Teacher Editio

Book 2

chemistry

FIFTH EDITION

bju press
Greenville, South Carolina

NOTE: The fact that materials produced by other publishers may be referred to in this volume does not constitute an endorsement of the content or theological position of materials produced by such publishers. Any references and ancillary materials are listed as an aid to the student or the teacher and in an attempt to maintain the accepted academic standards of the publishing industry.

CHEMISTRY Teacher Edition
Fifth Edition

Coordinating Writer
David M. Quigley, MEd

Writers
Christopher D. Coyle
Kelly Driskell

Consultants
Vincenzo Antignani, PhD
Verne Biddle, PhD
Carolyn Cowen, MAT
David Gardenghi, PhD
Carol Howell
Lynn Pert
Benjamin Zuehlke

Biblical Worldview
Renton Rathbun, ThM
Bryan Smith, PhD

Academic Oversight
Jeff Heath, EdD
Rachel Santopietro, MEd

Project Editor
Rick Vasso, MDiv

Cover, Design, and Interior Concept Design
Sarah Lompe

Page Layout
Carrie Walker

Illustration
Sarah Lompe

Permissions
Katie Jackson
Elizabeth Walker

Project Coordinators
Heather Chisholm
Chris Daniels

Photo credits appear on pages 630–35.

Teacher Edition photo credits: **ii** gameover/Alamy Stock Photo; **vi** real444/iStock/Getty Images Plus/Getty Images; **xii** skynesher/E+/Getty Images; **xiii** Nick Poon/Moment/Getty Images; **xiv** Jon Feingersh Photography Inc/The Image Bank/Getty Images; **xvi–xvii** kyoshino/iStock/Getty Images; **xviii** CherriesJD/iStock/Getty Images; **xix**t Jon Feingersh Photography Inc/The Image Bank/Getty Images; **xix**c SolStock/E+/Getty Images; **xix**b SDI Productions/E+/Getty Images; **600** fstop123/E+/Getty Images

The text for this book is set in Adobe Gil Sans, Adobe Minion Pro, Adobe Minion Variable Concept, Adobe Myriad Pro, Arial by Monotype Typography, Arial MT, Helvetica, IM FELL Great Primer by Igino Marini, Minion® Math by typoma® GmbH, Playfair Display by Claus Eggers Sørensen, Raleway, STIX, Symbol, and Times Roman.

The cover photo shows a close-up of a cluster of bubbles on a black background.

Greenville, South Carolina 29609

Printed in the United States of America

ISBN 978-1-62856-687-1

15 14 13 12 11 10 9 8 7 6 5 4 3 2 1

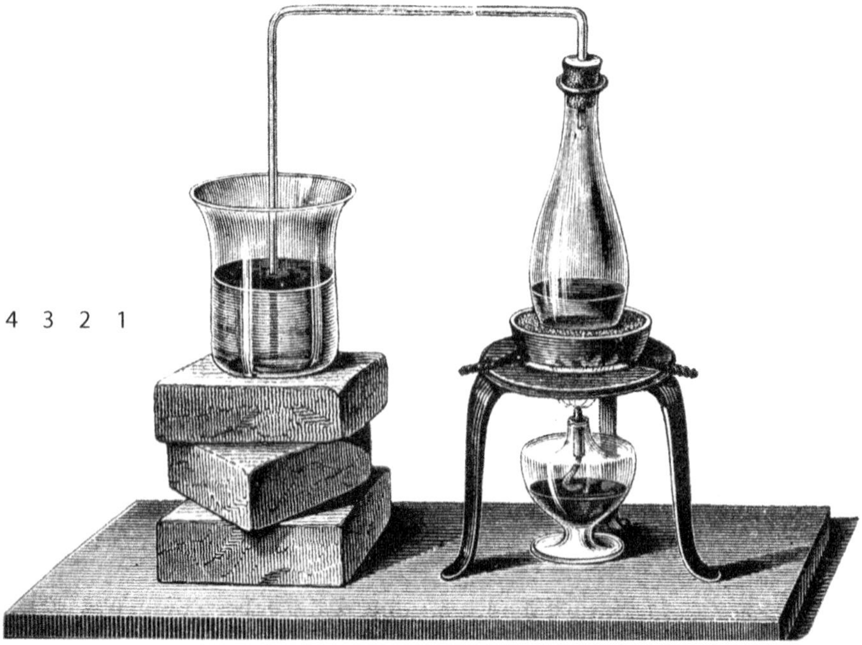

Contents

Contents

CASE STUDIES

ETHICS

HOW IT WORKS

MINI LABS

SERVING AS A(N)...

Contents

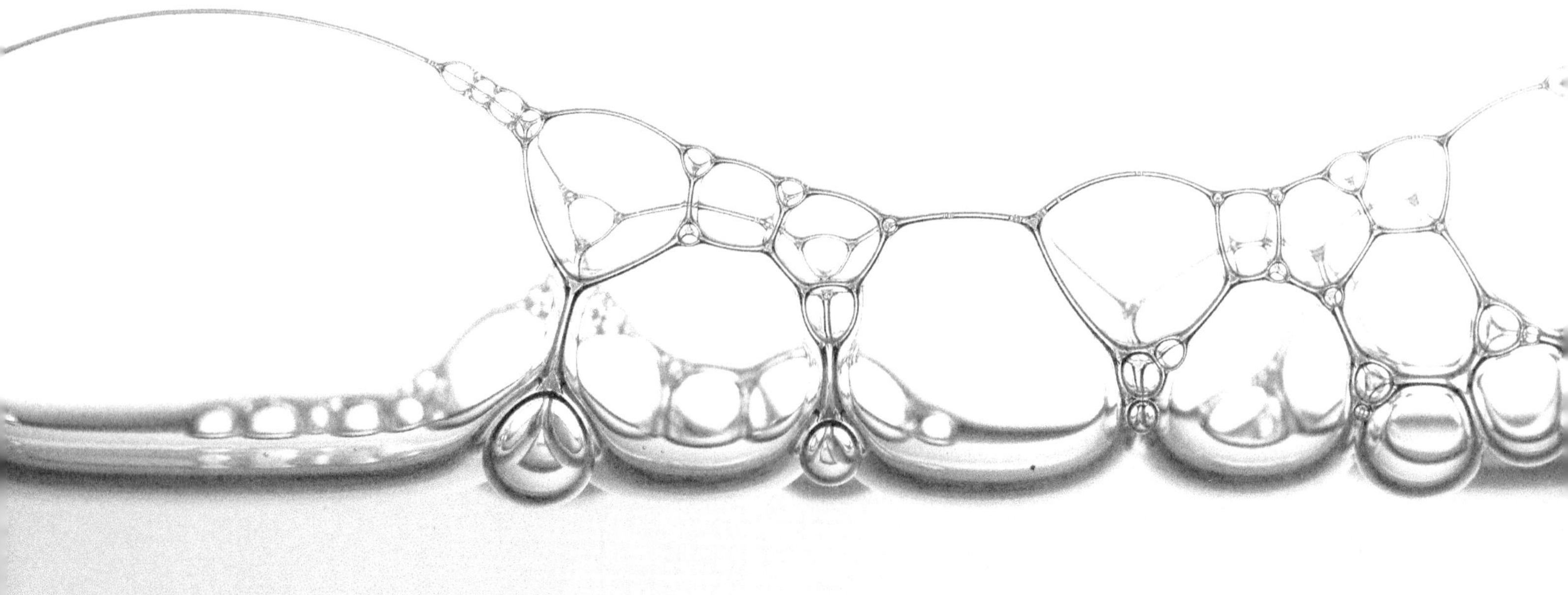

Left: Mockup of a futuristic base on Mars; *Top*: zinnia plant grown on the International Space Station (ISS) floating in microgravity; *Bottom*: astronauts outside the ISS.

CHEMISTRY AND BEYOND

People have been studying chemistry since Creation. There are numerous chemicals mentioned throughout Scripture. While we do know a lot about chemistry, we certainly don't know it all. As NASA looks to visit Mars and beyond, we need to expand our thinking about chemistry. We have a good grasp on much of chemistry here on Earth, but does that change in space?

A number of scientists are working on questions related to how various science fields differ in space. How do candles burn in reduced gravity? Do chemical reactions behave differently away from Earth's gravity? Could the science of photosynthesis help us in space exploration? Are biological processes different in space?

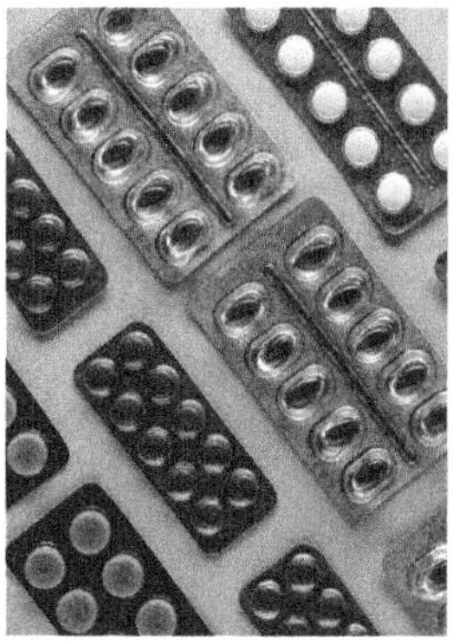

While there are numerous ways to investigate microgravity here on Earth, there is nothing better than experimenting about the effects of space than to actually be there. The International Space Station (ISS) has proven itself to be a vital research facility for all the nations involved in the program.

Investigating combustion in microgravity was one of the first experiments done on the ISS. NASA is currently conducting a series of combustion experiments on the ISS. They hope to learn more about how the process occurs so that they can find ways to burn fuels more efficiently and with less pollution. Combustion is one of the many chemistry concepts that scientists investigate on the ISS.

But chemistry isn't just for exploring space. Chemistry affects you all day every day—the clothes you wear, the food you eat, the car you drive, the medicine you take. You'll see in this textbook that chemistry is a powerful tool for us to use in God's world.

Chemistry could someday lead to cures for some of the diseases that plague us now, such as cancer, HIV, malaria, and others. It could revolutionize the cars we drive, the technology we use, and the way we generate electricity. It might even take us to Mars.

But *should* we try to do all these things? Should we try to establish a space station on Mars, isolating people from the earth that God created as a haven for life? Is chemistry the ultimate solution for all the problems we have now?

Chemistry alone can't answer these questions. But God's Word gives us the perspective we need to use chemistry in ways that glorify God and are truly helpful for His image-bearers. Let's explore how we can wisely use chemistry to take us above the clouds.

Features of This Textbook

This textbook is for you. We've designed it to help you learn. In the back of the textbook you will see other features, including an appendix section, glossary, index, and periodic table. We've designed this textbook with you in mind. We hope it will help you appreciate the wonders of God's creation even more. Flip through the following pages to see the features that we've included to lead you to success in chemistry.

❶ Chapter Opener
a short article that highlights issues and developments in chemistry that demonstrate how science intersects with your life

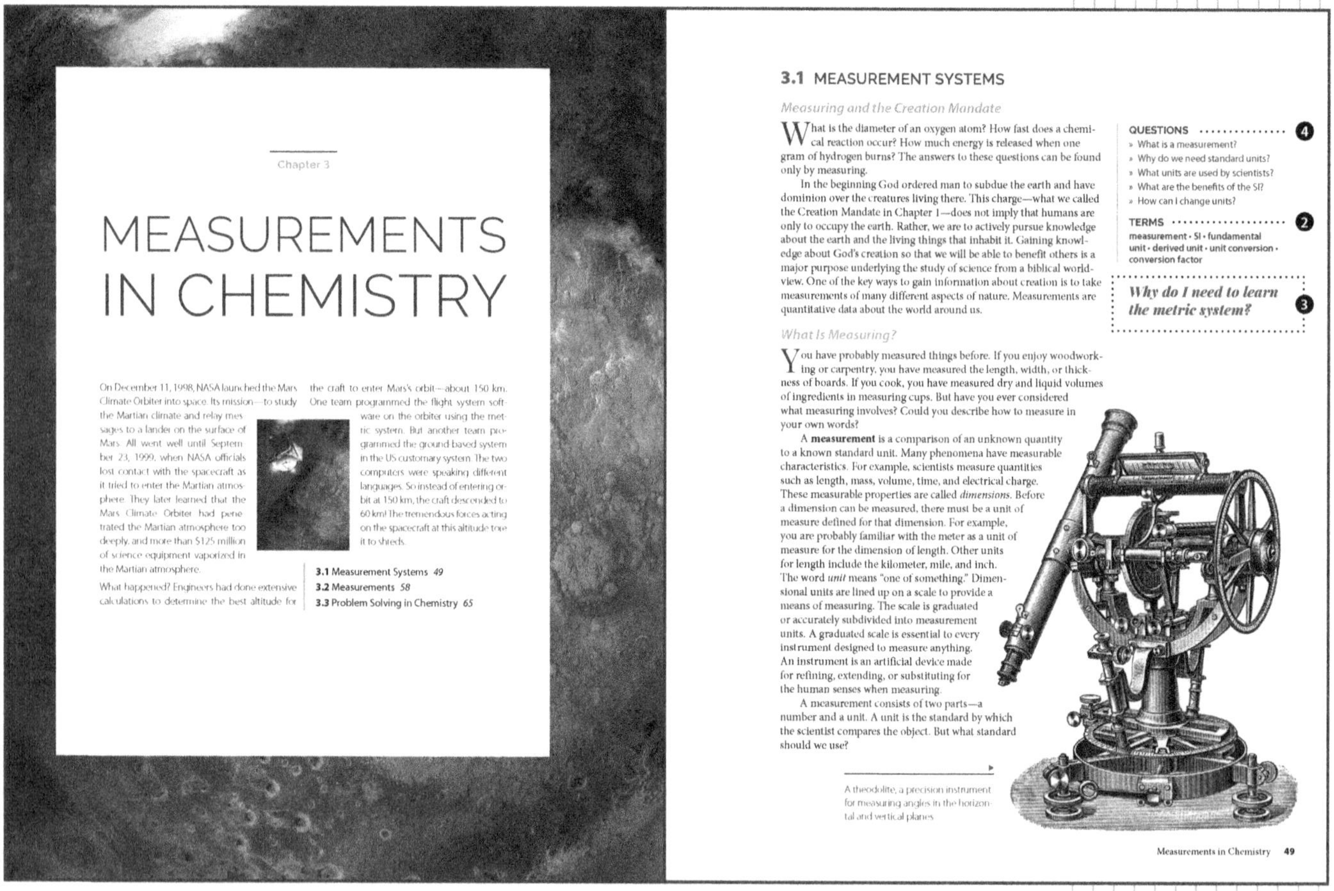

Chapter 3

MEASUREMENTS IN CHEMISTRY

On December 11, 1998, NASA launched the Mars Climate Orbiter into space. Its mission—to study the Martian climate and relay messages to a lander on the surface of Mars. All went well until September 23, 1999, when NASA officials lost contact with the spacecraft as it tried to enter the Martian atmosphere. They later learned that the Mars Climate Orbiter had penetrated the Martian atmosphere too deeply, and more than $125 million of science equipment vaporized in the Martian atmosphere.

What happened? Engineers had done extensive calculations to determine the best altitude for the craft to enter Mars's orbit—about 150 km. One team programmed the flight system software on the orbiter using the metric system. But another team programmed the ground-based system in the US customary system. The two computers were speaking different languages. So instead of entering orbit at 150 km, the craft descended to 60 km! The tremendous forces acting on the spacecraft at this altitude tore it to shreds.

3.1 Measurement Systems *49*
3.2 Measurements *58*
3.3 Problem Solving in Chemistry *65*

3.1 MEASUREMENT SYSTEMS

Measuring and the Creation Mandate

What is the diameter of an oxygen atom? How fast does a chemical reaction occur? How much energy is released when one gram of hydrogen burns? The answers to these questions can be found only by measuring.

In the beginning God ordered man to subdue the earth and have dominion over the creatures living there. This charge—what we called the Creation Mandate in Chapter 1—does not imply that humans are only to occupy the earth. Rather, we are to actively pursue knowledge about the earth and the living things that inhabit it. Gaining knowledge about God's creation so that we will be able to benefit others is a major purpose underlying the study of science from a biblical worldview. One of the key ways to gain information about creation is to take measurements of many different aspects of nature. Measurements are quantitative data about the world around us.

QUESTIONS ❹
» What is a measurement?
» Why do we need standard units?
» What units are used by scientists?
» What are the benefits of the SI?
» How can I change units?

TERMS ❷
measurement · SI · fundamental unit · derived unit · unit conversion · conversion factor

Why do I need to learn the metric system? ❸

What Is Measuring?

You have probably measured things before. If you enjoy woodworking or carpentry, you have measured the length, width, or thickness of boards. If you cook, you have measured dry and liquid volumes of ingredients in measuring cups. But have you ever considered what measuring involves? Could you describe how to measure in your own words?

A **measurement** is a comparison of an unknown quantity to a known standard unit. Many phenomena have measurable characteristics. For example, scientists measure quantities such as length, mass, volume, time, and electrical charge. These measurable properties are called *dimensions*. Before a dimension can be measured, there must be a unit of measure defined for that dimension. For example, you are probably familiar with the meter as a unit of measure for the dimension of length. Other units for length include the kilometer, mile, and inch. The word *unit* means "one of something." Dimensional units are lined up on a scale to provide a means of measuring. The scale is graduated or accurately subdivided into measurement units. A graduated scale is essential to every instrument designed to measure anything. An instrument is an artificial device made for refining, extending, or substituting for the human senses when measuring.

A measurement consists of two parts—a number and a unit. A unit is the standard by which the scientist compares the object. But what standard should we use?

A theodolite, a precision instrument for measuring angles in the horizontal and vertical planes

Measurements in Chemistry 49

❷ Vocabulary Terms
the key terms that will be introduced in a section

❸ Essential Question
the big question that you will learn about in a section

❹ Key Questions
the smaller questions that you can ask along the way through a section to help you answer the essential question

5

Element names come from many different sources. Latin names serve as the basis for many of the symbols for some elements that were known in ancient times. For example, *cuprum*, the Latin name for copper (Cu), means "from the island of Cyprus" and is the source for its symbol. Elements are named after many things.

color: iridium (Ir) from the Latin for "rainbow"

people: curium (Cm) for Pierre and Marie Curie, early researchers of radioactivity

places: californium (Cf) for California

heavenly bodies: helium (He) from *helios*, the Greek word for "sun"

miscellaneous words: bromine (Br) from the Greek word for "stench"

Today it is generally accepted that whoever discovers a new element has the honor of naming it, subject to the approval of the International Union of Pure and Applied Chemistry (IUPAC), an international organization responsible for standardization in chemistry. The periodic table of the elements in the back of this textbook displays the symbols for all the known elements.

Compounds

6 A pure substance that consists of two or more elements chemically combined in a fixed ratio is called a **compound**. Some compounds form distinct particles—molecules—while other compounds form vast crystalline arrays with repeating arrangements of ions. As you can imagine, there are many more compounds than elements. Just as chemical symbols are used to represent elements, chemists use **chemical formulas** to represent the millions of kinds of compounds.

7 The chemical formulas are made up of the chemical symbols for each element present. Numbers written at the lower right of a chemical symbol are called ***chemical subscripts***. They indicate the number of atoms or groups of atoms in a chemical formula. A molecule of water contains two hydrogen atoms and a single oxygen atom and so is written H_2O (the 1 for oxygen is assumed). When a subscript follows a group of symbols that are surrounded by parentheses, it refers to the entire group. The formula $Ca(HCO_3)_2$ consists of a calcium atom and two HCO_3 groups, for a total of one calcium atom, two hydrogen atoms, two carbon atoms, and six oxygen atoms. Notice that the subscripts act very much like exponents in mathematical expressions. The six oxygen atoms comes from the three oxygen atoms multiplied by two.

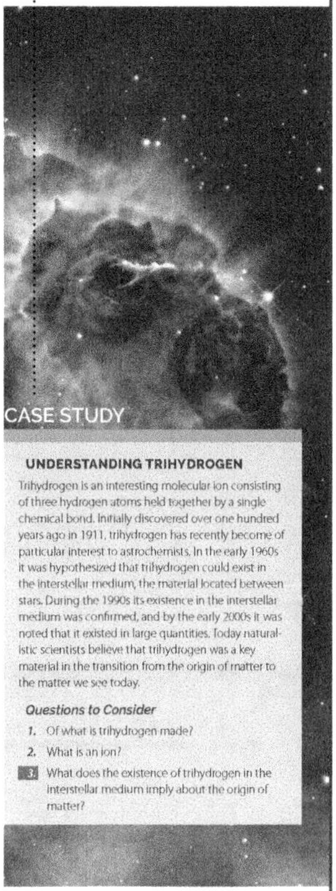

CASE STUDY

UNDERSTANDING TRIHYDROGEN

Trihydrogen is an interesting molecular ion consisting of three hydrogen atoms held together by a single chemical bond. Initially discovered over one hundred years ago in 1911, trihydrogen has recently become of particular interest to astrochemists. In the early 1960s it was hypothesized that trihydrogen could exist in the interstellar medium, the material located between stars. During the 1990s its existence in the interstellar medium was confirmed, and by the early 2000s it was noted that it existed in large quantities. Today naturalistic scientists believe that trihydrogen was a key material in the transition from the origin of matter to the matter we see today.

Questions to Consider

1. Of what is trihydrogen made?
2. What is an ion?
3. What does the existence of trihydrogen in the interstellar medium imply about the origin of matter?

Matter 29

5 Case Studies
opportunities to investigate specific areas in chemistry to apply what you have learned in a chapter

6 Bold-Faced Terms
vocabulary terms that you need to know

7 Italicized Terms
terms that will be defined later in the textbook or that are important terms in other scientific fields

10 CHAPTER REVIEW

8 *Chapter Summary*

TERMS
precipitate
chemical equation
reactant
product

10.1 CHEMICAL EQUATIONS

- Chemical reactions are a rearranging of the atoms in chemical substances to form new substances. Four signs that could indicate that a chemical reaction has occurred are a change in energy, the production of a gas, the formation of a precipitate, and a change of color.
- A balanced chemical equation shows the formulas and symbols for all substances involved in a chemical reaction and accounts for all atoms in both the reactants and the products to comply with the law of conservation of matter.
- Coefficients, subscripts, and special symbols provide more details on the quantities and conditions of a reaction.
- As a model of chemical reactions, chemical equations provide a lot of critical information but do not tell us everything about a reaction.

10.2 TYPES OF REACTIONS

- Five major categories of chemical reactions are synthesis, decomposition, combustion, single-replacement, and double-replacement.
- We can predict whether a single-replacement reaction will occur on the basis of the reactivity of the substances in the reaction. Double-replacement reactions will occur if at least one of the products is a precipitate, gas, or water.
- We can more accurately model what is going on in a double-replacement reaction with complete ionic and net ionic equations.

TERMS
synthesis reaction
decomposition reaction
combustion reaction
single-replacement reaction
double-replacement reaction
complete ionic equation
spectator ion
net ionic equation

9 *Chapter Review Questions*

RECALLING FACTS

1. What happens to chemical bonds in chemical reactions?
2. What is the only definitive way to know whether a chemical reaction has occurred?
3. Why is there typically a change in energy during a chemical reaction?
4. What is a precipitate?
5. Explain the steps to writing a balanced chemical equation.
6. Consider the reaction below.

   $HCl(aq) + H_2O(l) \rightleftharpoons Cl^-(aq) + H_3O^+(aq)$

   a. Why are two opposite arrows shown?
   b. Why is (*aq*) written after several of the substances?

Chemical Reactions and Equations 237

8 Chapter Summary
handy statements of the big ideas of the chapter, including vocabulary lists

9 Review Questions
questions at the end of each section and chapter that will have you recall facts, demonstrate your understanding of concepts, and cause you to use critical thinking

10

11

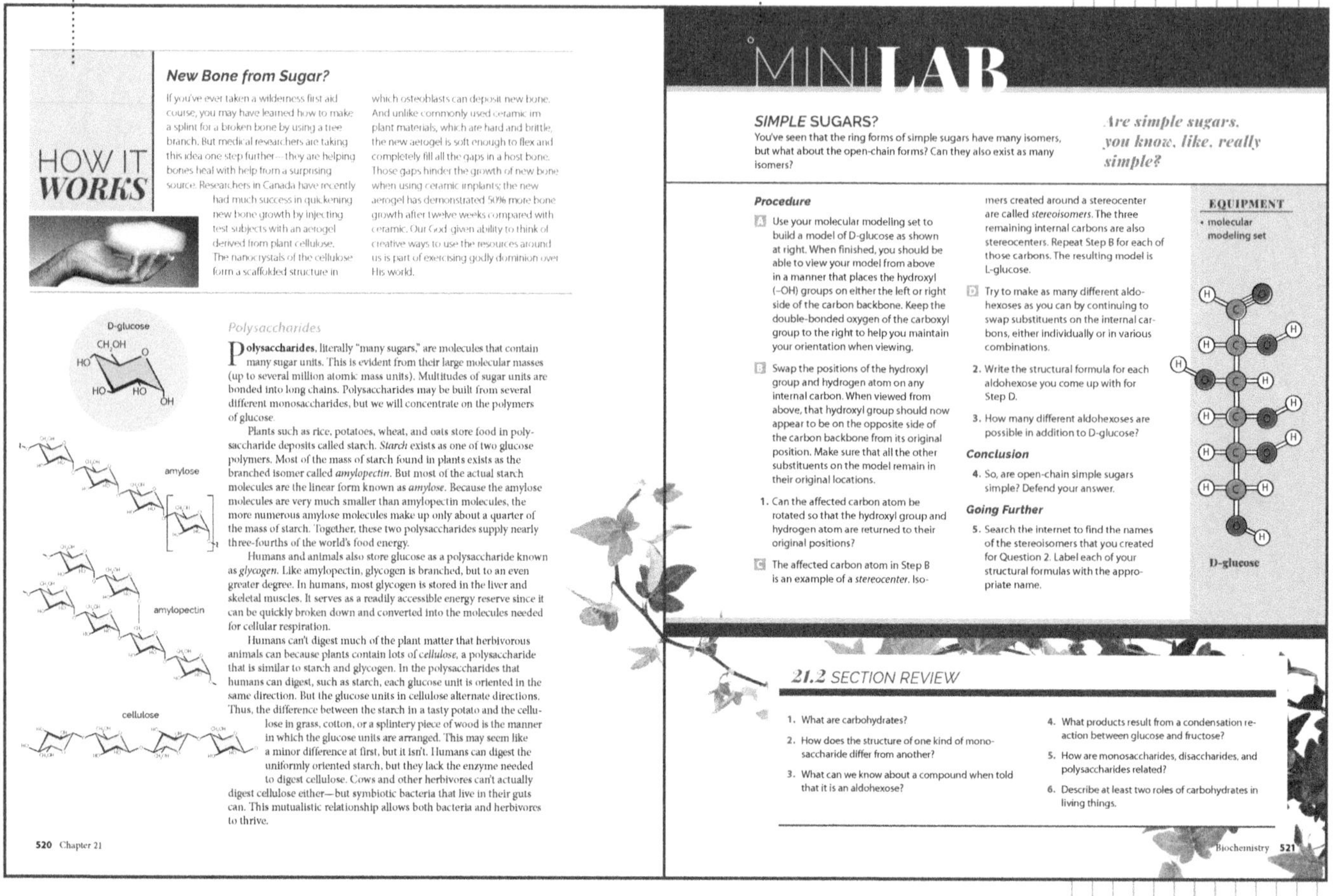
New Bone from Sugar?

HOW IT WORKS

If you've ever taken a wilderness first aid course, you may have learned how to make a splint for a broken bone by using a tree branch. But medical researchers are taking this idea one step further—they are helping bones heal with help from a surprising source. Researchers in Canada have recently had much success in quickening new bone growth by injecting test subjects with an aerogel derived from plant cellulose. The nanocrystals of the cellulose form a scaffolded structure in which osteoblasts can deposit new bone. And unlike commonly used ceramic implant materials, which are hard and brittle, the new aerogel is soft enough to flex and completely fill all the gaps in a host bone. Those gaps hinder the growth of new bone when using ceramic implants; the new aerogel has demonstrated 50% more bone growth after twelve weeks compared with ceramic. Our God-given ability to think of creative ways to use the resources around us is part of exercising godly dominion over His world.

Polysaccharides

Polysaccharides, literally "many sugars," are molecules that contain many sugar units. This is evident from their large molecular masses (up to several million atomic mass units). Multitudes of sugar units are bonded into long chains. Polysaccharides may be built from several different monosaccharides, but we will concentrate on the polymers of glucose.

Plants such as rice, potatoes, wheat, and oats store food in polysaccharide deposits called starch. *Starch* exists as one of two glucose polymers. Most of the mass of starch found in plants exists as the branched isomer called *amylopectin*. But most of the actual starch molecules are the linear form known as *amylose*. Because the amylose molecules are very much smaller than amylopectin molecules, the more numerous amylose molecules make up only about a quarter of the mass of starch. Together, these two polysaccharides supply nearly three-fourths of the world's food energy.

Humans and animals also store glucose as a polysaccharide known as *glycogen*. Like amylopectin, glycogen is branched, but to an even greater degree. In humans, most glycogen is stored in the liver and skeletal muscles. It serves as a readily accessible energy reserve since it can be quickly broken down and converted into the molecules needed for cellular respiration.

Humans can't digest much of the plant matter that herbivorous animals can because plants contain lots of *cellulose*, a polysaccharide that is similar to starch and glycogen. In the polysaccharides that humans can digest, such as starch, each glucose unit is oriented in the same direction. But the glucose units in cellulose alternate directions. Thus, the difference between the starch in a tasty potato and the cellulose in grass, cotton, or a splintery piece of wood is the manner in which the glucose units are arranged. This may seem like a minor difference at first, but it isn't. Humans can digest the uniformly oriented starch, but they lack the enzyme needed to digest cellulose. Cows and other herbivores can't actually digest cellulose either—but symbiotic bacteria that live in their guts can. This mutualistic relationship allows both bacteria and herbivores to thrive.

D-glucose

amylose

amylopectin

cellulose

520 Chapter 21

MINI LAB

SIMPLE SUGARS?

You've seen that the ring forms of simple sugars have many isomers, but what about the open-chain forms? Can they also exist as many isomers?

Are simple sugars, you know, like, really simple?

Procedure

A Use your molecular modeling set to build a model of D-glucose as shown at right. When finished, you should be able to view your model from above in a manner that places the hydroxyl (–OH) groups on either the left or right side of the carbon backbone. Keep the double-bonded oxygen of the carbonyl group to the right to help you maintain your orientation when viewing.

B Swap the positions of the hydroxyl group and hydrogen atom on any internal carbon. When viewed from above, that hydroxyl group should now appear to be on the opposite side of the carbon backbone from its original position. Make sure that all the other substituents on the model remain in their original locations.

1. Can the affected carbon atom be rotated so that the hydroxyl group and hydrogen atom are returned to their original positions?

C The affected carbon atom in Step B is an example of a *stereocenter*. Isomers created around a stereocenter are called *stereoisomers*. The three remaining internal carbons are also stereocenters. Repeat Step B for each of those carbons. The resulting model is L-glucose.

D Try to make as many different aldohexoses as you can by continuing to swap substituents on the internal carbons, either individually or in various combinations.

2. Write the structural formula for each aldohexose you come up with for Step D.
3. How many different aldohexoses are possible in addition to D-glucose?

Conclusion

4. So, are open-chain simple sugars simple? Defend your answer.

Going Further

5. Search the internet to find the names of the stereoisomers that you created for Question 2. Label each of your structural formulas with the appropriate name.

EQUIPMENT
- molecular modeling set

D-glucose

21.2 SECTION REVIEW

1. What are carbohydrates?
2. How does the structure of one kind of monosaccharide differ from another?
3. What can we know about a compound when told that it is an aldohexose?
4. What products result from a condensation reaction between glucose and fructose?
5. How are monosaccharides, disaccharides, and polysaccharides related?
6. Describe at least two roles of carbohydrates in living things.

Biochemistry 521

12 CAREERS

SERVING AS A CHEMICAL ABATEMENT SPECIALIST: *NOT YOUR AVERAGE CLEANUP CREW*

Asbestos, lead, mold, PCBs—what do these have in common? Each is a type of contaminant that might exist in a home, business, factory, or job site. Chemical agents like these can pose serious health risks to people, even if the contamination occurred many years in the past. The threat is often not readily apparent, either, since the problems usually exist in out-of-the-way places such as inside walls and ceilings, beneath floors, and even inside lamps, thermostats, and switches. Because of this, inspections take place whenever buildings are scheduled for demolition or renovation.

Chemical abatement specialists are specially trained technicians who identify chemical hazards and safely neutralize them. They use their knowledge of hazardous chemicals and the technologies needed to deal with them to help make safer working and living environments. As a chemical abatement specialist, you could demonstrate God's care for others by improving their lives through the wise remediation of chemical health risks.

EXAMPLE 11-12: MASS-TO-MOLE CONVERSIONS

How many moles of phosphoric acid can be formed from 3.550×10^3 g of diphosphorus pentoxide?

$$P_2O_5(s) + 3H_2O(l) \longrightarrow 2H_3PO_4(aq)$$

Write what you know and what you want to know.

3.550×10^3 g P_2O_5
? mol H_3PO_4

Note that the given value is in grams and the desired value is in moles. Since the conversion factors from the balanced equation are based on a mole ratio, the mass of diphosphorus pentoxide must first be converted to moles. Then the moles of diphosphorus pentoxide can be converted to moles of phosphoric acid according to the mole ratio from the equation above. These two steps should be done together as follows.

Convert g P_2O_5 to mol H_3PO_4.

$$3.550 \times 10^3 \text{ g } P_2O_5 \left(\frac{1 \text{ mol } P_2O_5}{141.94 \text{ g } P_2O_5}\right)\left(\frac{2 \text{ mol } H_3PO_4}{1 \text{ mol } P_2O_5}\right) = 50.02 \text{ mol } H_3PO_4$$

Chemical Calculations 255

10 How It Works Boxes

descriptions of how an everyday technology works and its relationship to the content of the chapter

11 Mini Labs

short hands-on activities to get you thinking and working like a scientist

12 Career Boxes

information about careers in chemistry (that could be yours!) that can be followed to wisely use God's world and help people

13

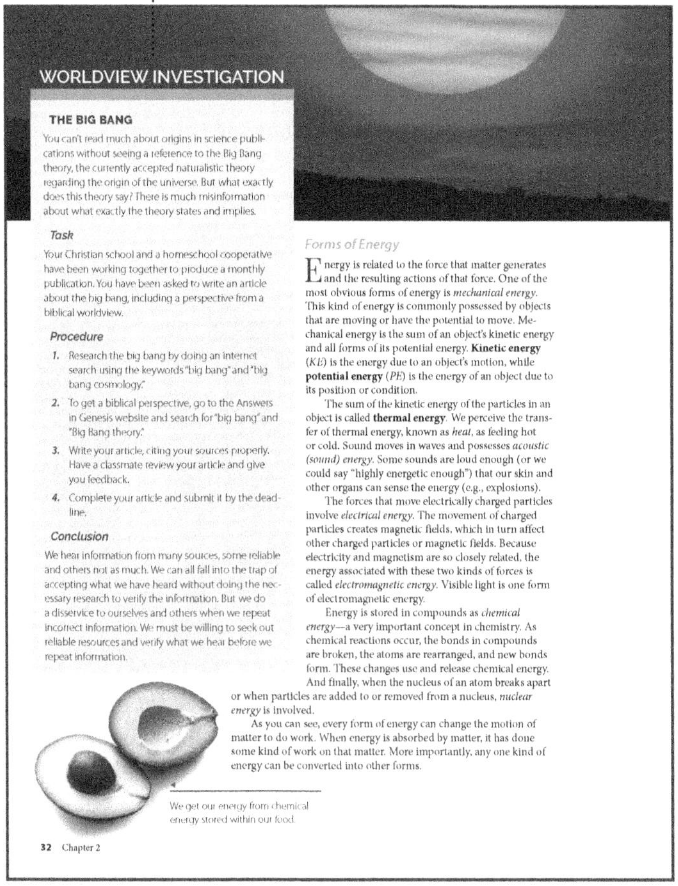

WORLDVIEW INVESTIGATION

THE BIG BANG

You can't read much about origins in science publications without seeing a reference to the Big Bang theory, the currently accepted naturalistic theory regarding the origin of the universe. But what exactly does this theory say? There is much misinformation about what exactly the theory states and implies.

Task

Your Christian school and a homeschool cooperative have been working together to produce a monthly publication. You have been asked to write an article about the big bang, including a perspective from a biblical worldview.

Procedure

1. Research the big bang by doing an internet search using the keywords "big bang" and "big bang cosmology."
2. To get a biblical perspective, go to the Answers in Genesis website and search for "big bang" and "Big Bang theory."
3. Write your article, citing your sources properly. Have a classmate review your article and give you feedback.
4. Complete your article and submit it by the deadline.

Conclusion

We hear information from many sources, some reliable and others not as much. We can all fall into the trap of accepting what we have heard without doing the necessary research to verify the information. But we do a disservice to ourselves and others when we repeat incorrect information. We must be willing to seek out reliable resources and verify what we hear before we repeat information.

Forms of Energy

Energy is related to the force that matter generates and the resulting actions of that force. One of the most obvious forms of energy is *mechanical energy*. This kind of energy is commonly possessed by objects that are moving or have the potential to move. Mechanical energy is the sum of an object's kinetic energy and all forms of its potential energy. **Kinetic energy** (*KE*) is the energy due to an object's motion, while **potential energy** (*PE*) is the energy of an object due to its position or condition.

The sum of the kinetic energy of the particles in an object is called **thermal energy**. We perceive the transfer of thermal energy, known as *heat*, as feeling hot or cold. Sound moves in waves and possesses *acoustic (sound) energy*. Some sounds are loud enough (or we could say "highly energetic enough") that our skin and other organs can sense the energy (e.g., explosions).

The forces that move electrically charged particles involve *electrical energy*. The movement of charged particles creates magnetic fields, which in turn affect other charged particles or magnetic fields. Because electricity and magnetism are so closely related, the energy associated with these two kinds of forces is called *electromagnetic energy*. Visible light is one form of electromagnetic energy.

Energy is stored in compounds as *chemical energy*—a very important concept in chemistry. As chemical reactions occur, the bonds in compounds are broken, the atoms are rearranged, and new bonds form. These changes use and release chemical energy. And finally, when the nucleus of an atom breaks apart or when particles are added to or removed from a nucleus, *nuclear energy* is involved.

As you can see, every form of energy can change the motion of matter to do work. When energy is absorbed by matter, it has done some kind of work on that matter. More importantly, any one kind of energy can be converted into other forms.

We get our energy from chemical energy stored within our food.

32 Chapter 2

13 Worldview Investigation Boxes
inquiry-based investigations that help you think through controversial areas of chemistry through the lens of Scripture

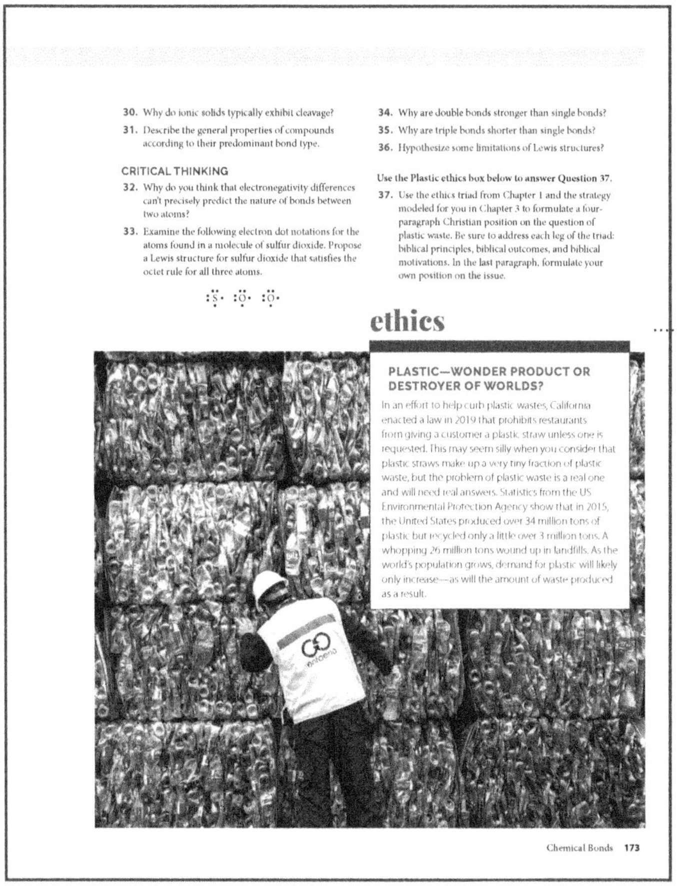

30. Why do ionic solids typically exhibit cleavage?
31. Describe the general properties of compounds according to their predominant bond type.

CRITICAL THINKING

32. Why do you think that electronegativity differences can't precisely predict the nature of bonds between two atoms?
33. Examine the following electron dot notations for the atoms found in a molecule of sulfur dioxide. Propose a Lewis structure for sulfur dioxide that satisfies the octet rule for all three atoms.

:S· :O· :O·

34. Why are double bonds stronger than single bonds?
35. Why are triple bonds shorter than single bonds?
36. Hypothesize some limitations of Lewis structures?

Use the Plastic ethics box below to answer Question 37.

37. Use the ethics triad from Chapter 1 and the strategy modeled for you in Chapter 3 to formulate a four-paragraph Christian position on the question of plastic waste. Be sure to address each leg of the triad: biblical principles, biblical outcomes, and biblical motivations. In the last paragraph, formulate your own position on the issue.

ethics

PLASTIC—WONDER PRODUCT OR DESTROYER OF WORLDS?

In an effort to help curb plastic wastes, California enacted a law in 2019 that prohibits restaurants from giving a customer a plastic straw unless one is requested. This may seem silly when you consider that plastic straws make up a very tiny fraction of plastic waste, but the problem of plastic waste is a real one and will need real answers. Statistics from the US Environmental Protection Agency show that in 2015, the United States produced over 34 million tons of plastic but recycled only a little over 3 million tons. A whopping 26 million tons wound up in landfills. As the world's population grows, demand for plastic will likely only increase—as will the amount of waste produced as a result.

Chemical Bonds 173

14 Ethics Boxes
opportunities to apply a biblical worldview to ethical issues in chemistry

To the Teacher

THIS IS FOR YOU!

Welcome to BJU Press *CHEMISTRY* 5th Edition! Your students are about to discover and explore the incredible richness of the universe that God has created. During this journey, students will find that people's views of chemistry vary drastically, depending on worldview—the overarching narrative that a person uses to see and interpret the world. And everyone has one. It shapes our beliefs and values, and each of us will make choices in life that are based on our worldview.

Since scientists who do chemistry all have worldviews, conflicts arise about their interpretations of what they observe. What is the origin of matter and energy? How do we determine the proper use of a new technology? What is man's duty in his treatment of the rest of creation? *CHEMISTRY* Student Edition 5th Edition helps students grapple with these questions from a biblical standpoint.

Though a good textbook is important, you as the teacher are essential to successful learning. Your job is to guide your students to learn through the lens of the Bible's narrative. Science class should be a time of discovery for both you and them. Your emphasis on glorifying God by obeying the Creation Mandate and helping other people through science will keep science exciting and will impact your students. These are the most important lessons that you can teach.

Make this course fit the needs of your students. *CHEMISTRY* Student Edition and *CHEMISTRY* Student Lab Manual both include more material than most teachers will be able to cover in one school year. You decide whether you will spend extra time on a particular topic, a lab activity, or a project.

New for 5th Edition

If you have used previous editions of CHEMISTRY *Student Edition, you will notice some changes in the 5th Edition.*

- **The writing style, vocabulary, and amount and distribution of content have been refined to better facilitate student learning at an eleventh-grade level.**
- **The text focuses on big ideas identified by essential questions.**
- **Emphasis has been placed on clearly explaining concepts and demonstrating how problems in chemistry are solved.**
- **Each chapter is identified as foundational, key, or enrichment. Foundational chapters are crucial for students to develop a basic understanding of chemistry. Key chapters are very important and may contain material that appears on standardized tests. Enrichment chapters may be skipped with little adverse effect on students; use them if a significant portion of your class is interested or if you have gifted students who need differentiated instruction.**
- **Case Studies, Worldview Investigations, How It Works boxes, and Career boxes engage student interest.**
- **Expanded examples model the problem-solving process and provide necessary scaffolding for student mastery of the content.**
- **Every chapter in the Student Edition includes a Mini Lab. These are small lab activities that help reinforce the objectives of the section and generally require less time and fewer materials than the lab activities in the Student Lab Manual.**
- **Ethics boxes found in many chapters present ethical dilemmas related to current fields of chemistry. Students formulate and apply a biblical understanding of the issues. Students are provided with a good deal of support early in the Student Edition and become more independent as they continue through the remainder of the textbook.**
- **Each chapter ends with a Chapter Review that presents in a few brief sentences the primary concepts of each section. This is followed by a set of chapter review questions. The reviews are divided into questions that require students to recall facts, those that compel students to demonstrate a thorough understanding of concepts, and those that require them to apply critical thinking.**

To the Teacher

FEATURES OF THE TEACHER EDITION

You have a lot of great material at your fingertips in this resource! *Chemistry* Teacher Edition 5th Edition features reduced student pages with side and bottom margins packed with educational content. Take a look at what it offers, whether you are a classroom teacher or a home educator.

LESSON PLAN OVERVIEW

The Lesson Plan Overview beginning on page xx is your year-at-a-glance schedule for teaching chemistry. This has been greatly enhanced for 5th Edition, integrating the accompanying Student Edition, Student Lab Manual, and Teacher Lab Manual to give you an idea of how much time you should spend on each chapter. The table also includes the essential question, objectives, and resources for each section. The schedule for each chapter includes a day of review and a test day.

THE TEACHING CYCLE

Each chapter or section begins with an overview. Section overviews include the lesson's essential question, objectives, and suggested resources. The overview is followed by a four-part teaching cycle: engage, instruct, apply, and assess.

- **Engage** students by capturing their attention, activating prior knowledge, and motivating them to connect with new content.
- **Instruct** students by using direct, indirect, and interactive strategies to expand and extend their knowledge and skills.
- **Apply** students' learning by practicing knowledge and skills and connecting them to real life.
- **Assess** students' understanding by using a variety of tools to systematically evaluate knowledge, skills, attitudes, and beliefs in order to improve student learning.

Each cycle includes research-based teaching strategies, ideas for demonstrations, tips for correcting misconceptions, formative assessments, suggestions for scheduling lab activities, and more. Differentiated instruction notes are located in the bottom margin and are easily identified by their yellow-tinted box. There are more teaching strategies than you will have time for, providing you the freedom and flexibility to choose those that best fit your students.

Margins also contain answers and expanded solutions to review questions.

Most margin notes are annotated with special icons to alert you to the type of note as described below. Notes that are not accompanied by an icon are additional information that you may find helpful in teaching the material.

Biblical Worldview Shaping—highlights worldview-shaping discussion questions and activities

Demonstration—provides materials and procedures for successful in-class demonstrations

Difficult Concept—points out common misconceptions or concepts that students may find difficult

Equipment—highlights notes and warnings about equipment used in different activities

Helpful Tip—provides suggestions for improving students' understanding or lesson management

Lab—flags where a Student Lab Manual activity best fits with the information in the chapter

Math—connects chemistry to concepts that are often taught in math classes

Recall—highlights topics from earlier chapters or courses that you may want to review to integrate and reinforce concepts

Safety—indicates that a demonstration has special safety concerns that you should consider before you attempt it

Teaching Strategies Icon—indicates notes that suggest ways to apply research-based educational strategies in your classroom, including group activities and discussions, activating prior knowledge, active learning, and formative assessments

Web Links—points out additional resources that might help in teaching the material, including web resources accessed through BJU Press *Chemistry* 5th Edition Web Links at TeacherToolsOnline.com

TEACHER RESOURCES

LAB MANUALS

The Student Lab Manual includes thought-provoking lab activities tied directly to the content of each chapter in the Student Edition. The Teacher Lab Manual provides all the instructions for conducting the activities, including information on the materials and equipment needed, answers to lab activity questions, and example data where applicable. Plan your lab activities on the basis of the equipment that you have and the needs of your students.

New in 5th Edition are inquiry lab activities. These provide opportunities for students to direct the investigation of a topic. Because inquiry lab activities are more open-ended, the Teacher Lab Manual includes a teacher guide for each one.

A companion science equipment kit is available from Logos Science. For more information visit **bjupress.com/category/science-secondary-christian-school-curriculum**.

ONLINE RESOURCES

Resources formerly available on the Teacher Toolkit CD are still available online.

RESOURCES AVAILABLE AT TEACHER TOOLS ONLINE
(purchased separately)

- visuals
- video content
- PowerPoint™ presentations
- Digital Teacher Edition
- ExamView™ testing software with editable test database

For more information, visit **TeacherToolsOnline.com**.

PRINTED ASSESSMENTS PACKAGE
(purchased separately)

- Quizzes and Tests (summative assessments) with Answer Keys

Biblical Worldview Shaping

IN CHEMISTRY 5TH EDITION

What makes matter and energy possible?

We will find that matter and energy are made possible only by the one who upholds all things by the word of His power (Heb. 1:3). As we examine five biblical worldview themes throughout this Teacher Edition, the following represent the many questions that we will be addressing.

Foundations of Chemistry

Although we are able to account for matter and energy by tracing them back to God's creative and sustaining work, our secular society views them as merely basic aspects of our universe.

- ***How does a scientist's worldview affect his work?***
- ***How does energy's origin relate to the laws of thermodynamics?***

Ch 1	Ch 2	Ch 3	Ch 6	Ch 8	Ch 15
E, E, Ev	**E, Ev**	**E**	**E**	**F**	**Ev**

See key below

Key

R—**Recall** biblical teaching

E—**Explain** biblical teaching

Ev—**Evaluate** controversial concepts

F—**Formulate** a Christian understanding of a controversial concept

A—**Apply** a Christian understanding to life

Implementation of the biblical worldview themes in their respective chapters

Community Obligations in Chemistry

Part of obeying God's command to love our neighbor is to enrich the lives of others through chemistry. But sometimes scientific knowledge is pursued without the consideration of others.

- ***What obligations do chemists have to their fellow humans?***
- ***How can chemical technology benefit my neighbor?***

Ch 1	Ch 3	Ch 14	Ch 18	Ch 21	Ch 22
E, E	E	E, A	Ev	A	A

Models in Chemistry

God made man's mind to understand the world through modeling. The secular scientist, however, does not acknowledge God but rather believes that modeling in chemistry determines what is real.

- ***Are scientific models capable of determining what is true about the world?***
- ***What do we learn about scientific knowledge when models are adjusted or changed to be more workable?***

Ch 1	Ch 2	Ch 3	Ch 4	Ch 5	Ch 6	Ch 8	Ch 12	Ch 22
E, E, Ev	E	E, Ev	E, E	E, E, F	E, Ev	F	E	E

Chemistry and Man's Use of the Environment

God made a beautiful world, and He commands man to cultivate and use this world with wisdom. Yet today man seeks either to abuse the environment or to worship it.

- ***Can electric cars actually be dangerous to our environment?***
- ***What should a Christian consider when debating the use of nuclear energy?***

Ch 1	Ch 12	Ch 14	Ch 19	Ch 22
E, E	F	E	A	A

Applied Ethics in Chemistry

God's law is practical and applies to every part of man's life, even his work in chemistry. Yet the secular world believes that Scripture is not equipped or appropriate to use as a measure for ethics in chemistry.

- ***How should a Christian evaluate risk assessments in businesses?***
- ***What should a Christian consider when debating medicinal uses of marijuana?***

Ch 1	Ch 3	Ch 4	Ch 6	Ch 7	Ch 9	Ch 10	Ch 11	Ch 13	Ch 16	Ch 22
R, E	E	Ev	Ev	Ev	F	F	F	F	A	A

Academic Rigor

BUILDING ACADEMIC RIGOR WITH CHEMISTRY 5TH EDITION

Desired Learning Outcomes

What do I want students to learn?

- Reading skills in informative texts with discipline-specific vocabulary
- Chemistry practices in scientific inquiry, data collection and analysis, model use and development, and formulating conclusions
- Perseverance in problem-solving
- Consistent scientific and mathematical precision and reasoning
- Visual analysis of process maps, graphs, and scientific diagrams
- Connecting chemistry to other disciplines
- 21st century skills—collaboration, creativity, critical thinking, problem solving, technology literacy
- Biblical worldview development regarding the foundations, models, community obligations, and applied ethics in chemistry as well as man's use of the environment

Teaching and Learning Supports

How will I help students learn?

- Highlight essential questions, key questions, and vocabulary.
- Give opportunities for scientific inquiry, data analysis, and model making through mini labs and lab activities.
- Model problem-solving skills, using case studies, ethics boxes, and examples.
- Provide regular practice of scientific and mathematical skills.
- Elicit and correct misconceptions with scaffolded Socratic dialogue and chemistry demonstrations.
- Guide visual interpretation of process maps, infographics, images, charts, and graphs.
- Make cross-curricular connections, employing educational technology with worldview investigation activities related to biblical worldview themes.

Evidence of Understanding

How do I evaluate student learning?

- Ask high-level questions that encourage scientific literacy and critical thinking.
- Employ frequent and varied preassessments and formative assessments.
- Evaluate student-created models and experimental conclusions.
- Assess the products of case study analyses and the formulation of positions on ethical issues.
- Monitor scientific and mathematical precision in student-generated solutions.
- Assess student-created graphic organizers, charts, and graphs.
- Evaluate student formulation and application of Christian positions on the foundations, models, community obligations, and applied ethics in chemistry as well as on man's use of the environment.

Academic Rigor

A PANORAMA OF ACADEMIC RIGOR

The Teacher's Role

The teacher is the person who crafts the learning environment. The teacher creates a learning community with high educational expectations, ignites interest and passion to help students persevere in challenging educational tasks, and inspires them by providing models of learning. She instructs, supports, critiques, and praises the efforts of the growing learners. Then she helps her students transfer their knowledge, understanding, and skills to life with the purpose of shaping their worldview.

The Learning Environment

Learning happens in a context. Physical and social environments create this context. For students to be stimulated and engaged and to perform at high levels, they need an environment that connects with and shapes their interests and values. Students need a flexible environment that adapts to remedy their deficits and capitalizes on their proficiencies. They need an interactive environment that intrinsically motivates them by giving them structure, freedom, and choices in learning. They need a safe environment that invites questioning, risk-taking, and honest discussion. Most importantly, students need positive relationships with mentors and peers and one-on-one time with caring, responsible instructors and parents. This kind of environment does not happen by accident; an educational climate like this must be crafted.

The Learning Experience

The textbook opens doors to the world of the learning experience. It captures student interest and significantly contributes to the educational environment. Educational and technological resources enable the teacher to develop knowledge, understanding, and skills in a scaffolded sequence to build a foundation that students can transfer to life. Teachers use educational tools to craft relevant, authentic learning experiences that develop creativity and problem-solving skills in a variety of contexts. These kinds of learning experiences allow students to take responsibility for their learning and discover the joy of serving God with their vocational knowledge and skills.

Lesson Plan Overview

Section	Student Edition Pages	Teacher Edition Pages	Teacher Resources	Essential Questions/Content Objectives
CHAPTER 12: *GASES* (9 days) Key Chapter				
12.1 Properties of Gases	269–73	269–73	Demonstrating the Diffusion and Reaction of Gases, Demonstrating Pressure	**EQ:** Why do gases behave as they do? **Objectives:** **12.1.1** State the kinetic-molecular theory of gases. **12.1.2** Convert measurements between different units of pressure. **12.1.3** Relate the pressure, volume, and temperature of gases to the kinetic-molecular theory.
12.2 Gas Laws	274–82	274–82	**Case Study:** When Oxygen Is Bad Demonstrating Boyle's Law #1, Demonstrating Boyle's Law #2, Demonstrating Charles's Law **Web Links:** Boyle's Law, Charles's Law, Gay-Lussac's Law **Mini Lab:** *Changing Volume*	**EQ:** Why do balloons stop getting bigger? **Objectives:** **12.2.1** State Boyle's, Charles's, Gay-Lussac's, and the combined gas laws qualitatively and mathematically. **12.2.2** Calculate the pressure, volume, or temperature of a gas under changing conditions. **12.2.3** Use the kinetic-molecular theory of gases to explain the gas laws. **12.2.4** Calculate the amount of gas produced from a solution by applying Dalton's law of partial pressures.
Lab Day 1	SLM* 107–10	TLM** 107–10	**Lab 12A:** *Cold and Calculating—* Finding Absolute Zero	**EQ:** How can we determine an impossibly cold temperature?
12.3 Gas Stoichiometry *(2 days)*	283–93	283–93	**How It Works:** Airbags **Worldview Investigation:** Greenhouse Gases	**EQ:** How do gases actually behave? **Objectives:** **12.3.1** State the law of combining volumes. **12.3.2** Explain why the kinetic-molecular theory is limited in its ability to describe real gases. **12.3.3** Calculate the pressure, volume, temperature, or moles of a gaseous substance present when given three of the four variables used in the ideal gas law. **12.3.4** Predict the amount of gas in a chemical reaction by using stoichiometric calculations. **12.3.5** Formulate a biblical position regarding greenhouse gases.
Lab Day 2	SLM 111–18	TLM 111–18	**Lab 12B:** *An Aquanaut's World—* Predicting the Production of Oxygen	**EQ:** How can we predict the volume of gas produced in a reaction?
Ethics Day	297	297	Deadly Safety Device?	**Objective:** **12.3.6** Formulate a biblical view of the appropriate use of airbag safety.
Review and Test Days				Chapter 12 Test

* SLM = Student Lab Manual **TLM = Teacher Lab Manual

Section	Student Edition Pages	Teacher Edition Pages	Teacher Resources	Essential Questions/Content Objectives
CHAPTER 13: ***SOLIDS AND LIQUIDS*** *(8 days)* Key Chapter				
13.1 Intermolecular Forces	299–303	299–303	**Web Links:** Hydrogen Bonding, Dispersion Forces	**EQ:** Why is oxygen a gas, water a liquid, and iron a solid at room temperature? **Objectives:** **13.1.1** Define *intermolecular force*. **13.1.2** Compare dipole-dipole forces, hydrogen bonds, and London dispersion forces. **13.1.3** Predict the intermolecular force(s) present in a substance on the basis of its composition. **13.1.4** Predict the melting point of a substance on the basis of the intermolecular forces present.
13.2 Solids	304–11	304–11	Demonstrating Sublimation and Deposition, Demonstrating Lattice Energy **How It Works:** Cryogenics **Web Links:** Sublimation of Iodine, Crystal Gallery, Liquid Crystal Gallery	**EQ:** Why can't I write with a diamond? **Objectives:** **13.2.1** Explain the properties of solids using the kinetic-molecular theory. **13.2.2** Compare crystalline and amorphous solids. **13.2.3** Explain the significance of the slopes and plateaus on a heating curve. **13.2.4** Describe what happens at the particle level during phase changes. **13.2.5** Summarize the three factors that produce network solids.
Lab Day 1	SLM 119–21	TLM 119–21	**Lab 13A:** *Cracking the Crystal—* Relating Geology to Chemistry	**EQ:** What determines the shape of a crystal?
13.3 Liquids	312–21	312–21	Demonstrating the High Surface Tension of Water, Demonstrating Viscosity, Demonstrating the Adhesion of Water, Demonstrating the Relationship between Vapor Pressure and Boiling **Web Links:** Straw Wrapper Capillary Action, Swamp Coolers **Mini Lab:** *Through the Void*	**EQ:** What makes water so special? **Objectives:** **13.3.1** Explain the properties of liquids on the basis of the kinetic-molecular theory and intermolecular attractions. **13.3.2** Compare evaporation and boiling. **13.3.3** Trace temperature changes and thermal energy flow during the process of evaporation. **13.3.4** Use a phase diagram to predict a substance's state of matter under various temperature and pressure conditions.
Lab Day 2	SLM 123–32	TLM 123–32	**Lab 13B:** *Forces of Nature*—Exploring Intermolecular Forces in Liquids	**EQ:** What determines the physical properties of liquids?
Ethics Day	325	325	Cryonics	**Objective:** **13.3.5** Respond to the claim that cryonics provides hope while science and technology advance.
Review and Test Days			Chapter 13 Test	

Lesson Plan Overview

Section	Student Edition Pages	Teacher Edition Pages	Teacher Resources	Essential Questions/Content Objectives
		CHAPTER 14: *SOLUTIONS* *(9 days)* Foundational Chapter		
14.1 The Dissolving Process	327–37	327–37	**Case Study:** Pharmaceutical Pollution **Demonstrating a Supersaturated Solution** **Web Links:** Polarity and Solubility, Hot Ice **Mini Lab**: *Off to the Races*	**EQ:** Why is it so difficult to dissolve sugar in my iced tea? **Objectives:** **14.1.1** Describe the parts of a solution. **14.1.2** Categorize examples of solutions. **14.1.3** Explain why certain solutes do not dissolve in certain solvents. **14.1.4** Explain how varying conditions will affect the rate of dissolving. **14.1.5** Solve solubility problems using a solubility curve. **14.1.6** Compare unsaturated, saturated, and supersaturated solutions.
Lab Day 1	SLM 133–36	TLM 133–36	**Lab 14A:** *One Giant Solution*—Making a Solubility Curve	**EQ:** How does temperature affect the solubility of a salt?
14.2 Measures of Concentration	338–42	338–42		**EQ:** How much sugar is really in my soda? **Objectives:** **14.2.1** Define *concentration*. **14.2.2** Compare the different ways to report the concentration of solutions. **14.2.3** Solve concentration problems. **14.2.4** Apply principles of solution concentrations to regulate personal sugar consumption.
Lab Day 2	SLM 137–42	TLM 137–42	**Lab 14B:** *Sugar, Sugar*—Determining the Sugar Content in Beverages	**EQ:** How much sugar is really in my favorite beverage?
14.3 Colligative Properties	343–48	343–48	**How It Works:** Reverse Osmosis **Web Link:** Osmosis	**EQ:** How can the same substance be both an antifreeze and a coolant? **Objectives:** **14.3.1** Define *colligative property*. **14.3.2** Relate colligative properties to changes in concentration. **14.3.3** Calculate boiling point elevation and freezing point depression. **14.3.4** Explain the process of osmosis. **14.3.5** Explain how colligative properties are used to benefit people.
14.4 Suspensions and Colloids	349–51	349–51	**Demonstrating the Tyndall Effect** **Careers:** Serving as an Environmental Scientist	**EQ:** How are eggs and Jell-O® related? **Objectives:** **14.4.1** Describe colloids using the terms *dispersing medium* and *dispersed phase*. **14.4.2** Compare solutions, suspensions, and colloids. **14.4.3** Give examples of common colloids.
Ethics Day	355	355	**Wastewater Management**	**Objective:** **14.4.4** Explain the importance of water treatment.
Review and Test Days			Chapter 14 Test	

Section	Student Edition Pages	Teacher Edition Pages	Teacher Resources	Essential Questions/Content Objectives
CHAPTER 15: *THERMOCHEMISTRY* (8 days) Key Chapter				
15.1 Thermodynamics and Phase Changes	357–63	357–63	**Demonstrating How to Create Your Own Heating Curve** **Web Link:** Phase Changes and Heat **Mini Lab:** *Comparing Thermal Energy Transfer* (p. 364)	**EQ: Does the temperature of water change as it freezes?** **Objectives:** **15.1.1** Define *thermochemistry*. **15.1.2** Compare temperature, thermal energy, and heat. **15.1.3** Relate the states of matter to the concepts of sensible heat and latent heat. **15.1.4** Calculate energy or temperature during phase changes.
Lab Day 1	SLM 143–48	TLM 143–48	**Lab 15A:** *Hot Shot*—Finding the Specific Heat of a Metal	**EQ: How can I measure how easily a material heats up?**
15.2 Thermodynamics and Chemical Changes	365–70	365–70	**Demonstrating Endothermic Reactions**	**EQ: Are chemical reactions ever cold?** **Objectives:** **15.2.1** Determine whether a given reaction is endothermic or exothermic by calculating its change in enthalpy. **15.2.2** Determine the enthalpy of a reaction on the basis of Hess's law.
15.3 Reaction Tendency *(2 days)*	371–81	371–81	**Case Study:** Entropy and Life **Worldview Investigation:** Heat Death **Web Link:** The Cosmological Argument	**EQ: Is dynamite dangerous?** **Objectives:** **15.3.1** Define *entropy* and give some common examples. **15.3.2** Predict reaction tendency on the basis of energy and entropy changes. **15.3.3** Calculate the change in entropy of a chemical reaction. **15.3.4** Predict the favorability of reactions on the basis of the four possible enthalpy-entropy combinations. **15.3.5** Evaluate the various theories of the end of the universe.
Lab Day 2	SLM 149–55	TLM 149–55	**Lab 15B:** *No Anchovies, Please!*—Exploring Enthalpies of Solution and Reaction	**EQ: How can I measure the energy change during the physical and chemical changes?**
Review and Test Days				Chapter 15 Test

Lesson Plan Overview

Section	Student Edition Pages	Teacher Edition Pages	Teacher Resources	Essential Questions/Content Objectives
			CHAPTER 16: *CHEMICAL KINETICS (7 days)* Key Chapter	
16.1 Reaction Rates	387–95	387–95	**Case Study:** Spontaneous Combustion Demonstrating the Effect of Concentration in a Reaction, Demonstrating the Effect of Surface Area and Temperature on Reaction Rates **Web Links:** Collision Theory, Catalysts **Mini Lab:** *Changing Reaction Rates*	**EQ:** How is a fire different from an explosion? **Objectives:** **16.1.1** Define *kinetics*. **16.1.2** Summarize the collision theory. **16.1.3** Explain why thermodynamically favorable reactions don't always occur. **16.1.4** Summarize changes in reaction rates in response to different reaction conditions.
Lab Day 1	SLM 157–62	TLM 157–62	**Lab 16A:** *Chemistry—A Contact Sport?*—Exploring Concentration's Effect on Reaction Rates	**EQ:** How does concentration affect reaction rate?
16.2 Reaction Mechanisms	396–404	396–404	**Careers:** Serving as a Pharmacologist **How It Works:** Sustained-Release Medicine	**EQ:** How does water form when hydrogen is burned? **Objectives:** **16.2.1** Explain how a reaction mechanism describes the steps that make up a chemical reaction. **16.2.2** Identify intermediate substances in the elementary steps of a reaction. **16.2.3** Interpret a rate law as it relates to changes in reactant concentration. **16.2.4** Relate the rate-determining steps to rate laws. **16.2.5** Formulate a rate law from a data table listing changes in reactant concentration.
Lab Day 2	SLM 163–68	TLM 163–68	**Lab 16B:** *Don't Overreact*—Determining a Rate Law	**EQ:** How can we determine the rate law for a chemical reaction?
Ethics Day	407	407	Medical Marijuana	**Objective:** **16.2.6** Determine an informed position on the personal use of medical marijuana.
Review and Test Days			Chapter 16 Test	

Section	Student Edition Pages	Teacher Edition Pages	Teacher Resources	Essential Questions/Content Objectives
CHAPTER 17: ***CHEMICAL EQUILIBRIUM*** *(8 days)* Key Chapter				
17.1 Equilibrium	409–15	409–15	**Web Links:** Dynamic Equilibrium, Blue Bottle Reaction, Dancing Gummi Bears **Mini Lab:** *Mix, Change, Repeat*	**EQ:** Can chemical reactions go in the reverse direction? **Objectives:** **17.1.1** Define *reversible reaction*. **17.1.2** Explain how a reaction at equilibrium continues to produce products without changing the amounts of products. **17.1.3** Write the equation for an equilibrium constant from a balanced chemical equation. **17.1.4** Solve problems involving equilibrium constants.
17.2 Le Châtelier's Principle	416–23	416–23	**Worldview Investigation:** Ethanol **How It Works:** The Haber Process **Demonstrating Reversible Color** **Web Links:** Le Châtelier's Principle, Watching the Haber Process	**EQ:** How can I produce more of the products without adding more of the reactants? **Objectives:** **17.2.1** Define *Le Châtelier's principle*. **17.2.2** Summarize the effects that various stresses will have on a system in equilibrium. **17.2.3** Predict the direction that a reaction will shift when stressed. **17.2.4** Formulate a biblical view of proper uses for ethanol.
Lab Day 1 *(2 days)*	SLM 169–70	TLM 169–70C	**Lab 17A:** *Stressed Out*—Inquiring into Le Châtelier's Principle	**EQ:** How do chemical systems respond to changing conditions?
17.3 Solution Equilibrium	424–29	424–29		**EQ:** Is it possible to calculate how much of a substance will dissolve? **Objectives:** **17.3.1** Relate the solubility of a salt to its solubility product. **17.3.2** Convert between solubilities and solubility products of solutes. **17.3.3** Predict whether a precipitate will form when two solutions are mixed when given the solubility product.
Lab Day 2	SLM 171–74	TLM 171–74	**Lab 17B:** *Precipitous Changes*—Exploring Solubility Products	**EQ:** How can we change the substance that precipitates from a chemical reaction?
Review and Test Days			Chapter 17 Test	

Lesson Plan Overview

Section	Student Edition Pages	Teacher Edition Pages	Teacher Resources	Essential Questions/Content Objectives
CHAPTER 18: *ACIDS, BASES, AND SALTS* (*7 days*) Key Chapter				
18.1 Defining Acids and Bases	435–39	435–39	**Case Study:** Royal Acid to the Rescue	**EQ:** Why do we have to test the pH of pool water? **Objectives:** **18.1.1** Describe acids and bases according to their physical and chemical properties. **18.1.2** Summarize the different definitions for acids and bases. **18.1.3** Classify a substance as an acid or base according to the Arrhenius, Brønsted-Lowry, and Lewis definitions. **18.1.4** Compare the three acid-base models. **18.1.5** Explain the relationship between conjugate acids and bases.
18.2 Acid Base Equilibria	440–51	440–51	**How It Works:** Breathalyzer **Demonstrating Red Cabbage and pH** **Web Links***:* Virtual pH Meter, Acid-Base Solutions **Mini Lab:** *Acid or Base?* (p. 452)	**EQ:** If vinegar is an acid, why can we put it on foods? **Objectives:** **18.2.1** Relate self-ionization of water to pH and pOH. **18.2.2** Solve pH and pOH problems. **18.2.3** Compare the strengths of acids. **18.2.4** Classify acids as monoprotic, polyprotic, diprotic, or triprotic on the basis of their chemical formulas. **18.2.5** Summarize how indicators work.
Lab Day 1	SLM 175–80	TLM 175–80	**Lab 18A:** *Colorful Chemistry—* Exploring Acid-Base Indicators	**EQ:** How does amount concentration of weak acids affect pH?
18.3 Neutralization	453–58	453–58	**Worldview Investigation:** Influencing Others **Web Links:** Neutralization, Buffers **Demonstrating Acids, Antacids, and pH**	**EQ:** How do antacids work? **Objectives:** **18.3.1** Write balanced chemical equations for neutralization reactions. **18.3.2** Summarize the titration process. **18.3.3** Calculate the concentration of a solution from acid-base titration data. **18.3.4** Define *buffer*. **18.3.5** Explain how a buffer system works. **18.3.6** Give examples of reactions in which buffers function. **18.3.7** Evaluate different standards of impairment.
Lab Day 2	SLM 181–86	TLM 181–86	**Lab 18B***: Say Cheese!*—Measuring Concentration by Titration	**EQ:** How do chemists determine amount concentration of acids and bases?
Review and Test Days			Chapter 18 Test	

Section	Student Edition Pages	Teacher Edition Pages	Teacher Resources	Essential Questions/Content Objectives
CHAPTER 19: *REDOX REACTIONS* (8 days) Key Chapter				
19.1 Redox Reactions *(2 days)*	463–70	463–70	**Web Links:** Redox Reaction, Screaming Gummy Reaction	**EQ:** How can I prevent my car from rusting? **Objectives:** **19.1.1** Define *oxidation-reduction reaction.* **19.1.2** Relate oxidation and reduction to the exchange of electrons. **19.1.3** Identify the oxidized and reduced substances in a redox reaction. **19.1.4** Balance redox reaction equations.
Lab Day 1	SLM 187–92	TLM 187–92	**Lab 19A:** *The Dead, Twitching Frog Mystery*—Investigating a Voltaic Cell	**EQ:** Where does the electricity in a battery come from?
19.2 Electrochemical Reactions	471–80	471–80	Demonstrating the Golden Touch, Demonstrating Electric Metal **Web Links:** Electroplating, Aluminum Smelting, How Batteries Work **Mini Lab:** *Observing a Voltaic Cell*	**EQ:** How do batteries transform chemical energy to electrical energy? **Objectives:** **19.2.1** Define *electrochemistry.* **19.2.2** Compare electrolytic and voltaic cells. **19.2.3** List (or explain) several practical applications of electrochemistry. **19.2.4** Compare rechargeable cells, fuel cells, and conventional voltaic cells. **19.2.5** Evaluate the need for battery recycling on the basis of a biblical worldview.
Lab Day 2	SLM 193–97	TLM 193–97	**Lab 19B:** *Danger under the Sink*—Using Redox Titration	**EQ:** How can I use titration of redox reactions?
Ethics Day	483	483–84	Electric Cars	**Objective:** **19.2.6** Argue for or against using electric cars to be better stewards of God's creation.
Review and Test Days			Chapter 19 Test	

Lesson Plan Overview

Section	Student Edition Pages	Teacher Edition Pages	Teacher Resources	Essential Questions/Content Objectives
CHAPTER 20: *ORGANIC CHEMISTRY* (8 days) Key Chapter				
20.1 Organic Compounds	485–87	485–87	**Careers:** Serving as an Odor Tester	**EQ:** How does organic chemistry fit within the broader study of chemistry in general? **Objectives:** **20.1.1** Define *organic compound*. **20.1.2** Explain why carbon forms so many compounds. **20.1.3** Describe the basic features of a structural formula. **20.1.4** Distinguish between aliphatic and aromatic organic compounds.
20.2 Hydrocarbons	488–96	488–96	**Web Link:** Interactive Molecular Structures	**EQ:** What chemicals are in my shampoo? **Objectives:** **20.2.1** Identify alkanes, alkenes, and alkynes from their names or formulas. **20.2.2** Draw structural formulas for compounds in common organic families. **20.2.3** Name alkanes, alkenes, and alkynes in accordance with IUPAC rules. **20.2.4** Relate the differences in physical and chemical properties to isomerism. **20.2.5** Contrast cyclic aliphatic compounds and aromatic substances.
20.3 Substituted Hydrocarbons	497–505	497–505	**Mini Lab:** *Isomerism in Substituted Hydrocarbons*	**EQ:** Does substituting one kind of atom for another in a hydrocarbon really make that big of a difference? **Objectives:** **20.3.1** Explain how functional groups affect a compound's properties. **20.3.2** Identify the functional group associated with each substituted organic compound. **20.3.3** Name substituted organic compounds using IUPAC rules. **20.3.4** Draw structural formulas for compounds with functional groups when given the IUPAC name.
Lab Day 1	SLM 199–202	TLM 199–202	**Lab 20A:** *Makes Scents!*—Synthesizing Esters	**EQ:** Where do artificial scents come from?
20.4 Organic Reactions	506–9	506–9		**EQ:** How are organic reactions classified? **Objectives:** **20.4.1** Identify reactions as redox, substitution, addition, or condensation. **20.4.2** Give examples of substitution, addition, and condensation reactions. **20.4.3** Summarize the different reactions involving organic compounds. **20.4.4** Predict the products from different organic reactions.
Lab Day 2	SLM 203–6	TLM 203–6	**Lab 20B:** *Squeaky Clean*—Investigating Soaps and Detergents	**EQ:** How do soaps and detergents work?
Review and Test Days				Chapter 20 Test

Section	Student Edition Pages	Teacher Edition Pages	Teacher Resources	Essential Questions/Content Objectives
CHAPTER 21: *BIOCHEMISTRY* (10 days) Key Chapter				
21.1 Chemistry of Life	515–16	515–16	**Web Link:** Metabolism	**EQ: Is biochemistry another name for organic chemistry?** **Objectives:** **21.1.1** Define *biochemistry*. **21.1.2** Explain the relationship between anabolism, catabolism, and metabolism.
21.2 Carbohydrates	517–21	517–21	**Demonstrating the Presence of Starch** **Mini Lab:** *Simple Sugars?*	**EQ: Are carbohydrates good or bad?** **Objectives:** **21.2.1** Define *carbohydrate*. **21.2.2** Explain the relationship between monosaccharides, disaccharides, and polysaccharides. **21.2.3** Explain the role of carbohydrates in living things.
21.3 Lipids	522–24	522–24		**EQ: Why can't I live without fats?** **Objectives:** **21.3.1** Define *lipids*. **21.3.2** Compare saturated and unsaturated fats. **21.3.3** Explain the role of lipids in living things.
Lab Day 1	SLM 207–11	TLM 207–11	**Lab 21A:** *A Balancing Act*—Testing Macronutrients in Food	**EQ: Am I eating balanced meals?**
21.4 Proteins	525–27	525–27	**Web Link:** Proteins	**EQ: What do proteins do for me?** **Objectives:** **21.4.1** Define *protein*. **21.4.2** Describe the formation and structure of proteins. **21.4.3** Explain the importance of the structure and shape of a protein molecule.
Lab Day 2	SLM 213–16	TLM 213–16	**Lab 21B:** *The Proof Is in the Jell-O*—Investigating Enzymes	**EQ: How do enzymes affect biochemical reactions?**
21.5 Nucleic Acids	528–32	528–32	**Worldview Investigation:** Abiogenesis **Web Link:** Replication, Transcription, and Translation	**EQ: How do cells know how to do things?** **Objectives:** **21.5.1** List the three parts of a nucleotide and describe their arrangement. **21.5.2** Describe how nucleic acids store information in cells. **21.5.3** Explain how information is transferred from the nucleus to other parts of cells. **21.5.4** Formulate a response to the theory of abiogenesis from a biblical worldview perspective.
Ethics Day	535	535	**Paleo Diets—Ancient Key to Modern Health?**	**Objective:** **21.5.5** Apply an understanding of biochemistry to decide whether to follow a paleo diet.
Review and Test Days			Chapter 21 Test	

Lesson Plan Overview

Section	Student Edition Pages	Teacher Edition Pages	Teacher Resources	Essential Questions/Content Objectives
CHAPTER 22: *NUCLEAR CHEMISTRY* (10 days) Enrichment Chapter				
22.1 Inside the Nucleus	537–44	537–44	**Careers:** Serving as a Nuclear Engineer	**EQ: Why do some atoms decay?** **Objectives:** **22.1.1** Define *radioactivity*. **22.1.2** Summarize the progression of scientists' understanding of radioactivity. **22.1.3** Determine whether a given nuclide is stable. **22.1.4** Relate the mass defect of a nucleus to its binding energy. **22.1.5** List instruments used to measure radiation.
22.2 Nuclear Decay	545–54	545–54	**Worldview Investigation:** Radiometric Dating (p. 555)	**EQ: How long will radioactive waste be around?** **Objectives:** **22.2.1** Compare the types of radioactive decay products. **22.2.2** Predict the type of decay that will occur for a particular isotope. **22.2.3** Write balanced equations for radioactive decay. **22.2.4** Solve half-life problems.
Lab Day 1 *(2 days)*	SLM 217–23	TLM 217–23	**Lab 22A:** *It's Only a Matter of Time*—Investigating Half-Life	**EQ: How can I model radioactive decay?**
22.3 Using Nuclear Chemistry *(2 days)*	556–65	556–65	**Web Links:** Nuclear Fission Simulation, How Do Nuclear Power Plants Work? **Mini Lab:** *Inquiring into Chain Reactions*	**EQ: Are nuclear power plants worth the risk?** **Objectives:** **22.3.1** Compare nuclear decay, nuclear reactions, and chemical reactions. **22.3.2** Distinguish between nuclear fission and fusion. **22.3.3** Write the nuclear equation for fission reactions. **22.3.4** Explain the relationship between mass of a fissionable substance and a chain reaction. **22.3.5** Calculate the energy released in a nuclear reaction. **22.3.6** Explain how worldview impacts assumptions about and conclusions drawn from radiometric dating.
Lab Day 2	SLM 225–29	TLM 225–29	**Lab 22B:** *Atomic Asteroids*—Determining Mass Defect and Binding Energy	**EQ: Where does the mass lost in a nuclear reaction go?**
Ethics Day	569	569, 569C	**Nuclear Power**	**Objective:** **22.3.7** Construct a position on whether to support or oppose building a nuclear plant near the local community.
Review and Test Days			Chapter 22 Test	

CHAPTER 12 *OBJECTIVES*

- Explain the properties of gases on the basis of the kinetic-molecular theory.
- Apply the gas laws under changing conditions.
- Predict quantities of gases involved in chemical reactions.
- Determine the molar volume of a gas in the laboratory.

OVERVIEW

Chapter 12 has key material that covers the chemistry of gases. The chapter builds upon the concepts of gas properties and laws learned in previous physical science course work and adds to these an introduction to gas stoichiometry.

12.1 PROPERTIES OF GASES

- *Kinetic-Molecular Description of Gases*
- *The Physical Properties of Gases*
- *How Gases Cause Pressure*
- *Pressure, Volume, and Temperature*

12.2 GAS LAWS

- *Standard Conditions*
- *Boyle's Law: Pressures and Volumes*
- *Charles's Law: Temperatures and Volumes*
- *Gay-Lussac's Law: Temperatures and Pressures*
- *The Combined Gas Law*
- *Dalton's Law of Partial Pressures: Mixtures of Gases*

12.3 GAS STOICHIOMETRY

- *Gases in Reactions*
- *The Molar Volume of a Gas*
- *Ideal Gases*
- *The Ideal Gas Law*
- *Stoichiometry Involving Gases*
- *The Densities of Gases*

LAB ACTIVITIES

Lab 12A: *Cold and Calculating*—Students create an air column to help them extrapolate the value of absolute zero.

Lab 12B: *An Aquanaut's World*—Students generate oxygen and predict its mass, both actual and theoretical.

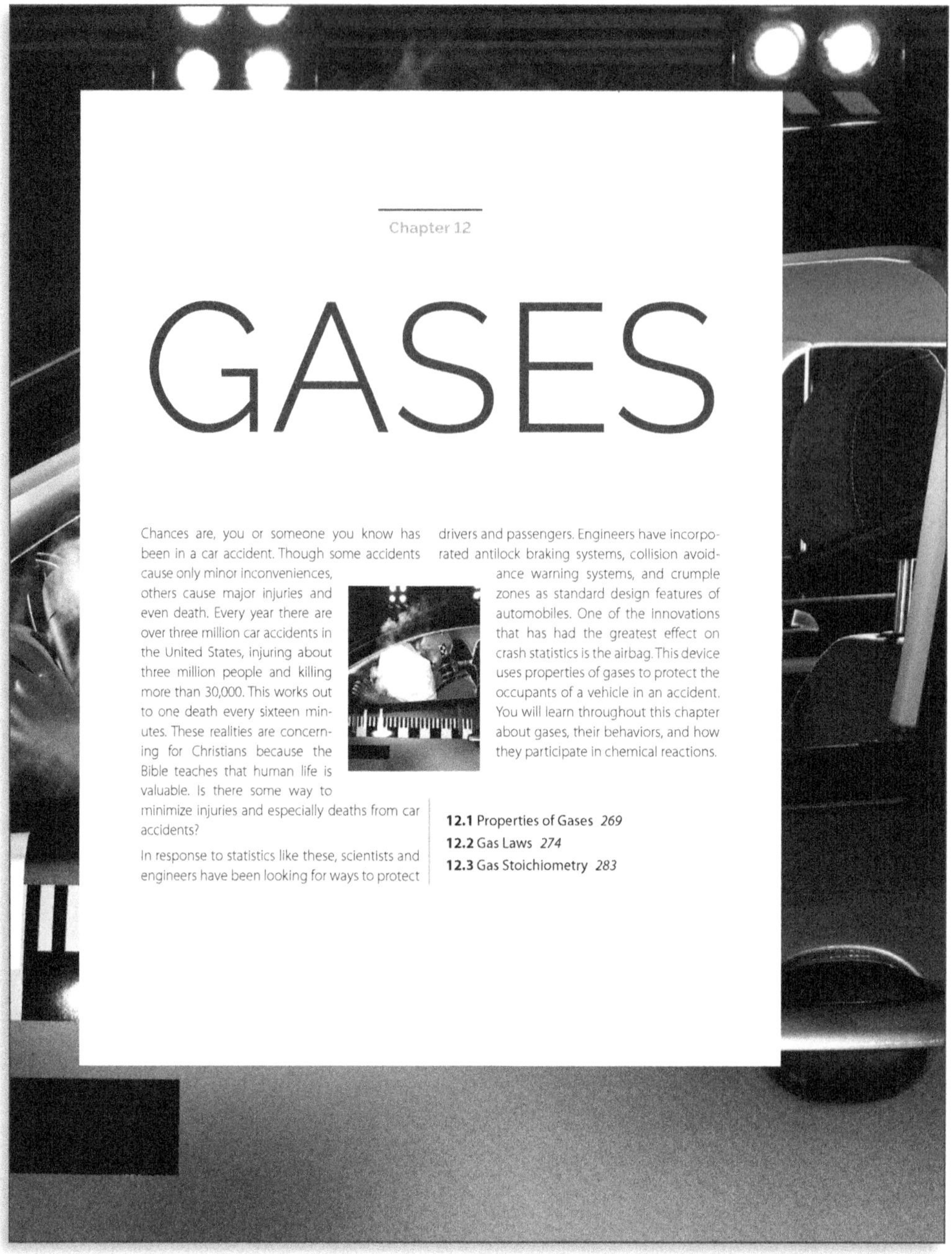

Chapter 12

GASES

Chances are, you or someone you know has been in a car accident. Though some accidents cause only minor inconveniences, others cause major injuries and even death. Every year there are over three million car accidents in the United States, injuring about three million people and killing more than 30,000. This works out to one death every sixteen minutes. These realities are concerning for Christians because the Bible teaches that human life is valuable. Is there some way to minimize injuries and especially deaths from car accidents?

In response to statistics like these, scientists and engineers have been looking for ways to protect drivers and passengers. Engineers have incorporated antilock braking systems, collision avoidance warning systems, and crumple zones as standard design features of automobiles. One of the innovations that has had the greatest effect on crash statistics is the airbag. This device uses properties of gases to protect the occupants of a vehicle in an accident. You will learn throughout this chapter about gases, their behaviors, and how they participate in chemical reactions.

The Chapter opener shows an image of the moment that an airbag is deployed during a crash test. This quick response occurs due to a series of rapid chemical reactions.

12.1 PROPERTIES OF GASES

Kinetic-Molecular Description of Gases

Have you ever let a helium balloon go, watching it rise into the sky and drift with the wind? It seems like it will never stop rising until it reaches space! At some point, however, the balloon does stop rising. Either the helium no longer has a density low enough to make the balloon continue to rise, or the balloon pops when it is stretched beyond its capacity due to the difference between internal and atmospheric pressures. The kinetic-molecular theory, introduced in Chapter 2, explains the behavior of gases, such as helium in a balloon, on the basis of the motion of particles. The theory was developed to explain the observations of physical properties of gases obtained from many experiments. This theory is summarized in the following five statements.

Why do gases behave as they do?

QUESTIONS

- How do scientists describe gas behavior?
- What causes gas pressure?
- How are temperature, pressure, and volume related in gases?

TERMS

diffusion • effusion • Graham's law of effusion • fluid • compressibility • expansibility • pressure

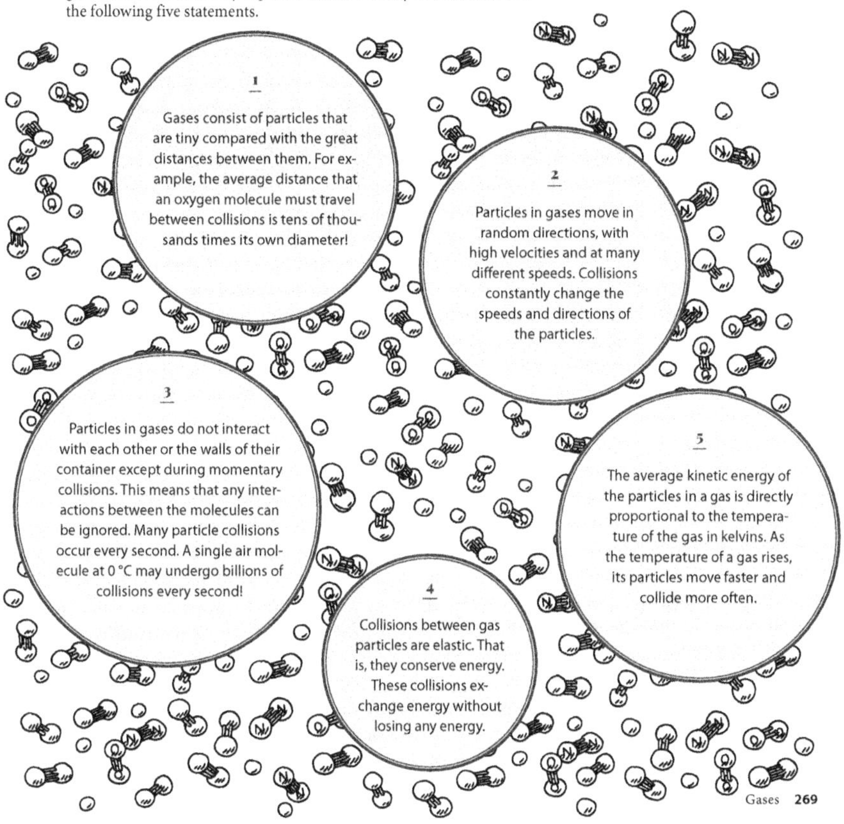

SECTION 12.1 *OVERVIEW*

Essential Question

Why do gases behave as they do?

Objectives

» **12.1.1** State the kinetic-molecular theory of gases.

» **12.1.2** Convert measurements between different units of pressure.

» **12.1.3** Relate the pressure, volume, and temperature of gases to the kinetic-molecular theory.

Resources

Demonstrating the Diffusion and Reaction of Gases, Demonstrating Pressure

ENGAGE

THINKING ABOUT GASES

Assess prior knowledge with a **think-pair-share**. Have students write down all they know about gases. Tell them to think of the properties of gases that they may have learned in physical science. Next, have them pair up with another student and direct each pair to share their information with each other. Select students to share their answers with the class. Take some time to discuss any misconceptions and highlight any correct descriptions.

INSTRUCT

KINETIC-MOLECULAR THEORY

Lead students to **recall** the kinetic-molecular theory, which was introduced in Chapter 2. Call on students to describe this theory and ask how it can apply to gases.

Remind students that this theory is a prediction, not an observation. It is a model to help scientists explain what they observe.

DEMONSTRATING THE DIFFUSION AND REACTION OF GASES

Demonstrate the diffusion and reaction of gases.

Materials: large, clear glass container; glass plate to cover container; petri dishes (2); cotton balls or swabs (2); tongs; household ammonia; 6 M hydrochloric acid

Note: Perform this demonstration in a fume hood or other well-ventilated area and wear gloves and goggles.

Procedure: Place the two petri dishes several feet apart. Pour a small amount of ammonia (NH_3) in one petri dish and a small amount of hydrochloric acid (HCl) in the other. Drop a cotton ball into each dish and let them soak up everything in the dishes. Remove the cotton balls with tongs and place them on opposite sides in the glass container. Don't let the cotton balls touch! Quickly cover the container. You should observe a faint white cloud appear between the cotton balls. Ask students where the cloud came from. *(from the diffusion and then reaction of NH_3 and HCl)*

Make sure that students understand that the aqueous solutions of NH_3 and HCl are not reacting; the gaseous forms of these compounds are. The reaction taking place is

$$NH_3(g) + HCl(g) \longrightarrow NH_4Cl(s).$$

Cleanup: Check your local laws and regulations for either neutralizing or disposing of the soaked cotton balls. Rinse all the dishes with a copious amount of water and then clean them with soap and water.

The Physical Properties of Gases

The kinetic-molecular theory is a very workable model for explaining the physical properties of gases that we observe.

DIFFUSION AND EFFUSION

When a gas enters a vacuum (a space containing no matter) or mixes with another gas, it spreads out to uniformly fill the entire volume over time. This process is called **diffusion**. Diffusion occurs because gas molecules are in constant motion. **Effusion** is a related process in which gas particles pass through a tiny opening into an evacuated chamber or space. Both of these processes are directly related to the speed and constant motion of gas particles.

In 1846 British chemist Thomas Graham experimented with various gases. In his studies he allowed gases at the same temperature to effuse into a vacuum. He discovered that the rate of effusion was inversely related to a gas's molar mass. Mathematically, **Graham's law of effusion**, also known as *Graham's law of diffusion*, states that the rate of effusion for a gas is inversely proportional to the square root of its molar mass. This relationship is true because at the same temperature, two different gases have the same kinetic energy. Therefore, the lighter of the two gases moves faster. Because lighter gas particles move faster, they spread more quickly. This law provides a way to experimentally compare molar masses.

$$\textit{rate of effusion} \propto \frac{1}{\sqrt{\textit{molar mass}}}$$

($\propto$ indicates "is proportional to")

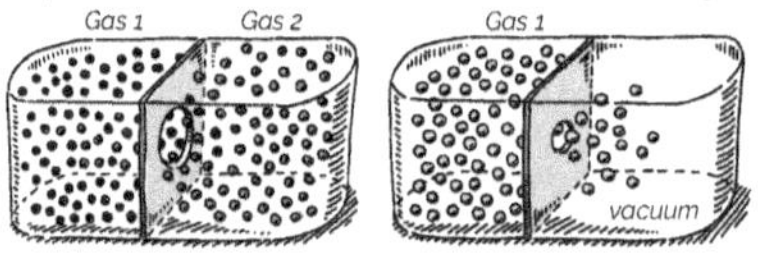

diffusion *effusion*

This same law allows us to calculate the ratio between effusion rates of two different gases using the following formula.

$$\frac{\textit{rate of effusion}_{\text{gas 1}}}{\textit{rate of effusion}_{\text{gas 2}}} = \frac{\sqrt{\textit{molar mass}_{\text{gas 2}}}}{\sqrt{\textit{molar mass}_{\text{gas 1}}}}$$

EXAMPLE 12-1: CALCULATING AN EFFUSION RATE RATIO

Calculate the ratio of effusion rates between nitrogen (N_2) and argon (Ar).

Write what you know.

$\textit{molar mass}_{N_2} = 28.02$ g/mol

$\textit{molar mass}_{Ar} = 39.95$ g/mol

$$\frac{\textit{rate of effusion}_{N_2}}{\textit{rate of effusion}_{Ar}} = ?$$

Write the formula and solve for the unknown.

$$\frac{\textit{rate of effusion}_{N_2}}{\textit{rate of effusion}_{Ar}} = \frac{\sqrt{\textit{molar mass}_{Ar}}}{\sqrt{\textit{molar mass}_{N_2}}}$$

Plug in known values and evaluate.

$$\frac{\textit{rate of effusion}_{N_2}}{\textit{rate of effusion}_{Ar}} = \frac{\sqrt{39.95 \frac{\cancel{g}}{\cancel{mol}}}}{\sqrt{28.02 \frac{\cancel{g}}{\cancel{mol}}}} = 1.194$$

This result indicates that the lighter nitrogen gas, which moves fast, will effuse 1.194 times faster than the argon gas.

FLUIDITY

Gas particles are able to move past one another like particles in liquids. Both liquids and gases can be poured, so both are considered **fluids**—they have the ability to flow, enabling them to take the shape of their container.

COMPRESSIBILITY AND EXPANSIBILITY

Though liquids do not easily compress, gases have the ability to change their volume to fit their containers. High pressures can squeeze gases into smaller volumes, a property that is called **compressibility**. When gases experience lower pressure, they quickly expand to fill the available space. This ability to spontaneously fill the available space is called **expansibility**. Gases will expand until they are constrained by an external force, thus they always fill their containers. Empty spaces between constantly moving gas molecules make these properties possible.

Helium gas is compressed into a canister for storage and shipping, but it quickly expands when released to inflate balloons.

How Gases Cause Pressure

Gas molecules collide with each other billions of times each second. They also collide with things like trees, buildings, people, and the walls of their containers. Though individual collisions are not very forceful, they add up to produce a significant force. **Pressure** is the average force exerted per unit of area when particles collide against a boundary. It is the observable result of billions of molecular collisions. The total pressure is dependent on the number of collisions that occur and how energetic those collisions are.

We experience gas pressure every moment of our lives due to the pressure exerted on us as the gas in the atmosphere collides with our bodies. These collisions result in a normal atmospheric pressure at sea level of 101 325 pascals (Pa). The pascal, which is named for French physicist Blaise Pascal, is the SI unit of pressure. A *pascal* is defined as the pressure produced by one newton (the SI unit of force) acting on an area of one square meter: 1 Pa = 1 N/m^2. A pascal is a small amount of pressure, so for many applications scientists will use kilopascals (kPa).

Pressure, Volume, and Temperature

A gas's volume depends not only on how many gas molecules are present but also on its temperature and pressure. According to the kinetic-molecular theory, a gas at a given temperature contains particles that are moving in random directions at many different speeds. These particles collide with the walls of their container, exerting a pressure on the walls. The average kinetic energy of these particles determines the gas's temperature. In a nonrigid vessel, the pressure exerted on the container will determine the volume of the container.

The graph at right shows how gas particles behave at different temperatures. At 0 °C, many hydrogen molecules move at speeds near 1500 m/s—some slower and some faster. The average speed of 1500 m/s causes the temperature to be 0 °C. At 500 °C, hydrogen molecules move faster, making the average speed greater. Let's look at three different scenarios to see how a gas's pressure, temperature, and volume are all related.

Notice how the average speed of hydrogen molecules shifts with temperature increase.

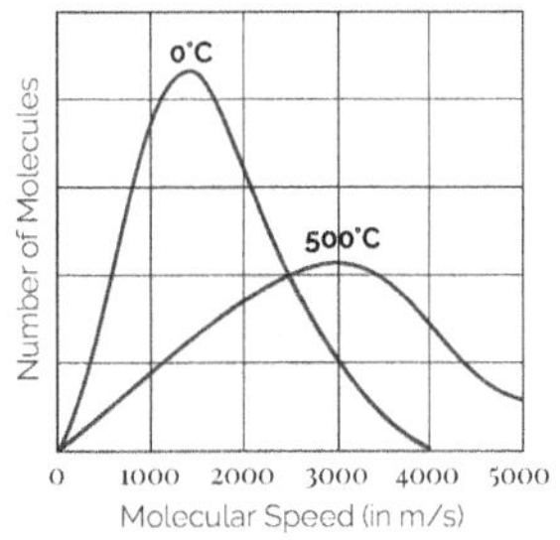

EXPANDING GASES

Some students may ask why the gases in the atmosphere don't just expand out into space. As stated in the Student Edition, the gases in the atmosphere will expand until constrained by an external force. In the case of atmospheric gases, the external force is Earth's gravity. Without sufficient gravity the gases in the atmosphere would fly off into space. This is the reason that the moon has no appreciable atmosphere.

Gases 271

DEMONSTRATING PRESSURE

Demonstrate the effects of pressure.

Materials: large syringe (without needle tip), marshmallows

Procedure: Place a marshmallow in the syringe and put your finger on the open tip so that air cannot escape.

Performance/Discussion: Give students an opportunity to handle the syringe. Have them depress and then pull back up on the plunger to see how pressure affects the marshmallow.

Ask students why the marshmallow decreases in size when the plunger is depressed and increases in size when it's pulled up. *(When the plunger is depressed in the syringe, the air molecules are compressed; the tiny air pockets inside the marshmallow also compress, increasing pressure and causing the marshmallow to decrease in size. When the plunger is pulled, the pressure decreases, allowing the expanding air to fill the syringe and causing the marshmallow to increase in size.)*

APPLY

RELATIONSHIP EXAMPLES

Lead students in a **collaborative learning** activity. Divide the class in groups of two to four. Tell each group to select one example from each case and explain how it relates pressure, temperature, and volume.

Case 1: using a plunger; underwater bubbles growing larger as they rise to the surface; popping your eardrums at higher altitudes *(relating pressure and volume)*

Case 2: inflating a hot air balloon; using a pop-up timer to heat meat to a certain temperature; heating a dented table tennis ball to pop out the dent *(relating temperature and volume)*

Case 3: a soft drink container exploding when left in a hot car *(relating temperature and pressure)*

Why Do Pressure, Temperature, and Volume Change?

In each case, parentheses indicate which statement of the kinetic-molecular theory is referenced (see page 269).

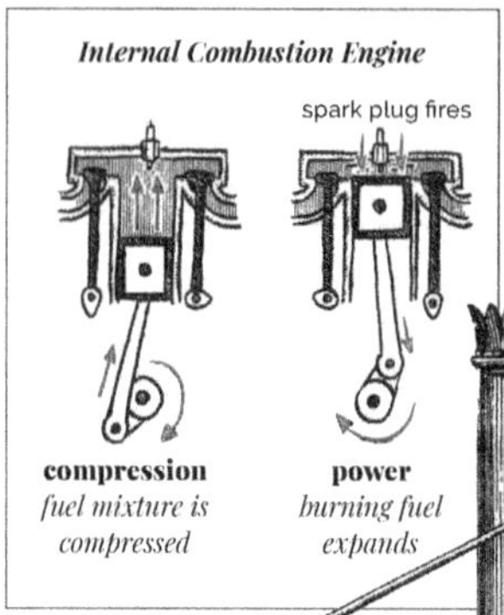

Case 1:
PRESSURE AND VOLUME

What happens to the pressure of a gas if we change its volume? As volume goes down and temperature is held constant, pressure increases. We can do this with a piston in a cylinder: the movable piston moves inward, decreasing the volume. By decreasing the volume, the particles are forced closer together (kinetic-molecular theory Statement 1, or S1), increasing the number of collisions with the walls (S2, S3). With more collisions, pressure on the walls also increases (S4). Additionally, there is a reduction in the surface area of the container. If we were to increase the volume at a constant temperature, pressure would decrease due to fewer collisions occurring. This is an inverse relationship.

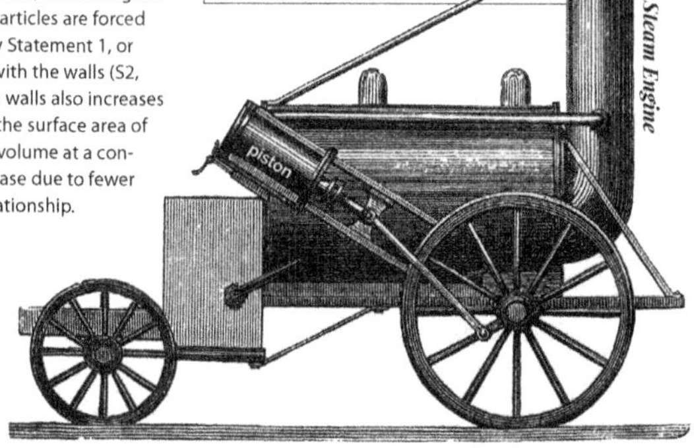

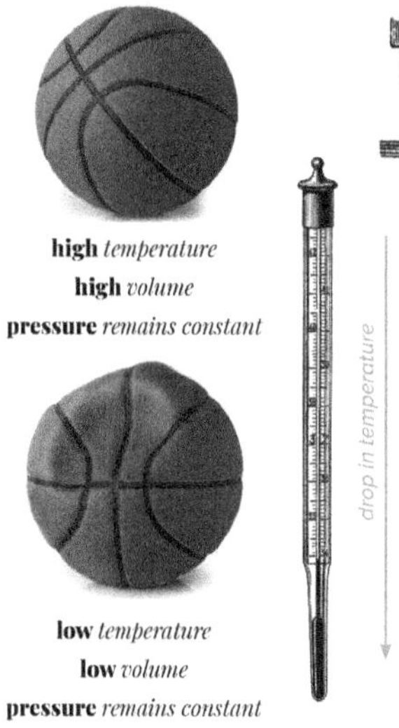

Case 2:
TEMPERATURE AND VOLUME

You left your basketball out overnight. You pick it up and try to dribble it and notice that it doesn't bounce like it did yesterday afternoon. What happened? As the air in the ball cooled, the gas particles moved slower (S5). The slower-moving particles collided with the interior of the ball less often (S3) and with less energy (S4, S5). Because the pressure remained constant, the ball contracted and so now has less volume. As gas temperature decreased with the pressure held constant, the volume of the gas also decreased.

This is a direct relationship. If you were to let the ball warm up again, the volume would also increase and the ball would bounce just like it did yesterday.

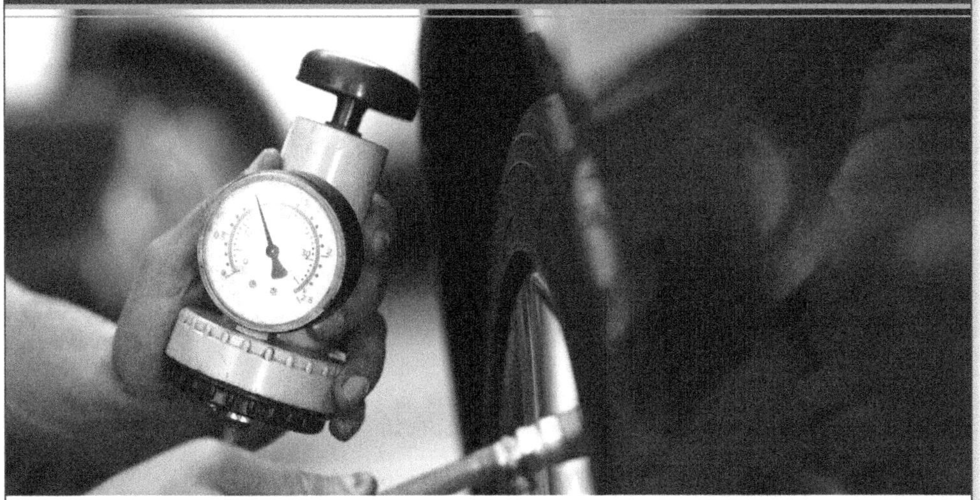

Case 3: TEMPERATURE AND PRESSURE

The owner's manual of your car tells you the proper *cold* tire pressure. Why does the temperature matter for having the proper pressure? As the temperature of a gas increases, its particles have a higher average kinetic energy (S5). The particles move faster, collide more often (S3), and strike with more force (S4). As force increases, pressure increases because of additional and more forceful collisions. Therefore, in a fixed volume, as in your tires, pressure will increase as temperature increases. The cold inflation pressure ensures that you won't exceed the limits of the tires as they warm up. The converse is also true, meaning that you will likely have to add air to your tires when the weather turns cold. This relationship is also direct.

The relationships between pressure, temperature, and volume shown in these three cases can be summarized with the following proportionalities.

$$P \propto \frac{1}{V} \text{ (constant } T\text{)}$$

$$T \propto V \text{ (constant } P\text{)}$$

$$P \propto T \text{ (constant } V\text{)}$$

12.1 SECTION REVIEW

1. List the five statements of the kinetic-molecular theory of gases.
2. Define *diffusion*.
3. If samples of oxygen and carbon dioxide are at the same temperature and are released into a large room, which sample will diffuse faster? Explain.
4. What causes gas pressure?
5. Use the statements of the kinetic-molecular theory to explain why pressure in a cylinder increases if you compress the gas in the cylinder to one-fifth its original volume.
6. You have a sample of gas in a 1 L balloon. Use the kinetic-molecular theory to explain what will happen to the volume of the balloon if the temperature of the gas is doubled at a constant pressure.
7. Aerosol cans display a label warning against incinerating them. According to the kinetic-molecular theory, why shouldn't an aerosol can be incinerated?

ASSESS

TICKET OUT THE DOOR

Check for understanding with this **summarizing activity**. Ask, "If you have a constant quantity of gas at constant temperature and you decrease the volume, will the pressure increase or decrease?" *(increase)*

12.1 REVIEW ANSWERS

1. (1) Gases consist of tiny, widely spaced particles. (2) Particles in gases move in random directions with high velocities. (3) Particles in gases do not interact with each other or with the walls of their container except during momentary collisions. (4) Collisions between gas particles are elastic, causing them to change their directions and velocities. (5) The average kinetic energy of the particles in a gas is related to its temperature. *(p. 269)*
2. In diffusion, gases spread out to fill their containers due to the constant movement of particles in random directions. *(p. 270)*
3. The oxygen will diffuse faster because the rate of diffusion is proportional to the inverse square root of the molar mass of the gas. Oxygen has a lower molar mass, resulting in a higher diffusion rate. *(p. 270)*
4. Gas pressure is caused by the constantly moving particles of a gas colliding with their container. *(p. 271)*
5. At a constant temperature, the particles in a gas have a constant average velocity. In a smaller space, the particles are closer together (Statement 1) and will collide with the container more often (S3), resulting in more force being applied (S4). Also, those collisions will occur over a decreased surface area. These factors will result in increased pressure. *(pp. 269, 272)*
6. As the temperature of the gas is doubled, the kinetic energy of the gas particles will also double. The higher kinetic energy will result in more collisions between the gas particles and the balloon. These collisions will also be more forceful. As the force on the balloon increases, the balloon will expand until the pressure in the balloon equals the pressure outside the balloon. Therefore, the volume will increase. Some students may recognize that the volume will also be doubled. *(p. 272)*
7. An aerosol can is rigid, so the volume of the gas is held constant. Incinerating a can would increase the temperature of the gas, causing the kinetic energy of the particles to increase (Statement 5). Therefore, there would be more collisions (S3) and more forceful collisions (S4). Under these conditions, the pressure of the gas would also increase, possibly to the point of structural failure of the can and potentially causing damage or injury. *(p. 273)*

SECTION 12.2 *OVERVIEW*

Essential Question

Why do balloons stop getting bigger?

Objectives

» **12.2.1** State Boyle's, Charles's, Gay-Lussac's, and the combined gas laws qualitatively and mathematically.

» **12.2.2** Calculate the pressure, volume, or temperature of a gas under changing conditions.

» **12.2.3** Use the kinetic-molecular theory of gases to explain the gas laws.

» **12.2.4** Calculate the amount of gas produced from a solution by applying Dalton's law of partial pressures.

Resources

Case Study: When Oxygen is Bad

Demonstrating Boyle's Law #1, Demonstrating Boyle's Law #2, Demonstrating Charles's Law

Web Links: Boyle's Law, Charles's Law, Gay-Lussac's Law

Mini Lab: *Changing Volume*; Lab 12A: *Cold and Calculating*—Finding Absolute Zero

ENGAGE

PROPERTIES OF GASES

Direct students in a **peer teacher** review activity. Before beginning, allow them three minutes to plan which concept from Section 12.1 that they would like to teach to a peer. When the time is up, tell students to gather in groups of two. Each student should then teach his chosen concept to his peer. Students may choose to illustrate or directly instruct from their books or use their notes as a guide. Inform the class that the goal is to make the concepts they teach clear and easy for their peers to understand. Circulate around the room as they are teaching and provide assistance as necessary.

QUESTIONS
» How can I predict the behavior of gases?
» How can I calculate changes in the pressure, temperature, and volume of a gas?
» Why do the gas laws work?
» How can I solve gas problems for mixtures of gases?

TERMS
standard temperature and pressure (STP) • Boyle's law • Charles's law • Gay-Lussac's law • combined gas law • Dalton's law of partial pressures

12.2 GAS LAWS

Standard Conditions

So far we have qualitatively described how gases behave. However, we can make these descriptions quantitative by using a series of gas laws that are based on the kinetic-molecular theory. These gas laws can be used to calculate volumes, pressures, and temperatures of gases at various conditions.

Why do balloons stop getting bigger?

Because the volume of a gas can change with temperature and pressure, reporting a volume without specifying these conditions is meaningless. Scientists have defined a standard temperature and pressure to be used when comparing volumes of gases. **Standard temperature and pressure (STP)** are 0 °C and 101.325 kPa.

Boyle's Law: Pressures and Volumes

Robert Boyle

Anglo-Irish physicist Robert Boyle was the first to study the relationship between the pressure and volume of a sample of gas. He summed up this relationship mathematically in what is called **Boyle's law**. The law states that the volume of a gas is inversely related to its pressure if the temperature is held constant (Case 1). In equation form, this law is

$$PV = k,$$

where P is pressure, V is volume, and k is a constant.

274 Chapter 12

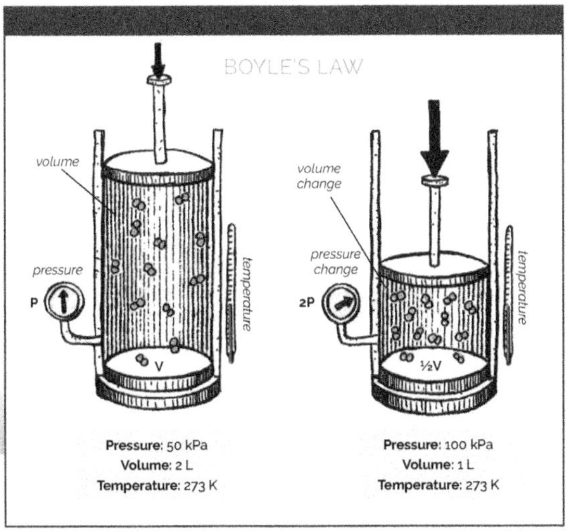

Think back to the cylinder in Case 1 on page 272. As the volume decreased, the particles were pushed together, increasing the number of collisions on a smaller surface area. So we see that, if the temperature is held constant, as the volume of a sample of gas goes down, pressure increases. The product of pressure and volume remains constant for the sample of gas. The equation below is a form of Boyle's law that can be used to solve problems when pressures and volumes of gases change.

$$P_1V_1 = k = P_2V_2$$

EXAMPLE 12-2: USING BOYLE'S LAW

Gas in a cylinder occupies 455 mL at 103.35 kPa. How much space does the gas occupy if we increase pressure to 113.48 kPa at a constant temperature?

Write what you know.

$V_1 = 455$ mL
$P_1 = 103.35$ kPa
$P_2 = 113.48$ kPa
$V_2 = ?$

Write the formula and solve for the unknown.

$$P_1V_1 = P_2V_2$$

$$\frac{P_1V_1}{P_2} = \frac{\cancel{P_2}V_2}{\cancel{P_2}}$$

$$V_2 = \frac{P_1V_1}{P_2}$$

Plug in known values and evaluate.

$$V_2 = \frac{(103.35\ \cancel{\text{kPa}})(455\ \text{mL})}{113.48\ \cancel{\text{kPa}}}$$

$$= 414\ \text{mL}$$

The increased pressure would compress the gas to 414 mL.

INSTRUCT

DEMONSTRATING BOYLE'S LAW #1

Demonstrate the effect of lowered pressure on volume.

Materials: vacuum pump; vacuum hose; bell jar; 50 mL beaker; can of shaving cream (not shaving gel), can of whipped cream, or marshmallows; tape

Preparation: Attach one end of the vacuum hose to the pump and the other end to the valve on the bell jar. Slightly inflate the balloon (5 cm diameter) and firmly tie the neck closed.

Performance/Discussion: Tape the neck of the balloon to the top of the inside of the bell jar. Place the bell jar on its base and turn on the pump. As air is evacuated, the pressure decreases and the balloon size increases. Make sure that students understand this relationship and its cause: gas particles in the balloon, with less pressure on them, spread out and expand the balloon.

Turn off the pump, remove the hose, and remove the balloon. The balloon will shrink; ask students why. *(The balloon is acclimating to atmospheric pressure.)*

Shake the shaving cream can and fill half the beaker with shaving cream. Place the beaker on the base, cover with the bell jar, attach the hose, and turn on the pump. The shaving cream will greatly expand as the pressure decreases. Ask students why the foam has expanded. *(The foam contains gas bubbles, and the decreased pressure allows each bubble to expand.)*

DEMONSTRATING BOYLE'S LAW #2

Demonstrate the effect of lowered volume on pressure.

Materials: hot plate, empty 12 oz soda can, water, tongs, large watertight container (at least 10 cm square and 15 cm deep)

Note: An aquarium or very large beaker will also work for the container.

Preparation: Fill three-fourths of the container with water. Place 25 mL of water in the soda can.

Performance/Discussion: Heat the can on the hot plate. When the water in the can has been boiling for thirty seconds, lift the can with the tongs and quickly invert it and place it in the container of water. Make sure that the mouth of the can is completely submerged. The can will instantly implode.

Conclusion: Ask students what happened. This demonstration is not quite as straightforward as the previous one, so you may have to guide students to the answer. Mention to them that 1 mol of liquid water has a volume of about 18 mL and 1 mol of gaseous water (steam) has a volume of about 30 600 mL—that's a big difference!

Lead students to the conclusion that heating the water in the can increases the water's volume as it turns to steam. Dunking the can in room-temperature water causes the steam in the can to rapidly condense. This change from high-volume steam to low-volume liquid lowers the pressure in the can. Since the can's mouth is sealed by the surrounding water, the low pressure in the can cannot equalize with the higher pressure surrounding it, and so the higher pressure outside the can crushes it.

This demonstration can also help you transition into presenting Charles's law because the first part (heating the water to increase its volume) shows the relationship between temperature and volume when pressure is constant.

BOYLE'S LAW

For an animation of Boyle's law, visit TeacherToolsOnline.com. Under Additional Resources, click on Chapter 12 Web Links. Then click on *Boyle's Law*.

MINI LAB: *CHANGING VOLUME*

Use this **mini lab** to help students understand how a change in the temperature of a gas affects its volume.

Answers

1. Answers will vary. Encourage students to develop a testable hypothesis. *Example*: A balloon deflates and sinks because it loses some of the air particles inside it.
2. A balloon inflates because more gas particles are being put into it. It stops inflating once the internal pressure balances with the external atmospheric pressure.
3. Answers will vary. Many students will recognize that the volume of the balloon will decrease.
4. It decreased.
5. It decreased.
6. As a balloon cools off, its volume decreases. Since its mass doesn't change and its volume is smaller, its density increases. A balloon sinks when its density is greater than the density of the surrounding air.

MINI LAB

CHANGING VOLUME

If you have ever watched a hot air balloon, you know that it rises as a burner heats the air in the balloon. If the burner is turned off, the balloon will begin to sink. We know that things float or sink depending on whether they are less dense or more dense than the fluid in which they are submerged. So a balloon sinks because it becomes more dense than the air around it. How does this happen?

How does a change in temperature of a gas affect its volume?

EQUIPMENT

- bucket
- ice
- balloon
- marker
- string
- spoon

1. Hypothesize why you think a hot air balloon sinks in the air around it.

Procedure

A Fill the bucket half full with ice.

B Add water until the bucket is three-quarters full.

C Inflate the balloon and tie it closed.

2. Why does a party balloon expand as you blow it up? Why doesn't it continue inflating after you stop blowing into it?

D Using the marker, draw a line around the circumference of the balloon.

E Using the string, measure the circumference of the balloon. Mark the circumference on the string.

3. What do you think will happen to the balloon if it is submerged in the ice water?

F Stir the water and then submerge the balloon.

G After ten minutes, retrieve the balloon and measure the circumference again.

Conclusion

4. What happened to the circumference?
5. What happened to the volume?

Going Further

6. Why does a hot air balloon sink when the burner below it is off?

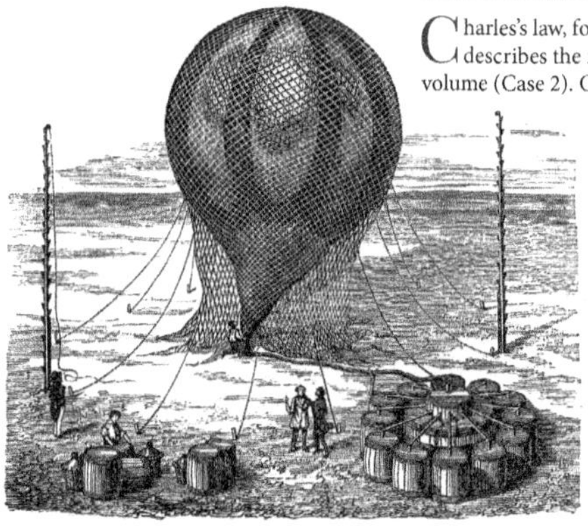

Charles's Law: Temperatures and Volumes

Charles's law, formulated by French physicist Jacques Charles, describes the relationship between a gas sample's temperature and volume (Case 2). Careful measurements of the volume of a gas at different temperatures and constant pressure yield data like that listed in Table 12-1. We can see from this table that temperature and volume are directly proportional when pressure is constant.

TABLE 12-1

Effect of Temperature on Volume

Temperature (K)	Volume (mL)
400	1000
200	500
100	250

Graphing these values with temperature on the x-axis and volume on the y-axis shows that the volume would approach zero at a temperature of 0 K. This extrapolation of gas volumes led to the development of the Kelvin temperature scale. On this scale, the lowest temperature that is theoretically possible (−273 °C) is labeled 0 K—absolute zero.

Charles's law states that when the pressure of a sample of a gas is held constant, the temperature in kelvins and the volume are directly related. Mathematically, this law is stated as

$$\frac{V}{T} = k,$$

where T is temperature in kelvins, V is volume, and k is a constant.

Remember the basketball (Case 2 on page 272) that sat out overnight? As the temperature decreased, the particles' kinetic energy decreased (S5). This meant that the particles collided with the inside of the ball less often (S3) and the collisions were less forceful (S4). Since the volume of the ball was changeable, the ball's volume also decreased to maintain a constant pressure. So when a sample of gas is held at a constant pressure, no matter what changes occur, the ratio between volume and temperature in kelvins will remain the same.

$$\frac{V_1}{T_1} = k = \frac{V_2}{T_2}$$

Remember that the temperature has to be in kelvins for Charles's law to work properly, though the volume can be measured in any unit. The reason for this is that the Kelvin scale is designed on the basis of thermodynamic temperature. Also, if you were to not use an absolute temperature scale, you could end up with negative volumes.

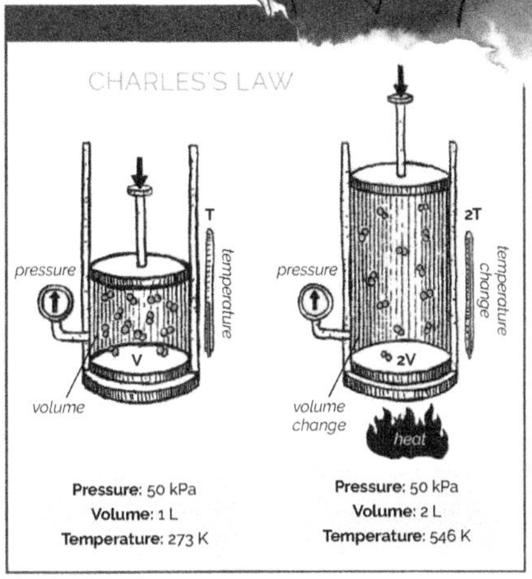

EXAMPLE 12-3: USING CHARLES'S LAW

A sample of gas occupies 3.75 L at 25 °C. Assuming that pressure is held constant, how much space will it occupy at standard temperature?

Write what you know.

$V_1 = 3.75$ L
$T_1 = 25$ °C $= 25 + 273.15 = 29\underline{8}.15$ K
$T_2 = 0$ °C $= 273$ K
$V_2 = ?$

Write the formula and solve for the unknown.

$$\frac{V_1}{T_1} = \frac{V_2}{T_2}$$

$$\left(\frac{V_1}{T_1}\right)T_2 = \left(\frac{V_2}{\cancel{T_2}}\right)\cancel{T_2}$$

$$V_2 = \left(\frac{V_1}{T_1}\right)T_2$$

Plug in known values and evaluate.

$$V_2 = \left(\frac{3.75\ \text{L}}{298.15\ \text{K}}\right)273\ \text{K}$$
$$= 3.43\text{L}$$

As the temperature decreased to standard temperature, the volume decreased to 3.43 L.

DEMONSTRATING CHARLES'S LAW

Demonstrate the effect of changing temperature on volume.

Material: balloon (the long kind used for making balloon animals), centimeter ruler, marker, baking sheet, oven, refrigerator

Procedure: Preheat the oven to 150 °F. Blow up a balloon to slightly less than its full length. On the balloon, draw a stick figure 10 cm long, his feet facing the tied end of the balloon. Place the balloon in a pan and place the pan in the oven.

Performance/Discussion: After ten minutes, remove the balloon and immediately measure the height of the stick figure. The balloon will have expanded and stretched its height. Ask students why the balloon expanded. *(When the gas in the balloon was heated, the gas particles moved faster and increased the pressure, expanding the balloon.)*

Place the same balloon in a freezer. After fifteen minutes, remove the balloon and measure the stick figure. The balloon will have contracted and the height of the stick figure will have decreased. Students should recognize by now the direct effect that a change in a gas's temperature has on its volume.

CHARLES'S LAW

For an animation of Charles's law, visit TeacherToolsOnline.com. Under Additional Resources, click on Chapter 12 Web Links. Then click on *Charles's Law*.

REARRANGING CHARLES'S LAW

Students can also solve Charles's law problems by plugging in the known values and cross multiplying to solve for the unknown.

TIRE PRESSURE

Use **Socratic questioning** to discuss temperature and pressure.

1. Why do people add air to their tires when it's cold outside? *(As temperature decreases, the volume of air in each tire also decreases.)*
2. When should you check air pressure in a tire? Why then? *(It's best to check before driving while tires are cold and when pressure is at its normal level. It's also inadvisable to check after a long trip when the friction from the road has raised the temperature of the tire, causing pressure to increase.)*
3. Why do people often add air to their tires but usually never let any out? *(Tires are permeable, and so the air slowly permeates the tire rubber and leaks out over time.)*

GAY-LUSSAC'S LAW

For an animation of Gay-Lussac's law, visit TeacherToolsOnline.com. Under Additional Resources, click on Chapter 12 Web Links. Then click on *Gay-Lussac's Law*.

COMBINING THE GAS LAWS

Direct students to create **Venn diagrams** for the three gas laws. This will help them differentiate between them and understand their similarities.

Gay-Lussac's Law: Temperatures and Pressures

The pressure in a car's tires increases as tires heat up on a lengthy trip. This is an example of **Gay-Lussac's law**, named in honor of French chemist Joseph Louis Gay-Lussac, which states that pressure is directly proportional to temperature in kelvins for a fixed mass of gas held at a constant volume (Case 3 on page 273). The law is expressed mathematically as

$$\frac{P}{T} = k,$$

where P is pressure, T is temperature in kelvins, and k is a constant.

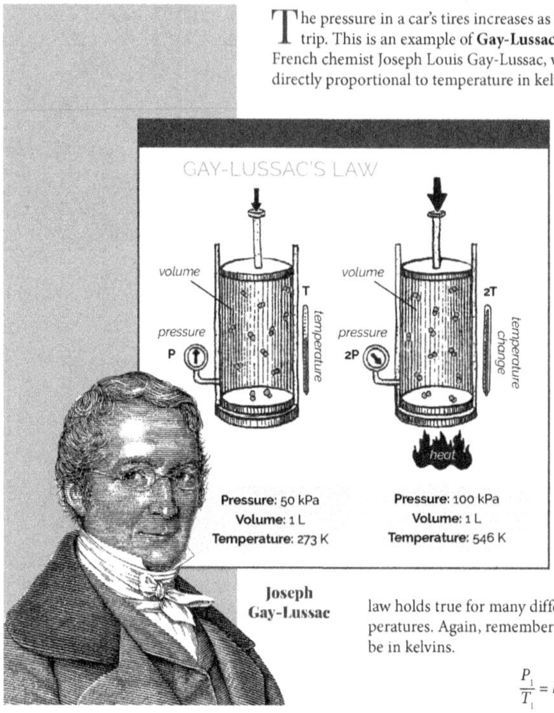

Joseph Gay-Lussac

As mentioned in Case 3, the pressure in the tires increased as temperature increased. Friction with the road raises the temperature of the air inside the tires. Gas molecules move faster (S5), collide more often (S3), and transfer more force (S4) to the inner walls of the tires. Since the volume is essentially fixed, pressure increases. As long as volume is held constant, Gay-Lussac's law holds true for many different pressures and temperatures. Again, remember that the temperature must be in kelvins.

$$\frac{P_1}{T_1} = k = \frac{P_2}{T_2}$$

EXAMPLE 12-4: USING GAY-LUSSAC'S LAW

Before Molly began a car trip, she measured the air pressure in her car tires and found that it was 221 kPa at 18 °C. After two hours of driving, she found that the pressure had increased to 248 kPa. What was the new temperature of the air in her tires?

Write what you know.

$P_1 = 221$ kPa
$T_1 = 18\ °C = 18 + 273.15 = 29\underline{1}.15$ K
$P_2 = 248$ kPa
$T_2 = ?$

Write the formula and solve for the unknown.

$$\frac{P_1}{T_1} = \frac{P_2}{T_2}$$

$$\left(\frac{P_1}{T_1}\right)T_2 = \left(\frac{P_2}{T_2}\right)T_2$$

$$\left(\frac{T_1}{P_1}\right)T_2\left(\frac{P_1}{T_1}\right) = P_2\left(\frac{T_1}{P_1}\right)$$

$$T_2 = P_2\left(\frac{T_1}{P_1}\right)$$

Plug in known values and evaluate.

$$T_2 = 248\ \text{kPa}\left(\frac{291.15\ \text{K}}{221\ \text{kPa}}\right)$$
$= 32\underline{6}.72$ K
$= 32\underline{6}.72 - 273.15 = 54$ °C

The air in her tires is now 54 °C.

The Combined Gas Law

The gas laws that we have discussed so far have applied to situations in which only two variables can change. But what happens when pressure, volume, and temperature all change? The three laws described so far can be combined to form a single equation called the **combined gas law**, which states that the pressure, volume, and temperature of a sample of gas vary jointly.

The formula for the combined gas law is

$$\frac{PV}{T} = k,$$

where P is pressure, V is volume, T is temperature in kelvins, and k is a constant.

$$\frac{P_1V_1}{T_1} = k = \frac{P_2V_2}{T_2}$$

The advantage of the combined gas law is that it uses one equation to solve problems in which pressure, volume, and temperature all change. The three previous gas laws can be derived from the combined gas law. For example, if temperature is constant in the above equation ($T_1 = T_2$) the two temperatures cancel from the combined gas law to produce Boyle's law.

EXAMPLE 12-5: USING THE COMBINED GAS LAW

A sample of gas has a volume of 3.6 L at 1.06×10^5 Pa and −15 °C. What will its volume be at STP?

Write what you know.

$V_1 = 3.6$ L
$P_1 = 1.06 \times 10^5$ Pa
$T_1 = -15$ °C $= 25\underline{8}.15$ K
$P_2 = 1.01 \times 10^5$ Pa
$T_2 = 0$ °C $= 27\underline{3}.15$ K
$V_2 = ?$

Write the formula and solve for the unknown.

$$\frac{P_1V_1}{T_1} = \frac{P_2V_2}{T_2}$$

$$\left(\frac{P_1V_1}{T_1}\right)\left(\frac{T_2}{P_2}\right) = \left(\frac{\cancel{P_2}V_2}{\cancel{T_2}}\right)\left(\frac{\cancel{T_2}}{\cancel{P_2}}\right)$$

$$V_2 = \frac{P_1V_1T_2}{T_1P_2}$$

Plug in known values and evaluate.

$$V_2 = \frac{(1.06 \times 10^5\ \cancel{\text{Pa}})(3.6\ \text{L})(273.15\ \cancel{\text{K}})}{(1.01 \times 10^5\ \cancel{\text{Pa}})(258.15\ \cancel{\text{K}})}$$

$$= 4.0\ \text{L}$$

By adjusting the temperature and pressure to STP, the volume expands to 4.0 L.

DIFFERENTIATED INSTRUCTION

Gas Laws Mnemonic

Lead students to create a **mnemonic** to help them recall the three gas laws. Have them put their mnemonic on a note card for later use as a reference when needed. They may choose to use the same mnemonic as written below or to create their own.

Bob **Boyle** **Pl**ays **V**ideogames on **T**uesdays. (Boyle's law relates pressure and volume when temperature is constant.)

Charles Loves **TV** **P**rograms. (Charles's law relates temperature and volume when pressure is constant.)

Gary **T**alks **P**olitics **V**oluminously. (Gay-Lussac's law relates temperature and pressure when volume is constant.)

GAS LAWS

Assess students' understanding with the following **formative assessment**.

1. A sample of gas occupying 275.0 mL at 12.0 °C is cooled to −22.0 °C. What volume will it occupy if the pressure remains constant?

What we know: $V_1 = 275.0$ mL,
$T_1 = 12$ °C $= 285$ K,
$T_2 = -22.0$ °C $= 251$ K

Unknown: V_2

Write the formula and solve for the unknown.

$$\frac{V_1}{T_1} = \frac{V_2}{T_2}$$

$$\left(\frac{V_1}{T_1}\right)T_2 = \left(\frac{V_2}{\cancel{T_2}}\right)\cancel{T_2}$$

$$V_2 = \left(\frac{V_1}{T_1}\right)T_2$$

Evaluate.

$$V_2 = \left(\frac{275.0\ \text{mL}}{285\ \cancel{\text{K}}}\right)251\ \cancel{\text{K}}$$

$$= 242\ \text{mL}$$

2. A sample of gas occupies 5.8 L at 125.99 kPa. What volume will it occupy at 100.0 kPa if the temperature remains constant?

What we know: $V_1 = 5.8$ L,
$P_1 = 125.99$ kPA, $P_2 = 100.0$ kPA

Unknown: V_2

Write the formula and solve for the unknown.

$$P_1V_1 = P_2V_2$$

$$\frac{P_1V_1}{P_2} = \frac{\cancel{P_2}V_2}{\cancel{P_2}}$$

$$V_2 = \frac{P_1V_1}{P_2}$$

Evaluate.

$$V_2 = \frac{(125.99\ \cancel{\text{kPa}})(5.8\ \text{L})}{100.0\ \cancel{\text{kPa}}}$$

$$= 7.3\ \text{L}$$

3. A sample of gas in a 550.0 mL vessel at 40.0 °C and 119.32 kPa is transferred to a second vessel where the temperature is 0 °C and the pressure is 99.32 kPa. What is the volume of the second vessel?

What we know: $V_1 = 550.0$ mL,
$T_1 = 40.0$ °C $= 313.15$ K,
$P_1 = 119.32$ kPa, $T_2 = 0$ °C $= 273.15$ K,
$P_2 = 99.32$ kPa

Unknown: V_2

(continued)

Write the formula and solve for the unknown. Since all three conditions change, the combined gas law applies.

$$\frac{P_1V_1}{T_1}=\frac{P_2V_2}{T_2}$$

$$\left(\frac{P_1V_1}{T_1}\right)\left(\frac{T_2}{P_2}\right)=\left(\frac{\cancel{P_2}V_2}{\cancel{T_2}}\right)\left(\frac{\cancel{T_2}}{\cancel{P_2}}\right)$$

$$V_2=\frac{P_1V_1T_2}{T_1P_2}$$

Evaluate.

$$V_2=\frac{(119.32\ \cancel{\text{kPa}})(550.0\ \text{mL})(273.15\ \cancel{\text{K}})}{(313.15\ \cancel{\text{K}})(99.32\ \cancel{\text{kPa}})}$$

$$=576.4\ \text{mL}$$

CASE STUDY

Answers

1. If the atmosphere were only oxygen, the partial pressure of oxygen would be too high and air-breathing creatures would suffer from oxygen toxicity.
2. Due to the increased external pressures experienced during deep diving, the pressure of the gases is also very high. The higher-than-normal partial pressures of nitrogen and oxygen lead to these dangerous conditions.
3. In a mixture of gases, the total pressure is the sum of the pressure of each individual gas. Each individual gas supplies part of the pressure, hence the term *partial pressure*.

John Dalton

Dalton's Law of Partial Pressures: Mixtures of Gases

It is rare to find a naturally occurring pure gas. Even gases produced in laboratories contain some impurities. These mixtures complicate gas law calculations. English chemist John Dalton formulated a law to describe how gaseous mixtures behave, called **Dalton's law of partial pressures**. This law states that the total pressure of a mixture of gases equals the sum of the pressures of each individual gas, called the *partial pressures*. The general formula for Dalton's law of partial pressures is

$$P_{\text{total}}=\Sigma P_i,$$

where P_{total} is the total gas pressure and ΣP_i (the uppercase Greek letter *sigma* combined with P_i) is the sum of the partial pressures.

Suppose that 1 L of oxygen is added to 1 L of nitrogen, both gases at STP, in a 1 L container. As long as the molecules do not chemically react, they behave independently of each other. So oxygen molecules collide with the container and exert a pressure of 101.325 kPa, just as they did before they were mixed with the nitrogen molecules. The nitrogen gas particles also collide with the container, exerting an additional 101.325 kPa of pressure, so the total pressure from the two gases is 202.650 kPa. This happens because there are twice as many particles colliding with the sides of the container.

As another example, a sample of air contains 78% nitrogen, 21% oxygen, 1% argon, and traces of other gases. These percentages are based on volume. If the air mixture is at normal atmospheric pressure, 101.325 kPa, we find that 78% of the pressure (79.0335 kPa) comes from nitrogen, 21% of the pressure (21.2783 kPa) comes from oxygen, and 1% of the pressure (1.013 25 kPa) comes from argon. The sum of all the partial pressures equals the total pressure of the mixture.

CASE STUDY

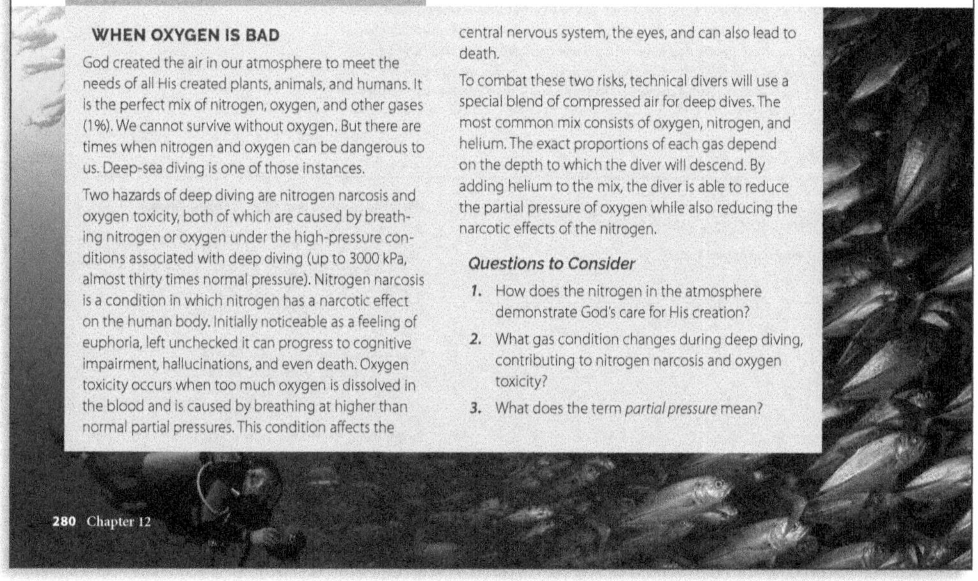

WHEN OXYGEN IS BAD

God created the air in our atmosphere to meet the needs of all His created plants, animals, and humans. It is the perfect mix of nitrogen, oxygen, and other gases (1%). We cannot survive without oxygen. But there are times when nitrogen and oxygen can be dangerous to us. Deep-sea diving is one of those instances.

Two hazards of deep diving are nitrogen narcosis and oxygen toxicity, both of which are caused by breathing nitrogen or oxygen under the high-pressure conditions associated with deep diving (up to 3000 kPa, almost thirty times normal pressure). Nitrogen narcosis is a condition in which nitrogen has a narcotic effect on the human body. Initially noticeable as a feeling of euphoria, left unchecked it can progress to cognitive impairment, hallucinations, and even death. Oxygen toxicity occurs when too much oxygen is dissolved in the blood and is caused by breathing at higher than normal partial pressures. This condition affects the central nervous system, the eyes, and can also lead to death.

To combat these two risks, technical divers will use a special blend of compressed air for deep dives. The most common mix consists of oxygen, nitrogen, and helium. The exact proportions of each gas depend on the depth to which the diver will descend. By adding helium to the mix, the diver is able to reduce the partial pressure of oxygen while also reducing the narcotic effects of the nitrogen.

Questions to Consider

1. How does the nitrogen in the atmosphere demonstrate God's care for His creation?
2. What gas condition changes during deep diving, contributing to nitrogen narcosis and oxygen toxicity?
3. What does the term *partial pressure* mean?

In the laboratory, chemists often collect a sample of a gas by trapping it at the top of a water-filled container. The gas bubbles up through the water, collects at the top, and forces water out the bottom. This technique is called *collecting over water* or *collection by water displacement*. The gas is initially pure, but as it bubbles through the water, some water evaporates and mixes with the gas being collected, forming a mixture called a wet gas. Accurate measurements of the gas cannot be made when it is mixed with water vapor. The total pressure, which equals the atmospheric pressure, is made up of the partial pressures of the gas and water vapor. To find the pressure due to the dry gas, the pressure from the water vapor must be subtracted from the atmospheric pressure. The pressure from the water vapor depends on its temperature. Table 12-2 lists vapor pressures of water at various temperatures.

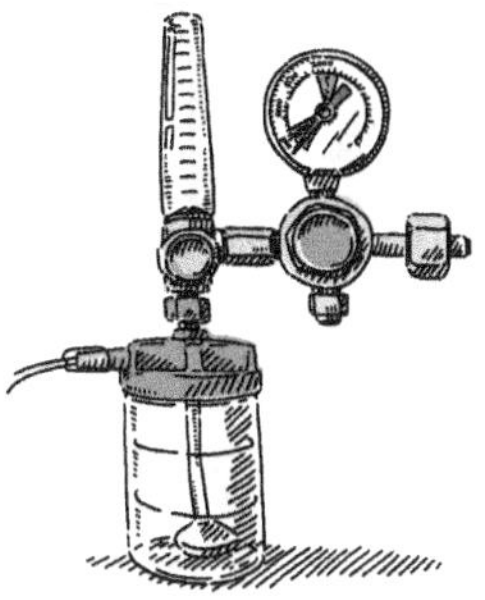

An oxygen humidifier. Ambulance equipment humidifies oxygen by bubbling it through water. Without this precaution, a patient's mouth, throat, and lungs would become dehydrated when receiving oxygen.

EXAMPLE 12-6: ADJUSTING FOR VAPOR PRESSURE

A 46 mL sample of O_2 gas is collected over water at 25 °C when the atmospheric pressure is 102 kPa. What volume of pure oxygen is this at STP?

Write what you know.

$V_1 = 46$ mL
$T_1 = 25$ °C $= 298.15$ K
$P_{total} = 102$ kPa
$T_2 = 273.15$ K
$P_2 = 101.325$ kPa
P_1 (sample of O_2) = ?
V_2 (sample of O_2) = ?

To use the combined gas law, we must find the pressure of pure oxygen. Use Table 12-2 to find the pressure of water vapor at 25 °C.

$P_{H_2O} = 3.1690$ kPa
$P_{total} = P_1 + P_{H_2O}$
$P_1 = P_{total} - P_{H_2O}$
$= 10\underline{2}$ kPa $- 3.1690$ kPa
$= 9\underline{8}.831$ kPa

Now we have what we need to use the combined gas equation. Notice that Celsius temperatures must be converted.

Write the formula and solve for the unknown.

$$\frac{P_1V_1}{T_1} = \frac{P_2V_2}{T_2}$$

$$\left(\frac{P_1V_1}{T_1}\right)\left(\frac{T_2}{P_2}\right) = \left(\frac{\cancel{P_2}V_2}{\cancel{T_2}}\right)\left(\frac{\cancel{T_2}}{\cancel{P_2}}\right)$$

$$V_2 = \frac{P_1V_1T_2}{T_1P_2}$$

Plug in known values and evaluate.

$$V_2 = \frac{(9\underline{8}.831\ \cancel{\text{kPa}})(4\underline{6}\ \text{mL})(273.15\ \cancel{\text{K}})}{(298.15\ \cancel{\text{K}})(101.325\ \cancel{\text{kPa}})}$$
$$= 41\ \text{mL}$$

Once we factor out the water vapor, we will have 41 mL of O_2, the dry gas.

TABLE 12-2 *Water Vapor Pressure at Various Temperatures*

Temperature (°C)	Vapor Pressure (kPa)
0.0	0.6113
5.0	0.8726
10.0	1.2281
15.0	1.7056
20.0	2.3388
25.0	3.1690
30.0	4.2455
35.0	5.6267
40.0	7.3814
45.0	9.5898
50.0	12.3440
55.0	15.7520
60.0	19.9320
65.0	25.0220
70.0	31.1760
75.0	38.5630
80.0	47.3730
85.0	57.8150
90.0	70.1170
95.0	84.5290
100.0	101.3200

BOILING WATER AND ATMOSPHERIC PRESSURE

Lead the class in a **discussion** by asking them why water's vapor pressure at 100 °C is 101.32 kPa. If students have difficulty explaining, help them see that for water to boil, it must push up as hard as the atmosphere pushes down. This is why a lower atmospheric pressure, such as at the top of a mountain, leads to a lower boiling point.

APPLY

LAB 12A: *COLD AND CALCULATING*

Once students have an understanding of the material in Section 12.2, they should be ready to work through Lab 12A.

ASSESS

TICKET OUT THE DOOR

As a **summarizing activity**, assess students' understanding by asking them how wet gas is formed.

12.2 REVIEW *ANSWERS*

* An asterisk following a question number indicates that a worked-out solution can be found on pages 297A–97B.

1. STP provides an agreed upon set of conditions to allow scientists to make direct comparisons of gas volumes. *(p. 274)*

2. Pressure is caused by the collisions of the constantly moving gas particles with their container. As the volume of the container changes, the pressure of the gas on the container changes inversely. If the volume increases, the surface area increases. The same force on a larger surface area causes a decrease in pressure. The particles can't apply the same force because with increased volume the particles are farther apart, and so they collide with the sides less often. Decreasing the volume has the opposite effect. *(pp. 274–75)*

3. Charles's law states that the volume and temperature of a sample of gas at a constant pressure vary directly with each other.

$\frac{V}{T} = k$ or $\frac{V_1}{T_1} = \frac{V_2}{T_2}$

$\left(\frac{T_1}{V_1} = \frac{T_2}{V_2}\right.$ is also acceptable.$\left.\right)$

(pp. 276–77)

4. The temperature and volume of a gas sample were carefully measured over a range of temperatures. When the data was graphed, scientists extrapolated back to the point where the gas would occupy zero volume, that is, its thermodynamic minimum. This was set to be absolute zero, which was one of the points that established the scale. *(p. 277)*

5.* a. 4.39×10^4 Pa

b. 149.8 mL

c. −199.27 °C

d. 863 kPa

e. 5.43 L

f. 70.1 mL

g. 6.17 L

h. 99.0 kPa *(pp. 274–79)*

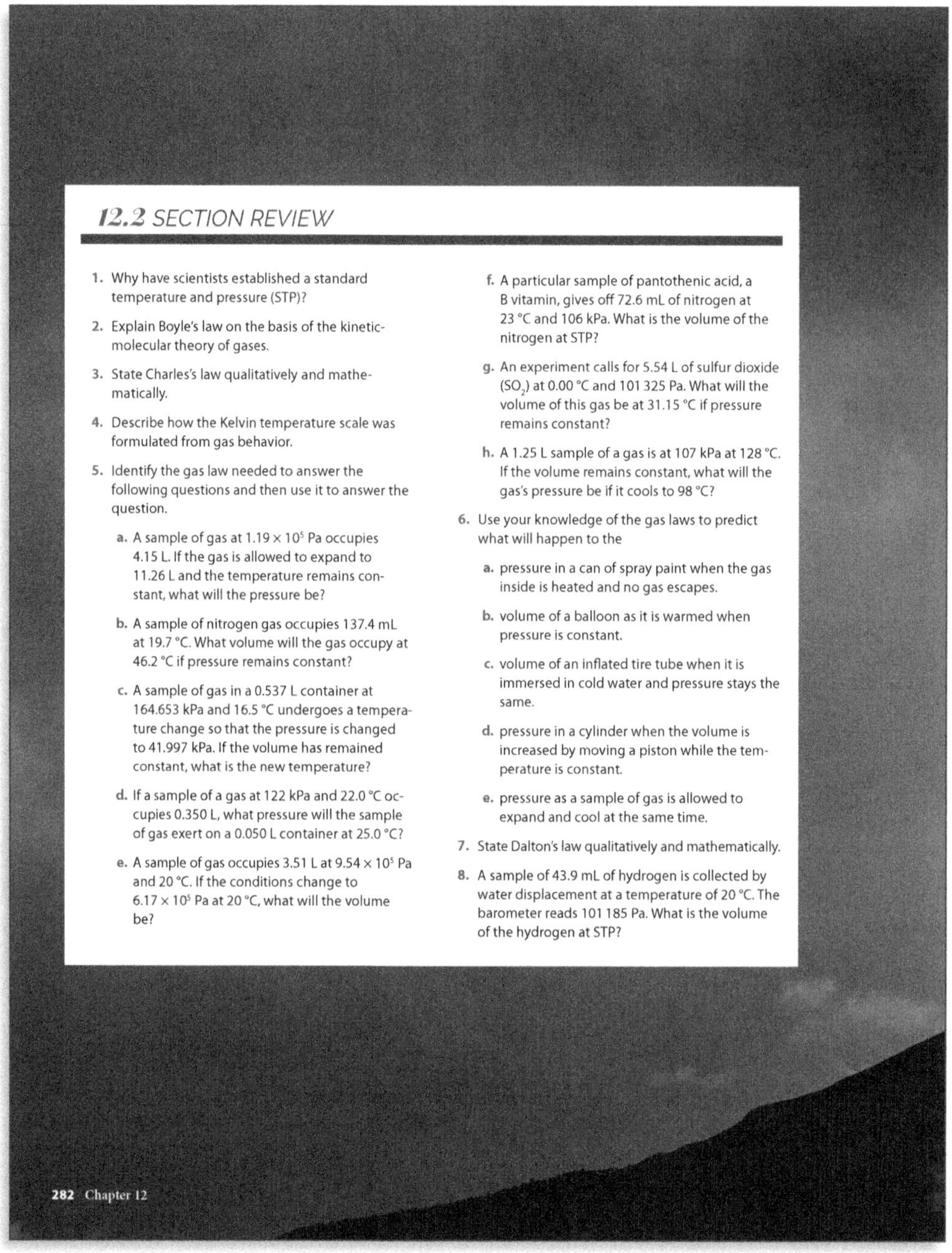

12.2 SECTION REVIEW

1. Why have scientists established a standard temperature and pressure (STP)?
2. Explain Boyle's law on the basis of the kinetic-molecular theory of gases.
3. State Charles's law qualitatively and mathematically.
4. Describe how the Kelvin temperature scale was formulated from gas behavior.
5. Identify the gas law needed to answer the following questions and then use it to answer the question.
   a. A sample of gas at 1.19×10^5 Pa occupies 4.15 L. If the gas is allowed to expand to 11.26 L and the temperature remains constant, what will the pressure be?
   b. A sample of nitrogen gas occupies 137.4 mL at 19.7 °C. What volume will the gas occupy at 46.2 °C if pressure remains constant?
   c. A sample of gas in a 0.537 L container at 164.653 kPa and 16.5 °C undergoes a temperature change so that the pressure is changed to 41.997 kPa. If the volume has remained constant, what is the new temperature?
   d. If a sample of a gas at 122 kPa and 22.0 °C occupies 0.350 L, what pressure will the sample of gas exert on a 0.050 L container at 25.0 °C?
   e. A sample of gas occupies 3.51 L at 9.54×10^5 Pa and 20 °C. If the conditions change to 6.17×10^5 Pa at 20 °C, what will the volume be?
   f. A particular sample of pantothenic acid, a B vitamin, gives off 72.6 mL of nitrogen at 23 °C and 106 kPa. What is the volume of the nitrogen at STP?
   g. An experiment calls for 5.54 L of sulfur dioxide (SO_2) at 0.00 °C and 101 325 Pa. What will the volume of this gas be at 31.15 °C if pressure remains constant?
   h. A 1.25 L sample of a gas is at 107 kPa at 128 °C. If the volume remains constant, what will the gas's pressure be if it cools to 98 °C?
6. Use your knowledge of the gas laws to predict what will happen to the
   a. pressure in a can of spray paint when the gas inside is heated and no gas escapes.
   b. volume of a balloon as it is warmed when pressure is constant.
   c. volume of an inflated tire tube when it is immersed in cold water and pressure stays the same.
   d. pressure in a cylinder when the volume is increased by moving a piston while the temperature is constant.
   e. pressure as a sample of gas is allowed to expand and cool at the same time.
7. State Dalton's law qualitatively and mathematically.
8. A sample of 43.9 mL of hydrogen is collected by water displacement at a temperature of 20 °C. The barometer reads 101 185 Pa. What is the volume of the hydrogen at STP?

282 Chapter 12

6. a. The pressure will increase (Gay-Lussac's law).

b. The volume will increase (Charles's law).

c. The volume will decrease (Charles's law).

d. The pressure will decrease (Boyle's law).

e. The pressure will decrease (combined gas law). *(all pp. 274–79)*

7. Dalton's law states that the total pressure in a container of a mixture of gases is equal to the sum of the pressures caused be each individual gas. The individual pressures are called partial pressures. $P_{total} = \Sigma P_i$ *(pp. 280–81)*

8.* 39.9 mL *(pp. 280–81)*

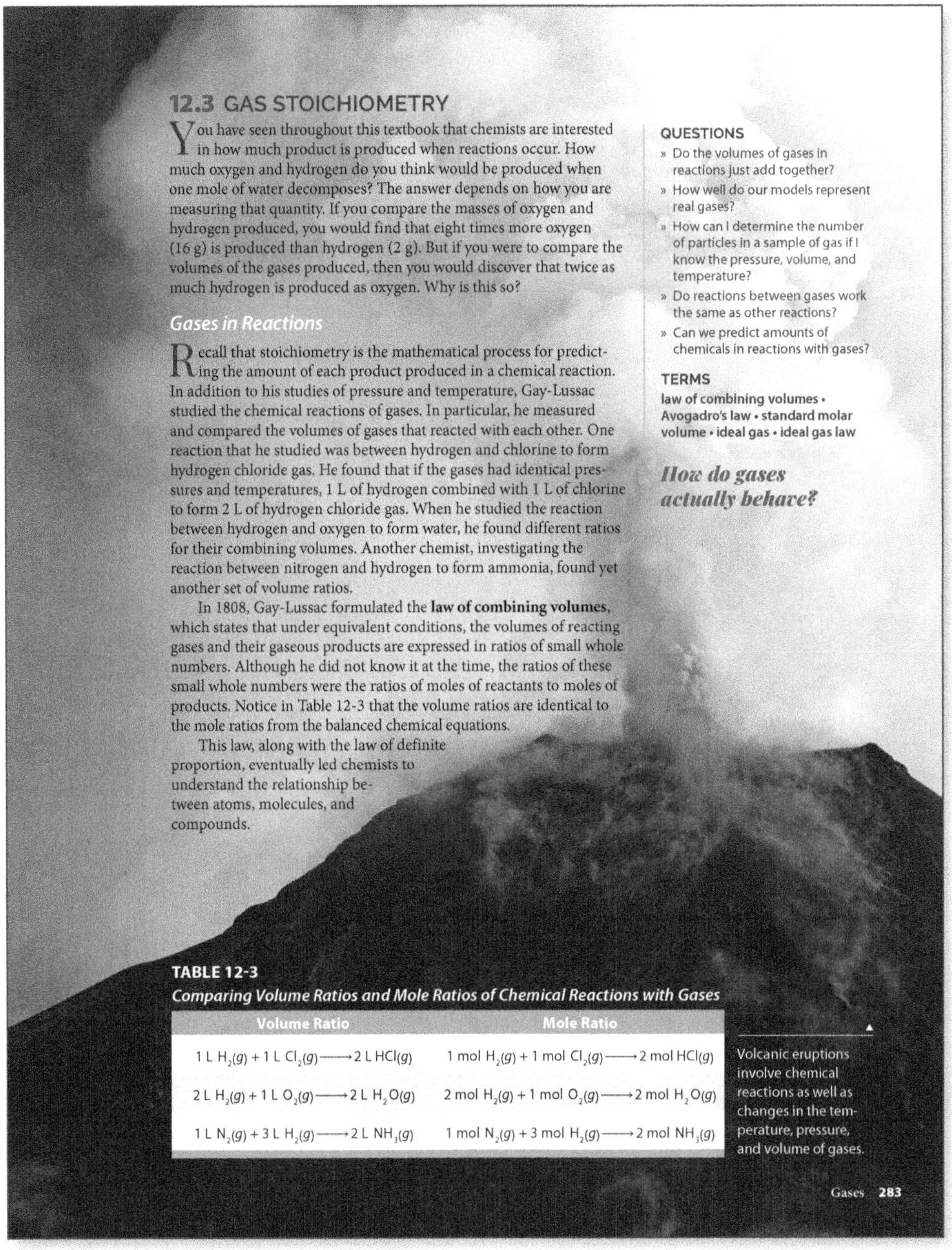

12.3 GAS STOICHIOMETRY

You have seen throughout this textbook that chemists are interested in how much product is produced when reactions occur. How much oxygen and hydrogen do you think would be produced when one mole of water decomposes? The answer depends on how you are measuring that quantity. If you compare the masses of oxygen and hydrogen produced, you would find that eight times more oxygen (16 g) is produced than hydrogen (2 g). But if you were to compare the volumes of the gases produced, then you would discover that twice as much hydrogen is produced as oxygen. Why is this so?

QUESTIONS
- Do the volumes of gases in reactions just add together?
- How well do our models represent real gases?
- How can I determine the number of particles in a sample of gas if I know the pressure, volume, and temperature?
- Do reactions between gases work the same as other reactions?
- Can we predict amounts of chemicals in reactions with gases?

TERMS
law of combining volumes • Avogadro's law • standard molar volume • ideal gas • ideal gas law

How do gases actually behave?

Gases in Reactions

Recall that stoichiometry is the mathematical process for predicting the amount of each product produced in a chemical reaction. In addition to his studies of pressure and temperature, Gay-Lussac studied the chemical reactions of gases. In particular, he measured and compared the volumes of gases that reacted with each other. One reaction that he studied was between hydrogen and chlorine to form hydrogen chloride gas. He found that if the gases had identical pressures and temperatures, 1 L of hydrogen combined with 1 L of chlorine to form 2 L of hydrogen chloride gas. When he studied the reaction between hydrogen and oxygen to form water, he found different ratios for their combining volumes. Another chemist, investigating the reaction between nitrogen and hydrogen to form ammonia, found yet another set of volume ratios.

In 1808, Gay-Lussac formulated the **law of combining volumes**, which states that under equivalent conditions, the volumes of reacting gases and their gaseous products are expressed in ratios of small whole numbers. Although he did not know it at the time, the ratios of these small whole numbers were the ratios of moles of reactants to moles of products. Notice in Table 12-3 that the volume ratios are identical to the mole ratios from the balanced chemical equations.

This law, along with the law of definite proportion, eventually led chemists to understand the relationship between atoms, molecules, and compounds.

TABLE 12-3
Comparing Volume Ratios and Mole Ratios of Chemical Reactions with Gases

Volume Ratio	Mole Ratio
$1\ L\ H_2(g) + 1\ L\ Cl_2(g) \longrightarrow 2\ L\ HCl(g)$	$1\ mol\ H_2(g) + 1\ mol\ Cl_2(g) \longrightarrow 2\ mol\ HCl(g)$
$2\ L\ H_2(g) + 1\ L\ O_2(g) \longrightarrow 2\ L\ H_2O(g)$	$2\ mol\ H_2(g) + 1\ mol\ O_2(g) \longrightarrow 2\ mol\ H_2O(g)$
$1\ L\ N_2(g) + 3\ L\ H_2(g) \longrightarrow 2\ L\ NH_3(g)$	$1\ mol\ N_2(g) + 3\ mol\ H_2(g) \longrightarrow 2\ mol\ NH_3(g)$

▲ Volcanic eruptions involve chemical reactions as well as changes in the temperature, pressure, and volume of gases.

ENGAGE

REVIEWING GAS LAWS

Review prior information learned in Section 12.2 with a **concept map**. Have each student create a concept map of all the material that he can recall from the section. When students have finished, select several to share their information with the class and discuss the content before beginning the section.

SECTION 12.3 *OVERVIEW*

Essential Question

How do gases actually behave?

Objectives

» **12.3.1** State the law of combining volumes.

» **12.3.2** Explain why the kinetic-molecular theory is limited in its ability to describe real gases.

» **12.3.3** Calculate the pressure, volume, temperature, or moles of a gaseous substance present when given three of the four variables used in the ideal gas law.

» **12.3.4** Predict the amount of gas in a chemical reaction by using stoichiometric calculations.

» **12.3.5** Formulate a biblical position regarding greenhouse gases. BWS

» **12.3.6** Formulate a biblical view of the appropriate use of airbag safety. BWS

Resources

Ethics: Deadly Saftey Device? (p. 297)

Airbags

How It Works: Airbags

Worldview Investigation: Greenhouse Gases

Lab 12B: *An Aquanaut's World:* Predicting the Production of Oxygen

INSTRUCT

DOES ONE SIZE REALLY FIT ALL?

Lead the class in a **discussion** about the standard molar volume of a gas. Ask students how gases with different-size molecules all fit the same number of molecules into 22.4 L.

The answer is that they really don't. Avogadro's law, like the other gas laws, is a model that works well to predict the behavior of gases. Because they are models, they work only for ideal gases, which will be discussed later in the chapter. Real gases don't behave ideally and therefore actually have slightly different molar volumes. A mole of a real gas is usually a little smaller or larger than 22.4 L. That being said, the molar volume is still a very workable model for most gases.

The Molar Volume of a Gas

Gay-Lussac's law of combining volumes led Amedeo Avogadro to hypothesize that under equivalent conditions, equal volumes of gases contain the same number of particles. A series of experiments supported his hypothesis, and additional work led to the development of **Avogadro's law**, which states that the volume of a gas, maintained at a constant temperature and pressure, is directly proportional to the number of moles of the gas. In equation form, this law is

$$\frac{V}{n} = k,$$

where V is volume, n is the number of particles in moles, and k is a constant.

Molar Volume

Every equivalent volume of gas in a reaction contains the same number of particles if the gases are at the same temperature and pressure.

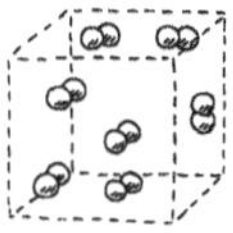
H_2

CH_4

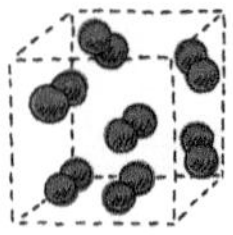
O_2

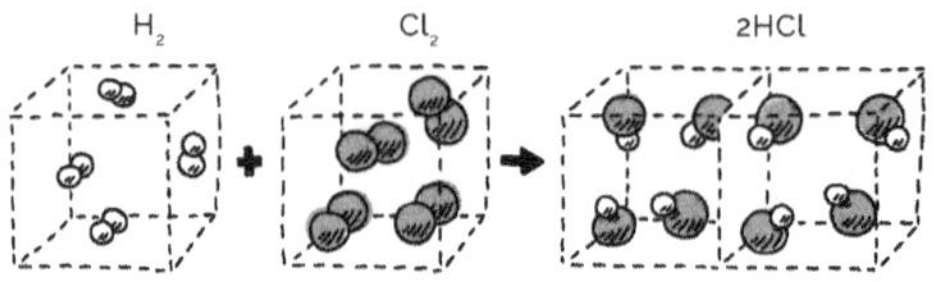

When hydrogen and chlorine react, 1 L of hydrogen contains the same number of molecules as 1 L of chlorine. One hydrogen molecule reacts with one chlorine molecule to form two hydrogen chloride molecules. Since twice as many hydrogen chloride molecules are produced, 2 L of gas results.

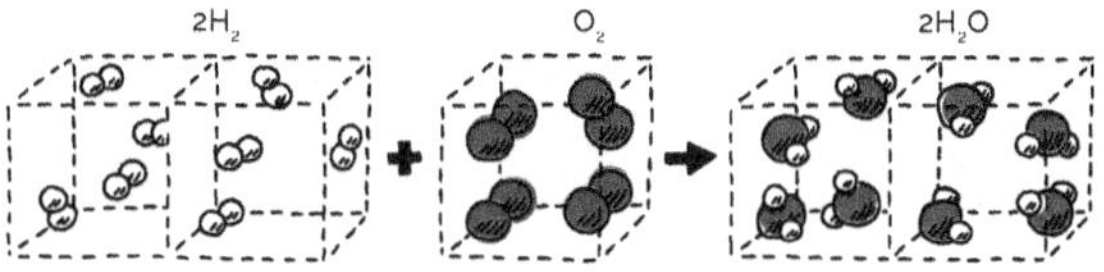

In the formation of water from hydrogen and oxygen, 2 L of hydrogen contain twice as many molecules as 1 L of oxygen. The 2 L of water vapor produced contain the same number of molecules as the 2 L of hydrogen and twice the number of molecules as the 1 L of oxygen.

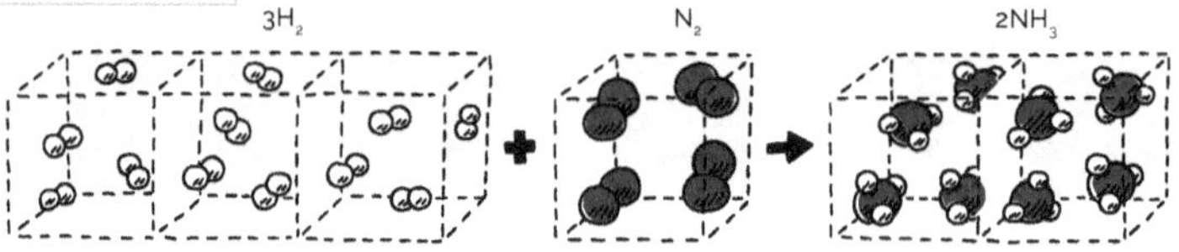

Likewise, the volumes of gases involved in the formation of ammonia (NH_3) show the relative number of molecules.

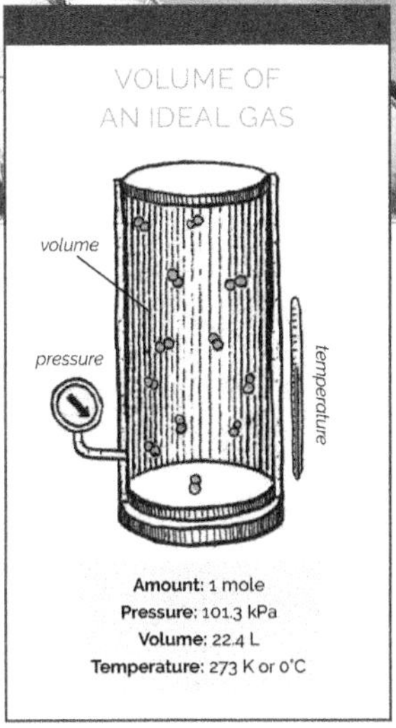

Avogadro's ideas eventually helped establish the mole as a unit of measure. Experiments also determined how many particles were present in a given volume. At STP, a volume of 22.4 L contains 6.022×10^{23} particles, or 1 mol, of a gas. For this reason, 22.4 L is called the **standard molar volume** of a gas. No matter what the gas is, 1 mol at STP occupies 22.4 L. The amount of space that a mole of gas will occupy—its molar volume—at other than STP will vary with temperature and pressure, but every gas will have the same molar volume at that same temperature and pressure.

The molar volume of a gas allows us to convert between moles of a gas and its volume as long as the gas is at STP. If the gas is not at STP, we can still determine the number of moles present by adjusting the volume of the gas by using the combined gas law that we studied in Section 12.2.

EXAMPLE 12-7:
CALCULATING GAS VOLUME FROM MOLES (STP)

What volume will 2.67 mol of ammonia occupy at STP?

Write what you know.

$n = 2.67$ mol
STP

Convert from moles to volume using molar volume.

$$2.67\ \cancel{\text{mol NH}_3}\left(\frac{22.4\ \text{L NH}_3}{1\ \cancel{\text{mol NH}_3}}\right) = 59.8\ \text{L NH}_3$$

As you can imagine, most of the time a sample of gas will be at conditions other than STP. We could still use the molar volume of a gas to convert between volume and moles, but we would have to use the combined gas law (Section 12.2) to first determine what the volume of the gas would be at STP. There is an easier way to find the moles at nonstandard conditions, and that is to use the ideal gas law, which you will learn about later in this section.

Gases 285

MAKING CONNECTIONS: REAL VERSUS IDEAL GASES

Lead students in a discussion through **Socratic questioning** on the two statements from the kinetic-molecular theory. For the first two questions, read the postulate and then ask the accompanying question regarding the limitations of the kinetic-molecular theory's ability to describe real gases.

1. **Postulate One**: When would the kinetic-molecular theory deviate from the behavior of real gases? *(Since the statement assumes that gas particles are tiny, the larger a gas's particle are, the less accurate the theory will be. Also, the statement assumes that the particles are far apart. Therefore, when the particles are close, the theory will less accurately predict behavior.)*
2. **Postulate Two**: When would the theory deviate from the behavior of real gases? *(This statement assumes little interaction between particles and the container. Any conditions in which the particles would be in frequent contact with the container or each other would result in deviations from the theory for the behavior of real gases.)*
3. State the gas conditions in which you would expect the kinetic-molecular theory to best predict the behavior of a gas. *(The kinetic-molecular theory should best predict gas behavior for small gas particles when they are spread apart [high temperature and low pressure].)*
4. Overall, what does this tell us about our ability to make and adjust models? *(Even the most thought-out models are limited by our own human reasoning and understanding. There will always be flaws in our ability to create and adjust models due to our finite understanding of God's creation.)*

Ideal Gases

Did you know that gases do not exactly obey Boyle's law for all pressures and temperatures? For that matter, Charles's law falls short too. Gas laws do not govern how gases behave—they merely describe. Boyle and Charles provided accurate descriptions of the volume, pressure, and temperature of gases, but the predictive ability of these laws depends on conditions. The gas laws that you have learned about are models—workable explanations or descriptions of the world around us.

Because the kinetic-molecular theory's description of gases is simple, it cannot exactly describe the behavior of most gases. An **ideal gas** is a gas whose behavior is perfectly predicted by the kinetic-molecular theory. Though no real-world gases are ideal, some come close under certain conditions. The kinetic-molecular theory makes several assumptions that are not always accurate. Let's reexamine two of the postulates of the kinetic-molecular theory.

1. Gas particles are tiny compared with the great distances between them.
2. Particles do not interact with each other or the walls of their container except during momentary collisions.

The kinetic-molecular theory assumes that particles, either atoms or molecules, are masses that take up no volume. Since gas particles, especially larger ones, take up at least some space, this postulate of the kinetic-molecular theory does not match the characteristics of real gases. The assumption that gas particles are separated by great distances is valid for gases at high temperatures and low pressures. However, high pressures or low temperatures can force gases to approach the point of *condensation*. Under these conditions, gas molecules slow down considerably and the spaces between them shrink. In these conditions, real gases behave quite differently than ideal gases. When a gas is near condensation, these interactions have an even greater impact on the particles. Consequently, the gas particles begin to coalesce, which results in pressures and volumes that are smaller than expected.

In general, real gases behave most like the ideal predicted by the kinetic-molecular theory when they have a low molar mass, are under low pressure (< 101.325 kPa), and are at a relatively high temperature (> 273 K). This is great news since we spend much of our time using gases at these high-temperature, low-pressure conditions, which means that the gas laws work well in our daily lives.

The molar volume of all gases is 22.4 L, right? Well, not exactly. The volume quantity 22.4 L is actually for ideal gases and is a useful approximation for real gases. When gaseous particles are large, molar volumes decline slightly because intermolecular forces become significant. Table 12-4 shows the molar volumes for some common gases.

TABLE 12-4
Values for Some Common Gases at STP

Gas	Gas Density (g/L)	Molar Mass (g/mol)	Standard Molar Volume (L)
H_2	0.0899	2.016	22.428
He	0.1785	4.003	22.426
Ne	0.9002	20.18	22.425
N_2	1.251	28.02	22.404
O_2	1.429	32.00	22.394
Ar	1.784	39.95	22.393
CO_2	1.977	44.01	22.256
NH_3	0.7710	17.03	22.094
Cl_2	3.214	70.90	22.063

IDEAL GAS LAW

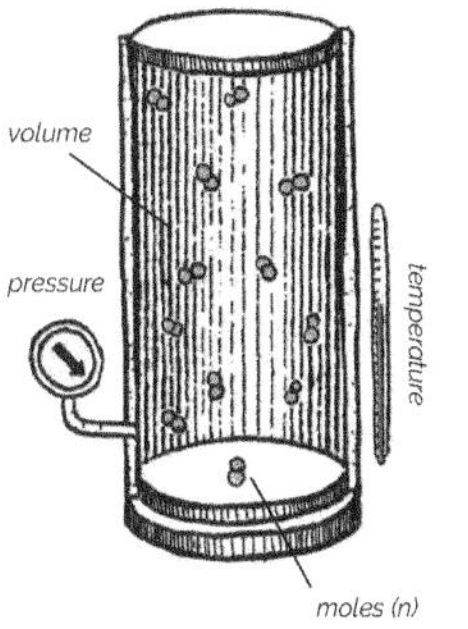

Pressure, temperature, volume, and number of moles are all considered by the ideal gas law.

The Ideal Gas Law

Boyle's law states that the volume of a gas is inversely proportional to its pressure when temperature remains constant. Charles's law states that volume is directly proportional to the Kelvin temperature when pressure is constant. Avogadro's law states that the volume is directly proportional to the number of moles of gas in the sample. These three laws can be written as shown below.

$$V \propto \frac{1}{P}$$

$$V \propto T$$

$$V \propto n$$

When they are combined, they give us the proportions below.

$$V \propto \frac{nT}{P} \text{ or } PV \propto nT$$

Using mathematics, we can change a proportion into an equation by including a constant. By including R, the *universal gas constant*, we change the proportionality into the **ideal gas law**, which relates the pressure, temperature, volume, and the number of moles in any sample of a gas. The ideal gas law allows us to solve for any of these quantities for a gas if we know the other three. The formula for the ideal gas law is

$$PV = nRT,$$

where P is the pressure, V is the volume, n is the number of particles in moles, and T is the temperature in kelvins. R is the universal gas constant. Rearranging the ideal gas law allows us to solve for the universal gas constant.

$$R = \frac{PV}{nT}$$

The gas constant's specific value depends on the units used for pressure, temperature, and volume (see Table 12-5). Since 1 mol of gas at STP (273.15 K and 101.325 kPa) occupies approximately 22.4 L, these values can be substituted into the equation. For example,

$$R = \frac{(101.325 \text{ kPa})(22.4 \text{ L})}{(1 \text{ mol})(273.15 \text{ K})}$$

$$= 8.31 \frac{\text{kPa} \cdot \text{L}}{\text{mol} \cdot \text{K}}$$

We can easily convert the value of the gas constant if working in other units.

TABLE 12-5

Universal Gas Constant Values

Pressure Unit	Volume Unit	*R* Value
kPa	L	$8.31 \frac{\text{kPa} \cdot \text{L}}{\text{mol} \cdot \text{K}}$
Pa	L	$8.31 \times 10^3 \frac{\text{Pa} \cdot \text{L}}{\text{mol} \cdot \text{K}}$
Pa	m^3	$8.31 \frac{\text{Pa} \cdot \text{m}^3}{\text{mol} \cdot \text{K}}$

THE DIFFERENCE BETWEEN THE COMBINED AND IDEAL GAS LAWS

Guide the class in a **discussion** regarding the differences between the combined and ideal gas laws. To get students thinking about this topic, ask the following questions.

1. When would you use the combined gas law? *(when the conditions [except for mass] are changing)*
2. When would you use the ideal gas law? *(when calculating one condition from a constant set of conditions)*

Explain that the combined gas law, like the other gas laws, allows us to account for changing conditions of a sample. It is used to calculate a change from one set of conditions to another set of conditions. The ideal gas law is used to calculate values for a single set of conditions (pressure, volume, temperature, or number of moles) for a sample of gas.

STOICHIOMETRY MAP

Lead students to update their stoichiometry **flow charts** from Chapter 11 by adding the ideal gas law. See Appendix M for an example.

EXAMPLE 12-8: CALCULATING MOLES OF A GAS

How many moles of a gas are present in a 3.32 L sample at 154 kPa and 29 °C?

Write what you know.

$V = 3.32\ \text{L}$
$P = 154\ \text{kPa}$
$T = 29\ °\text{C} = 30\underline{2}.15\ \text{K}$
$R = 8.31\ \dfrac{\text{kPa} \cdot \text{L}}{\text{mol} \cdot \text{K}}$ (from Table 12-5)
$n = ?$

Write the formula and solve for the unknown.

$$PV = nRT$$

$$\frac{PV}{RT} = \frac{n\cancel{RT}}{\cancel{RT}}$$

$$n = \frac{PV}{RT}$$

Plug in known values and evaluate.

$$n = \frac{(154\ \cancel{\text{kPa}})(3.32\ \cancel{\text{L}})}{(8.31\ \frac{\cancel{\text{kPa}} \cdot \cancel{\text{L}}}{\text{mol} \cdot \cancel{\text{K}}})(302.15\ \cancel{\text{K}})}$$

$$= 0.204\ \text{mol}$$

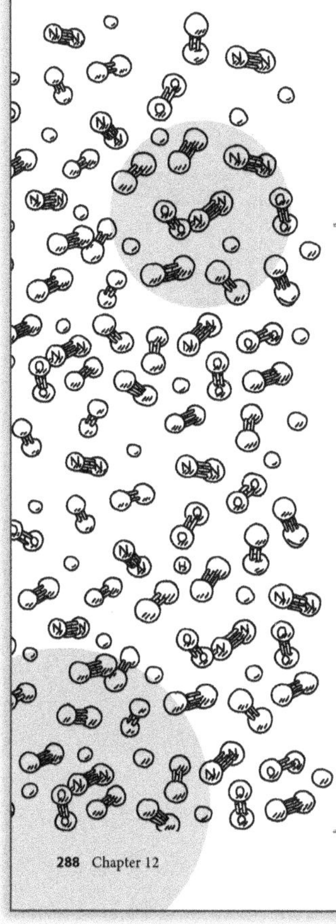

If chemists measure the mass, pressure, volume, and temperature of an unknown gas, they can determine its molar mass. They first use the ideal gas law to find the number of moles in the sample. They then form a ratio of the mass of the sample to the number of moles in the sample. This ratio is reduced to produce the molar mass of the gas.

EXAMPLE 12-9: CALCULATING MOLAR MASS OF A GAS MASS AT NONSTANDARD CONDITIONS

A 0.481 g sample of gas occupies $4.04 \times 10^{-4}\ \text{m}^3$ at 9.71×10^4 Pa and 297 K. What is the molar mass of this unknown gas?

Write what you know.

$m = 0.481\ \text{g}$
$V = 4.04 \times 10^{-4}\ \text{m}^3$
$P = 9.71 \times 10^4\ \text{Pa}$
$T = 297\ \text{K}$
$R = 8.31\ \dfrac{\text{Pa} \cdot \text{m}^3}{\text{mol} \cdot \text{K}}$ (from Table 12-5)
$n = ?$
molar mass = ?

Write the formula and solve for the unknown.

$n = \dfrac{PV}{RT}$ (see Example 12-8)

Plug in known values and evaluate.

$$n = \frac{(9.71 \times 10^4\ \cancel{\text{Pa}})(4.04 \times 10^{-4}\ \cancel{\text{m}^3})}{(8.31\ \frac{\cancel{\text{Pa}} \cdot \cancel{\text{m}^3}}{\text{mol} \cdot \cancel{\text{K}}})(297\ \cancel{\text{K}})}$$

$$= 0.015\underline{8}9\ \text{mol}$$

Now, by dividing the mass by the number of moles we can determine the molar mass.

$$\textit{molar mass} = \frac{0.481\ \text{g}}{0.015\underline{8}9\ \text{mol}}$$

$$= 30.3\ \text{g/mol}$$

Stoichiometry Involving Gases

In Chapter 11 you learned that the coefficients in balanced chemical equations give the molar ratios between reactants and products. The number of particles and their masses can be calculated once the number of moles is known. Throughout this section you have learned that by using the ideal gas law, we can convert between volume and moles of gases at any temperature and pressure. This allows us to accomplish stoichiometric calculations when given the volumes of gases in the reaction. Let's look at an example of a gas stoichiometry problem.

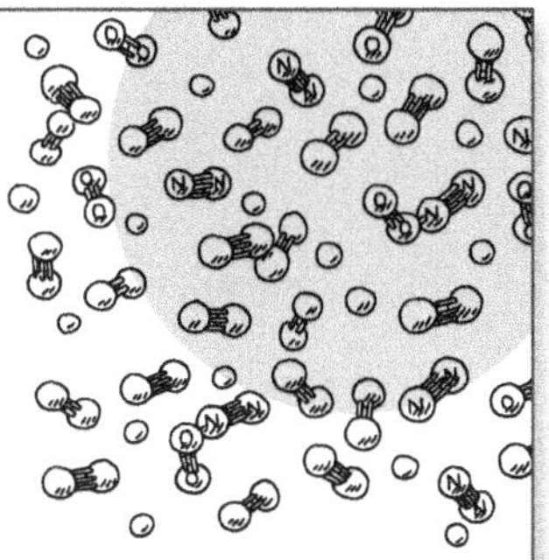

EXAMPLE 12-10: CALCULATING THE VOLUME OF A GASEOUS PRODUCT

When 78.5 g of calcium react with water to form calcium hydroxide and hydrogen gas, what volume of hydrogen gas will be produced at 315 K and 115 511 Pa?

Write what you know.

$$Ca(s) + 2H_2O(l) \longrightarrow Ca(OH)_2(aq) + H_2(g)$$

$m = 78.5$ g Ca

$P = 115\,511$ Pa

$T = 315$ K

$n_{H_2} = ?$

$V_{H_2} = ?$

Convert g Ca into mol H_2.

$$78.5\ \text{g Ca}\left(\frac{1\ \text{mol Ca}}{40.08\ \text{g Ca}}\right)\left(\frac{1\ \text{mol H}_2}{1\ \text{mol Ca}}\right)$$

$= 1.958582834$ mol H_2

Write what you know.

$n_{H_2} = 1.958$ mol H_2

$8.31 \times 10^3\ \frac{\text{Pa} \cdot \text{L}}{\text{mol} \cdot \text{K}}$ (from Table 12-5)

$V_{H_2} = ?$

Write the formula and solve for the unknown.

$$PV = nRT$$

$$\frac{PV}{P} = \frac{nRT}{P}$$

$$V = \frac{nRT}{P}$$

Plug in known values and evaluate.

$$V = \frac{(1.958\ \text{mol H}_2)(8.31 \times 10^3\ \frac{\text{Pa} \cdot \text{L}}{\text{mol} \cdot \text{K}})(315\ \text{K})}{(115\,511\ \text{Pa})}$$

$= 44.4$ L H_2

EXAMPLE 12-11: CALCULATING THE MASS OF PRODUCT FROM THE VOLUME OF A REACTANT

A volume of 3.58 L of oxygen gas at 180.3 kPa and 35 °C is reacted with hydrogen. How many grams of water will be produced?

Write what you know.

$$O_2(g) + 2H_2(g) \longrightarrow 2H_2O(l)$$

$V_{O_2} = 3.58$ L

$P = 180.3$ kPa

$T = 35\ °C = 308.15$ K

$R = 8.31\frac{\text{kPa} \cdot \text{L}}{\text{mol} \cdot \text{K}}$

$n_{O_2} = ?$

$m_{H_2O} = ?$

Write the formula and solve for the unknown.

$n = \frac{PV}{RT}$ (see Example 12-8)

Plug in known values and evaluate.

$$n = \frac{(180.3\ \text{kPa})(3.58\ \text{L O}_2)}{(8.31\ \frac{\text{kPa} \cdot \text{L}}{\text{mol} \cdot \text{K}})(308.15\ \text{K})}$$

$= 0.2520$ mol O_2

Convert mol O_2 into g H_2O.

$$0.2520\ \text{mol O}_2\left(\frac{2\ \text{mol H}_2\text{O}}{1\ \text{mol O}_2}\right)\left(\frac{18.02\ \text{g H}_2\text{O}}{1\ \text{mol H}_2\text{O}}\right)$$

$= 9.08$ g H_2O

IDEAL GAS LAW

Use the following **formative assessment** to check students' understanding.

1. How many moles of a gas are present in a 5.2 L sample at 202.68 kPa of pressure and 278.15 K?

   What we know: $V = 5.2$ L, $P = 202.68$ kPa, $T = 278.15$, $R = 8.31\frac{\text{kPa} \cdot \text{L}}{\text{mol} \cdot \text{K}}$

   Unknown: n

   Write the formula and solve for the unknown.

   $$PV = nRT$$

   $$\frac{PV}{RT} = \frac{nRT}{RT}$$

   $$n = \frac{PV}{RT}$$

   Evaluate.

   $$n = \frac{PV}{RT}$$

   $$n = \frac{(202.68\ \text{kPa})(5.2\ \text{L})}{\left(8.31\ \frac{\text{kPa} \cdot \text{L}}{\text{mol} \cdot \text{K}}\right)(278.15\ \text{K})}$$

   $= 0.46$ mol

2. What is the volume of 2.50 mol of nitrogen at STP?

   What we know: $n = 2.50$ mol, $P = 101.32$ kPa, $T = 273.15$ K, $R = 8.31\frac{\text{kPa} \cdot \text{L}}{\text{mol} \cdot \text{K}}$

   Unknown: V

   Write the formula and solve for the unknown.

   $$PV = nRT$$

   $$\frac{PV}{P} = \frac{nRT}{P}$$

   $$V = \frac{nRT}{P}$$

   Evaluate.

   $$V = \frac{(2.50\text{mol})\left(8.31\ \frac{\text{kPa} \cdot \text{L}}{\text{mol} \cdot \text{K}}\right)(273.15\ \text{K})}{101.32\ \text{kPa}}$$

   $= 56.0$ L

The Chapter opener discussed car crashes. Scientists have discovered how they can use chemistry and specifically chemical reactions that produce a gas to save lives during the milliseconds in which a car crash happens. Through the use of airbags, thousands of lives have been saved.

HOW IT *WORKS*

Airbags

Vehicles often come to a sudden stop during a car accident. While this is not good for the car, it is potentially deadly for the occupants. An airbag applies less force *over a relatively longer* time period compared with the greater force that the steering wheel would apply over a very short time. Airbags also spread the force over a larger area on the body, reducing the severity of any injures. All cars made since 1998 are equipped with front airbags, and with good reason. How does chemistry make this possible?

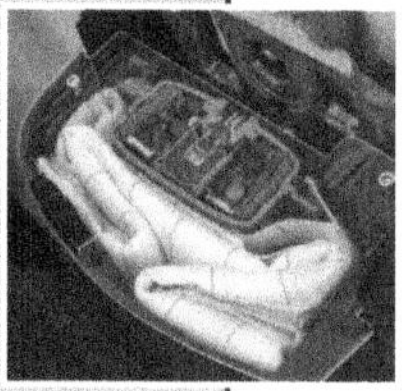

Airbags were first considered for aircraft in the 1940s. By the 1970s, scientists began planning for their use in cars. The original designers tried using compressed gases to inflate airbags. This approach was rejected due to issues with storing the compressed gas, maintaining consistency in inflation rates, and most importantly dealing with the limited inflation rate. To be effective, an airbag must inflate fast enough to make a difference. Since it takes only about fifty milliseconds after vehicle impact for a driver to strike the steering wheel, airbags must be designed to fully inflate before an occupant reaches them—faster than the blink of an eye.

An automobile airbag is folded and stored in the steering wheel or dashboard. When the airbag's control system senses a significant crash, it triggers a series of chemical reactions. In the primary reaction, sodium azide (NaN_3), a chemical also used in solid rockets, rapidly decomposes to form nitrogen gas and sodium metal.

$$2NaN_3(s) \longrightarrow 2Na(s) + 3N_2(g)$$

Since the sodium metal is hazardous, another reaction combines the sodium metal with potassium nitrate to form metal oxides and more nitrogen gas.

$$10Na(s) + 2KNO_3(s) \longrightarrow K_2O(s) + 5Na_2O(s) + N_2(g)$$

The nitrogen fills the airbag so quickly that it moves outward at about 89 m/s (about 200 mph)!

A third reaction with silicon dioxide consumes the hazardous metal oxides. Almost instantaneously, the airbag begins to deflate to provide softer cushioning before impact. After only two seconds, the airbag has completely deflated.

Scientists and engineers spend much of their time seeking ways to help others. Those who have worked on inventing and improving the airbag have saved many lives.

290 Chapter 12

The Densities of Gases

The density of a gas, as with all types of matter, is defined as mass per unit of volume. Compared with solids and liquids, gases have very low mass per unit of volume. This is not surprising since gases have so much empty space between their particles. Most gases have densities about one-thousandth the densities of their solid or liquid states.

Gas density is measured in grams per liter. Some people assume incorrectly that all gases have at least similar densities. Helium (0.1786 g/L at STP) has such a low density that it is used to lift weather balloons. Air at STP has a density of 1.2922 g/L. Some gases, such as nitrogen dioxide (1.880 g/L), are so dense that they tend to sink in air and roll along the ground.

Gases have different densities because of the variations in their molar masses. Since 1 mol of any gas occupies the same volume at any combination of temperature and pressure, the molar mass determines the density of the gas. Gases with low molar masses have low densities. Gases with higher molar masses have greater densities. In other words, the density and molar mass of a gas are directly related.

$$\rho_{gas} = \frac{\textit{molar mass}}{\textit{molar volume}}$$

This equation is a powerful tool for calculating the density of a gas if its molar mass is known.

EXAMPLE 12-12: CALCULATING GAS DENSITY

What is the density of hydrogen gas at STP?

Write what you know.

molar mass H_2 = 2.02 g/mol
standard molar volume = 22.4 L/mol.

Write the formula and solve for the unknown.

$$\rho_{gas} = \frac{\textit{molar mass}}{\textit{molar volume}}$$

Plug in known values and evaluate.

$$\rho_{H_2\text{ at STP}} = \frac{2.02\ \frac{g}{\cancel{mol}}}{22.4\ \frac{L}{\cancel{mol}}}$$

$$= 0.0902\ g/L$$

DENSITY AND FLOATING

To activate prior knowledge, use **Socratic questioning** to discuss the density of gases.

1. Why does wood float in water? *(It is less dense than water.)*
2. If you have two gases with different densities that won't mix in a container, how would you expect the gases to arrange themselves within the container? *(The less dense gas would end up floating on top of the denser gas.)*

Gases 291

WORLDVIEW INVESTIGATION: GREENHOUSE GASES

In this investigation students have the opportunity to research the topic of greenhouse gases, which will probably lead them to the topic of global warming. This subject has become very controversial due to much partisan political debate. For that reason, this may be a great time to discuss information sources. Point out that an organization's worldview may impact how they report on a certain topic.

The task does not state the length of the article. This was done intentionally to allow you as the teacher to decide on an appropriate length.

Appendix K includes a reproducible rubric to assess this worldview investigation activity.

WORLDVIEW INVESTIGATION

GREENHOUSE GASES

If you pay any attention to the news, you are aware that there is a lot of concern about greenhouse gases and global warming. Many people don't know what greenhouse gases are or how they affect the earth. And there is much confusion about the greenhouse effect and its relationship to global warming. Should we be trying to fix the greenhouse effect and global warming?

Task

Since you are a member of your school's science club, the editor of the school newspaper has asked you to write an article about greenhouse gases from a biblical worldview. She specifically wants you to address the following five questions. (1) What are greenhouse gases? (2) How do they affect the earth? (3) What biblical principles relate to greenhouse gases and climate change? (4) Are greenhouse gases and climate change significant issues? (5) How do biblical principles inform your position? While you have heard a lot about greenhouse gases and global warming on the news, you realize that you know very little about the subject since you have never researched the issue yourself.

Procedure

1. Do appropriate research on the topic. To get started, do an internet search using keywords such as "greenhouse effect" or "greenhouse gases." You could even search for "Are the greenhouse effect and global warming the same thing?"
2. Write your article, being careful to properly cite your sources.
3. Have a classmate read your article and provide feedback.
4. Edit your article and submit it before press time.

Conclusion

Greenhouse gases, the greenhouse effect, and global warming are issues that humans will continue to deal with. We have an obligation to be good stewards of the world that God created. We must wisely decide on appropriate action. But to make appropriate decisions, we must be informed on the issue.

292 Chapter 12

Analytical chemists can use this relationship to find the molar mass of an unknown gas. They can measure its density and then solve for its molar mass.

While understanding the densities of gases may seem like a novelty, the reality is that the behavior of gases on the basis of their densities can be a life or death matter. In 1986 many cattle (inset) and over 1700 people lost their lives when a large amount of carbon dioxide was released from deep within Lake Nyos in Cameroon. Because of its high density, the carbon dioxide gas remained at ground level and flowed through a river valley. Scientists investigated the event and determined that Lake Nyos experienced what is known as a *limnic eruption*—dissolved carbon dioxide being suddenly released from a lake. The tragedy of Lake Nyos led scientists to study other lakes with limnic activity to prevent a recurrence of this disaster. Their focus is on larger, more populated areas, such as the region surrounding Lake Kivu in East Central Africa. This is another example of scientists using their knowledge and skill to protect God's creation.

12.3 SECTION REVIEW

1. (True or False) Under equivalent conditions, equal volumes of gases contain the same number of particles.
2. How many moles of nitrogen gas occupy 14.7 L at STP?
3. When is the behavior of real gases most like ideal ones? Explain.
4. State the ideal gas law qualitatively and mathematically.
5. When do we use the combined gas law? the ideal gas law?
6. Use the ideal gas law to obtain the answers to the following questions.
   a. How many moles of oxygen will occupy 1.75 L at −118 °C and 5043 kPa?
   b. What is the temperature of 0.257 mol of oxygen occupying 6.78 L at 8.67×10^4 Pa?
   c. What is the pressure of 25.6 g of chlorine occupying 15.6 L at 218.6 °C?
   d. How much space will 0.514 mol of fluorine occupy at 58.5 °C and 1.076×10^5 Pa?
7. A technician produces hydrogen gas by reacting zinc with sulfuric acid. The equation for this single-replacement reaction is shown below.

   $$2Zn(s) + H_2SO_4(aq) \longrightarrow Zn_2SO_4(aq) + H_2(g)$$

   a. If the technician completely reacts 2.85 g Zn with excess acid, what volume of hydrogen gas will result at 98.29 kPa and 55.0 °C?
   b. When she finishes the procedure, she actually has 0.702 L of gas. Why did this occur?
8. How many grams of sodium azide are needed to produce enough nitrogen gas to fill a 57.6 L airbag at 98.8 kPa and 22 °C, assuming that only the nitrogen from the equation below is needed to fill it?

   $$2\,NaN_3(s) \longrightarrow 2Na(s) + 3\,N_2(g)$$

9. An unknown gas has a density of 0.714 g/L at STP. What is its molar mass?

APPLY

LAB 12B: *AN AQUANAUT'S WORLD*

Once students have an understanding of the material in Section 12.3, they should be ready to work through Lab 12B.

ASSESS

TICKET OUT THE DOOR

As a **summarizing activity**, assess students' understanding by asking them to list at least two of the three conditions under which gases behave most like ideal gases. *(when they have a low molar mass, the temperature is high, and the pressure is low)*

12.3 REVIEW ANSWERS

* An asterisk following a question number indicates that a worked-out solution can be found on pages 297B–97C.

1. True *(p. 284)*

2.* 0.656 mol N_2 *(p. 285)*

3. Real gases behave most like ideal gases when the particles are small and are under conditions of high temperature and low pressure. The kinetic-molecular theory assumes that gas particles take up no space and only momentarily interact with each other and the container. Small particles (low mass) take up the least space. When temperature is high and pressure is low, the gas particles have the greatest space between them and therefore interact infrequently. *(p. 286)*

4. The ideal gas law is a mathematical model that relates the pressure, temperature, volume, and the number of moles in any sample of a gas. $PV = nRT$ *(p. 287)*

5. The combined gas law is used when one sample of gas experiences a change in conditions. It allows us to solve for one variable (P, T, or V) when the other two variables change. The ideal gas law is used to solve for one of the four variables (P, V, T, and n) without a change in conditions. *(pp. 279, 287)*

6.*a. 6.85 mol O_2

b. 2 °C

c. 94.6 kPa

d. 13.2 L F_2 *(all pp. 287–88)*

7.*a. 0.605 L H_2

b. Since the reaction takes place in a solution, the gas is collected over water, and some of the volume of gas "produced" is water vapor. *(all pp. 280, 289)*

8.* 101 g NaN_3 *(pp. 289–90)*

9.* 16.0 g/mol *(p. 291)*

CHAPTER 12 *REVIEW ANSWERS*

Recalling Facts

1. Pressure is the average force exerted per unit of area when particles collide against a boundary. *(p. 271)*
2. Standard temperature is 0 °C and standard pressure is 1 atm. *(p. 274)*
3. The pressure and volume of a sample of gas, at a constant temperature, vary inversely with each other. $PV = k$ or $P_1V_1 = P_2V_2$ *(pp. 274–75)*
4. The combined gas law relates the pressure, temperature, and volume to each other in a joint equation.

   $\frac{PV}{T} = k$ or $\frac{P_1V_1}{T_1} = \frac{P_2V_2}{T_2}$ *(p. 279)*
5. The process of collecting a gas over water leads to some water vapor entering the gas sample. *(p. 280)*
6. Under equivalent conditions, the volumes of reacting gases and their gaseous products are expressed in ratios of small whole numbers. *(p. 283)*
7. The volume and number of particles (moles) of a gas, at a constant pressure and temperature, vary directly with each other.

   $\frac{V}{n} = k$ or $\frac{V_1}{n_1} = \frac{V_2}{n_2}$

   $\left(\frac{n_1}{V_1} = \frac{n_2}{V_2}\right.$ is also acceptable.$\left.\right)$ *(p. 284)*
8. Standard molar volume is the volume (22.4 L) occupied by any gas at STP. *(p. 285)*
9. An ideal gas is a gas whose behavior is perfectly predicted by the kinetic-molecular theory. *(p. 286)*

Understanding Concepts

* An asterisk following a question number indicates that a worked-out solution can be found on pages 297C–97G.

10. a. Gas particles are widely spaced, resulting in a small mass occupying a large volume.

    b. Gas particles are in constant motion in random directions. They collide with their container and other particles, causing gases to diffuse.

    c. Gases compress because there are large distances between particles.

12 CHAPTER REVIEW

Chapter Summary

TERMS
diffusion
effusion
Graham's law of effusion
fluid
compressibility
expansibility
pressure

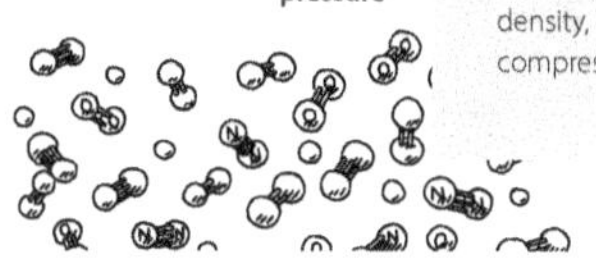

12.1 PROPERTIES OF GASES

- The kinetic-molecular theory describes the properties of gases on the basis of particle movement.
- Key properties of gases include low density, diffusion, effusion, fluidity, compressibility, and expansibility.
- Pressure results from the collision of molecules against a boundary.
- The pressure, temperature, and volume of a sample of gas are all interrelated, and those relationships can be explained by the kinetic-molecular theory.

12.2 GAS LAWS

- Standard temperature and pressure (STP) is defined as 0 °C and 101.325 kPa .
- Boyle's law states that when temperature is constant, the volume and pressure of a gas are inversely proportional to each other.
- Charles's law states that when pressure is constant, there is a direct relationship between the Kelvin temperature of a gas and its volume.
- Gay-Lussac's law states that when volume is constant, the pressure and Kelvin temperature of a gas are directly proportional.
- The combined gas law allows calculations when the pressure, volume, and temperature of a gas all change.
- Dalton's law of partial pressures states that the total pressure of a mixture of gases equals the sum of the partial pressures.

TERMS
standard temperature and pressure (STP)
Boyle's law
Charles's law
Gay-Lussac's law
combined gas law
Dalton's law of partial pressures

TERMS
law of combining volumes
Avogadro's law
standard molar volume
ideal gas
ideal gas law

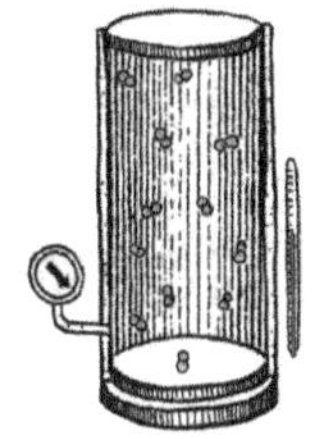

12.3 GAS STOICHIOMETRY

- Gay-Lussac's law of combining volumes states that the volumes of reacting gases and their gaseous products are expressed in ratios of small whole numbers. This principle allows the amounts of gases in moles to be calculated with stoichiometry.
- Avogadro's law states that the volume of a gas, maintained at a constant temperature and pressure, is directly proportional to the number of moles of the gas.
- At STP, 1 mol of any gas occupies approximately 22.4 L.
- The density of a gas can be determined by dividing its molar mass by its molar volume.
- The ideal gas law relates the pressure, volume, temperature, and quantity of gases.
- Scientists use the gas laws along with stoichiometric calculations to predict quantities of gases involved in chemical reactions.

294 Chapter 12

    d. The collisions between gas particles are elastic; that is, their kinetic energy is conserved. Temperature changes are due only to collisions with the container.

    e. The temperature of a gas is directly proportional to the average kinetic energy of its particles. Therefore, if we know the temperature of the gas samples, we can compare the average kinetic energies of the samples. *(all p. 269)*

11.* 1.19 *(p. 270)*

12. Since gases are compressible, they can be forced under pressure into small volumes. Canisters must be sufficiently sturdy to prevent rupture of the container. *(p. 271)*
13. The pressure will decrease. Some students may recognize that the pressure will be cut in half. *(p. 272)*
14. As temperature decreases, the particles move slower. Therefore, there will be fewer and less forceful collisions with the interior surface of the balloon. Since the pressure is constant, the balloon must contract so that the surface area is reduced to match the decrease in force. *(p. 272)*
15. As temperature decreases, particles move slower. This slow movement results in fewer collisions with the container and collisions that are less forceful. The net effect is decreased pressure on the container. *(p. 273)*

Chapter Review Questions

RECALLING FACTS

1. Define *pressure.*
2. Define *standard temperature and pressure* (STP).
3. State Boyle's law qualitatively and mathematically.
4. State the combined gas law qualitatively and mathematically.
5. Why is gas that is collected over water not pure?
6. State the law of combining volumes.
7. State Avogadro's law qualitatively and mathematically.
8. Define *standard molar volume.*
9. Define *ideal gas.*

UNDERSTANDING CONCEPTS

10. Use the kinetic-molecular theory of gases to explain why
    - **a.** air has a low density.
    - **b.** on a day with no wind, you can smell a dead skunk that is 500 yards away.
    - **c.** a large amount of air can be pumped into a small bicycle tire.
    - **d.** the temperature of a sample of gas doesn't change even though the collisions between particles transfer kinetic energy.
    - **e.** we can compare the average kinetic energy in samples of gases by comparing their temperatures.
11. Calculate the ratio of the effusion rates between nitrogen and argon gases.
12. Why is the carbon dioxide gas that carbonates fountain drinks and powers paintball guns stored in sturdy canisters?
13. You have a sample of gas in a 1 L bottle. What will happen to the pressure if the gas is allowed to expand into a 2 L bottle at a constant temperature?
14. Explain why an inflated balloon becomes smaller when placed in a freezer.
15. Why does the pressure of a gas at constant volume decrease with decreased temperature?
16. When dealing with gases, why is a standard value for temperature and pressure important?
17. Why do we have to use the Kelvin scale when working with the gas laws?
18. Explain Gay-Lussac's law on the basis of the kinetic-molecular theory of gases.
19. Solve each of the following questions using the appropriate gas law. Also identify the gas law that you used each time.
    - **a.** At 22.19 °C, a chemical reaction produces 74.30 mL of oxygen gas. How much space will the oxygen gas occupy at 54.37 °C if pressure remains constant?
    - **b.** A sample of gas at 112.7 kPa occupies 997.4 mL. What will the pressure be if the gas is compressed to 253.9 mL at a constant temperature?
    - **c.** A sample of nitrogen at 16 °C and 100.3 kPa has a volume of 2.60 L. What is the volume of the nitrogen at STP?

16. Standard values of temperature and pressure allow scientists to make direct comparisons of gas volumes since volumes are significantly affected by temperature and pressure. *(p. 274)*

17. The gas laws have to do with the energy of the particles in the sample. The Kelvin scale is founded upon absolute zero, the temperature at which the particles would have minimum energy. Also, other scales have negative temperatures. A negative temperature could result in calculated negative pressures and volumes, which don't make physical sense. This is especially true of negative volumes. *(pp. 276–77)*

18. The temperature of a substance is a measure of the average kinetic energy of its particles. As temperature increases, particles move faster. Faster-moving particles collide with the container more often and with more force. If the container is rigid, it cannot change in size, so these changes to the collisions apply more force on the container. As force increases while surface area remains constant, pressure increases. A decrease in temperature results in the opposite happening. *(p. 278)*

19.*a. 82.40 mL
b. 442.7 kPa
c. 2.43 L
d. 7.70×10^4 Pa
e. 90.9 mL
f. −14.5 °C
g. −159 °C
h. 9 °C *(all pp. 274–79)*

20.* 42.24 mL *(pp. 280–81)*

21. The volume of a gas is determined by the number of particles and the motion of those particles. If the temperature is held constant, the kinetic energy (motion) of the particles is constant. Therefore, by adding more particles, the number of collisions will increase. As the number of collisions increases, the net force on the container increases. In order to maintain a constant pressure, the surface area and therefore volume of the container must increase equally with the increased force. *(p. 284)*

22. Gas laws are useful because they are workable and provide a framework for scientific work. *(p. 286)*

23.*a. 0.0247 mol Kr

b. 10.4 L He

c. $39\underline{4}.711$ K = 122 °C

d. 3.88×10^5 Pa *(all pp. 287–88)*

24.*a. 561.12 L N_2

b. 715.1 L gases *(all p. 289)*

25.*a. 44.8 L NO

b. 18.1 g H_2O

c. 8.37 L O_2 *(all p. 289)*

26.* 3.17 g/L *(p. 289)*

Critical Thinking

27.* 70.93 g/mol *(p. 270)*

28. The changing of all three variables simultaneously is much more complex than a simple direct or inverse relationship. You can state whether one variable will increase or decrease in response to a general statement about the other two variables. *(pp. 272–73)*

29.* *(pp. 277, 279)*

30.* 66.7 mL *(p. 281)*

31. When something burns, the gaseous products are at high temperature. The high temperature results in low densities. These gaseous products rise to the top of a room on fire, and the unreacted, relatively cool air sinks toward the floor. *(p. 291)*

32.* *(p. 287)*

12 CHAPTER REVIEW

d. A 73.4 mL sample of gas is collected at 3.54×10^5 Pa and 114.6 °C. If the gas is allowed to expand to 269 mL and cooled to 35.9 °C, what is the new gas pressure?

e. A 95.1 mL sample of gas is collected at 124.8 kPa. How much space will the gas occupy if pressure is increased to 130.5 kPa and the temperature remains constant?

f. A 13.20 mL sample of hydrogen sulfide is at 1.875×10^5 Pa at 55.6 °C. At what temperature will the pressure drop to 1.475×10^5 Pa if the volume is held constant?

g. A sample of gas occupies 111 mL at 32.4 °C. What temperature is necessary to maintain a constant pressure if the gas is moved to a 41.3 mL container?

h. A 19.8 L sample of helium has a pressure of 1.142×10^5 Pa at 53.8 °C. If the volume is held constant, what temperature will result in 9.86×10^4 Pa of pressure?

20. A sample of 117.2 mL of chlorine is collected by water displacement at a temperature of 85.0 °C. The barometer reads 105.695 kPa. What is the volume of the chlorine at STP?

21. Explain Avogadro's law on the basis of the kinetic-molecular theory of gases.

22. If the behavior of real gases cannot be exactly predicted by gas laws, why are they still useful?

23. Answer the following questions using the ideal gas laws.

a. A canister holds 553 mL of krypton at STP. How many moles of Kr are present?

b. A weather balloon contains 0.465 mol He at STP. How much space will that gas occupy?

c. A 1.78 g sample of argon fill a 1.46 L tank at a pressure of 100.1 kPa. What is the temperature of the gas?

d. A tank of oxygen gas contains 89.0 g of O_2. If the volume of the tank is 17.54 L, what is the pressure (in Pa) of the O_2 if the temperature is 21.4 °C?

24. When nitroglycerine (227.1 g/mol) explodes, N_2, CO_2, H_2O, and O_2 gases are released initially. Assume that the gases from the explosion are allowed to change to STP without reacting further.

$$4C_3H_5N_3O_9(s) \longrightarrow 6N_2(g) + 12CO_2(g) + 10H_2O(g) + O_2(g)$$

a. If 16.7 mol of nitroglycerine reacts, how many liters of nitrogen are produced?

b. What is the total volume of gas produced when 1.000 kg of nitroglycerine reacts?

25. A reaction between ammonia and oxygen is the first step in the preparation of nitric acid (HNO_3) on a commercial scale. The reactants are mixed at STP. The products are produced at 1058 °C and at 98.7 kPa.

$$4NH_3(g) + 5O_2(g) \xrightarrow{\text{catalyst}} 4NO(g) + 6H_2O(g)$$

a. What volume of nitrogen monoxide (NO) is produced in the reaction vessel by the reaction of 0.500 mol O_2?

b. What mass of water is produced by the reaction of 15.0 L of ammonia at STP?

c. How many liters of oxygen must react to produce 33.5 L of nitrogen monoxide?

26. What is the density of chlorine gas (Cl_2) at STP?

CRITICAL THINKING

27. You set up an experiment comparing the diffusion rates of an unknown elemental gas with nitrogen gas. If the nitrogen diffused 1.591 times faster than the unknown gas, what is the molar mass of the unknown gas? Identify your unknown gas.

28. The descriptions of changes in pressure, temperature, and volume in Section 12.1 always stipulate that one of the properties is held constant. Since it seems unlikely that you can maintain one of these conditions constant in real-world situations, why do you think there is no description of these changing simultaneously?

29. Derive Charles's law from the combined gas law.

30. A sample of 75.6 mL of oxygen is collected by water displacement at a temperature of 48.1 °C. The barometer reads 116.5 kPa. What is the volume of the oxygen at STP?

31. Why are we taught to crawl out of a burning building?

32. Starting from the ideal gas law, explain Charles's law.

Use the ethics box to answer Question 33.

33. Write a four-paragraph response to the issue of airbag safety on the basis of a biblical worldview.

ethics

DEADLY SAFETY DEVICE?

The Chapter opener highlighted the dangers of automobile collisions. Scientists developed airbags to help protect occupants during a collision, and they have been instrumental in saving many thousands of lives in their five decades of use. Airbags inflate at about 200 mph in order to deploy quickly enough to protect vehicle occupants. Sadly, airbags have actually been the cause of a number of deaths. Because of this, some vehicle owners have considered deactivating the airbags in their cars. As a Christian, how do you balance the protective capabilities of airbags with their potential hazard? Is it appropriate to have your airbag disabled?

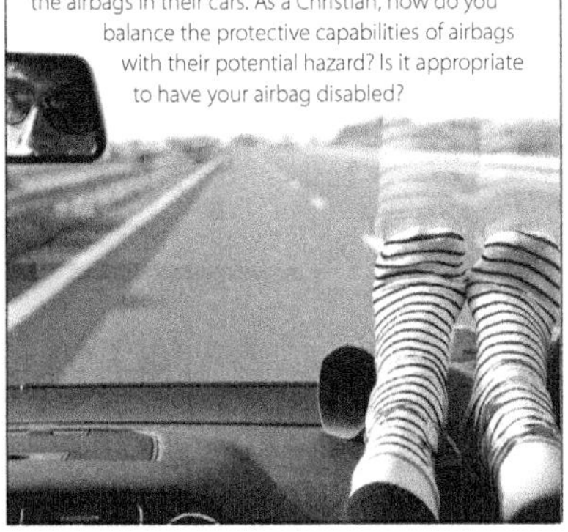

ETHICS: DEADLY SAFETY DEVICE?

Appendix L includes a reproducible rubric to assess the ethics essay.

33. People are valuable because they are God's image-bearers. The Bible places a high priority on protecting human life.

Since we are to protect God's image-bearers, any decisions regarding deactivating airbags should be made on the basis of the potential threat to people. Research shows that the number of lives saved is significantly higher than the lives lost due to malfunctioning airbags. Also, most of the deaths associated with airbags have been due to improper use.

I both glorify God and love others when I make decisions that obey God's commandments and help others. Making the right decision regarding airbags will glorify God, honor His commandment to protect human life, and protect those I love.

In most cases airbags should not be deactivated but should be used as specified in vehicle owner's manuals regarding seat position, occupant location in vehicle, and use in conjunction with seat belts. In some cases it is acceptable to have the bag disabled. There are medical reasons for deactivation. Also, if a child or other small occupant must sit in the front seat, it is much safer for the airbag to be disabled.

AIRBAGS

For a narrated video that focuses on airbag safety for children but includes principles that can also be applied to adults, visit TeacherToolsOnline.com. Under Additional Resources, click on the Chapter 12 Web Links. Then click on *Airbags*.

Section 12.2

5. a. What we know: $P_1 = 1.19 \times 10^5$ Pa, $V_1 = 4.15$ L, $V_2 = 11.26$ L

Unknown: P_2

Write the formula and solve for the unknown. Since temperature is constant, Boyle's law applies.

$$P_1V_1 = P_2V_2$$

$$\frac{P_1V_1}{V_2} = \frac{P_2\cancel{V_2}}{\cancel{V_2}}$$

$$P_2 = \frac{P_1V_1}{V_2}$$

Evaluate.

$$P_2 = \frac{(1.19 \times 10^5\ \text{Pa})(4.15\ \cancel{\text{L}})}{11.26\ \cancel{\text{L}}}$$

$$= 4.39 \times 10^4\ \text{Pa}$$

b. What we know: $V_1 = 137.4$ mL, $T_1 = 19.7$ °C = 292.85 K, $T_2 = 46.2$ °C = 319.35 K

Unknown: V_2

Write the formula and solve for the unknown. Since volume and temperature are being related, Charles's law applies.

$$\frac{V_1}{T_1} = \frac{V_2}{T_2}$$

$$\left(\frac{V_1}{T_1}\right)T_2 = \left(\frac{V_2}{\cancel{T_2}}\right)\cancel{T_2}$$

$$V_2 = \left(\frac{V_1}{T_1}\right)T_2$$

Evaluate.

$$V_2 = \left(\frac{137.4\ \text{mL}}{292.85\ \cancel{\text{K}}}\right)319.35\ \cancel{\text{K}}$$

$$= 149.8\ \text{mL}$$

c. What we know: $V_1 = V_2 = 0.537$ L, $P_1 = 164.653$ kPa, $T_1 = 16.5$ °C = 289.65 K, $P_2 = 41.997$ kPa

Unknown: T_2

Write the formula and solve for the unknown. Since pressure and temperature are being related, Gay-Lussac's law applies.

$$\frac{P_1}{T_1} = \frac{P_2}{T_2}$$

$$\left(\frac{P_1}{T_1}\right)T_2 = \left(\frac{P_2}{\cancel{T_2}}\right)\cancel{T_2}$$

$$\left(\frac{\cancel{P_1}}{\cancel{T_1}}\right)T_2\left(\frac{\cancel{T_1}}{\cancel{P_1}}\right) = P_2\left(\frac{T_1}{P_1}\right)$$

$$T_2 = P_2\left(\frac{T_1}{P_1}\right)$$

Evaluate.

$$T_2 = 41.997\ \cancel{\text{kPa}}\left(\frac{289.\underline{6}5\ \text{K}}{164.653\ \cancel{\text{kPa}}}\right)$$

$$= 73.8\underline{7}9\ \text{K} = -199.27\ \text{°C}$$

d. What we know: $P_1 = 122$ kPa, $T_1 = 22.0$ °C = 295.15 K, $V_1 = 0.350$ L, $V_2 = 0.050$ L, $T_2 = 25.0$ °C = 298.15 K

Unknown: P_2

Write the formula and solve for the unknown. Since all three conditions change, the combined gas law applies.

$$\frac{P_1V_1}{T_1} = \frac{P_2V_2}{T_2}$$

$$\left(\frac{P_1V_1}{T_1}\right)\left(\frac{T_2}{V_2}\right) = \left(\frac{P_2\cancel{V_2}}{\cancel{T_2}}\right)\left(\frac{\cancel{T_2}}{\cancel{V_2}}\right)$$

$$P_2 = \frac{P_1V_1T_2}{T_1V_2}$$

Evaluate.

$$P_2 = \frac{(122\ \text{kPa})(0.350\ \cancel{\text{L}})(298.15\ \cancel{\text{K}})}{(295.15\ \cancel{\text{K}})(0.050\ \cancel{\text{L}})}$$

$$= 863\ \text{kPa}$$

e. What we know: $V_1 = 3.51$ L, $P_1 = 9.54 \times 10^5$ Pa, $T_1 = T_2 = 20$ °C, $P_2 = 6.17 \times 10^5$ Pa

Unknown: V_2

Write the formula and solve for the unknown. Since temperature is constant, Boyle's law applies.

$$P_1V_1 = P_2V_2$$

$$\frac{P_1V_1}{P_2} = \frac{\cancel{P_2}V_2}{\cancel{P_2}}$$

$$V_2 = \frac{P_1V_1}{P_2}$$

Evaluate.

$$V_2 = \frac{(9.54 \times 10^5\ \cancel{\text{Pa}})(3.51\ \text{L})}{6.17 \times 10^5\ \cancel{\text{Pa}}}$$

$$= 5.43\ \text{L}$$

f. What we know: $V_1 = 72.6$ mL, $T_1 = 23$ °C = 296.15 K, $P_1 = 106$ kPa, $T_2 = 0$ °C = 273.15 K, $P_2 = 101.325$ kPa

Unknown: V_2

Write the formula and solve for the unknown. Since all three conditions change, the combined gas law applies.

$$\frac{P_1V_1}{T_1} = \frac{P_2V_2}{T_2}$$

$$\left(\frac{P_1V_1}{T_1}\right)\left(\frac{T_2}{P_2}\right) = \left(\frac{\cancel{P_2}V_2}{\cancel{T_2}}\right)\left(\frac{\cancel{T_2}}{\cancel{P_2}}\right)$$

$$V_2 = \frac{P_1V_1T_2}{T_1P_2}$$

Evaluate.

$$V_2 = \frac{(106\ \cancel{\text{kPa}})(72.6\ \text{mL})(273.15\ \cancel{\text{K}})}{(29\underline{6}.15\ \cancel{\text{K}})(101.325\ \cancel{\text{kPa}})}$$

$$= 70.1\ \text{mL}$$

g. What we know: $V_1 = 5.54$ L, $T_1 = 0.00$ °C = 273.15 K, $T_2 = 31.15$ °C = 304.30 K

Unknown: V_2

Write the formula and solve for the unknown. Since volume and temperature are being related, Charles's law applies.

$$\frac{V_1}{T_1} = \frac{V_2}{T_2}$$

$$\left(\frac{V_1}{T_1}\right)T_2 = \left(\frac{V_2}{\cancel{T_2}}\right)\cancel{T_2}$$

$$V_2 = \left(\frac{V_1}{T_1}\right)T_2$$

Evaluate.

$$V_2 = \left(\frac{5.54\text{ L}}{273.15\ \cancel{\text{K}}}\right)304.30\ \cancel{\text{K}}$$

$$= 6.17\text{ L}$$

h. What we know: $V_1 = V_2 = 1.25$ L, $P_1 = 107$ kPa, $T_1 = 128$ °C = 401.15 K, $T_2 = 98$ °C = 371.15 K

Unknown: P_2

Write the formula and solve for the unknown. Since pressure and temperature are being related, Gay-Lussac's law applies.

$$\frac{P_1}{T_1} = \frac{P_2}{T_2}$$

$$\left(\frac{P_1}{T_1}\right)T_2 = \left(\frac{P_2}{\cancel{T_2}}\right)\cancel{T_2}$$

$$P_2 = \left(\frac{P_1}{T_1}\right)T_2$$

Evaluate.

$$P_2 = \left(\frac{107\text{ kPa}}{40\underline{1}.15\ \cancel{\text{K}}}\right)37\underline{1}.15\ \cancel{\text{K}}$$

$$= 99.0\text{ kPa}$$

8. What we know: $P_{total} = 101\,185$ Pa, $T_1 = 20$ °C = 293.15 K, $P_{H_2O} = 2338.8$ Pa (from Table 12-2)

Unknown: P_{H_2}

Write the formula and solve for the unknown.

$$P_{total} = \Sigma P_i$$

$$P_{total} - P_{H_2O} = P_{H_2} \cancel{+ P_{H_2O}} \cancel{- P_{H_2O}}$$

$$P_{H_2} = P_{total} - P_{H_2O}$$

Evaluate.

$$P_{H_2} = 101\,185\text{ Pa} - 2338.8\text{ Pa}$$

$$= 98\,84\underline{6}.2\text{ Pa}$$

What we know: $V_1 = 43.9$ mL, $P_1 = 98\,846.2$ Pa, $T_1 = 20$ °C = 293.15 K, $T_2 = 0$ °C = 273.15 K, $P_2 = 101\,325$ Pa

Unknown: V_2

Write the formula and solve for the unknown.

$$\frac{P_1V_1}{T_1} = \frac{P_2V_2}{T_2}$$

$$\left(\frac{P_1V_1}{T_1}\right)\left(\frac{T_2}{P_2}\right) = \left(\frac{\cancel{P_2}V_2}{\cancel{T_2}}\right)\left(\frac{\cancel{T_2}}{\cancel{P_2}}\right)$$

$$V_2 = \frac{P_1V_1T_2}{T_1P_2}$$

Evaluate.

$$V_2 = \frac{(98\,84\underline{6}.2\ \cancel{\text{Pa}})(43.9\text{ mL})(273.15\ \cancel{\text{K}})}{(29\underline{3}.15\ \cancel{\text{K}})(101\,325\ \cancel{\text{Pa}})}$$

$$= 39.9\text{ mL}$$

Section 12.3

2. What we know: $V = 14.7$ mL N_2

Unknown: n

Convert L N_2 into mol N_2.

$$14.7\ \cancel{\text{L N}_2}\left(\frac{1\text{ mol N}_2}{22.4\ \cancel{\text{L N}_2}}\right) = 0.656\text{ mol N}_2$$

6. a. What we know: $V = 1.75$ L, $T = -118$ °C = 155.15 K, $P = 5043$ kPa, $R = 8.31\ \frac{\text{kPa}\cdot\text{L}}{\text{mol}\cdot\text{K}}$ (from Table 12 – 5)

Unknown: n

Write the formula and solve for the unknown.

$$PV = nRT$$

$$\frac{PV}{RT} = \frac{n\cancel{RT}}{\cancel{RT}}$$

$$n = \frac{PV}{RT}$$

Evaluate.

$$n = \frac{(5043\ \cancel{\text{kPa}})(1.75\ \cancel{\text{L}}\ O_2)}{\left(8.31\ \frac{\cancel{\text{kPa}}\cdot\cancel{\text{L}}}{\text{mol}\cdot\cancel{\text{K}}}\right)(15\underline{5}.15\ \cancel{\text{K}})}$$

$$= 6.85\text{ mol } O_2$$

b. What we know: $n = 0.257$ mol O_2, $V = 6.78$ L O_2, $P = 8.67 \times 10^4$ Pa, $R = 8.31 \times 10^3\ \frac{\text{Pa}\cdot\text{L}}{\text{mol}\cdot\text{K}}$

Unknown: T

Write the formula and solve for the unknown.

$$PV = nRT$$

$$\frac{PV}{nR} = \frac{\cancel{nR}T}{\cancel{nR}}$$

$$T = \frac{PV}{nR}$$

Evaluate.

$$T = \frac{(8.67 \times 10^4\ \cancel{\text{Pa}})(6.78\ \cancel{\text{L}}\ \cancel{O_2})}{(0.257\ \cancel{\text{mol}}\ \cancel{O_2})\left(8.31 \times 10^3\ \frac{\cancel{\text{Pa}}\cdot\cancel{\text{L}}}{\cancel{\text{mol}}\cdot\text{K}}\right)}$$

$$= 27\underline{5}.241\,961\,5\text{ K} = 2\text{ °C}$$

c. What we know: $m = 25.6\text{ g } Cl_2$, $V = 15.6\text{ L}$,

$T = 218.6\text{ °C} = 491.75\text{ K}$, $R = 8.31\dfrac{\text{kPa}\cdot\text{L}}{\text{mol}\cdot\text{K}}$,

$$n = 25.6\cancel{\text{g } Cl_2}\left(\frac{1\text{ mol } Cl_2}{70.90\cancel{\text{g } Cl_2}}\right) = 0.36\underline{1}\,07\text{ mol } Cl_2$$

Unknown: P

Write the formula and solve for the unknown.

$$PV = nRT$$

$$\frac{\cancel{V}P}{\cancel{V}} = \frac{nRT}{V}$$

$$P = \frac{nRT}{V}$$

Evaluate.

$$P = \frac{(0.36\underline{1}\,07\cancel{\text{mol } Cl_2})\left(8.31\dfrac{\text{kPa}\cdot\cancel{\text{L}}}{\cancel{\text{mol}}\cdot\cancel{\text{K}}}\right)(491.75\cancel{\text{K}})}{(15.6\cancel{\text{L } Cl_2})}$$

$= 94.6\text{ kPa}$

d. What we know: $n = 0.514\text{ mol } F_2$, $T = 58.5\text{ °C} = 331.65\text{ K}$,

$P = 1.076 \times 10^5\text{ Pa}$, $R = 8.31 \times 10^3\dfrac{\text{Pa}\cdot\text{L}}{\text{mol}\cdot\text{K}}$

Unknown: V

Write the formula and solve for the unknown.

$$PV = nRT$$

$$\frac{\cancel{P}V}{\cancel{P}} = \frac{nRT}{P}$$

$$V = \frac{nRT}{P}$$

Evaluate.

$$V = \frac{(0.514\cancel{\text{mol}}\,F_2)\left(8.31 \times 10^3\dfrac{\cancel{\text{Pa}}\cdot\text{L}}{\cancel{\text{mol}}\cdot\cancel{\text{K}}}\right)(331.65\cancel{\text{K}})}{(1.076 \times 10^5\cancel{\text{Pa}})}$$

$= 13.2\text{ L } F_2$

7. a. What we know: $m_{Zn} = 2.85\text{ g Zn}$, $T = 55\text{ °C} = 328.15\text{ K}$,

$P = 98.29\text{ kPa}$, $R = 8.31\dfrac{\text{kPa}\cdot\text{L}}{\text{mol}\cdot\text{K}}$

Unknowns: n_{H_2}, V

Use stoichiometry to find moles of H_2.

$$2.85\cancel{\text{g Zn}}\left(\frac{1\cancel{\text{mol Zn}}}{65.38\cancel{\text{g Zn}}}\right)\left(\frac{1\text{ mol } H_2}{2\cancel{\text{mol Zn}}}\right) = 0.021\,\underline{7}95\,656\,2\text{ mol } H_2$$

Write the formula and solve for the unknown.

$$PV = nRT$$

$$\frac{\cancel{P}V}{\cancel{P}} = \frac{nRT}{P}$$

$$V = \frac{nRT}{P}$$

Evaluate.

$$V = \frac{(0.021\,\underline{7}95\,656\,2\cancel{\text{mol}}\,H_2)\left(8.31\dfrac{\cancel{\text{kPa}}\cdot\text{L}}{\cancel{\text{mol}}\cdot\cancel{\text{K}}}\right)(32\underline{8}.15\cancel{\text{K}})}{(98.29\cancel{\text{kPa}})}$$

$= 0.605\text{ L } H_2$

8. What we know: $V = 57.6\text{ L}$, $P = 98.8\text{ kPa}$, $T = 22 = 295.15\text{ K}$,

$R = 8.31\dfrac{\text{kPa}\cdot\text{L}}{\text{mol}\cdot\text{K}}$

Unknown: m_{NaN_3}

Write the formula and solve for the unknown.

$$PV = nRT$$

$$\frac{PV}{RT} = \frac{n\cancel{RT}}{\cancel{RT}}$$

$$n = \frac{PV}{RT}$$

Evaluate.

$$n = \frac{(98.8\cancel{\text{kPa}})(57.6\cancel{\text{L}}\,N_2)}{\left(8.31\dfrac{\cancel{\text{kPa}}\cdot\cancel{\text{L}}}{\text{mol}\cdot\cancel{\text{K}}}\right)295.15\cancel{\text{K}}}$$

$= 2.320\,254\,463\text{ mol } N_2$

gas stoichiometry:

$$2.320\,254\,463\cancel{\text{mol } N_2}\left(\frac{2\cancel{\text{mol } NaN_3}}{3\cancel{\text{mol } N_2}}\right)\left(\frac{65.02\text{ g } NaN_3}{1\cancel{\text{mol } NaN_3}}\right) = 101\text{ g } NaN_3$$

9. What we know: *molar volume* $= 22.4\text{ L/mol}$, $\rho = 0.714\text{ g/L}$

Unknown: *molar mass*

Write the formula and solve for the unknown.

$$\rho_{gas} = \frac{molar\ mass}{molar\ volume}$$

$$(\rho_{gas})\,molar\ volume = \left(\frac{molar\ mass}{\cancel{molar\ volume}}\right)\cancel{molar\ volume}$$

$$molar\ mass = (\rho_{gas})\,molar\ volume$$

Evaluate.

$$molar\ mass = \left(0.714\frac{\text{g}}{\cancel{\text{L}}}\right)\left(22.4\frac{\cancel{\text{L}}}{\text{mol}}\right)$$

$= 16.0\text{ g/mol}$

Chapter Review

11. What we know: *molar mass*$_{N_2}$ $= 28.02\text{ g/mol}$,

molar mass$_{Ar}$ $= 39.95\text{ g/mol}$

Unknown: $\dfrac{rate\ of\ effusion_{N_2}}{rate\ of\ effusion_{Ar}}$

Write the formula and solve for the unknown.

$$\frac{rate\ of\ effusion_{N_2}}{rate\ of\ effusion_{Ar}} = \frac{\sqrt{molar\ mass_{Ar}}}{\sqrt{molar\ mass_{N_2}}}$$

Evaluate.

$$\frac{rate\ of\ effusion_{N_2}}{rate\ of\ effusion_{Ar}} = \frac{\sqrt{39.95\dfrac{\cancel{\text{g}}}{\cancel{\text{mol}}}}}{\sqrt{28.02\dfrac{\cancel{\text{g}}}{\cancel{\text{mol}}}}} = 1.19$$

19. a. What we know: $T_1 = 22.19\ °C = 295.34\ K$, $V_1 = 74.30\ mL$, $T_2 = 54.37\ °C = 327.52\ K$

Unknown: V_2

Write the formula and solve for the unknown. Relating volume and temperature requires the use of Charles's law.

$$\frac{V_1}{T_1} = \frac{V_2}{T_2}$$

$$\left(\frac{V_1}{T_1}\right)T_2 = \left(\frac{V_2}{\cancel{T_2}}\right)\cancel{T_2}$$

$$V_2 = \left(\frac{V_1}{T_1}\right)T_2$$

Evaluate.

$$V_2 = \left(\frac{74.30\ mL}{295.34\ \cancel{K}}\right)327.52\ \cancel{K}$$

$$= 82.40\ mL$$

b. What we know: $P_1 = 112.7\ kPa$, $V_1 = 997.4\ mL$, $V_2 = 253.9\ mL$

Unknown: P_2

Write the formula and solve for the unknown. Relating pressure and volume requires the use of Boyle's law.

$$P_1V_1 = P_2V_2$$

$$\frac{P_1V_1}{V_2} = \frac{P_2\cancel{V_2}}{\cancel{V_2}}$$

$$P_2 = \frac{P_1V_1}{V_2}$$

Evaluate.

$$P_2 = \frac{(112.7\ kPa)(997.4\ \cancel{mL})}{253.9\ \cancel{mL}}$$

$$= 442.7\ kPa$$

c. What we know: $T_1 = 16\ °C = 289.15\ K$, $P_1 = 100.3\ kPa$, $V_1 = 2.60\ L$, $T_2 = 0\ °C = 273.15\ K$, $P_2 = 101.325\ kPa$

Unknown: V_2

Write the formula and solve for the unknown. Relating changes in all three conditions requires the use of the combined gas law.

$$\frac{P_1V_1}{T_1} = \frac{P_2V_2}{T_2}$$

$$\left(\frac{P_1V_1}{T_1}\right)\left(\frac{T_2}{P_2}\right) = \left(\frac{\cancel{P_2}V_2}{\cancel{T_2}}\right)\left(\frac{\cancel{T_2}}{\cancel{P_2}}\right)$$

$$V_2 = \frac{P_1V_1T_2}{T_1P_2}$$

Evaluate.

$$V_2 = \frac{(100.3\ \cancel{kPa})(2.60\ L)(273.15\ \cancel{K})}{(289.15\ \cancel{K})(101.325\ \cancel{kPa})}$$

$$= 2.43\ L$$

d. What we know: $V_1 = 73.4\ mL$, $P_1 = 3.54 \times 10^5\ Pa$, $T_1 = 114.6\ °C = 387.75\ K$, $V_2 = 269\ mL$, $T_2 = 35.9\ °C = 309.05\ K$

Unknown: P_2

Write the formula and solve for the unknown. Relating changes in all three conditions requires the use of the combined gas law.

$$\frac{P_1V_1}{T_1} = \frac{P_2V_2}{T_2}$$

$$\left(\frac{P_1V_1}{T_1}\right)\left(\frac{T_2}{V_2}\right) = \left(\frac{P_2\cancel{V_2}}{\cancel{T_2}}\right)\left(\frac{\cancel{T_2}}{\cancel{V_2}}\right)$$

$$P_2 = \frac{P_1V_1T_2}{T_1V_2}$$

Evaluate.

$$P_2 = \frac{(3.54 \times 10^5\ Pa)(73.4\ \cancel{mL})(309.05\ \cancel{K})}{(387.75\ \cancel{K})(269\ \cancel{mL})}$$

$$= 7.70 \times 10^4\ Pa$$

e. What we know: $V_1 = 95.1 mL$, $P_1 = 124.8\ kPa$, $P_2 = 130.5\ kPa$

Unknown: V_2

Write the formula and solve for the unknown. Relating pressure and volume requires the use of Boyle's law.

$$P_1V_1 = P_2V_2$$

$$\frac{P_1V_1}{P_2} = \frac{\cancel{P_2}V_2}{\cancel{P_2}}$$

$$V_2 = \frac{P_1V_1}{P_2}$$

Evaluate.

$$V_2 = \frac{(124.8\ \cancel{kPa})(95.1\ mL)}{130.5\ \cancel{kPa}}$$

$$= 90.9\ mL$$

f. What we know: $V_1 = V_2 = 13.20\ mL$, $P_1 = 1.875 \times 10^5\ Pa$, $T_1 = 55.6\ °C = 328.75\ K$, $P_2 = 1.475 \times 10^5\ Pa$

Unknown: T_2

Write the formula and solve for the unknown. Relating pressure and temperature requires the use of Gay-Lussac's law.

$$\frac{P_1}{T_1} = \frac{P_2}{T_2}$$

$$\left(\frac{P_1}{T_1}\right)T_2 = \left(\frac{P_2}{\cancel{T_2}}\right)\cancel{T_2}$$

$$\left(\frac{\cancel{P_1}}{\cancel{T_1}}\right)T_2\left(\frac{\cancel{T_1}}{\cancel{P_1}}\right) = P_2\left(\frac{T_1}{P_1}\right)$$

$$T_2 = P_2\left(\frac{T_1}{P_1}\right)$$

Evaluate.

$$T_2 = 1.475 \times 10^5\ \cancel{Pa}\left(\frac{328.75\ K}{1.875 \times 10^5\ \cancel{Pa}}\right)$$

$$= 258.\underline{6}17\ K = -14.5\ °C$$

g. What we know: $V_1 = 111$ mL, $T_1 = 32.4\ °C = 305.55$ K, $V_2 = 41.3$ mL

Unknown: T_2

Write the formula and solve for the unknown. Relating volume and temperature requires the use of Charles's law.

$$\frac{V_1}{T_1} = \frac{V_2}{T_2}$$

$$\left(\frac{V_1}{T_1}\right)T_2 = \left(\frac{V_2}{\cancel{T_2}}\right)\cancel{T_2}$$

$$\left(\frac{\cancel{V_1}}{\cancel{T_1}}\right)T_2\left(\frac{\cancel{T_1}}{\cancel{V_1}}\right) = V_2\left(\frac{T_1}{V_1}\right)$$

$$T_2 = V_2\left(\frac{T_1}{V_1}\right)$$

Evaluate.

$$T_2 = 41.3\ \cancel{\text{mL}}\left(\frac{305.55\ \text{K}}{111\ \cancel{\text{mL}}}\right)$$

$$= 11\underline{3}.687\ \text{K} = -159\ °\text{C}$$

h. What we know: $V_1 = V_2 = 19.8$ L, $P_1 = 1.142 \times 10^5$ Pa, $T_1 = 53.8\ °C = 326.95$ K, $P_2 = 98.6$ kPa

Unknown: T_2

Write the formula and solve for the unknown. Relating pressure and temperature requires the use of Gay-Lussac's law.

$$\frac{P_1}{T_1} = \frac{P_2}{T_2}$$

$$\left(\frac{P_1}{T_1}\right)T_2 = \left(\frac{P_2}{\cancel{T_2}}\right)\cancel{T_2}$$

$$\left(\frac{\cancel{P_1}}{\cancel{T_1}}\right)T_2\left(\frac{\cancel{T_1}}{\cancel{P_1}}\right) = P_2\left(\frac{T_1}{P_1}\right)$$

$$T_2 = P_2\left(\frac{T_1}{P_1}\right)$$

Evaluate.

$$T_2 = 9.86 \times 10^4\ \cancel{\text{Pa}}\left(\frac{326.95\ \text{K}}{1.142 \times 10^5\ \cancel{\text{Pa}}}\right)$$

$$= 28\underline{2}.288\ \text{K} = 9\ °\text{C}$$

20. What we know: $P_{total} = 105.695$ kPa, $T_1 = 85.0\ °C = 358.15$ K, $P_{H_2O} = 57.8150$ kPa (from Table 12-3)

Unknown: P_{H_2}

Write the formula and solve for the unknown.

$$P_{total} = \Sigma P_i$$

$$P_{total} = P_{H_2} + P_{H_2O}$$

$$P_{H_2} = P_{total} - P_{H_2O}$$

Evaluate.

$$P_{H_2} = 105.695\ \text{kPa} - 57.8150\ \text{kPa}$$

$$= 47.880\ \text{kPa}$$

What we know: $V_1 = 117.2$ mL, $P_1 = 47.880$ kPa, $T_1 = 85.0\ °C = 358.15$ K, $T_2 = 0\ °C = 273.15$ K, $P_2 = 101.325$ kPa

Unknown: V_2

Write the formula and solve for the unknown.

$$\frac{P_1V_1}{T_1} = \frac{P_2V_2}{T_2}$$

$$\left(\frac{P_1V_1}{T_1}\right)\left(\frac{T_2}{P_2}\right) = \left(\frac{\cancel{P_2}V_2}{\cancel{T_2}}\right)\left(\frac{\cancel{T_2}}{\cancel{P_2}}\right)$$

$$V_2 = \frac{P_1V_1T_2}{T_1P_2}$$

Evaluate.

$$V_2 = \frac{(47.880\ \cancel{\text{kPa}})(117.2\ \text{mL})(273.15\ \cancel{\text{K}})}{(358.15\ \cancel{\text{K}})(101.325\ \cancel{\text{kPa}})}$$

$$= 42.24\ \text{mL}$$

23. a. What we know: $V = 553$ mL Kr, $T = 0\ °C = 273.15$ K, $P = 101.325$ kPa, $R = 8.31\ \frac{\text{kPa} \cdot \text{L}}{\text{mol} \cdot \text{K}}$

Unknown: n

Write the formula and solve for the unknown.

$$PV = nRT$$

$$\frac{PV}{RT} = \frac{n\cancel{RT}}{\cancel{RT}}$$

$$n = \frac{PV}{RT}$$

Evaluate.

$$n = \frac{(101.325\ \cancel{\text{kPa}})(0.553\ \cancel{\text{L}}\ \text{Kr})}{\left(8.31\ \frac{\cancel{\text{kPa}} \cdot \cancel{\text{L}}}{\text{mol} \cdot \cancel{\text{K}}}\right)(273.15\ \cancel{\text{K}})}$$

$$= 0.0247\ \text{mol Kr}$$

b. What we know: $n = 0.465$ mol He, $T = 0\ °C = 273.15$ K, $P = 101\ 325$ Pa, $R = 8.31 \times 10^3\ \frac{\text{Pa} \cdot \text{L}}{\text{mol} \cdot \text{K}}$

Unknown: V

Write the formula and solve for the unknown.

$$PV = nRT$$

$$\frac{\cancel{P}V}{\cancel{P}} = \frac{nRT}{P}$$

$$V = \frac{nRT}{P}$$

Evaluate.

$$V = \frac{(0.465\ \cancel{\text{mol}}\ \text{He})\left(8.31 \times 10^3\ \frac{\cancel{\text{Pa}} \cdot \text{L}}{\cancel{\text{mol}} \cdot \cancel{\text{K}}}\right)(273.15\ \cancel{\text{K}})}{(101\ 325\ \cancel{\text{Pa}})}$$

$$= 10.4\ \text{L He}$$

c. What we know: $m = 1.78$ g Ar, $V = 1.46$ L, $P = 101.1$ kPa, $R = 8.31\ \frac{\text{kPa} \cdot \text{L}}{\text{mol} \cdot \text{K}}$,

$$n = 1.78\ \cancel{\text{g Ar}}\left(\frac{1\ \text{mol Ar}}{39.95\ \cancel{\text{g Ar}}}\right) = 0.044\ \underline{5}56\ \text{mol Ar}$$

Unknown: T

Write the formula and solve for the unknown.

$PV = nRT$

$\frac{PV}{nR} = \frac{nRT}{nR}$

$T = \frac{PV}{nR}$

Evaluate.

$$T = \frac{(100.1\ \text{kPa})(1.46\ \text{L Ar})}{(0.044\underline{5}56\ \text{mol Ar})\left(8.31\ \frac{\text{kPa} \cdot \text{L}}{\text{mol} \cdot \text{K}}\right)}$$

$= 39\underline{4}.711\ \text{K} = 122\ °\text{C}$

d. What we know: $m = 89.0\ \text{g}\ O_2$, $V = 17.54\ \text{L}$, $T = 21.4\ °\text{C} = 294.55\ °\text{K}$, $P = 101.1\ \text{kPa}$, $R = 8.31 \times 10^3\ \frac{\text{Pa} \cdot \text{L}}{\text{mol} \cdot \text{K}}$,

$$n = 89.0\ \text{g}\ O_2 \left(\frac{1\ \text{mol}\ O_2}{32.00\ \text{g}\ O_2}\right) = 2.7\underline{8}1\ 25\ \text{mol}\ O_2$$

Unknown: P

Write the formula and solve for the unknown.

$PV = nRT$

$\frac{VP}{V} = \frac{nRT}{V}$

$P = \frac{nRT}{V}$

Evaluate.

$$P = \frac{(2.7\underline{8}1\ 255\ \text{mol}\ O_2)\left(8.31 \times 10^3\ \frac{\text{Pa} \cdot \text{L}}{\text{mol} \cdot \text{K}}\right)(294.\underline{5}5\ \text{K})}{(17.54\ \text{L}\ O_2)}$$

$= 3.88 \times 10^5\ \text{Pa}$

24. a. What we know: $n_{C_3H_5N_3O_9} = 16.7\ \text{mol}\ C_3H_5N_3O_9$, STP

Unknown: V_{N_2}

Use stoichiometry to find V_{N_2}.

$$16.7\ \text{mol}\ C_3H_5N_3O_9 \left(\frac{6\ \text{mol}\ N_2}{4\ \text{mol}\ C_3H_5N_3O_9}\right)\left(\frac{22.4\ \text{L}\ N_2}{1\ \text{mol}\ N_2}\right) = 561.12\ \text{L}\ N_2$$

b. What we know: $m_{C_3H_5N_3O_9} = 1.000\ \text{kg}\ C_3H_5N_3O_9$, STP

Unknown: V_{gases}

Use stoichiometry to find V_{gases}.

$$1.000\ \text{kg}\ C_3H_5N_3O_9 \left(\frac{1000\text{g}\ C_3H_5N_3O_9}{1\ \text{kg}\ C_3H_5N_3O_9}\right)\left(\frac{1\ \text{mol}\ C_3H_5N_3O_9}{227.1\ \text{g}\ C_3H_5N_3O_9}\right)$$

$$\left(\frac{29\ \text{mol gases}}{4\ \text{mol}\ C_3H_5N_3O_9}\right)\left(\frac{22.4\ \text{L gases}}{1\ \text{mol gases}}\right) = 715.1\ \text{L gases}$$

25. a. What we know: $T = 1058\ °\text{C} = 1331.15\ °\text{K}$, $P = 98.7\ \text{kPa}$, $n = 0.500\ \text{mol}\ O_2$, $R = 8.31\ \frac{\text{kPa} \cdot \text{L}}{\text{mol} \cdot \text{K}}$

Unknown: n_{NO}, V_{NO}

Use stoichiometry to find moles of NO.

$$0.500\ \text{mol}\ O_2 \left(\frac{4\ \text{mol NO}}{5\ \text{mol}\ O_2}\right) = 0.400\ \text{mol NO}$$

Write the formula and solve for the unknown.

$PV = nRT$

$\frac{RV}{R} = \frac{nRT}{P}$

$V = \frac{nRT}{P}$

Evaluate.

$$V_{NO} = \frac{(0.400\ \text{mol NO})\left(8.31\ \frac{\text{kPa} \cdot \text{L}}{\text{mol} \cdot \text{K}}\right)(1331.15\ \text{K})}{(98.7\ \text{kPa})}$$

$= 44.8\ \text{L NO}$

b. What we know: STP, $V_{NH_3} = 15.0\ \text{L}\ NH_3$

Unknown: m_{O_2}

Use stoichiometry to find mass O_2.

$$15.0\ \text{L}\ NH_3 \left(\frac{1\ \text{mol}\ NH_3}{22.4\ \text{L}\ NH_3}\right)\left(\frac{6\ \text{mol}\ H_2O}{4\ \text{mol}\ NH_3}\right)\left(\frac{18.02\ \text{g}\ H_2O}{1\ \text{mol}\ H_2O}\right) = 18.1\ \text{g}\ H_2O$$

c. What we know: $T = 1058\ °\text{C} = 1331.15\ °\text{K}$, $P = 98.7\ \text{kPa}$, $V_{NO} = 33.5\ \text{L}$, $R = 8.31\ \frac{\text{kPa} \cdot \text{L}}{\text{mol} \cdot \text{K}}$

Unknown: n_{NO}, n_{O_2}, V_{O_2}

Write the formula and solve for n_{NO}.

$PV = nRT$

$\frac{PV}{RT} = \frac{nRT}{RT}$

$n = \frac{PV}{RT}$

Evaluate.

$$n_{NO} = \frac{(98.7\ \text{kPa})(33.5\ \text{L NO})}{\left(8.31\ \frac{\text{kPa} \cdot \text{L}}{\text{mol} \cdot \text{K}}\right)(1331.15\ \text{K})}$$

$= 0.29\underline{8}\ 905\ 522\ 8\ \text{mol NO}$

Use stoichiometry to find moles of O_2.

$$0.29\underline{8}\ 905\ 522\ 8\ \text{mol}\ O_2 \left(\frac{5\ \text{mol}\ O_2}{4\ \text{mol NO}}\right) = 0.37\underline{3}\ 631\ 903\ 5\ \text{mol}\ O_2$$

What we know: STP, $n_{O_2} = 0.37\underline{3}\ 631\ 903\ 5\ \text{mol}\ O_2$, $R = 8.31\ \frac{\text{kPa} \cdot \text{L}}{\text{mol} \cdot \text{K}}$

Write the formula and solve for the unknown.

$PV = nRT$

$\frac{RV}{R} = \frac{nRT}{P}$

$V = \frac{nRT}{P}$

Evaluate.

$$V_{O_2} = \frac{(0.37\underline{3}\ 631\ 903\ 5\ \text{mol})\left(8.31\ \frac{\text{kPa} \cdot \text{L}}{\text{mol} \cdot \text{K}}\right)(273.15\ \text{K})}{(101.325\ \text{kPa})}$$

$= 8.37\ \text{L}\ O_2$

26. What we know: *molar mass* $Cl_2 = 70.90\ \text{g/mol}$, *molar volume* $= 22.4\ \text{L/mol}$

Unknown: ρ

Write the formula and solve for the unknown.

$$\rho_{gas} = \frac{\textit{molar mass}}{\textit{molar volume}}$$

Evaluate.

$$\rho_{gas} = \frac{70.90\ \text{g/mol}}{22.4\ \text{L/mol}}$$

$= 3.17\ \text{g/L}$

27. What we know: *molar mass*$_{N_2}$ = 28.02 g/mol,

$$\frac{rate\ of\ effusion_{N_2}}{rate\ of\ effusion_x} = 1.591$$

Unknown: *molar mass*$_x$

Write the formula and solve for the unknown.

$$\frac{rate\ of\ effusion_{N_2}}{rate\ of\ effusion_x} = \frac{\sqrt{molar\ mass_x}}{\sqrt{molar\ mass_{N_2}}}$$

$$\left(\frac{rate\ of\ effusion_{N_2}}{rate\ of\ effusion_x}\right)^2 = \frac{molar\ mass_x}{molar\ mass_{N_2}}$$

$$\left(\frac{rate\ of\ effusion_{N_2}}{rate\ of\ effusion_x}\right)^2 molar\ mass_{N_2} = \left(\frac{molar\ mass_x}{\cancel{molar\ mass_{N_2}}}\right)\cancel{molar\ mass_{N_2}}$$

$$molar\ mass_x = \left(\frac{rate\ of\ effusion_{N_2}}{rate\ of\ effusion_x}\right)^2 molar\ mass_{N_2}$$

Evaluate.

$molar\ mass_x = (1.591)^2(28.02\ \text{g/mol})$

$= 70.93\ \text{g/mol}$

While this molar mass doesn't match any element on the periodic table, we can divide it by 2 to see whether it is one of the diatomic elements. The molar mass of chlorine, a diatomic element, is 35.45 g/mol. Therefore, we conclude that the unknown gas is likely chlorine.

29. Start with the combined gas law: $\frac{P_1V_1}{T_1} = \frac{P_2V_2}{T_2}$. Charles's law relates volume and temperature at a constant pressure. Therefore, $P_1 = P_2 = P$. The combined gas law now becomes $\frac{PV_1}{T_1} = \frac{PV_2}{T_2}$. Dividing both sides by P $\left(\frac{\cancel{P}V_1}{\cancel{P}T_1} = \frac{\cancel{P}V_2}{\cancel{P}T_2}\right)$ leaves us with Charles's law $\left(\frac{V_1}{T_1} = \frac{V_2}{T_2}\right)$.

30. What we know: P_{total} = 116.5 kPa, T_1 = 48.1 °C = 321.25 K, P_{H_2O} = 11.2974 kPa (interpolated from Table 12-2)

Unknown: P_{H_2}

Write the formula and solve for the unknown.

$P_{total} = \Sigma P_i$

$P_{total} = P_{H_2} + P_{H_2O}$

$P_{H_2} = P_{total} - P_{H_2O}$

Evaluate.

$P_{H_2} = 116.5\ \text{kPa} - 11.2974\ \text{kPa}$

$= 105.\underline{2}02\ 6\ \text{kPa}$

What we know: V_1 =75.6 mL, P_1 = 105.202 6 kPa, T1 = 48.1 °C = 321.25 K, T_2 = 0 °C = 273.15 K, P_2 = 101.325 kPa

Unknown: V_2

Write the formula and solve for the unknown.

$$\frac{P_1V_1}{T_1} = \frac{P_2V_2}{T_2}$$

$$\left(\frac{P_1V_1}{T_1}\right)\left(\frac{T_2}{P_2}\right) = \left(\frac{\cancel{P_2}V_2}{\cancel{T_2}}\right)\left(\frac{\cancel{T_2}}{\cancel{P_2}}\right)$$

$$V_2 = \frac{P_1V_1T_2}{T_1P_2}$$

Evaluate.

$$V_2 = \frac{(105.\underline{2}02\ 6\ \cancel{\text{kPa}})(75.6\ \text{mL})(273.15\ \cancel{\text{K}})}{(321.25\ \cancel{\text{K}})(101.325\ \cancel{\text{kPa}})}$$

$= 66.7\ \text{mL}$

32. Charles's law relates changing volume and temperature when the pressure of a sample is held constant. We start with the ideal gas law.

$PV = nRT$

We then move the changing variables to the left side of the equation and all the constants to the right.

$$\frac{PV}{T} = \frac{nR\cancel{T}}{\cancel{T}}$$

$$\frac{\cancel{P}V}{\cancel{P}T} = \frac{nR}{P}$$

$$\frac{V}{T} = \frac{nR}{P}$$

Everything on the right side is held constant for Charles's law. We then replace the right side with a constant, *k*,

$$\frac{V}{T} = k,$$

leaving us with the equation in the form of Charles's law.

CHAPTER 13 *OBJECTIVES*

- » Explain the role of intermolecular forces in states of matter.
- » Relate the characteristics of solids and liquids to the kinetic-molecular theory.
- » Predict and test the effect of intermolecular forces on physical characteristics.

OVERVIEW

Chapter 13 is a key chapter. Section 13.1 describes the various intermolecular forces and their impact on the properties of different substances. Be sure that students understand the differences between intermolecular forces and bonds. Sections 13.2 and 13.3 relate the kinetic-molecular theory to the structure and properties of solids and liquids. These sections also cover phase changes and the calculations that help quantify them.

13.1 INTERMOLECULAR FORCES

- » *Defining Intermolecular Forces*
- » *Dipole-Dipole Forces*
- » *Hydrogen Bonds*
- » *London Dispersion Forces*

13.2 SOLIDS

- » *A Kinetic Description of Solids*
- » *Density of Solids*
- » *Crystalline and Amorphous Solids*
- » *Melting and Freezing*
- » *Sublimation and Deposition*
- » *Crystalline Structures*

13.3 LIQUIDS

- » *A Kinetic Description of Liquids*
- » *Density of Liquids*
- » *Effects of Intermolecular Attractions*
- » *Vaporization*
- » *Vapor Pressure and Boiling Point*
- » *Distilling Liquids*
- » *Phase Diagrams*
- » *Critical Temperatures and Pressures*
- » *Using Liquids to Solve Problems*

LAB ACTIVITIES

Lab 13A: *Cracking the Crystal*—Students create their own procedure for identifying crystals and their structures.

Lab 13B: *Forces of Nature*—Students compare the viscosity, surface tension, solubility, and volatility of four different liquids.

Chapter 13

SOLIDS & LIQUIDS

There are over 100,000 people in the United States on waiting lists for organ transplants. Those who make it to the top qualify for a transplant. More than 28,000 people receive organ transplants each year in the United States. That's 77 people every day who get a second chance at life.

After doctors remove an organ from a donor, surgeons have a brief window of time to transplant it into the person who needs it before the organ dies. A liver or pancreas can survive up to twelve hours, and kidneys can survive for twenty-four hours. But hearts and lungs must be transplanted within four to six hours. To last for even a few hours, organs need special storage. If a recipient is hundreds of miles away, every minute could make a difference. How can doctors preserve organs so that they stay alive long enough to bring new hope for the people who need them?

The Chapter Opener image shows a heart transplant operation in progress.

13.1 INTERMOLECULAR FORCES

Defining Intermolecular Forces

As you will see later in this chapter, medical professionals use their knowledge of states of matter to preserve donated organs during transport. The key to understanding the differences between one state of matter and another is to look at how particles of matter behave in the presence of other particles. Molecules interact with each other—some more than others. The electrostatic attractions between molecules are called **intermolecular forces**, also known as *van der Waals forces*. Recall from Chapter 7 that electrostatic attractions are the forces exerted between electrical charges—opposite charges attract and like charges repel. When these forces occur between different molecules, they are called intermolecular forces. Intermolecular forces are much weaker than the bonds that hold molecules together. On a scale from 0 to 100, the strength of bonds within a molecule would measure 100 while the strength of forces between molecules would be only 0.001 to 15. Nonetheless, these intermolecular forces influence the physical properties of many substances. They explain why, at room temperature, hydrogen is a gas, water is a liquid, and sugar is a solid.

Intermolecular forces are classified into three groups, each with a different strength. Each force is the result of attraction between regions of charge on some molecules and regions of opposite charge on other molecules.

QUESTIONS

- Are molecules attracted to each other in the same manner as atoms attract other atoms?
- Are all interactions between molecules equally strong?
- How can I tell which intermolecular forces are at work?
- How do intermolecular forces affect a substance's physical properties?

TERMS

intermolecular force • dipole-dipole force • hydrogen bond • London dispersion force

Why is oxygen a gas, water a liquid, and iron a solid at room temperature?

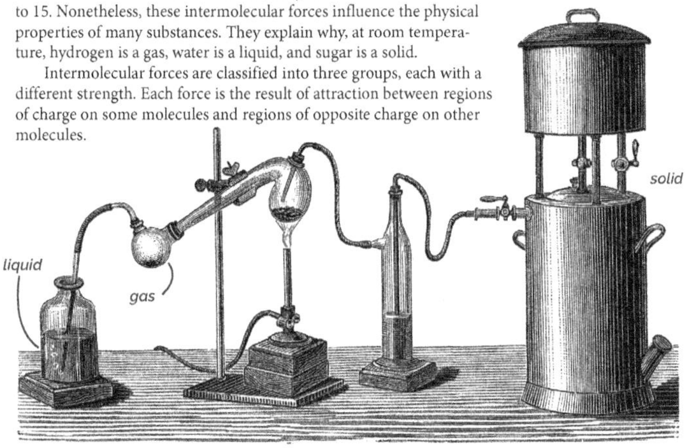

Dipole-Dipole Forces

Consider polar molecules, which have regions of unevenly distributed electrical charge. The positive areas of one molecule attract the negative areas of other molecules. The greater the polarity, the stronger the attraction between the two molecules. These polar molecules align themselves so that the positive end of one molecule is near the negative end of another molecule. This attraction is called a **dipole-dipole force**. The dipole-dipole forces of polar molecules are similar to the electrostatic attraction of ions in crystals of ionic compounds, but they are much weaker. They are strong enough, however, to have a significant influence on the physical properties of many compounds.

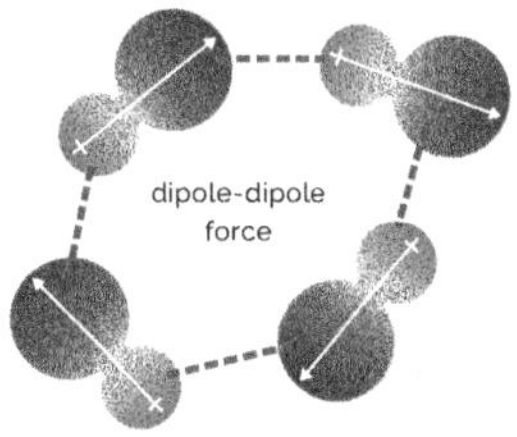

Solids & Liquids 299

SECTION 13.1 *OVERVIEW*

Essential Question

Why is oxygen a gas, water a liquid, and iron a solid at room temperature?

Objectives

- **13.1.1** Define *intermolecular force.*
- **13.1.2** Compare dipole-dipole forces, hydrogen bonds, and London dispersion forces.
- **13.1.3** Predict the intermolecular force(s) present in a substance on the basis of its composition.
- **13.1.4** Predict the melting point of a substance on the basis of the intermolecular forces present.

Resources

Web Links: Hydrogen Bonding, Dispersion Forces

ENGAGE

KINETIC-MOLECULAR THEORY

Activate prior knowledge with a **writing prompt**. On the board write, "What is the relationship between kinetic energy and states of matter?" *(The kinetic energy of a substance's particles determines its state. The particles in a gas have greater kinetic energy than those of the same substance as a liquid, and the liquid particles have greater kinetic energy than those in a solid.)*

DIFFERENTIATED INSTRUCTION

Visual Learning: Intermolecular Forces

Guide students in creating **concept definition maps** to help them recall the definitions of the various intermolecular forces. For each intermolecular force described in the Student Edition, have students place the force in a box or circle in the center of the map. Have them place four boxes around the center box. They should then write the definition of the force in the first box and describe an example in the second. In the third box, have them explain what the force is *not* and describe an example that does *not* illustrate that force. You may allow students to use other kinds of graphic organizers at your discretion.

INSTRUCT

BONDS BETWEEN ATOMS AND MOLECULES

Query students to identify any misconceptions about the difference between intermolecular forces and covalent bonding. The similarity of the terms *covalent bonding* and *hydrogen bonding* may generate some confusion. Emphasize that a hydrogen bond is not technically a bond at all but rather an electrostatic attraction between adjacent molecules or regions of molecules (as in a folded protein). It may also help students to think of covalent bonds as *intramolecular* forces (binding within) as opposed to *intermolecular* forces (external binding).

POLARITY OF ATOMS AND MOLECULES

Have students **review** Table 8-3 on page 189. Remind them that if atoms have polar bonds between them that are arranged symmetrically so that a dipole moment of 0 results, the molecule is nonpolar overall. Therefore, dipole-dipole interactions will not occur.

HYDROGEN BONDING

For a simple but informative animation to help clarify the concept of hydrogen bonds in water, visit TeacherToolsOnline.com. Under Additional Resources, click on Chapter 13 Web Links. Then click on *Hydrogen Bonding*.

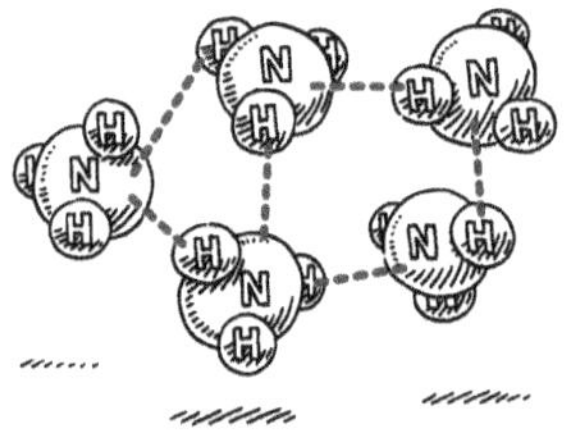

Hydrogen Bonds

Hydrogen bonds are a special type of dipole-dipole interaction in which one of the participating atoms is hydrogen and the other element is either nitrogen, oxygen, or fluorine. Whenever hydrogen is bonded to one of these very electronegative elements, the shared electrons shift away from the hydrogen atom because of the greater electronegativity of the other element. The hydrogen nucleus, essentially a proton, is left exposed. Any negatively charged regions of other molecules containing nitrogen, oxygen, or fluorine attract the exposed proton. Since hydrogen is so small, interacting molecules can get extremely close to it. The combination of high polarity and close proximity produces the strongest of the intermolecular forces.

HYDROGEN BONDS IN WATER

Hydrogen bonds form between the hydrogen atom of one water molecule and the oxygen atom of another water molecule.

They are not bonds in the same sense that ionic or covalent bonds are bonds; they are simply interactions between molecules. Like other intermolecular forces, hydrogen bonds are not as strong as the covalent bonds in water molecules. While the energy of covalent bonds in water is about 286 000 J/mol, the energy of hydrogen bonds in water is only about 20 000 J/mol.

The average hydrogen bond length between water molecules is 0.177 nm, compared with 0.099 nm for the O-H covalent bond. The longer length is indicative of a weaker attraction.

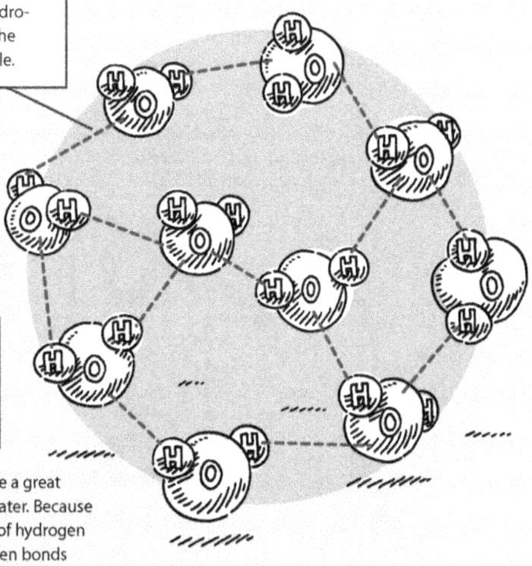

Despite the apparent weakness of these bonds, they have a great effect on the physical properties of substances such as water. Because there is a significant difference in the electronegativities of hydrogen and oxygen, water molecules are quite polar. The hydrogen bonds result in water remaining a liquid at room temperature.

TABLE 13-1 *Hydrogen Compounds Compared*

Compound	Molecular Mass (u)	Melting Point (°C)	Boiling Point (°C)
H_2Te	129.6	−49.0	−2.0
H_2Se	80.98	−65.7	−41.3
H_2S	34.09	−85.5	−59.6
H_2O	18.02	0.0	100.0

Table 13-1 compares water with other similar covalent compounds that contain hydrogen. Although water has a molecular mass that is much lower than that of the other compounds, hydrogen bonds raise its boiling and melting points.

300 Chapter 13

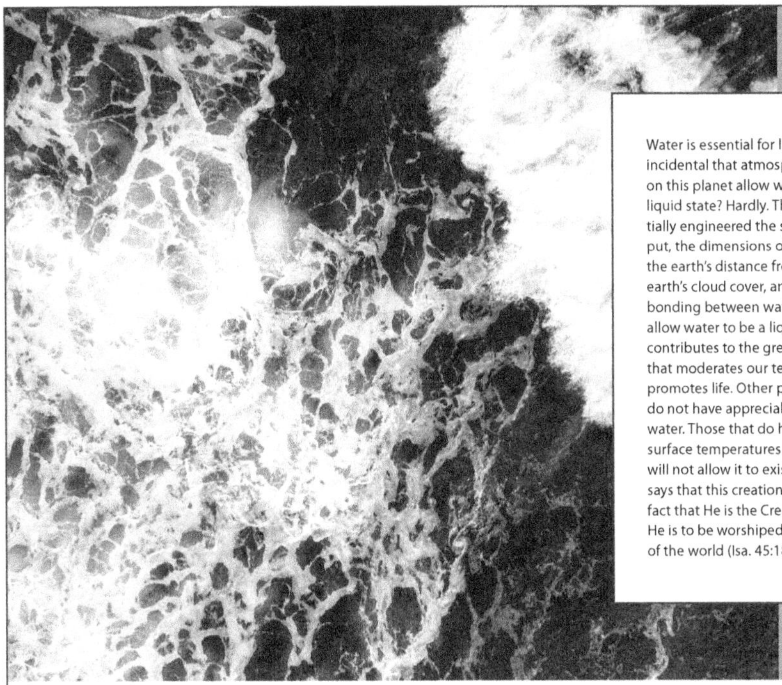

Water is essential for life. Is it merely coincidental that atmospheric conditions on this planet allow water to exist in the liquid state? Hardly. The Lord providentially engineered the sun's thermal output, the dimensions of the solar system, the earth's distance from the sun, the earth's cloud cover, and the hydrogen bonding between water molecules to allow water to be a liquid. Water vapor contributes to the greenhouse effect that moderates our temperatures and promotes life. Other planets and moons do not have appreciable amounts of water. Those that do have water have surface temperatures and pressures that will not allow it to exist as a liquid. God says that this creation testifies to the fact that He is the Creator God and that He is to be worshiped as the Sovereign of the world (Isa. 45:18).

London Dispersion Forces

Even nonpolar substances exist as either solids or liquids at room temperature. Why is this? Dipole-dipole interactions and hydrogen bonds are not the only intermolecular forces. There is a third type of intermolecular force called the **London dispersion force**, also called a *dispersion force* or *London force* after the physicist Fritz London. Nonpolar molecules do not have permanent regions of electrical charge, yet they still attract each other. On average, electrons in a nonpolar bond spend an equal amount of time around each atom. Yet at any point, these electrons can momentarily concentrate at one end of the molecule. These concentrations occur when the negative electrons of one molecule repel the electrons of a nearby molecule. The concentrations form temporary dipoles. Although the imbalance of charges occurs for just an instant, this is long enough to attract an oppositely charged region of a neighboring molecule. Thus, dispersion forces result from the random, unequal dispersion of electrons around the atoms in a molecule. Dispersion forces occur between all molecules, but they are the only intermolecular force acting on nonpolar molecules. Table 13-2 ranks the relative strengths of dispersion forces compared with other attractive forces, including bonds and intermolecular forces.

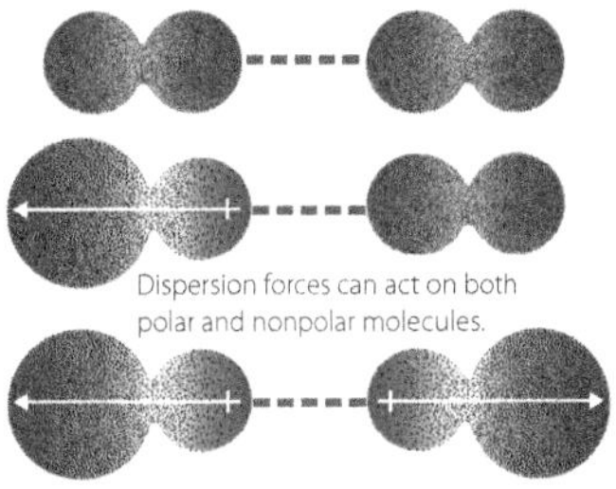

Dispersion forces can act on both polar and nonpolar molecules.

TABLE 13-2 *Relative Strengths of Attractive Forces*

1	ionic bond
2	metallic bond
3	covalent bond
4	hydrogen bond
5	dipole-dipole force
6	dispersion force

DISPERSION FORCES

For an animation showing the electron distribution of nonpolar molecules as they form temporary dipoles, creating dipoles in neighboring molecules, visit TeacherTools Online.com. Under Additional Resources, click on Chapter 13 Web Links. Then click on *Dispersion Forces*.

Solids & Liquids 301

JOINING FORCES

Lead students to **create a checklist** that joins the concepts of chemical bonds, molecule shapes, polarity, and intermolecular forces. Predicting boiling points of compounds in Example 13-2 helps students link these concepts. A sample checklist is provided below.

1. Determine the type of bond involved (ionic, covalent, or metallic).
2. Draw the Lewis structure.
3. Count the electron concentrations around the central atom and determine its shape.
4. Identify the intermolecular forces involved by determining whether the molecule is polar and whether it has the elements necessary for hydrogen bonding.

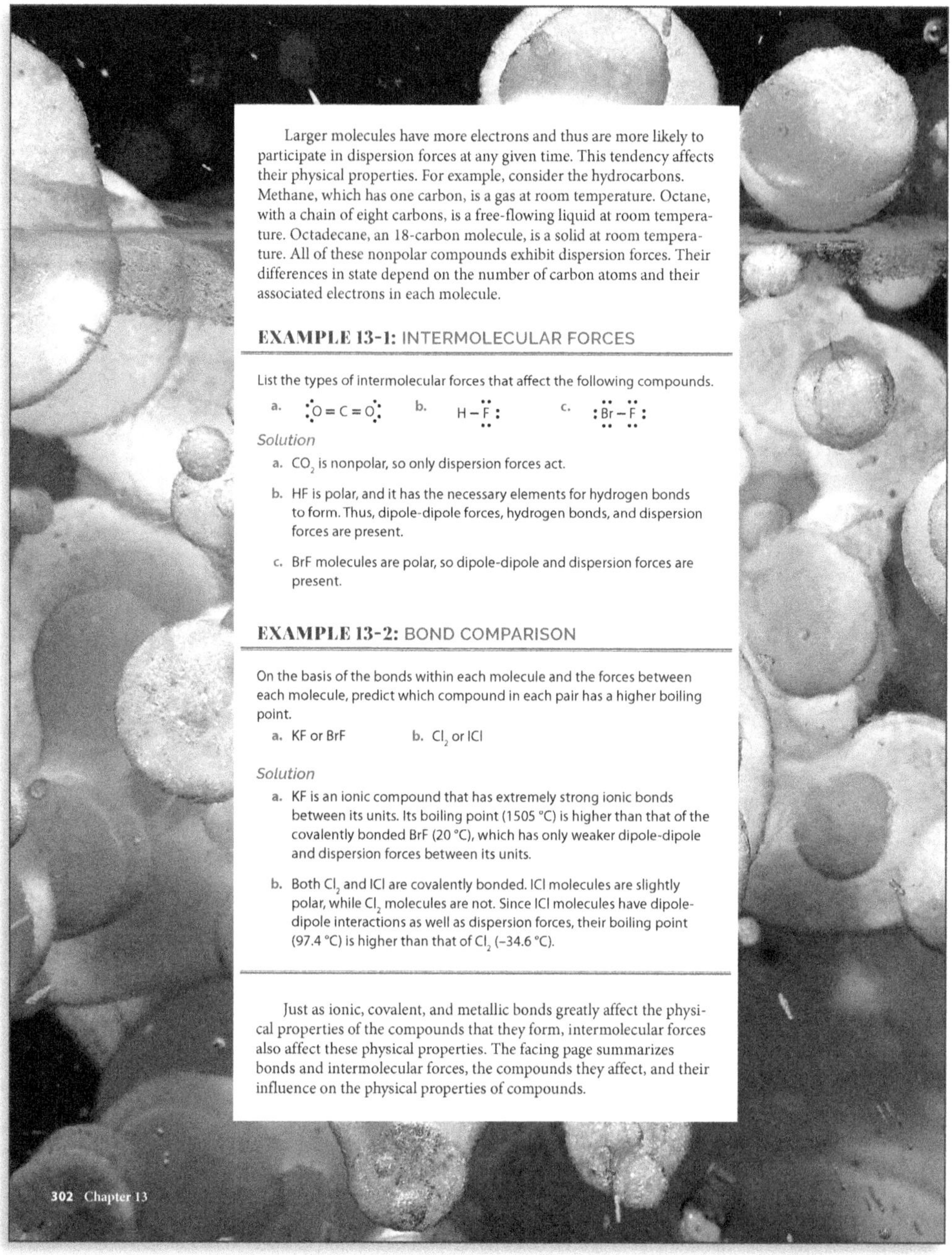

Larger molecules have more electrons and thus are more likely to participate in dispersion forces at any given time. This tendency affects their physical properties. For example, consider the hydrocarbons. Methane, which has one carbon, is a gas at room temperature. Octane, with a chain of eight carbons, is a free-flowing liquid at room temperature. Octadecane, an 18-carbon molecule, is a solid at room temperature. All of these nonpolar compounds exhibit dispersion forces. Their differences in state depend on the number of carbon atoms and their associated electrons in each molecule.

EXAMPLE 13-1: INTERMOLECULAR FORCES

List the types of intermolecular forces that affect the following compounds.

a. :O = C = O: b. H – F: c. :Br – F:

Solution

a. CO_2 is nonpolar, so only dispersion forces act.

b. HF is polar, and it has the necessary elements for hydrogen bonds to form. Thus, dipole-dipole forces, hydrogen bonds, and dispersion forces are present.

c. BrF molecules are polar, so dipole-dipole and dispersion forces are present.

EXAMPLE 13-2: BOND COMPARISON

On the basis of the bonds within each molecule and the forces between each molecule, predict which compound in each pair has a higher boiling point.

a. KF or BrF b. Cl_2 or ICl

Solution

a. KF is an ionic compound that has extremely strong ionic bonds between its units. Its boiling point (1505 °C) is higher than that of the covalently bonded BrF (20 °C), which has only weaker dipole-dipole and dispersion forces between its units.

b. Both Cl_2 and ICl are covalently bonded. ICl molecules are slightly polar, while Cl_2 molecules are not. Since ICl molecules have dipole-dipole interactions as well as dispersion forces, their boiling point (97.4 °C) is higher than that of Cl_2 (−34.6 °C).

Just as ionic, covalent, and metallic bonds greatly affect the physical properties of the compounds that they form, intermolecular forces also affect these physical properties. The facing page summarizes bonds and intermolecular forces, the compounds they affect, and their influence on the physical properties of compounds.

302 Chapter 13

TYPES OF
BONDS AND INTERMOLECULAR FORCES

STRUCTURAL UNITS	INTERACTION BETWEEN UNITS		PROPERTIES
ions	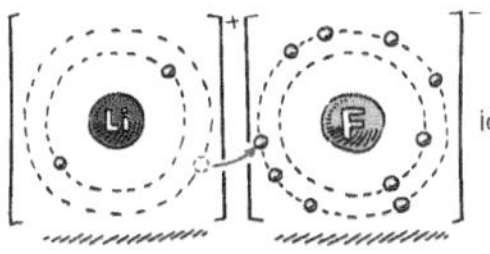	ionic bonds	very high melting/boiling points; usually soluble in polar solvents; electrical conductors when molten or dissolved
cations, mobile electrons (metals)	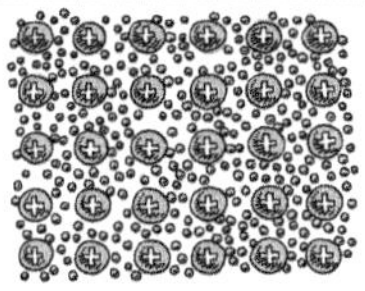	metallic bonds	high melting/boiling points; insoluble; electrical conductors in all states
polar molecules	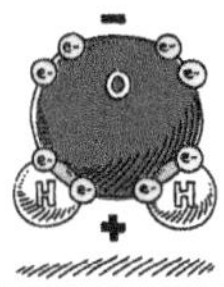	possibly hydrogen bonds, dipole-dipole forces, dispersion forces	melting/boiling points slightly higher than those of nonpolar molecules; usually soluble in polar solvents; nonconductors of electricity
nonpolar molecules	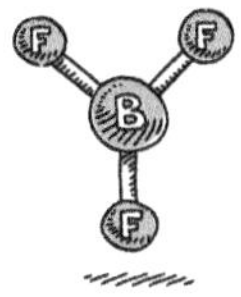	dispersion forces	low melting/boiling points; molecules soluble only in nonpolar solvents; nonconductors of heat and electricity

13.1 SECTION REVIEW

1. What are intermolecular forces?
2. How are the three types of intermolecular forces similar? How are they different?
3. How do you explain dispersion forces in nonpolar substances?
4. What types of intermolecular forces would you expect to find between molecules of H_2O? of BrCl? of hexane (C_6H_{14})?
5. Wax is nonpolar, yet it exists as a solid at room temperature. How can this be explained in terms of intermolecular forces?
6. Which substance, pure oxygen (O_2) or ozone (O_3), would you expect to have a higher boiling point? Explain.

ASSESS

TICKET OUT THE DOOR

Use a **quick write** to check students' understanding. Have them list the three types of intermolecular forces in order from strongest to weakest along with a definition for each. Select students to share their answers with the class and correct any errors or misconceptions. *(Hydrogen bonds are dipole-dipole forces that occur only between polar molecules that have the necessary atoms: H along with N, O, or F. They are the strongest intermolecular forces. Dipole-dipole forces exist only between polar molecules and are stronger than dispersion forces. Dispersion forces work between all kinds of molecules, polar and nonpolar, but are the only intermolecular forces affecting nonpolar molecules.)*

13.1 REVIEW *ANSWERS*

1. Intermolecular forces are the electrostatic attractions that exist between molecules. *(p. 299)*
2. The three types of intermolecular forces are all caused by the attraction of areas of opposite charge on a molecule. But they vary in strength and in the types of compounds that they affect. *(pp. 299–302)*
3. Dispersion forces occur because of temporary dipoles in the molecules due to the electrons moving around within the molecule. If the electrons momentarily end up in one area of the molecule, they have formed a temporary dipole. This dipole interacts with the electrons in adjacent molecules, producing a temporary dipole in them. These dipoles produce attractive forces between the molecules. Due to their temporary nature, these are the weakest of the intermolecular forces. *(p. 301)*
4. hydrogen bonds and dispersion forces; dispersion and dipole-dipole forces; dispersion forces *(pp. 299–302)*
5. Wax molecules still experience dispersion forces, even if they are nonpolar. For the wax to be a solid at room temperature on the basis of dispersion forces alone, its molecules must be large. *(pp. 301–2)*
6. Because it is a larger molecule with more electrons, ozone experiences greater dispersion forces than oxygen and thus has a higher boiling point, 161 K, compared with oxygen's 90 K. *(pp. 301–2)*

SECTION 13.2 *OVERVIEW*

Essential Question

Why can't I write with a diamond?

Objectives

» **13.2.1** Explain the properties of solids using the kinetic-molecular theory.

» **13.2.2** Compare crystalline and amorphous solids.

» **13.2.3** Explain the significance of the slopes and plateaus on a heating curve.

» **13.2.4** Describe what happens at the particle level during phase changes.

» **13.2.5** Summarize the three factors that produce network solids.

Resources

Demonstrating Sublimation and Deposition, Demonstrating Lattice Energy

How It Works: Cryogenics

Web Links: Sublimation of Iodine, Crystal Gallery, Liquid Crystal Gallery

Lab 13A: *Cracking the Crystal*—Relating Geology to Chemistry

ENGAGE

Use a **think-pair-share** to activate prior learning. Show a model of difluoromethane (CH_2F_2) or write its structural formula on the board; then ask students to state which of the three types of intermolecular forces described in the previous section are found in difluoromethane and be prepared to justify their answers. *(All three apply.)* Allow students to discuss their answer with a neighbor, and then select students to share their answers with the class. Correct any errors or misconceptions.

13.2 SOLIDS

QUESTIONS

» Why do solids have the properties they do?

» Do all solids have similar structures?

» How do I interpret a heating curve?

» What happens at the particle level during a phase change?

» What factors affect the formation of crystals?

TERMS

crystalline solid • amorphous solid • melting point • unit cell • allotrope • lattice energy

A Kinetic Description of Solids

The strength of bonds and intermolecular forces in a solid affects the internal movements of its own particles. According to the kinetic-molecular theory of matter, particles in solids are always moving—or more precisely, vibrating. At low temperatures, these particles barely vibrate. As temperatures approach a solid's melting point, the particles have more kinetic energy and the vibrations get faster and bigger. Strong intermolecular forces stifle these vibrations, while weak forces allow the particles to move more freely. For example, table salt exists as a solid up to the scorching temperature of 801°C because attractions between the Na^+ ions and the Cl^- ions are extremely strong. Nonpolar diatomic bromine molecules, with only weak dispersion forces, can move more freely. Consequently, bromine melts at −7 °C, allowing it to exist as a liquid at room temperature.

Why can't I write with a diamond?

Intermolecular forces affect other properties besides a substance's boiling and melting points. Because solid particles have little motion, they are not fluids, have a fixed shape and volume, and have low rates of diffusion. If a silver coin and a copper coin were clamped together for several years, a few atoms would diffuse between the metals, but the rate would be imperceptible compared with the diffusion rate of the same atoms if they were in the liquid phase.

Solid benzene sinks in liquid benzene (left). Solid water floats in liquid water (right).

Density of Solids

Because particles in solids are held closely together, they usually have high densities. Since solids are so dense and have fixed shapes and definite volumes, they resist compression. Atoms, molecules, or ions would have to be deformed for solid matter to compress significantly. A substance is typically about 10% denser as a solid than as a liquid. Consequently, when liquid and solid forms of the same substance are together, the solid form almost always sinks to the bottom.

304 Chapter 13

One notable exception to this trend is water. Down to a temperature of 4 °C, water becomes increasingly dense, but as it cools below this temperature, hydrogen bonds cause water molecules to orient themselves in a manner that spreads them farther apart from each other, forming an open hexagonal lattice. The increased space between the molecules causes ice to be less dense than water. This lower density is why ice cubes float in a glass of water. More importantly, open bodies of water such as lakes or ponds freeze from the top down. As ice forms on the surface, the water beneath is insulated. If the water is deep enough, it may never freeze solid during winter, allowing aquatic organisms to overwinter safely.

Crystalline and Amorphous Solids

Solids can occur in many shapes and forms. Some solids have naturally orderly shapes, forming regular three-dimensional patterns with distinct edges and sharp angles. When they are shattered, smaller shapes form with similar edges and angles. These solids are called **crystalline solids**. Ionic and metallic solids are usually crystalline. Other solids have no distinct shape or underlying pattern. When they split or shatter, irregular fragments result. Such solids are called **amorphous solids**. Covalent compounds can be crystalline or amorphous.

The differences between crystalline and amorphous solids result from the particular structures of the solids. The particles in crystalline solids—such as salt, sugar, and monoclinic sulfur—are arranged in well-defined, orderly, three-dimensional patterns. Atoms, ions, or molecules are stacked row upon row, column by column. The patterns, when repeated many times, result in crystals with regular shapes.

Particles in amorphous solids—such as rubber, asphalt, paraffin, or amorphous sulfur—are not arranged in any particular pattern. Their random, disordered structure results in globular shapes. Some amorphous solids are called *supercooled liquids*, or glasses. If a liquid can be cooled fast enough, its particles may not have time to form a preferred crystalline pattern. These molecules are locked in random positions. Volcanic obsidian is produced in this fashion.

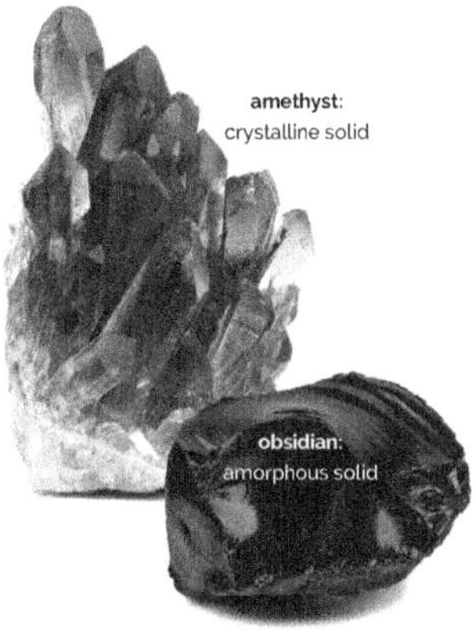

▲ The internal structure of amethyst is reflected in the external shape of its crystals. Obsidian is amorphous.

DIFFERENTIATED INSTRUCTION

Visual Learning: Properties of Solids and Liquids

Guide students through creating a **Venn diagram** to help them internalize the similarities and differences between the physical properties of solids and liquids. Have them draw three intersecting circles labeled "solid," "liquid," and "gas." As they read or hear about the properties of each phase of matter, they should place properties that all three have in common in the intersection of the circles, while placing properties that are unique to a particular phase in the nonintersecting portion of that phase's circle. For example, the phrase "definite volume, indefinite shape" would be placed in the circle for liquids. Since liquids, solids, and gases are made of atoms or molecules, that property would go in the intersection of the three circles. Students will need to recall the properties of gases from Chapter 12.

INSTRUCT

FREEZING POINT FOR MIXTURES

For substances that aren't pure, such as mixtures and certain organic compounds, the freezing point is actually lower than the melting point. This is because the different particles freeze at different rates, affecting the composition of particles that haven't frozen yet and lowering the overall freezing point.

DEMONSTRATING SUBLIMATION AND DEPOSITION

Demonstrate the sublimation and deposition of iodine.

Materials: ring stand and ring, wire gauze, laboratory burner, 100 mL beaker, evaporating dish, ice, iodine crystals

Preparation: Set up the ring stand, ring, and wire gauze so that the laboratory burner fits under the ring and gauze.

Performance/Discussion: Place approximately 10 g of iodine crystals in the beaker. Fill the evaporating dish with ice, and then cover the beaker with the dish. Gently heat the beaker under a fume hood until a purplish gas begins to form. Notice that the iodine crystals are sublimating—they are changing from solid to gas. As the gas rises and contacts the ice-filled dish, it deposits back into solid crystals that attach to the bottom of the dish.

Note: Iodine vapor is a strong irritant. Perform this demonstration under a fume hood or in another well-ventilated space.

Cleanup: If allowed by local disposal codes, flush the iodine crystals down the sink with copious amounts of water. Or you may keep them to use next year.

SUBLIMATION OF IODINE

You may opt to show a **video** of the previous demonstration. For one such video, visit TeacherToolsOnline.com. Under Additional Resources, click on Chapter 13 Web Links. Then click on *Sublimation of Iodine*.

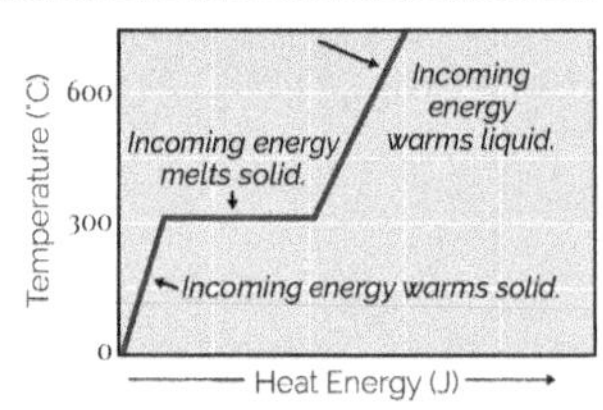

Melting and Freezing

Melting and freezing are changes between the solid and liquid states of a substance. Melting is the transition from a solid to a liquid. The temperature at which this process takes place is called the **melting point**. Freezing is the reverse process. For pure substances, the freezing point is the same as the melting point. Freezing points are not always cold temperatures. For example, iron freezes at 1538°C! When a lump of lead is placed in a ladle and heated, the atoms begin to vibrate more vigorously. Temperature, a measure of the vibrations of lead particles, rises (see graph at left). When the melting point of the lead is reached, the temperature stabilizes. At this point, all atoms are at the brink of liquefaction. Additional heat overcomes the attractive forces between lead atoms and melts the solid. Not until all the lead is melted will the temperature resume its upward climb.

The melting points of crystalline and amorphous solids are affected by the arrangements of their particles. Crystalline substances such as ice or lead have distinct melting points. Heating-curve graphs for crystalline substances show clear plateaus that correspond to sharp melting points. An entire sample melts at a clearly defined temperature because all particles are held by nearly identical forces. Amorphous solids, on the other hand, do not have sharp melting points. Their particles are in random positions at different distances from each other. Since the force strength varies with distance, not all of the particles are held together with identical force. As the temperature rises, only some intermolecular forces are overcome at each specific temperature. Amorphous solids gradually soften as more intermolecular forces are broken. The heating curve for an amorphous substance thus lacks the stairstep pattern seen in the heating curve for lead. Instead, the plateaus are replaced by a gradually ascending line.

Analytical chemists use melting points to determine the identity and purity of compounds. Many pure substances are crystalline, with their melting points listed in reference tables. Chemists can analyze the purity of a compound by observing its melting-point range. A narrow range indicates a pure sample, while a wide range indicates that impurities are present.

Sublimation and Deposition

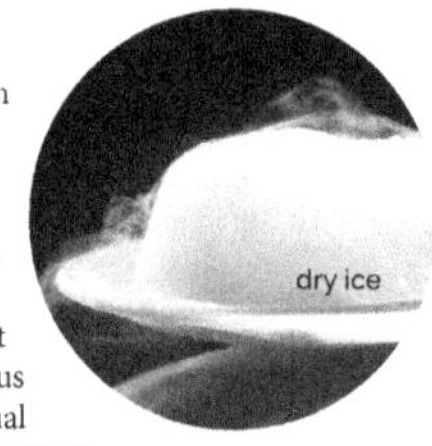

Many caterers use dry ice (solid carbon dioxide) to refrigerate their foods. When dry ice warms, it changes directly into a gas instead of melting into a liquid as ice does. This state change bypasses the liquid phase and alleviates the problems of messy puddles. Sublimation is the direct change in state from the solid to the gaseous state. Sublimation occurs because individual molecules leave the surface of a solid and become gaseous. For example, the smell of naphthalene or 1,4-dichlorobenzene mothballs comes from the individual molecules that have sublimed. Sublimation causes snow to slowly disappear, even when the temperature remains below freezing. Substances sublime readily if they have many molecules that can easily leave their surfaces.

306 Chapter 13

Deposition occurs when a substance changes directly from a gas to a solid—the reverse of sublimation. When frost forms on your windshield or lawn, deposition has taken place. Deposition of water vapor high above the earth forms snowflakes.

HOW IT *WORKS*

Cryogenics

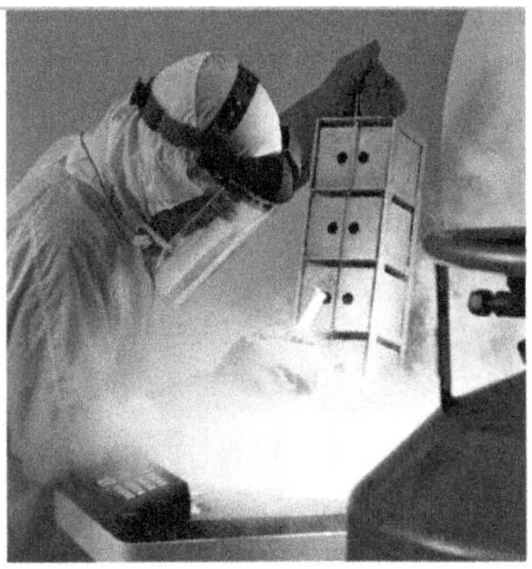

Imagine a world where you can use a banana to hammer nails into wood. In this world, a rubber bouncy ball shatters when it hits the ground. Believe it or not, this bizarre world actually exists—it is the world of cryogenics.

Cryogenics is the science of the supercold. The word *cryogenics* comes from the Greek word *kruos*, meaning "frost." Cryogenics does not deal with the moderately cold temperatures of your kitchen freezer, but with the intensely cold world of −150 °C and below. Applications of this fascinating area of science are found in such wide-ranging fields as space exploration, food preservation, and medicine.

Aerospace engineers use supercooled gases extensively in the space industry. Liquid hydrogen and oxygen are used together as a powerful fuel. Life support systems and space refrigeration systems also use cryogenic conditions.

Another application of cryogenics is rapidly freezing food. Some meats, pastries, and vegetables are frozen rapidly by being passed through cryogenic tunnels. As the food passes through frigid gases, its surface freezes rapidly. Cold temperatures then gradually spread to the core for an even freeze.

Liquefied gases have another interesting connection to food. Breeders can keep the eggs, sperm, and even embryos of livestock frozen in liquid nitrogen for years before being thawed and implanted into female animals. Some prize bulls that have been dead for years are still fathering calves through this technology.

Surgeons have used cryosurgery—the use of a freezing probe in place of a scalpel—with good success in removing warts, tonsils, and cataracts. Cryosurgery repairs and treats patients with less pain and hemorrhaging. Doctors have replaced many operations that previously required hospitalization with procedures that they can perform in the office.

As you can see, cryogenics deals with a wide range of applications. Scientists who specialize in applying an understanding of cryogenics to meeting the needs of people are called *cryogenic engineers*. It's a *cool* job that you might enjoy pursuing as a means to glorifying God and serving others.

Solids & Liquids 307

UNIT CELLS AND WALLPAPER

Use an **analogy** by comparing unit cells to repeating patterns in wallpaper, fabric, or flooring. Show students a piece of patterned material and have them isolate the repeating unit of the pattern. This two-dimensional pattern unit follows the same principle as a three-dimensional unit cell.

CRYSTAL GALLERY

Show your students more evidence of God's amazing creativity! For a colorful photo display of a large variety of crystals, visit TeacherToolsOnline.com. Under Additional Resources, click on Chapter 13 Web Links. Then click on *Crystal Gallery*.

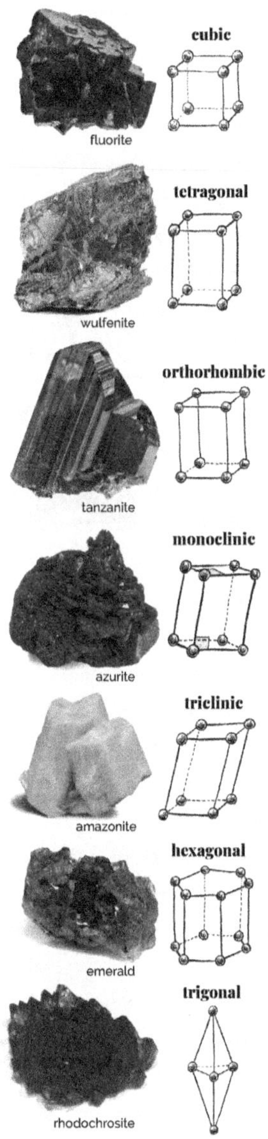

Crystalline Structures

The particles in crystals are arranged in orderly, repeating patterns. These patterns vary, as shown by the wide variety of beautiful shapes found in natural crystals. The beauty and predictability of naturally occurring crystals is yet another of God's fingerprints on our world. Several factors influence how the particles are arranged. Like electrical charges repel to maximize the distance between particles. At the same time, opposite charges seek to minimize that distance. These forces interact to produce the most stable crystal arrangement possible.

A crystal's three-dimensional pattern, or crystal lattice, depends on the number and kinds of particles involved, their relative sizes, and the charges of the ions. Scientists have found and classified seven basic classes of crystals—cubic, tetragonal, orthorhombic, monoclinic, triclinic, hexagonal, and trigonal.

Scientists mentally divide the natural structures of crystals into building blocks called **unit cells** that contain the fundamental patterns of the lattices. Unit cells usually consist of a specific number of ions. These portions of crystals can be compared to the basic pattern in a piece of wallpaper. The wallpaper pattern can be repeated indefinitely to cover large walls. Unit cells, when repeated many times in three dimensions, make up crystals.

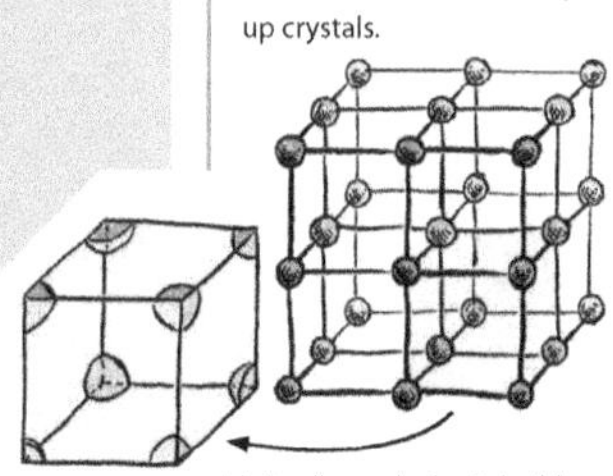

Unit cells are the basic building blocks for any type of crystal.

Some of the seven basic classes of crystals can be slightly modified by adding particles to the faces or interiors.

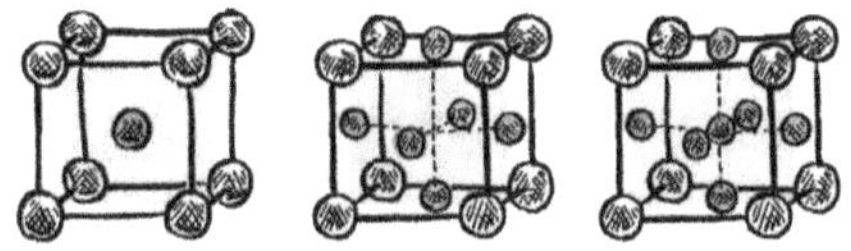

A body-centered crystal not only has particles at each of the corners, but it also has one in the center of the crystal.

A face-centered crystal has particles on the corners and on each face but no particle in the center of the crystal.

Some, but not all, of the seven basic crystal types have one or both of these modifications. These variations expand the seven basic classes into fourteen different lattices.

308 Chapter 13

Because crystals are three-dimensional arrangements of unit cells, they often assume the same shape as their unit cells. Salt crystals, for example, are tiny cubes. When they are formed, their units build upon themselves to form larger cubes with approximately the same number of units along each edge. A sodium chloride unit cell, which contains four Na^{+} ions and four Cl^{-} ions, has a length of 0.56 nm. A salt crystal 0.5 mm along each edge has nearly one million unit cells along each edge and approximately 10^{18} unit cells in its total structure.

But many crystals found in nature do not have the same shape as their constituent unit cells. Because of varying temperature, pressure, and other environmental factors, unit cells may stack in such a way that a different external structure forms. The "steps" on the surfaces of the crystals are only a fraction of a nanometer wide, so they are not visible to the eye. The crystal faces appear to be smooth even though they are ragged at the atomic level. Despite the fact that all the known minerals have one of the basic crystal structures, mineral crystals can exhibit a great variety of external forms.

POLYMORPHS AND ALLOTROPES

Some substances can form more than one type of crystal lattice. Such elements and compounds are said to be polymorphous. When Ca^{2+} and CO_3^{2-} ions crystallize at a low temperature, they fall into a rhombohedral lattice. Mineralogists call this form of calcium carbonate *calcite*. When these same ions crystallize at a high temperature, they orient themselves in an orthorhombic lattice and form a substance called *aragonite*, which is also calcium carbonate.

calcite

aragonite

Pure elements that are polymorphous are called *allotropic elements*, and their different forms are called **allotropes**. Sulfur, phosphorus, arsenic, and carbon are a few allotropic elements. You are probably familiar with some of carbon's allotropes. One of them, diamond, is Earth's hardest naturally occurring substance. This hardness is the result of the internal arrangement of diamond's carbon atoms and the strong covalent bonds between them. Most diamonds are used in industrial cutting tools, but high-grade diamonds are considered valuable gemstones. Another carbon allotrope, graphite, consists of sheets of carbon rings stacked layer on layer. The sheets are held together only by dispersion forces. This makes graphite extremely soft—it easily flakes if rubbed against a sheet of paper. It's the "lead" in ordinary pencils. In fact, graphite's name is derived from the Greek word meaning "to write."

BINDING FORCES IN CRYSTALS

Crystals are shaped by electrical forces. Oppositely charged regions attract, and similarly charged regions repel. The balance between attractions and repulsions determines how tightly the particles in the crystal are bound. If attractions just barely overcome the repulsions, the crystal will have weak bonds. If attractions are much greater than repulsions, the crystal will have strong binding forces.

DEMONSTRATING LATTICE ENERGY

Demonstrate the effect on temperature caused by dissolving salt in water.

Materials: glass filled with water, thermometer, salt sufficient to create a saturated solution (approximately 36 g of salt per 100 mL of water)

Preparation: none

Performance/Discussion: Fill a glass with water and measure its temperature. Dissolve salt to saturation in the water and measure its temperature again. Both the water and the glass will be noticeably cooler because the salt crystals absorb heat to overcome their lattice energy.

Cleanup: The saltwater solution may be disposed of down a drain.

POLYMORPHS VERSUS ALLOTROPES

Be sure to stress this difference between allotropes and polymorphs: allotropes must be elements, whereas polymorphs can be elements or compounds.

LIQUID CRYSTAL GALLERY

Not all crystals are solids. To see a beautiful collection of liquid crystal photomicrographs accompanied by explanations, visit TeacherToolsOnline.com. Under Additional Resources, click on Chapter 13 Web Links. Then click on *Liquid Crystal Gallery*.

SOLIDS

Use the following **formative assessment** to check students' understanding.

1. What type of solid has no preferred arrangement of particles? *(an amorphous solid)*
2. Describe the phase changes that are illustrated within a heating curve. *(Adding thermal energy affects the temperature and state of matter. During the phase changes, the temperature of a substance remains constant until the change is completed.)*
3. Explain the difference between sublimation and deposition. *(Sublimation is the direct change from the solid to the gaseous state. Deposition is the reverse process.)*
4. Why is lattice energy expressed as a negative number? *(Heat is released during crystallization, leaving less energy in the products than in the reactants.)*

APPLY

LAB 13A: *CRACKING THE CRYSTAL*

Once students have an understanding of the material in Section 13.2, they should be ready to work through Lab 13A.

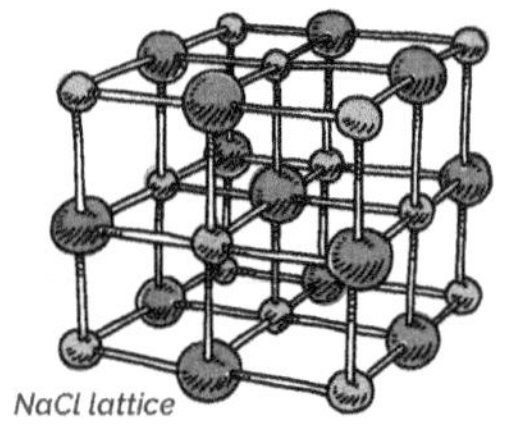

LATTICE ENERGY

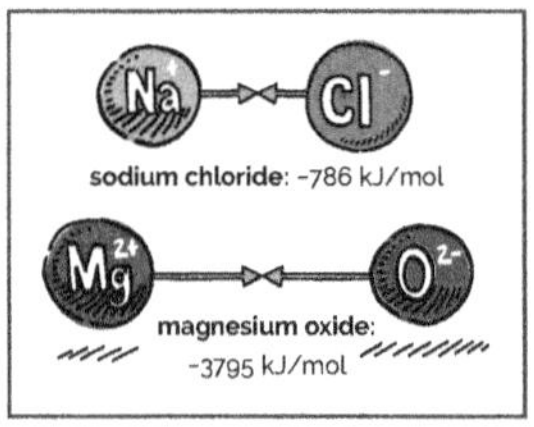

The **lattice energy** of a crystal is the energy released when gaseous particles form crystals. It is expressed as a negative number because heat is released during crystallization, leaving less energy in the products than in the reactants. Lattice energy is equal in magnitude to the energy necessary to pull a crystal apart. It shows the difference in energy between gas particles and those trapped in a crystal.

Binding forces must be overcome whenever a crystal is melted or dissolved. When a crystal melts, thermal energy is used to overcome binding forces. When a crystal dissolves, attractions between the particles of the crystal and the molecules of the solvent are able to break apart the crystal structure. For example, when table salt dissolves in water, its crystals absorb thermal energy from the water to overcome the lattice energy and break apart the ions. If a large amount of salt is added to a glass of water, you can feel the glass cool as the salt dissolves, using energy from its environment to break the crystal lattice.

What makes a crystal strong? In other words, what determines its lattice energy? The magnitude of the electrical charges in a crystal affects its stability. For example, sodium chloride, with a lattice energy of −786 kJ/mol, involves a sodium ion with a charge of 1+ and a chloride ion of 1−. But magnesium oxide, with a lattice energy of −3795 kJ/mol, involves a magnesium ion with a charge of 2+ and an oxide ion of 2−. Highly charged particles, like those in ionic compounds, interact strongly to produce strong crystals. The size of the particles also affects the binding forces. Small particles can be more tightly bound than large particles. A third factor—the geometric structure of the crystal—also affects the binding forces because both the structure and the size of the particles involved affect the distance between ions.

TYPES OF CRYSTALLINE SOLIDS

Crystalline substances can be classified by the types of particles they contain and how they are held together. This method of classification relies on an understanding of the types of bonds that we discussed in Chapter 7.

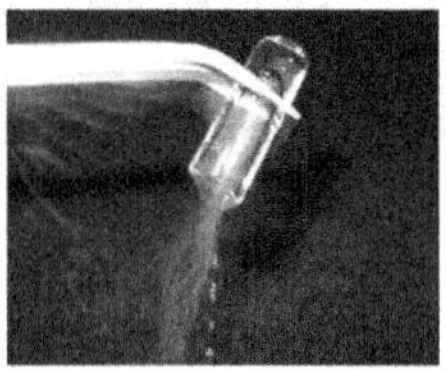

Atomic Crystals

These solids form only when noble gases freeze. The particles in these solids are individual atoms since noble gases do not typically form molecules. As you might expect, they are soft and are poor conductors of electricity.

Type: atomic
Unit Particles: atoms
Examples: Group 18 elements

Covalent Molecular Crystals

Molecular solids, such as table sugar, are made of covalently bonded atoms held together by any combination of dipole-dipole forces, hydrogen bonds, and dispersion forces. The intermolecular forces that attract the molecules to each other are weaker than the forces binding atoms together within each molecule. Thus, they have relatively low melting points. Their low melting points explain why molecular compounds are often gases or liquids at room temperature.

Type: covalent molecular
Unit Particles: molecules
Examples: H_2O (snowflake), CO_2 (dry ice), $C_{12}H_{22}O_{11}$ (table sugar)

Ionic Crystals

Ionic solids are made of a repeating network of ions defined by a unit cell. The ions may be monatomic or polyatomic. Remember from our earlier study that ionic compounds typically form between a metal and a nonmetal. The strong bonds between the alternating positive and negative ions in these crystals cause them to be strong and have high melting points. Many also fracture easily.

Covalent Network Solids

Some nonmetallic elements, such as carbon, are able to bond covalently to form a large network of atoms, as occurs with diamond. The particles in this and other covalent network solids are individual atoms bound together by covalent bonds. These crystals function more like giant molecules. The strength in these three-dimensional arrangements contributes to the generally high melting points of covalent network solids.

Type: Covalent network
Unit Particles: covalently bonded atoms
Examples: diamond (carbon atoms)

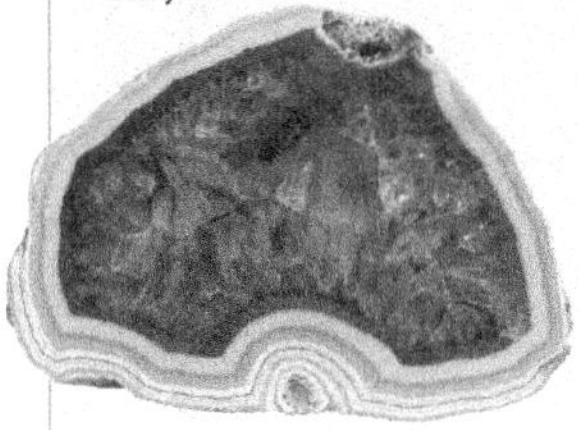

Type: ionic
Unit Particles: ions
Examples: NaCl, K_2SO_4

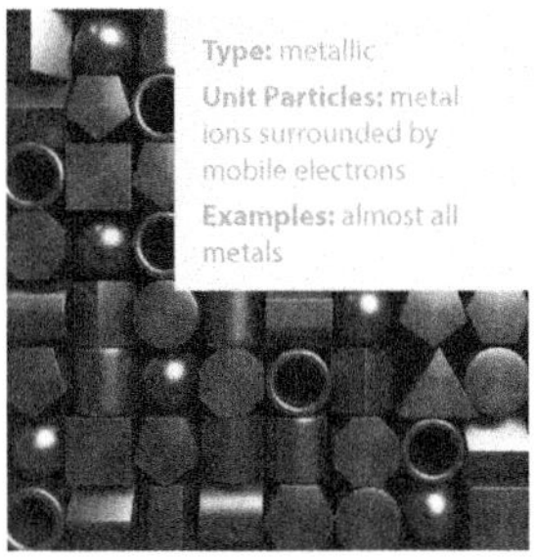

Type: metallic
Unit Particles: metal ions surrounded by mobile electrons
Examples: almost all metals

Metallic Crystals

Positive metal ions are surrounded by a sea of valence electrons in metallic solids. Because metals vary greatly in the strength of the metallic bonds that form between the metal ions and mobile electrons, metals have a wide range of physical properties. For example, mercury is a liquid at room temperature, while many others remain solid past 1000 °C. Most metals are lustrous and conduct electricity well because of their free electrons

13.2 SECTION REVIEW

1. How does the kinetic-molecular theory explain the properties of solids?
2. Explain the difference between crystalline and amorphous solids.
3. On a heating curve, what is indicated by the sloped portions? by the plateaued portions?
4. Draw a heating curve to represent a crystalline solid and one for an amorphous solid. Is there a difference between the two curves? If so, why?
5. How is a unit cell like a formula unit?
6. Explain why the lattice energy and the energy to break apart crystals of a substance differ in sign but are equal in magnitude.
7. How are covalent network solids similar to ionic solids?
8. Explain why covalent network crystals have relatively high melting points, while covalent molecular crystals, as a rule, melt at much lower temperatures.

ASSESS

TICKET OUT THE DOOR

Check students' understanding with this **summarizing activity**. Ask the following questions.

1. What type of crystal is table salt? *(ionic)*
2. What type is diamond? *(covalent network)*

13.2 REVIEW ANSWERS

1. According to the kinetic-molecular theory, the particles in solids have the least amount of energy relative to liquids and gases. Particles in solids do not have enough energy to overcome intermolecular forces and are thus locked into fixed positions and capable only of vibrating in place. Therefore, solids have fixed shapes and volumes with relatively high densities. *(p. 304)*
2. Crystalline solids are composed of unit cells arranged in an orderly, three-dimensional pattern, whereas amorphous solids are made of crystals that are arranged in no particular pattern. *(p. 305)*

QUESTIONS 3 AND 4

Questions 3 and 4 in the Student Edition use the term *warming curve*. This is a common term used to refer to the heating curves discussed in the chapter. Some students may be confused by this different term. The reduced student page has been updated with the term *heating curve*.

3. The sloped portions indicate that the temperature of the substance is rising. The plateaued portions indicate that added thermal energy is being used to overcome intermolecular forces, causing a phase change rather than increasing the substance's temperature. *(p. 306)*
4. Students' graphs should look similar to the one below.

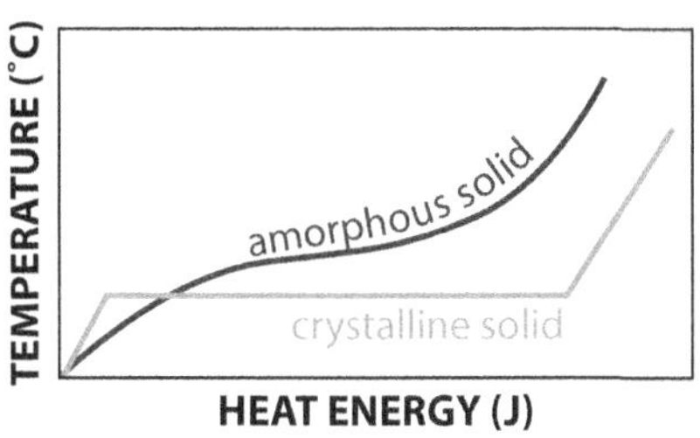

There is a difference between the two curves. Since amorphous particles are held together at random distances, the forces between them are of different strengths. Therefore, not all the forces will be overcome at the same temperature as they are in crystalline solids. *(p. 306)*

5. A formula unit is the simplest ratio between the different kinds of atoms in an ionic compound. A unit cell is the smallest part of a crystal that retains the structure of the crystal, and it is sometimes the same as a formula unit. *(p. 308)*
6. Lattice energy is the energy released when a crystal forms, and the same amount of energy must be provided to break down the crystal. *(p. 310)*
7. Covalent network solids and ionic solids are both large, three-dimensional networks of particles with great stability and high melting points. *(p. 311)*
8. Covalent molecules are held together by relatively weak intermolecular forces, while covalent network crystals have covalent bonds holding atoms tightly in a network. *(pp. 310–11)*

SECTION 13.3 *OVERVIEW*

Essential Question

What makes water special?

Objectives

» **13.3.1** Explain the properties of liquids on the basis of the kinetic-molecular theory and intermolecular attractions.

» **13.3.2** Compare evaporation and boiling.

» **13.3.3** Trace temperature changes and thermal energy flow during the process of evaporation.

» **13.3.4** Use a phase diagram to predict a substance's state of matter under various temperature and pressure conditions.

» **13.3.5** Respond to the claim that cryonics provides hope while science and technology advance. BWS

Resources

Ethics: Cryonics (p. 325)

Demonstrating the High Surface Tension of Water, Demonstrating Viscosity, Demonstrating the Adhesion of Water, Demonstrating the Relationship between Vapor Pressure and Boiling

Web Links: Straw Wrapper Capillary Action, Swamp Coolers

Lab 13B: *Forces of Nature*—Exploring Intermolecular Forces in Liquids; Mini Lab: *Through the Void*

ENGAGE

Activate prior knowledge with a **Socratic question**. Ask, "How do liquids compare with solids? with gases?" *(Liquids have definite volumes as solids do but have indefinite shapes. Liquids can flow, as gases do, and have indefinite shapes, but they do not have indefinite volumes as gases do.)*

LAB 13B: *FORCES OF NATURE*

Because students have already examined the effects of intermolecular forces in Section 13.1, Lab 13B can be done as an introductory activity prior to covering Section 13.3. In the activity, students explore the relationships between intermolecular forces and the properties of liquids. Alternatively, Lab 13B may be done as an application activity after covering Section 13.3.

13.3 LIQUIDS

QUESTIONS

» Why do liquids have the properties they do?

» Aren't evaporation and boiling the same thing?

» How does energy move through evaporation?

» How do I interpret a phase diagram?

TERMS

cohesion • adhesion • surface tension • surfactant • viscosity • meniscus • evaporation • boiling • boiling point • distillation • phase diagram • triple point • critical temperature • critical pressure

What makes water special?

If liquids were not so common, we would consider them amazing. Why does water form spherical drops? Why are bubbles round? Why does rubbing alcohol make your skin feel cold? What makes the surface of a liquid in a test tube curve? How can some insects skate across the surface of a pond? Although many properties of liquids are well known, they are not necessarily well understood.

A Kinetic Description of Liquids

Particles in liquids are held together by intermolecular forces that balance out their kinetic energy. The particles in a liquid substance move but with less energy than those same particles have as a gas. Because of the strength of their intermolecular forces, liquids are held closer together compared with gas particles having the same energy (temperature). Yet the attractive forces holding the particles together do not totally dominate, as in a solid. There is enough freedom for liquid particles to roll and slide over, around, and past each other. Liquid particles are not fixed in any one position, so liquids, like gases, are fluids that can flow and be poured.

Density of Liquids

Liquids have densities that are much greater than those of gases since there is little space between the particles of liquids. Because of this closeness, liquids cannot significantly expand or compress like gases can. People rely on this property every time they apply the brakes in their car. The pressure that is applied on the liquid through the brake pedal is transferred throughout the fluid, causing the brake pads to clamp down. Since the particles are already close together, liquids can transfer incredible pressures of even the most powerful hydraulic systems without being compressed much. The particles themselves would have to be crushed before a liquid could be appreciably compressed.

312 Chapter 13

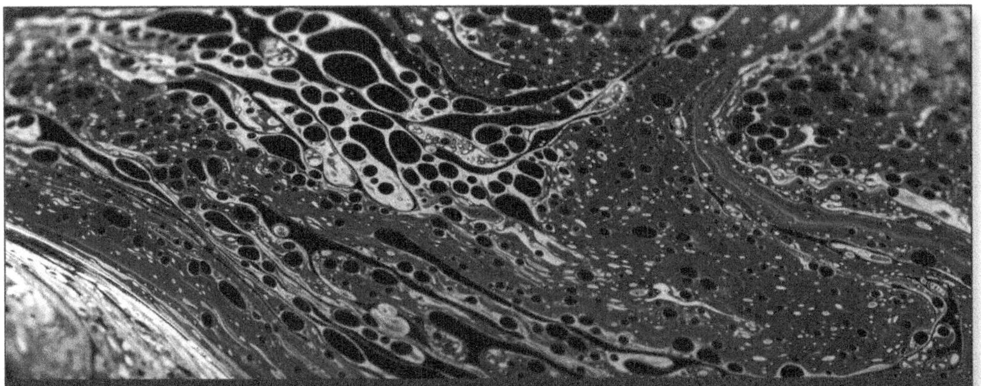

MINI LAB

THROUGH THE VOID

If you took a course in physical science, you may recall that certain chemicals, called indicators, will change color in the presence of an acid or base. Some indicators are liquids. Typically they are used by adding the indicator drop-wise into the solution being tested. Bromothymol blue (BTB), for example, is a greenish liquid that will change to yellow when added to an acid. But what if the two liquids don't touch? Will the indicator still work?

Can liquid particles move through empty space?

1. Write a hypothesis about whether BTB will change color when near an acid but not in direct contact with it.

Procedure

A. Place the petri dish on a blank sheet of paper for easier observation. Remove the cover and place one drop of vinegar and one drop of BTB in the dish, about 3 cm apart. Do not mix the drops or otherwise allow them to come in contact.

B. Replace the lid on the petri dish and observe.

2. Describe what happens in the dish.

Conclusion

3. Suggest an explanation for what you observed.

Going Further

4. The creative title of this lab activity suggests that there is "nothing" in the petri dish other than the two liquids. Is that true? Explain.

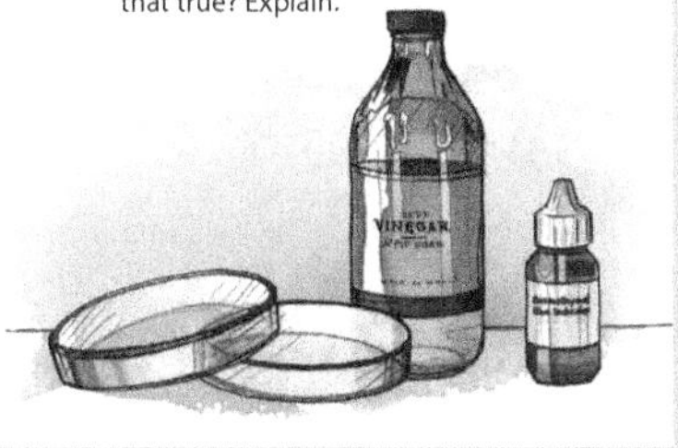

EQUIPMENT

- petri dish with cover
- vinegar
- bromothymol blue (BTB)

INSTRUCT

MINI LAB: *THROUGH THE VOID*

This **mini lab** is an introductory activity intended to get students thinking about the properties of liquids before moving on to the material in Section 13.3. Many students will be familiar with the concept of evaporation, but some may not recall that all liquids can evaporate under the right conditions. More advanced students may recognize that evaporation can account for the movement of particles between the two liquids, even without direct contact. For others, this may come as a bit of a surprise. They will learn more about how this process works as they work through the next section.

Answers

1. Answers will vary. Students should write a hypothesis that states that BTB either will or will not change color.
2. The drop of BTB changes from green to yellow.
3. Since the BTB changes color, particles from the vinegar must be coming in contact with it. Since the BTB and vinegar are not touching, vinegar particles must be traveling through the air in the container. Some of the vinegar must be evaporating.
4. No. There is air in the dish. Air is the medium through which the evaporated vinegar travels.

DEMONSTRATING THE HIGH SURFACE TENSION OF WATER

Demonstrate how to weaken the hydrogen bonds that create water's high surface tension.

Materials: paper clip or needle, 50 mL beaker or small glass, liquid dish soap

Preparation: Fill the beaker to the brim with water.

Performance/Discussion: Lower the paper clip or needle gently onto the surface of the water. You may have to use tweezers, toothpicks, a bent paper clip, or thread to lower it gently enough so that it floats. After students have seen the floating paper clip, carefully add a drop of dish soap to the water. The surface tension will reduce, and the paper clip will sink.

Conclusion: Why did the dish soap cause the paper clip to lose its ability to float? *(The dish soap is a surfactant, and it broke the hydrogen bonds in the water molecules, lessening the water's surface tension.)*

DEMONSTRATING VISCOSITY

Demonstrate how temperature affects the viscosity of liquids.

Materials: syrup or other viscous liquid, small glasses or test tubes (2), bowl

Preparation: Prepare two containers of syrup, one chilled or room temperature and the other warmed.

Performance/Discussion: Ask students whether viscosity and temperature are directly or inversely related. Lead them to the answer that it is an inverse relationship: as a liquid's temperature increases, its viscosity decreases. Demonstrate this by pouring the two samples of syrup into a bowl at the same time. The cold syrup, which is more viscous, flows much more slowly than the warm syrup.

Effects of Intermolecular Attractions

The properties of liquids are greatly affected by intermolecular forces. The attraction between the particles of a liquid is called **cohesion**. The attraction between the particles of a liquid and the particles of other materials is called **adhesion**. Cohesion and adhesion together cause many of the amazing properties of liquids that we observe.

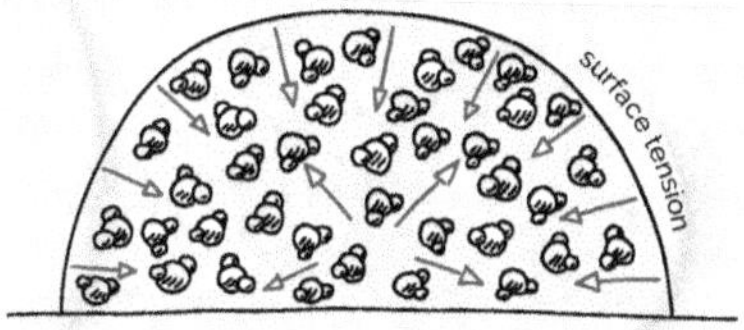

COHESION

Remember the water striders (How It Works on page 188)? You may recall that their ability to glide across the water's surface is partly due to a property of water itself. **Surface tension**, the elastic "skin" that forms on the surface of water and other liquids, is caused by the imbalance of intermolecular forces at the liquid's surface. A particle within a volume of liquid has neighbors on all sides. Each neighbor attracts interior particles equally in all directions. But a surface particle does not have other particles on one side. All forces exerted on surface particles are directed toward the interior of the liquid, and directionality of the forces binds surface particles together. If the force exerted by an object on the surface of a liquid is less than the liquid's surface tension, the object will be unable to penetrate the surface of the liquid. This phenomenon allows water striders and other insects to move across the surface of the water without sinking.

Surface tension affects the shapes of liquids. Raindrops are spherical because surface tension pulls water into the shape with the least surface area per unit of volume. Mercury, which has more surface tension than water, forms drops that are even more spherical than water drops.

Surface tension causes drops of mercury lying on a flat surface to curve under, around their edges.

Surface tension affects more than just the shape of raindrops. Have you ever tried to use water to get oil or grease off your hands with no soap? You need soap, or a detergent, to break down the grime. These both act as surface-active agents, or **surfactants**, meaning that they break down the normal surface tension of water by interfering with hydrogen bonds. This allows normally insoluble grease, oil, and other nonpolar liquids to dissolve. A soap molecule is a long molecule with a polar end and a nonpolar end. The polar end attracts water through dipole-dipole forces, while the nonpolar end attracts dirt, grease, and oil, allowing the water and the other substances to mix.

The attraction of liquid particles for one another affects their ability to flow. Thick and gooey liquids consist of particles that have a high cohesion. Liquids that flow easily consist of particles that have a low cohesion. The degree of cohesion and the shape of a fluid's particles affect a property called **viscosity**—a liquid's ability to resist flowing. The stronger the attractions between particles, the more viscous the

314 Chapter 13

fluid will be. Molasses is viscous, so it can be expected to have some strong attractions between its particles. Thinner, less viscous fluids like water and gasoline pour well and spread out quickly because they have weak intermolecular attractions. Temperature affects viscosity. At cold temperatures, intermolecular forces are more effective on slow-moving particles. That is why cold syrup flows more slowly than hot syrup.

ADHESION

The same intermolecular forces that cause surface tension affect how a liquid interacts with the particles in its container. Have you ever observed the curved surface of a liquid in a container with a narrow neck? This curved surface, called a **meniscus**, results from intermolecular attractions within the liquid and between the liquid and the container. When attractions between the container and the particles of the liquid exceed the attractions between the liquid particles, the liquid climbs the walls of the container, forming a concave meniscus. In narrow glass tubes called *capillary tubes*, this effect becomes greatly exaggerated. Water and other liquids rise up narrow capillary tubes easily by *capillary action*. Mercury, on the other hand, has little attraction for glass but has strong internal cohesive forces. These cohesive forces are so strong that the surface molecules are pulled away from the glass as the molecules try to form a sphere, producing a convex meniscus. Thus, mercury does not exhibit capillary action, as shown below.

Other fluid properties that liquids exhibit are *diffusibility* and *absorption*. A drop of food coloring spreads, or diffuses, throughout a glass of water. Spilled milk seeps into, or is absorbed by, a paper towel. Both cases are evidence that liquids consist of moving particles in unfixed positions. However, liquids diffuse in and are absorbed by other materials only when they are similar to one another. For instance, water wets a cotton cloth, but it does not wet wax candles. Water molecules are polar, so they readily adhere to sugar, cotton, skin, and other materials that have polar regions. Nonpolar materials, such as a freshly waxed car, cause water to bead up and roll away. On the other hand, nonpolar liquids wet nonpolar surfaces but not polar surfaces. In each case, intermolecular attractions determine how the liquid behaves.

DEMONSTRATING THE ADHESION OF WATER

Demonstrate the ability of water to adhere to glass surfaces.

Materials: glass microscope slides, liquid dish soap

Performance/Discussion: Hand out two glass slides to each student or group of students. Have them place a drop of water on one slide and then place the other slide on top, sandwiching the water between the slides. Then ask them to try to pull the slides apart without sliding or breaking them. Have them touch a drop of dish soap to one side of the joined slides, allowing the dish soap to wick in between them. Students should be able to easily separate the slides at this point.

Conclusion: Why could you not get the glass slides apart? *(The forces between the water and the glass were strong and had to be overcome with a surfactant.)*

STRAW WRAPPER CAPILLARY ACTION

For a scientific explanation of a common trick that teens like to do in restaurants, visit TeacherToolsOnline.com. Under Additional Resources, click on Chapter 13 Web Links. Then click on *Straw Wrapper Capillary Action*.

Solids & Liquids 315

SWAMP COOLERS

In desert climates, some buildings are air-conditioned by evaporative cooling systems, where air from the outside is pulled into the building through water-dampened filters. This type of system is often called a "swamp cooler." Since this process adds moisture to the air in the building, it is popular in the American Southwest and other hot, dry places. For more information about evaporative cooling systems, visit TeacherToolsOnline.com. Under Additional Resources, click on Chapter 13 Web Links. Then click on *Swamp Coolers*.

DYNAMIC EQUILIBRIUM

Use a **think-pair-share** to help students understand dynamic equilibrium. Ask, "What do you think is meant by the term *dynamic equilibrium*? Think about what each word means." (Dynamic means "changing, not static"; equilibrium means "a state of balance.") Have students discuss their answers with a partner, then choose several to share their answers with the class. Correct any errors or misconceptions. Dynamic equilibrium is an important concept for students to understand before they begin Chapter 14, so make sure that students get a good grasp of it here.

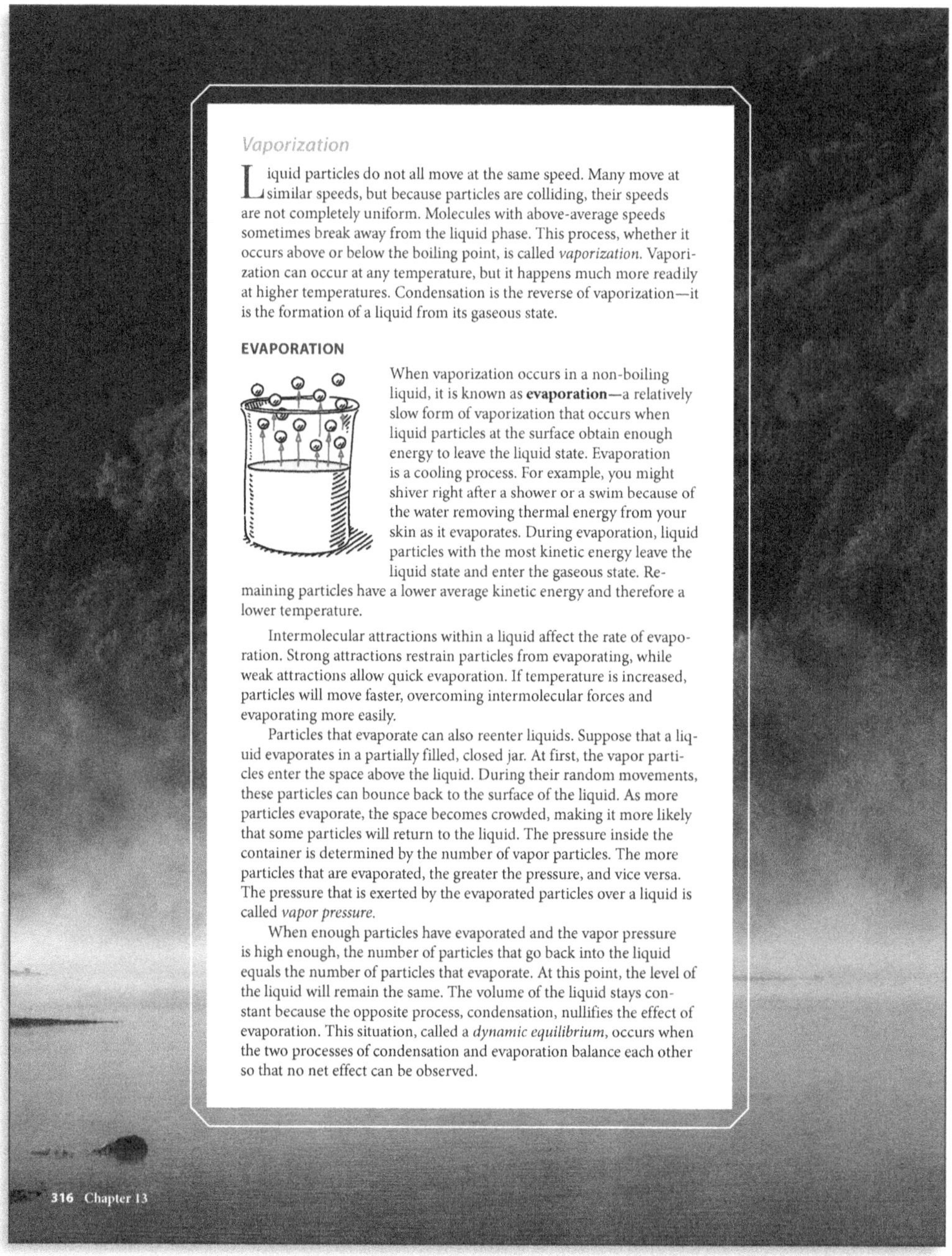

Vaporization

Liquid particles do not all move at the same speed. Many move at similar speeds, but because particles are colliding, their speeds are not completely uniform. Molecules with above-average speeds sometimes break away from the liquid phase. This process, whether it occurs above or below the boiling point, is called *vaporization*. Vaporization can occur at any temperature, but it happens much more readily at higher temperatures. Condensation is the reverse of vaporization—it is the formation of a liquid from its gaseous state.

EVAPORATION

When vaporization occurs in a non-boiling liquid, it is known as **evaporation**—a relatively slow form of vaporization that occurs when liquid particles at the surface obtain enough energy to leave the liquid state. Evaporation is a cooling process. For example, you might shiver right after a shower or a swim because of the water removing thermal energy from your skin as it evaporates. During evaporation, liquid particles with the most kinetic energy leave the liquid state and enter the gaseous state. Remaining particles have a lower average kinetic energy and therefore a lower temperature.

Intermolecular attractions within a liquid affect the rate of evaporation. Strong attractions restrain particles from evaporating, while weak attractions allow quick evaporation. If temperature is increased, particles will move faster, overcoming intermolecular forces and evaporating more easily.

Particles that evaporate can also reenter liquids. Suppose that a liquid evaporates in a partially filled, closed jar. At first, the vapor particles enter the space above the liquid. During their random movements, these particles can bounce back to the surface of the liquid. As more particles evaporate, the space becomes crowded, making it more likely that some particles will return to the liquid. The pressure inside the container is determined by the number of vapor particles. The more particles that are evaporated, the greater the pressure, and vice versa. The pressure that is exerted by the evaporated particles over a liquid is called *vapor pressure*.

When enough particles have evaporated and the vapor pressure is high enough, the number of particles that go back into the liquid equals the number of particles that evaporate. At this point, the level of the liquid will remain the same. The volume of the liquid stays constant because the opposite process, condensation, nullifies the effect of evaporation. This situation, called a *dynamic equilibrium*, occurs when the two processes of condensation and evaporation balance each other so that no net effect can be observed.

316 Chapter 13

BOILING

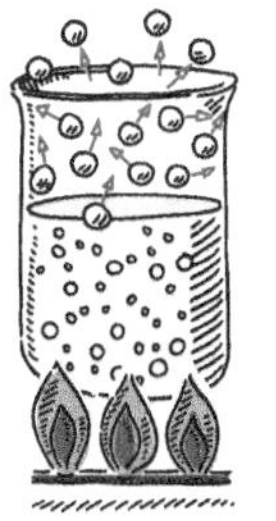

Boiling is a rapid change between the liquid and gaseous states caused by the application of heat or a dramatic decrease in pressure. Vapor bubbles form inside the liquid and rise to the surface. Vapor also escapes from a liquid's surface, as in evaporation.

Boiling is a relatively rapid form of vaporization that occurs when the vapor pressure of a liquid equals or exceeds the atmospheric pressure. Normally, atmospheric pressure is greater than vapor pressure at room temperature. The pressure prevents liquids from boiling. Table 13-3 shows that the vapor pressure of ethanol at 25 °C is only 9.07 kPa. The normal atmospheric pressure of 101.325 kPa can easily suppress this weak tendency to boil. But when the alcohol is heated to 78.4 °C, ethanol's vapor pressure equals normal atmospheric pressure and boiling occurs.

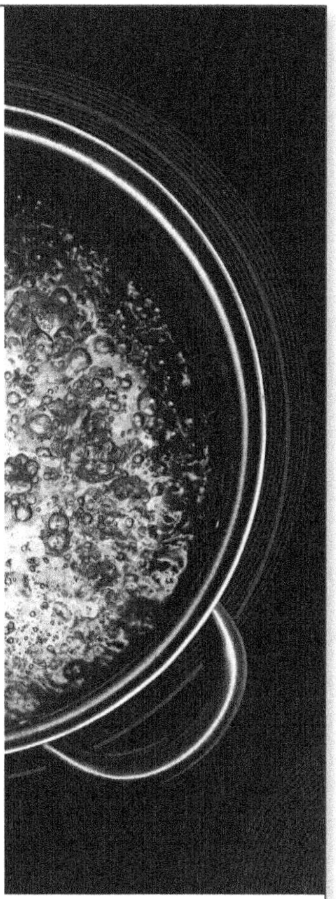

Vapor Pressure and Boiling Point

While most people equate boiling with particular temperatures, a liquid's temperature is not the sole deciding factor for when it boils. Climbers at the summit of Mount Everest would find that water boils at 70 °C, not at the expected 100 °C. At an elevation of 8850 m, the atmospheric pressure is only about 30 kPa, not the 101 kPa at sea level. Boiling occurs more readily because the vapor pressure of the liquid exceeds the lower atmospheric pressure at a lower temperature. When the vapor pressure reaches 30 kPa, the water will boil. Similarly, if atmospheric pressure is higher, a higher temperature is required for a liquid to boil, as is the case in hospital autoclaves or pressure cookers.

Because boiling points change with pressure, the **boiling point** of a liquid is defined as the temperature at which the vapor pressure equals the applied pressure. The *normal boiling point* is the temperature at which the vapor pressure equals 101.325 kPa. As you might expect, temperature and intermolecular forces affect vapor pressure just as they do evaporation. As the temperature in a liquid increases, its vapor pressure increases. The vapor pressure is less for a substance with strong intermolecular forces than for a substance with weaker intermolecular forces.

We can use the calculated vapor pressures of various substances to compare the rate at which they will evaporate. Suppose that mercury, water, and diethyl ether are spilled in a room at 25 °C. From Table 13-3 we can see that the mercury will exert 0.000 247 kPa of vapor pressure; water, 3.17 kPa; and diethyl ether, 72.1 kPa. These numbers show that diethyl ether will evaporate quickly, water will take longer to evaporate, and mercury will take decades to evaporate.

TABLE 13-3 *Vapor Pressures (in kPa)*

Substance	Temperature (°C)			
	0	25	50	100
Mercury	0.000 024 7	0.000 247	0.001 70	0.0364
Water	0.611	3.17	12.3	101
Ethanol	1.63	9.07	31.2	222
Methanol	3.16	16.3	53.9	—
Diethyl Ether	24.7	72.1	162	648

DEMONSTRATING THE RELATIONSHIP BETWEEN VAPOR PRESSURE AND BOILING

Demonstrate how vapor pressure affects the boiling point of water.

Materials: vacuum pump, bell jar, 50 mL beaker, thermometer

Preparation: Set up the vacuum pump and bell jar.

Performance/Discussion: Fill the beaker halfway with hot water and record the temperature. Place the beaker on the base of the bell jar, cover with the bell jar's dome, make sure that the seal is tight, and turn on the pump. As the pressure inside the bell jar is reduced, it will eventually become less than the vapor pressure of the hot water and the hot water will begin to boil. Keep the vacuum pump running until the boiling stops.

Remove the dome and measure the temperature. The temperature should be significantly less than the original reading; temperatures as low as 10 °C have been achieved in this way.

Conclusion: Ask students to use Table 13-3 to determine what the final vapor pressure of the water inside the bell jar was. For example, if the final temperature you measured was 50 °C, the final vapor pressure would be 12.3 kPa. You can confirm their answers if your vacuum pump has a pressure gauge. Then ask students how they could create their own vapor pressure curve like the one shown for Example 13-3 to show the relationship between vapor pressure and temperature for an unknown substance. They should conclude that taking regular measurements of temperature and pressure will generate a data set that can be graphed to show the relationship.

PHASE CHANGES

For an interactive phase diagram that allows you to manipulate conditions and shows the triple point of water, visit TeacherTools Online.com. Under Additional Resources, click on Chapter 13 Web Links. Then click on *Phase Changes*.

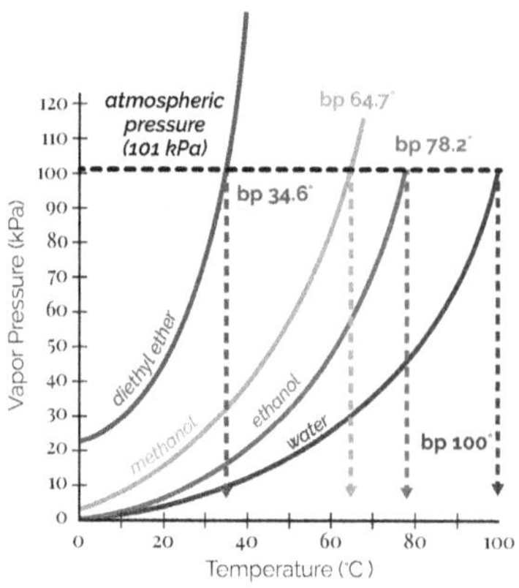

The vapor pressure of a substance at a specific atmospheric pressure can also be used to predict when a substance will boil. And we can use vapor pressure curves, such as the one at left, to answer questions related to boiling points. Let's look at how this works.

EXAMPLE 13-3: CALCULATING THE BOILING POINT

What is the boiling point of water that is subjected to an atmospheric pressure of 66.7 kPa?

Solution

Using the vapor pressure curve, draw a horizontal line from 66.7 kPa on the vertical axis to the curve that represents water's vapor pressure. From that intersection, drop a vertical line to the axis representing the temperature. It will intersect at approximately 89 °C. At this temperature, the vapor pressure of water will match the given atmospheric pressure, and the water will boil.

Distilling Liquids

The processes of vaporization and condensation can be used to separate mixtures. This technique is called **distillation**. This is one way in which salt water can be purified, and it is also used to separate combinations of liquids into pure samples called *fractions*.

In the laboratory, the mixture to be separated is placed into a distillation flask and heated. The temperature rises steadily until it reaches the boiling point of the liquid that boils at the lowest temperature. The vapor of this liquid enters a condenser and flows over its water-cooled glass walls. The vapor soon condenses and drips into a collecting flask. Once all of the first liquid has been vaporized, the temperature can rise until the boiling point of another substance is reached. The process is repeated, and the other liquid is collected in another flask. This technique works well as long as the substances in the mixture have distinctly different boiling points and do not strongly interact. If distillation is precisely controlled, substances with boiling points only a few degrees apart can be separated.

a simple distillation apparatus

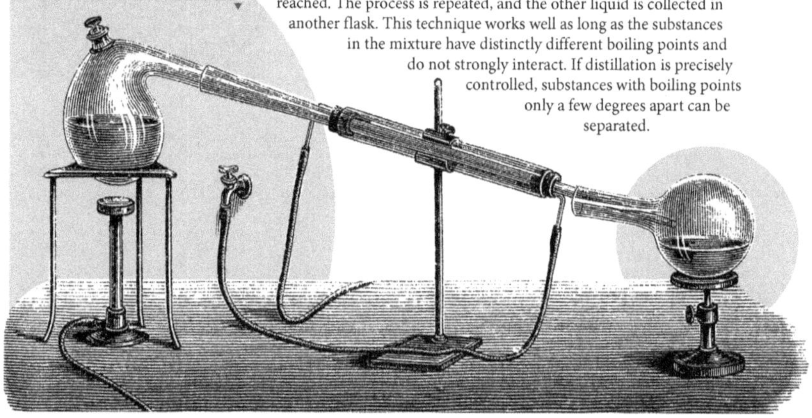

318 Chapter 13

Phase Diagrams

A **phase diagram** is a graphical way to represent the relationship between the temperature, pressure, and physical state of a substance. At right is a phase diagram of water. Note that all the points along the liquid-solid curve (AB) are melting points, all the points along the liquid-gas curve (AC) are boiling points, and all the points along the solid-gas curve (AD) are sublimation points.

Notice that the line of boiling points, the line of melting points, and the line of sublimation points intersect at point A. At this specific pressure and temperature (0.01 °C, 0.6 kPa), water can exist simultaneously in all three states. This specific set of conditions for a substance is called its **triple point**.

a phase diagram for water

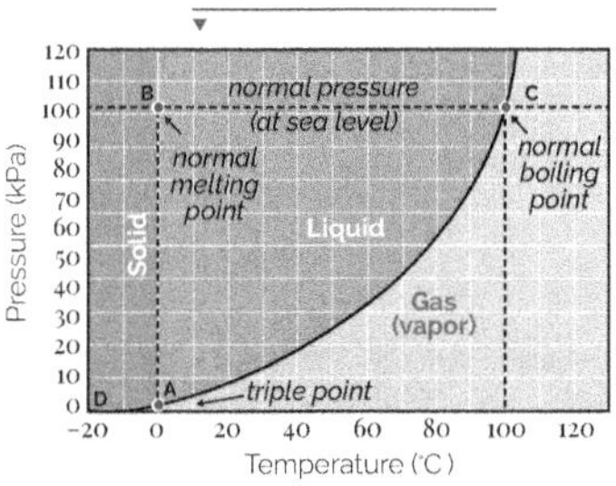

EXAMPLE 13-4: DETERMINING THE STATE OF MATTER

Using the phase diagram for water, determine the state of water at the following conditions:

a. 60 °C, 53.3 kPa

b. −10 °C, 133 kPa

c. 80 °C, 26.7 kPa

Solution

a. The point that corresponds to 60 °C and 53.3 kPa is between the line of melting points and the line of boiling points. This region represents the conditions at which water is in the liquid state.

b. The point corresponding to −10 °C and 133 kPa is to the left of the line of melting points. Water is a solid under these conditions.

c. The point corresponding to 80 °C and 26.7 kPa lies beyond the line of boiling points. Water will exist as a gas under these conditions.

Critical Temperatures and Pressures

Oxygen, hydrogen, nitrogen, and helium, though gases at room temperature, can be liquids under the proper conditions. Low temperatures and high pressures can condense and even solidify any gas. Low temperatures slow down the molecules; high pressures pack them together.

Scientists have found that high pressures alone cannot liquefy gases. Their temperatures must be lowered past a certain point. This value, called the **critical temperature** (T_c), is the highest temperature at which a gas can be liquefied. Each gas has its own characteristic critical temperature.

Hydrogen gas at 35 K cannot be liquefied, even at tremendous pressures. The molecules are moving too quickly. If the temperature is lowered to 33 K, it can be squeezed into a liquid if enough pressure is applied. Gases that have critical temperatures above room temperature can be liquefied at room temperature by pressure alone. Other gases require a combination of refrigeration and compression.

The pressure that is required to liquefy a gas at its critical temperature is called the **critical pressure** (P_c). Hydrogen gas at its critical temperature can be liquefied under a pressure of 1297 kPa. If the gas is colder than its critical temperature, less pressure is required to liquefy it.

TABLE 13-4
Critical Temperatures and Pressures

Substance	T_c (K)	P_c (kPa)
hydrogen (H_2)	33.1	1298
nitrogen (N_2)	126	3395
oxygen (O_2)	155	5043
carbon dioxide (CO_2)	304	7387
ammonia (NH_3)	406	11 277
chlorine (Cl_2)	417	7991
water (H_2O)	647	22 064

LIQUIDS

Use the following **formative assessment** to check students' understanding.

1. List three properties of liquids that are dependent on intermolecular forces. *(Accept any three: cohesion, adhesion, surface tension, and viscosity.)*
2. Explain the difference between vaporization and condensation. *(Vaporization is the change from a liquid to a gaseous state. Condensation is the change from a gas to a liquid state.)*
3. If particles in a liquid acquire enough energy to overcome the intermolecular forces, what type of vaporization will occur? *(evaporation)*
4. Describe how critical temperature relates to critical pressure. *(Critical temperature is the highest point at which a gas can be liquefied. Critical pressure is the pressure that is required to liquefy a gas at its critical temperature. If a gas gets colder than its critical temperature, there is less pressure needed to liquefy it.)*

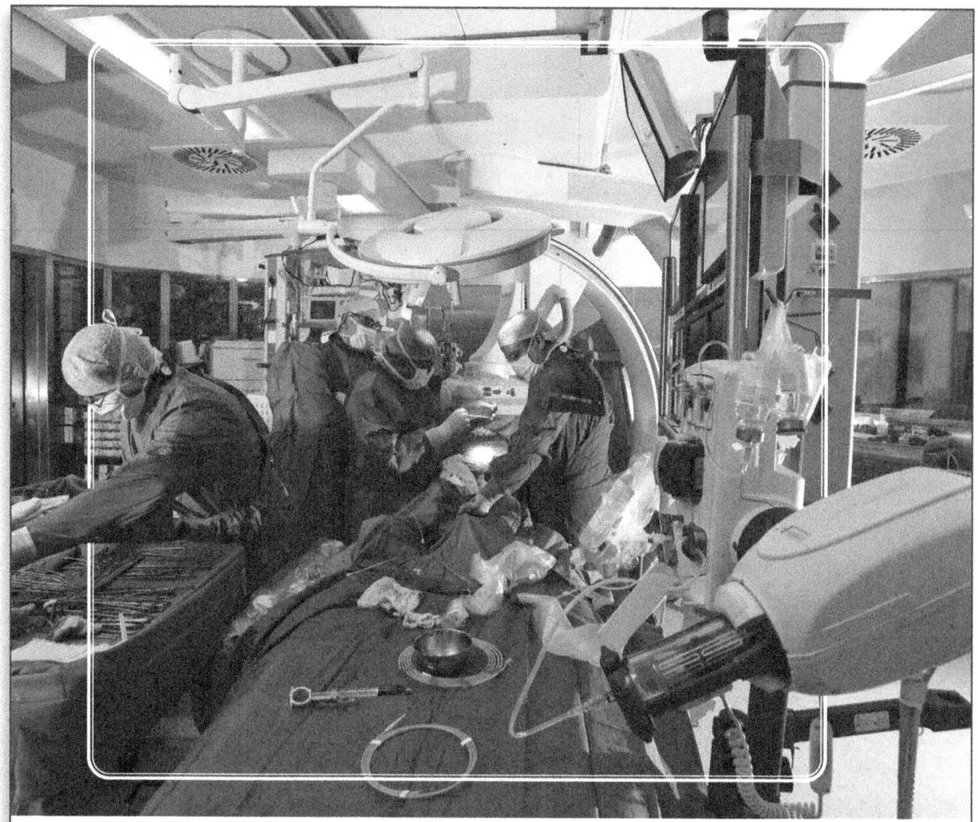

Using Liquids to Solve Problems

So how do doctors apply what you've learned in this chapter to help tackle the issue of organ donation described in the Chapter opener? People have been trying to transplant organs for thousands of years, mostly without success. Hundreds of years before Christ, Indian doctors performed skin grafts to treat burns. But it wasn't until the twentieth century that doctors developed safe and effective ways to transplant other organs to patients who needed them.

New types of transplants emerged during almost every decade between 1950 and 2000. The first successful kidney and bone marrow transplants were performed in the 1950s. The 1960s heralded the first successful pancreas and heart transplants. The 1980s saw the first successful lung and heart-lung transplants. And in the 1990s, cord-blood stem cell transplants and pancreatic islet transplants were successful. But how do all these organs and tissues stay alive in the transition from donor to recipient?

Currently, surgeons preserve most transplant organs by chilling them in the absence of blood flow, resulting in a condition called *cold ischemia*. Without blood flow, an organ will quickly die, so cooling is used to slow cell death and keep the organ viable during transport, at least for a little while. The organ is placed in a sterile container with special preservative solutions—liquids—surrounding it. This container is then placed in a beverage cooler filled with another icy solution designed to cool but not freeze the organ.

Kidneys get a different treatment. Doctors use a machine called a *pulsatile perfusion device* to continuously pump preservative solution through the kidney, keeping it viable for a longer period. Kidneys preserved in this fashion also survive transplantation better and are more likely to continue functioning after being transplanted into a recipient. Of course, the preserving liquid is different from the blood that normally pumps through the organ. As doctors continue to invent better ways to preserve organs, they use the properties of liquids to give new hope to those who are suffering. This is a way to use chemistry to show love to people.

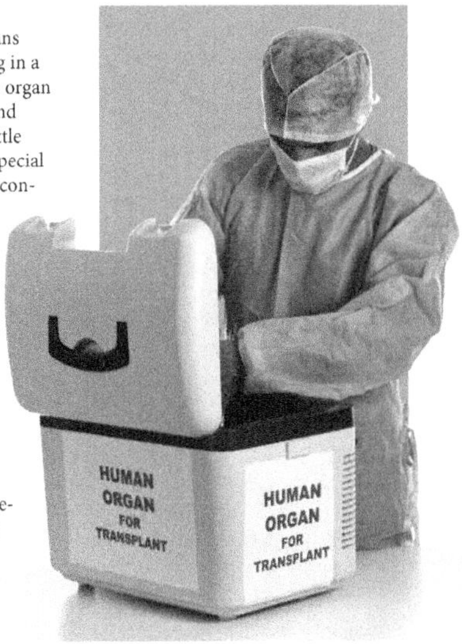

13.3 SECTION REVIEW

1. How does the kinetic-molecular theory explain the liquid phase of a substance?
2. What would happen to a paper clip floating on the surface of water if some detergent were added? Explain.
3. Explain the difference between cohesion and adhesion. Give an example of each.
4. Compare evaporation and boiling.
5. Why are the published values of the boiling points of substances always given for 101.325 kPa?
6. Describe what happens to the temperature of water as it changes phase from a solid to a gas.

Refer to the phase diagram for ethanol at right to answer Questions 7–8.

7. a. In what state is ethanol at 300 °C and 3000 kPa?
   b. In what state is ethanol at −145 °C and 1500 kPa?

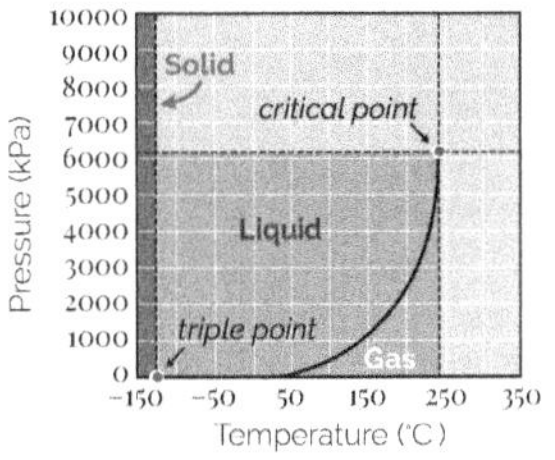

   c. At what combination of temperature and pressure can ethanol exist in all three phases of matter?
8. If ethanol is held at a constant temperature of 200 °C while the atmospheric pressure is increased from 900 kPa to 5250 kPa, will it undergo a phase change? If so, what kind?

ASSESS

TICKET OUT THE DOOR

Check for understanding with this **summarizing activity**. Ask students to write a definition for *triple point*. *(Triple point is the combination of temperature and pressure at which a substance can simultaneously exist as a gas, liquid, and solid.)*

13.3 REVIEW ANSWERS

1. According to the kinetic-molecular theory, particles in liquids have enough energy to partially overcome intermolecular forces between the particles. Unlike in solids, liquid particles can move around freely, but they cannot completely separate from each other as in a gas. *(p. 312)*
2. The paper clip would sink. The addition of detergent (a surfactant) would decrease the surface tension of the water. The weight of the paper clip could then overcome the surface tension and buoyant force. *(p. 314)*
3. Cohesion is the result of attractions between particles within a liquid. Adhesion results from the attractions that liquid particles have for other materials. Cohesion is responsible for the tendency of water to bead up on a flat surface. Adhesion accounts for water's tendency to climb the walls of narrow glass tubes (capillary action). (Other answers are possible.) *(pp. 314–15)*
4. Evaporation and boiling are two forms of vaporization. Evaporation occurs at any temperature at which a liquid state exists, typically at the interface between a liquid and another medium (e.g., air). Evaporation occurs because some particles in a liquid gain sufficient kinetic energy, allowing them to overcome intermolecular forces. Boiling occurs anywhere within a liquid whenever the liquid's vapor pressure equals or exceeds atmospheric pressure. Bubbles of vapor rise to the surface of the liquid and then enter the atmosphere. *(pp. 316–17)*
5. The boiling point of a substance will vary with pressure. For this reason, all comparisons with other substances must be made at standard pressure. *(p. 317)*
6. The temperature of ice rises until it begins to melt (reaches the melting point). At that point, additional thermal energy is being used to overcome the intermolecular forces that maintain ice's solid structure, not to increase the temperature of the ice-water mixture. Once all the ice is melted, the temperature of the liquid water increases until the boiling point is reached, where once again the temperature plateaus until the phase change is complete. After all the water enters the gas phase, the temperature rises again. *(pp. 306, 316–17)*
7. **a.** gas
   b. solid
   c. −123 °C, 0 kPa *(all p. 319)*
8. Yes. It will condense from a gas to a liquid. *(p. 319)*

13 CHAPTER REVIEW

Chapter Summary

TERMS
intermolecular force
dipole-dipole force
hydrogen bond
London dispersion force

13.1 INTERMOLECULAR FORCES

- Intermolecular forces are the electrostatic forces due to temporarily or permanently charged regions on particles. These forces influence the physical properties of substances.
- Hydrogen bonds, dipole-dipole forces, and dispersion forces are the three main types of intermolecular forces in order from strongest to weakest.
- The intermolecular forces present in a substance can be predicted on the basis of its composition and structure.
- The physical properties of a substance can be predicted on the basis of its intermolecular forces.

13.2 SOLIDS

- The properties of solids can be described and explained by the kinetic-molecular theory.
- Amorphous solids have no preferred arrangement of particles, whereas crystalline solids form regular three-dimensional patterns called crystal lattices. These can be described using the concept of unit cells.
- Melting is the change from the solid to the liquid state; freezing is the reverse process.
- Heating curves illustrate how adding thermal energy affects the temperature and state of matter.
- Phase changes can be explained on the basis of the interplay between kinetic-molecular theory and intermolecular forces. During phase changes, the temperature of a substance remains constant until the change is completed.
- Sublimation is the direct change from the solid to the gaseous state; deposition is the reverse process.
- The lattice energy of a crystal is reflected in its melting point and solubility and is partly determined by its particles' electric charge and size.
- Allotropes are different crystal lattice structures formed by an element.

TERMS
crystalline solid
amorphous solid
melting point
unit cell
allotrope
lattice energy

322 Chapter 13

13.3 LIQUIDS

- As is true for solids, the properties of liquids can be described and explained by the kinetic-molecular theory.
- Cohesion, adhesion, surface tension, capillary action, and viscosity are all dependent on intermolecular forces.
- Vaporization is the change from the liquid to the gaseous state; condensation is the reverse process.
- There are two types of vaporization. Evaporation is vaporization any time the liquid phase is present and particles of the liquid get enough energy to overcome the intermolecular forces. Boiling is vaporization when the vapor pressure of a liquid equals the atmospheric pressure.
- Distillation is a technique used to separate mixtures by vaporizing and condensing the components, or fractions, on the basis of their boiling points.
- Phase diagrams show the temperature and pressure conditions under which a substance is solid, liquid, or gaseous.

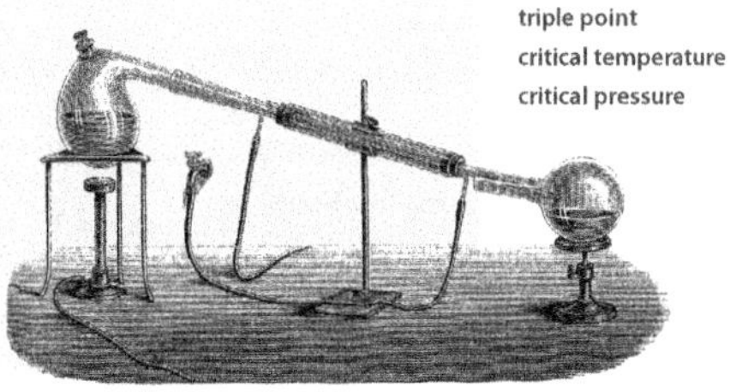

TERMS
cohesion
adhesion
surface tension
surfactant
viscosity
meniscus
evaporation
boiling
boiling point
distillation
phase diagram
triple point
critical temperature
critical pressure

Chapter Review Questions

RECALLING FACTS

1. What is a hydrogen bond?
2. Arrange the attractive forces (bonds and intermolecular forces) within substances in order of increasing strength.
3. What makes water different from other substances in regard to the density of its solid and liquid states?
4. What is the major difference between crystalline and amorphous solids?
5. Name three factors that determine the structure of a crystal.
6. Name three factors that determine the strength of a crystal.
7. What causes surface tension?
8. Why do raindrops not assume triangular or cubic shapes?
9. Why does the surface of water in a glass test tube curve upward at the edges?
10. How does perspiration cool the skin on a person's body?
11. What is the essential difference between boiling and evaporation?

UNDERSTANDING CONCEPTS

12. A study buddy claims that the bonds between atoms within a molecule are stronger than the forces that exist between molecules. Is he correct? Explain.
13. Explain how you would determine which type(s) of intermolecular forces exist within a substance.
14. Predict the types of intermolecular forces that may act between the molecules in the following substances.
    a. CO_2
    b. NH_3
    c. HCl
    d. C_3H_8
15. Assume that the particles in table salt (NaCl) vibrate just as forcefully as the particles in lead (Pb). Explain why table salt remains a solid at 500 °C while lead exists as a liquid.
16. When thermal energy is being removed from a liquid, why does the temperature of the liquid at its freezing point remain constant until all the liquid freezes?

CHAPTER 13 REVIEW ANSWERS

Recalling Facts

1. A hydrogen bond is a particularly strong dipole-dipole force between molecules that contain strongly polar bonds, such as those between hydrogen and nitrogen, oxygen, or fluorine. *(p. 300)*
2. dispersion force, dipole-dipole force, hydrogen bond, covalent bond, metallic bond, ionic bond *(p. 301)*
3. Unlike most other substances, water is less dense as a solid than as a liquid. *(p. 304)*
4. Particles are arranged randomly in an amorphous solid but are orderly and regular in a crystal. *(p. 305)*
5. The structure of a crystal is determined by the number and kinds of particles, the size of the particles, and the electrical charges on the particles. *(p. 308)*
6. The strength of a crystal is determined by the magnitude of the electrical charges, the size of the particles, and the geometric structure of the crystal. *(pp. 308–10)*
7. unbalanced forces at the surface of a liquid *(p. 314)*
8. Surface tension pulls raindrops into the shape that has the least surface area per unit volume, that is, a sphere. *(p. 314)*
9. Attractive forces between the glass and the water overcome the attractive forces within the liquid. *(pp. 314–15)*
10. When water molecules evaporate, they take thermal energy with them, and the average kinetic energy of the remaining molecules decreases. *(p. 316)*
11. Boiling can occur anywhere within a liquid when the vapor pressure of the liquid equals the atmospheric pressure. Evaporation occurs at the surface when particles of the liquid obtain sufficient energy to leave the liquid, regardless of the vapor pressure. *(pp. 316–17)*

Understanding Concepts

12. Yes. All intermolecular forces are much weaker than the covalent bonds that exist within molecules. *(p. 299)*
13. All substances have dispersion forces. Polar substances have dipole-dipole forces. If a polar substance contains hydrogen bonded with nitrogen, oxygen, or fluorine, the material will have hydrogen bonds. *(pp. 300–303)*
14. **a.** dispersion
    b. hydrogen bonds, dispersion
    c. dipole-dipole, dispersion
    d. dispersion *(all pp. 300–303)*
15. The attractive forces (ionic bonds) between the ions in table salt (NaCl) are stronger than the attractive forces between the lead (Pb) atoms. *(pp. 300–303)*
16. The loss of thermal energy allows intermolecular forces to lock the particles in place, changing the liquid to a solid. Afterward any additional loss of thermal energy will lower the temperature of the solid. *(p. 306)*

17. a. NH_3; NF_3 does not have hydrogen bonds.

b. NaCl; NaCl is ionic.

c. CHF_3; CF_4 is nonpolar and does not have hydrogen bonds.

d. C_2H_5Cl; Cl_2 is nonpolar. *(all pp. 300–303)*

18. a. Particles gain enough kinetic energy to break away from the attractive forces that hold them in a liquid. *(pp. 316–17)*

b. Particles with high kinetic energy escape the attractive forces at the surface. *(p. 316)*

c. Particles lose kinetic energy until attractive forces prevail and hold them in fixed positions. *(p. 306)*

d. Particles held in a solid gain enough kinetic energy to break away from the attractive forces and go directly to the gaseous state. *(p. 306)*

19. a. When wax molecules are heated, they gain enough kinetic energy to overcome the intermolecular forces holding them rigidly in place. *(p. 306)*

b. Kinetic energy is removed from the water molecules as the water is cooled. The water solidifies as the molecules' motion decreases and attractive forces take hold. *(p. 306)*

c. Liquids like ginger ale flow because their molecules have enough kinetic energy to overcome intermolecular forces to the point that the molecules are not held rigidly in place. *(p. 312)*

d. Some water molecules gain sufficient kinetic energy to escape from the surface of the water. *(p. 316)*

e. When the water vapor molecules encounter the cold glass, some of their kinetic energy is removed. The vapor molecules slow down and become liquid. *(p. 316)*

f. The molecules of ice in snow exert vapor pressure even below freezing because they still have kinetic energy. Some snow molecules have enough energy to sublimate, going directly from the solid to the gaseous state. *(p. 306)*

g. The particles in solids and liquids are already about as close as they can be. *(p. 304)*

13 CHAPTER REVIEW

17. Using your understanding of intermolecular forces, determine which substance in each of the pairs should have the higher boiling point. Give your reasoning.

a. NF_3, NH_3 **c.** CF_4, CHF_3

b. NaCl, HCl **d.** Cl_2, C_2H_5Cl

18. In terms of attractive forces and kinetic energies of particles, explain what happens during the following phase changes. *Example*: In melting, the particles gain enough kinetic energy to overcome the attractive forces that hold them in fixed positions.

a. boiling **c.** freezing

b. evaporation **d.** sublimation

19. Use the kinetic-molecular theory to explain each observation given.

a. Wax melts near the flame of a burning candle.

b. Liquid water may be converted into ice cubes in a freezer.

c. Ginger ale flows to match the shape of a glass.

d. Water gradually evaporates from a swimming pool.

e. Water vapor condenses inside house windows on cold days.

f. Snow gradually disappears, even when the temperature remains below freezing.

g. Solids and liquids cannot be compressed as much as gases.

20. A white powder contains tiny cube-shaped grains and melts at a temperature between 141.6 °C and 142.2 °C. Is this solid more likely to be a crystalline solid or an amorphous solid?

21. Automobile engines are designed to be lubricated with motor oils of specific viscosities. These are rated from the lowest viscosity of 5W up to the highest viscosity of 70W. What can you conclude about the intermolecular attractions in an oil rated 10W?

22. Water rolls off a duck's back but thoroughly wets a head of human hair. What do these observations reveal about the chemical nature of these two surfaces?

23. After a jar of liquid has been sealed, the level of the liquid decreases slightly because of evaporation. After a slight decrease, the level of the liquid ceases to change. Why?

24. Crude oil is purified or refined through a process called *fractional distillation*. In this process the different components of oil (e.g., lubricating oil, grease, gasoline, and natural gas) are separated by distillation. What do you conclude about the physical properties of the different components?

25. Water in a truck's radiator can get hotter than 100 °C when the radiator is sealed tightly. How is it possible for water to exist as a liquid at temperatures above its normal boiling point?

CRITICAL THINKING

26. In this chapter, hydrogen bonds are described as a force between molecules, but might there be conditions under which it could also exist as a force *within* a molecule? Explain.

27. Predict which member in each of the following pairs of crystals has the stronger binding forces. Explain the reasons for your prediction.

a. NaCl, I_2

b. KBr, NaBr

c. CaI_2, KI

28. Refer to the diagram below to determine

a. the boiling point of ethanol when it is at normal atmospheric pressure.

b. the boiling point of methanol at 96.0 kPa.

c. the atmospheric pressure at which diethyl ether boils at 20 °C.

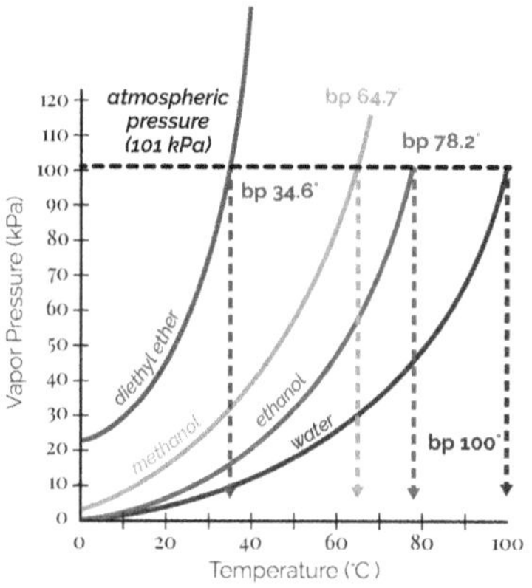

20. The powder is most likely crystalline because it has a definite melting point. *(pp. 305–6)*

21. Oil rated 10W would have weaker intermolecular attractions than 70W oil but would be a little stronger than 5W oil. *(pp. 314–15)*

22. The surface of a duck's back must have a nonpolar covering that repels water. Hair has regions of polar substances that attract water. *(pp. 314–15)*

23. Initially, the rate of evaporation exceeds the rate of condensation, causing the level to fall. Once the air above the liquid becomes saturated, the rate of condensation matches the rate of evaporation and the liquid level stabilizes, demonstrating a dynamic equilibrium. *(p. 316)*

24. The components all have distinct boiling points. *(p. 318)*

25. Increased pressure on the liquid's surface holds down the escaping molecules. Higher temperatures and higher vapor pressures are then required for boiling to occur. *(p. 319)*

29. Refer to the phase diagram of water below to determine the state of water at the given conditions.

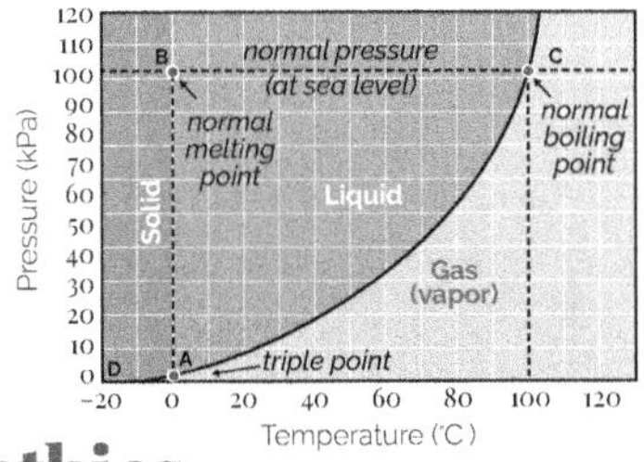

a. 80 °C, 40.0 kPa

b. 100 °C, 120.0 kPa

c. −10 °C, 66.7 kPa

30. A scientist claims to have a cooling apparatus kept at −100 °C by liquid nitrogen. Is this possible? Why or why not?

Use the ethics box below to answer Question 31.

31. Use the ethics process from pages 74–75 to write a four-paragraph assessment of the notion that cryonics offers hope as science advances our understanding of medicine.

ethics

CRYONICS

As you read in Section 13.2, applications of cryogenics are very useful, but there are a few dubious uses. *Cryonics*, one of the more macabre uses of cryogenics, is the process of deep freezing and storing a person who has been declared legally dead. People hope that a preserved person can be brought back to life at some time in the future.

Why would someone choose to do this? Some people hope that they can be stored until a cure is found for their incurable diseases. They are looking for healing for themselves or for their loved ones. People recognize that things are not the way they should be. Or there is the hope for a future reunion with loved ones, as with baseball great Ted Williams, probably the most famous person to undergo cryonics. Our desire for healing and life shows that we long for the world to be the way that God created it. However, there is currently no possibility of reviving a person preserved by cryonics since, as far as science has been able to determine, the biological processes of death are irreversible. Despite these facts, some people still put all their hope in science.

Ted Williams

What if advances in scientific technology did someday produce a way to bring these people back to life? Even if this happened, that person would still ultimately die, and their most fundamental problem would not be cured. People are still sinners, and death—both physical and spiritual—is part of God's penalty for sin. Adam and Eve's sin brought disease and death into the world, and as their children, we follow them in sin. But God's solution is far better than the faint hope of cryonics. All the promises of God for healing and eternal life find fulfillment in Jesus. He alone can save us from the deadly effects of sin and restore us to the abundant life that God wants us to enjoy. Whoever believes in Jesus will "not perish, but have everlasting life" (John 3:16).

Critical Thinking

26. Yes. If a molecule is large enough, it is possible for hydrogen bonding to occur between one part of the molecule and another part.

27. a. NaCl; NaCl is ionic, while I_2 molecules have only dispersion forces between them.

b. NaBr; The smaller Na^+ ions can exert more forces of attraction than K^+ ions.

c. CaI_2; The 2+ charge on Ca_2^+ ions acts more forcefully than the 1+ charge on K^+ ions. *(all pp. 301, 310)*

28. a. 78.4 °C

b. approximately 63 °C

c. approximately 40 kPa *(all p. 318)*

29. a. gas

b. liquid

c. solid *(all p. 319)*

30. No. The critical temperature of nitrogen is −147 °C (126 K), and nitrogen cannot exist as a liquid above this temperature. *(p. 319)*

ETHICS: CRYONICS

Appendix L includes a reproducible rubric to assess the ethics essay.

31. Answers will vary.

The Bible teaches that physical death, a consequence of the Fall, is something that all people will experience. Instances from the Scriptures of the dead being brought back to life are rare and were done to validate the ministry of the person doing the miracle. The Bible also teaches that after death comes judgment. For the believer, physical death is not something to be feared, for Christ has paid the penalty for sin. Upon death, believers enter into the eternal presence of their Savior. For the unbeliever, death is ultimately followed by final judgment and eternal punishment.

For the believer, there is no point in preserving a physical body through cryonics because the Bible teaches that at the resurrection, believers will receive glorified bodies. Choosing to preserve one's body after death is ultimately an exercise in futility, both spiritually and physically, since there is as yet no means of reanimating dead tissue nor evidence that it will be possible in the future.

Believers should be motivated to take care of their earthly bodies since they are a gift from God. Exercising good dominion includes maintaining a healthy body, thereby honoring God and helping a person remain fit for service to others. But Christians should not be unduly concerned about what happens to their bodies after death. Love for others should also motivate believers to share the gospel with those who through unbelief live in fear of death.

CHAPTER 14 *OBJECTIVES*

- Summarize the dissolving process.
- Use measures of concentration to solve problems.
- Analyze the effect of added solute on the properties of solvents.
- Describe colloids and their uses.
- Compare the concentration of sugar in beverages with those reported on nutrition labels.

OVERVIEW

Chapter 14 is a foundational chapter that covers material on solutions. Students should already be familiar with a wide variety of solutions encountered in everyday life. Throughout the chapter students will discover what makes something a solution and how to determine the amount of substances that are within a solution. Knowing the properties of solutions and the measures of concentration is essential to understanding the concepts covered in future chapters.

14.1 THE DISSOLVING PROCESS
- *Defining Solutions*
- *Types of Solutions*
- *The Dissolving Process*
- *Solvent Selectivity*

14.2 MEASURES OF CONCENTRATION
- *Defining Concentration*
- *Mass Fraction*
- *Volume Fraction*
- *Amount Concentration*
- *Molality*

14.3 COLLIGATIVE PROPERTIES
- *Vapor Pressure Depression*
- *Boiling Point Elevation*
- *Freezing Point Depression*
- *Increased Osmotic Pressure*

14.4 SUSPENSIONS AND COLLOIDS
- *Suspensions*
- *Colloids*
- *Solving Problems with Solution Properties*

Chapter 14

SOLUTIONS

Water covers about 70% of the earth's surface, yet many consider water scarcity to be one of the world's greatest health issues. Over 1.1 billion people do not have an adequate source of clean water. That's more than 14% of the world's population.

You may be wondering if there is so much water on the earth, why do so many people struggle to find water to drink? For some, there simply is no source of fresh water nearby. (The vast majority of Earth's water is salt water.) Even when we have fresh water, pollution is a big issue. Between water's salt content and contamination, much of the planet's available water is not potable. Therefore, many people suffer from dehydration, parasites, cholera, dysentery, and other conditions.

A growing issue is chemical pollution, fed by sources such as agriculture, manufacturing, and chemical and pharmaceutical industries. Throughout this chapter, we will investigate the use of chemical solutions and other means to remove hazardous dissolved chemicals from the water that people desperately need.

LAB ACTIVITIES

Lab 14A: *One Giant Solution*—Students create a solubility curve.

Lab 14B: *Sugar, Sugar*—Students determine the sugar content in beverages.

The Chapter opener shows an image of clean water in the hands of children in Africa. Although 2.6 billion people have been able to get access to improved drinking water since 1990, there are still roughly 785 million people who rely on contaminated water sources for survival.

14.1 THE DISSOLVING PROCESS

Defining Solutions

We use solutions and their properties when we add antifreeze to a car's radiator, spread salt on an icy sidewalk, wear sterling silver, disinfect a cut, or clean windows. Many chemical reactions take place in solution. People breathe a solution called air, and most of the human body is a water-based solution. The study of chemistry is saturated with solutions!

Shampoos, soft drinks, and perfumes are mixtures of many ingredients. Their ingredients do not clump together, separate from each other, or fall to the bottom of a container. Their components cannot be filtered out because they are very small, typically less than 1 nm. These products are homogeneous mixtures since their compositions are uniform. They are not compounds because they are physically combined, not chemically bonded together.

Why is it so difficult to dissolve sugar in my iced tea?

The substances mentioned above are all **solutions**—homogeneous mixtures of variable composition in a single phase. The most abundant substance in a solution is called the **solvent**. In shampoo and soft drinks, the solvent is water; in perfume, the solvent is often an alcohol. Dissolved substances are called **solutes**. Solutes dissolved in a solvent make a solution.

QUESTIONS
- » What are the parts of a solution?
- » Are there different types of solutions?
- » Why doesn't everything dissolve?
- » How can I get sugar to dissolve more quickly in my tea?
- » How can I get more sugar to dissolve in my tea?

TERMS
solution • solvent • solute • miscibility • solvation • dissociation • ionization • enthalpy of solution • solubility • unsaturated solution • saturated solution • supersaturated solution • Henry's law

Properties of Solutions

- Solutes cannot be filtered out of a solution.
- Solutes do not settle out of a solution.
- Solutions are uniform.
- Solutions are not chemically combined.
- Solutions can vary in their concentrations.

SECTION 14.1 *OVERVIEW*

Essential Question

Why is it so difficult to dissolve sugar in my iced tea?

Objectives

- » **14.1.1** Describe the parts of a solution.
- » **14.1.2** Categorize examples of solutions.
- » **14.1.3** Explain why certain solutes do not dissolve in certain solvents.
- » **14.1.4** Explain how varying conditions will affect the rate of dissolving.
- » **14.1.5** Solve solubility problems using a solubility curve.
- » **14.1.6** Compare unsaturated, saturated, and supersaturated solutions.

Resources

Case Study: Pharmaceutical Pollution

Demonstrating a Supersaturated Solution

Web Links: Polarity and Solubility, Hot Ice

Mini Lab: *Off to the Races*; Lab 14A: *One Giant Solution*—Making a Solubility Curve

ENGAGE

RECALLING MIXTURES

Activate prior knowledge with a **game** of "Mixture Pictionary." Before beginning, ask students to define what a mixture is. They may recall from Chapter 2 that a mixture is two or more substances that are physically combined in a variable ratio. They may be either heterogeneous or homogeneous. The components within heterogeneous mixtures retain their physical properties and are easily separated. The components within a homogeneous mixture cannot be easily seen nor separated.

Setting Up: Create approximately twenty note cards with examples of different homogeneous and heterogeneous mixtures. Prepare a dry erase board by separating it into two parts with a line dividing the sides. Have students split into two separate groups. Explain that one person from each group will compete simultaneously against one person in the other group to see which group can draw a mixture (can be heterogeneous or homogeneous) and have their team guess the quickest-drawn mixture. They can either

(continued)

select from a preselected mixture that you created or come up with their own mixture, but it must be identifiable.

Playing the Game:

1. Select one person from each group to draw an example of a mixture. They must preselect a card with a predetermined mixture or must tell you what they plan to draw.
2. Set a timer for one minute and have the teams simultaneously draw the mixture on the board. If the team doesn't correctly answer within that minute, the time stops, and the next player draws and tries to get his team to correctly guess his mixture.

Winning the Game: Points are awarded for correct answers given within the allotted time. To determine the winner, tally up the points. The team with the most points has won the game of Mixture Pictionary!

INSTRUCT

MISCIBLE LIQUIDS

Stress that the term *miscible* applies only to liquids.

TYPES OF

Solutions

miscible
seawater

LIQUID SOLUTIONS

Most of the solutions that we use are liquids because the solvent is a liquid. Liquid solvents can dissolve solids, other liquids, and even gases. Sweetened tea and seawater are common examples of solutions made by dissolving solid solutes in a liquid solvent.

A common liquid-liquid solution is rubbing alcohol. Rubbing alcohol is a mixture of 30% water and 70% isopropyl alcohol. Both the solute and solvent are liquids. But not all liquid-liquid mixtures form a solution. We all know that oil and water don't mix. Scientists use the term **miscibility** to describe whether two liquids will mix to form a solution. When two liquids, like alcohol and water, mix to form a homogeneous mixture, they are said to be *miscible*. But liquids that separate after mixing, like oil and water, are said to be *immiscible*.

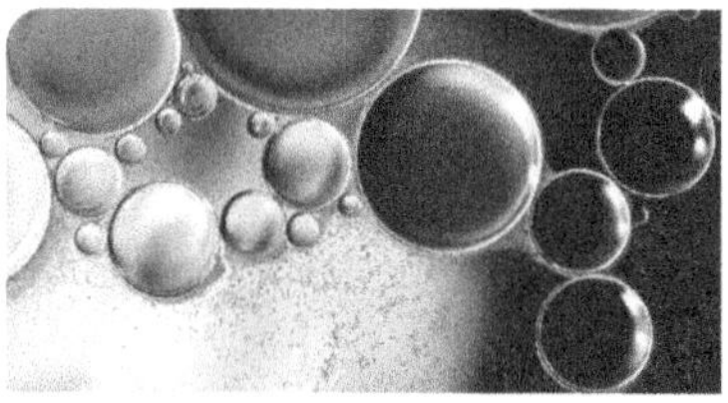

immiscible
oil and water

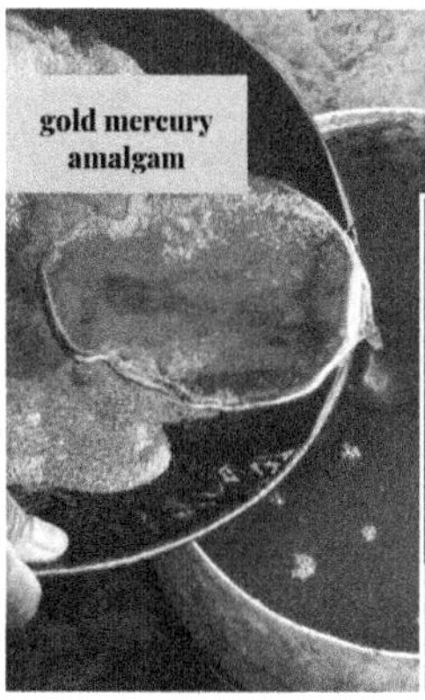

gold mercury amalgam

pewter: *an alloy made with tin, lead, and copper*

SOLID SOLUTIONS

Solids can also act as solvents. Liquids, gases, and even other solids can dissolve in solid solvents. The most common solid-solid solutions are metal alloys. Brass, a copper and zinc alloy, is a blend of the two metals in a uniform mixture. Gold and mercury can form a solid-liquid solution that in the past was used in the process for mining gold. A solution containing mercury is called an *amalgam*. Hydrogen gas can dissolve in palladium metal and produce a solid-gas solution. Scientists have used this process to purify hydrogen by allowing it to dissolve into the metal and then forcing it out with heat.

GASEOUS SOLUTIONS

Gases can also act as solvents. Although some scientists may argue the point, there is only one type of permanent gas solution at ordinary pressures—gaseous solvents dissolving gaseous solutes.

Gases cannot dissolve liquids or solids because the gaseous solvent can't separate liquids and solids into individual particles. The collection of liquid or solid particles is too large to give the mixture a single phase, so the mixture is not considered a solution. Scientists categorize these mixtures as *colloids* or *suspensions* (see Section 14.4). An example of a gaseous solution is the air we breathe. It is a solution of oxygen, carbon dioxide, argon, and trace amounts of other gases dissolved in nitrogen.

SCUBA tanks contain gaseous solutions.

TABLE 14-1 *Solutions*

		Solvents		
		Gas	**Liquid**	**Solid**
Solutes	**Gas**	gas-in-gas (air)	gas-in-liquid (soft drink)	gas-in-solid (H_2 in Pd)
	Liquid	does not exist	liquid-in-liquid (vinegar)	liquid-in-solid (amalgam)
	Solid	does not exist	solid-in-liquid (salt water)	solid-in-solid (alloy)

CASE STUDY

PHARMACEUTICAL POLLUTION

When most of us think of pharmaceutical products, we think of medicines that make us well. But there is a side to pharmaceuticals that is not so beneficial. In recent years, environmental scientists have identified a problem—pharmaceutical pollution in wastewater and ultimately in our water supply.

Most of these dissolved chemicals enter water systems from human waste, which we already know how to remove. Other chemicals enter systems through the disposal of unused chemicals. A small percentage enter the water supply from manufacturing. Today we know the chemicals that are present, but in many cases we need to develop a process for removing them at water treatment facilities.

Questions to Consider

1. Since these chemicals are in solution, why might filtering not eliminate them?
2. What process might work for removing these smaller solute particles?
3. How does the process that you mentioned in Question 2 remove pollution from water?

SOLUTIONS

Lead students to create a **graphic organizer** like Table 14-1 in the Student Edition. You may opt to have students research different solutions to add more examples to their organizer.

CASE STUDY: PHARMACEUTICAL POLLUTION

Answers

1. Filtration is a method of separation that works on the basis of particle size. If the particles are too small, they will pass through the filter.
2. Answers will vary. *Example:* osmosis
3. Answers will vary. *Example:* Osmosis is the process of water moving across a semipermeable membrane due to concentration differences on either side of the membrane. By controlling the solutions in a system, water is moved out of the wastewater, leaving the pollution behind.

INTERMOLECULAR FORCES AND THE FORMATION OF HYDROGEN BONDS

Lead students in a **review** of hydrogen bonds by asking the following questions.

1. Does the forming of hydrogen bonds release or require energy? *(It releases energy.)*
2. What is required for hydrogen bonds to break down? *(energy)*

The Dissolving Process

So how does a solute dissolve in a solvent? For example, how does sugar dissolve in coffee? The dissolving mechanisms for each type of solution are different. To dissolve a substance in a liquid solution, the intermolecular forces within both the solute and solvent must be overcome.

DISSOLVING FOR LIQUID SOLUTIONS

Solvation is the dissolving process in solid-in-liquid solutions. In solvation, the particles of the solvent surround and separate the ions or molecules of the solute. Solvation in water is called *hydration*. The more general term, solvation, describes the dissolving of a solid compound in any liquid solvent. If the solute is an ionic compound, solvent molecules break up the crystal into ions in a process called **dissociation**. In some cases, covalent compounds form ions when they dissolve in solution, a process known as **ionization**.

A Sugar Solution

Dissolving sugar in water provides a good example of how this process works. In a sugar-water solution, the solvent molecules (water) separate the solute particles (sugar molecules) from each other. Before this happens, energy is needed to overcome the attractions between solvent particles. The positive regions of the water molecules attract the negative regions of the sugar molecules. Negative regions of water molecules attract positive regions of sugar molecules in the same manner. Hydrogen bonds form and dispersion forces take effect. The water molecules then pull sugar molecules away from their neighbors. After solvation, diffusion carries the dissolved particles throughout the solution.

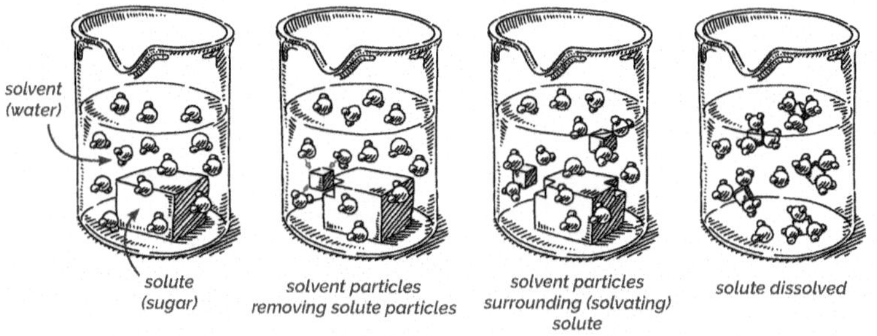

Thermal energy is necessary to overcome the intermolecular forces between the solvent particles and between the solute particles. Therefore, the first steps of solvation are endothermic, absorbing thermal energy from the surroundings. After the separation, solute and solvent particles mix and begin to attract each other. This mixing produces a more stable arrangement of particles, releasing energy. This part of the solution process is exothermic. The net energy change during the dissolving process is the **enthalpy of solution** ($\Delta H_{solution}$), also known as the *heat of solution*. This value, specific to each solute, is expressed in kilojoules per mole (kJ/mol). The concept of enthalpy is discussed more in Chapter 15.

330 Chapter 14

DISSOLVING FOR SOLID AND GASEOUS SOLUTIONS

In solid and gaseous solutions, solute and solvent particles mix predominantly by the process of diffusion. In gaseous solutions, molecules mix by random, constant motion. For solid solutions, mixing typically takes place while the components are in liquid form, allowing diffusion to take place.

MINI LAB

OFF TO THE RACES

Many people find an ice-cold glass of tea refreshing. While we may differ on how sweet tea is supposed to be, many of us like some sugar in our tea.

How can we increase the rate of dissolving?

1. Name two conditions that you think might affect the rate at which sugar will dissolve in water.
2. In relationship to dissolving, what is different between the granulated sugar and the sugar cube?

Procedure

A. Copy the table below onto a piece of paper.

B. Label the four beakers 1–4.

C. Use the laboratory balance and three of the weighing dishes to measure three 3.60 g samples of granulated sugar. Place the sugar cube in the fourth dish.

D. Add 100 mL of room temperature water to Beakers 1–3 and 100 mL of hot water to Beaker 4.

E. Start the stopwatch as you simultaneously add the granulated sugar to Beakers 1, 2, and 4 and the sugar cube to Beaker 3. Stir Beaker 2.

F. Note the time when each sample of sugar finishes dissolving.

Conclusion

3. In which beaker did the sugar dissolve fastest?
4. From your observations, summarize the effect that different conditions had on dissolving the sugar.

Going Further

5. How can we most quickly dissolve sugar in a glass of tea?

EQUIPMENT

- laboratory balance
- beakers, 250 mL (4)
- weighing dishes (4)
- stopwatch
- stirring rod
- marker
- granulated sugar, 11 g
- sugar cube
- room temperature water, 300 mL
- hot water, 100 mL

Beaker	Conditions			Time (s)
	Water	Sugar	Other	
1	room temperature	granulated	none	
2	room temperature	granulated	stirred	
3	room temperature	cube	none	
4	hot	granulated	none	

MINI LAB: *OFF TO THE RACES*

Use this **mini lab** to demonstrate how to increase the rate of dissolving substances.

Answers

1. Answers will vary. Students may say temperature, stirring, surface area, or pressure.
2. The granulated sugar will have more of its surface area exposed to the solvent.
3. Answers will vary. Beakers 2 and 4 should be fastest and Beaker 3 slowest.
4. Increased temperature increased the rate of dissolving. An increased amount of surface area of the solute exposed to the solvent increased the rate of dissolving. Stirring increased the rate of dissolving.
5. Stirring granulated sugar in hot tea allows for the fastest dissolving of sugar.

DIFFERENTIATED INSTRUCTION

Endo Enters, Exo Exits

Use a **mnemonic device** to help students remember the difference between endothermic and exothermic reactions.

Endothermic—Enters: Thermal energy is absorbed.

Exothermic—Exits: Thermal energy is released.

POLARITY AND SOLUBILITY

For an informative video demonstrating how polarity affects solubility, visit TeacherToolsOnline.com. Under Additional Resources, click on Chapter 14 Web Links. Then click on *Polarity and Solubility*.

MIXING POLARITIES

Lead a quick **demonstration** to test for miscibility and immiscibility. Have students set up one mixture of water and vinegar and another of water and oil. You may opt to add food coloring to the water to make the substances more distinct. This will quickly demonstrate that the oil and water will not mix, showing the immiscibility of a polar substance in a nonpolar substance. The vinegar and water will mix, showing that they are both polar and therefore miscible.

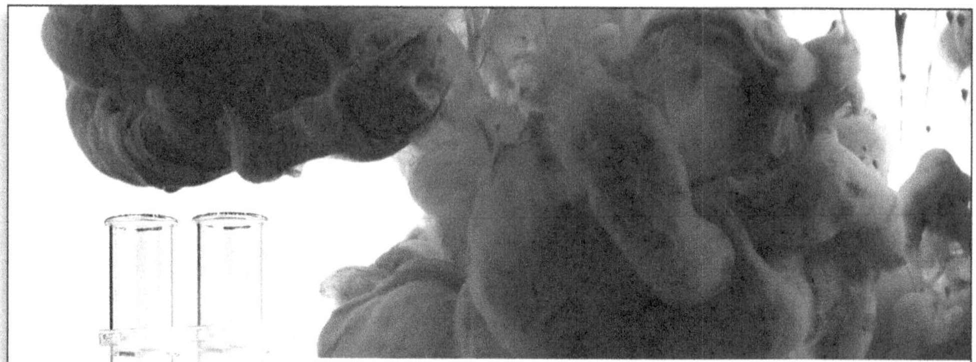

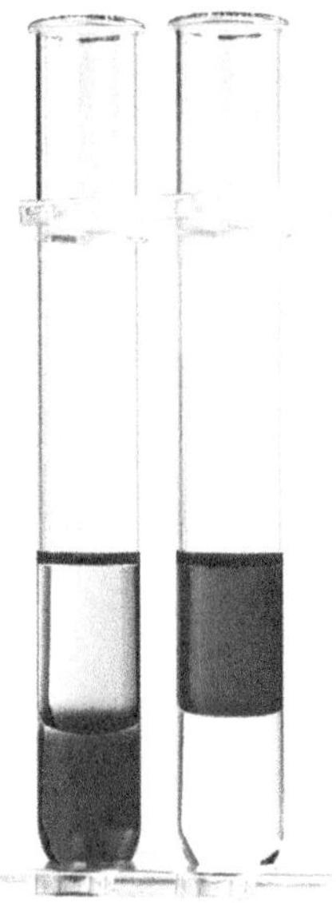

Nonpolar hexane (clear liquid on left) and water (tinted with bromine) are immiscible and remain in distinct phases. Over time the bromine migrates to the hexane (top layer, right) because it is more soluble in hexane than in water.

Solvent Selectivity

Why do isopropyl alcohol and water mix but not oil and water? What determines which substances can mix or dissolve in others? The governing principle in solutions is *like dissolves like.* Polar solvents dissolve polar solutes, and nonpolar solvents dissolve nonpolar solutes.

Ionic compounds and polar covalent molecules have regions of electrical charge. These regions of charge can interact with neighboring ions or with other polar molecules. Isopropyl alcohol (C_3H_8O), acetic acid ($C_2H_4O_2$), ammonia (NH_3), and hydrogen chloride (HCl) are all polar substances. They dissolve in water because of dipole-dipole forces. Electrostatic forces also separate ions, as in a saltwater solution. Positive sodium ions are strongly attracted to the negative pole of water molecules, while negatively charged chloride ions are attracted to the positive pole. When a solute can dissolve in a solvent, it is said to be *soluble* in that solvent. **Solubility** is the maximum amount of a solute that can dissolve in a specific solvent under specific conditions, such as temperature and pressure. Typically chemists report solubility as the mass of solute that will dissolve in 100 mL of solvent.

Nonpolar substances such as hexane, pentane, and petroleum ether cannot mix with polar substances. Consequently, they are pushed out of polar solvents, forming distinct layers in the container. If you were to try to mix water and hexane, they would remain in two layers.

EXAMPLE 14-1: COMPARISONS OF SOLUBILITY

Considering the polarity of methanol, hexane, and aluminum chloride, determine which of the following substances can dissolve in water.

methanol **hexane** **aluminum chloride**

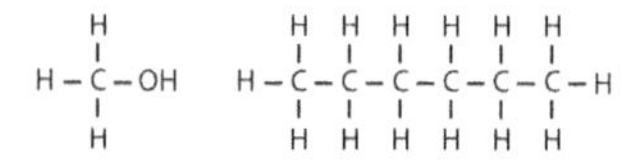

$[Al^{3+}][Cl^-]_3$

Solution

Polar water molecules can dissolve polar methanol molecules and ionic aluminum chloride, but they cannot dissolve nonpolar hexane molecules.

Soluble versus insoluble: NaCl in water (left) and calcium carbonate in water (right)

Like dissolves like is a general rule, but there are several exceptions. Calcium chloride ($CaCl_2$) dissolves in water, but calcium carbonate ($CaCO_3$) does not. Both compounds are ionic, so why aren't both soluble in the polar solvent water? The strength of ionic attractions within compounds accounts for differences in the solubility of different solutes. Dissociation must overcome the lattice energy of the crystalline structures. Some ions so strongly attract each other that a specific solvent cannot break them apart; the solute is *insoluble* in that solvent. Table 14-2 describes the solubility of many ions and compounds. Salts are considered soluble if at least 1 g of solute will dissolve in 100 g of H_2O. They are insoluble if less than 0.1 g of solute will dissolve in 100 g of H_2O. Scientists identify solutes with solubility values between these values as slightly soluble. Substances such as calcium carbonate (chalk), though considered insoluble in water, do have limited solubility. Almost no substances have zero solubility.

TABLE 14-2 *Solubility Rules*

	Soluble (remains aqueous)	Exceptions (forms precipitate)
1	NO_3^-	
2	Li^+, Na^+, K^+, Rb^+, NH_4^+	
3	Cl^-, B^-, I^-	Cu^+, Ag^+, Hg_2^{2+}, Pb^{2+}
4	SO_4^{2-}	Ag^+, Ba^{2+}, Ca^{2+}, Sr^{2+}, Pb^{2+}, Hg_2^{2+}
	Insoluble (forms precipitate)	**Exceptions (remains aqueous)**
5	S^{2-}	Mg^{2+}, Ba^{2+}, Ca^{2+}, Sr^{2+}
6	CO_3^{2-}, PO_4^{3-}	Na^+, K^+, NH_4^+
7	OH^-	Na^+, K^+, Ca^{2+}, Ba^{2+}
8	O^{2-}	Na^+, K^+, Ca^{2+}, Ba^{2+}, Sr^{2+}

EXAMPLE 14-2: SALT SOLUBILITY

Using Table 14-2, determine whether the following salts will be soluble in water.

a. KCl

b. $PbSO_4$

c. BeO

d. MgS

Solution

a. soluble; Line 2 indicates that potassium compounds are soluble.

b. insoluble; Line 4 indicates that sulfate compounds are soluble, but Pb^{2+} is an exception.

c. insoluble; Line 8 indicates that oxides are insoluble.

d. soluble; Line 5 indicates that sulfides are insoluble, but Mg^{2+} is an exception.

SOLUBILITY RULES

Students should recall this solubility rules chart from Chapter 10. If they need a review on how to apply these rules, refer to page 234.

Solution Equilibria

Consider dissolving table salt in a beaker of water. Initially, during the dissociation process, the solution has not yet reached its maximum solubility. Since the solution contains less than the maximum amount of solute that it could hold at the current conditions, we consider this an **unsaturated solution**. The thermal energy required for the dissociation of salt is greater than the thermal energy given off in hydration. Energy is therefore absorbed in the solution process, and the solution becomes slightly cooler.

$$NaCl(s) + \text{heat} \longrightarrow Na^+(aq) + Cl^-(aq)$$

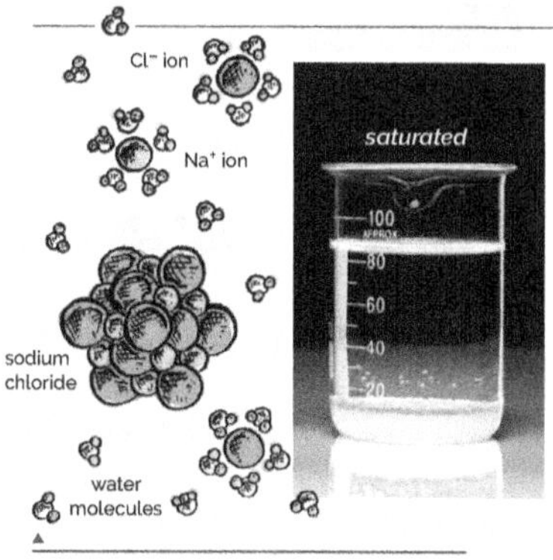

As sodium chloride dissociates, negative portions of water molecules attach to the Na⁺ ions. Positive portions of water molecules interact with Cl⁻ ions.

If we continue to add more and more salt, eventually no more salt appears to dissolve. The temperature and the amount of salt at the bottom of the glass remain constant. When a solution contains the maximum amount of solute at a given temperature, we call it a **saturated solution.** But this condition does not stop the dissolving process. The water molecules are still moving, dissociating ions. The amount of salt at the bottom of the glass remains constant because the reverse process, precipitation, also occurs.

$$Na^+(aq) + Cl^-(aq) \longrightarrow NaCl(s) + \text{heat}$$

When both processes occur at the same rate, no noticeable changes occur. This condition is called a *dynamic equilibrium*. We discuss equilibrium reactions more in Chapter 17.

$$NaCl(s) + \text{heat} \rightleftharpoons Na^+(aq) + Cl^-(aq)$$

As strange as it may seem, it is possible to dissolve more than the maximum amount of solute—we call it a **supersaturated solution**. For example, the solubility of sodium thiosulfate ($Na_2S_2O_3$) in water is about 73 g/100 mL at room temperature. But if we raise the temperature of the solution to 100 °C, the solubility increases to 231 g/100 mL; thus, more sodium thiosulfate can dissolve. If the solution is then slowly and carefully cooled back to room temperature, the excess sodium thiosulfate will not crystallize out. Instead, 231 g of sodium thiosulfate remain in 100 mL of water—more than three times the expected amount! Supersaturated solutions are not in equilibrium—they are unstable. A scratch on the inner surface of the container, the addition of a small crystal of sodium thiosulfate, or even a sudden disturbance can cause the excess solute to crystallize rapidly, returning the solution to its saturated level.

334 Chapter 14

Equilibria can also exist for liquid-gas solutions. Carbonated drinks are solutions of carbon dioxide. When you open a bottle of carbonated beverage, carbon dioxide gas escapes with a fizz. If you replace the cap, the escaping gas collects above the liquid in the bottle. As the partial pressure of carbon dioxide increases, the rate at which carbon dioxide escapes from the solution decreases. Eventually, the rate at which carbon dioxide reenters the solution will match the rate at which it leaves the solution. Because the two processes oppose each other, the drink does not lose all its carbonation right away.

FACTORS THAT AFFECT THE *Rate of Solution*

The rate at which a solute dissolves depends on its solubility and the frequency of collisions with solvent particles. The more collisions there are between the solute and solvent particles, the faster the solute dissolves. Temperature, stirring, and the amount of surface area of the solute exposed to the solvent all affect the frequency of these collisions.

The temperature of a solution affects the number of molecular collisions. Consider a glass of warm, unsweetened tea. Which should be put into the tea first—sugar or ice? If the sugar is to dissolve quickly, you should add it first. The faster moving particles in warm tea will dissolve sugar faster than the slower moving particles in iced tea.

Stirring a solvent increases the number of collisions. A moving spoon brings the solvent molecules into contact with the sugar at the bottom of the glass more rapidly.

The number of collisions also depends on the amount of surface area exposed to solvent action, which explains why granulated sugar will dissolve more quickly than a sugar cube will. In a sugar cube, the bulk of the cube shields most of the solute from the solvent. In granulated sugar, the solvent has access to many more sugar molecules. Increased surface area speeds up the rate of dissolving.

Solutions 335

DEMONSTRATING A SUPERSATURATED SOLUTION

Demonstrate the effect of a seed crystal on a supersaturated solution.

Materials: ring stand and ring, wire gauze, laboratory burner, 250 mL Erlenmeyer flask, sodium acetate trihydrate (100 g), wash bottle with distilled water, aluminum foil, clear evaporating dish or watch glass

Note: Perform this demonstration on a hard, nonporous surface in case the solution splashes out and crystallizes.

Preparation: Place the ring on the ring stand and the wire gauze on the ring. Adjust the ring's height so that the laboratory burner will fit underneath. To the flask add 100 g of sodium acetate trihydrate crystals and 10 mL of distilled water. The inside of the flask must be clean and scratch-free, or the solution will instantly crystallize.

Place the flask onto the ring and heat while stirring until all the crystals dissolve. Carefully rinse the inside of the flask with a small amount of distilled water. Remove the flask from the ring. Cover the flask with aluminum foil and let it cool to room temperature (one to three hours). Be careful handling the flask; simply moving it might cause the solution to crystallize.

Performance/Discussion: Before starting the demonstration, remove the foil from the flask and ensure that the sodium acetate trihydrate has not precipitated. If it has, the preparation steps must be repeated. Add 1 g of sodium acetate trihydrate crystals to the evaporating dish. Slowly pour the supersaturated solution over the crystals and watch a tall "stalagmite" form. Point out to students that the stalagmite is warm to the touch, and then ask them what that means. They should determine that the reaction is exothermic.

Cleanup: Place the stalagmite in a beaker, cover with plastic wrap, label, and save for next year. Or you may decide to crush the stalagmite with a mortar and pestle to reuse the crystals. You can also reverse the reaction by placing the stalagmite in a beaker with a little water and heating until a supersaturated solution is formed.

HOT ICE

As an alternative to the demonstration above, you may want to show a video of the creation of "hot ice." A video entitled "Hot Ice" shows the rapid crystallization of sodium acetate initiated by a seed crystal in a supersaturated solution. To see the video, visit TeacherTools Online.com. Under Additional Resources, click on Chapter 14 Web Links. Then click on *Hot Ice*.

THE DISSOLVING PROCESS

As a **formative assessment**, have students answer the following questions.

1. What type of mixtures are solutions? *(homogeneous)*
2. Is CH_4 soluble or insoluble in water? *(insoluble)*
3. Describe how we know when a solution is saturated. *(when it can dissolve no more solute at its current temperature and pressure)*
4. What three factors affect the rate of solutions? *(temperature, stirring, and increased surface area; Students may also mention pressure for gaseous solutes.)*

RATE OF SOLUTION VERSUS SOLUBILITY

Use **word association** to help students remember the difference between rate of solution and solubility. The *rate of solution* refers to how fast (fast = speed = rate) something dissolves or becomes a solution. *Solubility* has to do with how much solute can dissolve in a specific solvent under specific conditions, such as temperature and pressure.

FACTORS THAT AFFECT

Solubility

TEMPERATURE

Solid and Liquid Solutes

Will the solubility of a solute increase or decrease as temperature increases? In general, higher temperatures help more of a solid and liquid dissolve by increasing the space between the solvent particles. Increased temperature also increases solubility because most solids and liquids require thermal energy to dissolve. Suppose that a saturated solution of potassium chlorate ($KClO_3$) is at equilibrium.

$$KClO_3(s) + \text{heat} \rightleftharpoons K^+(aq) + ClO_3^-(aq)$$

Adding thermal energy is equivalent to adding more of a reactant. This energy favors the forward reaction, causing more of the potassium chlorate to dissolve until the solution reaches a new equilibrium position.

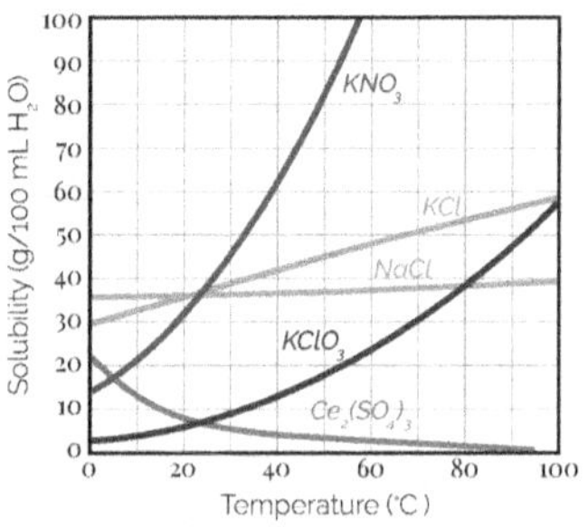

The graph above shows the solubility of different substances at temperatures from 0 °C to 100 °C. We can see on the graph the solubility curve for $KClO_3$, which shows how much $KClO_3$ can be dissolved in 100 mL of water.

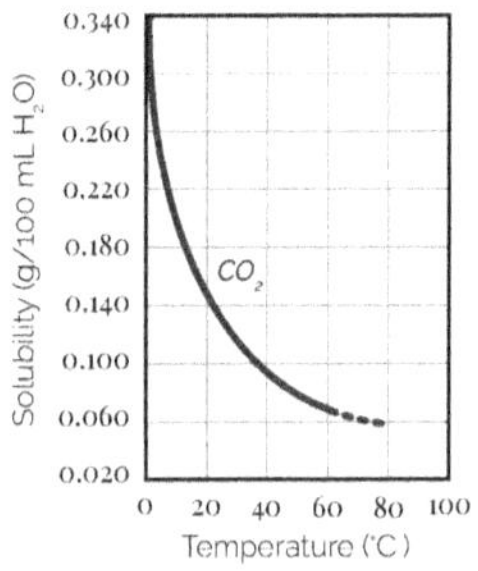

Gaseous Solutes

However, when gases dissolve, the opposite usually occurs—thermal energy is released.

$$CO_2(g) + H_2O(l) \rightleftharpoons H_2CO_3(aq) + \text{heat}$$

We could, therefore, think of thermal energy as a product of the process. Adding thermal energy is equivalent to adding more product to the reaction vessel. This additional energy drives the reverse reaction and causes carbon dioxide to escape from the solution until it establishes a new equilibrium position. Note on the graph at left how the solubility of carbon dioxide changes with temperature.

EXAMPLE 14-3: SOLUBILITY AND TEMPERATURE CHANGE

Use the solubility curves above to answer the following questions.

a. What is the solubility of KNO_3 in 100 mL of water at 50 °C?

b. At what temperature is the solubility of CO_2 0.160 g in 100 mL of water?

Solution

a. Enter the graph on the *x*-axis at 50 °C, move vertically until you intersect the KNO_3 curve, and then move horizontally until you reach the *y*-axis. The solubility of KNO_3 is approximately 83 g.

b. Enter the graph on the *y*-axis at 0.160 g, move horizontally until you intersect the CO_2 curve, and then move vertically until you reach the *x*-axis. The temperature is approximately 18 °C.

GASES AND PRESSURE

Make sure that students realize that Henry's law is just for gases; pressure has very little effect on the solubility of liquids and solids. When a gas is being dissolved into a liquid, air pressure helps push the gas into the liquid. When a liquid or solid is being dissolved, it is not being pushed by air pressure into the solution, so pressure has minimal effect.

EXAMPLE 14-4: SOLUBILITY AND TEMPERATURE CHANGE

Use the solubility curves on the previous page to answer the following questions about the solubility of various compounds in water at different temperatures.

a. Which compound is the most soluble at 0 °C?

b. Which compound is the most soluble at 60 °C?

c. Which compounds show decreasing solubility as the temperature increases?

Solution

a. NaCl

b. KNO_3

c. $Ce_2(SO_4)_3$ and CO_2

Pressure

While pressure had little effect on the solubility of solid and liquid solutes, pressure drastically affects the solubility of gases in liquids. **Henry's law** states that the solubility of a gas is directly proportional to the partial pressure of the gas above the solution. We use the formula

$$\frac{S_1}{P_1} = k,$$

where *S* is the solubility of a gas at different partial pressures (*P*).

This law is vividly illustrated whenever we open a bottle of soda. Opening the bottle reduces the pressure from 385 kPa to atmospheric pressure, and the solubility of carbon dioxide in the beverage decreases, allowing the excess gas to escape. The escape of a gas from a liquid-gas solution is called *effervescence*.

14.1 SECTION REVIEW

1. Give an example of a liquid solution, a solid solution, and a gaseous solution.
2. Predict whether each of the following pairs of liquids is miscible or immiscible.
   a. olive oil and avocado oil
   b. gasoline and water
   c. iced tea and salt water
   d. olive oil and tea
3. Why do you think that water is often called the universal solvent? What makes it such a good solvent?
4. Define *solubility*.
5. Compare unsaturated, saturated, and supersaturated solutions.
6. Using the kinetic-molecular theory, explain each of the following observations.
   a. Sugar dissolves faster in hot coffee than it does in cold coffee.
   b. Finely ground salt dissolves faster than large chunks of salt do.
   c. Solutes dissolve faster when stirred.
7. Use the solubility curves on page 336 to answer the following questions.
   a. What is the solubility of KCl at 35 °C?
   b. At what temperature is 30 g the solubility of $KClO_3$?
   c. Consider the curve for KNO_3. What locations on the graph represent supersaturated, saturated, and unsaturated solutions?
8. Will a carbonated drink go flat faster if it is heated? Why?

Solutions 337

14.1 REVIEW *ANSWERS*

1. Answers will vary. *Examples:* liquid: salt water; solid: steel; gaseous: air *(pp. 328–29)*
2. **a.** miscible
   b. immiscible
   c. miscible
   d. immiscible *(all p. 328)*
3. Water can dissolve many different solutes. It is also abundant on our planet. Its polar character and its ability to form hydrogen bonds make it capable of dissolving both ionic and polar covalent substances. *(p. 332)*
4. Solubility is the maximum amount of a solute that can dissolve in a specific solvent under specific conditions, such as temperature and pressure. *(p. 332)*
5. All three terms are related to the solubility of a solute in a particular solvent at a particular temperature and pressure. An *unsaturated* solution is one that contains less solute than the solubility amount, while *saturated* solutions contain the solubility amount for those conditions. *Supersaturated* solutions contain more than the solubility amount of solute. *(p. 334)*
6. **a.** The frequency of collisions is greater in hot coffee.
   b. Finely ground salt crystals expose more solute particles to the solvent.
   c. Stirring increases the number of collisions. *(all p. 335)*
7. **a.** approximately 40 g
   b. approximately 70 °C
   c. supersaturated: above the curve; saturated: on the curve; unsaturated: below the curve *(all p. 336)*
8. Yes. Carbon dioxide becomes less soluble at a higher temperature. Therefore, as the drink is heated, carbon dioxide will escape faster, and the drink will become flat quicker. *(p. 336)*

MORE THAN EFFERVESCENCE

Lead a **discussion** by asking students why it is that a carbonated drink will spray out quickly after it has been shaken or dropped but will not if it is allowed to sit for a while. They should be able to figure out that the drink is a supersaturated solution of CO_2 in a liquid. The agitation causes CO_2 to leave the solution as bubbles that rapidly rise to the surface, much more rapidly than in effervescence. If opening is delayed, much of the gas will reenter the solution and regain equilibrium.

APPLY

LAB 14A: *ONE GIANT SOLUTION*

Once students have an understanding of the material in Section 14.1, they should be ready to work through Lab 14A.

ASSESS

TICKET OUT THE DOOR

Check for understanding with this **summarizing activity**. Ask, "What effect does the increase of pressure have on a solid, liquid, and gas?" *(Increasing pressure increases the solubility of a gas but has little effect on the solubility of a liquid or solid.)*

SECTION 14.2 *OVERVIEW*

Essential Question

How much sugar is really in my soda?

Objectives

» **14.2.1** Define *concentration.*

» **14.2.2** Compare the different ways to report the concentration of solutions.

» **14.2.3** Solve concentration problems.

» **14.2.4** Apply principles of solution concentrations to regulate personal sugar consumption. BWS

Resource

Lab 14B: *Sugar, Sugar*—Determining the Sugar Content in Beverages

ENGAGE

Activate prior knowledge through a one-minute **quick write** activity. Tell students they have one minute to write down the definitions of two terms or concepts from Section 14.1. Once they have finished, have them share with their neighbor what they have written down. As a class, discuss several of the terms or concepts and eliminate any misunderstandings.

INSTRUCT

COMPARING CONCENTRATIONS BY MASS FRACTION

Mass fractions cannot be compared for different substances. For example, while a 10% salt solution is twice as concentrated as a 5% salt solution, it is not necessarily twice as concentrated as a 5% sugar solution.

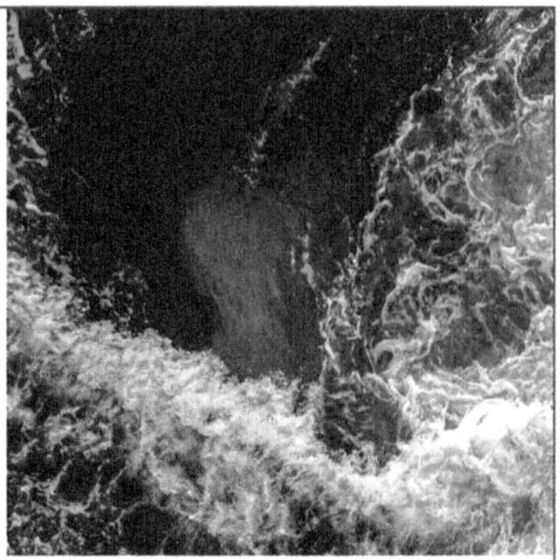

14.2 MEASURES OF CONCENTRATION

QUESTIONS

» How can we describe the amount of dissolved solute?

» How can we calculate the amount of solute needed to make a solution?

TERMS

concentration • mass fraction • volume fraction • amount concentration • molality

How much sugar is really in my soda?

Defining Concentration

What is the best way to describe how much solute is in a solution? Terms such as *diluted* and *concentrated* refer to relative amounts of solute in a solvent. These qualitative descriptions are not sufficient to precisely describe the amount of solute in a solution. Quantitative measurements of solutes are much more useful in chemistry. **Concentration** is a measure of the amount of a solute in a certain volume or mass of either the solvent alone or the entire solution.

The most common ways to express concentration are mass fraction, volume fraction, amount concentration, and molality. Each has its advantages and unique uses. Let's look at each of these calculations.

Mass Fraction

One common method of expressing concentrations compares the mass of the solute with the mass of the solution. Known as **mass fraction**, this method reports the concentration as a decimal value or as a percent. We use the formula

$$w_{\text{solute}} = \left(\frac{m_{\text{solute}}}{m_{\text{solution}}}\right) 100\%,$$

where w_{solute} is the mass fraction, m_{solute} is the mass of the solute, and m_{solution} is the mass of the solution. For example, oceanographers typically measure the salinity, or salt concentration, of seawater using the mass fraction. Typically, ocean water has 3.5 g of dissolved salts in every 100 g of solution.

$$w_{\text{salt}} = \left(\frac{3.5\,\cancel{g}}{100\,\cancel{g}}\right) 100\%$$
$$= 3.5\%$$

Although ecologists often use this measure of concentration, other measures are more common in chemical applications.

Volume Fraction

Another common method of expressing concentrations relates the volume of the solute to the volume of the solution. **Volume fractions** often appear on the ingredient labels of many household products, especially liquid-liquid solutions. Volume fraction is reported as a decimal value or as a percent. We use the formula

$$\varphi_{\text{solute}} = \left(\frac{V_{\text{solute}}}{V_{\text{solution}}}\right) 100\%,$$

where φ_{solute} is the volume fraction, V_{solute} is the volume of the solute, and V_{solution} is the volume of the solution. Vinegar is an example of a solution whose concentration is reported as a volume fraction, as it consists of approximately 5.0% acetic acid by volume. That means that acetic acid contributes 5 mL for every 100 mL of solution. While you may see this measure of concentration used for some foods and medicines, chemists use it infrequently.

Amount Concentration

The most common expression of concentration in chemistry is called **amount concentration**, or *molar concentration*, and compares the moles of solute with the volume of the solution. You will often hear this measurement called *molarity*. The formula for amount concentration is

$$c_{\text{solute}} = \frac{n_{\text{solute}}}{V_{\text{solution}}},$$

where c_{solute} is the amount concentration in moles per liter, n_{solute} is the number of moles of the solute, and V_{solution} is the volume of the solution in liters. For example, a solution containing 6 mol of NaCl per liter of solution has an amount concentration of

$$\frac{6 \text{ mol NaCl}}{1 \text{ L water}} = \frac{6 \text{ mol}}{\text{L}} \text{ NaCl}.$$

You may hear this referred to as a "six molar sodium chloride solution," and it is often written as "6 M NaCl solution."

MOLES AND MOLAR MASS

Lead students through a **review** by asking why moles are used in conversions in chemistry. *(Moles allow scientists to convert easily from a measured quantity [grams] to a known number of particles, that is, Avogadro's number—6.022 × 10^{23}.)*

If students are having difficulty remembering this concept, review how to calculate molar mass (Ch. 11). This is important because they will need to do conversions from grams to moles in many problems throughout this chapter.

STOICHIOMETRY MAP

Lead students to update their stoichiometry **flow charts** from Chapters 11 and 12 by adding the volume of solution. See Appendix M for an example.

Solutions 339

PREPARING SOLUTIONS

Dispel the common misunderstanding that a solvent is the same volume as the solution. For example, if you ask students to make a 100 mL saltwater solution, many will measure out 100 mL of water (the solvent). But when they add the solute (salt), the volume of the solution will increase, changing the amount concentration of the solution.

EXAMPLE 14-5: CALCULATING AMOUNT CONCENTRATION

What is the amount concentration of a solution that contains 3.40 mol of solute in 245 mL of solution?

Solution

Write what you know.

$n = 3.40$ mol
$V = 245$ mL $= 0.245$ L
$c_{solute} = ?$

Write the formula and solve for the unknown.

$$c_{solute} = \frac{n_{solute}}{V_{solution}}$$

Plug in known values and evaluate.

$$c_{solute} = \frac{3.40 \text{ mol}}{0.245 \text{ L}}$$

$$= 13.9 \frac{\text{mol}}{\text{L}}$$

The amount concentration of the solution is 13.9 mol/L.

EXAMPLE 14-6: CALCULATING MOLES FROM AMOUNT CONCENTRATION

You have 0.615 L of a 0.50 M HCl solution. How many moles of HCl does this solution contain?

Solution

Write what you know.

$V_{solution} = 0.615$ L
$c_{HCl} = 0.50$ mol/L
$n_{solute} = ?$

Write the formula and solve for the unknown.

$$c_{HCl} = \frac{n_{solute}}{V_{solution}}$$

$$c_{HCl}V_{solution} = \frac{n_{solute}}{\cancel{V_{solution}}}\cancel{V_{solution}}$$

$$n_{solute} = c_{HCl}V_{solution}$$

Plug in known values and evaluate.

$$n_{solute} = \left(0.50 \frac{\text{mol}}{\cancel{\text{L}}}\right)(0.615 \cancel{\text{L}})$$

$$= 0.31 \text{ mol}$$

The solution contains 0.31 mol HCl.

EXAMPLE 14-7: CALCULATING VOLUME FROM AMOUNT CONCENTRATION

A chemical reaction requires 0.180 mol of silver nitrate ($AgNO_3$). How many milliliters of a 0.800 M solution should be added to the reaction vessel to provide this amount?

Solution

Write what you know.

$n_{AgNO_3} = 0.180$ mol
$c_{AgNO_3} = 0.800$ mol/L
$V_{solution} = ?$

Write the formula and solve for the unknown.

$$c_{AgNO_3} = \frac{n_{AgNO_3}}{V_{solution}}$$

$$c_{AgNO_3}V_{solution} = \frac{n_{AgNO_3}}{\cancel{V_{solution}}}\cancel{V_{solution}}$$

$$\frac{\cancel{c_{AgNO_3}}V_{solution}}{\cancel{c_{AgNO_3}}} = \frac{n_{AgNO_3}}{c_{AgNO_3}}$$

$$V_{solution} = \frac{n_{AgNO_3}}{c_{AgNO_3}}$$

Plug in known values and evaluate.

$$V_{solution} = \frac{0.180 \cancel{\text{mol}}}{0.800 \frac{\cancel{\text{mol}}}{\text{L}}}$$

$$= 0.225 \cancel{\text{L}}\left(\frac{1000 \text{ mL}}{1 \cancel{\text{L}}}\right) = 225 \text{ mL}$$

You will need to add 225 mL of the solution to the reaction vessel.

DILUTING SOLUTIONS

To prepare a solution with a specific amount concentration, chemists add the solute to a small amount of solvent and then dilute the solution up to its required volume. Special pieces of glassware called *volumetric flasks* are carefully calibrated to yield exact amounts of solutions.

We sometimes also have a need to make a solution with a particular amount concentration from a stock solution with a high amount concentration. Let's look at an example of this type of calculation. We can solve many dilution problems with the equation

$$c_1V_1 = c_2V_2,$$

where c is the amount concentration and V is the volume.

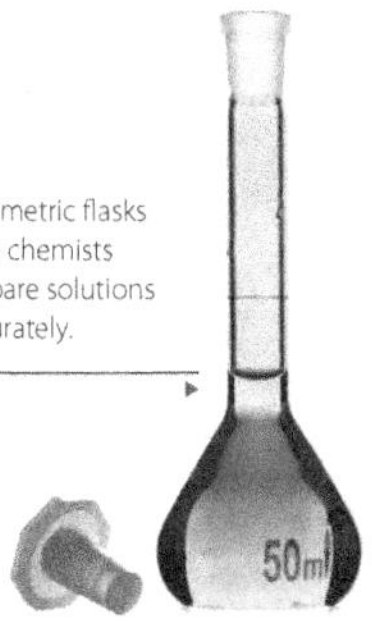

Volumetric flasks help chemists prepare solutions accurately.

EXAMPLE 14-8: CALCULATING VOLUME DURING DILUTION

You need 565 mL of 1.54 M HCl. In the stock room, you have a stock solution of 12 M HCl. What volumes of stock solution and water should you mix to produce the required solution?

Solution

Start by determining the volume of stock solution that will provide the necessary amount of solute.

Write what you know.

$V_{solution} = 565$ mL
$c_{solution} = 1.54$ mol/L
$c_{stock\ solution} = 12$ mol/L
$V_{stock\ solution} = ?$

Write the formula and solve for the unknown.

$$c_{solution}V_{solution} = c_{stock\ solution}V_{stock\ solution}$$

$$\frac{c_{solution}V_{solution}}{c_{stock\ solution}} = \frac{\cancel{c_{stock\ solution}}V_{stock\ solution}}{\cancel{c_{stock\ solution}}}$$

$$V_{stock\ solution} = \frac{c_{solution}V_{solution}}{c_{stock\ solution}}$$

Plug in known values and evaluate.

$$V_{stock\ solution} = \frac{\left(1.54\ \frac{\cancel{mol}}{\cancel{L}}\right)(565\ mL)}{12\ \frac{\cancel{mol}}{\cancel{L}}} = 72.5\ mL$$

Now find the volume of water required to make 565 mL of solution.

Write the formula and solve for the unknown.

$$V_{solution} = V_{water} + V_{stock\ solution}$$

$$V_{water} = V_{solution} - V_{stock\ solution}$$

Plug in known values and evaluate.

$$V_{water} = 565\ mL - 72.5\ mL = 492.5\ mL$$

To make the necessary solution, you will need 72.5 mL of 12 M HCl and 492.5 mL H_2O.

Molality

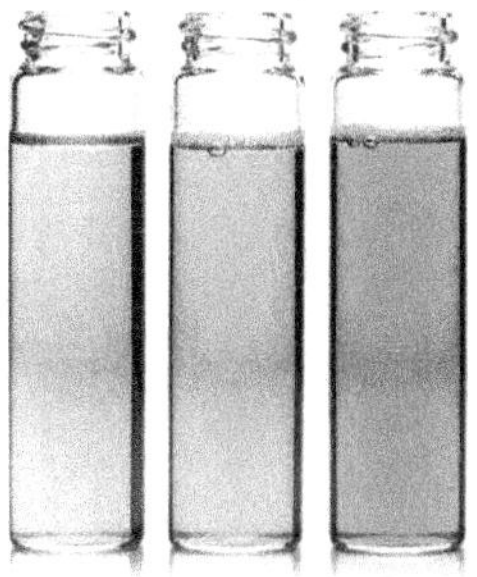

A fourth measure of a solution's concentration is called **molality**, which is the number of moles of solute per kilogram of solvent. We use the formula

$$b_{solute} = \frac{n_{solute}}{m_{solvent}},$$

wheres b_{solute} is the molality of the solution in moles per kilogram, n_{solute} is the number of moles of the solute, and $m_{solvent}$ is the mass of the solvent in kilograms. For example, a solution containing 6 mol of HCl per kilogram of solvent has a molality of 6 mol/kg. You may see this written "6 m HCl solution," which is read as "six molal hydrochloric acid."

Molality has the advantage that it is not affected by changes in temperature and pressure as amount concentration is. You will see one application that uses molality when you study colligative properties in Section 14.3.

DILUTION

Use the following **formative assessment** to check students' understanding.

A volume of 175 mL of a 1.6 M stock solution of LiCl is diluted to 1.0 L. Determine the new concentration of the solution.

What we know: $c_{stock\ solution} = 1.6$ M LiCl,
$V_{stock\ solution} = 175$ mL LiCl,
$V_{solution} = 1$ L $= 1000$ mL LiCl

Unknown: $c_{solution}$

Write the formula and solve for the unknown.

$$c_1V_1 = c_2V_2$$

$$\frac{c_1V_1}{V_2} = \frac{c_2\cancel{V_2}}{\cancel{V_2}}$$

$$c_2 = \frac{c_1V_1}{V_2}$$

Evaluate.

$$c_{solution} = \frac{(1.6\ mol/L\ LiCl)(175\ \cancel{mL})}{1000\ \cancel{mL}}$$

$$= 0.28\ mol/L\ LiCl$$

APPLY

LAB 14B: *SUGAR, SUGAR*

Once students have an understanding of the material in Section 14.2, they should be ready to work through Lab 14B.

ASSESS

TICKET OUT THE DOOR

As a **summarizing activity**, assess students' understanding by asking them to describe how to find the amount concentration of a solute. *(Find the moles of solute per volume of solution.)*

14.2 REVIEW *ANSWERS*

* An asterisk following a question number indicates that a worked-out solution can be found on pages 355A–55B.

1. Concentration is a measure of the amount of a solute in a certain volume or mass of the solvent or of the solution itself. *(p. 338)*

2.* 4.8% *(p. 338)*

3.* 39 mL *(pp. 339–40)*

4. Amount concentration compares the moles of solute with the volume (in liters) of the entire solution. *(p. 339)*

5.*a. 0.965 mol/L $NaNO_3$

b. 0.62 mol NaOH

c. 72.9 g K_2SO_4

d. 0.2669 L *(all pp. 339–40)*

6.* 0.465 L *(p. 341)*

7.*a. 1.75 mol/kg NaCl

b. 6.76 mol/kg $C_2H_6O_2$

c. 4.85 kg

d. 805 g KI *(all pp. 341–42)*

SEM of sodium nitrate

EXAMPLE 14-9: MOLALITY CALCULATION

What is the molality of a solution composed of 31.2 g of sodium nitrate ($NaNO_3$) dissolved in 415 g of water?

Solution

Write what you know.

$m_{NaNO_3} = 31.2\text{ g }NaNO_3$

$m_{H_2O} = 415\text{ g }H_2O = 0.415\text{ kg }H_2O$

$n_{NaNO_3} = ?$

$b_{NaNO_3} = ?$

Convert mass sodium nitrate into moles.

$$31.2\text{ g }NaNO_3\left(\frac{1\text{ mol }NaNO_3}{85.00\text{ g }NaNO_3}\right) = 0.36\underline{7}\text{ mol }NaNO_3$$

Write the formula and solve for the unknown.

$$b_{solute} = \frac{n_{solute}}{m_{solvent}}$$

Plug in known values and evaluate.

$$b_{NaNO_3} = \frac{0.36\underline{7}\text{ mol }NaNO_3}{0.415\text{ kg}} = 0.884\ \frac{\text{mol}}{\text{kg}}\ NaNO_3$$

Your solution has a molality of 0.884 mol/kg $NaNO_3$.

14.2 SECTION REVIEW

1. Define *concentration.*
2. What is the mass fraction of a solution made by dissolving 6.3 g NaCl in 125.0 g H_2O?
3. A scientist is working with 460.0 mL of vinegar solution with an 8.5% volume fraction. How much vinegar does the solution contain?
4. What does amount concentration compare?
5. Solve the following solution concentration problems.
   a. What is the amount concentration if we dissolve 38.97 g of sodium nitrate ($NaNO_3$) in water to make 475 mL of solution?
   b. How many moles of sodium hydroxide (NaOH) need to be dissolved in 725 mL of solution to produce a 0.85 M NaOH solution?
   c. What mass of solute should you measure out to prepare 0.550 L of 0.761 M K_2SO_4 solution?
   d. What volume of solution will produce a 1.750 M KNO_3 solution using 47.23 g KNO_3?
6. A scientist needs to dilute a 9.75 M HCl stock solution so that he has 2.54 L of 1.75 M HCl solution. How much stock solution does he need to add to water to make his new solution?
7. Solve the following solution concentration problems.
   a. A scientist dissolves 4.51 moles of sodium chloride (NaCl) in 2.57 kg of water. What is the molality of the solution?
   b. A radiator contains a mixture of 3.25 kg of ethylene glycol ($C_2H_6O_2$) in 7.75 kg of water. Calculate the molality of this solution.
   c. While making jelly, a confectioner boils a sugar solution, removing water, until it is a 2.74 molal sucrose ($C_{12}H_{22}O_{11}$) solution with 4.55 kg $C_{12}H_{22}O_{11}$ in it. How much water remains?
   d. How many grams of potassium iodide are needed to make a 2.77 m KI solution using 1.75 kg of water?

342 Chapter 14

14.3 COLLIGATIVE PROPERTIES

As solutes are introduced to solutions, those solutions begin to behave differently than their pure solvents do. Vapor pressure, boiling point, freezing point, and osmotic pressure all change as the number of particles in the solution increases. **Colligative properties** are those properties of solvents that change as the number of solute particles in the solution change.

QUESTIONS

- Do dissolved particles change the physical properties of solvents?
- Why do they put rock salt in ice cream makers?
- What is osmosis?

TERMS

colligative property • vapor pressure depression • boiling point elevation • freezing point depression • osmosis • osmotic pressure

Vapor Pressure Depression

How can the same substance be both an antifreeze and a coolant?

At the surface of a solution, solute particles fill positions that are normally occupied by solvent molecules. If the solute is less likely to become a gas—that is, it is less *volatile*—fewer of the more volatile solvent particles will have access to the surface. Since fewer solvent particles have a chance to evaporate, the vapor pressure of the solution is lower than the vapor pressure of the pure solvent. This lowering of vapor pressure due to the presence of solute particles in a solution is called **vapor pressure depression**.

If we add a mole of sugar to a liter of water, the vapor pressure of the solution will be lower than that of pure water. If we add a mole of sodium chloride to a liter of water, the vapor pressure will be even lower. This is because sodium chloride, an ionic compound, dissociates into Na^+ and Cl^- ions, while covalent sugar remains as an intact molecule when dissolved. The larger number of particles in the salt solution more effectively lowers the vapor pressure. If we dissolve aluminum chloride ($AlCl_3$) in a liter of water, four moles of ions for every one mole of aluminum chloride will be released, further decreasing the vapor pressure.

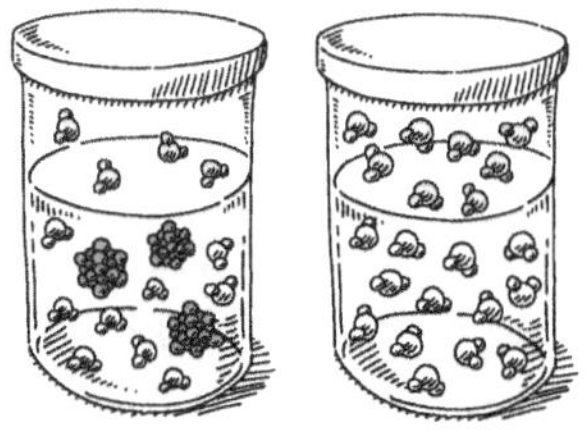

▲ The presence of the solute particles in the solution (left) causes a lower vapor pressure than in the pure solvent (right).

ENGAGE

CHANGE IN PROPERTIES OF SOLVENTS

Lead students to participate in a **think-pair-share**. Before beginning, remind them that in the last section we learned how to calculate a solution's mass fraction, volume, and molality. To get them thinking about the properties of newly created solutions, ask, "Once solutes are added to solvents, what properties of solvents do you think change?"

Give students some time to think about their answers and have them pair up with a classmate to share responses. Once they have finished sharing, select several to discuss their answers with the class. After a short discussion, you can segue into the section to talk about the colligative properties of solvents that change after a solute is added to a solution.

SECTION 14.3 *OVERVIEW*

Essential Question

How can the same substance be both an antifreeze and a coolant?

Objectives

- » **14.3.1** Define *colligative property*.
- » **14.3.2** Relate colligative properties to changes in concentration.
- » **14.3.3** Calculate boiling point elevation and freezing point depression.
- » **14.3.4** Explain the process of osmosis.
- » **14.3.5** Explain how colligative properties are used to benefit people. BWS

Resources

How It Works: Reverse Osmosis

Web Link: Osmosis

INSTRUCT

DELTA SYMBOL = CHANGE

The Greek letter *delta* (Δ) will be used in future chapters, so make sure that students know that it indicates change.

Boiling Point Elevation

Recall that boiling occurs when the vapor pressure of a liquid is equal to or exceeds the atmospheric pressure. Since the presence of solute particles lowers the vapor pressure, the vapor pressure at the expected boiling point will be lower than atmospheric pressure. Therefore, the solution will have to be heated more to raise the vapor pressure to atmospheric pressure. We call this **boiling point elevation** (ΔT_b)—the phenomenon that occurs when solute particles raise the boiling point of a solution.

A 1 molal (1 mol sugar/1 kg water) solution of sugar in water boils at 100.512 °C—an increase of 0.512 °C. The change in boiling temperature is the difference between the new boiling point and the original boiling point.

$$\Delta T_b = T_2 - T_1$$

For water, 1 mol of particles—molecules, atoms, or ions—in 1 kg of water elevates the boiling point of water 0.512 °C. This value is called the *molal boiling point constant (K_b)* for water. Other solvents have their own unique molal boiling point constants, as shown in Table 14-3.

As we dissolve more particles in a solution, the boiling point elevation increases. We calculate this value using the equation

$$\Delta T_b = iK_b b_{solute},$$

where ΔT_b is the change in boiling point in degrees Celsius, K_b is the molal boiling point constant for the solvent, and b_{solute} is the molality of the solution. The i in the formula is the van't Hoff factor, which accounts for the number of particles dissolved for each molecule or formula of the solute. In this textbook, we will assume that all molecules remain together and all ions dissociate completely. Therefore, for sugar, $i = 1$; for NaCl, $i = 2$; and for $AgCl_3$, $i = 4$.

A concentrated sugar solution boils at a temperature well above 100 °C.

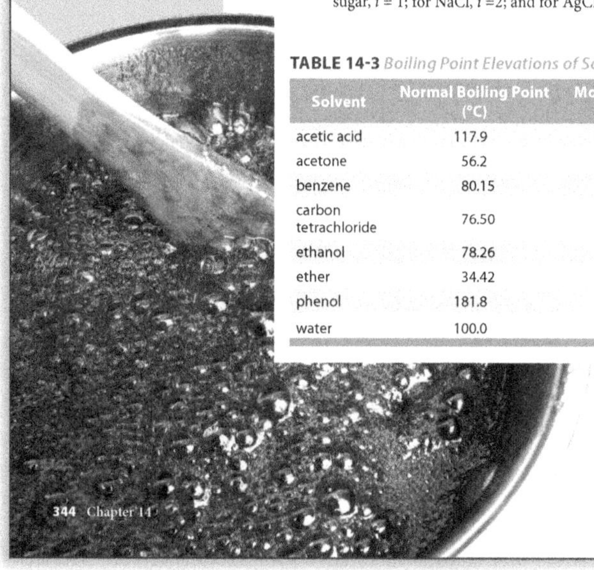

TABLE 14-3 *Boiling Point Elevations of Solvents*

Solvent	Normal Boiling Point (°C)	Molal Boiling Point Constant (K_b) (°C·kg/mol)
acetic acid	117.9	3.07
acetone	56.2	1.71
benzene	80.15	2.53
carbon tetrachloride	76.50	5.03
ethanol	78.26	1.22
ether	34.42	2.02
phenol	181.8	3.56
water	100.0	0.512

Let's look at an example of calculating boiling point elevation in a solution with a molecular solute.

EXAMPLE 14-10: CALCULATING BOILING POINT WITH A MOLECULAR SOLUTE

To make maple syrup, people boil maple sap (sugar water mixture) until the solution concentration is that of 1.34 kg of sugar dissolved in 0.500 kg of water. (Assume that the sugar is all sucrose, $C_{12}H_{22}O_{11}$). What is the final boiling point of this mixture?

Write what you know.

$m_{solute} = 1.34$ kg $C_{12}H_{22}O_{11}$
$i = 1$ (Sucrose is a molecular substance.)
$m_{solvent} = 0.500$ kg
$K_b = 0.512$ °C·kg/mol
$T_1 = 100.0$ °C
$n_{solute} = ?$
$b_{solute} = ?$
$\Delta T_b = ?$
$T_2 = ?$

Convert mass of sucrose to moles of sucrose.

$$1340 \text{ g } C_{12}H_{22}O_{11}\left(\frac{1 \text{ mol } C_{12}H_{22}O_{11}}{342.34 \text{ g } C_{12}H_{22}O_{11}}\right) = 3.914 \text{ mol } C_{12}H_{22}O_{11}$$

Determine the molality of the syrup.

Write the formula and solve for the unknown.

$$b_{solute} = \frac{n_{solute}}{m_{solvent}}$$

Plug in known values and evaluate.

$$b_{solute} = \frac{3.914 \text{ mol } C_{12}H_{22}O_{11}}{0.500 \text{ kg}} = 7.828 \frac{\text{mol}}{\text{kg}} C_{12}H_{22}O_{11}$$

Determine the boiling point elevation.

Write the formula and solve for the unknown.

$$\Delta T_b = iK_b b_{solute}$$

Plug in known values and evaluate.

$$\Delta T_b = (1)\left(0.512 \frac{°\text{C} \cdot \text{kg}}{\text{mol}}\right)\left(7.828 \frac{\text{mol}}{\text{kg}}\right) = 4.007 \text{ °C}$$

Determine the new boiling point.

Write the formula and solve for the unknown.

$$\Delta T_b = T_2 - T_1$$
$$T_2 = T_1 + \Delta T_b$$

Plug in known values and evaluate.

$$T_2 = 100.0 \text{ °C} + 4.007 \text{ °C} = 104.0 \text{ °C}$$

The final temperature is 104.0 °C

The calculation of boiling point elevation in a solution with an ionic solute is identical except for the van't Hoff factor. For an ionic solute, we have to identify the number of ions that each formula unit contributes.

EXAMPLE 14-11: CALCULATING MOLALITY FROM BOILING POINT ELEVATION

What is the molality of a solution of NaCl in water if the solution has a boiling point that is 0.400 °C higher than water?

Write what you know.

$\Delta T_b = 0.400$ °C
$i = 2$ (NaCl is an ionic substance.)
$K_b = 0.512$ °C·kg/mol
$b_{solute} = ?$

Write the formula and solve for the unknown.

$$\Delta T_b = iK_b b_{solute}$$

$$\frac{\Delta T_b}{iK_b} = \frac{iK_b b_{solute}}{iK_b}$$

$$b_{solute} = \frac{\Delta T_b}{iK_b}$$

Plug in known values and evaluate.

$$b_{solute} = \frac{0.400 \text{ °C}}{(2)\left(0.512 \frac{°\text{C} \cdot \text{kg}}{\text{mol}}\right)} = 0.391 \frac{\text{mol}}{\text{kg}} \text{ NaCl}$$

This is a 0.391 m NaCl solution.

BOILING POINT

Lead students to create a **flow chart** for calculating boiling point. Using the steps indicated within the sample problems and formulas, have students create a method of recalling how to solve for boiling point elevation and the change in boiling point.

COMPARING VAPOR PRESSURE AND FREEZING POINT DEPRESSION

Use a **discussion question** to get students thinking about freezing point depression. Ask, "Since solute particles raise the boiling point of a solution, what do you think they will do to its freezing point?" Select students to share their responses with the class and defend their choices. Then explain that in the same way that solute particles lower the vapor pressure of a solution, they also lower its freezing point. During the freezing process, the solute particles interfere with the crystal structure of the solvent as the solvent tries to solidify. Therefore, more thermal energy must be removed (i.e., the temperature must be colder) for the entire solution to freeze.

FREEZING POINT

Lead students to create a **flow chart** for calculating freezing point, as they did with boiling point. Using the steps indicated within the sample problems and formulas, have students create a method of recalling how to solve for freezing point depression and the change in freezing point.

TABLE 14-4 *Freezing Point Depressions of Solvents*

Solvent	Normal Freezing Point (°C)	Molal Freezing Point Constant (K_f) (°C·kg/mol)
acetic acid	16.6	−3.90
benzene	5.48	−5.12
ether	−116.3	−1.79
phenol	40.9	−7.40
water	0.00	−1.86

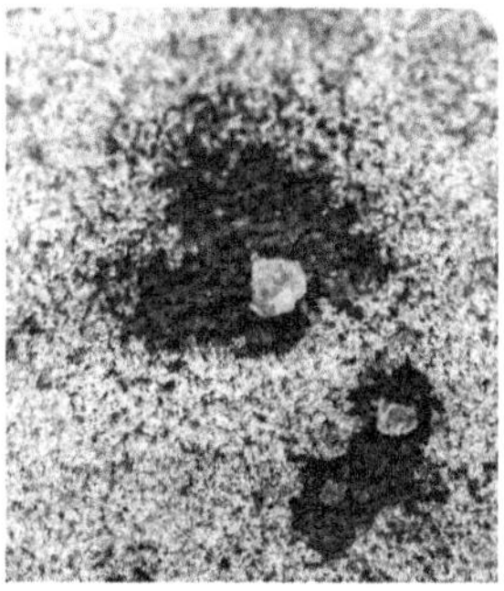

Freezing Point Depression

While dissolving solute in a solution will raise the boiling point, the same solute particles will cause solutions to freeze at temperatures lower than that of their pure solvents. A 1 molal solution of sugar in water freezes at −1.86 °C, which is 1.86 °C lower than the normal freezing point of water. This change in freezing point is called the **freezing point depression** (ΔT_f). This quantity is calculated similarly to boiling point elevation.

$$\Delta T_f = T_2 - T_1$$

As with changes to the boiling point, each solvent has its own *molal freezing point constant* (K_f), which allows us to calculate freezing point depression with the equation

$$\Delta T_f = iK_f b_{solute},$$

where ΔT_f is the change in freezing point in degrees Celsius, i is the van't Hoff factor, K_f is the molal freezing point constant for the solvent, and b_{solute} is the molality of the solution.

One application of freezing point depression is the addition of antifreeze to a car's engine cooling system. Antifreeze is a 25% (by volume) solution of ethylene glycol that depresses the freezing point by about 12 °C. As a dissolved solute, it also raises the boiling point. So the antifreeze in a car's radiator prevents the water in the radiator from freezing in the winter and also prevents it from vaporizing in the summer, which is why it is also considered a coolant.

Another cold weather application of freezing point depression occurs in regions that deal with snow and ice on roads. The salts sodium chloride and calcium chloride are often used to lower the freezing point of water and prevent ice from forming on roads. Calcium chloride ($CaCl_2$) lowers the freezing point of water more than sodium chloride (NaCl) because it dissociates into more ions than sodium chloride does. A mole of calcium chloride dissociates into three, rather than two, moles of ions. The effective concentration of the solution is tripled, rather than doubled, so there is a greater depression in the freezing point. This temperature depression prevents the water from freezing until the water is cooled to lower temperatures. Solid calcium chloride also has the added benefit of actively absorbing water from the air to dissolve itself, thus increasing the rate at which it dissolves and lowers the freezing point.

You might think that calcium chloride would be the natural choice for deicing all roads, but there is a catch. Sodium chloride in its raw form as rock salt is much cheaper than calcium chloride and is often effective enough to get the job done. In locations with heavy precipitation or extremely low temperatures, calcium chloride may be used alone or in combination with sodium chloride.

346 Chapter 14

EXAMPLE 14-12: FREEZING POINT DEPRESSION FOR IONIC COMPOUNDS

Compare the freezing points of aqueous solutions of 3.00 m $CaCl_2$ and 3.00 m NaCl.

Write what you know.

$b_{CaCl_2} = 3.00\ \text{mol/L}\ CaCl_2$
$b_{NaCl} = 3.00\ \text{mol/L NaCl}$
$i_{CaCl_2} = 3$
$i_{NaCl} = 2$
$K_f = -1.86\ °C \cdot \text{kg/mol}$ (water from Table 14-4)
$T_1 = 0.00\ °C$ (water from Table 14-4)
$\Delta T_{f\,CaCl_2} = ?$
$T_{2\,CaCl_2} = ?$
$\Delta T_{f\,NaCl} = ?$
$T_{2\,NaCl} = ?$

Determine the boiling point elevation.

Write the formula and solve for the unknown.

$$\Delta T_f = iK_f b_{solute}$$

Plug in known values and evaluate.

$$\Delta T_{f\,CaCl_2} = (3)\left(-1.86\ \frac{°C \cdot \cancel{kg}}{\cancel{mol}}\right)\left(3.00\ \frac{\cancel{mol}}{\cancel{kg}}\right) = -16.\underline{7}4\ °C$$

$$\Delta T_{f\,NaCl} = (2)\left(-1.86\ \frac{°C \cdot \cancel{kg}}{\cancel{mol}}\right)\left(3.00\ \frac{\cancel{mol}}{\cancel{kg}}\right) = -11.\underline{1}6\ °C$$

Determine the new boiling point.

Write the formula and solve for the unknown.

$$\Delta T_f = T_2 - T_1$$
$$T_2 = T_1 + \Delta T_f$$

Plug in known values and evaluate.

$$T_{2\,CaCl_2} = 0.00\ °C + (-16.\underline{7}4\ °C) = -16.7\ °C$$
$$T_{2\,NaCl} = 0.00\ °C + (-11.\underline{1}6\ °C) = -11.2\ °C$$

The calcium chloride will lower the freezing point to −16.7 °C while the sodium chloride will lower it only to −11.2 °C.

Molecular substances will also lower freezing points. The calculation of freezing point when using a molecular solute is identical to the above example except that molecular solutes will have a van't Hoff factor of 1. We have this scenario when adding antifreeze to a car's cooling system.

Increased Osmotic Pressure

Peel a fresh potato and slice it into strips. Add these immediately to a strong sugar solution. What happens? The semipermeable membrane that surrounds each cell in the potato pieces allows the small water molecules within to pass through it and enter the sugar solution. But the membrane prevents the larger sugar molecules from entering into the cells. Only a few water molecules leave the sugar solution to enter the cells. Many more enter the solution from the water within the cells. As a result, the potato slices will shrink as they lose water. If we wait about thirty minutes and then remove the potato slices, pat them dry, and put them on a balance, we can determine how much water they have lost. The change in mass is due to **osmosis**—the movement of a solvent across a semipermeable membrane due to differences in the solution concentration on each side of the membrane. You may remember osmosis from biology, where living organisms move water in and out of cells through osmosis. In the example of the potato, the solvent is water and the semipermeable membrane is the cell membrane. Osmosis occurs as the water molecules attempt to equalize the concentration on each side of the membrane.

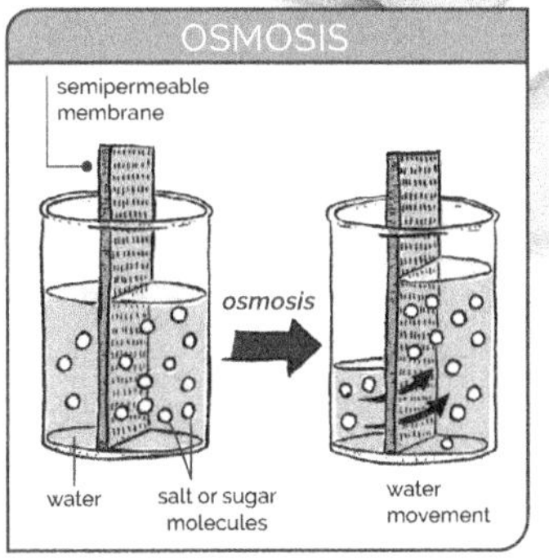

The **osmotic pressure** of a solution is the amount of pressure required to prevent osmosis from occurring. The more solute particles there are in a solution, the greater the osmotic pressure. The osmotic pressure of a solution is a colligative property because it depends on the number of particles in solution.

CORRECTION

In Example 14-12, the subscripts on *K* and *T* are incorrect in the Student Edition but have been corrected in the Teacher Edition. You may want to point out to students that since we are solving a freezing point depression problem, the correct subscript is f.

A LARGE-SCALE SEMIPERMEABLE MEMBRANE

Lead students in a review **discussion** of osmosis. They may recall learning about osmosis during biology. Review the concept that osmosis is the movement of solvent molecules through a semipermeable membrane. Ask students whether they can think of any examples of osmosis. If they have difficulty understanding, provide an example such as a window screen or porch screen being a semipermeable membrane that allows tiny gas molecules to flow freely but prevents the "flow" of insects.

OSMOSIS

For a video demonstrating osmosis in potato slices, visit TeacherToolsOnline.com. Under Additional Resources, click on Chapter 14 Web Links. Then click on *Osmosis*.

DIFFERENTIATED INSTRUCTION

Colligative Properties Project

Direct students to complete a **research project** on three different ways that colligative properties can be used to benefit people. For example, salt (NaCl) and calcium chloride ($CaCl_2$) lower the freezing point of water, helping to melt snow and ice and making roadways safer. Students may choose to create a website, write a paper, create a project board, perform a demonstration, or do a visual or video presentation.

ASSESS

TICKET OUT THE DOOR

Assess students' understanding of colligative properties with a **summarizing activity** by asking them to state three properties that change when a solute is added to a solution. *(Boiling point is raised, freezing point is lowered, and osmotic pressure is increased.)*

14.3 REVIEW *ANSWERS*

* An asterisk following a question number indicates that a worked-out solution can be found on pages 355B–55C.

1. A colligative property is a property of solutions that changes due to the number of particles dissolved in a solution. *(p. 343)*
2. Vapor pressure is related to the number of solvent particles that can enter the vapor phase from the liquid. The presence of solute particles lowers the total number of solvent particles at the surface and therefore decreases the number that can leave the liquid phase. *(p. 343)*
3. Na_3PO_4; It will release 4 mol of ions—3 Na^+ and 1 PO_4^{3-}—and so has the greatest influence. *(p. 343)*
4.* 101.43 °C *(pp. 344–45)*
5.* −5.20 °C *(pp. 346–47)*
6. molality; Boiling point elevation and freezing point depression both involve changing temperatures. Since neither moles of solute or mass of solvent are affected by changes in temperature, molality provides an unchanging measure of concentration. *(pp. 344–47)*
7. Osmosis is the movement of a solvent across a semipermeable membrane due to differences in the solution concentration on each side of the membrane. *(p. 347)*
8. **a.** The osmotic pressure of the solution in the cell is greater than that of the pure water; therefore, water enters the cell. In blood plasma, the osmotic pressures of the cell contents and surrounding plasma are very similar—the cell can handle any small differences in the osmotic pressures.

   b. The osmotic pressure of the solution around the cell is greater than that inside the cell, causing water to leave the cell and making it shrink. *(all p. 347)*

HOW IT *WORKS*

Reverse Osmosis

Osmosis is the movement of a solvent across a semipermeable membrane due to differences in solution concentration. In this section, you learned that the presence of solute particles increases the osmotic pressure—a colligative property. Scientists have discovered a way to use osmosis to address the issue of clean water around the world.

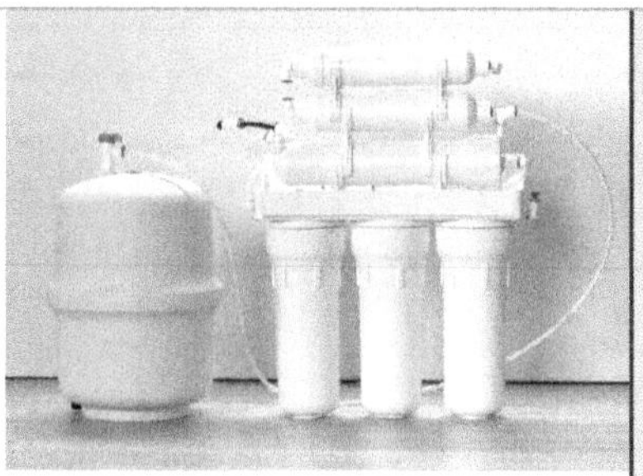

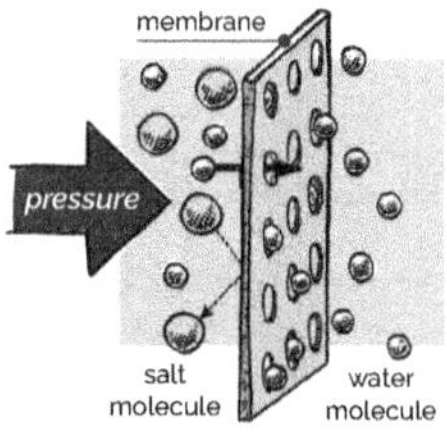

The process to purify water is called *reverse osmosis* (RO). In RO, the solvent is still moving across the membrane, but it is moving *away* from the high concentration solution rather than *toward* it—the opposite, or reverse direction, of what normally happens. In an RO system, the untreated water enters the system under high pressure. This pressure must be higher than the osmotic pressure, and the higher the pressure, the more effective the system. Under this high pressure, the solvent—pure water—leaves the solution and is collected on the "clean" side of the membrane. Depending on the intended use of the water, there may be additional sanitizing steps needed.

RO has many applications, with the most common being desalination to obtain drinking water from seawater. Other applications include drinking water purification, food production, military uses, and aquariums. RO has the advantage of having low energy costs compared with purification processes that involve high temperatures. Current research in RO technology is looking into using nanotechnology in the membrane.

14.3 SECTION REVIEW

1. What is a colligative property?
2. Explain how the presence of solute particles lowers the vapor pressure.
3. If we add one mole each of KCl, NaCl, Na_3PO_4, and $PbSO_4$ to equal amounts of water, which substance causes the greatest decrease in vapor pressure? Explain.
4. What is the boiling point of an aqueous solution of 75.5 g of glucose ($C_6H_{12}O_6$) dissolved in 150 g of water?
5. What is the freezing point of an aqueous solution of 75.5 g of glucose ($C_6H_{12}O_6$) dissolved in 150 g of water?
6. Which measure of concentration do we use in boiling point elevation and freezing point depression calculations? Explain.
7. What is osmosis?
8. Explain why
   a. red blood cells that are placed in pure water absorb water until they burst but do not absorb water when surrounded by blood plasma.
   b. red blood cells shrink when they are in a very concentrated salt solution.

14.4 SUSPENSIONS AND COLLOIDS

Up to this point, we have spent our time discussing solutions—homogeneous mixtures with a single phase. What about heterogeneous mixtures, which have more than one phase? Such mixtures can be further categorized on the basis of their particle sizes and are called either *suspensions* or *colloids*.

How are eggs and Jell-O® related?

QUESTIONS
- » What is a colloid?
- » What is the difference between solutions, suspensions, and colloids?
- » What common substances are colloids?

TERMS
suspension • colloid • dispersed phase • dispersing medium • Tyndall effect • Brownian motion

Suspensions

Solutions are homogeneous mixtures because the dissolved particles are so small that we cannot see them. These particles are typically smaller than 1 nm. **Suspensions**, on the other hand, contain larger particles—greater than 1 µm. These particles are so large that they will eventually settle out of a mixture. This means that a suspension is a heterogeneous mixture. Two common suspensions are aerosols, which consist of a liquid suspended in a gas, and dust—solid particles suspended in a gas. If you have ever dusted the furniture, you know that eventually more dust will settle out of the air.

If solutions have dissolved particles of less than a nanometer and suspensions contain particles larger than a micrometer, what do we call a mixture with particles between a nanometer and a micrometer?

TABLE 14-5 *Particle Size Comparison*

Mixture	Particle Size
solution	< 1 nm
colloid	> 1 nm and < 1 µm
suspension	> 1 µm

Colloids

A **colloid** is a heterogeneous mixture that contains intermediate-sized particles dispersed in a medium. The particles are sometimes called the **dispersed phase**; the medium is called the **dispersing medium**. A very familiar colloid is clouds, which consist of water droplets (dispersed phase) in the air (dispersing medium). The size of particles in a colloid cannot exceed 1 µm since particles any larger quickly settle out from their medium. Intermolecular collisions buffet particles smaller than 1 µm with sufficient force to counteract the constant tug of gravity. Since colloids are different from solutions, terms such as *solute*, *dissolved*, and *solvent* do not apply.

ENGAGE

HOMOGENEOUS AND HETEROGENEOUS MIXTURES

Lead students in a **collaborative mind warm-up** activity. On the board, create a T-chart with headers for homogeneous and heterogeneous mixtures. Do a quick review of the properties of each type of mixture by calling on students to share their answers. As students call out their responses, write the answers under the appropriate header. Have them also create a similar T-chart, which they will add to when learning the material in this section.

INSTRUCT

SUSPENSIONS AND COLLOIDS

Direct students to fill in the **T-chart** they created in the engagement activity, with suspensions under the homogeneous mixture heading and colloids under the heterogeneous mixture heading. Be sure to have them add a brief description and examples for each term.

SECTION 14.4 *OVERVIEW*

Essential Question

How are eggs and Jell-O related?

Objectives

- » **14.4.1** Describe colloids using the terms *dispersing medium* and *dispersed phase.*
- » **14.4.2** Compare solutions, suspensions, and colloids.
- » **14.4.3** Give examples of common colloids.
- » **14.4.4** Explain the importance of water treatment. BWS

Resources

Ethics: Wastewater Management (p. 355)

Demonstrating the Tyndall Effect

Careers: Serving as an Environmental Scientist

DEMONSTRATING THE TYNDALL EFFECT

Demonstrate that colloidal particles reflect light but that particles in a solution do not.

Materials: laser pointer; chalkboard erasers; chalk dust, baby powder, flour, or aerosol hairspray; several different solutions and colloids

Preparation: Fill the erasers with chalk dust or baby powder.

Performance/Discussion: Darken the room, and then turn on the laser pointer and aim it at the wall. *Avoid shining it into anyone's eyes.* Point out that the light is not visible as it passes through the air (a solution) and strikes the wall. It is seen only when it hits an object (in this case, the wall) and is reflected.

Have a student stand at one end of the room and turn on the laser pointer, aiming at the opposite wall. Holding an eraser in each hand, hit the erasers together (or blow dust or powder from your hand) above the laser beam. Walk from the laser to the opposite wall, releasing more particles as you go. As the dust particles fall and enter the path of the laser beam, they reflect the light, making the beam visible. If you don't have chalk dust, powder, or flour, spraying the laser beam with hairspray will give a similar effect.

Conclusion: If you have time, set out several substances and have students use the laser test to determine whether the substances are solutions or colloids. Examples of solutions are water, tea, rubbing alcohol, coffee, and vinegar. Examples of colloids are milk, lotion, muddy water, and gelatin. The colloids can be diluted with water and still exhibit the Tyndall effect.

In a colloid, both the dispersing medium and dispersed phase can be in any of eight possible combinations of states. Mixtures of gases with gases are the exception—they are always solutions. Table 14-6 summarizes the possible combinations of states for colloids.

TABLE 14-6 *Types of Colloids*

Dispersing Medium	Dispersed Phase	Common Name	Examples
Gas	gas	does not exist	
	liquid	liquid aerosol	fog, clouds, mist
	solid	solid aerosol	smoke, dust in the air
Liquid	gas	foam	shaving cream, whipped cream
	liquid	emulsion	hand cream, mayonnaise (oil dispersed in water)
	solid	sol	paint, blood
Solid	gas	solid foam	plastic foam, marshmallows
	liquid	gel	gelatin, jelly
	solid	solid sol	cranberry glass (glass with dispersed metal)

PROPERTIES OF *Colloids*

In 1869, an Irish physicist named John Tyndall demonstrated that the particles in colloids were large enough to scatter light waves. This **Tyndall effect** is often used to distinguish colloids from solutions. A beam of light will pass through a solution without being seen because dissolved particles are too small to disturb light waves. The outline of a light beam will not show up in air because air is a solution. But when a beam of light goes through a colloid, the beam's outline shows up distinctly. The perfect illustration of the Tyndall effect is seen when automobile headlights shine through the air into a patch of fog (a colloid).

Tyndall effect. Can you tell which cylinder contains a colloid and which one contains a solution?

John Tyndall

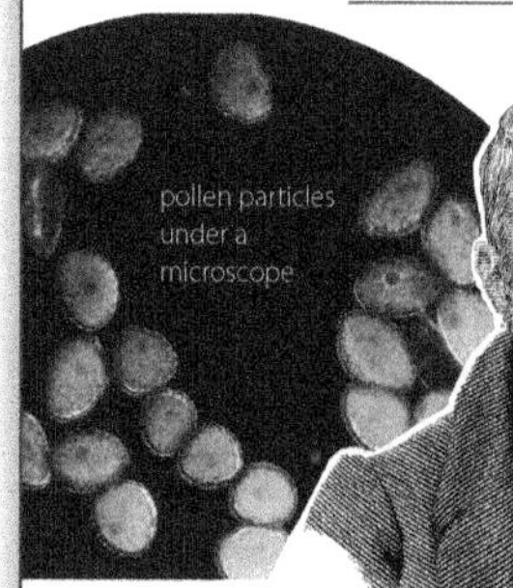

pollen particles under a microscope

A British botanist named Robert Brown discovered major proof for the kinetic-molecular theory by observing a colloid. In 1827, he watched pollen particles dispersed in water. He saw that the pollen particles moved slightly as if many small collisions were jostling them. This type of movement, called **Brownian motion**, results from colloidal particles colliding with fluid particles. This observation led scientists to accept the particle model of matter.

Robert Brown

350 Chapter 14

Solving Problems with Solution Properties

In the Chapter opener, we discussed the challenge of providing clean drinking water to people around the world. Even if we address the issue of the proximity of people to water, we still haven't solved the problem of impurities in the water. Between bacteria, viruses, pollutants, and minerals in the water, we have a lot of work to do to provide clean drinking water to people. The good news is that we can address many of these issues with the chemistry concepts that we have discussed in this chapter.

Practical water treatment involves three steps. First, pathogens are killed by chlorinating the water with chlorine dioxide or a similar compound, forming a dilute solution. Then other compounds are added to clump impurities together, causing *coagulation*. This step, also called *flocculation*, clumps the impurities. This transitions the water from a colloid to a suspension. The suspended particles settle out over time. To speed the process, the water can also be passed through a filtration system. Finally, the water passes through a filter under pressure to quickly remove impurities. Even after all these processes, some toxins remain in the water as they are too small to be removed. As a result, people in some locations still have to boil their water before using it.

CAREERS

SERVING AS AN ENVIRONMENTAL SCIENTIST: ***WATER WATCHER***

The Chapter opener highlights the challenge of providing drinking water to people around the world. While proximity to water is an issue, a much bigger problem are the pollutants that are in the water that may be available. This is a matter of particular interest for many environmental scientists.

Environmental science takes a multidisciplinary approach to solving problems. Environmental scientists need to incorporate knowledge and skills applicable to biology, chemistry, physics, and many other fields. Dr. Christopher Higgins from the Colorado School of Mines is an environmental engineer. Much of his work centers on what happens to organic compounds in wastewater and reclaimed water. He researches how those contaminants interact with biological systems.

Environmental science is an excellent career for someone interested in many fields of science. It is also a career in which you have tremendous opportunities to help others.

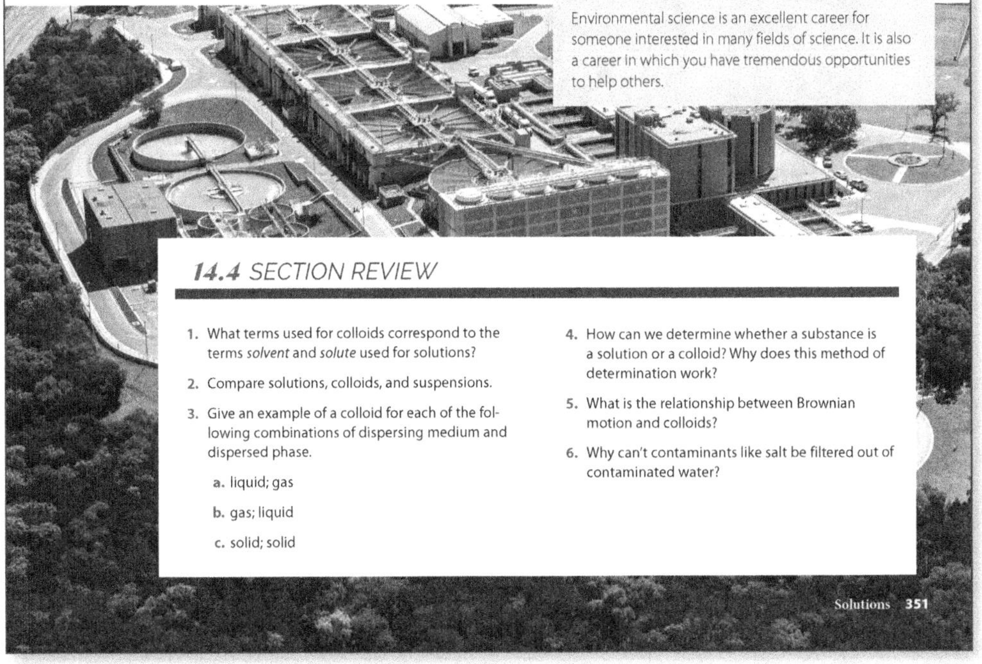

14.4 SECTION REVIEW

1. What terms used for colloids correspond to the terms *solvent* and *solute* used for solutions?
2. Compare solutions, colloids, and suspensions.
3. Give an example of a colloid for each of the following combinations of dispersing medium and dispersed phase.
   a. liquid; gas
   b. gas; liquid
   c. solid; solid
4. How can we determine whether a substance is a solution or a colloid? Why does this method of determination work?
5. What is the relationship between Brownian motion and colloids?
6. Why can't contaminants like salt be filtered out of contaminated water?

DIFFERENTIATED INSTRUCTION

Emergency Water

Lead students to complete a **research paper** on the importance of water treatment and the three best methods for purifying water during an emergency—boiling, chlorinating, and distilling. Direct them to write a paragraph on each method, all of which are endorsed by the American Red Cross. Knowing how each method works might one day save someone's life!

ASSESS

TICKET OUT THE DOOR

Check for understanding with this **summarizing activity**. Ask students to describe the difference between suspensions and colloids. *(Suspensions are heterogeneous mixtures whose particles are large enough to settle out. Colloids have intermediate-sized particles that will not.)*

14.4 REVIEW *ANSWERS*

1. Since the particles in a colloid are not dissolved, the terms *solute* and *solvent* don't apply. The particles are considered the dispersed phase instead of the solute. The material in which the particles are dispersed is the dispersing medium, not the solvent. *(p. 349)*
2. Particle size is the determining factor. Suspensions have the largest particles (greater than 1 μm), which are so large that they eventually settle to the bottom. Colloids have intermediate-sized particles (between 1 nm and 1 μm), which are large enough to scatter light. Solutions have the smallest particles (less than 1 nm), which cannot be macroscopically observed and therefore give the mixture a uniform appearance. *(p. 349)*
3. Answers will vary. *Examples:*
   a. shaving cream, whipped cream
   b. fog, clouds, mist
   c. cranberry glass *(all p. 350)*
4. Apply the Tyndall effect by shining a beam of light through the substance. If the substance is a colloid, it will scatter the light and the beam will be seen. If it is a solution, the beam will not be seen. Colloidal particles are large enough to scatter light, whereas particles in a solution are not. *(p. 350)*
5. The movement of particles is known as Brownian motion, which Robert Brown observed in a colloid. *(p. 350)*
6. Particles in solution are extremely small (less than 1 nm), and there is a limit to how fine a filter can be. *(pp. 327, 351)*

14 CHAPTER REVIEW

Chapter Summary

TERMS
solution
solvent
solute
miscibility
solvation
dissociation
ionization
enthalpy of solution
solubility
unsaturated solution
saturated solution
supersaturated solution
Henry's law

14.1 THE DISSOLVING PROCESS

- Solutions are homogeneous mixtures of variable composition in a single phase. The majority substance is the solvent, and it contains one or more solutes dissolved in it.
- Substances able to dissolve in a given solvent are soluble. Mutually soluble liquids are miscible.
- Solvation is the dissolving process of solids in liquids. First, solvent and solute particles have to be separated from like particles, an endothermic process. Next, the solvent and solute particles attract each other and release energy, an exothermic process. The enthalpy of solution is the change in energy.
- Solubility is the maximum amount of a solute that can dissolve in a specific solvent under specific conditions, such as temperature and pressure.
- A solution is saturated when it can dissolve no more solute at its current temperature and pressure.
- An increase in the temperature of a liquid solvent generally increases the solubility of solid solutes but decreases the solubility of gas solutes.
- An increase in pressure has little effect on the solubility of solids and liquids but increases the solubility of gases.

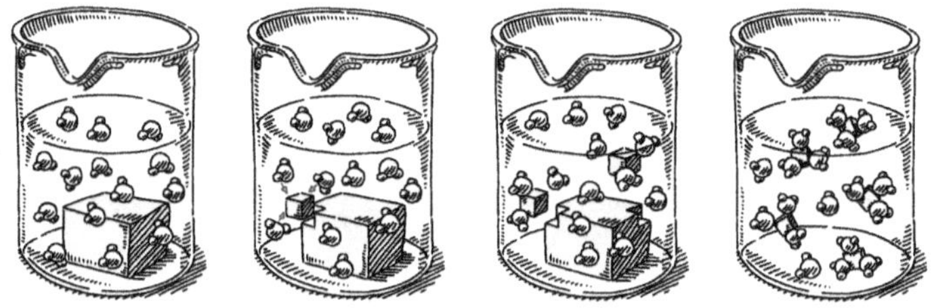

14.2 MEASURES OF CONCENTRATION

- Solution concentration is a comparison of the amount of solute with the amount of solution or solvent.
- The two most useful measures of concentration are amount concentration (moles of solute per liter of solution) and molality (moles of solute per kilogram of solvent).

TERMS
concentration
mass fraction
volume fraction
amount concentration
molality

14.3 COLLIGATIVE PROPERTIES

- Colligative properties are physical properties of a solution that are related to the number of particles in solution.
- Colligative properties include vapor pressure depression, boiling point elevation, freezing point depression, and osmotic pressure.

TERMS

colligative property
vapor pressure depression
boiling point elevation
freezing point depression
osmosis
osmotic pressure

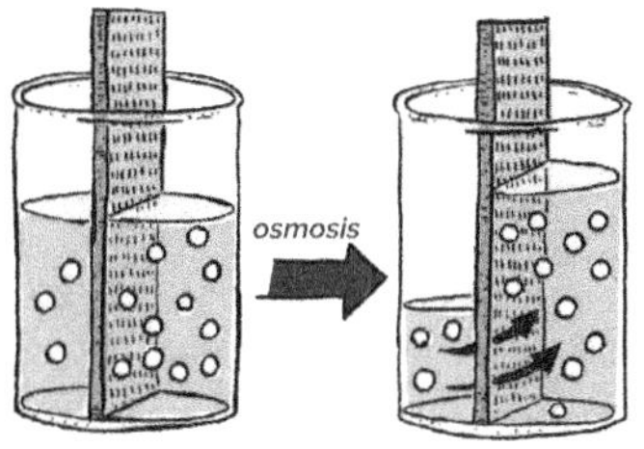

14.4 SUSPENSIONS AND COLLOIDS

- The main factor that determines whether substances will form a suspension, colloid, or solution is particle size.
- Suspensions have large particles that will eventually settle out.
- Colloids have particles of intermediate size—too small to settle out but too large to be considered dissolved.
- The Tyndall effect is the ability of colloidal particles to scatter light.

TERMS

suspension
colloid
dispersed phase
dispersing medium
Tyndall effect
Brownian motion

Chapter Review Questions

RECALLING FACTS

1. Define *solution.*
2. List the five properties of solutions.
3. What is the formula for calculating mass fraction?
4. What does volume fraction compare?
5. How does molality differ from the other measurements of concentration described in this chapter? How is this beneficial?
6. Which is the most common measure of concentration used in chemistry? Which is the least common?
7. How does a solute affect the colligative properties of a solution?
8. Define *freezing point depression.*
9. What is a suspension?
10. Define *colloid.*
11. What determines whether a mixture is a solution, colloid, or suspension?
12. Give an example of a colloid for each of the following combinations of dispersing medium and dispersed phase.
    a. liquid; liquid
    b. gas; solid
    c. solid; gas
13. What is the Tyndall effect? How is it used?

CHAPTER 14 *REVIEW ANSWERS*

Recalling Facts

1. A solution is a homogeneous mixture of variable composition with a uniform appearance throughout. *(p. 327)*
2. **(a)** Solutes cannot be filtered out of a solution.

   (b) Solutes do not settle out of a solution.

   (c) Solutions are uniform.

   (d) Solutions are not chemically combined.

   (e) Solutions can vary in their concentrations. *(p. 327)*
3. $w_{\text{solute}} = \left(\frac{m_{\text{solute}}}{m_{\text{solution}}}\right)100\%$ *(p. 338)*
4. the volume of the solute and the volume of the entire solution *(p. 339)*
5. Molality compares the amount of solute (in moles) with the amount of solvent (in kilograms), while all the other measures compare the amount of solute with the amount of the entire solution. By comparing the amount of solute with the mass of solvent, molality is not affected by changes in temperature or pressure. *(p. 341)*
6. mass fraction; percent by mass *(pp. 338–41)*
7. The greater the number of solute particles, the greater the changes in the property. *(p. 343)*
8. Freezing point depression is a measure of how much lower the freezing point of a solution is compared with the freezing point of the solvent alone. *(p. 346)*
9. A suspension is a heterogeneous mixture with suspended particles larger than 1 µm. *(p. 349)*
10. A colloid is a heterogeneous mixture with intermediate-sized particles (between 1 nm and 1 µm) dispersed in a medium. The particles are called the *dispersed phase*, and the material in which they are dispersed is called the *dispersing medium*. *(p. 349)*
11. Particle size is the determining factor. Suspensions have the largest particles (greater than 1 µm), which are so large that they eventually settle to the bottom. Colloids have intermediate-sized particles (between 1 nm and 1 µm), which are large enough to scatter light. Solutions have the smallest particles (less than 1 nm), which cannot be macroscopically observed and give the mixture a uniform appearance. *(p. 349)*
12. Answers will vary. *Examples:*

    a. hand cream, mayonnaise, oil in water

    b. smoke, dust floating in the air

    c. foam, marshmallow *(all p. 350)*
13. The Tyndall effect is the scattering of light as it passes through a substance, thus making the light beam visible. It is used to determine whether an unknown mixture is a colloid or a solution. *(p. 350)*

Understanding Concepts

* An asterisk following a question number indicates that a worked-out solution can be found on pages 355C–55G.

14. **a.** water; salt

    b. water; CO_2

    c. nitrogen; oxygen and other gases

    d. Fe; Mn and C *(all pp. 328–29)*
15. Dissociation occurs when an ionic compound separates into separate ions when dissolved. Ionization occurs when a covalent compound reacts with water to produce ions when dissolved. *(p. 330)*

16. For one substance to dissolve another, the intermolecular forces between both the solvent particles and the solute particles must be overcome. This requires an input of energy. As the intermolecular forces between solute and solvent particles form, energy is released. The entire process can be exothermic or endothermic. *(p. 330)*

17. Like dissolves like. Water is a polar solvent; therefore, it dissolves polar and ionic solutes. Lithium chloride is ionic and so dissolves in water. Carbon tetrachloride is insoluble in water because it is nonpolar but typically dissolves in a nonpolar solvent. *(p. 332)*

18.* *(pp. 327–34)*

19. a. approximately 42 °C

b. approximately 11 g

c. The solution will be unsaturated because the solubility of NH_4Cl at 50 °C is 50 g. You have dissolved less than the maximum solute that the water can hold at this temperature. *(all p. 336)*

20.* 3.68×10^3 g *(p. 338)*

21.* 0.1039 L *(p. 339)*

22.*a. 0.740 mol/L $Na_2B_4O_7$

b. 0.749 mol/L $Na_2B_4O_7$

c. 0.942 mol $Na_2B_4O_7$

d. 135.1 mL *(all p. 340)*

23.* 1.228 L *(pp. 339–40)*

24.*a. 0.540 mol/kg Na_2PO_3F

b. 2.48×10^{-3} mol Na_2PO_3F

c. 1.61×10^3 Na_2PO_3F *(all pp. 441–42)*

25. a. The 2.9 m CH_3OH solution has the lowest vapor pressure because it is the most concentrated.

b. The 0.5 m $Al_2(SO_4)_3$ solution releases the most ions upon dissociation. *(all p. 343)*

26. Boiling occurs when the vapor pressure of the liquid equals or exceeds atmospheric pressure. Since the dissolved solute particles lower the liquid's vapor pressure, the liquid will need to be heated to a higher temperature to get its vapor pressure to equal or exceed the atmospheric pressure. *(pp. 343–44)*

14 CHAPTER REVIEW

UNDERSTANDING CONCEPTS

14. Identify the solvent and solute(s) in each of the following solutions.

a. salt water

b. carbonated water

c. air

d. carbon steel (1% Mn, 0.9% C, 98.1% Fe)

15. How are dissociation and ionization different?

16. Explain changes in energy when a substance is dissolving.

17. Explain why water will dissolve lithium chloride but not carbon tetrachloride (CCl_4).

18. Create a graphic organizer for solutions. At a minimum, use the following terms: *concentrated solution, concentration, dilute solution, heterogeneous mixture, homogeneous mixture, mixture, saturated solution, solubility, solute, solution, solvent, supersaturated solution, unsaturated solution.*

19. Use the solubility curves on page 336 to answer the following questions.

a. At what temperature will the solubility of KNO_3 be 65 g?

b. What is the solubility of $KClO_3$ at 35 °C?

c. If you dissolve 40 g of KCl in 100 mL of water at 50 °C, will the solution be supersaturated, saturated, or unsaturated? Explain.

20. A solute with a mass of 135.5 g needs to be dissolved in water to make a solution with a 3.55% mass fraction. How much water is needed?

21. A lab technician is mixing 1.754 L of solvent to make a solution with a 5.593% volume fraction. How much solute is needed?

22. An aqueous solution of anhydrous sodium tetraborate ($Na_2B_4O_7$) is sometimes used to fireproof wood.

a. What is the amount concentration of 2.50 L of a solution that contains 1.85 mol $Na_2B_4O_7$?

b. What is the amount concentration of 45.0 L of a solution that contains 6.78 kg $Na_2B_4O_7$?

c. How many moles of $Na_2B_4O_7$ are in 600.0 mL of a 1.57 M $Na_2B_4O_7$ solution?

d. A chemist needs 50.85 g $Na_2B_4O_7$ for a reaction. How many milliliters of a 1.870 M solution does she need?

23. For an experiment, you need 1.250 L of 0.300 M H_2SO_4 solution. If your stock solution is 17.4 M H_2SO_4, how much stock solution and water do you need to prepare the solution?

24. Disodium phosphorofluoridate (Na_2PO_3F) is a common source of fluoride in some modern toothpastes.

a. What is the molality of a solution containing 2.75 mol Na_2PO_3F in 5.09 kg H_2O?

b. How many moles of Na_2PO_3F would be contained in 125.0 g of H_2O if the solution were 0.0198 molal?

c. What mass of disodium phosphorofluoridate is needed to make a 0.0223 m Na_2PO_3F solution with 500.0 kg of water?

25. From each of the following sets, choose the solution that has the lowest vapor pressure. Explain.

a. 1.8 m CH_3OH	**b.** 0.5 m Na_3PO_4
0.7 m CH_3OH	0.5 m $MgCl_2$
2.9 m CH_3OH	0.5 m NaCl
0.2 m CH_3OH	0.5 m $Al_2(SO_4)_3$

26. How does the lowering of the vapor pressure due to dissolved particles explain the elevation of the boiling point in a solution?

27. A chef adds salt to the water when cooking eggs because she believes that the eggs will cook faster.

a. Is this an accurate statement? Explain.

b. What is the boiling point of the salt water if she dissolves 10.0 g NaCl in 1.00 L of pure water?

c. How many grams of NaCl must be added to 1.00 L of water to raise its boiling point to 105.0 °C?

d. In light of the answers to Questions 27b and 27c, do you think that adding salt to water is a convenient method for decreasing the cooking time of eggs?

28. Automobile coolant additive consists primarily of ethylene glycol ($C_2H_6O_2$). Manufacturers also add small amounts of dye and anticorrosion substances.

a. The coldest temperature of the year in Augusta, Maine, is expected to be −26.0 °C. What must the molality of a solution of water (solvent) and ethylene glycol (solute) be for the radiator fluid to prevent the water from freezing?

b. How many grams of ethylene glycol must be added to 4.00 L of water to attain this molality?

27.*a. Yes. In theory this is accurate. The boiling point of a solution of water should be higher than that of pure water. Therefore, the boiling salted water should be hotter than the unsalted water.

b. 100.2 °C

c. 2.9×10^2 g NaCl

d. No. It would take a large amount of salt to raise the boiling point enough to shorten the cooking time. *(pp. 344–45)*

28.*a. 14.0 mol/kg

b. 3.47×10^3 g $C_2H_6O_2$

c. 3.12 L $C_2H_6O_2$

d. Antifreeze not only lowers the freezing point of water but also raises its boiling point. A vehicle can operate at a higher temperature in the summer with antifreeze.

e. 107.2 °C *(all pp. 346–47)*

29. Answers will vary. Students could discuss vapor pressure depression, boiling point elevation, freezing point depression, or increased osmotic pressure. Boiling point elevation is used when adding antifreeze to car radiators and in candy making. Freezing point depression is used in adding antifreeze to car radiators and ice melt on roadways. Some students may mention using solutions in living organisms to allow or prevent osmosis or methods of desali-

c. How many liters of antifreeze is this? Assume that the density of antifreeze is 1.113 g/mL and ignore the fact that there are small amounts of other substances present.

d. Why is it important to have a solution of coolant in a car's radiator during the summer?

e. What is the boiling point for this solution?

29. Describe two ways that colligative properties are used to make life better.

30. What is the only combination of phases that cannot form a colloid? Why?

31. Why do you think that water has the potential to be so contaminated?

CRITICAL THINKING

32. The Chapter opener focuses on the scarcity of drinking water for many around the world. Some Christians may minimize these kinds of concerns. How would you respond to the following statement?

"The poor people of Africa and Asia don't need drinking water nearly as much as they need the gospel. Christians should not put time and resources into water purification. They should put all their efforts into sending missionaries who can preach the Bible and plant churches."

33. The chief engineer at a soft drink bottling plant wants to increase the amount of carbonation in soda. What can he do to increase the amount of gas dissolved in soda?

34. Suppose that all the water on our planet had to be replaced by another liquid. List the physical and chemical properties that the new compound would need.

35. A 9.168 M aqueous solution of H_2SO_4 has a density of 1.4987 g/mL at 20 °C. How many grams of H_2SO_4 are in 50.00 g of this solution?

36. You mix 2.45 L of 6.51 M HCl solution with 4.30 L of 3.75 M HCl solution. What is the molarity of your new mixture?

37. An aqueous solution of an unknown molecular compound boils at 101.00 °C.

a. What is the molality of the solution?

b. What is the freezing point of the solution?

c. What would the molar mass of the unknown compound be if we added 7.80 g of solute to 100.0 g of water to make the solution?

Use the ethics box below to answer Question 38.

38. Use the process for ethical decision making modeled in Chapter 3 to write a four-paragraph response on how to balance treatment cost, water usage, and discharge pollution.

ethics

WASTEWATER MANAGEMENT

You have probably noticed that water treatment is an important topic. The method used to treat wastewater is a multistep process, with each step adding cost. Most municipal water treatment plants balance the cost of treatment with the intended use of the water discharged from the plant. The water treatment plants in some cities release water with high levels of bacteria because the system discharges water to a stream or to the ocean. They reason that they are releasing the water to the environment, so there's no need to clean it any more than necessary. The downside to such thinking is that the body of water may become unusable for recreational uses like fishing or swimming.

nation by reverse osmosis. Other uses are possible. *(pp. 343–47)*

30. There are no gas-in-gas colloids. Because of the small size of gas particles, mixtures of gases with gases always form solutions. *(p. 350)*

31. Because water is a universal solvent, many pollutants will easily dissolve in it. *(pp. 332, 351)*

Critical Thinking

32. While everyone's greatest need is for salvation, we are also called to meet the physical needs of those around us. James teaches us that refusal to meet the physical needs is an example of faith without works. We can often reach people with the gospel after we have first met their physical needs.

33. He can increase the pressure of the gas over the liquid (Henry's law) and decrease the temperature of the system. *(p. 337)*

34. Answers will vary. The new compound would need to remain a liquid over a wide range of temperatures (0 °C–100 °C). It should evaporate easily with the introduction of thermal energy but have a high enough specific heat value to absorb large amounts of heat. It should be colorless to allow light to penetrate it and should be capable of dissolving a wide range of gases, especially oxygen, so that it could support life. It should be able to hold gases in solution, even at higher temperatures. This liquid should also dissolve most solid solutes. It should be a polar molecule to aid the dissociation of ionic compounds. It should be safe for plants to absorb and animals to drink.

35.* 30.00 g H_2SO_4 *(p. 319)*

36.* 4.75 mol/L HCl *(p. 319)*

37.*a. 2.0 mol/kg

b. −3.63 °C

c. 4.0×10^1 g/mol solute *(all pp. 341, 346)*

ETHICS: WASTEWATER MANAGEMENT

Appendix L includes a reproducible rubric to assess the ethics essay.

38. Water treatment is a challenging topic because everyone needs water. To completely treat water is a costly proposition; no one would argue against the expense to treat water for people in need of drinking water. But there is much pressure on governments and other organizations to save money when discharge water is not intended for human consumption. Students should find references to God's command to protect life, manage the created world, and be good stewards of the resources that He has given us.

Different outcomes will relate to giving more emphasis to one of the competing aspects than is given to others. An improper outcome would place saving money over the protection of life and the created world. Another improper outcome would be paying extra to purify water that a system discharges into already polluted water. An appropriate outcome would include a well-reasoned balancing of the competing aspects of the issue.

We are to both glorify God and love others when making decisions. We must clean water sufficiently for the next intended use while paying attention to the unintended consequences of our actions.

In most cases water treatment needs to be to the standard required for the next intended use of the water. But if the discharge water reduces the water quality in the discharge body to an unacceptable level, additional treatment is warranted.

Section 14.2

2. What we know: $m_{solute} = 6.3$ g, $m_{solvent} = 125.0$ g,
$m_{solution} = m_{solute} + m_{solvent} = 6.3\text{ g} + 125.0\text{ g} = 131.3\text{ g}$

Unknown: w_{solute}

Write the formula and solve for the unknown.

$$w_{solute} = \left(\frac{m_{solute}}{m_{solution}}\right)100\%$$

Evaluate.

$$w_{NaCl} = \left(\frac{6.3\ \cancel{\text{g}}}{131.3\ \cancel{\text{g}}}\right)100\%$$
$$= 4.8\%$$

3. What we know: $V_{solution} = 460.0$ mL, $\varphi_{solute} = 8.5\%$

Unknown: V_{solute}

Write the formula and solve for the unknown.

$$\varphi_{solute} = \left(\frac{V_{solute}}{V_{solution}}\right)100\%$$

$$\left(\frac{\varphi_{solute}}{100\%}\right)V_{solution} = \left(\frac{V_{solute}}{\cancel{V_{solution}}}\right)\left(\frac{\cancel{100\%}}{\cancel{100\%}}\right)\cancel{V_{solution}}$$

$$V_{solute} = \left(\frac{\varphi_{solute}}{100\%}\right)V_{solution}$$

Evaluate.

$$V_{solute} = \left(\frac{8.5\cancel{\%}}{100\cancel{\%}}\right)460.0\text{ mL}$$
$$= 39\text{ mL}$$

5. a. What we know: $m_{solute} = 38.97$ g $NaNO_3$,
$V_{solution} = 475.0\text{ mL} = 0.475\text{ L}$

Unknown: n_{solute}, c_{solute}

Convert mass sodium nitrate into moles sodium nitrate.

$$38.97\ \cancel{\text{g NaNO}_3}\left(\frac{1\text{ mol NaNO}_3}{85.00\ \cancel{\text{g NaNO}_3}}\right) = 0.458\underline{4}7\text{ mol NaNO}_3$$

Write the formula and solve for the unknown.

$$c_{solute} = \frac{n_{solute}}{V_{solution}}$$

Evaluate.

$$c_{solute} = \frac{0.458\underline{4}7\text{ mol NaNO}_3}{0.475\text{ L}}$$
$$= 0.965\text{ mol/L NaNO}_3$$

b. What we know: $V_{solution} = 725.0\text{ mL} = 0.725\text{ L}$,
$c_{solute} = 0.85$ M NaOH

Unknown: n_{solute}

Write the formula and solve for the unknown.

$$c_{solute} = \frac{n_{solute}}{V_{solution}}$$

$$c_{solute}V_{solution} = \frac{n_{solute}\cancel{V_{solution}}}{\cancel{V_{solution}}}$$

$$n_{solute} = c_{solute}V_{solution}$$

Evaluate.

$$n_{solute} = (0.85\text{ mol}/\cancel{\text{L}}\text{ NaOH})(0.725\ \cancel{\text{L}})$$
$$= 0.62\text{ mol NaOH}$$

c. What we know: $V_{solution} = 0.550$ L, $c_{solute} = 0.761$ M K_2SO_4

Unknown: n_{solute}, m_{solute}

Write the formula and solve for the unknown.

$$c_{solute} = \frac{n_{solute}}{V_{solution}}$$

$$c_{solute}V_{solution} = \frac{n_{solute}\cancel{V_{solution}}}{\cancel{V_{solution}}}$$

$$n_{solute} = c_{solute}V_{solution}$$

Evaluate.

$$n_{solute} = (0.761\text{ mol}/\cancel{\text{L}}\ K_2SO_4)(0.550\ \cancel{\text{L}})$$
$$= 0.41\underline{8}5\text{ mol } K_2SO_4$$

Convert moles potassium sulfate into mass potassium sulfate.

$$0.41\underline{8}5\ \cancel{\text{mol } K_2SO_4}\left(\frac{174.26\text{ g } K_2SO_4}{1\ \cancel{\text{mol } K_2SO_4}}\right) = 72.9\text{ g } K_2SO_4$$

d. What we know: $m_{solute} = 47.23$ g KNO_3, $c_{solute} = 1.750$ M KNO_3

Unknown: n_{solute}, $V_{solution}$

Convert mass potassium nitrate into moles potassium nitrate.

$$47.23\ \cancel{\text{g KNO}_3}\left(\frac{1\text{ mol KNO}_3}{101.11\ \cancel{\text{g KNO}_3}}\right) = 0.467\underline{1}1\text{ mol KNO}_3$$

Write the formula and solve for the unknown.

$$c_{solute} = \frac{n_{solute}}{V_{solution}}$$

$$c_{solute}V_{solution} = \frac{n_{solute}\cancel{V_{solution}}}{\cancel{V_{solution}}}$$

$$\frac{\cancel{c_{solute}}V_{solution}}{\cancel{c_{solute}}} = \frac{n_{solute}}{c_{solute}}$$

$$V_{solution} = \frac{n_{solute}}{c_{solute}}$$

Evaluate.

$$V_{solution} = \frac{0.467\underline{1}1\ \cancel{\text{mol KNO}_3}}{1.750\ \cancel{\text{mol}}/\text{L}\ \cancel{\text{KNO}_3}}$$
$$= 0.2669\text{ L}$$

6. What we know: $c_{stock\ solution} = 9.75$ M HCl, $V_{solution} = 2.54$ L,
$c_{solution} = 1.75$ M HCl

Unknown: $V_{stock\ solution}$

Write the formula and solve for the unknown.

$$c_1V_1 = c_2V_2$$

$$\frac{\cancel{c_1}V_1}{\cancel{c_1}} = \frac{c_2V_2}{c_1}$$

$$V_1 = \frac{c_2V_2}{c_1}$$

Evaluate.

$$V_{\text{stock solution}} = \frac{\left(1.75\ \frac{\cancel{\text{mol}}}{\cancel{\text{L}}}\ \cancel{\text{HCl}}\right)(2.54\ \text{L})}{9.75\ \frac{\cancel{\text{mol}}}{\cancel{\text{L}}}\ \cancel{\text{HCl}}}$$

$$= 0.456\ \text{L}$$

7. a. What we know: $n_{\text{solute}} = 4.51$ mol NaCl, $m_{\text{solvent}} = 2.57$ kg

Unknown: b_{solute}

Write the formula and solve for the unknown.

$$b_{\text{solute}} = \frac{n_{\text{solute}}}{m_{\text{solvent}}}$$

Evaluate.

$$b_{\text{solute}} = \frac{4.51\ \text{mol NaCl}}{2.57\ \text{kg}}$$

$$= 1.75\ \text{mol/kg NaCl}$$

b. What we know: $m_{\text{solute}} = 3.25$ kg $C_2H_6O_2 = 3.25 \times 10^3$ g $C_2H_6O_2$, $m_{\text{solvent}} = 7.75$ kg

Unknown: n_{solute}, b_{solute}

Convert mass $C_2H_6O_2$ to moles.

$$3.25 \times 10^3\ \cancel{\text{g}\ C_2H_6O_2}\left(\frac{1\ \text{mol}\ C_2H_6O_2}{62.08\ \cancel{\text{g}\ C_2H_6O_2}}\right)$$

$$= 52.\underline{3}5\ \text{mol}\ C_2H_6O_2$$

Write the formula and solve for the unknown.

$$b_{\text{solute}} = \frac{n_{\text{solute}}}{m_{\text{solvent}}}$$

Evaluate.

$$b_{\text{solute}} = \frac{52.\underline{3}5\ \text{mol}\ C_2H_6O_2}{7.75\ \text{kg}}$$

$$= 6.75\ \text{mol/kg}\ C_2H_6O_2$$

c. What we know: $b_{\text{solute}} = 2.74$ mol/kg $C_{12}H_{22}O_{11}$, $m_{\text{solute}} = 4.55$ kg $C_{12}H_{22}O_{11} = 4.55 \times 10^3$ g $C_{12}H_{22}O_{11}$

Unknown: n_{solute}, m_{solvent}

Convert mass $C_{12}H_{22}O_{11}$ to moles.

$$4.55 \times 10^3\ \cancel{\text{g}\ C_{12}H_{22}O_{11}}\left(\frac{1\ \text{mol}\ C_{12}H_{22}O_{11}}{342.34\ \cancel{\text{g}\ C_{12}H_{22}O_{11}}}\right)$$

$$= 13.\underline{2}9\ \text{mol}\ C_{12}H_{22}O_{11}$$

Write the formula and solve for the unknown.

$$b_{\text{solute}} = \frac{n_{\text{solute}}}{m_{\text{solvent}}}$$

$$b_{\text{solute}} m_{\text{solvent}} = \frac{n_{\text{solute}}}{\cancel{m_{\text{solvent}}}} \cancel{m_{\text{solvent}}}$$

$$\frac{\cancel{b_{\text{solute}}} m_{\text{solvent}}}{\cancel{b_{\text{solute}}}} = \frac{n_{\text{solute}}}{b_{\text{solute}}}$$

$$m_{\text{solvent}} = \frac{n_{\text{solute}}}{b_{\text{solute}}}$$

Evaluate.

$$m_{\text{solvent}} = \frac{13.\underline{2}9\ \cancel{\text{mol}\ C_{12}H_{22}O_{11}}}{2.74\ \cancel{\text{mol}}/\text{kg}\ \cancel{C_{12}H_{22}O_{11}}}$$

$$= 4.85\ \text{kg}$$

d. What we know: $b_{\text{solute}} = 2.77$ mol/kg KI, $m_{\text{solvent}} = 1.75$ kg

Unknown: n_{solute}, m_{solute}

Write the formula and solve for the unknown.

$$b_{\text{solute}} = \frac{n_{\text{solute}}}{m_{\text{solvent}}}$$

$$b_{\text{solute}} m_{\text{solvent}} = \frac{n_{\text{solute}}}{\cancel{m_{\text{solvent}}}} \cancel{m_{\text{solvent}}}$$

$$n_{\text{solute}} = b_{\text{solute}} m_{\text{solvent}}$$

Evaluate.

$$n_{\text{solute}} = (2.77\ \text{mol}/\cancel{\text{kg}}\ \text{KI})(1.75\ \cancel{\text{kg}})$$

$$= 4.8\underline{4}7\ \text{mol KI}$$

Convert moles KI to mass.

$$4.8\underline{4}7\ \cancel{\text{mol KI}}\left(\frac{166.00\ \text{g KI}}{1\ \cancel{\text{mol KI}}}\right) = 805\ \text{g KI}$$

Section 14.3

4. What we know: $m_{\text{solute}} = 75.5$ g $C_6H_{12}O_6$, $i = 1$ (molecular solute), $m_{\text{solvent}} = 150$ g $= 0.150$ kg, $K_b = 0.512$ °C·kg/mol, $T_1 = 100.0$ °C

Unknown: n_{solute}, b_{solute}, ΔT_b, T_2

Convert mass $C_6H_{12}O_6$ to moles.

$$75.5\ \cancel{\text{g}\ C_6H_{12}O_6}\left(\frac{1\ \text{mol}\ C_6H_{12}O_6}{180.18\ \cancel{\text{g}\ C_6H_{12}O_6}}\right) = 0.41\underline{9}0\ \text{mol}\ C_6H_{12}O_6$$

Write the formula and solve for the unknown.

$$b_{\text{solute}} = \frac{n_{\text{solute}}}{m_{\text{solvent}}}$$

Evaluate.

$$b_{\text{solute}} = \frac{0.41\underline{9}0\ \text{mol}\ C_6H_{12}O_6}{0.150\ \text{kg}}$$

$$= 2.7\underline{9}3\ \text{mol/kg}\ C_6H_{12}O_6$$

Write the formula and solve for the unknown.

$$\Delta T_b = iK_b b_{\text{solute}}$$

Evaluate.

$$\Delta T_b = (1)(0.512\ \text{°C} \cdot \cancel{\text{kg}}/\cancel{\text{mol}})(2.7\underline{9}3\ \cancel{\text{mol}}/\cancel{\text{kg}})$$

$$= 1.43\ \text{°C}$$

Write the formula and solve for the unknown.

$$\Delta T_b = T_{b_2} - T_{b_1}$$

$$T_{b_2} = \Delta T_b + T_{b_1}$$

Evaluate.

$$T_{b_2} = 1.43\ \text{°C} + 100.0\ \text{°C} = 101.43\ \text{°C}$$

5. What we know: $m_{solute} = 75.5\ g\ C_6H_{12}O_6$, $i = 1$ (molecular solute), $m_{solvent} = 150\ g = 0.150\ kg$, $K_f = -1.86\ °C{\cdot}kg/mol$, $T_1 = 0.0\ °C$

Unknown: n_{solute}, b_{solute}, ΔT_f, T_2

Convert mass $C_6H_{12}O_6$ to moles.

$$75.5\ \cancel{g\ C_6H_{12}O_6}\left(\frac{1\ mol\ C_6H_{12}O_6}{180.18\ \cancel{g\ C_6H_{12}O_6}}\right) = 0.4190\ mol\ C_6H_{12}O_6$$

Write the formula and solve for the unknown.

$$b_{solute} = \frac{n_{solute}}{m_{solvent}}$$

Evaluate.

$$b_{solute} = \frac{0.4190\ mol\ C_6H_{12}O_6}{0.150\ kg}$$

$$= 2.793\ mol/kg\ C_6H_{12}O_6$$

Write the formula and solve for the unknown.

$$\Delta T_f = iK_f b_{solute}$$

Evaluate.

$$\Delta T_f = (1)(-1.86\ °C \cdot \cancel{kg}/\cancel{mol})(2.793\ \cancel{mol}/\cancel{kg})$$

$$= -5.195\ °C$$

Write the formula and solve for the unknown.

$$\Delta T_f = T_{f_2} - T_{f_1}$$

$$T_{f_2} = \Delta T_f + T_{f_1}$$

Evaluate.

$$T_{f_2} = -5.195\ °C + 0.00\ °C = -5.20\ °C$$

Chapter 14 Review

18.

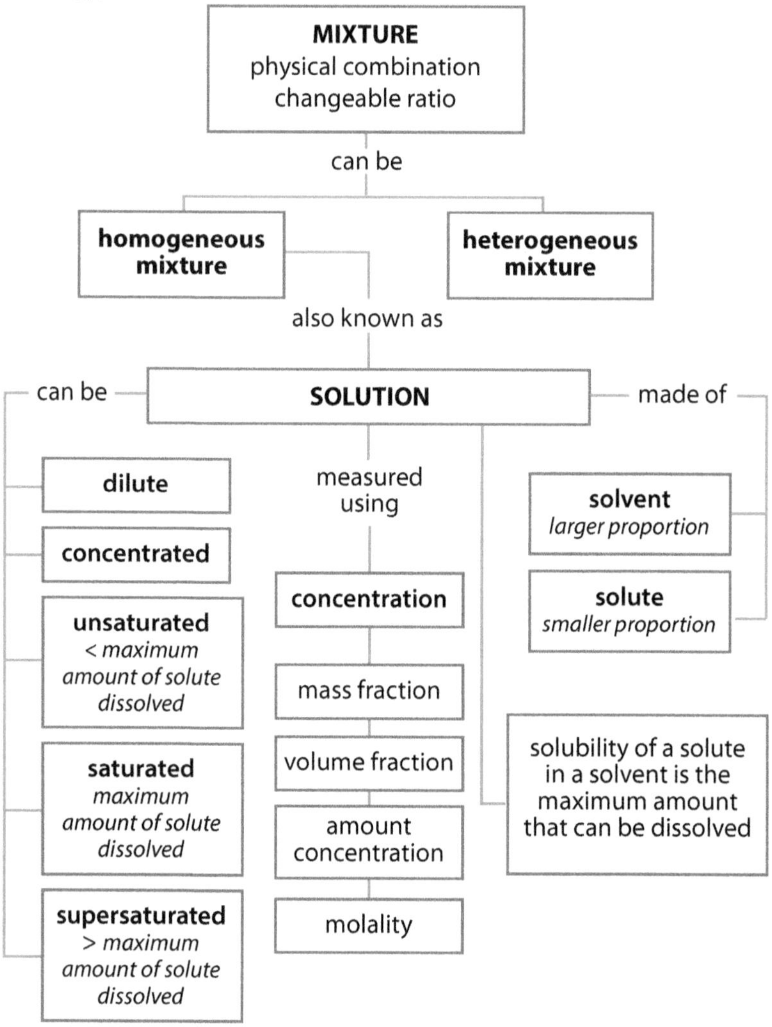

20. What we know: $m_{solute} = 135.5\text{ g}$, $w_{solute} = 3.55\%$

Unknown: $m_{solvent}$

Write the formula and solve for the unknown.

$$w_{solute} = \left(\frac{m_{solute}}{m_{solution}}\right)100\%$$

$$w_{solute} = \left(\frac{m_{solute}}{m_{solute} + m_{solvent}}\right)100\%$$

$$w_{solute}(m_{solute} + m_{solvent}) = \left(\frac{m_{solute}}{\cancel{m_{solute} + m_{solvent}}}\right)\cancel{(m_{solute} + m_{solvent})}100\%$$

$$\frac{\cancel{w_{solute}}(m_{solute} + m_{solvent})}{\cancel{w_{solute}}} = \frac{m_{solute}}{w_{solute}}100\%$$

$$\cancel{m_{solute}} + m_{solvent} - \cancel{m_{solute}} = \frac{m_{solute}}{w_{solute}}100\% - m_{solute}$$

$$m_{solvent} = \frac{m_{solute}}{w_{solute}}100\% - m_{solute}$$

Evaluate.

$$m_{solvent} = \frac{(100\cancel{\%})(135.5\text{ g})}{3.55\cancel{\%}} - 135.5\text{ g}$$

$$= 38\underline{1}6\text{ g} - 135.5\text{ g}$$

$$= 3.68 \times 10^3\text{ g}$$

21. What we know: $V_{solvent} = 1.754\text{ L}$, $\varphi_{solute} = 5.593\%$

Unknown: V_{solute}

Write the formula and solve for the unknown.

$$\varphi_{solute} = \left(\frac{V_{solute}}{V_{solution}}\right)100\%$$

$$\varphi_{solute} = \left(\frac{V_{solute}}{V_{solute} + V_{solvent}}\right)100\%$$

$$\varphi_{solute}(V_{solute} + V_{solvent}) = \left(\frac{V_{solute}}{\cancel{V_{solute} + V_{solvent}}}\right)(100\%)\cancel{(V_{solute} + V_{solvent})}$$

$$\cancel{\varphi_{solute}V_{solute}} + \varphi_{solute}V_{solvent} - \cancel{\varphi_{solute}V_{solute}} = V_{solute}(100\%) - \varphi_{solute}V_{solute}$$

$$\varphi_{solute}V_{solvent} = V_{solute}(100\% - \varphi_{solute})$$

$$\frac{\varphi_{solute}V_{solvent}}{(100\% - \varphi_{solute})} = \frac{V_{solute}\cancel{(100\% - \varphi_{solute})}}{\cancel{(100\% - \varphi_{solute})}}$$

$$V_{solute} = \frac{\varphi_{solute}V_{solvent}}{(100\% - \varphi_{solute})}$$

Evaluate.

$$V_{solute} = \frac{(5.593\%)(1.754\text{ L})}{(100\% - 5.593\%)}$$

$$= \frac{9.81\underline{0}\,1\cancel{\%}\text{ L}}{(94.40\underline{7}\cancel{\%})}$$

$$= 0.1039\text{ L}$$

22. a. What we know: $V_{solution} = 2.50\text{ L}$, $n_{solute} = 1.85\text{ mol } Na_2B_4O_7$

Unknown: c_{solute}

Write the formula and solve for the unknown.

$$c_{solute} = \frac{n_{solute}}{V_{solution}}$$

Evaluate.

$$c_{solute} = \frac{1.85\text{ mol } Na_2B_4O_7}{2.50\text{ L}}$$

$$= 0.740\text{ mol/L } Na_2B_4O_7$$

b. What we know: $V_{solution} = 45.0\text{ L}$,
$m_{solute} = 6.78\text{ kg } Na_2B_4O_7 = 6.78 \times 10^3\text{ g } Na_2B_4O_7$

Unknown: c_{solute}

Convert grams $Na_2B_4O_7$ to moles.

$$6.78 \times 10^3\ \cancel{\text{g } Na_2B_4O_7}\left(\frac{1\text{ mol } Na_2B_4O_7}{201.22\ \cancel{\text{g } Na_2B_4O_7}}\right)$$

$$= 33.\underline{6}9\text{ mol } Na_2B_4O_7$$

Write the formula and solve for the unknown.

$$c_{solute} = \frac{n_{solute}}{V_{solution}}$$

Evaluate.

$$c_{solute} = \frac{33.\underline{6}9\text{ mol } Na_2B_4O_7}{45.0\text{ L}}$$

$$= 0.749\text{ mol/L } Na_2B_4O_7$$

c. What we know: $V_{solution} = 600.0\text{ mL} = 0.6000\text{ L}$,
$c_{solute} = 1.57\text{ M } Na_2B_4O_7$

Unknown: n_{solute}

Write the formula and solve for the unknown.

$$c_{solute} = \frac{n_{solute}}{V_{solution}}$$

$$c_{solute}V_{solution} = \frac{n_{solute}\cancel{V_{solution}}}{\cancel{V_{solution}}}$$

$$n_{solute} = c_{solute}V_{solution}$$

Evaluate.

$$n_{solute} = (1.57\text{ mol}/\cancel{\text{L}}\ Na_2B_4O_7)(0.6000\ \cancel{\text{L}})$$

$$= 0.942\text{ mol } Na_2B_4O_7$$

d. What we know: $m_{solute} = 50.85\text{ g } Na_2B_4O_7$, $c_{solute} = 1.870\text{ M } Na_2B_4O_7$

Unknown: n_{solute}, $V_{solution}$

Convert grams $Na_2B_4O_7$ to moles.

$$50.85\text{ g } Na_2B_4O_7\left(\frac{1\text{ mol } Na_2B_4O_7}{201.22\text{ g } Na_2B_4O_7}\right)$$

$= 0.252\underline{7}0\text{ mol } Na_2B_4O_7$

Write the formula and solve for the unknown.

$$c_{solute} = \frac{n_{solute}}{V_{solution}}$$

$$c_{solute}V_{solution} = \frac{n_{solute}}{V_{solution}}V_{solution}$$

$$\frac{c_{solute}V_{solution}}{c_{solute}} = \frac{n_{solute}}{c_{solute}}$$

$$V_{solution} = \frac{n_{solute}}{c_{solute}}$$

Evaluate.

$$V_{solution} = \frac{0.252\underline{7}0\text{ mol } Na_2B_4O_7}{1.870\text{ mol/L } Na_2B_4O_7}$$

$= 0.1351\text{ L} = 135.1\text{ mL}$

23. What we know: $V_{solution} = 1.250\text{ L}$, $c_{solution} = 0.300\text{ M } H_2SO_4$, $c_{stock\ solution} = 17.4\text{ M } H_2SO_4$

Unknown: $V_{stock\ solution}$, V_{water}

Write the formula and solve for the unknown.

$$c_1V_1 = c_2V_2$$

$$\frac{c_1V_1}{c_2} = \frac{c_2V_2}{c_2}$$

$$V_2 = \frac{c_1V_1}{c_2}$$

Evaluate.

$$V_{stock\ solution} = \frac{(0.300\text{ mol/L } H_2SO_4)(1.250\text{ L})}{17.4\text{ mol/L } H_2SO_4}$$

$= 0.021\underline{5}5\text{ L}$

Write the formula and solve for the unknown.

$$V_{solution} = V_{water} + V_{stock\ solution}$$

$$V_{water} = V_{solution} - V_{stock\ solution}$$

Plug in known values and evaluate.

$V_{water} = 1.250\text{ L} - 0.021\underline{5}5\text{ L} = 1.228\text{ L}$

24. a. What we know: $n_{solute} = 2.75\text{ mol } Na_2PO_3F$, $m_{solvent} = 5.09\text{ kg}$

Unknown: b_{solute}, m_{solute}

Write the formula and solve for the unknown.

$$b_{solute} = \frac{n_{solute}}{m_{solvent}}$$

Evaluate.

$$b_{solute} = \frac{2.75\text{ mol } Na_2PO_3F}{5.09\text{ kg}}$$

$= 0.540\text{ mol/kg } Na_2PO_3F$

b. What we know: $b_{solute} = 0.0198\text{ m } Na_2PO_3F$, $m_{solvent} = 125.0\text{ g} = 0.125\text{ kg}$

Unknown: n_{solute}

Write the formula and solve for the unknown.

$$b_{solute} = \frac{n_{solute}}{m_{solvent}}$$

$$b_{solute}m_{solvent} = \frac{n_{solute}}{m_{solvent}}m_{solvent}$$

$$n_{solute} = b_{solute}m_{solvent}$$

Evaluate.

$n_{solute} = (0.0198\text{ mol/kg } Na_2PO_3F)(0.125\text{ kg})$

$= 2.48 \times 10^{-3}\text{ mol } Na_2PO_3F$

c. What we know: $b_{solute} = 0.0223\text{ m } Na_2PO_3F$, $m_{solvent} = 500.0\text{ kg}$

Unknown: n_{solute}, m_{solute}

Write the formula and solve for the unknown.

$$b_{solute} = \frac{n_{solute}}{m_{solvent}}$$

$$b_{solute}m_{solvent} = \frac{n_{solute}}{m_{solvent}}m_{solvent}$$

$$n_{solute} = b_{solute}m_{solvent}$$

Evaluate.

$n_{solute} = (0.0223\text{ mol/kg } Na_2PO_3F)(500.0\text{ kg})$

$= 11.\underline{1}5\text{ mol } Na_2PO_3F$

Convert moles Na_2PO_3F to mass.

$$11.\underline{1}5\text{ mol } Na_2PO_3F\left(\frac{143.95\text{ g } Na_2PO_3F}{1\text{ mol } Na_2PO_3F}\right)$$

$= 1.61 \times 10^3\text{ g } Na_2PO_3F$

27. b. What we know: $m_{solute} = 10.0\text{ g NaCl}$, $i = 2$ (ionic solute), $V_{solvent} = 1.00\text{ L} = 1.00 \times 10^3\text{ mL}$, $K_b = 0.512\text{ °C·kg/mol}$, $T_1 = 100\text{ °C}$

Unknown: n_{solute}, b_{solute}, ΔT_b, T_2

Convert mass NaCl to moles.

$$10.0\text{ g NaCl}\left(\frac{1\text{ mol NaCl}}{58.44\text{ g NaCl}}\right) = 0.17\underline{1}1\text{ mol NaCl}$$

Convert volume H_2O to mass.

$$1.00 \times 10^3\text{ mL } H_2O\left(\frac{1\text{ g } H_2O}{1\text{ mL } H_2O}\right)\left(\frac{1\text{ kg } H_2O}{1000\text{ g } H_2O}\right) = 1.00\text{ kg } H_2O$$

Write the formula and solve for the unknown.

$$b_{solute} = \frac{n_{solute}}{m_{solvent}}$$

Evaluate.

$$b_{solute} = \frac{0.171\underline{1}\text{ mol NaCl}}{1.00\text{ kg}}$$
$$= 0.171\underline{1}\text{ mol/kg NaCl}$$

Write the formula and solve for the unknown.

$$\Delta T_b = iK_b b_{solute}$$

Evaluate.

$$\Delta T_b = (2)(0.512\ °\text{C} \cdot \cancel{\text{kg/mol}})(0.171\underline{1}\ \cancel{\text{mol/kg}})$$
$$= 0.17\underline{5}2\ °\text{C}$$

Write the formula and solve for the unknown.

$$\Delta T_b = T_{b_2} - T_{b_1}$$
$$T_{b_2} = \Delta T_b + T_{b_1}$$

Evaluate.

$$T_{b_2} = 0.1752\ °\text{C} + 100.0\ °\text{C} = 100.175\ °\text{C}$$

c. What we know: $i = 2$ (ionic solute), $m_{solvent} = 1.00$ kg, $T_1 = 100.0$ °C, $T_2 = 105.0$ °C, $K_b = 0.512$ °C·kg/mol

Unknown: ΔT_b, b_{solute}, n_{solute}, m_{solute}

Write the formula and solve for the unknown.

$$\Delta T_b = T_{b_2} - T_{b_1}$$

Evaluate.

$$\Delta T_b = 105.0\ °\text{C} - 100.0\ °\text{C} = 5.0\ °\text{C}$$

Write the formula and solve for the unknown.

$$\Delta T_b = iK_b b_{solute}$$
$$\frac{\Delta T_b}{iK_b} = \frac{\cancel{iK_b} b_{solute}}{\cancel{iK_b}}$$
$$b_{solute} = \frac{\Delta T_b}{iK_b}$$

Evaluate.

$$b_{solute} = \frac{5.0\ \cancel{°\text{C}}}{(2)(0.512\ \cancel{°\text{C}} \cdot \text{kg/mol})}$$
$$= 4.\underline{8}8\text{ mol/kg}$$

Write the formula and solve for the unknown.

$$b_{solute} = \frac{n_{solute}}{m_{solvent}}$$
$$b_{solute} m_{solvent} = \frac{n_{solute}}{\cancel{m_{solvent}}} \cancel{m_{solvent}}$$
$$n_{solute} = b_{solute} m_{solvent}$$

Evaluate.

$$n_{solute} = (4.\underline{8}82\text{ mol/}\cancel{\text{kg}})(1.00\ \cancel{\text{kg}})$$
$$= 4.\underline{8}82\text{ mol NaCl}$$

Convert moles NaCl to mass.

$$4.\underline{8}82\ \cancel{\text{mol NaCl}}\left(\frac{58.44\text{ g NaCl}}{1\ \cancel{\text{mol NaCl}}}\right) = 2.9 \times 10^2\text{ g NaCl}$$

28. a. What we know: $i = 1$ (molecular solute), $K_f = -1.86$ °C·kg/mol, $T_1 = 0.0$ °C, $T_2 = -26.0$ °C

Unknown: ΔT_f, b_{solute}

Write the formula and solve for the unknown.

$$\Delta T_f = T_{f_2} - T_{f_1}$$

Evaluate.

$$\Delta T_f = -26.0\ °\text{C} - 0.00\ °\text{C} = -26.0\ °\text{C}$$

Write the formula and solve for the unknown.

$$\Delta T_f = iK_f b_{solute}$$
$$\frac{\Delta T_f}{iK_f} = \frac{\cancel{iK_f} b_{solute}}{\cancel{iK_f}}$$
$$b_{solute} = \frac{\Delta T_f}{iK_f}$$

Evaluate.

$$b_{solute} = \frac{-26.0\ \cancel{°\text{C}}}{(1)(-1.86\ \cancel{°\text{C}} \cdot \text{kg/mol})}$$
$$= 13.\underline{9}7\text{ mol/kg}$$
$$= 14.0\text{ mol/kg}$$

b. What we know: $i = 1$ (molecular solute), $b_{solute} = 13.\underline{9}7$ mol/kg, $V_{solvent} = 4.00$ L, $m_{solvent} = 4.00$ kg

Unknown: m_{solute}

Convert molality of ethylene glycol to mass.

$$4.00\ \cancel{\text{kg H}_2\text{O}}\left(\frac{13.\underline{9}7\ \cancel{\text{mol C}_2\text{H}_6\text{O}_2}}{1\ \cancel{\text{kg H}_2\text{O}}}\right)\left(\frac{62.08\text{ g C}_2\text{H}_6\text{O}_2}{1\ \cancel{\text{mol C}_2\text{H}_6\text{O}_2}}\right)$$
$$= 34\underline{6}9\text{ g C}_2\text{H}_6\text{O}_2$$
$$= 3.47 \times 10^3\text{ g C}_2\text{H}_6\text{O}_2$$

c. Convert grams ethylene glycol to liters.

$$34\underline{6}9\ \cancel{\text{g C}_2\text{H}_6\text{O}_2}\left(\frac{1\ \cancel{\text{mL}}\text{ C}_2\text{H}_6\text{O}_2}{1.113\ \cancel{\text{g C}_2\text{H}_6\text{O}_2}}\right)\left(\frac{1\text{ L}}{1000\ \cancel{\text{mL}}}\right)$$
$$= 3.12\text{ L C}_2\text{H}_6\text{O}_2$$

e. What we know: $i = 1$ (molecular solute), $b_{solute} = 13.97$ mol/kg, $K_b = 0.512$ °C · kg/mol, $T_{b_1} = 100.0$ °C,

Unknown: ΔT_b, T_{b_2}

Write the formula and solve for the unknown.

$$\Delta T_b = iK_b b_{solute}$$

Evaluate.

$$\Delta T_b = (1)(0.512\ °\text{C} \cdot \cancel{\text{kg/mol}})(13.\underline{9}7\ \cancel{\text{mol/kg}})$$
$$= 7.1\underline{5}2\ °\text{C}$$

Write the formula and solve for the unknown.

$$\Delta T_b = T_{b_2} - T_{b_1}$$
$$T_{b_2} = \Delta T_b + T_{b_1}$$

Evaluate.

$$T_{b_2} = 7.1\underline{5}2\ °\text{C} + 100.0\ °\text{C} = 107.15\ °\text{C}$$

35. What we know: $c_{solute} = 9.168\ M\ H_2SO_4$, $\rho_{solution} = 1.4987\ g/mL$, $m_{solution} = 50.0\ g$

Unknown: $V_{solution}$, n_{solute}, m_{solute}

Use density to convert mass solution to volume solution.

$$50.0\ \cancel{g}\left(\frac{1\ mL}{1.4987\ \cancel{g}}\right) = 33.3\underline{6}2\ mL$$

$$= 0.033\ 3\underline{6}2\ L$$

Write the formula and solve for the unknown.

$$c_{solute} = \frac{n_{solute}}{V_{solution}}$$

$$c_{solute}V_{solution} = \frac{n_{solute}}{\cancel{V_{solution}}}\cancel{V_{solution}}$$

$$n_{solute} = c_{solute}V_{solution}$$

Evaluate.

$$n_{solute} = \left(9.168\ \frac{mol}{\cancel{L}}\ H_2SO_4\right)(0.033\ 3\underline{6}2\ \cancel{L})$$

$$= 0.305\ \underline{8}6\ mol\ H_2SO_4$$

Convert moles of H_2SO_4 to grams.

$$0.305\ \underline{8}6\ \cancel{mol\ H_2SO_4}\left(\frac{98.08\ g\ H_2SO_4}{1\ \cancel{mol\ H_2SO_4}}\right) = 30.00\ g\ H_2SO_4$$

36. What we know: $V_1 = 2.45\ L$, $c_1 = 6.51\ M\ HCl$, $V_2 = 4.30\ L$, $c_2 = 3.75\ M\ HCl$

Unknown: n_1, n_2, c_{new}

Write the formula and solve for the unknown.

$$c_{solute} = \frac{n_{solute}}{V_{solution}}$$

$$c_{solute}V_{solution} = \frac{n_{solute}}{\cancel{V_{solution}}}\cancel{V_{solution}}$$

$$n_{solute} = c_{solute}V_{solution}$$

Evaluate.

$$n_1 = (6.51\ mol/\cancel{L}\ HCl)(2.45\ \cancel{L}) = 15.\underline{9}4\ mol\ HCl$$

$$n_2 = (3.75\ mol/\cancel{L}\ HCl)(4.30\ \cancel{L}) = 16.\underline{1}2\ mol\ HCl$$

Write the formula and solve for the unknown.

$$c_{solute} = \frac{n_{solute}}{V_{solution}}$$

Evaluate.

$$c_{solute} = \frac{n_1 + n_2}{V_1 + V_2}$$

$$= \frac{15.\underline{9}4\ mol\ HCl + 16.\underline{1}2\ mol\ HCl}{2.45\ L + 4.30\ L}$$

$$= \frac{32.\underline{0}6\ mol\ HCl}{6.75\ L}$$

$$= 4.75\ mol/L\ HCl$$

37. a. What we know: $i = 1$ (molecular solute), $T_{b_2} = 101.0\ °C$, $K_b = 0.512\ °C \cdot kg/mol$, $T_{b_1} = 100.0\ °C$

Unknown: ΔT_b, b_{solute}

Write the formula and solve for the unknown.

$$\Delta T_b = T_{b_2} - T_{b_1}$$

Evaluate.

$$\Delta T_b = 101.0\ °C - 100.0\ °C = 1.0\ °C$$

Write the formula and solve for the unknown.

$$\Delta T_b = iK_b b_{solute}$$

$$\frac{\Delta T_b}{iK_b} = \frac{\cancel{iK_b}b_{solute}}{\cancel{iK_b}}$$

$$b_{solute} = \frac{\Delta T_b}{iK_b}$$

Evaluate.

$$b_{solute} = \frac{1.0\ \cancel{°C}}{(1)(0.512\ \cancel{°C} \cdot kg/mol)}$$

$$= 1.\underline{9}5\ mol/kg = 2.0\ mol/kg$$

b. What we know: $i = 1$, $b_{solute} = 1.\underline{9}5\ mol/kg$, $K_f = -1.86\ °C \cdot kg/mol$, $T_{f_1} = 0.00\ °C$

Unknown: ΔT_f, T_{f_2}

Write the formula and solve for the unknown.

$$\Delta T_f = iK_f b_{solute}$$

Evaluate.

$$\Delta T_f = (1)(-1.86\ °C \cdot \cancel{kg/mol})(1.\underline{9}5\ \cancel{mol/kg})$$

$$= -3.\underline{6}2\ °C$$

Write the formula and solve for the unknown.

$$\Delta T_f = T_{f_2} - T_{f_1}$$

$$T_{f_2} = \Delta T_f + T_{f_1}$$

Evaluate.

$$T_{f_2} = -3.\underline{6}2\ °C + 0.00\ °C = -3.6\ °C$$

c. What we know: $m_{solute} = 7.80\ g$, $m_{solvent} = 100.0\ g$, $b_{solute} = 1.95\ mol/kg$

Unknown: *molar mass*

Convert mass solute/mass solvent to mass solute/mole solute.

$$\left(\frac{7.80\ g}{100.0\ \cancel{g\ solvent}}\right)\left(\frac{1\ \cancel{kg\ solvent}}{1.\underline{9}5\ mol\ solute}\right)\left(\frac{1000\ \cancel{g\ solvent}}{1\ \cancel{kg\ solvent}}\right)$$

$$= 4.0 \times 10^1\ g/mol\ solute$$

CHAPTER 15 *OBJECTIVES*

- Analyze the energy changes during phase changes.
- Analyze the energy changes during chemical changes.
- Predict whether a reaction will spontaneously occur by calculating the change in free energy.
- Determine the specific heat of a substance using calorimetry.

OVERVIEW

Chapter 15 has key material. In this chapter students will predict whether a reaction will occur by applying their knowledge of thermochemistry. It is important for students to have a firm understanding of the mole concept from Chapter 11 before engaging with this material. Students will use their understanding of moles and thermochemistry to calculate the enthalpy, entropy, and free energy of reactions.

15.1 THERMODYNAMICS AND PHYSICAL CHANGES
- *Measuring Heat and Temperature*
- *Enthalpy of Phase Changes*
- *Specific Heat*

15.2 THERMODYNAMICS AND CHEMICAL CHANGES
- *Enthalpy (Heat) of Reaction*
- *Enthalpy (Heat) of Formation*
- *Enthalpy (Heat) of Combustion*
- *Calculating Enthalpies of Reaction*

15.3 REACTION TENDENCY
- *Chemical Bonds and Enthalpy*
- *Entropy and Reaction Tendency*
- *Calculating Entropy Changes*
- *Calculating Free-Energy Change*
- *Worldview Conflict in Thermodynamics*

LAB ACTIVITIES

Lab 15A: *Hot Shot*—Students determine the specific heat of a metal.

Lab 15B: *No Anchovies, Please!*—Students determine how to find the enthalpy of reaction.

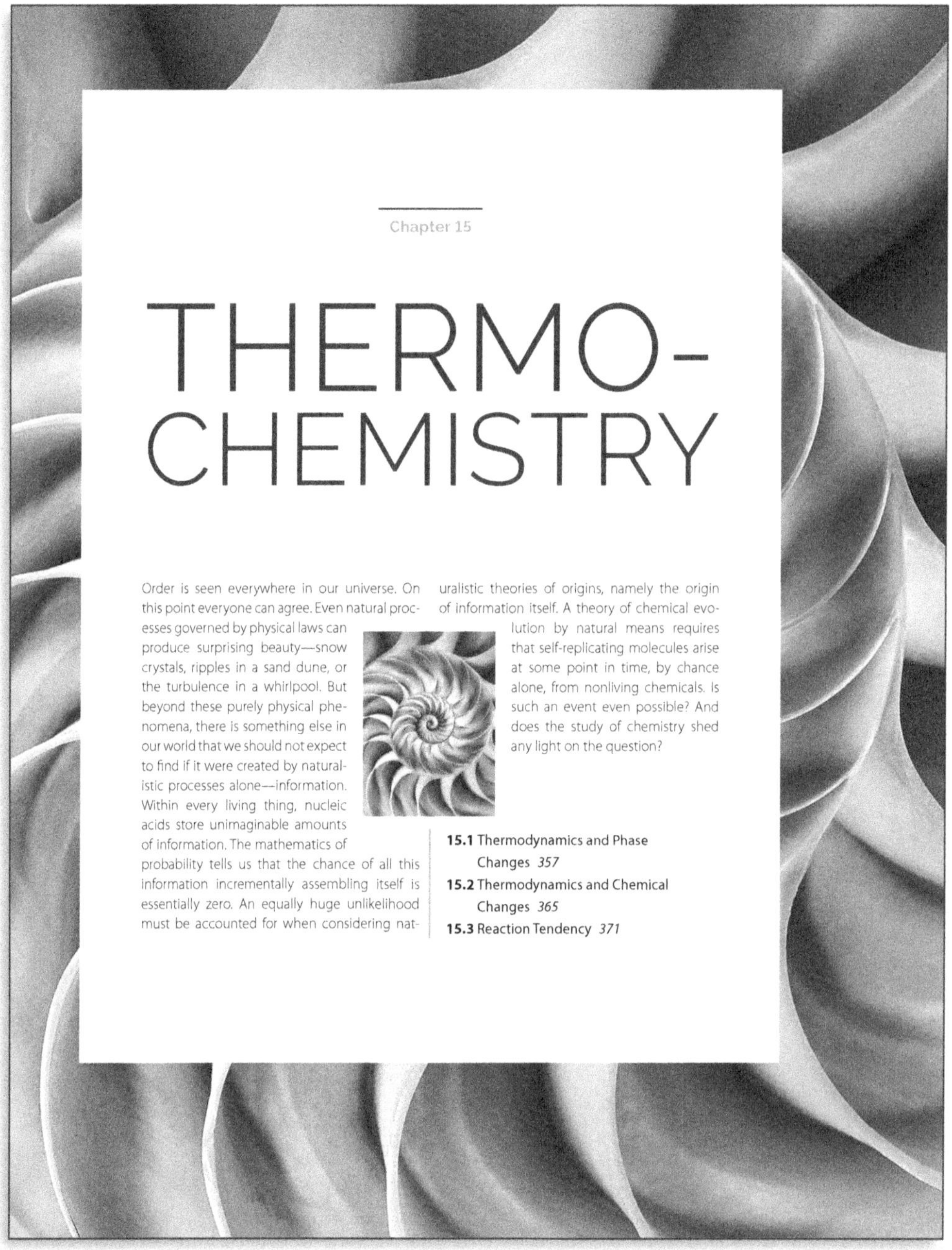

Chapter 15

THERMO-CHEMISTRY

Order is seen everywhere in our universe. On this point everyone can agree. Even natural processes governed by physical laws can produce surprising beauty—snow crystals, ripples in a sand dune, or the turbulence in a whirlpool. But beyond these purely physical phenomena, there is something else in our world that we should not expect to find if it were created by naturalistic processes alone—information. Within every living thing, nucleic acids store unimaginable amounts of information. The mathematics of probability tells us that the chance of all this information incrementally assembling itself is essentially zero. An equally huge unlikelihood must be accounted for when considering naturalistic theories of origins, namely the origin of information itself. A theory of chemical evolution by natural means requires that self-replicating molecules arise at some point in time, by chance alone, from nonliving chemicals. Is such an event even possible? And does the study of chemistry shed any light on the question?

The image in the Chapter opener shows the intricate design of the inner chambers of a nautilus shell. Our world is filled with patterns, designs, and information that confirm the existence of an omnipotent Creator.

15.1 THERMODYNAMICS AND PHASE CHANGES

The formation of a strand of DNA requires many chemical reactions. Can such reactions produce ever-increasing order in living things? In Chapter 2, we introduced the laws of thermodynamics. Those laws describe energy changes in matter. In summary, they state that matter and energy can be neither created nor destroyed but can be converted from one form to another. During these conversions, some energy becomes unusable. **Thermochemistry**, the branch of science that studies the transfer of energy during phase or chemical changes, is an important application of these laws. As you will see, thermochemistry has something to say about the order that we see in our universe, including in DNA molecules.

QUESTIONS
- What is thermochemistry?
- Is there a difference between thermal energy and heat?
- Do all phase changes require the same amount of added energy?

TERMS
thermochemistry • enthalpy • calorimeter • sensible heat • latent heat • molar enthalpy of fusion • molar enthalpy of vaporization • specific heat

Does the temperature of water change as it freezes?

Measuring Heat and Temperature

In many investigations scientists are interested in thermal energy, the total kinetic energy of the particles within a substance. But we can't directly measure thermal energy, so scientists rely on measurements of two different properties: temperature and heat. Remember that temperature, measured in degrees Celsius or kelvins, expresses the average kinetic energy in the particles of a sample. Heat, on the other hand, measures the amount of thermal energy transferred from one substance to another. Heat is typically expressed in joules (J). The joule is the standard SI unit of work and can be used to measure any kind of energy.

Because it is impossible to determine the absolute amount of thermal energy in a substance, chemists measure the change in energy that occurs during a chemical reaction. This measurement is more useful to them anyway. Scientists have defined a property of matter called enthalpy to help them quantify the change in energy. **Enthalpy** (H) is the thermal energy content of a system at a constant pressure. For the most part, chemical reactions in nature or in the laboratory occur at a constant pressure.

Changes in enthalpy can be measured in a reaction vessel called a calorimeter. A **calorimeter** is an insulated container, similar to a thermos, in which a thermometer detects the temperature change that occurs during a chemical reaction. In one common kind of calorimeter, a chemical reaction occurs in a sealed reaction chamber submerged in a measured quantity of water. The change in the water temperature indirectly indicates how much energy the reaction has released or absorbed.

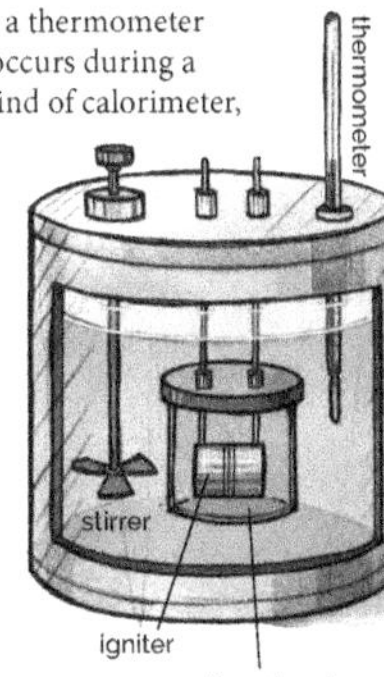

In this calorimeter, the enthalpy of the reaction is captured by the water and calculated from the temperature change.

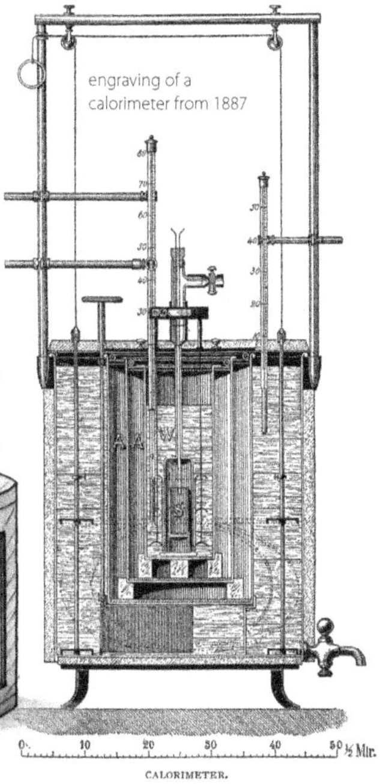

engraving of a calorimeter from 1887

SECTION 15.1 *OVERVIEW*

Essential Question

Does the temperature of water change as it freezes?

Objectives

- **15.1.1** Define *thermochemistry*.
- **15.1.2** Compare temperature, thermal energy, and heat.
- **15.1.3** Relate the states of matter to the concepts of sensible heat and latent heat.
- **15.1.4** Calculate energy or temperature during phase changes.

Resources

- Demonstrating How to Create Your Own Heating Curve
- Web Link: Phase Changes and Heat
- Lab 15A: *Hot Shot*—Finding the Specific Heat of a Metal; Mini Lab: *Comparing Thermal Energy Transfer* (p. 364)

ENGAGE

PHASE CHANGE

Activate prior knowledge with a review **discussion** regarding phase changes learned in Chapter 2. To get students thinking of the study of thermodynamics, ask them the following questions.

1. What determines a substance's state of matter? *(the kinetic energy of the particles and the attractive forces between the particles, all of which is explained by the kinetic-molecular theory)*
2. What is thermal energy? *(the sum of the kinetic energies of the particles in an object)*
3. What is the difference between heat and temperature? *(Heat is the movement of thermal energy, and temperature is the average kinetic energy of a system's particles.)*

After discussing the foundational concepts of thermochemistry, transition to Section 15.1 by explaining to students that in this chapter they will learn how to quantitatively define the transfer of thermal energy.

INSTRUCT

THERMODYNAMICS

Lead students to create **Sketchnotes** on the information in this chapter. Encourage them to be creative when listing vocabulary terms, creating illustrations, and adding diagrams and formulas.

ENTHALPY AND WARMTH

The word *enthalpy* comes from a Greek word that means "to warm." When thermal energy flows into a substance (an endothermic process), the enthalpy change will be positive—positive warmth. When thermal energy flows out from a substance (an exothermic process), the enthalpy change will be negative—negative warmth.

SENSIBLE HEAT

Sensible heat does not refer to "heat that makes sense." Rather, it refers to heat that can be sensed. In other words, sensible heat can be measured with a thermometer or felt with the hand.

PHASE CHANGES AND HEAT

For an interactive activity that explores the changes that occur to a substance during phase changes, visit TeacherToolsOnline .com. Under Additional Resources, click on Chapter 15 Web Links. Then click on *Phase Changes*.

ENTHALPY *of Phase Changes*

The thermal energy transferred between substances can be divided into two categories. **Sensible heat** is the transfer of thermal energy that produces a temperature change in a substance. We can sense, or detect, this type of heat by a change in temperature.

A second category, called **latent heat**, is the thermal energy that produces a phase change when transferred to a substance. No temperature change is observed. Examine the heating curve below to see where sensible and latent heat affect water.

This heating curve for water shows three states of matter and how adding thermal energy affects its temperature and state.

358 Chapter 15

Changing ice into liquid water involves both sensible and latent heat. Ice, at a temperature that is below its melting point, can be heated until it reaches a temperature of 0 °C (sensible heat). Any thermal energy added at this point does not raise the temperature. Instead, it serves to supply the energy needed to overcome the intermolecular forces (latent heat). Not until the last piece of ice has melted will the temperature of the water rise above 0 °C.

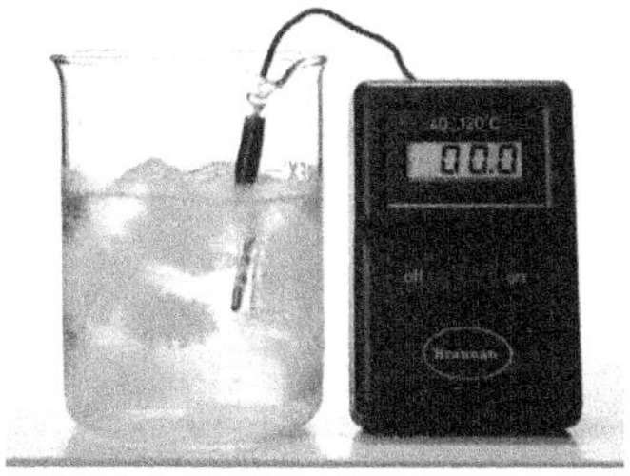

A significant amount of energy must be added to a solid at its melting point to overcome intermolecular forces, and that amount differs for each substance. The thermal energy required is called the *heat of fusion*, or the **molar enthalpy of fusion** (ΔH_{fus}). It is defined as the quantity of energy required to melt one mole of a solid to a liquid with no temperature change. The same amount of energy is released when one mole of the liquid freezes.

TABLE 15-1

Molar Enthalpies of Fusion and Vaporization

Substance	Formula	ΔH_{fus} (kJ/mol)	ΔH_{vap} (kJ/mol)
ammonia	NH_3	5.66	23.3
ethanol	C_2H_5OH	4.94	38.6
methanol	CH_3OH	3.17	35.2
water	H_2O	6.01	40.7

The amount of energy required to convert a mole of a liquid at its boiling point to its vapor at the same temperature is called the *heat of vaporization*, or the **molar enthalpy of vaporization** (ΔH_{vap}). The reverse of the enthalpy of vaporization is called the *enthalpy of condensation*; this quantity is equal in magnitude but opposite in sign to the enthalpy of vaporization.

Enthalpies of vaporization differ widely because the strength of intermolecular attractions in different liquids varies. For instance, it takes 40.7 kJ to vaporize 1 mol of water at 100 °C and 101.325 kPa, while a mole of ammonia at its boiling point can be vaporized by adding 23.3 kJ of energy.

EXAMPLE 15-1: CALCULATING LATENT HEAT

How much energy would be required to melt 3.54 kg of ice at 0 °C to water without any temperature change?

Write what you know.

$m = 3.54$ kg

$\Delta H_{fus} = 6.01$ kJ/mol

Convert mass of water to energy required.

$$3.54\ \cancel{\text{kg } H_2O}\left(\frac{1000\ \cancel{\text{g } H_2O}}{1\ \cancel{\text{kg } H_2O}}\right)\left(\frac{1\ \cancel{\text{mol } H_2O}}{18.02\ \cancel{\text{g } H_2O}}\right)\left(\frac{6.01\ \text{kJ}}{1\ \cancel{\text{mol } H_2O}}\right) = 1.18 \times 10^3\ \text{kJ}$$

You would need to add 1.18×10^3 kJ of energy to melt the ice.

WHAT'S THE POINT OF FUSION AND VAPORIZATION?

Use a **discussion question** to assess students' understanding. Ask, "Why do we need enthalpies of fusion and vaporization before we can calculate total enthalpy?" *(We must first find the amount of thermal energy that a particle requires before it can change from a solid to a liquid and from a liquid to a gas.)*

MOLAR ENTHALPIES OF FUSION AND VAPORIZATION

Direct students to create a **chart** similar to the molar enthalpies of fusion and vaporization table on this page. This will help them be more familiar with the molar enthalpies of several of the most common substances used throughout the Student Edition.

POWER PLANT FIELD TRIP

Arrange for a tour of a local power plant. Be sure that the tour guide is aware of specific information that you would like to cover during the tour, such as the processes that occur as energy is released from coal, uranium, or water and transformed into electricity for use by the community.

SPECIFIC HEATS

Direct students to add the formula for thermal energy to their **Sketchnotes**. Encourage them to add an example problem.

Specific Heat

Have you ever noticed that an aluminum pan on a stove heats up faster than the water inside it? Why does this happen? You might explain this by observing that the pan receives the heat before the water does, but there is a better explanation.

Not all substances heat at the same rate or change temperature by the same amount under the same conditions. The amount of thermal energy that raises 1 g of water by 1 °C will raise the temperature of 1 g of aluminum by approximately 5 °C. Given the same amount of energy, the aluminum will have a greater temperature change. The **specific heat** (c_{sp}) of a substance is the amount of thermal energy required to raise the temperature of 1 g of the substance by 1 °C. The usual unit for this quantity is joules per gram kelvin (J/g · K). Degrees Celsius may be substituted for kelvins since the degree sizes are equal. For example, 1 g of water can be raised 1 °C with the input of 4.18 J of energy. Thus, the specific heat of water is 4.18 J/g ·°C.

Specific heats of some common substances are listed in Table 15-2. Substances with high specific heats require large amounts of energy for a given temperature change and will change temperature only slowly. Substances with low specific heats require comparatively small amounts of energy for a given temperature change and will change temperature rapidly under the same conditions. The thermal energy input can be found with the equation

$$Q = c_{sp} m \Delta T,$$

where Q is the thermal energy in joules, c_{sp} is its specific heat in joules per gram degree Celsius, m is the mass of the substance in grams, and ΔT is its change in temperature in degrees Celsius.

TABLE 15-2 *Specific Heats*

Substance	Specific Heat (J/g · °C)
lead	0.13
mercury	0.14
silver	0.23
copper	0.38
iron	0.45
chlorine	0.48
carbon (diamond)	0.51
aluminum	0.90
oxygen	0.92
benzene	1.73
steam	2.00
acetic acid	2.05
ice	2.11
ethanol	2.53
water	4.18

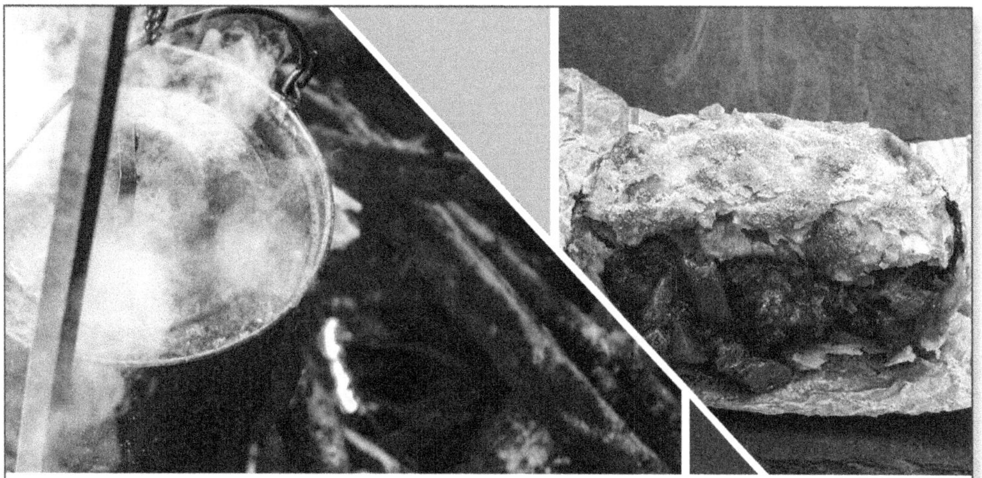

Rates of cooling are also related to specific heat. Substances with high specific heat values retain heat for longer periods than those with low specific heats. For example, the dry crust of a meat turnover may be slightly warm while the filling is still hot enough to scorch your tongue. Like enthalpies of vaporization, specific heats serve as rough indicators of intermolecular attractions. Particles that are strongly attracted to each other require extra thermal energy to increase their kinetic energies. Using the equation above for a cooling process, that is, releasing heat, would produce a negative change in temperature and a negative value for Q.

The heating curve of a substance reveals its relative specific heat. If temperature rises quickly with the addition of thermal energy, the specific heat must be low. In such a case, a small amount of heat results in a large change in temperature. A substance that has a gentle slope on its heating curve has a high specific heat because added energy does not change the temperature very much.

EXAMPLE 15-2: CALCULATING THERMAL ENERGY

A 28.35 g sample of silver is heated from 15.2 °C to 85.6 °C. How many joules were added to the sample?

Write what you know.

$c_{sp\ silver} = 0.23\ J/g \cdot °C$ (from Table 15-2)
$m = 28.35\ g$
$T_i = 15.2\ °C$
$T_f = 85.6\ °C$
$Q = ?$

Write the formula and solve for the unknown.

$$Q = c_{sp}m\Delta T$$
$$= c_{sp}m(T_f - T_i)$$

Plug in known values and evaluate.

$$Q = \left(\frac{0.23\ J}{\cancel{g} \cdot °C}\right)(28.35\ \cancel{g})(85.6\ °C - 15.2\ °C)$$
$$= \left(\frac{0.23\ J}{\cancel{°C}}\right)(28.35)(70.4\ \cancel{°C})$$
$$= 459\ J$$

The given change in temperature requires the addition of 459 J of energy.

Thermochemistry 361

UNDERSTANDING SPECIFIC HEAT

Use **Socratic questioning** to help students understand specific heat.

1. Why do you believe that a large body of water stays warm even after it has been cold outside for a while? *(The specific heat of water is so much higher than the specific heat of air that it requires much more energy and time to change the water's temperature.)*
2. Why is the specific heat of water higher than the specific heat of air? (Lead them to recall the properties of water.) *(The specific heat of water is higher due to the hydrogen bonds that join the multitude of water molecules. For the temperature of water to increase, the water molecules must vibrate to break the hydrogen bonds. To break these strong bonds, a high amount of energy must be added.)*

THERMAL ENERGY

Use the following **formative assessment** to check students' understanding.

1. If 1254 J of energy are added to 232 g of benzene at 22.0 °C, what will its final temperature be?

   What we know: $Q = 1254\ J$, $m = 232\ g$, $T_i = 22.0\ °C$, $c_{sp} = 1.73\ J/g \cdot °C$

   Unknown: T_f

   Write the formula and solve for the unknown.

   $$Q = c_{sp}m\,\Delta T$$
   $$Q = c_{sp}m(T_f - T_i)$$
   $$\frac{Q}{c_{sp}m} = \frac{\cancel{c_{sp}}\cancel{m}(T_f - T_i)}{\cancel{c_{sp}}\cancel{m}}$$
   $$T_f \cancel{- T_i} \cancel{+ T_i} = \frac{Q}{c_{sp}m} + T_i$$
   $$T_f = \frac{Q}{c_{sp}m} + T_i$$

   Evaluate.

   $$T_f = \frac{1254\ \cancel{J}}{\left(1.73\ \frac{\cancel{J}}{\cancel{g} \cdot °C}\right)(232\ \cancel{g})} + 22.0\ °C$$
   $$= 3.1\underline{2}4\ °C + 22.0\ °C$$
   $$= 25.1\ °C$$

2. A 31.35 g mass of iron is heated from 29.7 °C to 74.3 °C. How many joules were added to accomplish this?

   What we know: $m = 31.35\ g$, $T_i = 29.7\ °C$, $T_f = 74.3\ °C$, $c_{sp} = 0.45\ J/g \cdot °C$

   Unknown: Q

   Write the formula and solve for the unknown.

   $$Q = c_{sp}m\Delta T$$
   $$= c_{sp}m(T_f - T_i)$$

   Evaluate.

   $$Q = \left(0.45\ \frac{J}{\cancel{g} \cdot °C}\right)(31.35\ \cancel{g})(74.3\ °C - 29.7\ °C)$$
   $$= \left(0.45\ \frac{J}{\cancel{°C}}\right)(31.35)(44.6\ \cancel{°C})$$
   $$= 629\ J$$

DEMONSTRATING HOW TO CREATE YOUR OWN HEATING CURVE

Demonstrate the latent heat in the phase change of ice to water.

Materials: ring stand and iron ring, wire gauze, laboratory burner, 500 mL beaker, crushed ice, water, thermometer, timer, graph paper

Preparation: Set up the ring stand, iron ring, and wire gauze with the burner underneath. You can also perform this demonstration on a kitchen stovetop with a double boiler and a candy thermometer.

Performance/Discussion: Fill a beaker with crushed ice and water. Record the temperature, and then heat the beaker over a laboratory burner. Measure and record the temperature in the beaker every minute until all the ice is melted. If you have time, continue heating the water until it boils and begins to turn to steam. Make sure that the thermometer doesn't touch the side or bottom of the beaker.

Have students use the data to create a graph in which the *x*-axis is time and the *y*-axis is temperature. Their graphs should look very similar to the graph on pages 358 and 363.

APPLY

LAB 15A: *HOT SHOT*

Once students have an understanding of the material in Section 15.1, they should be ready to work through Lab 15A.

ASSESS

TICKET OUT THE DOOR

As a **summarizing activity**, assess students' understanding by assigning each student to use the information learned in Section 15.1 to create a quiz question on a note card. Students should write the answers to their questions on the back of the note card. This can be used as a class review for Section 15.1 by having students post their questions and answers to Quizlet or another quiz generating application or website.

EXAMPLE 15-3: CALCULATING TEMPERATURE CHANGE

If 942 J of thermal energy are added to 50.0 g of water at 25.1 °C, what will its final temperature be?

Write what you know.

$Q = 942\text{ J}$
$c_{\text{sp water}} = 4.18\text{ J/g}\cdot\text{°C}$ (from Table 15-2)
$m = 50.0\text{ g}$
$T_i = 25.1\text{ °C}$
$T_f = ?$

Write the formula and solve for the unknown.

$$Q = c_{sp} m\,\Delta T$$
$$= c_{sp} m\,(T_f - T_i)$$

$$\frac{Q}{c_{sp}m} = \frac{\cancel{c_{sp}m}\,(T_f - T_i)}{\cancel{c_{sp}m}}$$
$$T_f \cancel{- T_i} \cancel{+ T_i} = \frac{Q}{c_{sp}m} + T_i$$
$$T_f = \frac{Q}{c_{sp}m} + T_i$$

Plug in known values and evaluate.

$$T_f = \frac{942\,\cancel{\text{J}}}{(4.18\,\cancel{\text{J}}/\cancel{\text{g}}\cdot\text{°C})(50.0\,\cancel{\text{g}})} + 25.1\text{ °C}$$
$$= 4.5\underline{0}7\text{ °C} + 25.1\text{ °C}$$
$$= 29.6\text{ °C}$$

The final temperature is 29.6 °C.

A Complex Thermodynamic Problem

The last two subsections have described measurements of energy changes in substances. These include molar enthalpy of fusion, molar enthalpy of vaporization, and specific heat. How can this information be used?

Suppose you try your hand at frying ice cubes. You start with an ice cube with a mass of 5.00 g at a temperature of 0 °C. If that ice cube is heated until it is completely converted to steam at 100 °C, how many joules of energy must be added?

Remember, latent heat is thermal energy added to make a phase change with no change in temperature, and sensible heat is thermal energy added with a noticeable temperature change.

In this example, ice is being converted to water and then to steam. The first step is to gather all the needed values from Tables 15-1 and 15-2.

Use the heating curve at right to guide your calculations. You will need to calculate the energy needed to melt the ice (Segment 1), heat the liquid water (Segment 2), and finally, vaporize the water (Segment 3).

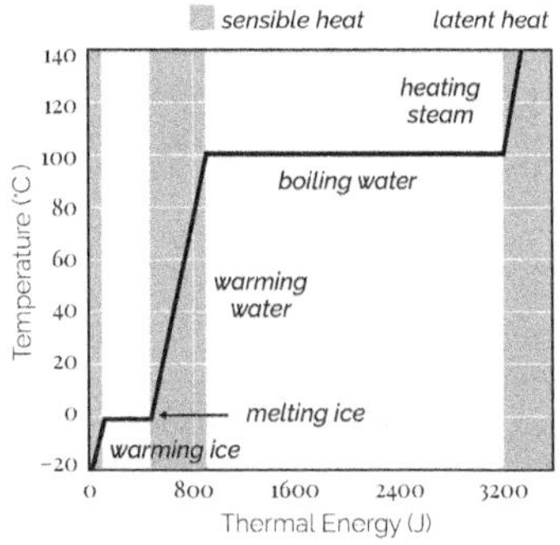

EXAMPLE 15-4:
CALCULATING ENERGY IN A COMPLEX THERMODYNAMIC PROBLEM

Write what you know.

$c_{sp\,water} = 4.18\ J/g\cdot°C$ (from Table 15-2)
$m = 5.00\ g$
$\Delta H_{fus} = 6.01\ kJ/mol$ (from Table 15-1)
$\Delta H_{vap} = 40.7\ kJ/mol$ (from Table 15-1)
$T_i = 0.0\ °C$
$T_f = 100.0\ °C$
$Q = ?$

Segment 1 (melting ice)
Convert mass of ice to energy required to melt.

$$Q_1 = 5.00\ \cancel{g\ H_2O}\left(\frac{1\ \cancel{mol\ H_2O}}{18.02\ \cancel{g\ H_2O}}\right)\left(\frac{6.01\ kJ}{1\ \cancel{mol\ H_2O}}\right) = 1.667\ kJ$$

Segment 2 (heating water)
Write the formula and solve for the unknown.

$$Q = c_{sp}m\ \Delta T$$
$$Q = c_{sp}m\ (T_f - T_i)$$

Plug in known values and evaluate.

$$Q_2 = \left(\frac{4.18\ J}{\cancel{g}\cdot°C}\right)(5.00\ \cancel{g})(100.0\ °C - 0.0\ °C)$$
$$= \left(\frac{4.18\ J}{\cancel{°C}}\right)(5.00\ \cancel{g})(100.0\ \cancel{°C})$$
$$= 2090\ J = 2.090\ kJ$$

Segment 3 (boiling water)
Convert mass of water to energy required to boil.

$$Q_3 = 5.00\ \cancel{g\ H_2O}\left(\frac{1\ \cancel{mol\ H_2O}}{18.02\ \cancel{g\ H_2O}}\right)\left(\frac{40.7\ kJ}{1\ \cancel{mol\ H_2O}}\right) = 11.29\ kJ$$

Total Energy

$$Q_{total} = Q_1 + Q_2 + Q_3 = 1.667\ kJ + 2.090\ kJ + 11.29\ kJ$$
$$= 15.0\ kJ$$

It will take 15.0 kJ of energy to convert 5.00 g of ice at 0.0 °C to steam at 100.0 °C.

15.1 SECTION REVIEW

1. Define *thermochemistry*.
2. What is the difference between thermal energy, heat, and temperature? What units are used to measure each?
3. What does a scientist use a calorimeter for?
4. Compare sensible heat and latent heat.
5. Explain how sensible heat and latent heat interact to change a substance from a solid to a gas.
6. How does the specific heat of a substance relate to its ability to change temperature?
7. Define *molar enthalpy of fusion*, *molar enthalpy of vaporization*, and *specific heat*.
8. How much thermal energy is needed to accomplish the change in each case below?
   a. melt 355 g of ethanol at its melting point
   b. vaporize 515 g of methanol at its boiling point
9. How much heat energy is lost by a 53.6 g piece of copper when it cools from 95.7 °C to 22.5 °C?

DIFFERENTIATED INSTRUCTION

A Muggy Scenario

Prompt students to do a **turn and talk**. Ask the following question and have students turn to a peer nearby and allow them two minutes to talk with their partner about the answer to the question.

"If the specific heat of the air is about 1 J/(g·°C), how do the conditions on a muggy day affect the temperature of the atmosphere?" *(On a muggy day, there is more water in the air. Since water has a higher specific heat than air, the atmosphere will change temperature much more slowly.)*

When the time is up, select students to share their answers with the class and discuss anything that needs clarifying.

15.1 REVIEW ANSWERS

* An asterisk following a question number indicates that a worked-out solution can be found on page 385A.

1. Thermochemistry is the branch of science that studies the transfer of energy during physical and chemical changes. *(p. 357)*

2. *Thermal energy* is the total kinetic energy of the particles in a sample. *Heat* is the amount of thermal energy transferred from one substance to another. *Temperature* is a measure of the average kinetic energy of the particles in a sample. Thermal energy and heat are both measured in joules. Temperature is measured in kelvins or degrees Celsius. *(p. 357)*

3. A calorimeter is used to accurately determine the enthalpy change that occurs during a chemical reaction. *(p. 357)*

4. *Sensible heat* is the transfer of thermal energy that causes a temperature change in a substance. *Latent heat* is the transfer of thermal energy that causes a change in state without changing the temperature of a substance. *(p. 358)*

5. These two forms of energy work together to change a substance from a solid to a gas. Sensible heat is the thermal energy needed to warm a solid to its melting point, a liquid from its melting point to its boiling point, and a gas to any temperature above its boiling point. Latent heat is the thermal energy needed to change the state of a substance at each point—solid to liquid and liquid to gas. *(pp. 358–59)*

6. The lower the specific heat of a substance, the less energy is required to increase its temperature. Thus, a substance with a low specific heat will warm faster than a substance with a high specific heat. *(p. 360)*

7. All three terms indicate the amount of energy needed to cause a change in a given amount of a substance. The *molar enthalpy of fusion* is the amount of thermal energy needed to melt a mole of a given substance. The *molar enthalpy of vaporization* is the amount of thermal energy needed to change a mole of a given substance from a liquid to a gas. The *specific heat* is the amount of thermal energy needed to change 1 g of a substance 1 °C. *(pp. 359–60)*

8.* **a.** 38.1 kJ
b. 566 kJ *(all p. 359)*

9.* $-1530\ J = -1.53 \times 10^3\ J$ *(pp. 360–62)*

MINI LAB: *COMPARING THERMAL ENERGY TRANSFER*

Use this **mini lab** to help students determine whether equal volumes of metal contain the same amount of energy.

Answers

1. Answers will vary. *Example*: Two cubes of the same size but made of different materials will transfer the same amount of thermal energy.
2. Heating the two cubes to the boiling point of water and leaving them in the boiling water for 3 min ensures that both cubes will be at the same temperature. The temperature will be that of the boiling water—approximately 100 °C.
3. nickel
4. The two cubes, nickel and aluminum, have equal volumes. Aluminum has a higher specific heat, so it transfers more energy per degree temperature change. But nickel is denser than aluminum, so it has more mass, that is, particles, per unit of volume. The greater mass means that volume for volume, nickel contains more total thermal energy than aluminum.
5. A materials engineer who is considering using a metal in a situation involving thermal energy transfer must consider not only the volume and type of metal involved but also the density of the metal since specific heat is a measure of energy per unit of mass, not volume.

MINI LAB

COMPARING THERMAL ENERGY TRANSFER

In days gone by, some people used to keep their feet warm at night by placing a pan of hot coals from a fire under the covers at the foot of the bed. Sounds risky, but it did demonstrate that thermal energy can be transferred from one object (a burning coal) through another object (the pan) to a third object (the cold feet). In this lab activity, you will use a similar process to test the heat-transferring abilities of some metal cubes.

Do equal volumes of metal contain the same amount of thermal energy?

1. Do you think that cubes of two different metals with equal volumes will transfer the same amount of thermal energy? State your answer in the form of a hypothesis.

Procedure

A. Fill each of the beakers with 300 mL of water. Place one beaker on the hot plate and record the starting temperature of the water in the other two beakers.

B. Use the tongs to place the aluminum and nickel cubes into the beaker on the hot plate. Set the hot plate on high and bring the water to a boil. Leave the cubes in the boiling water for 3 min.

2. What do we know about the temperatures of the two cubes at this point? Explain.

C. Turn off the hot plate. Carefully use tongs to remove one of the blocks and place it into one of the room-temperature beakers. Place the remaining block in the other beaker.

D. Monitor the temperature in the beakers with the cubes until each temperature no longer changes. Record the final temperature for each beaker. Subtract the initial temperature from the final temperature to determine the temperature change in each beaker.

3. Which cube caused a greater temperature change?

Conclusion

4. Suggest an explanation for the result that you observed.

Going Further

5. How might what you observed be important for a materials engineer to consider?

EQUIPMENT
- hot plate
- beaker, 400 mL (3)
- thermometers (2)
- tongs
- density cubes, aluminum and nickel (one of each)
- goggles

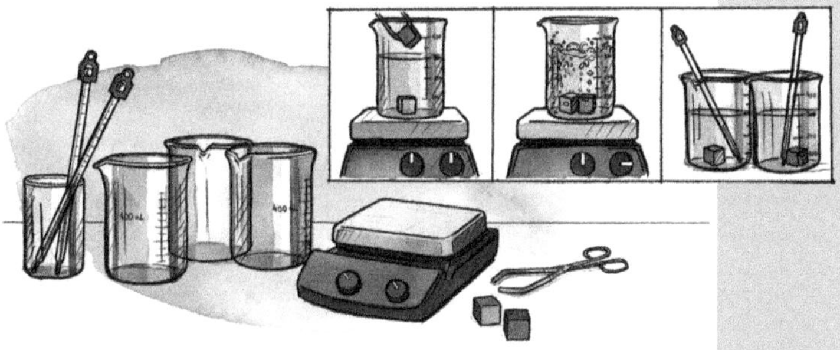

15.2 THERMODYNAMICS AND CHEMICAL CHANGES

QUESTIONS

- » How can I know whether a reaction is exothermic or endothermic?
- » How can I determine the energy change in a multistep reaction?

TERMS

enthalpy of reaction • thermochemical equation • standard molar enthalpy of formation • standard molar enthalpy of combustion • Hess's law

Enthalpy (Heat) of Reaction

The concept of enthalpy is especially valuable to scientists studying the energy changes of chemical reactions. They call the change in enthalpy that occurs during a reaction the **enthalpy** (heat) **of reaction** (ΔH_r). The enthalpy change of a reaction is the difference between the enthalpy of the products and the enthalpy of the reactants.

$$\Delta H_r = H_{products} - H_{reactants}$$

The formation of water from its two elements illustrates this process. When 1 mol of hydrogen gas is ignited in the presence of 0.5 mol of oxygen gas, an explosive reaction forms 1 mol of water. Careful measurements reveal that 285.8 kJ of thermal energy are released in the explosion.

$$H_2(g) + 0.5O_2(g) \longrightarrow H_2O(l) \quad \Delta H_r = -285.8 \text{ kJ}$$

Because the coefficients in this balanced equation represent moles of substances and not particles, it is permissible to use fractions in order to show the formation of a single mole of a product. The above equation shows the formation of 1 mol of water. Since there is a direct relationship between enthalpy and molar quantities, the standard balanced equation shown below is used. Note that 2 mol of water is produced.

$$2H_2(g) + O_2(g) \longrightarrow 2H_2O(l) \quad \Delta H_r = -571.6 \text{ kJ}$$

A chemical equation such as this one that shows the reactants, products, and amount of energy that is released or absorbed as heat is called a **thermochemical equation**. These equations show the physical state of each substance because the physical states affect how ΔH for the reaction is calculated.

Are chemical reactions ever cold?

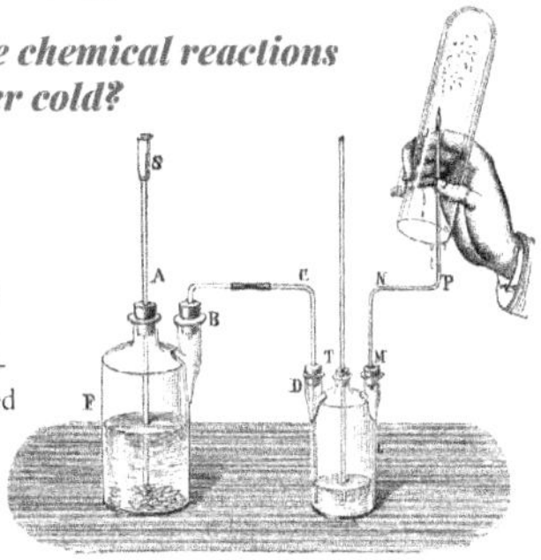

▲ Hydrogen combustion. The experiment shown above is demonstrating the production of water from hydrogen and oxygen.

SECTION 15.2 *OVERVIEW*

Essential Question

Are chemical reactions ever cold?

Objectives

- » **15.2.1** Determine whether a given reaction is endothermic or exothermic by calculating its change in enthalpy.
- » **15.2.2** Determine the enthalpy of a reaction on the basis of Hess's law.

Resource

Demonstrating Endothermic Reactions

ENGAGE

PHASE CHANGE REVIEW

Review prior information using the **student generated quiz** questions from the Ticket Out the Door activity in Section 15.1. Have students trade their quiz questions with a nearby peer. Each student should answer the question on a separate sheet of paper without looking at the answer on the back of the note card. Have students then give their answer sheets and questions back to their peers for grading. Allow time for students who got a correct answer to teach the material to their peers.

After everyone has finished, discuss any difficult concepts with the class and allow for any necessary discussion.

INSTRUCT

CHEMICAL CHANGES

Direct students to create a **concept map** for the terms that they will see throughout Sections 15.2 and 15.3. The title written in the center of the map should be "Chemical Changes." The branches extending from the center should indicate the section's highlighted terms. Students should begin with enthalpy of reaction and then write the equation and definition. As you cover the section, have students add terms, definitions, equations, and examples.

TYPES OF CHEMICAL REACTIONS

Lead a **review** on the types of chemical reactions from Chapter 10. Ask students to identify the types of chemical reactions. *(synthesis, decomposition, combustion, single-replacement, and double-replacement)* Students should be able to describe and give examples of each type of reaction.

EXOTHERMIC REACTIONS

Assess prior knowledge with a **review** of exothermic reactions (Ch. 2). Ask students where the thermal energy comes from in an exothermic reaction. *(Thermal energy comes out of chemical bonds when they are formed.)*

Lead students to recall that breaking the old bonds absorbs a small amount of energy, and forming the new bonds releases a large amount of energy. Therefore, the net change is a release of energy: the energy leaves the bonds and is transferred to either the motion of the particles or the surroundings.

DEMONSTRATING ENDOTHERMIC REACTIONS

Demonstrate the endothermic reaction below.

$$Ba(OH)_2 + 8H_2O\,(s) + 2NH_4Cl\,(s) \longrightarrow BaCl_2\,(s) + 10H_2O\,(l) + 2NH_3(g)$$

Materials: $Ba(OH)_2 \cdot 8H_2O$ (barium hydroxide octahydrate, 20 g), NH_4Cl (ammonium chloride, 10 g), water, 125 mL Erlenmeyer flask, digital thermometer, petri dish or other dish large enough to hold the flask, stirring rod

Note: Barium hydroxide is toxic and can be deadly if ingested. Work in a well-ventilated area and use gloves and goggles.

Preparation: Place the thermometer and 20 g of $Ba(OH)_2 \cdot 8H_2O$ into a clean, dry flask. Add 1 mL of water to the petri dish.

Procedure: Place the flask in the petri dish. Add 10 g of NH_4Cl to the flask and carefully stir. From a distance, record the temperature and watch while the mixture goes from a *solid* to a slushy liquid as the reaction progresses. Ammonia gas will be released during the reaction; you may choose to pass a piece of litmus paper over the flask to show the alkalinity of ammonia. Wait several minutes for the reaction to finish, and then record the final temperature and carefully lift the beaker.

Note: The flask may be extremely cold. Wear gloves or an oven mitt when handling the frozen flask.

Heat of Reaction

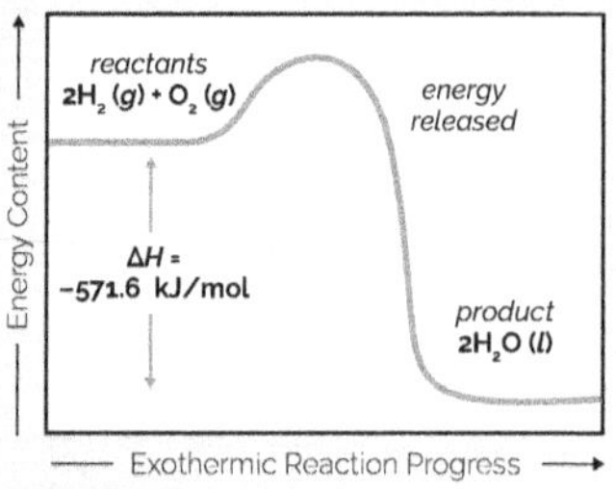

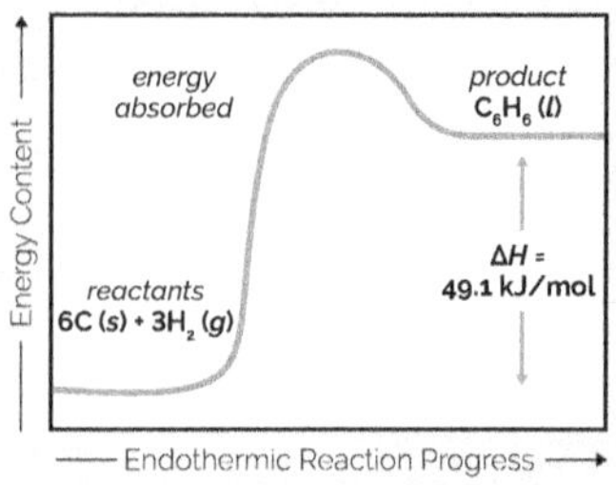

Exothermic

The products in an exothermic reaction have a lower enthalpy than the reactants. This means that energy is released during the reaction and the enthalpy of the reaction (ΔH_r) is a negative value. Therefore, all exothermic reactions have negative values for ΔH_r. The graph above illustrates the energy changes in exothermic reactions. The products have a lower enthalpy than the reactants, and the difference is released as energy.

Endothermic reactions absorb energy, resulting in a greater amount of energy in the products.

Endothermic

Products of endothermic reactions have a higher enthalpy than the reactants because energy has been absorbed. An endothermic reaction has a positive value for ΔH_r. The graph above illustrates the difference in energies between the reactants and the products of an endothermic reaction.

The endothermic formation of one mole of benzene has the following thermochemical equation.

$$6C(s) + 3H_2(g) \longrightarrow C_6H_6(l)$$
$$\Delta H_f = 49.1\ \text{kJ}$$

If the ΔH_f is known, the ΔH_r of the reverse reaction can be easily calculated. The ΔH_r of the reverse reaction has the same magnitude but the opposite sign of the ΔH_f of the forward reaction.

For example, the reaction that formed a mole of liquid water had a ΔH_f of −285.8 kJ (the negative sign indicates that energy is given off). A reaction that decomposes the same amount of water has a ΔH_r of 285.8 kJ (energy absorbed).

Enthalpy (Heat) of Formation

Chemists could measure the change in enthalpy for thousands of known reactions, but measuring so many reactions would be difficult and the data would fill several volumes of books. Therefore, a quick technique for calculating changes in enthalpy was devised. Enthalpy in a substance varies with temperature and pressure, so these conditions must be specified. In thermodynamics, the *standard state* is defined as 25 °C (298 K, or roughly room temperature) and 101.325 kPa of pressure (normal atmospheric pressure at sea level).

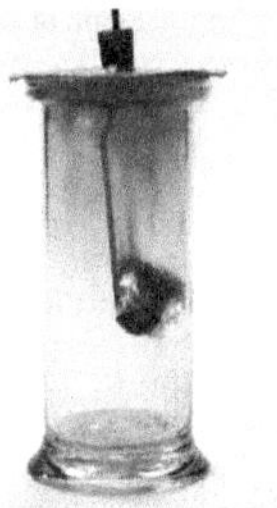

iron burning in chlorine gas

366 Chapter 15

Results: The reaction is so strongly endothermic that the water in the petri dish will freeze and stick to the flask. Ask students whether this reaction has a negative or positive enthalpy of reaction (ΔH). *(positive)* You may also want to ask students where they think the water in the flask came from. Point out the waters of hydration in barium hydroxide's chemical formula to help them answer.

Cleanup: The barium chloride salt produced in this reaction is a toxic chemical. Check your local and state regulations before discarding.

DIFFERENT STATES OF ENTHALPY

Stress to students that the state of matter is important. For example, liquid water has a different ΔH°_f than gaseous water does. See Appendix H in the Student Edition for the various ΔH°_f values of water.

The **standard molar enthalpy of formation** is defined as the enthalpy change to produce 1 mol of a compound in its standard state from its elements in their standard states. We use the notation ΔH°_f; the degree symbol signifies that this ΔH refers to standard conditions. For example, the standard state of water is liquid; the standard state of gold is solid. Table 15-3 lists several standard molar enthalpies of formation. Appendix H contains a more extensive listing. A quick look at the appendix will show that most values for ΔH°_f are negative. Thus the synthesis reactions that produce most of the common compounds are exothermic. Compounds with large negative numbers release large amounts of energy when they form. Molecules such as Cl_2, H_2, and O_2 have no enthalpies of formation because these substances are the reference points with which the enthalpies of compounds are compared. This is true for every element in its naturally occurring pure form.

TABLE 15-3 *Standard Molar Enthalpies of Formation*

Compound	ΔH°_f (kJ/mol)
Fe_2O_3 (*s*)	−824.2
NH_4NO_3 (*s*)	−365.6
NO (*g*)	91.3
NO_2 (*g*)	33.2
$PbCl_2$ (*s*)	−359.4

EXAMPLE 15-5: CALCULATING ΔH°_F

What is the ΔH°_f for $N_2 + 2O_2 \longrightarrow 2NO_2$?

Solution

Table 15-3 shows that the standard molar enthalpy of formation of nitrogen dioxide is 33.2 kJ/mol. The given reaction forms 2 mol of nitrogen dioxide.

$$2\ \cancel{\text{mol } NO_2}\left(\frac{33.2\ \text{kJ}}{1\ \cancel{\text{mol } NO_2}}\right) = 66.4\ \text{kJ}$$

Enthalpy (Heat) of Combustion

Combustion reactions produce energy in the form of heat and light. They all involve a reaction with oxygen. The most significant combustion reactions occur with hydrocarbons—organic compounds containing carbon and hydrogen. Carbon dioxide and water are the typical products. The **standard molar enthalpy of combustion** (ΔH°_c) is defined as the thermal energy released by the complete burning of one mole of a substance at standard conditions. For example, propane, the gas used for most outdoor grills, is useful because of the heat released during its combustion. The thermochemical equation for the complete combustion of propane is shown below.

$$C_3H_8(g) + 5O_2(g) \longrightarrow 3CO_2(g) + 4H_2O(l)$$

$$\Delta H^\circ_c = -2219.2\ \text{kJ/mol}$$

A list of values for the enthalpy of combustion for some other common compounds is found in Table 15-4. All the values are negative because these reactions are all exothermic. As a rule, the larger the molecule is, the more energy is released.

TABLE 15-4 *Standard Molar Enthalpies of Combustion*

Substance	Formula	ΔH°_c (kJ/mol)
carbon monoxide (*g*)	CO	−283.4
graphite (*s*)	C	−393.5
hydrogen (*g*)	H_2	−285.8
methane (*g*)	CH_4	−890.8
propane (*g*)	C_3H_8	−2219.2
sucrose (*s*)	$C_{12}H_{22}O_{11}$	−5647

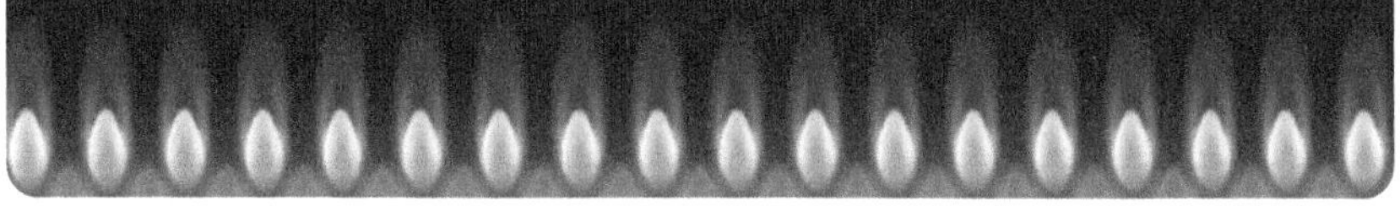

Thermochemistry 367

CALCULATING ENTHALPIES OF REACTION

Prompt students to create a **sequence chart** on calculating enthalpies of reaction. After reviewing the example provided on this page, have students list the steps for calculating enthalpies of reaction. They will need to refer to Appendix H in the Student Edition to find the enthalpies of formation.

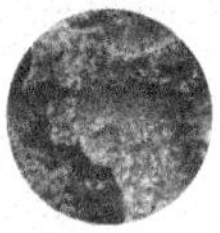

CALCULATING ENTHALPIES *of Reaction*

A chemical reaction can be viewed as two chemical processes. In the first step, each reactant breaks down to its elements in their standard states. In the second step, the elements in their standard states recombine to form the products. Remember that the formation and breakdown of a particular substance are opposite processes and must therefore have opposite signs. If a reaction is endothermic in one direction, it will be exothermic in the other.

The following reaction between lead(II) oxide and carbon monoxide will illustrate this two-process approach.

$$PbO(s) + CO(g) \longrightarrow Pb(s) + CO_2(g) \quad \Delta H^\circ r = -65.7 \text{ kJ}$$

1 The first step in the reaction is the breakdown of lead(II) oxide and carbon monoxide.

The ΔH°_f for lead(II) oxide is −217.3 kJ/mol (Appendix H). The breakdown of lead(II) oxide, which is the reverse reaction, requires 217.3 kJ.

$$PbO(s) \underset{-217.3 \text{ kJ}}{\overset{217.3 \text{ kJ}}{\rightleftharpoons}} Pb(s) + \tfrac{1}{2}O_2(g)$$

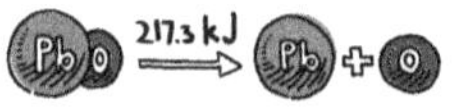

The ΔH°_f for carbon monoxide is −110.5 kJ/mol, so the breakdown of carbon monoxide to its elements requires 110.5 kJ/mol.

$$CO(g) \underset{-110.5 \text{ kJ}}{\overset{110.5 \text{ kJ}}{\rightleftharpoons}} C(s) + \tfrac{1}{2}O_2(g)$$

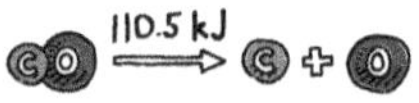

The ΔH° for the first part of the reaction is obtained by adding together the two quantities of energy required to break the compounds apart. Their sum is 327.8 kJ.

2 The second part of the reaction is the formation of products.

The ΔH° for each of these changes can be easily found in the table listing values of ΔH°_f. Since lead is an element in its standard state, its ΔH°_f is zero. The ΔH°_f for the formation of 1 mol of carbon dioxide from its elements at standard conditions is −393.5 kJ.

$$C(s) + O_2(g) \underset{393.5 \text{ kJ}}{\overset{-393.5 \text{ kJ}}{\rightleftharpoons}} CO_2(g)$$

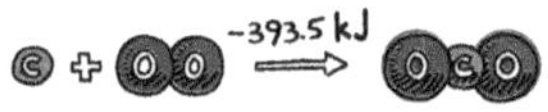

The total ΔH° for the formation of products is therefore −393.5 kJ.

By adding the enthalpy for the breakdown of reactants to the enthalpy for the formation of products, we get the ΔH°_r for the reaction, which is −65.7 kJ. This result shows that the reaction is exothermic.

In this problem, calculating the ΔH°_r of the whole reaction involved combining the values for ΔH°_f in two partial reactions.

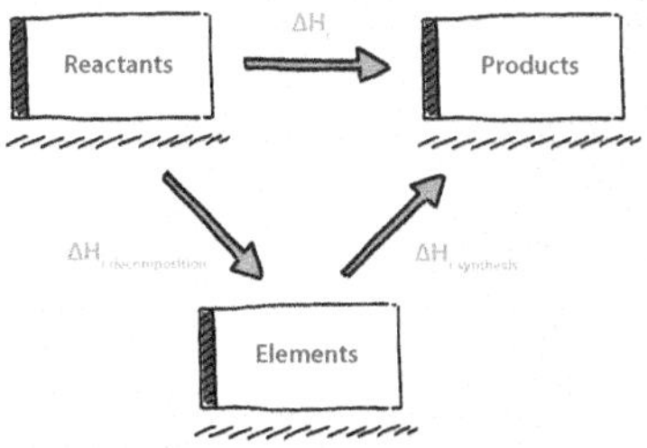

Hess's law states that the enthalpy change of a reaction equals the sum of the enthalpy changes for each step of the process.

The example below shows how one reaction could be thought of as the sum of two other reactions. The first reaction breaks apart the reactants and the second puts them back together in a different arrangement.

$PbO + CO \longrightarrow \cancel{Pb} + \cancel{O_2} + \cancel{C}$ $\Delta H° = 327.8$ kJ

$\cancel{Pb} + \cancel{O_2} + \cancel{C} \longrightarrow Pb + CO_2$ $\Delta H° = -393.5$ kJ

$PbO + CO \longrightarrow Pb + CO_2$ $\Delta H° = -65.7$ kJ

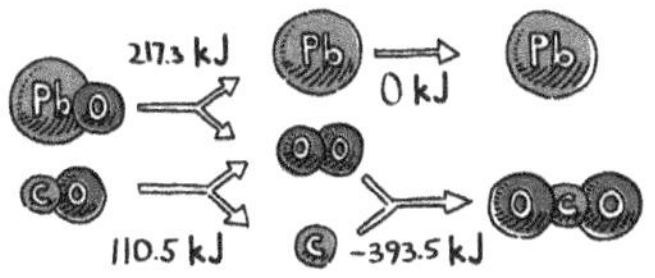

The enthalpy change of the net reaction equals the sum of the enthalpy changes for the two steps. Notice how the common reactants and products cancel each other. The mathematical version of this statement is shown below.

$$\Delta H°_{reaction} = \Delta H°_{reactant\ decomposition} + \Delta H°_{product\ synthesis}$$

Because the $\Delta H°_f$ values in the table refer to the formation of compounds from elements, the values for reactant-decomposition enthalpies will be opposite in sign to those listed. Consequently, the equation can be changed to a form that uses the data in Appendix H without changing the signs. The symbol Σ in this equation is the Greek letter *sigma*. It signifies a summation of numbers.

$$\Delta H°_{reaction} = \Sigma\Delta H°_{f\ (products)} - \Sigma\Delta H°_{f\ (reactants)}$$

There are two general principles for combining thermochemical equations.

1. When using Hess's law, you may use any valid balanced equation, but remember to change the sign on the $\Delta H°$ if you reverse the equation.
2. Multiply the coefficients of a balanced equation to get the desired equation when the coefficients are added together, but remember to also multiply the $\Delta H°$ by the same number.

Thermochemistry **369**

CALCULATING ENTHALPIES OF REACTION

Use the following **formative assessment** to check students' understanding.

1. Calculate the standard change in enthalpy ($\Delta H°_r$) for the following reaction.

   $3NO_2\ (g) + H_2O\ (l) \longrightarrow 2HNO_3\ (l) + NO\ (g)$

   What we know: $\Delta H_f\ (NO_2) = 33.2$ kJ/mol, $\Delta H°_f\ (H_2O) = -285.8$ kJ/mol, $\Delta H°_f\ (HNO_3) = -174.1$ kJ/mol, $\Delta H°_f\ (NO) = 91.3$ kJ/mol

   Unknown: $\Delta H°_r$

   Write the formula and solve for the unknown.

   $\Delta H°_r = \Sigma H°_{products} - \Sigma H°_{reactants}$

   Plug in known values and evaluate.

   $$\Delta H°_r = \left[(2\ \cancel{mol\ HNO_3})\left(\frac{-174.1\ kJ}{\cancel{mol\ HNO_3}}\right) + (1\ \cancel{mol\ NO})\left(\frac{91.3\ kJ}{\cancel{mol\ NO}}\right)\right] - \left[(3\ \cancel{mol\ NO_2})\left(\frac{33.2\ kJ}{\cancel{mol\ NO_2}}\right) + (1\ \cancel{mol\ H_2O})\left(\frac{-285.8\ kJ}{\cancel{mol\ H_2O}}\right)\right]$$

   $= -256.9\ kJ - (-186.2\ kJ)$

   $= -70.7\ kJ$

2. Is the following reaction endothermic or exothermic, given that the $\Delta H°_f\ (PCl_3) = -319.7$ kJ/mol?

   $P_4 + 6Cl_2 \longrightarrow 4PCl_3$

   $\Delta H° = (4\ mol)(-319.7\ kJ/mol) = -1279\ kJ$

   It is exothermic.

DIFFERENTIATED INSTRUCTION

Hess's Law

Lead students to create an **illustration** of Hess's law like the one on the reduced student page above. They should include the information within the black box regarding the two general principles for combining thermochemical equations. Be sure to have them emphasize the equation used to calculate enthalpy change:

$$\Delta H°_r = \Sigma H°_{products} - \Sigma H°_{reactants}$$

After students have illustrated Hess's law, apply it by going over the example on page 370. Direct students to add to their illustration the steps used to calculate the change in enthalpy.

ASSESS

TICKET OUT THE DOOR

Check for understanding with this **summarizing activity**. Ask, "In an endothermic reaction, how does the enthalpy of the reactants compare to the enthalpy of the products?" *(The reactants have less enthalpy.)*

15.2 REVIEW ANSWERS

* An asterisk following a question number indicates that a worked-out solution can be found on page 385A.

1. An *endothermic reaction* is a reaction that takes in energy, meaning that the products have more thermal energy than the reactants had. An *exothermic reaction* is a reaction that gives off energy—the products have less thermal energy than the reactants had. *(p. 366)*

2. Enthalpy is the amount of thermal energy in a system. During a chemical reaction we calculate the change in enthalpy. An exothermic reaction loses thermal energy, so the products have less thermal energy than the reactants had. The negative change in enthalpy indicates the amount of energy lost by the system. *(p. 366)*

3. *Enthalpy of reaction* is the change in thermal energy during a chemical reaction. *Standard molar enthalpy of formation* is the thermal energy change to produce 1 mol of a compound in its standard state from its elements in their standard states. *Standard molar enthalpy of combustion* is the thermal energy released by the complete burning of 1 mol of a substance at standard conditions. *(pp. 365–67)*

4. STP is defined as 273 K and 101.325 kPa of pressure, respectively. Standard state has the same pressure of 101.325 kPa, but the temperature is 298 K. *(p. 366)*

5. Find the sum of the enthalpies of reaction for each of the subordinate steps. *(p. 369)*

6.*a. –91.8 kJ; exothermic

b. 108.5 kJ; endothermic *(all pp. 368–69)*

7.* 14.7 kJ *(pp. 368–69)*

8. Ammonium chloride would be less effective because it is not as endothermic as ammonium nitrate and absorbs only half as much energy. *(pp. 368–69)*

9. 5075 kJ/mol C_8H_{18} *(pp. 368–69)*

EXAMPLE 15-6: CALCULATING $\Delta H°$

Estimate the $\Delta H°_f$ for the combustion of methane using standard enthalpies of formation.

$$CH_4(g) + 2O_2(g) \longrightarrow CO_2(g) + 2H_2O(l)$$

Write what you know.

The equation requires the use of the following enthalpies of formation from Appendix H.

$\Delta H°_f\,(CO_2) = -393.5$ kJ/mol
$\Delta H°_f$ (liquid H_2O) = –285.8 kJ/mol
$\Delta H°_f\,(CH_4) = -79.6$ kJ/mol
$\Delta H°_f\,(O_2) = 0$ kJ/mol

A total of 2 mol of oxygen and water participate in the reaction. This is included when calculating the enthalpy change of the entire reaction.

Write the formula and solve for the unknown.

$$\Delta H° = \Sigma\Delta H°_{f\,(products)} - \Sigma\Delta H°_{f\,(reactants)}$$

$$\Delta H° = [\Delta H°_f\,(CO_2) + \Delta H°_f\,(H_2O)] - [\Delta H°_f\,(CH_4) + \Delta H°_f\,(O_2)]$$

Plug in known values and evaluate.

$$\Delta H_r = \left[1\,\cancel{\text{mol CO}_2}\left(\frac{-393.5\text{ kJ}}{1\,\cancel{\text{mol CO}_2}}\right) + 2\,\cancel{\text{mol H}_2\text{O}}\left(\frac{-285.8\text{ kJ}}{1\,\cancel{\text{mol H}_2\text{O}}}\right)\right] - \left[1\,\cancel{\text{mol CH}_4}\left(\frac{-79.6\text{ kJ}}{1\,\cancel{\text{mol CH}_4}}\right) + 2\,\cancel{\text{mol O}_2}\left(\frac{0\text{ kJ}}{1\,\cancel{\text{mol O}_2}}\right)\right]$$

$$= (-393.5\text{ kJ} + -571.6\text{ kJ}) - (-79.6\text{ kJ} + 0\text{ kJ})$$
$$= -885.5\text{ kJ}$$

This reaction is highly exothermic.

15.2 SECTION REVIEW

1. Define *endothermic reaction* and *exothermic reaction*.
2. Does an exothermic reaction have a negative or positive change in enthalpy? Explain.
3. Define *enthalpy of reaction*, *standard molar enthalpy of formation*, and *standard molar enthalpy of combustion*.
4. What is the difference between standard temperature and pressure (STP) and standard state?
5. How can we determine the energy in a multistep reaction?
6. Calculate $\Delta H°$ for each of the following reactions and tell whether each reaction is endothermic or exothermic.
   a. $N_2\,(g) + 3H_2\,(g) \longrightarrow 2NH_3\,(g)$
   b. $Ca(OH)_2\,(s) \longrightarrow CaO\,(s) + H_2O\,(g)$
7. Some instant ice packs contain ammonium chloride (NH_4Cl), which dissolves to produce two ions in a process similar to that involving ammonium nitrate. Given that the ammonium ion has a $\Delta H°_f$ of –132.5 kJ/mol and that the $\Delta H°_f$ of the chloride ion is –167.2 kJ/mol, calculate the enthalpy of solution. Remember from Chapter 14 that the enthalpy of solution is the net energy change during the dissolving process.
8. Compare the cooling efficiency of ice packs that use ammonium chloride with those that use ammonium nitrate, assuming that each reaction involves the same volume of water and molar quantity of salt. The equation for dissolving ammonium nitrate is shown below.

$$NH_4NO_3\,(s) \longrightarrow NH_4^+\,(aq) + NO_3^-\,(aq)$$
$$\Delta H_{soln} = 28.1\text{ kJ/mol}$$

9. A key component in gasoline is octane (C_8H_{18}). If $\Delta H_f = -249.7$ kJ/mol, calculate the enthalpy of combustion for octane.

15.3 REACTION TENDENCY

Chemical compounds store energy. As long as bonds are not changed, the energy that they contain cannot be released. For chemical substances to react, there must be a transfer of energy, and this change in energy is more observable. Chemical bonds can be broken through *vibration*. In some cases, this vibration may be indirectly caused by the *rotation* or *translation* (lateral motion) of the molecule. An outside source of energy, such as a laser, can cause the vibration. The atoms can be vibrated so strongly that the attraction holding them together is overcome.

QUESTIONS

- What is entropy?
- What determines the likelihood of a reaction occurring?
- How do I determine the change in entropy of a system?
- Can I predict the favorability of a reaction?

TERMS

entropy • Gibbs free energy

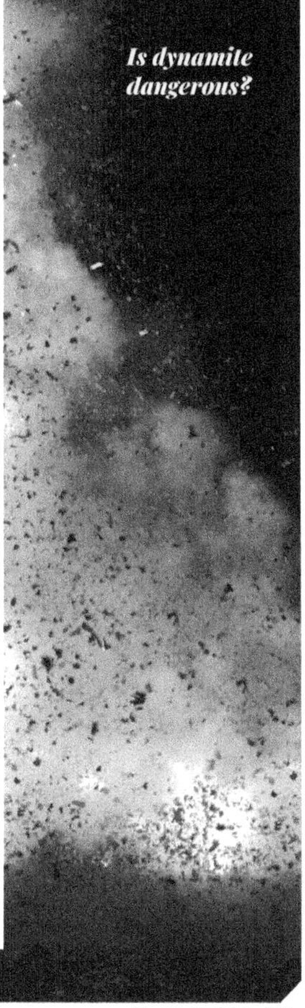

Is dynamite dangerous?

Chemical Bonds and Enthalpy

Siege mortars, like this one intended for use in the Crimean War, rely on bond formation to release large amounts of energy.

In Section 15.2, you calculated the enthalpies of a reaction by using enthalpies of formation. Another method of analyzing the enthalpy changes of chemical reactions is to focus on the bonds between pairs of atoms. The strength of the bond between any two atoms depends on the elements that are bonding and on the length of the bond. Because bonded atoms are more stable than unbonded atoms, energy is always required to break bonds—that is, it is an endothermic process. Conversely, the formation of bonds always releases energy and is thus exothermic. The stronger the bond is, the more energy is released.

These relationships can help explain why some reactions give off energy and others require energy. Strong, stable bonds require large amounts of energy to break them. Strong bonds also give off large amounts of energy when they form. Weak bonds can be broken with small amounts of energy. Predictably, they give off small amounts of energy when they form.

A reaction that breaks strong bonds and forms weak bonds requires energy. More energy is required to break the strong bonds than is released when the weak bonds form. As a result, reactions that produce compounds with weaker, less stable bonds are endothermic.

$$\text{stronger bonds} \longrightarrow \text{weaker bonds; } \Delta H_r > 0 \text{ (endothermic)}$$

A reaction that forms stable, low-energy compounds from compounds with high-energy and weak bonds releases energy. The amount of energy that must be used to break the weak bonds is small compared with all the energy that is given off when the strong bonds form.

$$\text{weaker bonds} \longrightarrow \text{stronger bonds; } \Delta H_r < 0 \text{ (exothermic)}$$

In most cases, exothermic processes are thermodynamically favorable and endothermic processes are not. But this rule does not always hold true; a negative ΔH does not always indicate that a process is favorable.

ENGAGE

ENTHALPY

Review prior knowledge from Section 15.2 with a **peer teacher** activity. Have students break into groups of three. Every student selects one of the three concepts: enthalpy of reaction, standard molar enthalpy of formation, and standard molar enthalpy of combustion. Once concepts have been selected, each student is given two minutes to teach the material to his group. To help students with this activity, you may want to allow them to use examples within their notes or textbook.

When students have finished with the activity, do a quick review of the concepts. Explain that Section 15.2 focused primarily on using enthalpies of formation to calculate enthalpies of reaction. In this section, however, the focus will be more on the bonds between atoms to help describe enthalpy changes.

SECTION 15.3 *OVERVIEW*

Essential Question

Is dynamite dangerous?

Objectives

- **15.3.1** Define *entropy* and give some common examples.
- **15.3.2** Predict reaction tendency on the basis of energy and entropy changes.
- **15.3.3** Calculate the change in entropy of a chemical reaction.
- **15.3.4** Predict the favorability of reactions on the basis of the four possible enthalpy-entropy combinations.
- **15.3.5** Evaluate the various theories of the end of the universe. BWS

Resources

Case Study: Entropy and Life

Worldview Investigation: Heat Death

Web Link: The Cosmological Argument

Lab 15B: *No Anchovies, Please!*—Exploring Enthalpies of Solution and Reaction

INSTRUCT

THE FIRST AND SECOND LAWS

Lead students through a **review** of the first and second law of thermodynamics.

1. Explain the first law of thermodynamics. *(The first law of thermodynamics states that matter and energy can be neither created nor destroyed, only converted from one form into another.)*
2. Explain the second law of thermodynamics. *(The second law of thermodynamics, also called the law of increasing entropy, states that natural processes tend toward the highest entropy, decreasing the usable energy in the universe.)*

DESCRIBING ENTROPY

Direct students to create **illustrations** that describe entropy. One example could be ice melting, water evaporating, creamer dissolving in coffee, or hot pans cooling down. Within their illustrations, make sure that students have the correct definition of entropy, as well as a couple of examples of what entropy is not. (Entropy is not disorder or the measure of chaos.)

ENTROPY MISCONCEPTION

Dispel any misconceptions about the term *entropy*. A messy room is often used as an example of entropy—the room naturally moves toward a state of complete disorder until energy is applied to it to clean it up. But this is not the case. Entropy is not disorder nor the measure of chaos; rather it describes the dispersal of energy. The energy expended to clean up the room is a form of entropy: energy is dispersed when we place items back where they belong.

ENTHALPY VERSUS ENTROPY

Stress the difference between enthalpy and entropy: *enthalpy* is the thermal energy content of a system at a constant pressure, while *entropy* is the dispersal of energy in a system.

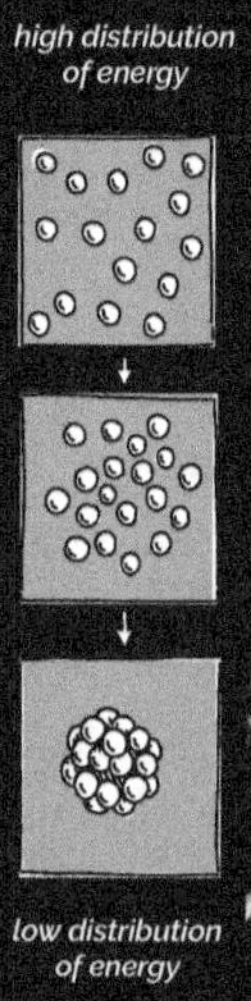

Entropy and Reaction Tendency

We are surrounded by processes that occur *spontaneously*, yet many of those processes absorb rather than give off energy. In other words, they are endothermic. One example is the release of compressed gas into the atmosphere. As gas under high pressure is released, it gets colder. You may have noticed this phenomenon when dispensing whipped cream from a can. In Chapter 14 you learned that the formation of many solutions causes the temperature of the solvent to decrease. Ice cubes absorb thermal energy from their surroundings to melt into water. All of these are endothermic processes. Clearly, something in addition to enthalpy influences spontaneity.

Each of these examples shows us that processes tend to proceed naturally in a way that spreads out energy. The *second law of thermodynamics* relates this tendency to a very large system when it states that natural processes tend to decrease the usable energy in the universe. The energy of gas molecules is less concentrated after being released from the pressure of a can. The energy of solute particles is dispersed after solvation.

Entropy (S) is a measure of the dispersal of energy in a system. In natural processes, energy tends to spread out, not concentrate. A hot pan cooling off on a stovetop is an example of entropy in action. Gases, with their free-flying particles, have high entropies. Crystalline solids have particles arranged in definite, repeating, organized systems with energy stored in bonds; therefore, they possess low entropies and high energy density.

Because entropy is related to the kinetic energy of a substance, entropy increases as temperature increases. As the temperature becomes greater, the increased kinetic energy gives the particles greater motion. But it's not always directly proportional. For example, when ice (a crystalline solid) melts, entropy is increased because attractions in the crystal that store energy are broken and energy is dispersed. But the temperature does not change. Because the amount of entropy in a substance varies with temperature as well as pressure, these conditions must be specified. Table 15-5 lists the entropies per mole of several common substances at standard conditions (again indicated by the degree symbol). Although enthalpy values for pure elements are not listed in the extensive table in Appendix H, entropies are included because all substances have some entropy.

TABLE 15-5 *Standard Molar Entropies*

Substance	Formula	$S°$ (J/mol · K)
ammonia (*g*)	NH_3	192.8
ammonium chloride (*s*)	NH_4Cl	94.6
hydrogen bromide (*g*)	HBr	198.7
hydrogen chloride (*g*)	HCl	186.9

Calculating Entropy Changes

From the data in Appendix H, the entropy changes of many reactions can be calculated. An entropy change is the difference between the sum of the entropies of the products and the sum of the entropies of the reactants, similar to how the enthalpy of a reaction is calculated.

$$\Delta S = \text{total entropy in products} - \text{total entropy in reactants}$$

$$\Delta S = \Sigma S_{\text{products}} - \Sigma S_{\text{reactants}}$$

A reaction with a positive ΔS increases entropy and spreads out energy. The products have more entropy than the reactants. A negative ΔS signifies a decrease in entropy and a concentration of energy in that part of the universe, though it results in a net loss of usable energy in the universe.

EXAMPLE 15-7: CALCULATING ΔS°

Does the reaction $NH_3\ (g) + HCl\ (g) \longrightarrow NH_4Cl\ (s)$ produce an increase or decrease in entropy at standard conditions?

Write what you know.

Using entropies from Appendix H:

$S°\ (NH_3) = 192.8\ \text{J/mol} \cdot \text{K}$
$S°\ (HCl) = 186.9\ \text{J/mol} \cdot \text{K}$
$S°\ (NH_4Cl) = 94.6\ \text{J/mol} \cdot \text{K}$

Write the formula and solve for the unknown.

$$\Delta S° = \Sigma S°_{\text{products}} - \Sigma S°_{\text{reactants}}$$

Plug in known values and evaluate.

$$\Delta S° = (1\ \cancel{\text{mol } NH_4Cl})\left(\frac{94.6\ \text{J}}{\cancel{\text{mol } NH_4Cl} \cdot \text{K}}\right) - \left[(1\ \cancel{\text{mol } NH_3})\left(\frac{192.8\ \text{J}}{\cancel{\text{mol } NH_3} \cdot \text{K}}\right) + (1\ \cancel{\text{mol } HCl})\left(\frac{186.9\ \text{J}}{\cancel{\text{mol } HCl} \cdot \text{K}}\right)\right]$$

$$= 94.6\ \text{J/K} - 379.7\ \text{J/K}$$

$$= -285.1\ \text{J/K}$$

The amount of entropy has decreased.

While the entropy of a specific system may increase or decrease, all processes, whether spontaneous or nonspontaneous, increase the total entropy of the universe. A positive $\Delta S°$ means a reaction is more favorable. A reaction with a negative $\Delta S°$ decreases entropy, and thus is less favorable.

The 70 m wide Darvaza gas crater in Turkmenistan burns methane gas that seeps from the ground.

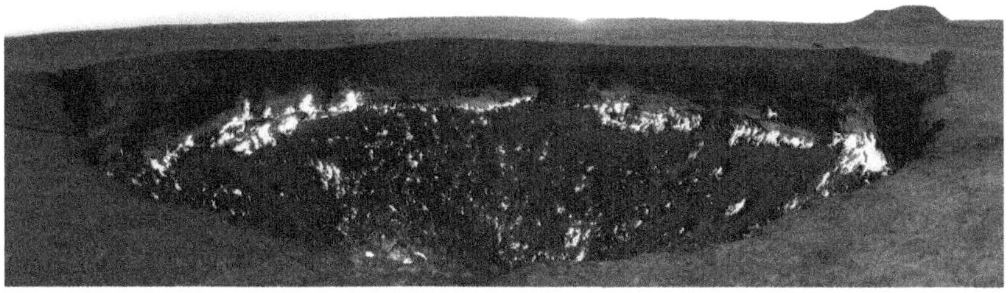

ENTROPY CHANGE

Direct students to add to the **concept map** that they began in Section 15.2. Have them begin with adding "entropy change" by writing its equation, definition, and reaction favorability. As you cover the section, have students add terms, definitions, equations, reaction favorability, and examples.

ENTROPY AND LIFE

The case study on this page discusses the dispersal of energy along each step of the ATP energy cycle. Without entropy, our bodies wouldn't be able to break down sugar molecules into a usable form of energy. The efficient energy system that God has put in place in our bodies is designed to use entropy to its advantage.

CASE STUDY

ENTROPY AND LIFE

You've just finished a long, hard soccer game. The next thing on your mind is a cold drink, so you go to the vending machine. All you have is a $20 bill, so your shoulders sag in dejection when you see that the machine accepts only $1, $5, and $10 bills. Sure, you have enough money to get ten bottles, but your money isn't in a usable form.

This situation is similar to the way that your body gets and uses energy. When you eat food, your body is getting a great source of energy. But that energy is similar to your $20—there's plenty of it, but it's not in a usable form. If your body released the energy stored in fats, sugars, and other molecules in that food all at once, great damage would result. Your body's cells must break down food into a usable form. This is where entropy comes in to save the day.

Sugars from the digestive system are carried by the circulatory system to cells all over your body. Once these molecules reach body cells, the work of energy conversion begins. The energy-rich sugar molecules must be converted into a more usable form of energy for the cell. This conversion requires a process called *aerobic cellular respiration*. Aerobic cellular respiration requires oxygen—hence the word *aerobic*—which you obtain from breathing. Through a complicated series of steps, aerobic cellular respiration takes energy from the sugar molecules and stores that energy in less-energy-rich molecules of adenosine triphosphate—ATP. This process is less than 50% efficient, so over half the energy dissipates into forms that don't fuel the body. Most of the "lost" energy is given off as thermal energy and is used to maintain body temperature, so it is actually being put to good use. The secret to ATP's success lies in its three phosphate groups. The bonds holding each of the phosphates in place are high-energy bonds. By breaking the bonds, energy is released, and your body can use that energy for work.

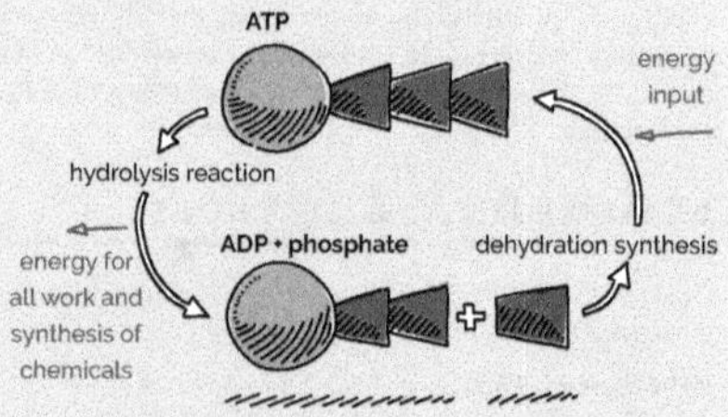

The body's supply of energy is maintained by recycling ATP. When a phosphate is broken off from ATP and energy is released, the ATP molecule is transformed into ADP—adenosine diphosphate. Through another type of reaction, a phosphate can be added back onto ADP, once again creating ATP. In just one of your muscle cells at work during that soccer game, ten million ATP molecules were used and recycled every second! Your body requires a constant source of ATP, and God's design and provision of energy for us is amazing. And it all demonstrates the second law of thermodynamics and entropy at work.

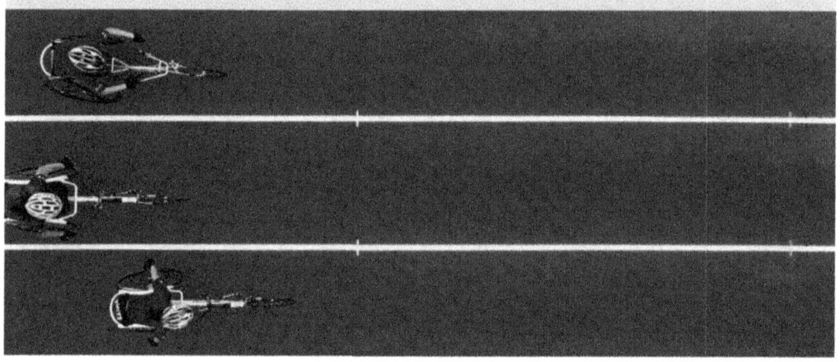

374 Chapter 15

FREE-ENERGY CHANGE

Two tendencies drive reactions. The first is the tendency to decrease enthalpy (exothermic), and the second is the tendency to increase entropy. Reactions can be either exothermic or endothermic, and they can either increase or decrease entropy.

Four possible enthalpy/entropy combinations exist.

1. exothermic and increasing entropy ($-\Delta H, +\Delta S$)
2. exothermic and decreasing entropy ($-\Delta H, -\Delta S$)
3. endothermic and increasing entropy ($+\Delta H, +\Delta S$)
4. endothermic and decreasing entropy ($+\Delta H, -\Delta S$)

Reactions are driven by the combined effects of change in enthalpy (ΔH) and change in entropy (ΔS). A single expression that relates ΔH and ΔS is needed to determine how they combine.

In the 1800s, American physicist J. Willard Gibbs (right) formulated a single criterion of favorability. He combined the change in enthalpy and the change in entropy into a single term called *free energy*, which is sometimes called **Gibbs free energy** (G) in his honor.

The free-energy change (ΔG) for a reaction can be calculated by the equation

$$\Delta G = \Delta H - T\Delta S,$$

where ΔG is the change in the free energy in joules, ΔH is the change in the enthalpy in joules, T is the temperature in kelvins, and ΔS is the change in the entropy in joules per kelvin.

A negative ΔG indicates a decline in free energy and signifies that a reaction may occur spontaneously (or is favorable). A positive ΔG indicates a net increase in free energy and signifies that a reaction is not favorable—nonspontaneous. The free-energy change can be negative under several conditions. A negative ΔH and a positive ΔS always contribute to a negative ΔG. When the two tendencies oppose each other, the temperature at which the reaction takes place determines the sign of ΔG. Table 15-6 shows the conditions at which ΔG is negative and the reaction is spontaneous.

TABLE 15-6 *When ΔG Is Negative*

	ΔH	ΔS	ΔG
Case 1	−	+	$-\Delta G$ at all T
Case 2	−	−	$-\Delta G$ at low T
Case 3	+	+	$-\Delta G$ at high T
Case 4	+	−	$+\Delta G$ at all T

FREE-ENERGY CHANGE

Direct students to add "Free-Energy Change" to their **concept map**. Have them write the Gibbs free energy equation, definition, and reaction favorabilities (according to Table 15-6 and pages 376–79).

As you review this section, encourage students to write the cases in which a reaction is favorable (spontaneous) and not favorable (nonspontaneous). This information (pp. 376–79) is important in understanding reaction tendencies.

CALCULATING ΔG

In situations where no temperature is given, assume standard state.

DIFFERENTIATED INSTRUCTION

Free-Energy Change

Lead students to create an **illustration** of the four cases for calculating free-energy change (pp. 376–79). Give each student four note cards. Each note card represents a case. The front of the note card should be the illustration of the case. For example, Case 1 would have an illustration on the front of the note card similar to the drawing on page 376, which represents a decrease in enthalpy and an increase in entropy producing a favorable, spontaneous reaction. On the back of the note card, have students work through an example problem, include the steps for solving, and practice how to calculate free-energy change.

TEMPERATURE AND FAVORABILITY

Somewhere between 298 K and 1000 K a reaction may change from unfavorable to favorable as ΔG becomes negative. To find the point where this change occurs, find the temperature at which $\Delta G = 0$. Use the free-energy equation and the values for ΔH and ΔS, and then solve for T.

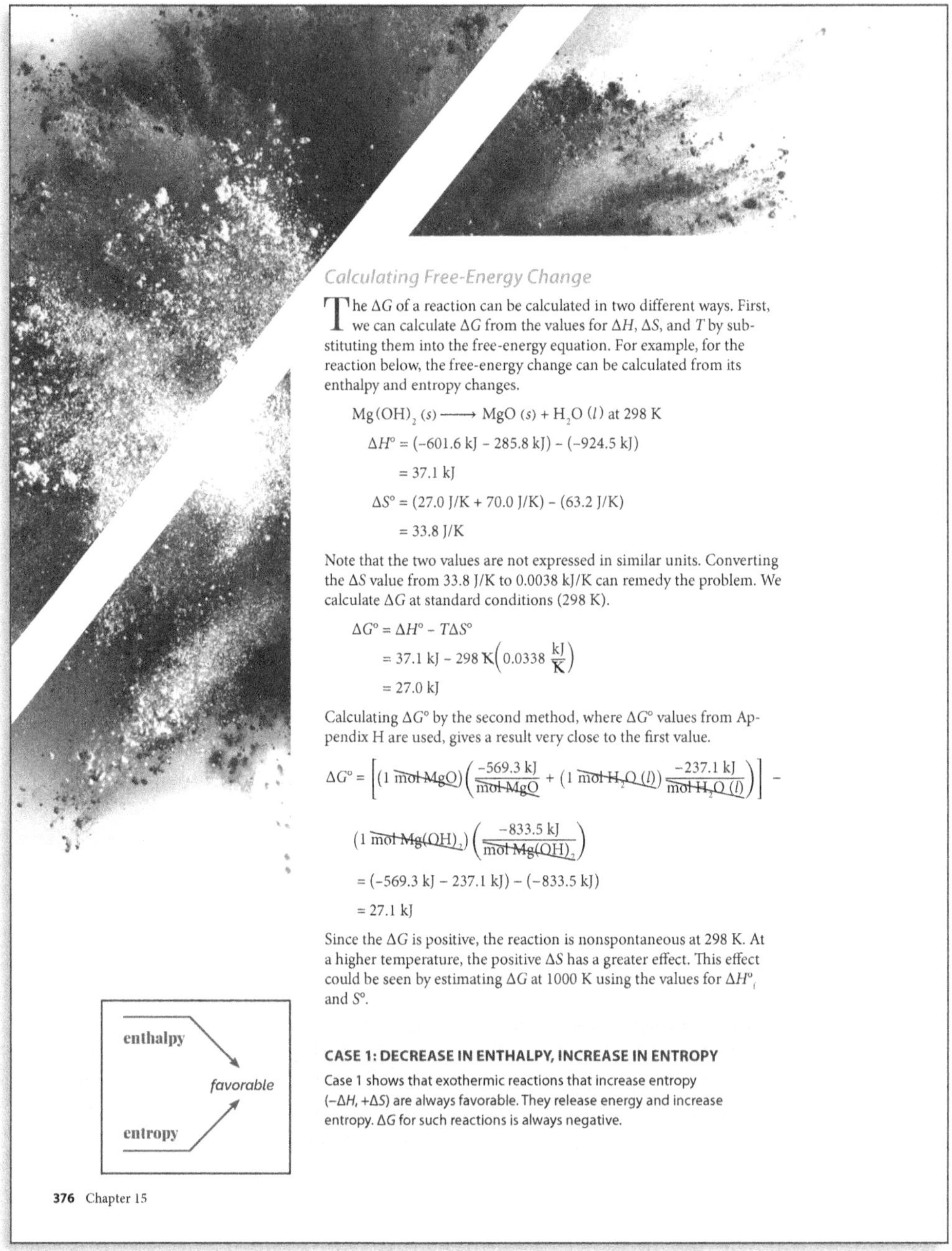

Calculating Free-Energy Change

The ΔG of a reaction can be calculated in two different ways. First, we can calculate ΔG from the values for ΔH, ΔS, and T by substituting them into the free-energy equation. For example, for the reaction below, the free-energy change can be calculated from its enthalpy and entropy changes.

$$Mg(OH)_2\ (s) \longrightarrow MgO\ (s) + H_2O\ (l) \text{ at } 298\ K$$

$$\Delta H^\circ = (-601.6\ kJ - 285.8\ kJ) - (-924.5\ kJ)$$

$$= 37.1\ kJ$$

$$\Delta S^\circ = (27.0\ J/K + 70.0\ J/K) - (63.2\ J/K)$$

$$= 33.8\ J/K$$

Note that the two values are not expressed in similar units. Converting the ΔS value from 33.8 J/K to 0.0038 kJ/K can remedy the problem. We calculate ΔG at standard conditions (298 K).

$$\Delta G^\circ = \Delta H^\circ - T\Delta S^\circ$$

$$= 37.1\ kJ - 298\ \cancel{K}\left(0.0338\ \frac{kJ}{\cancel{K}}\right)$$

$$= 27.0\ kJ$$

Calculating ΔG° by the second method, where ΔG° values from Appendix H are used, gives a result very close to the first value.

$$\Delta G^\circ = \left[(1\ \cancel{mol\ MgO})\left(\frac{-569.3\ kJ}{\cancel{mol\ MgO}}\right) + (1\ \cancel{mol\ H_2O\ (l)})\left(\frac{-237.1\ kJ}{\cancel{mol\ H_2O\ (l)}}\right)\right] -$$

$$(1\ \cancel{mol\ Mg(OH)_2})\left(\frac{-833.5\ kJ}{\cancel{mol\ Mg(OH)_2}}\right)$$

$$= (-569.3\ kJ - 237.1\ kJ) - (-833.5\ kJ)$$

$$= 27.1\ kJ$$

Since the ΔG is positive, the reaction is nonspontaneous at 298 K. At a higher temperature, the positive ΔS has a greater effect. This effect could be seen by estimating ΔG at 1000 K using the values for ΔH°_f and S°.

CASE 1: DECREASE IN ENTHALPY, INCREASE IN ENTROPY

Case 1 shows that exothermic reactions that increase entropy ($-\Delta H$, $+\Delta S$) are always favorable. They release energy and increase entropy. ΔG for such reactions is always negative.

376 Chapter 15

EXAMPLE 15-8: CALCULATING ΔG, CASE 1

Calculate the Gibbs free-energy change for the following reaction.

$$2Ag\,(s) + S\,(s) \longrightarrow Ag_2S\,(s) \text{ at } 298\text{ K}$$

Write what you know.

$\Delta H^\circ\,(Ag_2S) = -32.6$ kJ
$S^\circ\,(Ag_2S) = 144.0$ J/mol · K
$S^\circ\,(Ag) = 42.6$ J/mol · K
$S^\circ\,(S) = 32.1$ J/mol · K
$T = 298$ K

Write the formula and solve for the unknown.

$$\Delta H^\circ = \Sigma H^\circ_{products} - \Sigma H^\circ_{reactants}$$
$$\Delta S^\circ = \Sigma S^\circ_{products} - \Sigma S^\circ_{reactants}$$

Plug in known values and evaluate.

$$\Delta H^\circ = (-32.6\text{ kJ}) - (-0.0\text{ kJ} - 0.0\text{ kJ}) = -32.6\text{ kJ}$$

$$\Delta S^\circ = (1\text{ mol }Ag_2S)\left(\frac{144.0\text{ J}}{\text{mol }Ag_2S\cdot K}\right) - \left[(2\text{ mol }Ag)\left(\frac{42.6\text{ J}}{\text{mol }Ag\cdot K}\right) + (1\text{ mol }S)\left(\frac{32.1\text{ J}}{\text{mol }S\cdot K}\right)\right]$$
$$= 144.0\,\frac{J}{K} - \left(85.2\,\frac{J}{K} + 32.1\,\frac{J}{K}\right)$$
$$= 26.7\,\frac{J}{K} = 0.0267\,\frac{kJ}{K}$$

Write the formula and solve for the unknown.

$$\Delta G^\circ = \Delta H^\circ - T\Delta S^\circ$$

Plug in known values and evaluate.

$$\Delta G^\circ = -32.6\text{ kJ} - 298\text{ K}\left(0.0267\,\frac{kJ}{K}\right) = -40.6\text{ kJ}$$

The reaction is spontaneous.

CASE 2: DECREASE IN ENTHALPY, DECREASE IN ENTROPY

Case 2 shows that exothermic reactions that decrease entropy ($-\Delta H, -\Delta S$) may or may not be favorable. The two tendencies oppose each other. In cases like this, the temperature determines whether the reaction is favorable. The entropy change hinders the reaction less at low temperatures than it does at high temperatures, so ΔG is negative at low temperatures.

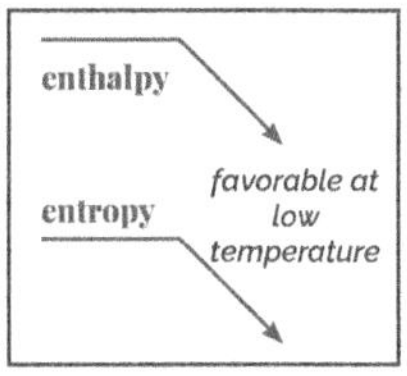

EXAMPLE 15-9: CALCULATING ΔG, CASE 2

Calculate the Gibbs free-energy change for the following reaction.

$$2\,Fe\,(s) + \frac{3}{2}O_2\,(g) \longrightarrow Fe_2O_3\,(s) \text{ at } 298\text{ K}$$

Write what you know.

$\Delta H^\circ\,(Fe_2O_3) = -824.2$ kJ
$S^\circ\,(Fe_2O_3) = 87.4$ J/mol · K
$S^\circ\,(Fe) = 27.3$/mol · K
$S^\circ\,(O_2) = 205.2$ J/mol · K
$T = 298$ K

Write the formula and solve for the unknown.

$$\Delta H^\circ = \Sigma H^\circ_{products} - \Sigma H^\circ_{reactants}$$
$$\Delta S^\circ = \Sigma S^\circ_{products} - \Sigma S^\circ_{reactants}$$

Plug in known values and evaluate.

$$\Delta H^\circ = (-824.2\text{ kJ}) - (-0.0\text{ kJ} - 0.0\text{ kJ}) = -824.2\text{ kJ}$$

$$\Delta S^\circ = (1\text{ mol }Fe_2O_3)\left(\frac{87.4\text{ J}}{\text{mol }Fe_2O_3\cdot K}\right) - \left[(2\text{ mol }Fe)\left(\frac{27.3\text{ J}}{\text{mol }Fe\cdot K}\right) + \left(\frac{3}{2}\text{ mol }O_2\right)\left(\frac{205.2\text{ J}}{\text{mol }O_2\cdot K}\right)\right]$$
$$= 87.4\,\frac{J}{K} - \left(54.6\,\frac{J}{K} + 307.8\,\frac{J}{K}\right)$$
$$= -275\,\frac{J}{K} = -0.275\,\frac{kJ}{K}$$

Write the formula and solve for the unknown.

$$\Delta G^\circ = \Delta H^\circ - T\Delta S^\circ$$

Plug in known values and evaluate.

$$\Delta G^\circ = -824.2\text{ kJ} - 298\text{ K}\left(-0.275\,\frac{kJ}{K}\right) = -742.3\text{ kJ}$$

The reaction is spontaneous.

SEEING RELATIONSHIPS

Initiate a **discussion** by asking students to compare the changes in enthalpy, entropy, and free energy of a few compounds in Appendix H. For example, the S° for carbon is 5.7 J/(mol · K); for calcium carbonate it is 917 J/(mol · K). This shows that calcium carbonate requires much more energy to be drawn from its surroundings to maintain its form at standard state. This is why solids at room temperature tend to have low S° values, and gases at room temperature have high S° values. Ask students whether they see any more connections between the values.

REACTION TENDENCY

Use the following **formative assessment** to check students' understanding.

1. Define ΔH, ΔS, and ΔG. *(ΔH is the change in enthalpy [heat energy] of a reaction. ΔS is the change in entropy [dispersal of energy] of a reaction. ΔG is the combined change of enthalpy and entropy of a reaction.)*
2. State the case in which a reaction is not favorable. *(in an endothermic reaction with a decrease in entropy and an increase in enthalpy)*
3. In an exothermic reaction with a decrease in enthalpy and a decrease in entropy, will a high or low temperature determine its favorability? *(low temperature)*
4. In an endothermic reaction with an increase in enthalpy and an increase in entropy, will a high or low temperature determine its favorability? *(high temperature)*
5. Consider the reaction below.

   $3NO_2\ (g) + H_2O\ (l) \longrightarrow 2HNO_3\ (l) + NO\ (g)$

   Calculate the change in free energy (ΔG) for the reaction at 298 K ($\Delta H = -70.7$ kJ; $\Delta S = -0.2686$ kJ/K). State whether the reaction is favorable (spontaneous) or unfavorable (nonspontaneous) at this temperature.

   What we know: $\Delta H = -70.7$ kJ, $\Delta S = -0.2686$ kJ/K, $T = 298$ K

   Unknown: ΔG

   Write the formula and solve for the unknown.

   $\Delta G = \Delta H - T\Delta S$

   Plug in known values and evaluate.

   $\Delta G = -70.7\ \text{kJ} - 298\ \text{K}(-0.2686\ \text{kJ/K})$

   $= 9.3$ kJ; unfavorable

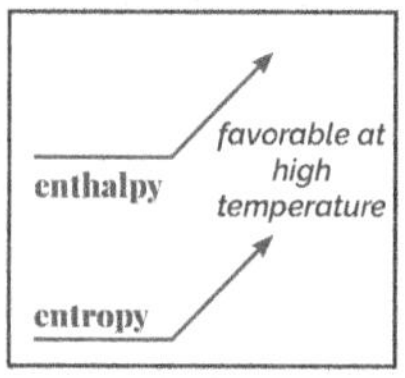

CASE 3: INCREASE IN ENTHALPY, INCREASE IN ENTROPY

Case 3 represents endothermic reactions that increase entropy ($+\Delta H$, $+\Delta S$). These reactions can be favorable if the entropy change is greater than the enthalpy change. High temperatures magnify the effect of the entropy change and make ΔG negative. As a result, these reactions can proceed. At lower temperatures, however, they have positive ΔG values, making them unfavorable.

EXAMPLE 15-10: CALCULATING ΔG, CASE 3

Calculate the Gibbs free-energy change for the following reaction.

$2C\ (s) + H_2\ (g) \longrightarrow C_2H_2\ (g)$ at 298 K

Write what you know.

$\Delta H°\ (C_2H_2) = 227.4$ kJ
$S°\ (C_2H_2) = 200.9$ J/mol · K
$S°\ (C) = 5.7$/mol · K
$S°\ (H_2) = 130.7$ J/mol · K
$T = 298$ K

Write the formula and solve for the unknown.

$$\Delta H° = \Sigma H°_{products} - \Sigma H°_{reactants}$$
$$\Delta S° = \Sigma S°_{products} - \Sigma S°_{reactants}$$

Plug in known values and evaluate.

$$\Delta H° = (227.4\ \text{kJ}) - (-0.0\ \text{kJ} - 0.0\ \text{kJ}) = 227.4\ \text{kJ}$$

$$\Delta S° = (1\ \text{mol}\ C_2H_2)\left(\frac{200.9\ \text{J}}{\text{mol}\ C_2H_2 \cdot \text{K}}\right) - \left[(2\ \text{mol C})\left(\frac{5.7\ \text{J}}{\text{mol C} \cdot \text{K}}\right) + (1\ \text{mol}\ H_2)\left(\frac{130.7\ \text{J}}{\text{mol}\ H_2 \cdot \text{K}}\right)\right]$$
$$= 200.9\ \frac{\text{J}}{\text{K}} - \left(11.4\ \frac{\text{J}}{\text{K}} + 130.7\ \frac{\text{J}}{\text{K}}\right)$$
$$= 58.8\ \frac{\text{J}}{\text{K}} = 0.0588\ \frac{\text{kJ}}{\text{K}}$$

Write the formula and solve for the unknown.

$$\Delta G° = \Delta H° - T\Delta S°$$

Plug in known values and evaluate.

$$\Delta G° = 227.4\ \text{kJ} - 298\ \text{K}\left(0.0588\ \frac{\text{kJ}}{\text{K}}\right) = 209.9\ \text{kJ}$$

The reaction is nonspontaneous.

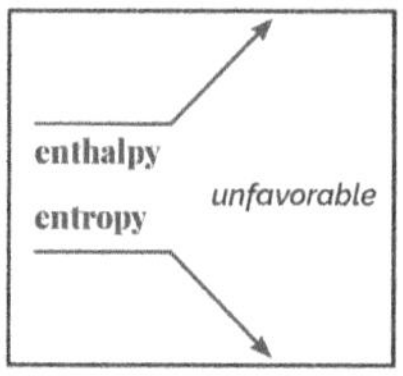

CASE 4: INCREASE IN ENTHALPY, DECREASE IN ENTROPY

Case 4 shows that endothermic reactions that decrease entropy ($+\Delta H$, $-\Delta S$) do not occur naturally. To proceed spontaneously, these reactions would have to concentrate energy by adding it to the chemical substances. Reactions that exhibit positive enthalpy changes can be forced if other types of energy are used. Otherwise, they are unfavorable at any temperature.

EXAMPLE 15-11: CALCULATING ΔG, CASE 4

Calculate the Gibbs free-energy change for the following reaction.

$2C\,(s) + 2H_2\,(g) \longrightarrow C_2H_4\,(g)$ at 298 K

Write what you know.

$\Delta H^\circ\,(C_2H_4) = 52.4$ kJ
$S^\circ\,(C_2H_4) = 219.3$ J/mol · K
$S^\circ\,(C) = 5.7$/mol · K
$S^\circ\,(H_2) = 130.7$ J/mol · K
$T = 298$ K

Write the formula and solve for the unknown.

$$\Delta H^\circ = \Sigma H^\circ_{products} - \Sigma H^\circ_{reactants}$$
$$\Delta S^\circ = \Sigma S^\circ_{products} - \Sigma S^\circ_{reactants}$$

Plug in known values and evaluate.

$$\Delta H^\circ = (52.4\ \text{kJ}) - (-0.0\ \text{kJ} - 0.0\ \text{kJ})$$
$$= 52.4\ \text{kJ}$$
$$\Delta S^\circ = (1\ \cancel{\text{mol}\ C_2H_4})\left(\frac{219.3\ \text{J}}{\cancel{\text{mol}\ C_2H_4}\cdot \text{K}}\right) - \left[(2\ \cancel{\text{mol}\ C})\left(\frac{5.7\ \text{J}}{\cancel{\text{mol}\ C}\cdot \text{K}}\right) + (2\ \cancel{\text{mol}\ H_2})\left(\frac{130.7\ \text{J}}{\cancel{\text{mol}\ H_2}\cdot \text{K}}\right)\right]$$
$$= 219.3\ \frac{\text{J}}{\text{K}} - \left(11.4\ \frac{\text{J}}{\text{K}} + 261.4\ \frac{\text{J}}{\text{K}}\right)$$
$$= -53.5\ \frac{\text{J}}{\text{K}} = -0.0535\ \frac{\text{kJ}}{\text{K}}$$

Write the formula and solve for the unknown.

$$\Delta G^\circ = \Delta H^\circ - T\Delta S^\circ$$

Plug in known values and evaluate.

$$\Delta G^\circ = 52.4\ \text{kJ} - 298\ \cancel{\text{K}}\left(-0.0535\ \frac{\text{kJ}}{\cancel{\text{K}}}\right)$$
$$= 68.3\ \text{kJ}$$

The reaction is nonspontaneous.

EXAMPLE 15-12: CALCULATING ΔG AT DIFFERENT TEMPERATURES

Determine whether the reaction between ammonia and hydrogen chloride is probable at 298 K and at 985 K according to the values shown in Appendix H.

$NH_3(g) + HCl(g) \longrightarrow NH_4Cl(s)$

Write what you know.

$H^\circ\,(NH_3) = -45.9$ kJ/mol
$H^\circ\,(HCl) = -92.3$ kJ/mol
$H^\circ\,(NH_4Cl) = -314.4$ kJ/mol
$S^\circ\,(NH_3) = 192.8$ J/mol · K
$S^\circ\,(HCl) = 186.9$ J/mol · K
$S^\circ\,(NH_4Cl) = 94.6$ J/mol · K
$T_1 = 298$ K
$T_2 = 985$ K

Write the formula and solve for the unknown.

$$\Delta H^\circ = \Sigma H^\circ_{products} - \Sigma H^\circ_{reactants}$$
$$\Delta S^\circ = \Sigma S^\circ_{products} - \Sigma S^\circ_{reactants}$$

Plug in known values and evaluate.

$$\Delta H^\circ = (1\ \cancel{\text{mol}\ NH_4Cl})\left(\frac{-314.4\ \text{kJ}}{\cancel{\text{mol}\ NH_4Cl}}\right) - \left[(1\ \cancel{\text{mol}\ NH_3})\left(\frac{-45.9\ \text{kJ}}{\cancel{\text{mol}\ NH_3}}\right) + (1\ \cancel{\text{mol}\ HCl})\left(\frac{-92.3\ \text{kJ}}{\cancel{\text{mol}\ HCl}}\right)\right]$$
$$= -314.4\ \text{kJ} - (-138.2\ \text{kJ})$$
$$= -176.2\ \text{kJ}$$

$$\Delta S^\circ = (1\ \cancel{\text{mol}\ NH_4Cl})\left(\frac{94.6\ \text{J}}{\cancel{\text{mol}\ NH_4Cl}\cdot \text{K}}\right) - \left[(1\ \cancel{\text{mol}\ NH_3})\left(\frac{192.8\ \text{J}}{\cancel{\text{mol}\ NH_3}\cdot \text{K}}\right) + (1\ \cancel{\text{mol}\ HCl})\left(\frac{186.9\ \text{J}}{\cancel{\text{mol}\ HCl}\cdot \text{K}}\right)\right]$$
$$= 94.6\ \text{J/K} - 379.7\ \text{J/K}$$
$$= -285.1\ \text{J/K} = -0.2851\ \text{kJ/K}$$

Write the formula and solve for the unknown

$$\Delta G^\circ = \Delta H^\circ - T\Delta S^\circ$$

Plug in known values and evaluate. ($T_1 = 298$ K)

$$\Delta G^\circ = -176.2\ \text{kJ} - 298\ \cancel{\text{K}}\left(-0.2851\ \frac{\text{kJ}}{\cancel{\text{K}}}\right)$$
$$= -91.2\ \text{kJ}$$

Since ΔG° is negative, the reaction is probable at 298 K, making it spontaneous.

Even though the values of ΔH and ΔS at 985 K are not known, the value of ΔG can be estimated by using the 298 K figures in the free-energy equation and solving for ΔG.

Plug in known values and evaluate. ($T_2 = 985$ K)

$$\Delta G = -176.2\ \text{kJ} - 985\ \cancel{\text{K}}\left(-0.2851\ \frac{\text{kJ}}{\cancel{\text{K}}}\right)$$
$$= 104.6\ \text{kJ}$$

The positive ΔG shows that the reaction is unfavorable at 985 K, making it nonspontaneous.

Thermochemistry 379

WORLDVIEW INVESTIGATION: HEAT DEATH

Appendix K includes a reproducible rubric to assess the worldview investigation activity on this page.

WORLDVIEW INVESTIGATION

HEAT DEATH

A cup of hot coffee cools off and a sound gets quieter as you get farther from its source. Some people have called entropy "time's arrow" because we naturally assume that a process continues in a direction that results in energy being spread out. And as energy spreads out, it becomes less useful for doing work. That's not a problem for a system as small as a cup of coffee—we can easily brew a new cup. But what about larger systems, such as our universe? If the naturalistic worldview were true, what consequences would the concept of entropy have for our universe?

Task

You're watching a TV documentary on the solar system. As often happens in such films, the narrator describes how the universe arose during the big bang, which you have heard of before. He also mentions that the solar system will die a "heat death." What does that mean?

Procedure

1. Research the concept of heat death by doing an internet search using the keywords "heat death" and "big freeze."
2. To get a biblical perspective, go to the Creation Ministries International website and search for "heat death."
3. Write a summary of your findings, including the concept of heat death, the evidence that it is based on, and a Christian response to the idea on the basis of what the Bible teaches about Earth's future state. Have a classmate review your summary and give you feedback.
4. Complete your summary and submit it by the deadline.

Conclusion

We are often exposed to popular ideas about the fate of our universe, many of which are voiced from a naturalistic perspective. Such narratives offer little hope for those who put stock in them. In contrast, the Bible offers an encouraging description of both the future state of believers and the new earth in which they will dwell.

Worldview Conflict in Thermodynamics

Energy radiates from the sun. Warmth from a fire in a fireplace spreads throughout the room. Natural processes in the universe tend to spread energy out, not concentrate it. In other words, it's very likely that in any natural process, spreading energy will happen. Entropy is a measure of the extent to which energy is spread out. The entropy of most objects decreases as they lose energy and increases as they gain energy. For example, the entropy of water vapor decreases as it deposits to form a snowflake. But the energy lost by the water vapor dissipates into the cooler environment and produces an even larger increase in its entropy. The net result is an increase of entropy in the universe.

So how is the formation of snowflakes different from the formation of the very first molecules that supposedly kick-started the evolution of life? Can we simply pump energy into a system to produce order and complexity? The molecules of life—amino acids, proteins, and DNA—are very energy dense and have low entropy compared with the smaller molecules from which they are formed. This means that according to the second law of thermodynamics, it is unlikely that these molecules would spontaneously form in any warm ocean of chemicals on an early earth. Adding energy from the sun wouldn't solve this problem either; there is no initial "machine" or process to convert that energy into a useful form to manufacture the molecules necessary for life. Life comes only from life.

Living things are energy converters. For example, plants live by converting energy from the sun into a form they can use. But this concentration of energy in the plant also produces a loss of usable energy somewhere else in the universe. In fact, only about 1%–2% of the energy that a plant receives from the sun is converted into sugars that the plant can use for food. Spontaneous chemical processes can produce only a limited degree of order and no degree of complexity and information. Living systems have an organization and complexity that spontaneous processes in nonliving systems cannot reproduce.

But entropy is not the enemy of complexity, nor is disorder. The second law shows how our world operates in ways that are predictable and reliable. God uses entropy to sustain the world and protect life through a helpful flow of energy, like energy from the sun or energy from our food. We can also see how God has provided for life by giving the universe a reservoir of usable energy. In the laws of thermodynamics, we can see the goodness and faithfulness of God at work.

15.3 SECTION REVIEW

1. A classmate tells you that since most chemical reactions are exothermic, breaking bonds must release energy. How do you respond?
2. What is entropy?
3. State whether each of the following is a case of increasing or decreasing entropy and give your reasoning for each answer.
   a. A car rolls to a stop.
   b. Ice forms on a car windshield overnight.
   c. Sugar dissolves in a cup of tea.
   d. A book falls from your desk.
4. Arrange the following examples in order of increasing entropy. (Assume that entropy usually increases with temperature.)
   a. 1 mol of H_2O (*g*) at 125 °C
   b. 1 mol of H_2O (*g*) at 140 °C
   c. 1 mol of H_2O (*s*)
   d. 1 mol of H_2O (*l*)
5. Calculate the standard entropy change ($\Delta S°$) for each reaction. On the basis of the entropy change, indicate whether the reaction tends to proceed naturally.
   a. $2KClO_3(s) \longrightarrow 2KCl(s) + 3O_2(g)$
   b. $SnO_2(s) + 2H_2(g) \longrightarrow Sn(s) + 2H_2O(l)$
6. Calculate the change in free energy ($\Delta G°$) for each reaction from Question 5 at 298 K, and tell whether the reactions are spontaneous or nonspontaneous at this temperature.
7. Which combinations of ΔH and ΔS signs (+ and –) always result in a reaction that is favorable? never result in a reaction that is favorable?
8. Under what conditions will a reaction with positive ΔH and ΔS values result in a reaction that is favorable? Explain.

THE COSMOLOGICAL ARGUMENT

For a video that presents a clear argument for the creation of the universe, visit TeacherToolsOnline.com. Under Additional Resources, click on Chapter 15 Web Links. Then click on *The Cosmological Argument*.

Please be sure students understand that this video is merely demonstrating that belief in God is "reasonable." However, reason cannot tell us what is true. Only Scripture can account for the truth of God.

APPLY

LAB 15B: *NO ANCHOVIES, PLEASE!*

Once students have an understanding of the material in Section 15.3, they should be ready to work through Lab 15B.

ASSESS

TICKET OUT THE DOOR

As a **summative assessment**, ask students to describe the three cases in which reactions are more favorable. *(Case 1: reactions decrease in enthalpy, increase in entropy; Case 2: reactions decrease in enthalpy, decrease in entropy; Case 3: reactions increase in enthalpy, increase in entropy)*

15.3 REVIEW ANSWERS

* An asterisk following a question number indicates that a worked-out solution can be found on page 385B.

1. Most chemical reactions are exothermic. The energy released in exothermic reactions is the difference in energy between the reactants and products. Breaking any bond actually requires energy, while the forming of bonds releases energy. Therefore, in an exothermic reaction the energy released by forming bonds in the new substances must be more than the energy required to break the bonds in the reactants. *(p. 371)*
2. Entropy is a measure of the dispersal of energy in a system. *(p. 372)*
3. **a.** increasing; Friction is what stops the car, and friction causes a dispersion of thermal energy.
   b. decreasing; The ordered ice crystals have less dispersed energy than the molecules in water vapor.
   c. increasing; Dissolving a solute increases the randomness of the motion of its particles.
   d. increasing; The book has less potential energy on the floor than it had on the desk; the energy was transferred to the ground and spread out. *(all p. 372)*
4. c, d, a, b *(p. 372)*
5.* **a.** 494.6 J/K = 0.4946 kJ/K; favorable
   b. –119.2 J/K = –0.1192 kJ/K; unfavorable *(all p. 373)*
6.* **a.** –225.0 kJ; spontaneous
   b. 41.5 kJ; nonspontaneous *(all pp. 375–79)*
7. The combination of a negative ΔH and positive ΔS always results in a reaction that is favorable. One with a positive ΔH and negative ΔS never results in a reaction that is favorable. *(pp. 375–79)*
8. Reactions with positive ΔH and ΔS values will be favorable at high temperatures because the condition magnifies the effect of the entropy change. *(pp. 375–79)*

15 CHAPTER REVIEW

Chapter Summary

15.1 THERMODYNAMICS AND PHASE CHANGES

- Thermochemistry studies the transfer of energy during chemical reactions or phase changes.
- Thermal energy is the total kinetic energy of the particles in a substance. Temperature measures the average kinetic energy of the particles in a substance. Heat is the transfer of thermal energy between substances.
- The thermal energy of a system at constant pressure is enthalpy.
- Latent heat is the transfer of thermal energy that causes a phase change in a substance, while sensible heat is the transfer of thermal energy that causes a temperature change in the substance.
- The molar enthalpy of fusion is the thermal energy needed to melt 1 mol of a solid at its melting point with no temperature change. The thermal energy required to convert 1 mol of a liquid at its boiling point to its vapor at the same temperature is its molar enthalpy of vaporization.
- The specific heat of a substance is the amount of thermal energy required to raise the temperature of 1 g of the substance 1 °C.

TERMS

thermochemistry
enthalpy
calorimeter
sensible heat
latent heat
molar enthalpy of fusion
molar enthalpy of vaporization
specific heat

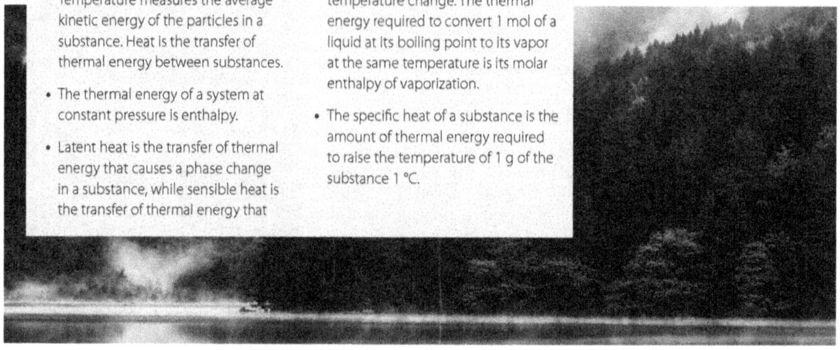

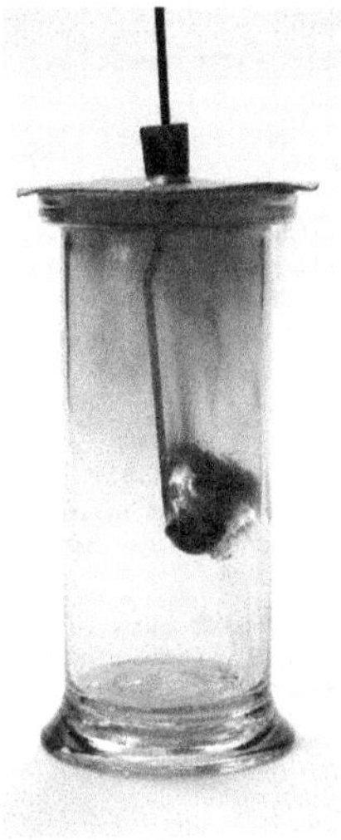

15.2 THERMODYNAMICS AND CHEMICAL CHANGES

- When scientists study the energy changes in a reaction, they measure the enthalpy of reaction, which is defined as the total enthalpy of the products minus the total enthalpy of the reactants.
- The standard molar enthalpy of formation is the change in enthalpy that occurs when 1 mol of a compound is formed in its standard state from its elements in their standard states.
- Standard state refers to the state of matter that a substance has at 298 K and 101.325 kPa.
- The standard molar enthalpy of combustion is defined as the energy released by the complete burning of 1 mol of a substance at standard conditions.
- Hess's law states that the enthalpy change of a reaction equals the sum of the enthalpy changes for each step of the process. That law can be used to calculate the enthalpy of reaction.

TERMS

enthalpy of reaction
thermochemical equation
standard molar enthalpy of formation
standard molar enthalpy of combustion
Hess's law

382 Chapter 15

15.3 REACTION TENDENCY

TERMS

entropy

Gibbs free energy

- Entropy (S) is the tendency of natural processes to spread out energy in the universe. The change in entropy (ΔS) is the entropy in the products minus the entropy in the reactants ($\Delta S = \Sigma S_{products} - \Sigma S_{reactants}$).
- Reactions that increase entropy (i.e., they have a positive ΔS) tend to be favorable, while reactions that decrease entropy (they have a negative ΔS) tend to be unfavorable.
- Gibbs free energy is helpful in determining whether overall reactions are spontaneous (favorable) or not. The free-energy change (ΔG) for a reaction can be calculated by the equation $\Delta G = \Delta H - T\Delta S$, where T is the temperature in kelvins.

Chapter Review Questions

RECALLING FACTS

1. What is enthalpy?
2. Why must a calorimeter be insulated?
3. Why is it necessary to designate the state of matter of each substance in a thermochemical equation?
4. Does a compound with a negative molar enthalpy of formation value result from an endothermic or exothermic reaction?
5. Why are most of the standard molar enthalpies of formation (ΔH°_f) negative?
6. What law allows you to combine the steps of a chemical reaction to compute change in entropy?
7. Which kind of reaction is more thermodynamically favorable: exothermic or endothermic?
8. What two tendencies influence all chemical reactions?
9. Which of the following situations are possible according to the laws of thermodynamics?
   a. insect larvae spontaneously forming in rotting meat
   b. the human body converting the energy in food to other forms of energy
   c. the energy and matter in the universe coming into being from nothing without any intervention from God
   d. the invention of an automobile engine that is 100% efficient
10. Which combination(s) of ΔH and ΔS values will result in favorability depending on temperature?

CHAPTER 15 REVIEW ANSWERS

Recalling Facts

1. Enthalpy is the thermal energy content of a system at a constant pressure. *(p. 357)*
2. A calorimeter is used to measure energy changes in a system. It must be insulated to prevent thermal energy transfer with the environment. *(p. 357)*
3. Enthalpy values for substances vary depending on which state of matter they occur in. *(p. 365)*
4. exothermic *(pp. 366–67)*
5. The reactions that produce most of the common compounds are exothermic. *(p. 367)*
6. Hess's law *(p. 369)*
7. exothermic *(p. 371)*
8. All chemical reactions tend to decrease enthalpy and increase entropy. *(p. 375)*
9. b *(p. 375)*
10. when ΔH and ΔS have the same sign *(pp. 375–79)*

Understanding Concepts

* An asterisk following a question number indicates that a worked-out solution can be found on pages 385B–85E.

11. Its temperature would not change, but the entire sample would change to a gas. *(p. 359)*

12. Soup, being mostly water, will take more time to cool because of its high specific heat. *(p. 360)*

13. Though there are exceptions, solids tend to have lower specific heats than liquids or gases. *(p. 360)*

14.* 41.7 °C *(pp. 361–62)*

15.* 971 J *(pp. 361–62)*

16.* 24.1 kJ *(pp. 362–63)*

17.* 221.0 kJ *(pp. 366–67)*

18.*a. −58.2 kJ; exothermic

b. 58.2 kJ; endothermic

c. 52.4 kJ; endothermic

d. −52.4 kJ; exothermic *(all pp. 368–69)*

CORRECTION

Have students make the following correction to the equation in the a. reaction before answering Questions 19–24: Change the second reactant to $5O_2$.

19.*a. −902.0 kJ; exothermic

b. −70.7 kJ; exothermic

c. −236.0 kJ; exothermic *(all pp. 368–69)*

20.*a. 0.1788 kJ/K

b. −0.2686 kJ/K

c. 1.0414 kJ/K *(all p. 373)*

21.*a. −955.3 kJ; favorable

b. 9.3 kJ; unfavorable

c. −546.3 kJ; favorable *(all pp. 376–79)*

22.*a. −1078.1 kJ; favorable

b. 193.9 kJ; unfavorable

c. −1261.8 kJ; favorable *(all pp. 376–79)*

23.*a. −5045 K; Since a negative kelvin value is impossible, this reaction never switches to nonspontaneous.

b. 263 K

c. −227 K; Since a negative kelvin value is impossible, this reaction never switches to nonspontaneous. *(all pp. 376–79)*

15 CHAPTER REVIEW

UNDERSTANDING CONCEPTS

11. What would happen to the temperature and physical state of 1 mol of liquid diethyl ether at its standard boiling point if its molar enthalpy of vaporization (26.52 kJ/mol) were added?

12. Will soup take more or less time to cool than an equal volume of toast? Explain.

13. From the specific heat table (Table 15-2), what general conclusions can you draw about the relationship between specific heat values and the three common states of matter?

14. If 2586 J of energy are added to 128 g of benzene at 30.0 °C, what will its final temperature be?

15. A 47.35 g mass of copper is heated from 32.7 °C to 85.3 °C. How many joules were added to accomplish this?

16. Suppose you have an ice cube with a mass of 8.00 g at a temperature of 0.0 °C. How many joules of heat must be added to completely convert the ice cube to steam at 100.0 °C?

17. What is the enthalpy of formation (ΔH°_f) for the following equation?

$2\,C\,(s) + O_2\,(g) \longrightarrow 2CO\,(g)$

18. For each of the following reactions, find the enthalpy of reaction and tell whether the reaction is endothermic or exothermic.

a. $Hg\,(l) + S\,(s) \longrightarrow HgS\,(s)$

b. $HgS\,(s) \longrightarrow Hg\,(l) + S\,(s)$

c. $2\,C\,(s) + 2H_2\,(g) \longrightarrow C_2H_4\,(g)$

d. $C_2H_4\,(g) \longrightarrow 2\,C\,(s) + 2H_2\,(g)$

For Questions 19–23, refer to the following reactions.

a. $4NH_3\,(g) + 5O_2\,(g) \longrightarrow 4NO\,(g) + 6H_2O\,(g)$

b. $3NO_2\,(g) + H_2O\,(l) \longrightarrow 2HNO_3\,(l) + NO\,(g)$

c. $2NH_4NO_3\,(s) \longrightarrow 2N_2\,(g) + O_2\,(g) + 4H_2O\,(g)$

19. Calculate the standard change in enthalpy (ΔH°_r) for each reaction, and tell whether each reaction is endothermic or exothermic.

20. Calculate the standard entropy change (ΔS°) for each reaction.

21. Calculate the change in free energy (ΔG°) for each reaction at 298 K, and tell whether each reaction is favorable (spontaneous) or unfavorable (nonspontaneous) at this temperature.

22. Estimate ΔG for each reaction at 985 K and tell whether each reaction is favorable (spontaneous) or unfavorable (nonspontaneous) at this temperature.

23. Estimate the temperature (if any) at which each reaction changes from being spontaneous to nonspontaneous (the temperature at which $\Delta G = 0$).

24. Under what conditions will a reaction with negative ΔH and ΔS values result in a reaction that is favorable? Explain.

24. Reactions with negative ΔH and ΔS values will be favorable at low temperatures because this will reduce the effect of the entropy change. *(pp. 375–79)*

CRITICAL THINKING

25. What is wrong with the statement, "As a substance freezes, it absorbs energy equal to its enthalpy of fusion"?

26. A 79.8 g piece of iron at 98.7 °C is placed in 215.0 g of water at 22.7 °C in a calorimeter. What is the final temperature of the water and iron?

27. One method of manufacturing sulfuric acid involves the four-step process shown below. Given the chemical equations for each step, determine the enthalpy of reaction for the overall reaction.

$$2S(s) + 3O_2(g) + 2H_2O(l) \longrightarrow 2H_2SO_4(l)$$

1. $S(s) + O_2(g) \longrightarrow SO_2(g) \quad \Delta H_r^\circ = -296.8\ \text{kJ}$
2. $SO_3(g) \longrightarrow SO_2(g) + \frac{1}{2}O_2(g) \quad \Delta H_r^\circ = 49.5\ \text{kJ}$
3. $H_2SO_4(g) \longrightarrow SO_3(g) + H_2O(l) \quad \Delta H_r^\circ = 101.1\ \text{kJ}$
4. $H_2SO_4(g) \longrightarrow H_2SO_4(l) \quad \Delta H_r^\circ = -68.9\ \text{kJ}$

28. How is developing an ice pack that uses enthalpy to help heal injuries an example of obeying two important commands from God?

Critical Thinking

25. As a substance freezes, the solid releases energy in an amount equal to its enthalpy of fusion. *(p. 359)*

26.* $T_f = 25.7\ °C$ *(pp. 360–62)*

27.* Overall reaction:

$2S(s) + 3O_2(g) + 2H_2O(l) \longrightarrow 2H_2SO_4(l)$; $\Delta H_r = -1032.6$ kJ or 516.3 kJ/mol *(pp. 368–69)*

28. Developing an ice pack obeys the Creation Mandate and the command to love our neighbor. It demonstrates understanding and using God's creation to help others.

Section 15.1

8. a. What we know: $m = 355$ g (ethanol, C_2H_6O), $\Delta H_{fus} = 4.94$ kJ/mol

Unknown: Q

Convert mass ethanol to energy required.

$$355\ \cancel{g\ C_2H_6O}\left(\frac{1\ \cancel{mol\ C_2H_6O}}{46.08\ \cancel{g\ C_2H_6O}}\right)\left(\frac{4.94\ kJ}{1\ \cancel{mol\ C_2H_6O}}\right) = 38.1\ kJ$$

b. What we know: $m = 515$ g (methanol, CH_4O), $\Delta H_{fus} = 35.2$ kJ/mol

Unknown: Q

Convert mass methanol to energy required.

$$515\ \cancel{g\ CH_4O}\left(\frac{1\ \cancel{mol\ CH_4O}}{32.05\ \cancel{g\ CH_4O}}\right)\left(\frac{35.2\ kJ}{1\ \cancel{mol\ CH_4O}}\right) = 566\ kJ$$

9. What we know: $m = 53.6$ g, $T_i = 95.7$ °C, $T_f = 22.5$ °C, c_{sp} (copper) = 0.39 J/g·°C

Unknown: Q

Write the formula and solve for the unknown.

$$Q = c_{sp}\, m\Delta T$$

$$Q = c_{sp} m(T_f - T_i)$$

Evaluate.

$$Q = \left(\frac{0.39\ J}{\cancel{g}\cdot °C}\right)(53.6\ \cancel{g})(22.5\ °C - 95.7\ °C)$$

$$= \left(\frac{0.39\ J}{\cancel{°C}}\right)(53.6)(-73.2\ \cancel{°C})$$

$$= -1530\ J = -1.53 \times 10^3\ J$$

Section 15.2

6. a. What we know: $\Delta H°_{f(N_2)} = 0$ kJ/mol, $\Delta H°_{f(H_2)} = 0$ kJ/mol,

$\Delta H_{f(NH_3)} = -45.9$ kJ/mol

Unknown: ΔH_r

Write the formula and solve for the unknown.

$$\Delta H_r = \Sigma\Delta H_{products} - \Sigma\Delta H_{reactants}$$

Evaluate.

$$\Delta H_r = (2\ \cancel{mol\ NH_3})\left(\frac{-45.9\ kJ}{\cancel{mol\ NH_3}}\right) - \left[(1\ \cancel{mol\ N_2})\left(\frac{0\ kJ}{\cancel{mol\ N_2}}\right) + (3\ \cancel{mol\ H_2})\left(\frac{0\ kJ}{\cancel{mol\ H_2}}\right)\right]$$

$$= -91.8\ kJ - 0\ kJ$$

$$= -91.8\ kJ;\ \text{exothermic}$$

b. What we know: $\Delta H_{f(Ca(OH)_2)} = -985.2$ kJ/mol, $\Delta H_{f(CaO)} = -634.9$ kJ/mol, $\Delta H_{f(H_2O(g))} = -241.8$ kJ/mol

Unknown: ΔH_r

Write the formula and solve for the unknown.

$$\Delta H_r = \Sigma\Delta H_{products} - \Sigma\Delta H_{reactants}$$

Evaluate.

$$\Delta H_r = \left[(1\ \cancel{mol\ CaO})\left(\frac{-634.9\ kJ}{\cancel{mol\ CaO}}\right) + (1\ \cancel{mol\ H_2O})\left(\frac{-241.8\ kJ}{\cancel{mol\ H_2O}}\right)\right] - (1\ \cancel{mol\ Ca(OH)_2})\left(\frac{-985.2\ kJ}{\cancel{mol\ Ca(OH)_2}}\right)$$

$$= (-634.9\ kJ - 241.8\ kJ) - (-985.2\ kJ)$$

$$= -876.7\ kJ - (-985.2\ kJ)$$

$$= 108.5\ kJ;\ \text{endothermic}$$

7. What we know: $\Delta H_f\,(NH_4^+) = -132.5$ kJ/mol, $\Delta H_{f(Cl^-)} = -167.2$ kJ/mol, $\Delta H_{f(NH_4Cl)} = -314.4$ kJ/mol,

$$NH_4Cl(s) \longrightarrow NH_4^+(aq) + Cl^-(aq)$$

Unknown: ΔH_{sol}

Write the formula and solve for the unknown.

$$\Delta H_{sol} = \Sigma\Delta H_{f\ products} - \Sigma\Delta H_{f\ reactants}$$

Evaluate.

$$\Delta H_r = \left[(1\ \cancel{mol\ NH_4^+})\left(\frac{-132.5\ kJ}{\cancel{mol\ NH_4^+}}\right) + (1\ \cancel{mol\ Cl^-})\left(\frac{-167.2\ kJ}{\cancel{mol\ Cl^-}}\right)\right] - (1\ \cancel{mol\ NH_4Cl})\left(\frac{-314.4\ kJ}{\cancel{mol\ NH_4Cl}}\right)$$

$$= (-132.5\ kJ - 167.2\ kJ) - (-314.4\ kJ)$$

$$= -299.7\ kJ - (-314.4\ kJ)$$

$$= 14.7\ kJ$$

9. What we know: $2C_8H_{18}(g) + 25O_2(g) \longrightarrow 16CO_2(g) + 18H_2O(l)$, $\Delta H_{f(C_8H_{18})} = -249.7$ kJ/mol, $\Delta H_{f(O_2)} = 0.0$ kJ/mol, $\Delta H_{f(CO_2(g))} = -393.5$ kJ/mol, $\Delta H_{f(H_2O(l))} = -241.8$ kJ/mol

Unknown: ΔH_c

Write the formula and solve for the unknown.

$$\Delta H_r = \Sigma\Delta H_{products} - \Sigma\Delta H_{reactants}$$

Evaluate.

$$\Delta H_c = \left[(16\ \cancel{mol\ CO_2})\left(\frac{-393.5\ kJ}{\cancel{mol\ CO_2}}\right) + (18\ \cancel{mol\ H_2O})\left(\frac{-241.8\ kJ}{\cancel{mol\ H_2O}}\right)\right] - \left[(2\ \cancel{mol\ C_8H_{18}})\left(\frac{-249.7\ kJ}{\cancel{mol\ C_8H_{18}}}\right) + (25\ \cancel{mol\ O_2})\left(\frac{0.0\ kJ}{\cancel{mol\ O_2}}\right)\right]$$

$$= (-6296.0\ kJ + (-4352.4\ kJ)) - (-499.4\ kJ + 0.0\ kJ)$$

$$= -10\,648.4\ kJ - (-499.4\ kJ)$$

$$= -10\,149\ kJ\ \text{(for the 2 mol in the equation)}$$

$$= -5075\ kJ/mol\ C_8H_{18}$$

Section 15.3

5. a. What we know: $S°$ ($KClO_3$) = 143.1 J/mol · K, $S°$ (KCl) = 82.6 J/mol · K, $S°$ (O_2) = 205.2 J/mol · K

Unknown: ΔS

Write the formula and solve for the unknown.

$$\Delta S° = \Sigma S°_{products} - \Sigma S°_{reactants}$$

Plug in known values and evaluate.

$$\Delta S° = \left[(2\ \text{mol KCl})\left(\frac{82.6\ \text{J}}{\text{mol KCl} \cdot \text{K}}\right) + (3\ \text{mol } O_2)\left(\frac{205.2\ \text{J}}{\text{mol } O_2 \cdot \text{K}}\right)\right] - (2\ \text{mol } KClO_3)\left(\frac{143.1\ \text{J}}{\text{mol } KClO_3 \cdot \text{K}}\right)$$

$$= 780.8\ \text{J/K} - 286.2\ \text{J/K}$$

$$= 494.6\ \text{J/K} = 0.4946\ \text{kJ/K; favorable}$$

b. What we know: $S°$ (SnO_2) = 49.0 J/mol · K, $S°$ (H_2) = 130.7 J/mol · K, $S°$ (Sn) = 51.2 J/mol · K, $S°$ (H_2O (*l*)) = 70.0 J/mol · K

Unknown: ΔS

Write the formula and solve for the unknown.

$$\Delta S° = \Sigma S°_{products} - \Sigma S°_{reactants}$$

Plug in known values and evaluate.

$$\Delta S° = \left[(1\ \text{mol Sn})\left(\frac{51.2\ \text{J}}{\text{mol Sn} \cdot \text{K}}\right) + (2\ \text{mol } H_2O\ (l))\left(\frac{70.0\ \text{J}}{\text{mol } H_2O\ (l) \cdot \text{K}}\right)\right] - \left[(1\ \text{mol } SnO_2)\left(\frac{49.0\ \text{J}}{\text{mol } SnO_2 \cdot \text{K}}\right) + (2\ \text{mol } H_2)\left(\frac{130.7\ \text{J}}{\text{mol } H_2 \cdot \text{K}}\right)\right]$$

$$= 191.2\ \text{J/K} - 310.4\ \text{J/K}$$

$$= -119.2\ \text{J/K} = -0.1192\ \text{kJ/K; unfavorable}$$

6. a. What we know: $H°_f$ ($KClO_3$) = −397.7 kJ/mol, $H°_f$ (KCl) = −436.5 kJ/mol, $H°_f$ (O_2) = 0.0 kJ/mol, ΔS = 0.4946 kJ/mol · K

Unknown: $\Delta G°$

Write the formula and solve for the unknown.

$$\Delta H° = \Sigma H°_{products} - \Sigma H°_{reactants}$$

Plug in known values and evaluate.

$$\Delta H°_r = \left[(2\ \text{mol KCl})\left(\frac{-436.5\ \text{kJ}}{\text{mol KCl}}\right) + (3\ \text{mol } O_2)\left(\frac{0.0\ \text{kJ}}{\text{mol } O_2}\right)\right] - (2\ \text{mol } KClO_3)\left(\frac{-397.7\ \text{kJ}}{\text{mol } KClO_3}\right)$$

$$= -873.0\ \text{kJ} - (-795.4\ \text{kJ})$$

$$= -77.6\ \text{kJ}$$

Write the formula and solve for the unknown.

$$\Delta G° = \Delta H° - T\Delta S°$$

Plug in known values and evaluate.

$$\Delta G° = -77.6\ \text{kJ} - 298\ \text{K}(0.4946\ \text{kJ/K})$$

$$= -225.0\ \text{kJ; spontaneous}$$

b. What we know: $H°_f$ (SnO_2) = −577.6 kJ/mol, $H°_f$ (H_2) = 0.0 kJ/mol, $H°_f$ (Sn) = 0.0 kJ/mol, $H°_f$ (H_2O (*l*)) = −285.8 kJ/mol, $\Delta S°$ = −0.1192 kJ/K

Unknown: $\Delta G°$

Write the formula and solve for the unknown.

$$\Delta H° = \Sigma H°_{products} - \Sigma H°_{reactants}$$

Plug in known values and evaluate.

$$\Delta H° = \left[(1\ \text{mol Sn})\left(\frac{0.0\ \text{kJ}}{\text{mol Sn}}\right) + (2\ \text{mol } H_2O\ (l))\left(\frac{-285.8\ \text{kJ}}{\text{mol } H_2O\ (l)}\right)\right] - \left[(1\ \text{mol } SnO_2)\left(\frac{-577.6\ \text{kJ}}{\text{mol } SnO_2}\right) + (2\ \text{mol } H_2)\left(\frac{0.0\ \text{kJ}}{\text{mol } H_2}\right)\right]$$

$$= -571.6\ \text{kJ} - (-577.6\ \text{kJ})$$

$$= 6.0\ \text{kJ}$$

Write the formula and solve for the unknown.

$$\Delta G° = \Delta H° - T\Delta S°$$

Plug in known values and evaluate.

$$\Delta G° = 6.0\ \text{kJ} - 298\ \text{K}(-0.1192\ \text{kJ/K})$$

$$= 41.5\ \text{kJ; nonspontaneous}$$

Chapter Review

14. What we know: Q = 2586 J, m = 128 g, T_i = 30.0 °C, c_{sp} = 1.73 J/g· °C

Unknown: T_f

Write the formula and solve for the unknown.

$$Q = c_{sp}m\Delta T$$

$$Q = c_{sp}m(T_f - T_i)$$

$$\frac{Q}{c_{sp}m} = \frac{c_{sp}m(T_f - T_i)}{c_{sp}m}$$

$$T_f - T_i + T_i = \frac{Q}{c_{sp}m} + T_i$$

$$T_f = \frac{Q}{c_{sp}m} + T_i$$

Evaluate.

$$T_f = \frac{2586\ \text{J}}{\left(1.73\ \frac{\text{J}}{\text{g} \cdot °\text{C}}\right)(128\ \text{g})} + 30.0\ °\text{C}$$

$$= 11.\underline{6}8\ °\text{C} + 30.0\ °\text{C}$$

$$= 41.7\ °\text{C}$$

15. What we know: m = 47.35 g, T_i = 32.7 °C, T_f = 85.3 °C, c_{sp} = 0.39 J/g· °C

Unknown: Q

Write the formula and solve for the unknown.

$$Q = c_{sp}m\Delta T$$

$$= c_{sp}m(T_f - T_i)$$

(continued)

Evaluate.

$$Q = \left(0.39 \frac{\text{J}}{\text{g}\cdot{}^\circ\text{C}}\right)(47.35\ \text{g})(85.3\ {}^\circ\text{C} - 32.7\ {}^\circ\text{C})$$

$$= \left(0.39 \frac{\text{J}}{{}^\circ\text{C}}\right)(47.35)(52.6\ {}^\circ\text{C})$$

$$= 971\ \text{J}$$

16. What we know: $m = 8.00$ g, $T_i = 0.0$ °C, $T_f = 100.0$ °C, $c_{sp} = 4.18$ J/g· °C, $\Delta H_{fus} = 6.01$ kJ/mol H_2O, $\Delta H_{vap} = 40.7$ kJ/mol H_2O

Unknown: Q_{melt}, Q, Q_{boil}, Q_{total}

Convert mass into Q_{melt} and Q_{boil}.

$$8.00\ \text{g H}_2\text{O}\left(\frac{1\ \text{mol H}_2\text{O}}{18.02\ \text{g H}_2\text{O}}\right)\left(\frac{6.01\ \text{kJ}}{1\ \text{mol H}_2\text{O}}\right) = 2.668\ \text{kJ} = Q_{melt}$$

$$8.00\ \text{g H}_2\text{O}\left(\frac{1\ \text{mol H}_2\text{O}}{18.02\ \text{g H}_2\text{O}}\right)\left(\frac{40.7\ \text{kJ}}{1\ \text{mol H}_2\text{O}}\right) = 18.06\ \text{kJ} = Q_{boil}$$

Write the formula and solve for the unknown.

$$Q = c_{sp} m \Delta T$$

Evaluate.

$$Q = (8.00\ \text{g})\left(4.18 \frac{\text{J}}{\text{g}\cdot{}^\circ\text{C}}\right)(100.0\ {}^\circ\text{C} - 0.00\ {}^\circ\text{C})$$

$$= (8.00)\left(4.18 \frac{\text{J}}{{}^\circ\text{C}}\right)(100.0\ {}^\circ\text{C})$$

$$= 3344\ \text{J} = 3.344\ \text{kJ}$$

$$Q_{total} = \Sigma Q = Q_{melt} + Q + Q_{boil}$$

$$= 2.668\ \text{kJ} + 18.06\ \text{kJ} + 3.344\ \text{kJ}$$

$$= 24.1\ \text{kJ}$$

17. $2\ \text{mol CO}\left(\frac{-110.5\ \text{kJ}}{1\ \text{mol CO}}\right) = 221.0\ \text{kJ}$

18. a. $\Delta H^\circ_r = (1\ \text{mol HgS})\left(\frac{-58.2\ \text{kJ}}{\text{mol HgS}}\right) - \left[(1\ \text{mol Hg})\left(\frac{0.0\ \text{kJ}}{\text{mol Hg}}\right) + (1\ \text{mol S})\left(\frac{0.0\ \text{kJ}}{\text{mol S}}\right)\right]$

$= -58.2$ kJ; exothermic

b. $\Delta H^\circ_r = \left[(1\ \text{mol Hg})\left(\frac{0.0\ \text{kJ}}{\text{mol Hg}}\right) + (1\ \text{mol S})\left(\frac{0.0\ \text{kJ}}{\text{mol S}}\right)\right] - (1\ \text{mol HgS})\left(\frac{-58.2\ \text{kJ}}{\text{mol HgS}}\right)$

$= 58.2$ kJ; endothermic

c. $\Delta H^\circ_r = (1\ \text{mol C}_2\text{H}_2)\left(\frac{52.4\ \text{kJ}}{1\ \text{mol C}_2\text{H}_2}\right) - \left[(1\ \text{mol C})\left(\frac{0.0\ \text{kJ}}{\text{mol C}}\right) + (1\ \text{mol H})\left(\frac{0.0\ \text{kJ}}{\text{mol H}}\right)\right]$

$= 52.4$ kJ; endothermic

d. $\Delta H^\circ_r = \left[(1\ \text{mol C})\left(\frac{0.0\ \text{kJ}}{\text{mol C}}\right) + (1\ \text{mol H})\left(\frac{0.0\ \text{kJ}}{\text{mol H}}\right)\right] - (1\ \text{mol C}_2\text{H}_2)\left(\frac{52.4\ \text{kJ}}{1\ \text{mol C}_2\text{H}_2}\right)$

$= -52.4$ kJ; exothermic

19. a. What we know: $\Delta H^\circ_f (NH_3) = -45.9$ kJ/mol, $\Delta H^\circ_f (O_2) = 0.0$ kJ/mol, ΔH°_f (NO) $= 91.3$ kJ/mol, ΔH°_f (H_2O (*g*)) $= -241.8$ kJ/mol

Unknown: ΔH°_r

Write the formula and solve for the unknown.

$$\Delta H^\circ_r = \Sigma H^\circ_{products} - \Sigma H^\circ_{reactants}$$

Plug in known values and evaluate.

$$\Delta H^\circ_r = \left[(4\ \text{mol NO})\left(\frac{91.3\ \text{kJ}}{1\ \text{mol NO}}\right)(6\ \text{mol H}_2\text{O}\ (g))\left(\frac{-241.8\ \text{kJ}}{1\ \text{mol H}_2\text{O}\ (g)}\right)\right] - \left[(4\ \text{mol NH}_3)\left(\frac{-45.9\ \text{kJ}}{1\ \text{mol NH}_3}\right) + (5\ \text{mol O}_2)\left(\frac{0.0\ \text{kJ}}{1\ \text{mol O}_2}\right)\right]$$

$= -1085.6$ kJ $- (-183.6$ kJ)

$= -902.0$ kJ; exothermic

b. What we know: $\Delta H^\circ_f (NO_2) = 33.2$ kJ/mol, ΔH°_f (H_2O (*l*)) $= -285.8$ kJ/mol, $\Delta H^\circ_f (HNO_3) = -174.1$ kJ/mol, ΔH°_f (NO) $= 91.3$ kJ/mol

Unknown: ΔH°_r

Write the formula and solve for the unknown.

$$\Delta H^\circ_r = \Sigma H^\circ_{products} - \Sigma H^\circ_{reactants}$$

Plug in known values and evaluate.

$$\Delta H^\circ_r = \left[(2\ \text{mol HNO}_3)\left(\frac{-174.1\ \text{kJ}}{\text{mol HNO}_3}\right) + (1\ \text{mol NO}\ (g))\left(\frac{91.3\ \text{kJ}}{\text{mol NO}\ (g)}\right)\right] - \left[(3\ \text{mol NO}_2)\left(\frac{33.2\ \text{kJ}}{\text{mol NO}_2}\right) + (1\ \text{mol H}_2\text{O})\left(\frac{-285.8\ \text{kJ}}{\text{mol H}_2\text{O}}\right)\right]$$

$= -256.9$ kJ $- (-186.2$ kJ)

$= -70.7$ kJ; exothermic

c. What we know: $\Delta H^\circ_f (NH_4NO_3) = -365.6$ kJ/mol, $\Delta H^\circ_f (N_2) = 0.0$ kJ/mol, $\Delta H^\circ_f (O_2) = 0.0$ kJ/mol, ΔH°_f (H_2O (*g*)) $= -241.8$ kJ/mol

Unknown: ΔH°_r

Write the formula and solve for the unknown.

$$\Delta H^\circ_r = \Sigma H^\circ_{products} - \Sigma H^\circ_{reactants}$$

Plug in known values and evaluate.

$$\Delta H^\circ_r = \left[(2\ \text{mol N}_2)\left(\frac{0.0\ \text{kJ}}{\text{mol N}_2}\right) + (1\ \text{mol O}_2)\left(\frac{0.0\ \text{kJ}}{\text{mol O}_2}\right) + (4\ \text{mol H}_2\text{O}\ (g))\left(\frac{-241.8\ \text{kJ}}{\text{mol H}_2\text{O}\ (g)}\right)\right] - (2\ \text{mol NH}_4\text{NO}_3)\left(\frac{-365.6\ \text{kJ}}{\text{mol NH}_4\text{NO}_3}\right)$$

$= -967.2$ kJ $- (-731.2$ kJ)

$= -236.0$ kJ; exothermic

20. a. What we know: $S°(NH_3) = 192.8$ J/mol · K, $S°(O_2) = 205.2$ J/mol · K, $S°(NO) = 210.8$ J/mol · K, $S°(H_2O(g)) = 188.8$ J/mol · K

Unknown: ΔS

Write the formula and solve for the unknown.

$$\Delta S° = \Sigma S°_{products} - \Sigma S°_{reactants}$$

Plug in known values and evaluate.

$$\Delta S° = \left[(4\ \cancel{\text{mol NO}})\left(\frac{210.8\ \text{J}}{\cancel{\text{mol NO}}\cdot\text{K}}\right) + (6\ \cancel{\text{mol H}_2\text{O}(g)})\left(\frac{188.8\ \text{J}}{\cancel{\text{mol H}_2\text{O}(g)}\cdot\text{K}}\right)\right] - \left[(4\ \cancel{\text{mol NH}_3})\left(\frac{192.8\ \text{J}}{\cancel{\text{mol NH}_3}\cdot\text{K}}\right) + (5\ \cancel{\text{mol O}_2})\left(\frac{205.2\ \text{J}}{\cancel{\text{mol O}_2}\cdot\text{K}}\right)\right]$$

$$= 1976.0\ \frac{\text{J}}{\text{K}} - 1797.2\ \frac{\text{J}}{\text{K}}$$

$$= 178.8\ \text{J/K} = 0.1788\ \text{kJ/K}$$

b. What we know: $S°(NO_2) = 240.2$ J/mol · K, $S°(H_2O(l)) = 70.0$ J/mol · K, $S°(HNO_3) = 155.6$ J/mol · K, $S°(NO) = 210.8$ J/mol · K

Unknown: ΔS

Write the formula and solve for the unknown.

$$\Delta S° = \Sigma S°_{products} - \Sigma S°_{reactants}$$

Plug in known values and evaluate.

$$\Delta S° = \left[(2\ \cancel{\text{mol HNO}_3})\left(\frac{155.6\ \text{J}}{\cancel{\text{mol HNO}_3}\cdot\text{K}}\right) = (1\ \cancel{\text{mol NO}(g)})\left(\frac{210.8\ \text{J}}{\cancel{\text{mol NO}(g)}\cdot\text{K}}\right)\right] - \left[(3\ \cancel{\text{mol NO}_2})\left(\frac{240.2\ \text{J}}{\cancel{\text{mol NO}_2}\cdot\text{K}}\right) + (1\ \cancel{\text{mol H}_2\text{O}})\left(\frac{70.0\ \text{J}}{\cancel{\text{mol H}_2\text{O}}\cdot\text{K}}\right)\right]$$

$$= 522.0\ \text{J/K} - 790.6\ \text{J/K}$$

$$= -268.6\ \text{J/K} = -0.2686\ \text{kJ/K}$$

c. What we know: $S°(NH_4NO_3) = 151.1$ J/mol · K, $S°(N_2) = 191.6$ J/mol · K, $S°(O_2) = 205.2$ J/mol · K, $S°(H_2O(g)) = 188.8$ J/mol · K

Unknown: $\Delta S°$

Write the formula and solve for the unknown.

$$\Delta S° = \Sigma S°_{products} - \Sigma S°_{reactants}$$

Plug in known values and evaluate.

$$\Delta S° = \left[(2\ \cancel{\text{mol N}_2})\left(\frac{191.6\ \text{J}}{\cancel{\text{mol N}_2}\cdot\text{K}}\right) + (1\ \cancel{\text{mol O}_2})\left(\frac{205.2\ \text{J}}{\cancel{\text{mol O}_2}\cdot\text{K}}\right) + (4\ \cancel{\text{mol H}_2\text{O}(g)})\left(\frac{188.8\ \text{J}}{\cancel{\text{mol H}_2\text{O}(g)}\cdot\text{K}}\right)\right] - (2\ \cancel{\text{mol NH}_4\text{NO}_3})\left(\frac{151.1\ \text{J}}{\cancel{\text{mol NH}_4\text{NO}_3}\cdot\text{K}}\right)$$

$$= 1343.6\ \text{J/K} - 302.2\ \text{J/K}$$

$$= 1041.4\ \text{J/K} = 1.0414\ \text{kJ/K}$$

21. a. What we know: $\Delta H°_r = -902.0$ kJ, $\Delta S° = 0.1788$ kJ/K, $T = 298$ K

Unknown: $\Delta G°$

Write the formula and solve for the unknown.

$$\Delta G° = \Delta H° - T\Delta S°$$

Plug in known values and evaluate.

$$\Delta G° = -902.0\ \text{kJ} - 298\ \cancel{\text{K}}(0.1788\ \text{kJ}/\cancel{\text{K}})$$

$$= -955.3\ \text{kJ; favorable}$$

b. What we know: $\Delta H°_r = -70.7$ kJ, $\Delta S° = -0.2686$ kJ/K, $T = 298$ K

Unknown: $\Delta G°$

Write the formula and solve for the unknown.

$$\Delta G° = \Delta H° - T\Delta S°$$

Plug in known values and evaluate.

$$\Delta G° = -70.7\ \text{kJ} - 298\ \cancel{\text{K}}(-0.2686\ \text{kJ}/\cancel{\text{K}})$$

$$= 9.3\ \text{kJ; unfavorable}$$

c. What we know: $\Delta H°_r = -236.0$ kJ, $\Delta S° = 1.0414$ kJ/K, $T = 298$ K

Unknown: $\Delta G°$

Write the formula and solve for the unknown.

$$\Delta G° = \Delta H° - T\Delta S°$$

Plug in known values and evaluate.

$$\Delta G° = -236.0\ \text{kJ} - 298\ \cancel{\text{K}}(1.0414\ \text{kJ}/\cancel{\text{K}})$$

$$= -546.3\ \text{kJ; favorable}$$

22. a. What we know: $\Delta H_r = -902.0$ kJ, $\Delta S = 0.1788$ kJ/K, $T = 985$ K

Unknown: ΔG

Write the formula and solve for the unknown.

$$\Delta G = \Delta H - T\Delta S$$

Plug in known values and evaluate.

$$\Delta G = -902.0\ \text{kJ} - 985\ \cancel{\text{K}}(0.1788\ \text{kJ}/\cancel{\text{K}})$$

$$= -1078.1\ \text{kJ; favorable}$$

b. What we know: $\Delta H_r = -70.7$ kJ, $\Delta S = -0.2686$ kJ/K, $T = 985$ K

Unknown: ΔG

Write the formula and solve for the unknown.

$$\Delta G = \Delta H - T\Delta S$$

Plug in known values and evaluate.

$$\Delta G = -70.7\ \text{kJ} - 985\ \cancel{\text{K}}(-0.2686\ \text{kJ}/\cancel{\text{K}})$$

$$= 193.9\ \text{kJ; unfavorable}$$

c. What we know: $\Delta H_r = -236.0$ kJ, $\Delta S = 1.0414$ kJ/K, $T = 985$ K

Unknown: ΔG

Write the formula and solve for the unknown.

$$\Delta G = \Delta H - T\Delta S$$

Plug in known values and evaluate.

$$\Delta G = -236.0\ \text{kJ} - 985\ \cancel{\text{K}}(1.0414\ \text{kJ}/\cancel{\text{K}})$$

$$= -1261.8\ \text{kJ; favorable}$$

23. Write the formula and solve for the unknown.

$\Delta G = \Delta H - T\Delta S$

Reactions change from spontaneous when $\Delta G = 0$.

Set $\Delta G = 0$ and solve for T.

$0 = \Delta H - T\Delta S$

$0 + T\Delta S = \Delta H - T\Delta S + T\Delta S$

$\frac{T\Delta S}{\Delta S} = \frac{\Delta H}{\Delta S}$

$T = \frac{\Delta H}{\Delta S}$

a. What we know: $\Delta H_r = -902.0$ kJ, $\Delta S = 0.1788$ kJ/K, $\Delta G = 0$ kJ

Unknown: T

Plug in known values and evaluate.

$T = \frac{-902.0 \text{ kJ}}{0.1788 \text{ kJ/K}}$

$= -5045$ K

b. What we know: $\Delta H_r = -70.7$ kJ, $\Delta S = -0.2686$ kJ/K, $\Delta G = 0$ kJ

Unknown: T

$T = \frac{\Delta H}{\Delta S}$

$= \frac{-70.7 \text{ kJ}}{-0.2686 \text{ kJ/K}}$

$= 263$ K

c. What we know: $\Delta H_r = -236.0$ kJ, $\Delta S = 1.0414$ kJ/K, $\Delta G = 0$ kJ

Unknown: T

$T = \frac{\Delta H}{\Delta S}$

$= \frac{-236.0 \text{ kJ}}{1.0414 \text{ kJ/K}}$

$= -227$ K

26. What we know: $m_{Fe} = 79.8$ g, $T_{i\,Fe} = 98.7$ °C, $m_{water} = 215.0$ g, $T_{i\,water} = 22.7$ °C, $c_{sp\,Fe} = 0.46$ J/g·°C, $c_{sp\,water} = 4.18$ J/g·°C, $Q_{water} = -Q_{Fe}$

Unknown: $T_{f\,Fe} = T_{f\,water} = T_f$

Write the formula and solve for the unknown.

$$Q_{water} = -Q_{Fe}$$

$c_{sp\,water} m_{water} (T_f - T_{i\,water}) = -c_{sp\,Fe} m_{Fe} (T_f - T_{i\,Fe})$

In this case, it is easiest to substitute for Q_{water} and Q_{Fe} and solve for T_f.

$\left(4.18 \frac{\text{J}}{\text{g}\cdot°\text{C}}\right)(215.0 \text{ g})(T_f - 22.7\text{ °C})$
$= -\left(0.46 \frac{\text{J}}{\text{g}\cdot°\text{C}}\right)(79.8 \text{ g})(T_f - 98.7\text{ °C})$

$898.7 \frac{\text{J}}{°\text{C}}(T_f - 22.7\text{ °C}) = -36.71 \frac{\text{J}}{°\text{C}}(T_f - 98.7\text{ °C})$

$898.7 \frac{\text{J}}{°\text{C}} T_f - 20\,400 \frac{\text{J}}{°\text{C}}\text{°C} = -36.71 \frac{\text{J}}{°\text{C}} T_f + 3623 \frac{\text{J}}{°\text{C}}\text{°C}$

$898.7 \frac{\text{J}}{°\text{C}} T_f - 20\,400 \frac{\text{J}}{°\text{C}}\text{°C} + 36.71 \frac{\text{J}}{°\text{C}} T_f =$
$-36.71 \frac{\text{J}}{°\text{C}} T_f + 3623 \frac{\text{J}}{°\text{C}}\text{°C} + 36.71 \frac{\text{J}}{°\text{C}} T_f$

$935 \frac{\text{J}}{°\text{C}} T_f - 20\,400\text{ J} + 20\,400\text{ J} = 3623\text{ J} + 20\,400\text{ J}$

$$\frac{935.4 \frac{\text{J}}{°\text{C}} T_f}{935.4 \frac{\text{J}}{°\text{C}}} = \frac{24\,023 \text{ J}}{935.4 \frac{\text{J}}{°\text{C}}}$$

$$T_f = 25.7\text{ °C}$$

27. We need 2 mol of sulfur on the left side of the equation and it is there in Equation 1, but there is only 1 mol of it, so we must multiply Equation 1 by 2. We need 3 mol of oxygen on the left side of the equation and it is there in Equation 1 but on the right in Equation 2, so we may need to make an adjustment later. We need 2 mol of water on the left side of the equation and it is only in Equation 3, but it is on the right side and there is only 1 mol so we have to reverse Equation 3 and multiply it by 2. We need 2 mol of liquid sulfuric acid on the right. It is there in Equation 4, but we need to double Equation 4. We need to eliminate the SO_2 and SO_3. We can accomplish this by reversing Equation 2 and multiplying it by 2. This change to Equation 2 also gives us 3 mol of oxygen on the left side (in Equations 1 and 2).

1. ~~$S(s) + O_2(g) \longrightarrow SO_2(g)$ $\Delta H°_r = -296.8$ kJ~~
   $2S(s) + 2O_2(g) \longrightarrow 2SO_2(g)$ $\Delta H°_r = -593.6$ kJ

2. ~~$SO_3(g) \longrightarrow SO_2(g) + \frac{1}{2}O_2(g)$ $\Delta H°_r = 49.5$ kJ~~
   $2SO_2(g) + O_2(g) \longrightarrow 2SO_3(g)$ $\Delta H°_r = -99.0$ kJ

3. ~~$H_2SO_4(g) \longrightarrow SO_3(g) + H_2O(l)$ $\Delta H°_r = 101.1$ k~~
   $2SO_3(g) + 2H_2O(l) \longrightarrow 2H_2SO_4(g)$ $\Delta H°_r = -202.2$ kJ

4. ~~$H_2SO_4(g) \longrightarrow H_2SO_4(l)$ $\Delta H°_r = -68.9$ k~~
   $2H_2SO_4(g) \longrightarrow 2H_2SO_4(l)$ $\Delta H°_r = -137.8$ kJ

We should be able to add the four intermediate equations to make the overall chemical equation. If successful, we can then add the enthalpies of reaction for each intermediate step to determine the enthalpy of the overall reaction.

1. $2S(s) + 2O_2(g) \longrightarrow 2SO_2(g)$ $\Delta H°_r = -593.6$ kJ
2. $2SO_2(g) + O_2(g) \longrightarrow 2SO_3(g)$ $\Delta H°_r = -99.0$ kJ
3. $2SO_3(g) + 2H_2O(l) \longrightarrow 2H_2SO_4(g)$ $\Delta H°_r = -202.2$ kJ
4. $2H_2SO_4(g) \longrightarrow 2H_2SO_4(l)$ $\Delta H°_r = -137.8$ kJ

Overall: $2S(s) + 3O_2(g) + 2H_2O(l) \longrightarrow 2H_2SO_4(l)$
$\Delta H°_r = -1032.6$ kJ or 516.3 kJ/mol

CHAPTER 16 *OBJECTIVES*

- Explain how kinetics differs from chemical thermodynamics.
- Write a chemical equation from its elementary steps.
- Determine the conditions that affect reaction rates.

OVERVIEW

Chapter 16 has key material that will help students understand the mechanisms that occur within a reaction. Students will discover the requirements needed for a reaction to occur as well as the factors that affect the rates of reactions.

16.1 REACTION RATES

- *Kinetics*
- *Energy Diagrams*
- *Collision Theory*
- *Activation Energy and the Activated Complex*
- *Rates of Reactions*
- *Factors That Affect Reaction Rates*

16.2 REACTION MECHANISMS

- *Mechanisms*
- *Rate Laws and Reaction Orders*
- *Kinetics in the Real World*

LAB ACTIVITIES

Lab 16A: *Chemistry—A Contact Sport?*—Students gain an understanding of factors that affect the rates of reactions and how to determine the concentration of a reactant on the basis of the reaction time.

Lab 16B: *Don't Overreact*—Students learn how to determine the rate law for a chemical reaction.

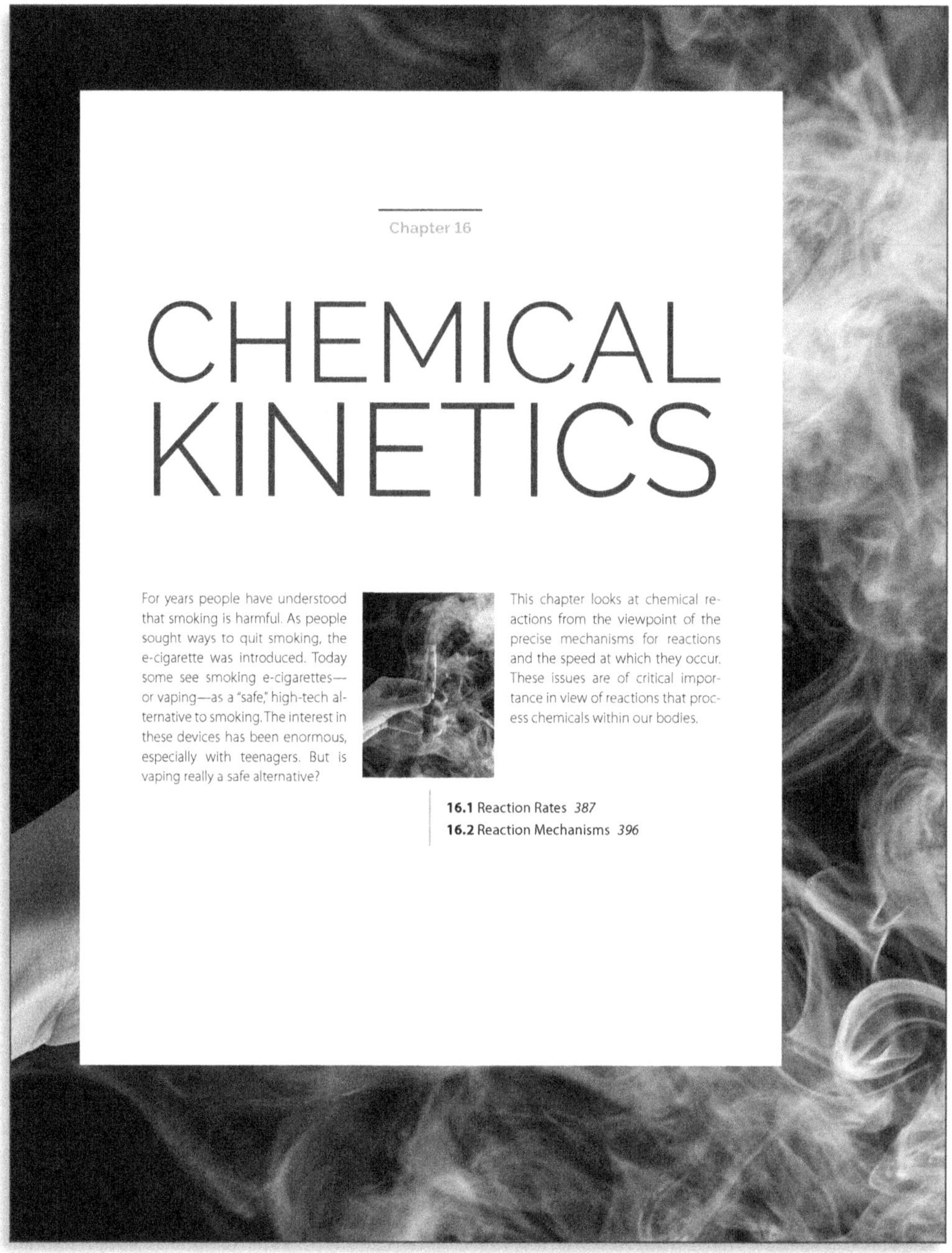

Chapter 16

CHEMICAL KINETICS

For years people have understood that smoking is harmful. As people sought ways to quit smoking, the e-cigarette was introduced. Today some see smoking e-cigarettes—or vaping—as a "safe," high-tech alternative to smoking. The interest in these devices has been enormous, especially with teenagers. But is vaping really a safe alternative?

This chapter looks at chemical reactions from the viewpoint of the precise mechanisms for reactions and the speed at which they occur. These issues are of critical importance in view of reactions that process chemicals within our bodies.

The image in the Chapter opener shows vapor being emitted from an e-cigarette. Although popular among the younger generation, research studies have shown that vaping poses many health risks.

16.1 REACTION RATES

Kinetics

What is the difference between the decomposition of nitroglycerine in dynamite and the decomposition of food? For one, there is a huge difference in the amount of energy released, as you learned when studying thermodynamics in Chapter 15. But another part of the difference is how fast the reaction takes place. The field of chemistry called *kinetics* answers questions about the speed at which reactions occur and the way in which they get started. While thermodynamics answers the basic question, "Can it react?," kinetics answers the more specific questions, "Will it react?" and "How fast will it react?" **Kinetics** is the study of the rates of reactions and the steps by which they occur.

How is a fire different from an explosion?

The fact that a reaction is thermodynamically favorable does not mean that it will proceed automatically. Some reactions proceed at an extremely slow rate; others are rapid. Some need a push to get started; others proceed on their own.

QUESTIONS

- How can I tell how quickly a reaction will occur?
- Why don't all favorable reactions occur?
- How do reactions actually occur?
- What affects reaction rates?

TERMS

kinetics • collision theory • activation energy • activated complex • reaction rate • catalyst • homogeneous catalyst • heterogeneous catalyst • enzyme • inhibitor

FAVORABLE REACTIONS

As an example, consider the following three reactions. Each of them has a negative Gibbs free energy (ΔG), so they are all favorable (spontaneous) under the proper conditions of temperature and pressure.

the oxidation of a diamond

$\Delta G = -395.4$ kJ

This reaction occurs, but not at a significant rate.

the burning of methane

$\Delta G = -882.0$ kJ

Combustion of methane will not start unless it is given an energetic push (from a lighted match, for example) and is very rapid.

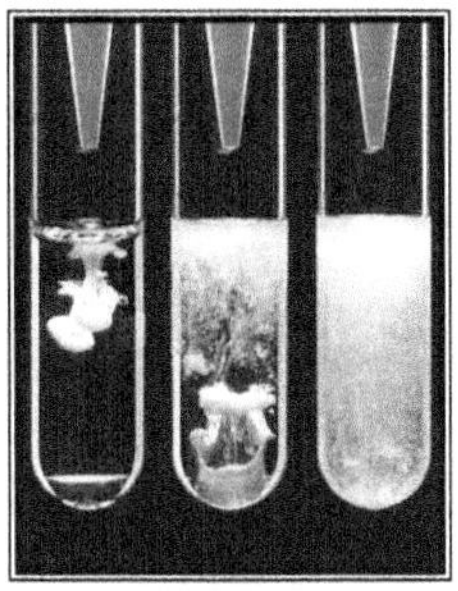

the mixing and the neutralization of $Ba(OH)_2$ and H_2SO_4

$\Delta G = -286.1$ kJ

This third reaction proceeds as soon as the reactants are mixed together and occurs quickly.

Something besides thermodynamics must be used to explain why reactions have such a wide variety of rates. That something is kinetics.

SECTION 16.1 *OVERVIEW*

Essential Question

How is a fire different from an explosion?

Objectives

» **16.1.1** Define *kinetics*.

» **16.1.2** Summarize the collision theory.

» **16.1.3** Explain why thermodynamically favorable reactions don't always occur.

» **16.1.4** Summarize changes in reaction rates in response to different reaction conditions.

Resources

Case Study: Spontaneous Combustion

Demonstrating the Effect of Concentration in a Reaction, Demonstrating the Effect of Surface Area and Temperature on Reaction Rates

Web Links: Collision Theory Resources, Catalysts

Mini Lab: *Changing Reaction Rates*; Lab 16A: *Chemistry—A Contact Sport?—Exploring Concentration's Effect on Reaction Rates*

ENGAGE

WHAT HAVE WE LEARNED?

Prompt students to do a **turn and talk** activity. On the board write "Name some concepts that you have learned about in chemistry so far." Tell them that they will be given three minutes to turn to their neighbor and discuss and record their answers. Once students have finished discussing their answers, select several to share their answers. As they do, write their answers on the board. Students should recall concepts such as elements, groups, ions, oxidation numbers, types of reactions, chemical equations, stoichiometry, bonds, measures of concentration, and calculating enthalpy, entropy, and free energy.

Ask, "Is there anything that seems to be missing from this list?" Lead students to understand that although they've learned how to predict whether a reaction will occur, they haven't yet discovered the speed of reactions or how they get started in the first place.

INSTRUCT

KINETICS

Lead a **visual analysis** of the graphs on page 388. Ask the following questions to help students understand the difference between thermodynamics and kinetics.

1. On the basis of the graphs, where would you apply the concept of thermodynamics? *(only in the starting and ending points of the reaction)* (This answer implies that thermodynamics is concerned only with the energy before and after a reaction.)
2. On the basis of the graphs, where would you apply the concept of kinetics? *(in the middle of the reaction)* (This answer implies that kinetics is concerned with the energy between the beginning and end of the reaction.)

Thermodynamics and kinetics complement each other and work together to tell the whole story of a reaction.

COLLISION THEORY RESOURCES

For a video that helps to explain the collision theory, visit TeacherToolsOnline.com. Under Additional Resources, click on Chapter 16 Web Links. Then click on *Collision Theory*.

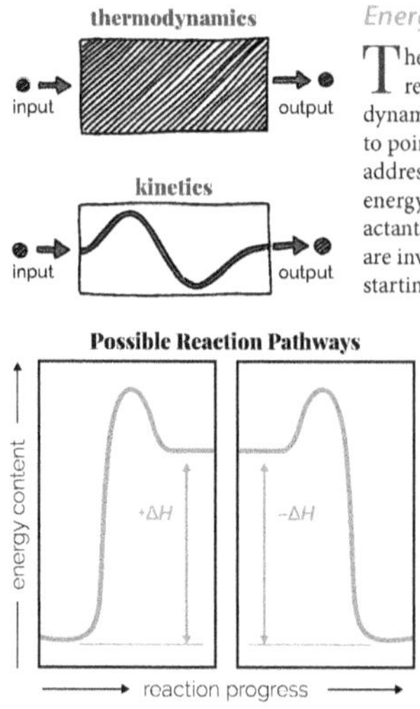

Energy Diagrams

Thermodynamics relates only to the starting and ending points of a reaction and is therefore path independent. In chemistry, thermodynamics is concerned only with the change in energy from point A to point B. On the other hand, kinetics is path-dependent. Kinetics addresses how a reaction proceeds from point A to point B. Are the energy changes during a reaction simple and direct, or must the reactants gain some energy before the reaction can proceed? What steps are involved? Kinetics seeks to determine what happens between the starting point and end point of a reaction.

To understand the difference between thermodynamics and kinetics, consider a shopper strolling through a multilevel mall. She may change levels and go in and out of stores. Thermodynamics is concerned only with what level she entered and exited the mall, that is, with her beginning and ending energies. But kinetics would be interested in the specific path she took through the mall—which stores she entered and for how long, along with when and where she changed levels.

It can be helpful to graph the energy changes in a reaction on an energy diagram (see left). The horizontal scale represents the progress of the reaction being considered, and the vertical scale represents energy. The highest point on the energy diagram corresponds to the energy needed by the reactants to form products.

Collision Theory

Recall that, according to the kinetic-molecular theory, particles are in constant motion in random directions at speeds related to their temperature. With all that motion, collisions are bound to happen, and colliding particles may react. Suppose a hypothetical gas molecule (X_2) can combine with a different hypothetical gas molecule (Y_2). A sufficiently energetic collision will disrupt the electron orbitals of these molecules. For a moment, the four atoms form a single high-energy group; then the group separates into two new molecules (2XY) according to the equation below.

$$X_2 + Y_2 \longrightarrow 2XY$$

The **collision theory** of reactions states three conditions that must be met for any reaction to occur. First, the particles must collide in order to react, though a collision alone does not guarantee a reaction. The particles must also collide in the proper orientation necessary for the rearrangement of atoms and electrons. Finally, the collision must be energetic enough to form products. The theory can be summarized by saying that reactions follow only *effective collisions*—those that are sufficiently energetic and properly oriented.

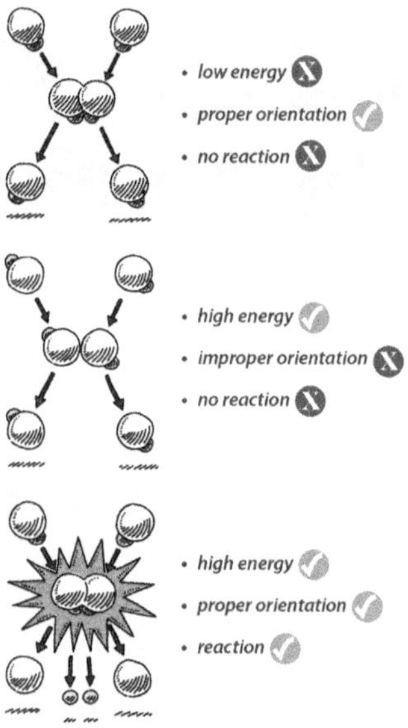

The collision theory explains why reactions occur at faster or slower rates, depending on reaction conditions. Any factor that increases the number of effective collisions increases the rate of a reaction. Therefore, the rate at which a chemical reaction proceeds is directly related to the frequency of effective collisions. Fast reactions occur when the three criteria are easily met: (1) collisions with (2) proper orientation and (3) sufficient energy. But if meeting even one criterion is difficult, the reaction will occur more slowly.

MINILAB

CHANGING REACTION RATES

We all know that when there is little traffic on the highway, the probability of collision is low. As the amount of traffic increases, the chances of two cars colliding is greater. Do chemical reactions work the same way? Does increasing the concentration of the reactants affect the number of collisions and therefore the reaction rate?

How does concentration affect reaction rate?

1. Write a hypothesis regarding the effect of concentration on the rate of reaction.
2. Justify why you think concentration will affect the rate as you indicated in your hypothesis.

Procedure

A. Copy the table below onto a piece of paper.

B. Label the test tubes 1–4.

C. Fill the test tubes with vinegar and water according to the table.

3. What is being compared in Tubes 1 and 2?
4. What is being compared in Tubes 2, 3, and 4?

D. Add the indicated strip of metal to each test tube and record your observations.

Conclusion

5. What was the effect of using different metals? Why do you think this was true?
6. What was the effect of changing the concentration of the vinegar?

Test Tube	Vinegar (mL)	Water (mL)	Metal	Reaction
1	20	0	Cu	
2	20	0	Mg	
3	10	10	Mg	
4	5	15	Mg	

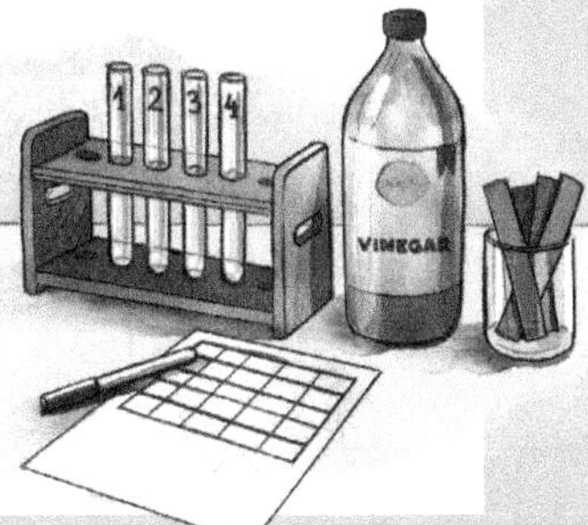

EQUIPMENT

- test tubes (4)
- test tube rack
- graduated cylinder, 25 mL
- vinegar, 55 mL
- water, 25 mL
- magnesium strips, 2 cm (3)
- copper strip, 2 cm
- marker

CHANGING REACTION RATES

Use this **mini lab** to demonstrate how different concentrations of reactants will affect a reaction rate.

Answers

1. Answers will vary. *Example:* As the concentration of reactants increases, the reaction rate will increase.
2. As the concentration of reactants increases, more particles will come in contact with each other. As this happens, they are more likely to react with each other.
3. the type of metal
4. the concentration of the vinegar
5. The copper didn't react, but the magnesium did. According to the activity series, copper is less active than magnesium.
6. As expected, the more concentrated vinegar reacted more quickly than the less concentrated vinegar.

DIFFERENTIATED INSTRUCTION

Collision Theory

Direct students to create a **demonstration** of the collision theory like the image shown on page 388 of the Student Edition. They may opt to use different objects to represent different molecules, or they can choose to sketch their demonstration. Ask students to demonstrate both collisions that *will* and those that *will not* result in reactions. To assess their understanding, ask them to show their demonstration to you and state why reactions occur or not.

ENERGY BOTH WAYS

If the activated complex reverts to the original reactants, energy is also released, but to a lesser degree than in the forward reaction.

Exothermic reactions are very often self-sustaining because the release of energy from the activated complex activates more reactants to continue the forward reaction until one of the reactants is used up.

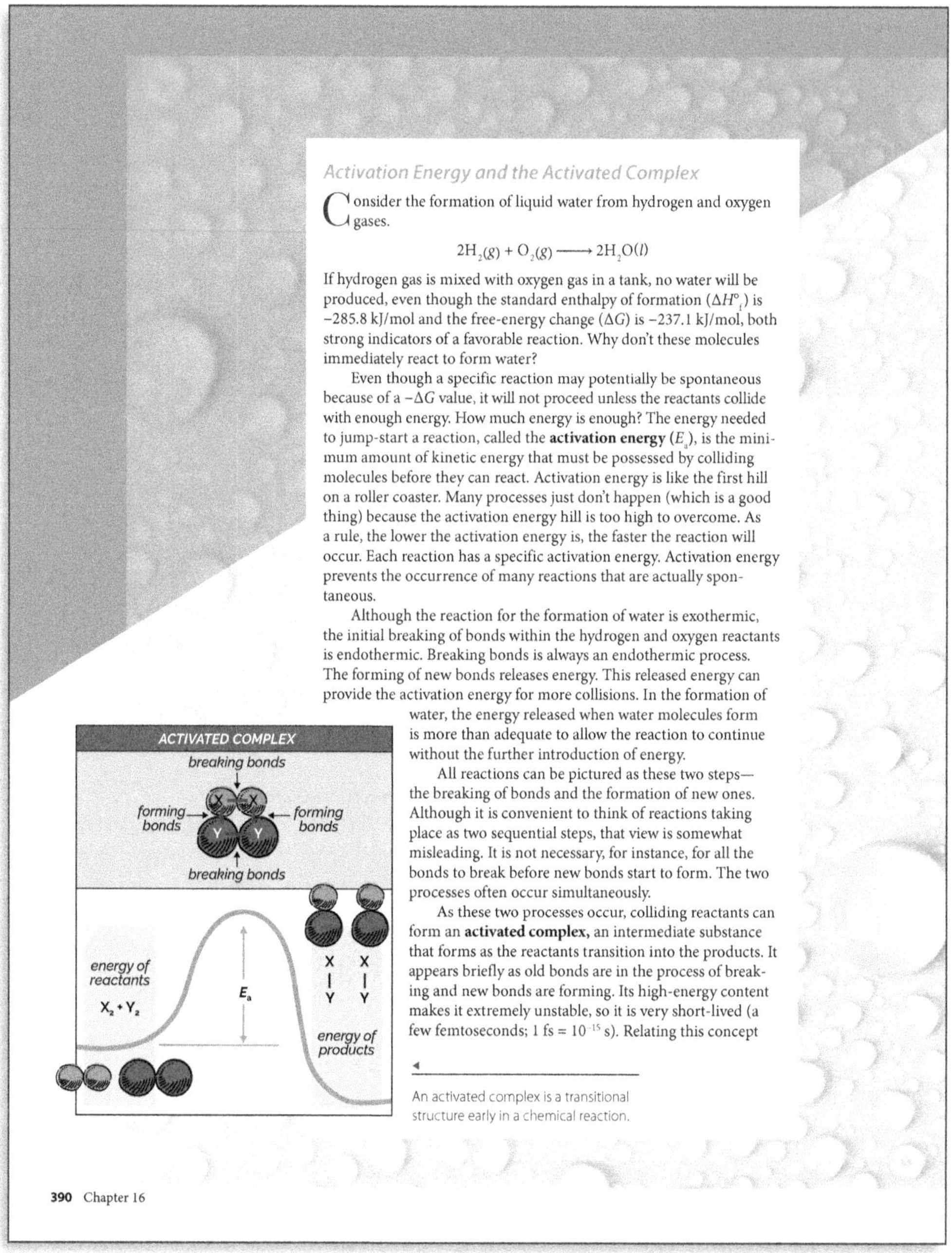

Activation Energy and the Activated Complex

Consider the formation of liquid water from hydrogen and oxygen gases.

$$2H_2(g) + O_2(g) \longrightarrow 2H_2O(l)$$

If hydrogen gas is mixed with oxygen gas in a tank, no water will be produced, even though the standard enthalpy of formation (ΔH°_f) is −285.8 kJ/mol and the free-energy change (ΔG) is −237.1 kJ/mol, both strong indicators of a favorable reaction. Why don't these molecules immediately react to form water?

Even though a specific reaction may potentially be spontaneous because of a $-\Delta G$ value, it will not proceed unless the reactants collide with enough energy. How much energy is enough? The energy needed to jump-start a reaction, called the **activation energy** (E_a), is the minimum amount of kinetic energy that must be possessed by colliding molecules before they can react. Activation energy is like the first hill on a roller coaster. Many processes just don't happen (which is a good thing) because the activation energy hill is too high to overcome. As a rule, the lower the activation energy is, the faster the reaction will occur. Each reaction has a specific activation energy. Activation energy prevents the occurrence of many reactions that are actually spontaneous.

Although the reaction for the formation of water is exothermic, the initial breaking of bonds within the hydrogen and oxygen reactants is endothermic. Breaking bonds is always an endothermic process. The forming of new bonds releases energy. This released energy can provide the activation energy for more collisions. In the formation of water, the energy released when water molecules form is more than adequate to allow the reaction to continue without the further introduction of energy.

All reactions can be pictured as these two steps—the breaking of bonds and the formation of new ones. Although it is convenient to think of reactions taking place as two sequential steps, that view is somewhat misleading. It is not necessary, for instance, for all the bonds to break before new bonds start to form. The two processes often occur simultaneously.

As these two processes occur, colliding reactants can form an **activated complex,** an intermediate substance that forms as the reactants transition into the products. It appears briefly as old bonds are in the process of breaking and new bonds are forming. Its high-energy content makes it extremely unstable, so it is very short-lived (a few femtoseconds; 1 fs = 10^{-15} s). Relating this concept

An activated complex is a transitional structure early in a chemical reaction.

390 Chapter 16

to the energy diagrams discussed previously, we see that the activation energy can also be defined in terms of the activated complex. It can be thought of as the minimum amount of energy needed to convert the reactants into the activated complex.

In conclusion, activation energy plays a crucial role in determining how fast a reaction will proceed under given temperature and pressure conditions. A large activation energy can prevent an otherwise favorable reaction from proceeding quickly or even at all.

Which reaction is most likely to proceed rapidly?

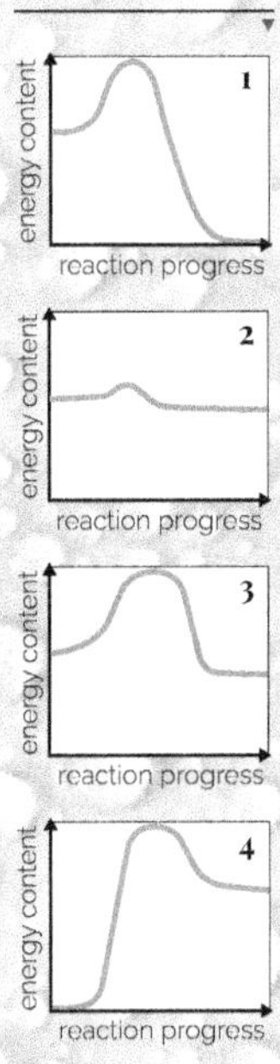

Rates of Reactions

During a reaction, the concentrations of reactants and products change constantly. At the beginning of a reaction, the reactants are at their highest concentrations. As the reaction progresses, product concentrations increase as the concentrations of reactants decrease by being consumed. Consider the reaction between iodine chloride and hydrogen.

$$2ICl(g) + H_2(g) \longrightarrow I_2(g) + 2HCl(g)$$

The graph below shows how the concentrations of the substances in this reaction vary with time. Notice that the reactants are being consumed as the products form. Also note that the changes are most rapid early in the reaction and then gradually slow.

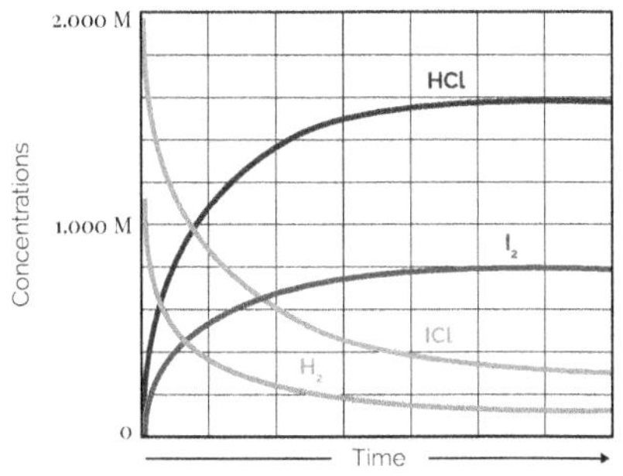

Reaction rate is a measure of how quickly reactants change into products. It can describe how fast the reactants disappear or how fast the products appear. Although reaction rates may be measured in several different units, they usually tell how fast concentrations change with time. Units such as amount concentration per second or moles per liter per hour are common.

RAPID REACTION

Employ a **class poll** to assess students' understanding of reaction rates using the question and illustrations in the margin of page 391. You may want to have students use a polling website. (Do an internet search using the keywords "polling website for teachers.") Or you may opt to have them hold up a paper stating which answer they believe is correct.

Question (in Student Edition margin): Which reaction is most likely to proceed rapidly?

Answer: Reaction 2. It has the smallest barrier to overcome, so it is the most likely to proceed rapidly as soon as reactants are mixed.

Discussion: Why won't the other reactions occur as quickly? *(Reaction 4 requires a large initial input and a net gain in energy. It is doubtful that such a reaction would proceed rapidly on its own. The other reactions release energy but must overcome the activation energy barrier to do so.)*

NATURAL REACTIVITY

Lead a **review** of chemical reactivity by asking students the following questions.

1. What property determines a chemical's reactivity? *(electron configuration)*
2. How many valence electrons do extremely reactive elements have? *(usually one or seven, though exceptions exist; The most reactive elements are those that need to lose or gain only one electron to obtain a full valence shell.)*

FACTORS THAT AFFECT REACTION RATES

Direct students to create a **concept map** for the factors that affect reaction rates. As you teach this section, have students add the types of factors to their concept map, along with illustrations.

DEMONSTRATING THE EFFECT OF CONCENTRATION IN A REACTION

Demonstrate how concentration affects the rate at which a piece of zinc dissolves.

Materials: hydrochloric acid solutions (0.1 M, 1.0 M, and 2.0 M), test tubes (3), strips of zinc metal (3), funnel, 10 mL graduated cylinder, nitrile gloves, safety goggles, timer

Procedure: Label three test tubes as 0.1 M, 1.0 M, and 2.0 M. Use a 10 mL graduated cylinder to measure 5 mL of 0.1 M, 1.0 M, and 2.0 M HCl into its corresponding test tube.

Performance/Discussion: Carefully drop one zinc strip into each test tube and observe. Have students record their observations.

Students should observe that a lower concentration of HCl decreases the rate of reaction. When the concentration levels are increased, a higher reaction rate results. When the concentration of HCl is 0.1 M, the zinc metal will not dissolve, and no chemical reaction should take place. When the concentration is increased to 1.0 M, the zinc metal will dissolve. When it's dissolved in the 2.0 M HCl, it will dissolve more quickly.

Remember that reactions depend on collisions that are properly oriented and have enough energy. Anything that increases the frequency, energy, and efficiency of these collisions should increase the rate of a reaction. Five of the most important factors affecting reaction rates are considered on this page spread.

Factors That Affect REACTION RATES

Nature of Reactants

The most obvious factor that controls the rate of a reaction is the chemical nature of the reactants. Logically enough, reactive substances react quickly. Phosphorus, in its white form, spontaneously bursts into flames when exposed to air. It is so reactive that it must be stored under water. At the other extreme, the noble gases rarely or never react.

white phosphorus in water

phosphorus reacting with air

Another variable is the particular combination of elements. Hydrogen and chlorine, under certain conditions, react vigorously; under those same conditions, hydrogen and nitrogen will react only weakly. The three test tubes shown below contain three metals in hydrochloric acid. Magnesium reacts the most, zinc reacts mildly, and copper doesn't react at all. This is related to the activity series that we saw in Chapter 10.

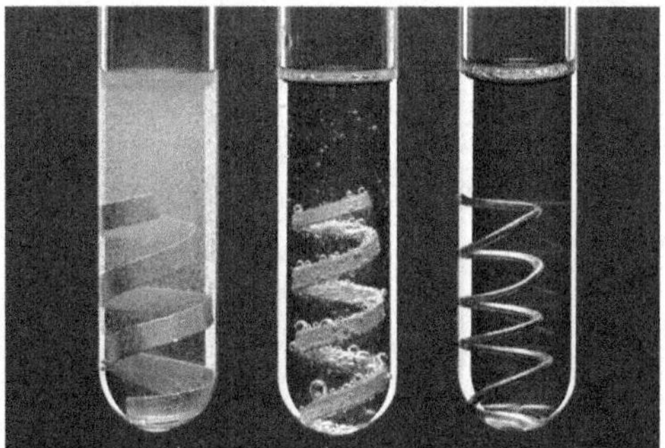
magnesium zinc copper

Concentration

Since changing the conditions of a reaction so that more collisions occur increases the reaction rate, there should be a definite connection between concentration and reaction rate. Notice in the two test tubes below that copper barely reacts in 1 M nitric acid, but reacts vigorously in 17 M nitric acid.

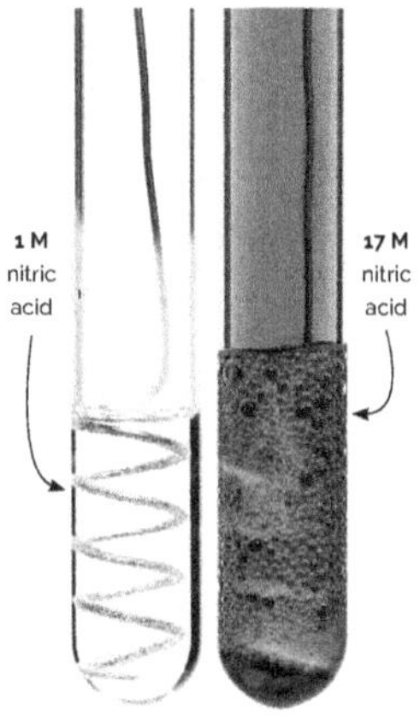

Since there are seventeen times more hydrogen ions in the concentrated solution, there are many more collisions that can cause reactions with the copper. The effect of concentration on the reaction rate varies from reaction to reaction. Thus, each reaction must be studied experimentally.

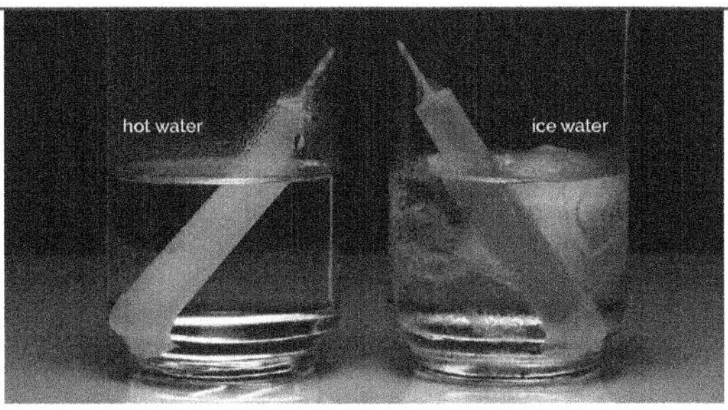

Temperature

A rule of thumb in kinetics is that reaction rates double for every 10 °C rise in temperature. Higher temperatures increase reaction rates because they increase the kinetic energy of the reactants. According to the kinetic-molecular theory, increased kinetic energy results in faster-moving particles, which collide more often. These collisions will generally have more energy, meaning that they are more likely to react. Higher temperatures increase the number of effective collisions, increasing the reaction rate. Notice the two glow sticks shown above. The one intensely emitting light is in hot water, while the dimmer one is in ice water.

Presence of Catalysts

A **catalyst** is a substance that changes a reaction's rate without being consumed by the reaction. It is present during the reaction, but it is neither a reactant nor a product. A catalyst provides an alternative *reaction mechanism* from reactants to products that has a lower activation energy. A catalyst does not affect the concentration of products at the conclusion of a reaction, only the rate at which these products are formed. The catalyst also does not affect the enthalpy change (ΔH) of a reaction. Neither will it enable a thermodynamically impossible reaction to occur.

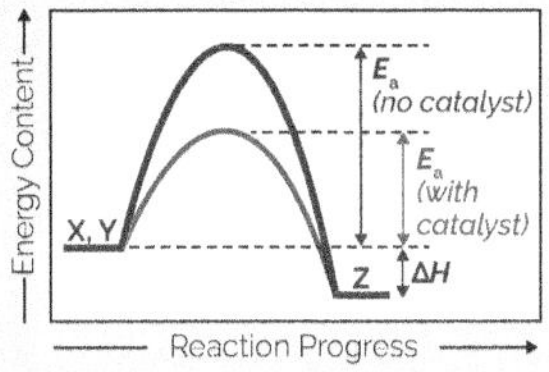

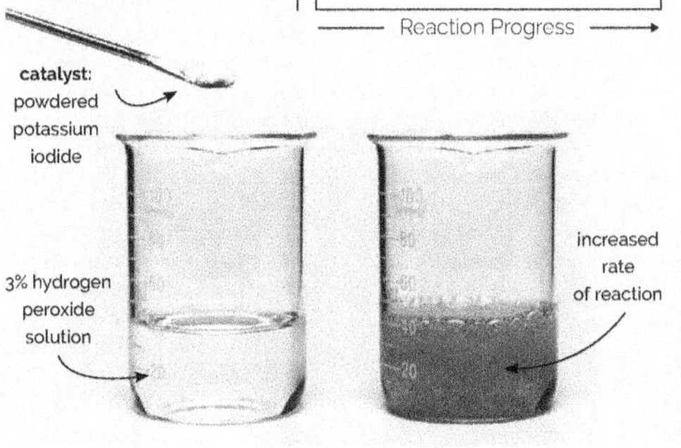

Surface Area

In a mixture of gases or in a solute dissolved in a solvent, frequent collisions allow reactions, once started, to progress rapidly. But if the reactants are in two different phases, the reaction rate is dependent on how much contact occurs between the substances at their interface. Increasing the amount of exposed surface area allows more collisions to occur. If a substance is broken up into pieces rather than being in one piece, more surface area is exposed and the reaction will occur faster due to an increase in collision rate. For example, we all know that sugar has plenty of energy that is typically released slowly by digestion. But if sugar is in the form of fine dust with a greatly increased surface area, it can be deadly. The image above shows the results of a sugar explosion at a manufacturing facility.

DEMONSTRATING THE EFFECT OF SURFACE AREA AND TEMPERATURE ON REACTION RATES

Demonstrate the effect of surface area and temperature on reaction rates.

Note: If you have the time and resources, have students perform this demonstration in small groups. Once all groups have finished, average the class's results.

Materials: identical beakers or glasses (2), effervescent tablets (4), water, ice cubes, heat source to boil water

Preparation 1: Fill the two beakers halfway with tap water of the same temperature. Crush one effervescent tablet and set aside.

Performance/Discussion 1: Simultaneously place an unbroken effervescent tablet in one glass and the crushed tablet in the other. The crushed tablet should dissolve much faster than the whole tablet.

Preparation 2: Fill one beaker halfway with boiling water and the other halfway with ice water.

Performance/Discussion 2: Simultaneously place an unbroken effervescent tablet in each beaker. The tablet in hot water should dissolve faster than the one in ice water.

Conclusion: Ask students why the crushed tablet and the tablet in hot water dissolved faster. Lead them to the idea that increasing the temperature and the surface area will increase the rate of reaction. Then ask them what they think would happen to a crushed tablet in hot water. They should be able to figure out that the tablet would dissolve even faster.

CATALYSTS

For a video on catalysts, visit TeacherTools Online.com. Under Additional Resources, click on Chapter 16 Web Links. Then click on *Catalysts*.

MORE ABOUT *Catalysts*

How do catalysts work? One theory states that catalysts hold reactants in just the right positions for favorable collisions.

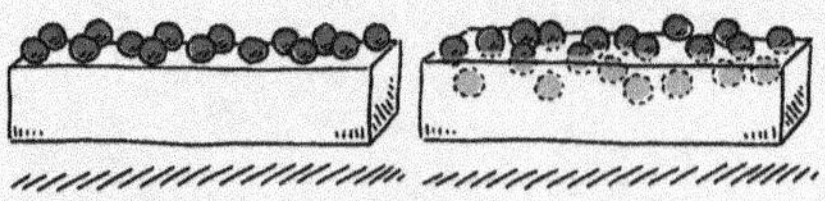

adsorption
the collection of one substance on the surface of another

absorption
the entering of one substance into another

For example, a mixture of hydrogen and oxygen gas does not react to form water at room temperature. But if a catalyst of powdered platinum is first introduced, the platinum causes an explosion as its surface becomes covered with adsorbed oxygen. *Adsorption* refers to the collection of one substance on the surface of another. It is different from absorption, which involves one substance entering into another. The platinum atoms stretch and weaken the bonds of the O_2 molecules as they are held in place, lowering the activation energy required for the reaction. The oxygen atoms then react rapidly with the hydrogen molecules to form water.

SEVERAL TYPES OF CATALYSTS

A **homogeneous catalyst** is in the same phase as the reactants or in solution with a reactant. Homogeneous catalysts combine with one of the reactants to form an intermediate compound that will react more readily with the other reactant or reactants. A catalyst that is in a phase different than the reactants is a **heterogeneous catalyst**. Heterogeneous catalysts are materials capable of adsorbing molecules onto their surfaces. Platinum, nickel, palladium, and other powdered metals and metalloids are examples of heterogeneous catalysts.

palladium

One distinct class of catalysts comprises the naturally occurring biological substances known as **enzymes**. Enzymes are responsible for most of the essential biochemical reactions. More than a thousand enzymes have been identified, and each one is specific to a chemical reaction occurring within a living organism. The presence of an enzyme typically causes a reaction to occur millions of times faster than when the reaction is uncatalyzed. Without enzymes, these same processes would occur too slowly to be of any use to an organism. Enzymes also aid living things by providing a lower activation energy and thus a lower temperature at which chemical reactions can occur. The temperature that would be required for most reactions to proceed without an enzyme would cook cells and result in tissue damage or death for an organism.

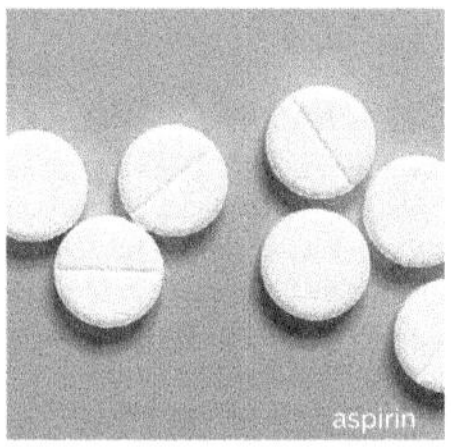

aspirin

Some catalysts, such as those that promote spoiling of food, are undesirable. An **inhibitor** is a substance used to reduce a catalyst's undesirable effects. Inhibitors work by bonding to a catalyst to decrease the catalyzed reaction rate or even completely stop the process. Like adsorption, this effect is the result of holding molecules in a certain position, but in this case the effect is to prevent effective collisions. Many important food preservatives act as inhibitors. Aspirin is another valuable inhibitor that works by blocking the action of two different enzymes that cause inflammation and pain.

CASE STUDY: SPONTANEOUS COMBUSTION

Answers:

1. Increased temperatures mean that particles are moving faster. Faster moving particles collide more often, and their collisions are more energetic.
2. The nature of the material seems to have a significant impact. All the examples of spontaneous combustion mentioned in the case study involve materials that are combustible.

CASE STUDY

SPONTANEOUS COMBUSTION

It was a hot June day in 1933 in North Arlington, New Jersey. Swimmers seeking relief from the oppressive heat swarmed a beach along the bank of the Passaic River. Nearby was a storehouse full of pyroxylin—a highly combustible material used in lacquers, plastics, and artificial leather.

At 9:12 p.m., lingering swimmers noticed fire coming from the roof of the storehouse. With a puff, both ends of the building blew out, showering the crowd with bricks. Burning celluloid fell on everyone, and a vast flame swept over the surrounding area. Another blast occurred, and flames engulfed the beach as well as nine nearby buildings. Before it was over, ten people died and 180 were injured. The burning of the Atlantic Pyroxylin Waste Company remains a sobering yet predictable example of spontaneous combustion.

Spontaneous combustion starts without a flame or spark. Fires begun this way ignite because of the role that thermal energy plays in speeding up reaction rates. The Atlantic Pyroxylin Waste Company stored pyroxylin scraps swept up from factory floors. These scraps often had machine oil on them. The heat necessary for the fire to start came from the reaction between this oil and atmospheric oxygen.

Typically, a spontaneous combustion reaction doesn't generate great amounts of heat because it occurs slowly and the energy disperses. But if thermal energy cannot escape, it accumulates and the temperature increases. As the temperature increases, the reaction occurs faster, producing more heat. If unchecked, the reaction can generate temperatures above the autoignition point of the surrounding material.

Spontaneous combustion can occur in places other than factories. It can happen in soft coal, freshly cut bales of hay, and even in workshops, where oily and paint-saturated rags pose a threat. Preventing spontaneous combustion fires is a matter of controlling the rates of chemical reactions. Caution should be taken with combustible materials in powdered forms. The large amount of surface area allows reactions to proceed more quickly. More importantly, combustible material should be stored in a well-ventilated place where heat can be removed as fast as it is produced. Such actions will prevent heat from accumulating in a place where it can increase the rate of reaction.

Questions to Consider

1. Why does increased temperature increase a reaction rate?
2. What other factor seems to significantly impact spontaneous combustion? Explain.

16.1 SECTION REVIEW

1. Define *kinetics*.
2. Contrast thermodynamics and kinetics by indicating which question or questions each can answer.
3. Explain what an effective collision is according to the collision theory.
4. Give two reasons why a collision between two reactive molecules might not result in a reaction.
5. Why is the initial stage of almost all reactions endothermic?
6. Write the chemical equation for the reaction shown in the graph at right.
7. What are the five variables that can affect the rate of reaction?
8. How does a catalyst speed up a reaction rate?

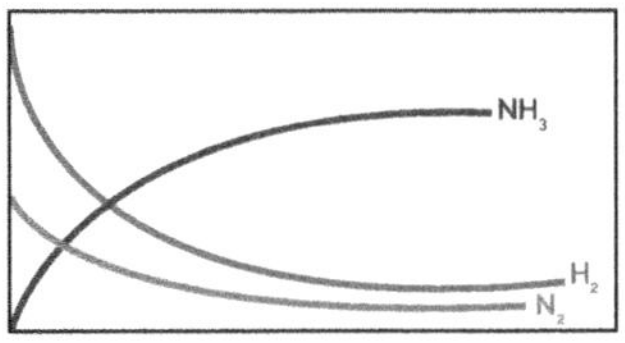

DIFFERENTIATED INSTRUCTION

Reactions and Rates

Use an **interactive activity** to demonstrate how reactions respond to different conditions. To access this activity, visit TeacherToolsOnline.com. Under Chapter 16 Additional Resources, click on *Reactions and Rates*.

Lead students to relate the graph within the activity to the reaction pathways shown on page 388. Discuss what happens to the molecules as the concentration and temperature increase within the reaction. Help students to see how the number of collisions increases as temperature and concentration increase. Allow them to take turns selecting different conditions to see how they affect the molecules as well as the reaction rate. Ask them what other conditions could affect the rates of reactions. *(the nature of reactants, surface area, and catalysts present)*

To assess students' understanding, have them write or use illustrations to give a general conclusion about the activity. Students should relate the terms *molecule*, *concentration*, *temperature*, *activation energy*, and *reaction rate*.

APPLY

LAB 16A: *CHEMISTRY—A CONTACT SPORT?*

Once students have an understanding of the material in Section 16.1, they should be ready to work through Lab 16A.

ASSESS

TICKET OUT THE DOOR

As a **summarizing activity**, assess students' understanding of the material from Section 16.1 by asking them to name two types of catalysts. *(Students should be able to identify at least two: homogeneous catalysts, heterogeneous catalysts, enzymes, inhibitors.)*

16.1 REVIEW *ANSWERS*

1. Kinetics is the study of the rates of reactions and the steps by which they occur. *(p. 387)*
2. Thermodynamics answers the question, "Can the reaction occur?" Kinetics answers the questions, "Will the reaction occur? How quickly will the reaction happen?" *(p. 387)*
3. An effective collision is any collision between two reactants with the proper orientation and sufficient energy. It is a collision that causes a reaction to occur. *(p. 388)*
4. The collision may not be properly oriented or it may not be energetic enough. *(p. 388)*
5. For a reaction to occur, any existing chemical bonds must be broken, requiring an input of energy. *(p. 390)*
6. $3H_2(g) + N_2(g) \longrightarrow 2NH_3(g)$ *(p. 391)*
7. the reactants' chemical nature, concentration, temperature, surface area, and the presence of a catalyst *(pp. 392–93)*
8. A catalyst provides an alternate route from reactants to products with a lower activation energy. Catalysts may also hold reactants in the right orientation for favorable collisions. *(p. 393)*

SECTION 16.2 *OVERVIEW*

Essential Question

How does water form when hydrogen is burned?

Objectives

» **16.2.1** Explain how a reaction mechanism describes the steps that make up a chemical reaction.

» **16.2.2** Identify intermediate substances in the elementary steps of a reaction.

» **16.2.3** Interpret a rate law as it relates to changes in reactant concentration.

» **16.2.4** Relate the rate-determining steps to rate laws.

» **16.2.5** Formulate a rate law from a data table listing changes in reactant concentration.

» **16.2.6** Determine an informed position on the personal use of medical marijuana. BWS

Resources

Careers: Serving as a Pharmacologist

How It Works: Sustained-Release Medicine

Ethics: Medical Marijuana (p. 407)

Lab 16B: *Don't Overreact*—Determining a Rate Law

ENGAGE

REACTION RATES

Review Section 16.1 with a **fact swap** activity. Have students write three facts from Section 16.1 on a piece of paper. Tell them that they will have three minutes to walk around the room, verbally swap facts with their peers, and write down the new facts that they accumulate. To swap facts, a student must share one fact in order to get one from his peer—one that is different from a fact he already has! After the time is up, see who was able to accumulate the most facts. Take a few minutes to review some of the information that students have collected.

Explain to students that in Section 16.2 they will discover the steps that occur during a reaction that ultimately form a product.

QUESTIONS

» What are the steps in a chemical reaction?

» Are there substances formed in reactions that are not products?

» What determines the rate of a reaction?

» How can I write a rate law?

TERMS

reaction mechanism • elementary step • rate-determining step • complex reaction • intermediate • reaction order • rate law • specific rate constant

16.2 REACTION MECHANISMS

Mechanisms

Chemists can easily identify the reactants of a chemical process. They also routinely analyze the products. But other molecules that form and then re-form during reactions are much more difficult to pinpoint. For chemists, observing reactions is like studying a factory's processes from outside the building. They can see the raw materials going in and the finished products coming out, but the individual steps involved in forming the products are more difficult to understand. The series of steps that make up a reaction is called a **reaction mechanism**.

How does water form when hydrogen is burned?

Understanding Reaction Mechanisms

To understand reaction mechanisms, consider the decomposition of NO_2.

- How does this reaction take place?
- Do two molecules collide to form an activated complex that splits into nitrogen monoxide and oxygen molecules?
- Do the three atoms in nitrogen dioxide all split apart and then rearrange themselves?
- Does an atom of oxygen separate from a molecule of nitrogen dioxide and then combine with another free oxygen atom?
- Or does something totally different occur?

Theoretically, any one of these proposed mechanisms could produce nitrogen monoxide and oxygen from nitrogen dioxide.

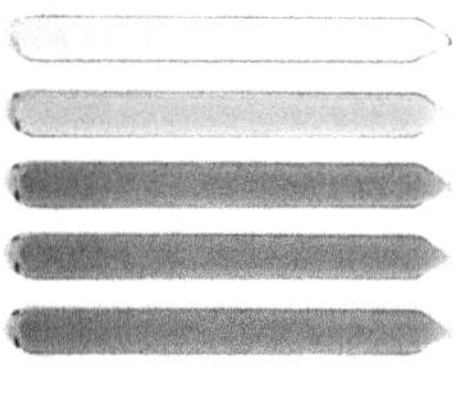

These vials show the color change as a reaction progresses to equilibrium.

Often, a reaction mechanism is made of two or more steps, called **elementary steps**. A possible reaction mechanism for the decomposition of nitrogen dioxide looks like the following.

Elementary Step 1: $2NO_2(g) \longrightarrow NO_3(g) + NO(g)$

Elementary Step 2: $NO_3(g) \longrightarrow NO(g) + O_2(g)$

The rate at which the reaction occurs is dependent on the rates of the elementary steps. The reaction can proceed only as fast as the slowest elementary step, which is known as the **rate-determining step**. To understand this limiting factor, compare the reaction mechanism with an assembly line. Suppose that one job on an assembly line requires a worker to perform a task that is much more difficult than that of any other worker. The product can be produced only as fast as the worker with the most difficult task can complete his job. Similarly, a reaction can proceed only as fast as the rate-determining step. In the example of the decomposition of NO_2, the first step is the slowest, so it is the rate-determining step.

Elementary Step 1: $2NO_2(g) \longrightarrow NO_3(g) + NO(g)$ slow

Elementary Step 2: $NO_3(g) \longrightarrow NO(g) + O_2(g)$ fast

Together, the individual elementary steps make up a **complex reaction**, or *net reaction*. During a complex reaction, there are substances that are formed in one step and consumed in the next. These substances are called **intermediates**. Intermediates do not appear in the chemical equation for the net reaction. So we can cancel the intermediates out of our elementary steps and add the two steps together to get the net equation.

Elementary Step 1: $2NO_2(g) \longrightarrow \cancel{NO_3(g)} + NO(g)$

Elementary Step 2: $\cancel{NO_3(g)} \longrightarrow NO(g) + O_2(g)$

Net Equation: $2NO_2(g) \longrightarrow 2NO(g) + O_2(g)$

INSTRUCT

MECHANISMS

Direct students to create **Sketchnotes** of the vocabulary and examples within Section 16.2.

Be sure that students have a firm understanding of elementary steps, rate-determining steps, complex reactions, and how to cancel out intermediates before moving on to the next subsection.

As another example, consider the reaction between hydrogen and iodine gases, one of the first to be studied in the field of kinetics.

$$H_2(g) + I_2(g) \longrightarrow 2HI(g)$$

Several reaction mechanisms for the production of hydrogen iodide (HI) are possible. In the illustrations below, the phases have been omitted to make it easier to follow the steps. However, all the reactants and products of this reaction are gases. Since they are all in the same phase, the reaction is a *homogeneous reaction*.

We cancel out the iodine atoms since they are intermediates and add the two elementary steps to obtain the net equation.

Elementary Step 1: $I_2 \longrightarrow \cancel{2I}$

Elementary Step 2: $\cancel{2I} + H_2 \longrightarrow 2HI$

Net Equation: $I_2 + H_2 \longrightarrow 2HI$

A second possible reaction mechanism has three steps. And again, by canceling the intermediates, we can add the steps to get the net equation.

Elementary Step 1: $I_2 \longrightarrow \cancel{2I}$

Elementary Step 2: $\cancel{I} + H_2 \longrightarrow \cancel{H_2I}$

Elementary Step 3: $\cancel{H_2I} + \cancel{I} \longrightarrow 2HI$

Net Equation: $I_2 + H_2 \longrightarrow 2HI$

Note that this reaction mechanism has an additional intermediate—H_2I.

Reaction mechanisms are temperature dependent; therefore, temperature is the deciding factor in determining which of the possible mechanisms will actually occur.

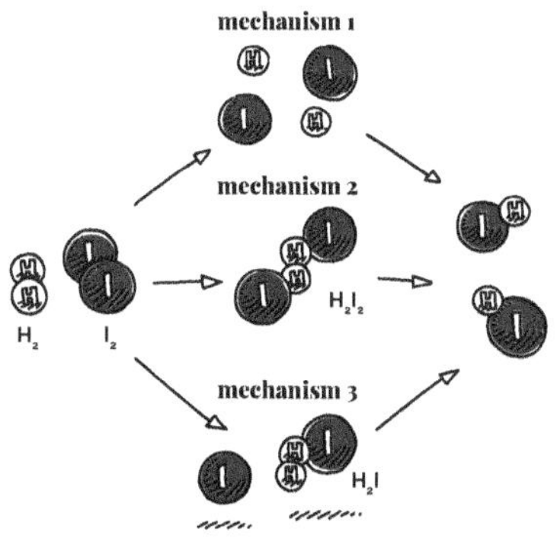

Three other possible reaction mechanisms for the reaction between hydrogen gas and iodine gas

Chemical Kinetics 397

NOT VERY CONSTANT

The specific rate constant is constant for a reaction only at a certain temperature, hence the word "specific" in the constant's name. Because of this, a reaction may have several specific rate constants depending on the temperature conditions during the reaction.

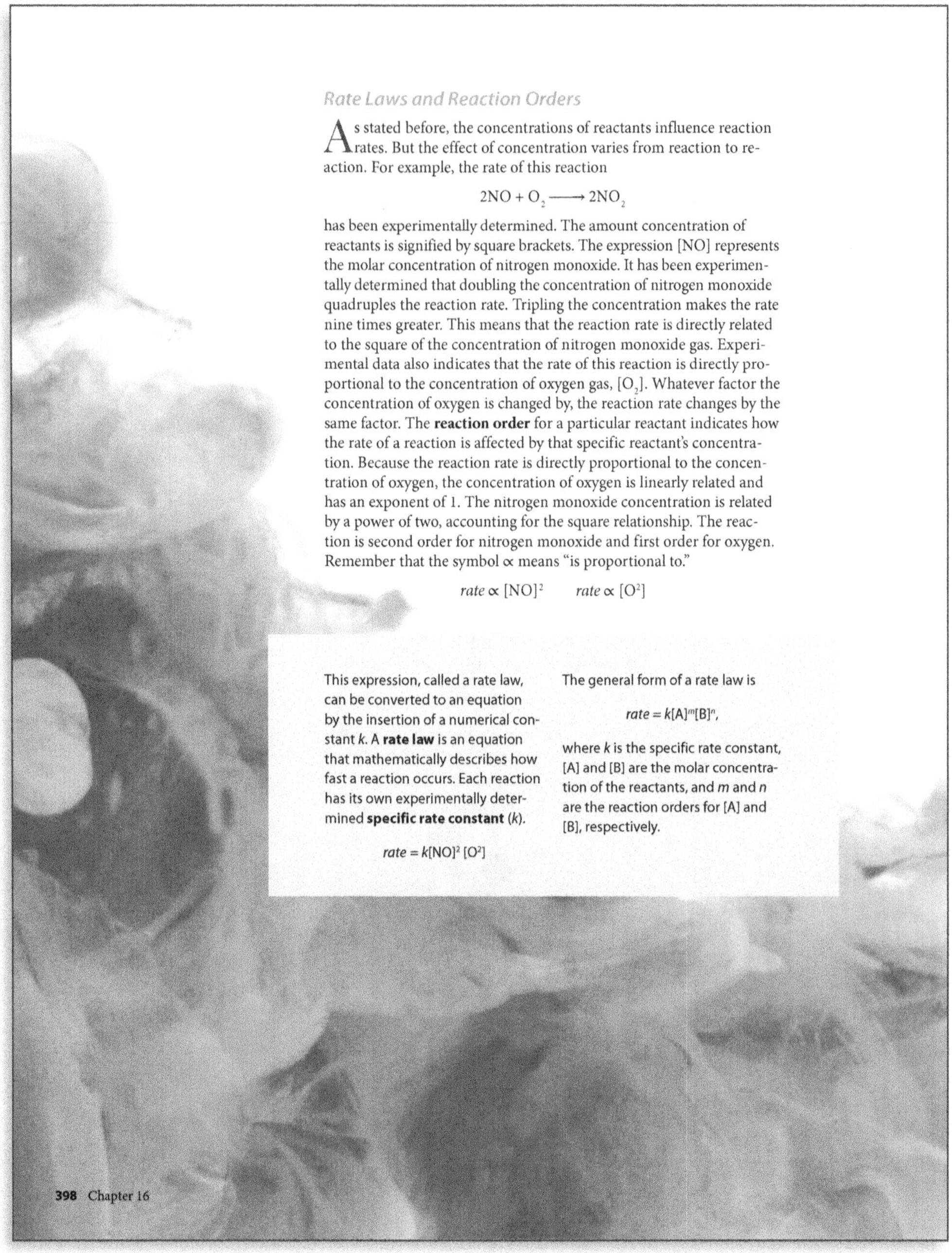

Rate Laws and Reaction Orders

As stated before, the concentrations of reactants influence reaction rates. But the effect of concentration varies from reaction to reaction. For example, the rate of this reaction

$$2NO + O_2 \longrightarrow 2NO_2$$

has been experimentally determined. The amount concentration of reactants is signified by square brackets. The expression [NO] represents the molar concentration of nitrogen monoxide. It has been experimentally determined that doubling the concentration of nitrogen monoxide quadruples the reaction rate. Tripling the concentration makes the rate nine times greater. This means that the reaction rate is directly related to the square of the concentration of nitrogen monoxide gas. Experimental data also indicates that the rate of this reaction is directly proportional to the concentration of oxygen gas, $[O_2]$. Whatever factor the concentration of oxygen is changed by, the reaction rate changes by the same factor. The **reaction order** for a particular reactant indicates how the rate of a reaction is affected by that specific reactant's concentration. Because the reaction rate is directly proportional to the concentration of oxygen, the concentration of oxygen is linearly related and has an exponent of 1. The nitrogen monoxide concentration is related by a power of two, accounting for the square relationship. The reaction is second order for nitrogen monoxide and first order for oxygen. Remember that the symbol ∝ means "is proportional to."

$$rate \propto [NO]^2 \qquad rate \propto [O^2]$$

This expression, called a rate law, can be converted to an equation by the insertion of a numerical constant *k*. A **rate law** is an equation that mathematically describes how fast a reaction occurs. Each reaction has its own experimentally determined **specific rate constant** (*k*).

$$rate = k[NO]^2\,[O^2]$$

The general form of a rate law is

$$rate = k[A]^m[B]^n,$$

where *k* is the specific rate constant, [A] and [B] are the molar concentration of the reactants, and *m* and *n* are the reaction orders for [A] and [B], respectively.

398 Chapter 16

Table 16-1 gives several examples of rate laws. It is important to note that rate laws must be determined experimentally. If every chemical reaction occurred in a single step—an elementary reaction, as shown in its balanced chemical equation with no intermediates—it would be accurate to use the coefficients from the reactants as exponents for those substances. Single-step reactions are rare, however, so this is seldom an accurate method for writing rate laws. Remember that the exponents in the rate law are experimentally determined. They do not come from the stoichiometric coefficients in the chemical reaction.

In some cases, not all reactants appear in the rate law for the reaction. Changing the concentration of these reactants has no impact at all on the reaction rate. For those reactants, the reaction is zero order. The reactant would therefore not be included in the rate law. Can you find an example of such a reaction in Table 16-1?

TABLE 16-1 *Rate Laws for Several Reactions*

Reaction	Rate =
$2H_2 + 2NO \longrightarrow N_2 + 2H_2O$	$k[H_2][NO]^2$
$2NO + Br_2 \longrightarrow 2NOBr$	$k[NO]^2[Br_2]$
$NO + O_3 \longrightarrow NO_2 + O_2$	$k[O_3][NO]$
$2NO + O_2 \longrightarrow 2NO_2$	$k[NO]^2[O_2]$
$C_4H_9Br + 2H_2O \longrightarrow C_4H_9OH + Br^- + H_3O^+$	$k[C_4H_9Br]$

Balanced chemical equations show only the reactants and the products they form, not the steps that the reactants take to form those products. Reactions often have several possible mechanisms, and an equation alone cannot reveal which mechanism occurred. If there are several possible reaction mechanisms, the rate law can sometimes be used to eliminate one or more of the possibilities. A possible mechanism can be eliminated if the experimentally determined rate law does not match the theoretical rate law derived from the proposed mechanism.

The reaction between nitrogen dioxide and carbon monoxide at low temperatures has the following rate law.

$$NO_2(g) + CO(g) \longrightarrow NO(g) + CO_2(g);\ rate = k[NO_2]^2$$

According to the rate law, changing the concentration of carbon monoxide [CO] has no effect on the rate of the reaction. Therefore, the concentration of carbon monoxide does not appear in the rate law. If this reaction is broken apart into its two most likely elementary steps as shown below, an examination of them will show why this is true.

Elementary Step 1:	$NO_2 + \cancel{NO_2} \longrightarrow \cancel{NO_3} + NO$
Elementary Step 2:	$\cancel{NO_3} + CO \longrightarrow \cancel{NO_2} + CO_2$
Net Equation:	$NO_2 + CO \longrightarrow NO + CO_2$

carbon dioxide nitrogen dioxide

WHEN REACTANTS DO NOT APPEAR IN A RATE LAW

Lead students in a **Socratic questioning** activity.

1. Which reaction in Table 16-1 shows a rate law which is missing one of the reactants? *(the last one)*
2. Why would it be missing the reactant? *(It indicates that the $2H_2O$ does not impact the reaction rate. Thus, the reaction is zero order for that reactant and the reactant is not included in the rate law.)*

ORDER OF THE REACTANT

The exponent in a rate law is also called the *order of the reactant.* In this Student Edition, it is always a positive integer, but fractions and negative integers are also possible.

RATE LAW

Use the following **formative assessment** to check students' understanding of the material.

1. What is the slowest step in a reaction? *(the rate-determining step)*
2. What does *k* represent in a rate law? *(the specific rate constant)*
3. If a reaction is second order for a reactant, how would doubling the concentration of that reactant affect the rate of the reaction? *(It would increase fourfold, or make it go four times faster.)*
4. In a reaction with a rate law of $k[NO]^2[O_2]$, how would doubling the concentration of NO compare with doubling the concentration of O_2? *(Because this reaction is second order in NO, doubling its concentration will affect the reaction rate fourfold. The reaction is first order in O_2, so doubling its concentration will only double the reaction rate.)*

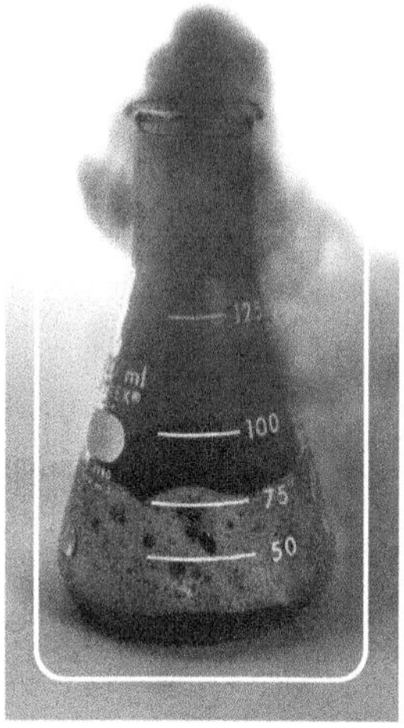

Concentrated nitric acid reacts with copper, generating nitrogen dioxide gas.

Scientists have experimentally determined that the first step, in which the molecules collide, occurs at a slower rate than the second step. Consequently, the first step is the rate-determining step. In reactions with a single step, the rate law would then be based on the original balanced equation. Because carbon monoxide does not appear in the rate-determining step, the reaction rate does not depend on its concentration. *Remember that rate laws are always based on the rate-determining step.*

The exponent 2 on the $[NO_2]^2$ term of the rate law indicates that the concentration of nitrogen dioxide plays the crucial role in determining how fast the reaction occurs. The reaction is second order in NO_2. If the concentration of nitrogen dioxide is tripled, the rate is nine times faster. This relationship occurs because the coefficient 3 is also raised to the second power, $(3[NO_2])^2$.

EXAMPLE 16-1: FORMULATING A RATE LAW

Nitrogen monoxide gas and chlorine gas combine as shown in the following equation.

$$2NO + Cl_2 \longrightarrow 2NOCl$$

A laboratory scientist collects the following data on three trials of this reaction. State the reaction order for each reactant and determine an appropriate rate law.

REACTION DATA

Trial	Initial [NO] (M)	Initial [Cl_2] (M)	Initial Rate (mol/L min)
1	0.50	0.50	0.0190
2	1.00	0.50	0.0760
3	0.50	1.00	0.0380

Solution

Notice that when the concentration of NO was doubled from Trial 1 to Trial 2, the reaction rate increased fourfold (0.0760/0.0190 = 4). Therefore, the reaction is second order in NO.

When the concentration of Cl_2 was doubled from Trial 1 to Trial 3, the reaction rate also doubled. The reaction is first order in Cl_2. In light of this,

$$rate = k[NO]^2[Cl_2].$$

EXAMPLE 16-2: INTERPRETING A RATE LAW

For the rate law $rate = k[A][B]^3$, what will happen to the rate of the reaction

a. if the initial concentration of A is doubled?

b. if the initial concentration of A is cut in half?

c. if the initial concentration of B is doubled?

Solution

a. The reaction rate will double.

b. The reaction rate will be cut in half.

c. The reaction rate will be eight times faster.

CAREERS

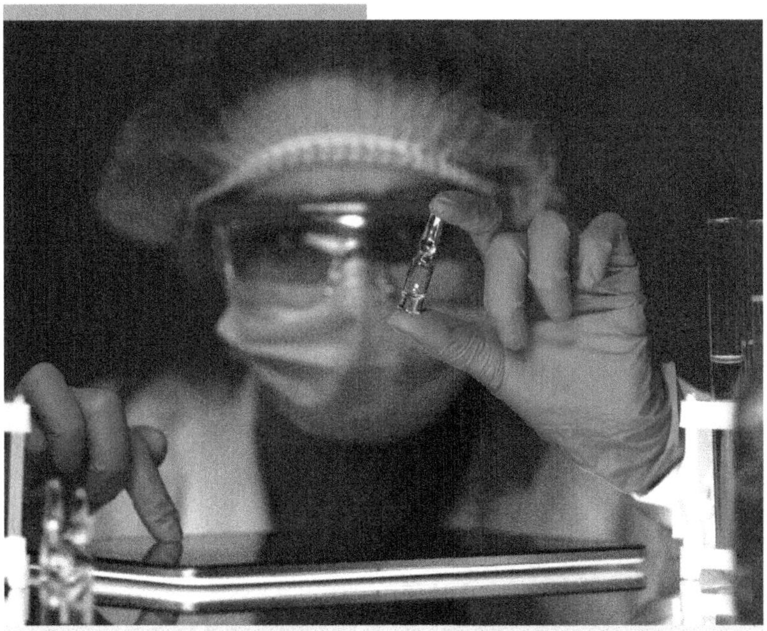

SERVING AS A PHARMACOLOGIST: *LIFESAVING CHEMISTRY*

Daniella is a toddler from St. Petersburg, Russia. She was in the hospital recovering from surgery for a life-threatening condition when she contracted HIV during a blood transfusion. Now she will fight a lifelong battle with the disease—and she is not alone. Worldwide, 37.9 million people have contracted HIV, and another 1.7 million join them every year. Pharmacologists around the world are working to develop new drug regimens for diseases like HIV.

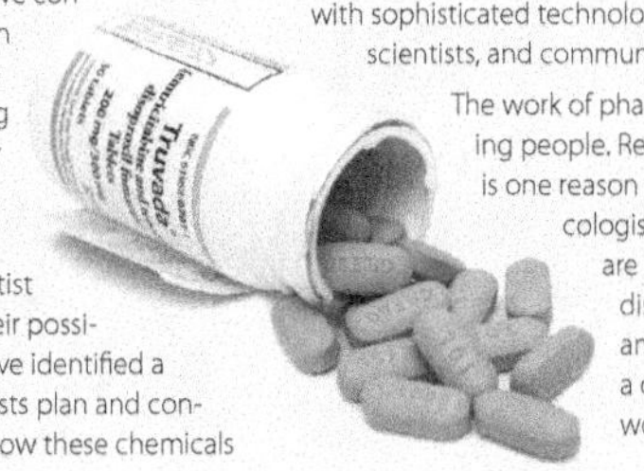

A cure for HIV starts in the laboratory of a pharmacologist—a scientist who investigates chemicals for their possible medicinal value. Once they have identified a potential medicine, pharmacologists plan and conduct experiments, testing to see how these chemicals will interact with biological processes in living things. As a drug goes through the approval process for use as a medication, a pharmacologist will test the drug in the laboratory, on animals, and later on people. When testing a medicine for conditions such as HIV, which requires lifelong medication, a pharmacologist must assess the long-term safety of the chemical. Pharmacologists need to be able to solve problems, work with sophisticated technology, collaborate with other scientists, and communicate with and lead others.

The work of pharmacologists helps suffering people. Relieving human suffering is one reason why Jesus came. Pharmacologists help people who are suffering with pain and disease, following Christ's example of shining as lights in a dark world through good works (Matt. 5:16).

Chemical Kinetics 401

PHARMACOKINETICS

For more information or videos on this topic, perform an internet search using the keyword "pharmacokinetics."

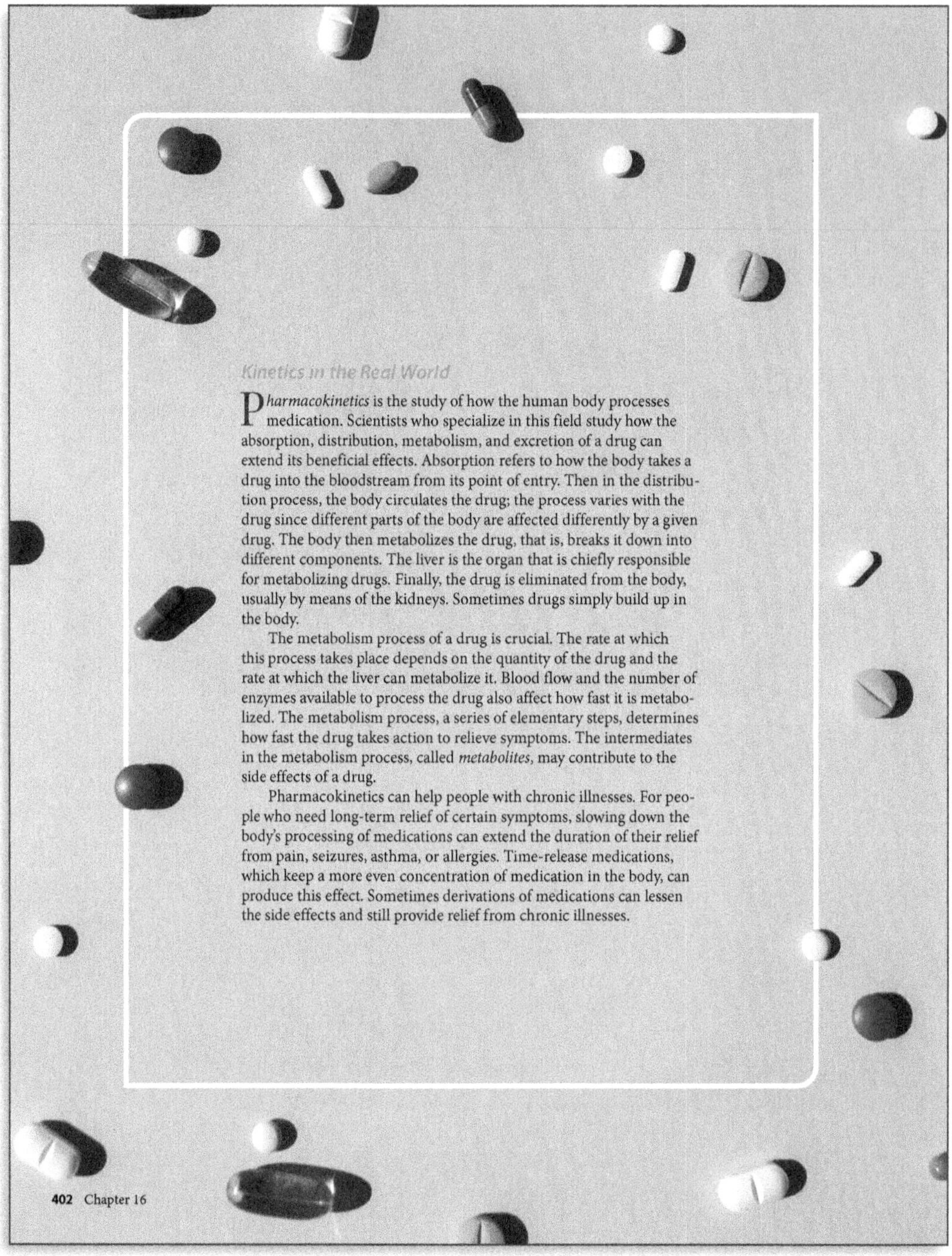

Kinetics in the Real World

Pharmacokinetics is the study of how the human body processes medication. Scientists who specialize in this field study how the absorption, distribution, metabolism, and excretion of a drug can extend its beneficial effects. Absorption refers to how the body takes a drug into the bloodstream from its point of entry. Then in the distribution process, the body circulates the drug; the process varies with the drug since different parts of the body are affected differently by a given drug. The body then metabolizes the drug, that is, breaks it down into different components. The liver is the organ that is chiefly responsible for metabolizing drugs. Finally, the drug is eliminated from the body, usually by means of the kidneys. Sometimes drugs simply build up in the body.

The metabolism process of a drug is crucial. The rate at which this process takes place depends on the quantity of the drug and the rate at which the liver can metabolize it. Blood flow and the number of enzymes available to process the drug also affect how fast it is metabolized. The metabolism process, a series of elementary steps, determines how fast the drug takes action to relieve symptoms. The intermediates in the metabolism process, called *metabolites,* may contribute to the side effects of a drug.

Pharmacokinetics can help people with chronic illnesses. For people who need long-term relief of certain symptoms, slowing down the body's processing of medications can extend the duration of their relief from pain, seizures, asthma, or allergies. Time-release medications, which keep a more even concentration of medication in the body, can produce this effect. Sometimes derivations of medications can lessen the side effects and still provide relief from chronic illnesses.

402 Chapter 16

Sustained-Release Medication

HOW IT *WORKS*

In the use of pharmaceutical chemicals, the goal is to maintain the amount of the substance in the body at optimal levels. When we take medicines, the substance goes through a number of physical and chemical processes. The substance often has to be dissolved to be available for transport throughout the body. It then goes through a number of chemical reactions with other substances. Over time, the chemical is processed by the body and usually eliminated. So what happens to the level of the drug in our system?

Upon dissolving, the concentration of the chemical usually increases to a maximum value and then decreases over time depending on the chemical reaction rates and metabolic rate of the individual. Doctors will calculate the dosing and administration schedule to maintain the drug close to the optimal level. But taking medication often can be a hassle and sometimes results in patients missing doses. Pharmacologists have been working on new medications that can alleviate many of these issues.

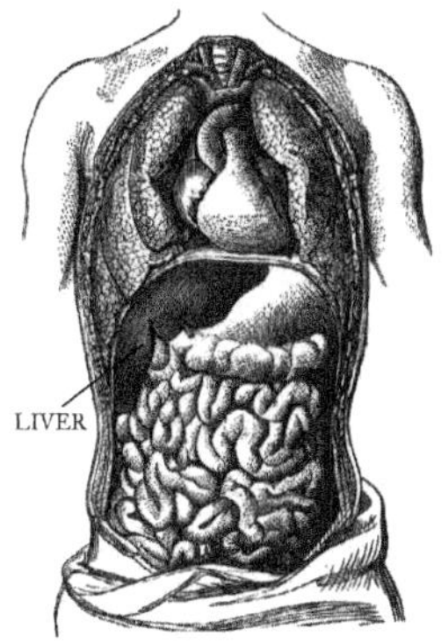

Pharmacologists often work on existing medicines to make their administration more effective. One advancement has been in the field of sustained-release medications. These are medications that typically contain a higher dose of the medicine but are formulated to release the chemicals over time. This allows doctors to reduce the number of times a medicine is taken and ensures that the chemical remains at the target concentrations longer.

There are a number of approaches that are used to control the release rate of these medicines. In some cases, the medicine is contained within a slow dissolving material. Other times it is enclosed by an insoluble material through which the medicine can diffuse. Some even use osmosis to move water into a capsule enclosing the drug, pushing it out of the capsule and into the body. Some of the most amazing technology actually releases the medicine in response to conditions in the body (e.g., pH levels).

In all these approaches, the pharmacologist is working to improve the lives of people around him. He strives to develop new ways to help doctors treat people in ways that allow them to live productive lives.

TIMELY MEDICINE

Most medications require about ten years to create and test before they are released for patient use. In special cases, some pharmaceutical companies give patients experimental drugs (an act known as *compassionate use*), but the next step to better help people is to shorten the research time for *all* patients. Without sacrificing the quality of the research, medications should go on the market as soon as is reasonably possible. This would show good stewardship and love for our neighbors. Impress on students that this is a great opportunity to serve the Lord.

APPLY

LAB 16B: *DON'T OVERREACT*

Once students have an understanding of the material in Section 16.2, they should be ready to work through Lab 16B.

ASSESS

TICKET OUT THE DOOR

Assess students' understanding of rate laws with a **summarizing activity** by asking them to explain what has happened if a reactant does not appear in the rate law. *(The concentration of the reactant did not affect the rate of the reaction, and the reaction is zero order for that reactant. The reactant also will not appear in the balanced chemical equation.)*

16.2 REVIEW *ANSWERS*

1. elementary steps *(p. 396)*
2. Intermediates are formed in one elementary step and consumed in a subsequent step. *(p. 396)*
3. The rate-determining step is the slowest step in the reaction mechanism and sets the rate of the reaction. *(p. 396)*
4. **a.** NO_3

   b. Elementary Step 1

   c. $NO_2 + CO \longrightarrow NO + CO_2$
   (all pp. 396–97)
5. $2O_3 \longrightarrow 3O_2$ *(pp. 396–97)*
6. Reaction order for a reactant indicates how the rate of a reaction is affected by that specific reactant's concentration. *(p. 398)*
7. **a.** reaction mechanisms

   b. by experimentally measuring rates

   c. Step A is the rate-determining step because it involves both reactants. He cannot determine which mechanism is correct because they both would work with the data given.
   (all pp. 396, 398–400)

16.2 SECTION REVIEW

1. What term refers to the steps that make up a reaction mechanism?
2. Why do intermediates not appear in a net equation?
3. There is usually one step in a multi-step reaction that is rate-determining. How does the rate-determining step affect the overall rate of the reaction?
4. Use the reaction mechanism below containing the two elementary steps to answer the following questions.

   1: $2NO_2 \longrightarrow NO_3 + NO$ (slow)

   2: $NO_3 + CO \longrightarrow NO_2 + CO_2$ (fast)

   a. What is the intermediate?

   b. Which step is the rate-determining step?

   c. Write the net equation.
5. What is the net equation the mechanism of the complex reaction shown below?

   Elementary Step 1: $Cl + O_3 \longrightarrow O_2 + ClO$

   Elementary Step 2: $O_3 \longrightarrow O_2 + O$

   Elementary Step 3: $ClO + O \longrightarrow Cl + O_2$
6. What is reaction order?
7. The reaction $2NO(g) + 2H_2(g) \longrightarrow N_2(g) + 2H_2O(l)$ occurs in two steps, which could be either

   A: Elementary Step 1: $2NO + H_2 \longrightarrow N_2 + H_2O_2$

   Elementary Step 2: $H_2O_2 + H_2 \longrightarrow 2H_2O$

   or

   B: Elementary Step 1: $2NO + H_2 \longrightarrow N_2O + H_2O$

   Elementary Step 2: $N_2O + H_2 \longrightarrow N_2 + H_2O$

   a. What are processes A and B called?

   b. How can scientists decide whether A or B is correct?

   c. Suppose a scientist experimentally determines that both gases influence the reaction rate. Which step is the rate-determining step for this reaction? Can the scientist determine whether process A or B is the correct one from the information given? Explain.
8. A scientist is studying the following reaction.

   $2NO + 2H_2 \longrightarrow N_2 + 2H_2O$

   She collects the following data on three trials of this reaction. State the reaction order for each reactant and determine an appropriate rate law. Explain.

REACTION DATA

Trial	Initial [NO] (M)	Initial [H_2] (M)	Initial Rate (mol/L min)
1	0.20	0.20	3.76×10^{-3}
2	0.40	0.20	1.50×10^{-2}
3	0.20	0.40	7.52×10^{-3}

8. NO is a second-order reactant. (When the concentration of NO was doubled from the first to the second trial, the reaction rate quadrupled.)

   H_2 is a first-order reactant. (When the concentration of H_2 was doubled from the first trial to the third trial, the reaction rate also doubled.)

   rate = $k[NO]^2[H_2]$ *(all pp. 398–400)*

16 CHAPTER REVIEW

Chapter Summary

TERMS
kinetics
collision theory
activation energy
activated complex
reaction rate
catalyst
homogeneous catalyst
heterogeneous catalyst
enzyme
inhibitor

16.1 REACTION RATES

- Kinetics is the study of the rates of reactions and the steps by which they occur.
- Energy diagrams show the changes in energy through a reaction, including the activation energy and enthalpy changes.
- According to the collision theory, chemical reactions are caused by collisions that are properly oriented and energetic enough to form products.
- The activation energy (E_a) is the minimum amount of kinetic energy that must be possessed by colliding particles before they can react.
- The activated complex is a transitional structure between the reactants and the products. It is unstable and short-lived.
- Reaction rates tell how quickly reactants change into products. They are affected by the nature, concentration, temperature, and surface area of the reactants, along with the presence of catalysts.

TERMS
reaction mechanism
elementary step
rate-determining step
complex reaction
intermediate
reaction order
rate law
specific rate constant

16.2 REACTION MECHANISMS

- The series of steps that make up a reaction is called a reaction mechanism.
- Complex reactions have at least two elementary steps and form intermediate substances that do not appear in the equation for the net reaction.
- A rate law is an equation that mathematically describes how fast a reaction occurs. These equations take the form

$$rate = k[A]^m[B]^n,$$

where k is the specific rate constant, [A] and [B] are the molar concentrations of the reactants, and m and n are the reaction orders for [A] and [B], respectively.

CHAPTER 16 REVIEW ANSWERS

Recalling Facts

1. Thermodynamics asks, "Can these react?" Kinetics asks, "Will these react? If so, how quickly?" *(p. 387)*
2. activation energy *(p. 390)*
3. a short-lived transitional structure between reactants and products *(p. 390)*
4. Reaction rate is a measure of how quickly reactants change into products. *(p. 391)*
5. inhibitor *(p. 394)*
6. A homogeneous catalyst is in the same phase as the reactants or is in solution with the reactants. In a homogeneous reaction, all the reactants and products are in the same phase. *(pp. 394, 397)*

16 CHAPTER REVIEW

Chapter Review Questions

RECALLING FACTS

1. What questions do chemical thermodynamics and kinetics answer?
2. What term do we use to refer to the energy needed for a reaction to occur according to the collision theory?
3. What is an activated complex?
4. Define *reaction rate*.
5. A consumer product is available that, when applied to apple slices, prevents the enzymatic process that normally causes an apple slice to react with atmospheric oxygen and turn brown. Chemically speaking, what term describes this antibrowning agent?
6. What is the difference between a homogeneous catalyst and a homogeneous reaction?
7. What is a reaction mechanism?
8. What is an intermediate?
9. In reactions that have several possible reaction mechanisms, what factor determines the path that the reaction will follow?
10. In addition to the concentration of one or more of the reactants, what is found in all rate laws?

UNDERSTANDING CONCEPTS

11. How is the study of kinetics different from the study of thermodynamics?
12. When the reactants for a reaction with a negative ΔG are mixed, no reaction appears to occur. Suggest an explanation for the nonreaction.
13. According to the collision theory:
    a. Why does an increased temperature increase the reaction rate?
    b. Why does a greater concentration of reactants often increase the reaction rate?
    c. Why do powders react more quickly than a single mass of reactant?
    d. How does the presence of catalysts increase the reaction rate?
14. Draw an energy diagram for both an endothermic and an exothermic reaction. Include the following labels in your diagram: reactants, products, activated complex, activation energy, and ΔH.
15. The two curves in the energy diagram below represent the reaction shown below occurring under two different sets of reaction conditions. Assume that the two graphs are to scale with each other.

$$2KClO_3(s) \longrightarrow 2KCl(s) + 3O_2(g)$$

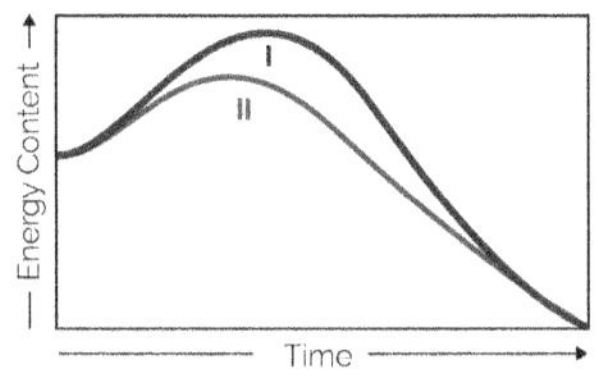

    a. Which set of conditions requires the lower activation energy? Justify your answer.
    b. Which reaction pathway would more likely include a catalyst? Justify your answer.
    c. Which reaction pathway requires higher temperatures? Justify your answer.
16. Of the three energy diagrams shown below, which is the most thermodynamically favorable? Which is the most likely to occur quickly? Explain.

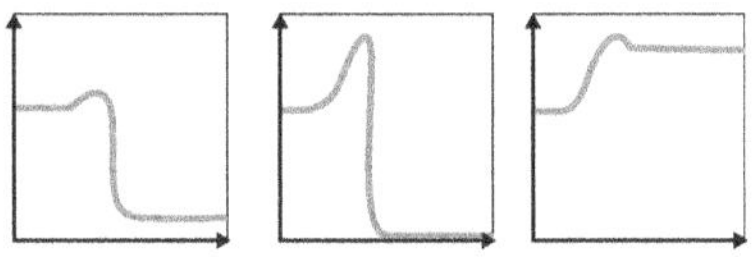

17. What happens to the concentration of the reactants and products in a chemical reaction? Explain.
18. Sugar needs temperatures much higher than 98.6 °F in order to burn. Yet sugar can be "burned" in your cells at this temperature. What is responsible for the ability of your body to burn sugar at this low temperature? Draw energy diagrams that illustrate the difference between the two situations.
19. Create a graphic organizer for kinetics using the terms *activated complex, activation energy, collision theory, complex reaction, elementary step, intermediate, kinetics, rate-determining step, reaction mechanism*, and *reaction rate*.
20. Why do activated complexes and intermediates not appear in net equations?

406 Chapter 16

---

7. a series of steps that make up a chemical reaction *(p. 396)*

8. An intermediate is a chemical substance that is produced in an elementary step of a reaction mechanism and is then used as a reactant in another elementary step. Intermediates are not products of the complex reaction. *(p. 396)*

9. the temperature at which the reaction occurs *(p. 397)*

10. a constant (k) that is specific to a reaction *(p. 398)*

Understanding Concepts

11. Thermodynamics is the study of the favorability of a reaction. Kinetics is the study of the conditions under which a reaction will occur, the rate of the reaction, and the steps involved. Thermodynamics is path-independent, focused only on the initial and final energy of reaction, while kinetics is path-dependent, concerned with the entire process of the reaction. *(pp. 387–88)*

12. The reaction may be happening too slowly to be observed or may not have sufficient energy. *(p. 388)*

13. a. At higher temperatures, more collisions occur, and on average the collisions are more energetic.

b. Greater concentrations result in more collisions.

c. More reactant particles are exposed to each other on the surface of a powder than on the surface of a crystal.

d. Catalysts provide an alternate pathway from reactants to products with a lower activation energy, meaning that more collisions will have enough energy to be effective. *(all pp. 388–89)*

14. See diagram on page 407A. *(p. 390)*

15. a. II; Activation energy is the difference in energy between the reactants and the top of the hill. Curve II has the lower difference in energy.

b. II; The presence of a catalyst increases the rate of a reaction by providing an alternative pathway with a lower activation energy. Since Curve II has a lower activation energy, it includes a catalyst.

c. I; As activation energy increases, the particles need more energy to have effective collisions; therefore, Curve I needs a high temperature for its particles to have sufficient energy to react. *(all p. 390)*

16. The second graph represents the most thermodynamically favorable reaction because of the large ΔH. The first graph is the one that is most likely to occur and occur quickly because of its negative ΔH and its small activation energy. *(pp. 390–91)*

17. As a reaction occurs, the concentration of the reactants decreases as reactants are changed into products. As the products are produced, the concentration of products increases. The rates are initially high because there are many collisions. As the concentration of reactants decreases, so does the reaction rate, slowing the rate of change in the concentrations. *(p. 391)*

18. Enzymes in the body lower the activation energy of the reaction. See diagram on page 407A. Student diagrams should show an exothermic reaction with a high activation energy that is modified significantly by enzymes. *(p. 394)*

19. See graphic organizer on page 407B. *(pp. 388–400)*

20. Activated complexes and intermediates exist only during the reaction and are completely consumed. *(p. 396)*

21. a. N_2O_2, N_2O

b. Elementary Step 2

c. $2NO + 2H_2 \longrightarrow N_2 + 2H_2O$ *(all p. 396)*

22. Chemical equations show only the reactants and their products, not the steps that the reactants underwent to form the products. Also, reactions have several

21. Use the elementary steps for the reaction mechanism below to answer the following questions.

1: $2NO \longrightarrow N_2O_2$ (fast)

2: $N_2O_2 + H_2 \longrightarrow N_2O + H_2O$ (slow)

3: $N_2O + H_2 \longrightarrow N_2 + H_2O$ (fast)

a. What are the intermediates?

b. Which step is the rate-determining step?

c. Write the net equation.

22. Why is it generally impossible to use only a balanced chemical equation to predict a rate law for a particular reaction?

23. A scientist postulates two possible rate laws for a reaction as shown below.

A: $rate = k[NO_2][F_2]$ or B: $rate = k[NO_2]^2[F_2]$

a. How can you tell which rate law is correct?

b. What is the reaction order of F_2 in each rate law?

c. What is the reaction order of NO_2 in each rate law?

d. In which of the rate laws would a change in the concentration of NO_2 have a greater influence? Explain.

e. How would doubling the concentration of F_2 in Rate Law A affect the reaction rate?

f. From this information, can you tell whether the reaction is a complex reaction or a single-step reaction? Explain.

24. Acetone and bromine combine as shown in the equation below.

$C_3H_6O + Br_2 \longrightarrow C_3H_5OBr + HBr$

A scientist collects the following data on three trials of this reaction. State the reaction order for each reactant and determine an appropriate rate law.

REACTION DATA

Trial	Initial $[C_3H_6O]$ (M)	Initial $[Br_2]$ (M)	Initial Rate (mol/L·min)
1	0.10	0.10	1.64×10^{-5}
2	0.10	0.20	1.64×10^{-5}
3	0.20	0.10	3.28×10^{-5}

CRITICAL THINKING

25. Why will a reaction involving the collision of three molecules proceed more slowly than one involving the collision of two molecules, all other things being equal?

26. Propose a possible two-step mechanism for the decomposition of HgO according to the equation below.

$2HgO(s) \longrightarrow 2Hg(l) + O_2(g)$

Use the ethics box below to answer Question 27.

27. Research the issue of medical marijuana and write a four-paragraph response to the question of how a Christian should respond to a push within his state to legalize marijuana for medical uses.

ethics

MEDICAL MARIJUANA

Drug laws vary around the world. Even within countries there can be tremendous variation in the laws that exist and how they should be enforced. Within the United States, the federal government maintains a ban on the use of marijuana, while several states have legalized it for medical and even recreational use. Each state has its own program regarding regulation, sale, and enforcement. While some states recognize medical marijuana for patients from outside their state, others do not.

Chemical Kinetics 407

possible mechanisms, so rate laws must be determined experimentally. *(p. 399)*

23. a. The correct rate law can be found by conducting experiments in which the concentrations of NO_2 and F_2 are changed to determine how those changes affect the reaction rate.

b. first order *(both rate laws)*

c. first order in Rate Law A and second order in Rate Law B

d. Rate Law B; NO_2 is a second-order reactant, so it affects the reaction rate by a squared factor.

e. It would double the reaction rate.

f. While it is most likely a complex reaction, we can't be certain of that from the information given. If we had the chemical equation and the reaction orders matched the coefficients, the reaction might be simpler. *(all pp. 399–400)*

24. C_3H_6O is a first-order reactant. Br_2 is a zero-order reactant. $rate = k[C_3H_6O]$ *(pp. 399–400)*

Critical Thinking

25. A simultaneous collision involving three molecules is far less likely to occur than a collision between two molecules. *(pp. 388–89)*

ETHICS: MEDICAL MARIJUANA

Appendix L includes a reproducible rubric to assess the ethics essay.

26. Answers do not need to be identical to the example shown below, but they must contain steps that add up to the overall reaction when common terms are canceled.

Elementary Step 1:
$HgO \longrightarrow Hg + \frac{1}{2}O_2$

Elementary Step 2:
$\frac{1}{2}O_2 + HgO \longrightarrow Hg + O_2$

Net Chemical Equation:
$2HgO\ (s) \longrightarrow 2Hg\ (l) + O_2\ (g)$
(pp. 396–97)

27. Students' responses should appropriately address the issues of biblical principles, biblical outcomes, and biblical motivations.

Students will find a number of sources on both sides of the issue. Most legitimate medical sources do not support recreational use, though that is not the focus of this assignment.

The principles involved include not being controlled by anything other than the Holy Spirit. Students may point out warnings against other intoxicating substances (e.g., wine and strong drink). Balanced with this are the needs of those around us, including the need for medical treatment, which involves medications that may have adverse side effects.

Biblical outcomes could include the outright prohibition of the medical use of marijuana, in spite of some medical evidence indicating the efficacy of its medical use (research is ongoing), possibly resulting in continued suffering and reduction in quality of life for some patients. Legalization could result in more abuse of marijuana, to the detriment of people and society. Another possible outcome is a balanced program of using it in cases that have a proven medical use while maintaining enforcement against illegal uses. This balanced approach would also involve proper recognition across jurisdictions.

Biblical motivations should include seeking to love others while glorifying God. We should always seek human prospering and strive for what is best for all of God's image-bearers.

Chapter Review Answers

14.

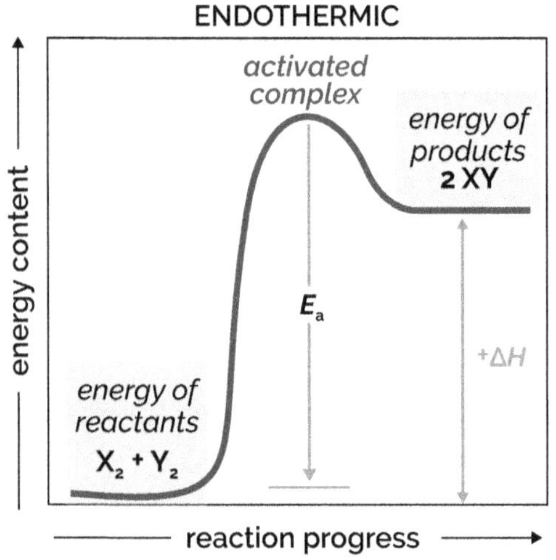

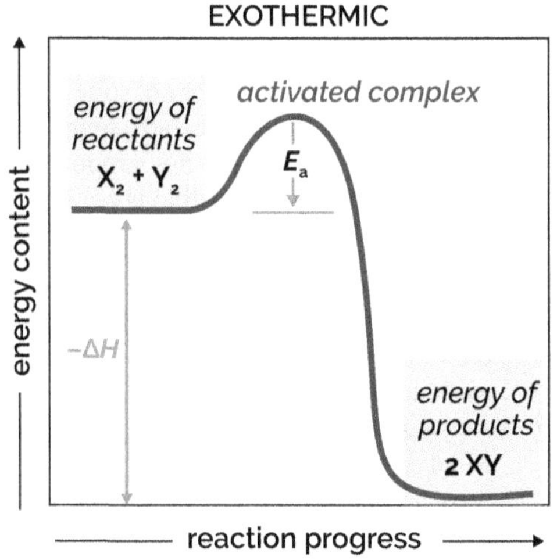

18.

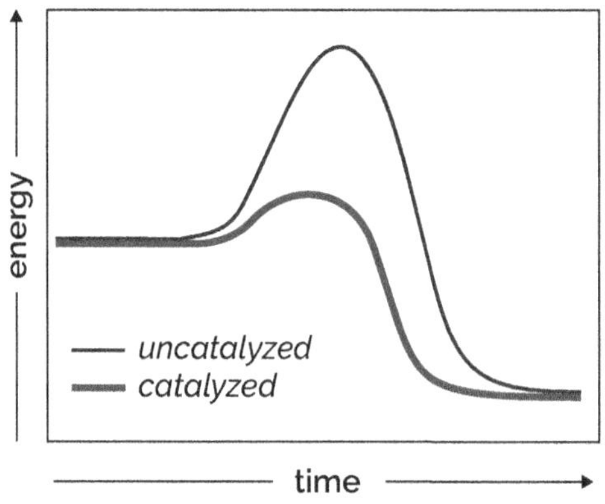

19.

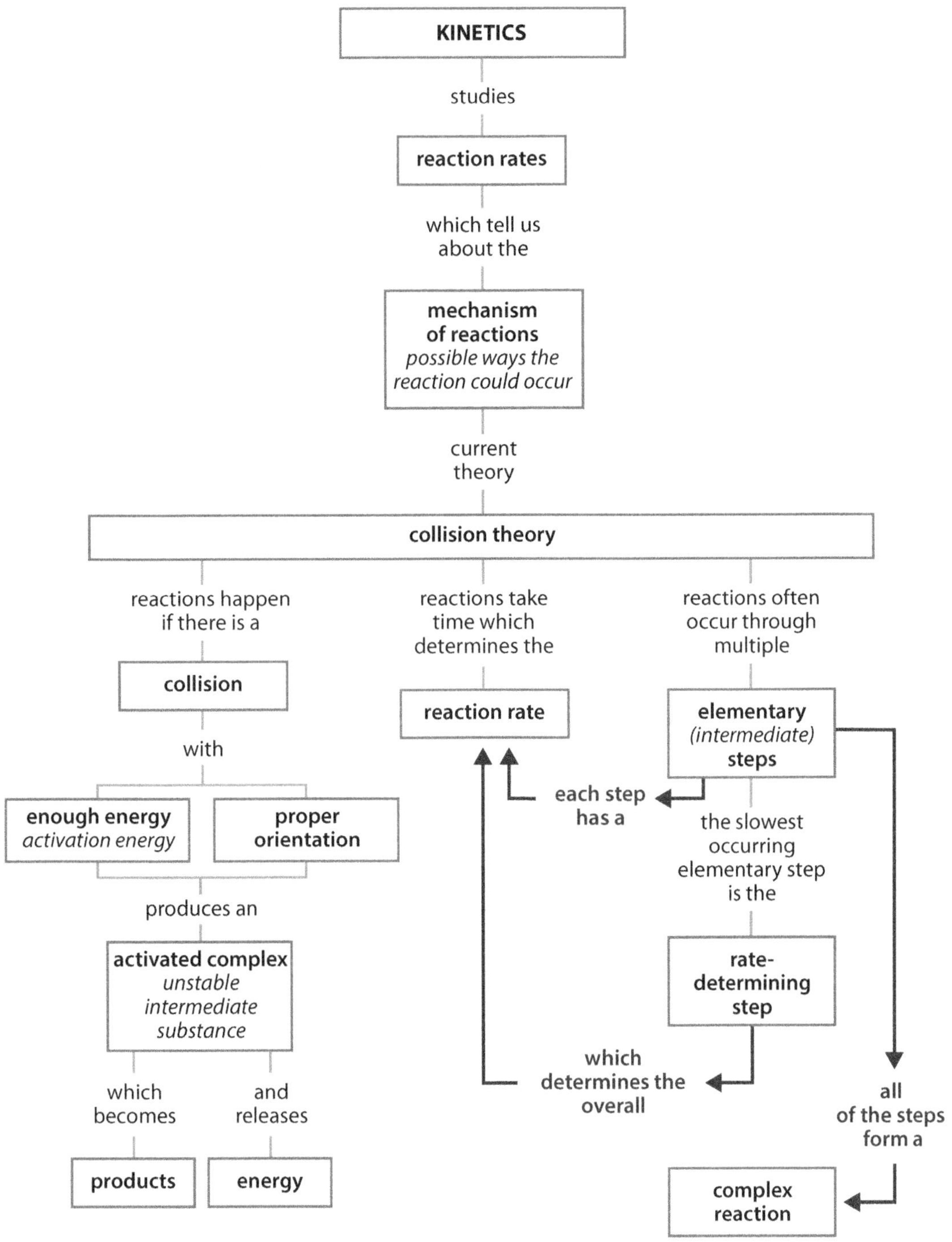
KINETICS
studies
reaction rates
which tell us about the
mechanism of reactions
possible ways the reaction could occur
current theory
collision theory
reactions happen if there is a
collision
with
enough energy
activation energy
proper orientation
produces an
activated complex
unstable intermediate substance
which becomes
and releases
products
energy
reactions take time which determines the
reaction rate
reactions often occur through multiple
elementary (intermediate) steps
each step has a
the slowest occurring elementary step is the
rate-determining step
which determines the overall
all of the steps form a
complex reaction

CHAPTER 17 *OBJECTIVES*

- Predict the concentration of a substance at its equilibrium position.
- Predict how stresses on a system will change the equilibrium position.
- Solve solubility problems by using the solubility product constant.
- Verify predictions made on the basis of Le Châtelier's principle.

OVERVIEW

Chapter 1 has key material which will help students understand chemical equilibrium. The two preceding chapters focused on *whether* and *how fast* a reaction will occur. Chapter 17 addresses *how many* reactant particles will be transformed into product particles. The chapter dispels the common misconception that all reactions proceed in a forward direction to completion, using up all the reactants and leaving only products.

17.1 EQUILIBRIUM

- *What Is Chemical Equilibrium?*
- *Dynamic Equilibrium*
- *Getting to Equilibrium*
- *Equilibrium Constants*

17.2 LE CHÂTELIER'S PRINCIPLE

- *The Effect of Concentration*
- *The Effect of Pressure*
- *The Effect of Temperature*
- *The Effect of Catalysts*
- *Equilibria and Industry*
- *Worldview Conflict and Equilibrium*

17.3 SOLUTION EQUILIBRIUM

- *Ionic Equilibria*
- *Solubility and Equilibria*
- *Common-Ion Effect*
- *Precipitation Reactions*

LAB ACTIVITIES

Lab 17A: *Stressed Out*—Students observe and evaluate various stresses on a chemical reaction in equilibrium.

Lab 17B: *Precipitous Changes*—Students observe and alter the equilibrium position within a precipitation reaction.

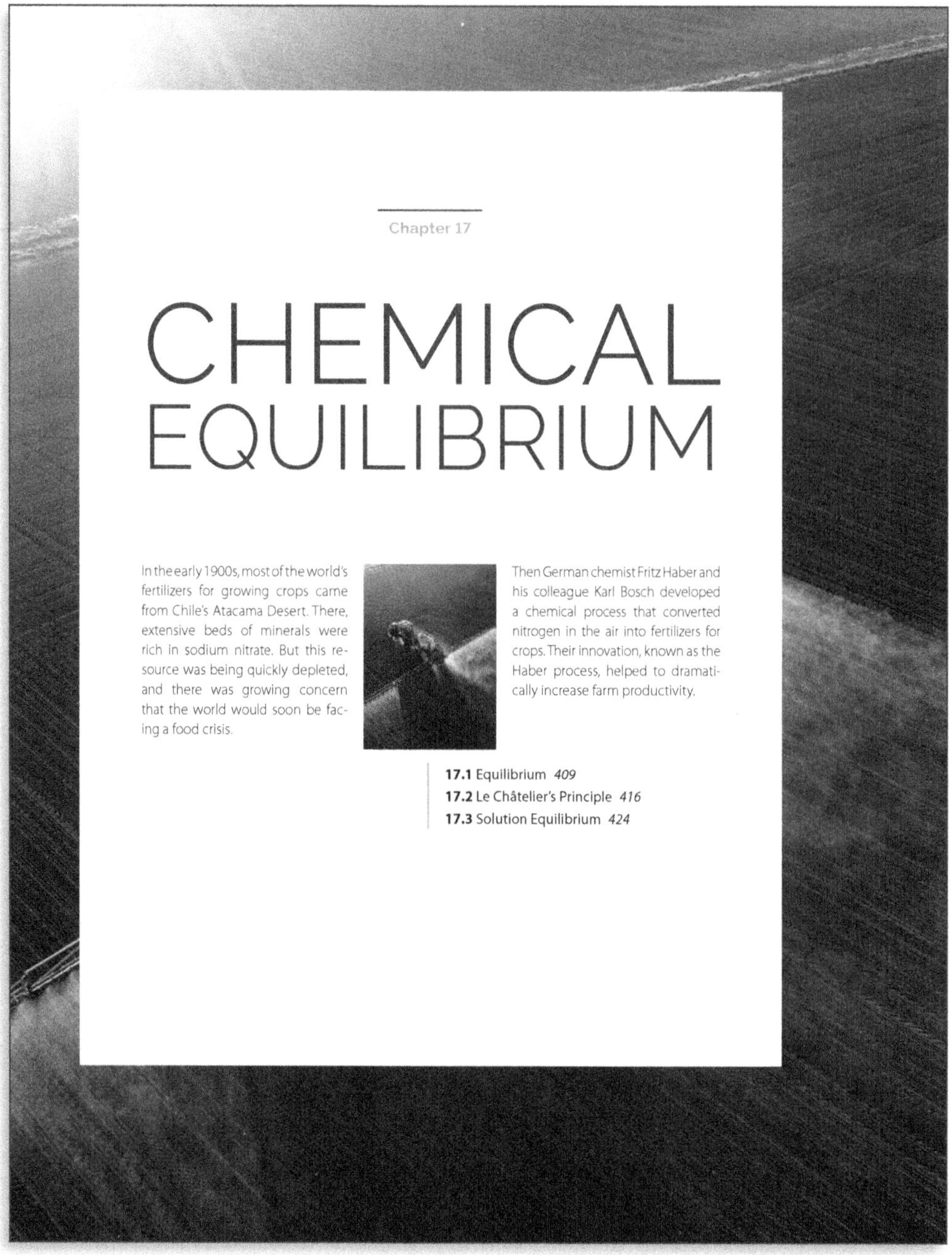

Chapter 17

CHEMICAL EQUILIBRIUM

In the early 1900s, most of the world's fertilizers for growing crops came from Chile's Atacama Desert. There, extensive beds of minerals were rich in sodium nitrate. But this resource was being quickly depleted, and there was growing concern that the world would soon be facing a food crisis.

Then German chemist Fritz Haber and his colleague Karl Bosch developed a chemical process that converted nitrogen in the air into fertilizers for crops. Their innovation, known as the Haber process, helped to dramatically increase farm productivity.

The Chapter opener shows a photo of a tractor spraying a large field with fertilizer. Although fertilizers used in agriculture have been helpful in providing vast amounts of food, there are disadvantages in the overuse of such chemicals. Beyond providing a quick method for obtaining food, the ammonia used in many types of fertilizers can seep into our groundwater and contaminate our food and bodies. Today, however, there is ongoing research being done with the intention to develop alternative methods to eradicate these issues and improve our current methods of fertilization.

17.1 EQUILIBRIUM

What Is Chemical Equilibrium?

When you think about chemical reactions, like the Haber process, you might assume that most of them continue in the forward direction to completion and then stop, and indeed some do. These are known as *irreversible reactions*. But most natural processes are **reversible reactions**—reactions that occur in both the forward and reverse directions. As products form, a portion of those products simultaneously reverts to reactants. The Haber process is based on a reversible reaction of hydrogen and nitrogen. Left on its own, the reaction would quickly reach a balance between forward and reverse reactions. The Haber process gets around this reality by favoring the forward reaction at a high temperature and continuously removing the product as it forms, reducing the likelihood of the reverse reaction occurring.

Can chemical reactions go in the reverse direction?

QUESTIONS

- What does it mean that a reversible reaction is complete?
- Is a reversible reaction ever really finished?
- How can I derive the equation for an equilibrium constant from a balanced chemical equation?
- How can I calculate an equilibrium constant?

TERMS

reversible reaction • chemical equilibrium • equilibrium position • equilibrium constant • law of chemical equilbrium

REVERSIBLE REACTIONS SHARE THE FOLLOWING CHARACTERISTICS:

- Both reactants and products exist together as a mixture.
- The ratio in which reactants and products are present in the reaction vessel depends on the relative speeds of the forward and reverse reactions.
- Changing the rate of either the forward or the reverse reaction changes the ratio of products and reactants in the reaction vessel.

▲ 1928 photo of a chemical and pharmaceutical production facility located along the Rhine River in Ludwigshafen, Germany

Chemical equilibrium results when the forward and reverse reactions proceed at the same rate. The high temperature and product removal of the Haber process ensure that this point is never reached. Like the kinetic-molecular and atomic theories, chemical equilibrium is one of the big ideas of chemistry and explains many observations. While the study of thermodynamics determines whether a reaction can occur and kinetics determines how fast it will occur, the study of equilibrium determines how far a reaction will proceed toward completion.

SECTION 17.1 *OVERVIEW*

Essential Question

Can chemical reactions go in the reverse direction?

Objectives

» **17.1.1** Define *reversible reaction.*

» **17.1.2** Explain how a reaction at equilibrium continues to produce products without changing the amounts of products.

» **17.1.3** Write the equation for an equilibrium constant from a balanced chemical equation.

» **17.1.4** Solve problems involving equilibrium constants.

Resources

Web Links: Dynamic Equilibrium, Blue Bottle Reaction, Dancing Gummi Bears

Mini Lab: *Mix, Change, Repeat*

ENGAGE

CHEMICAL REACTIONS

Preassess students' knowledge of reactions with a **think-pair-share**. Ask the essential question, "Can chemical reactions go in the reverse direction?" You may want to have them recall the yield symbol for reversible reactions (Ch. 10). Pair up students and have them discuss what they believe the answer to this question is. After they have discussed their answers, have them record any reactions that they have observed that seem irreversible. They may mention burning wood, cooking eggs and meat, baking cakes, and so on.

Once students have finished, discuss the activity as a class and introduce the characteristics of reversible reactions.

INSTRUCT

NOTICEABLE REACTIONS

Students will not usually see the equilibrium between precipitation reactions or the dissolving that occurs with gases in a container because these reactions are not that noticeable. Reversible reactions at equilibrium do not appear to be doing anything because the forward and reverse reactions are happening at the same rate, resulting in very little observable change, unless the equilibrium is stressed in some way.

DYNAMIC EQUILIBRIUM

For a video about dynamic equilibrium, visit TeacherToolsOnline.com. Under Additional Resources, click on Chapter 17 Web Links. Then click on *Dynamic Equilibrium*.

SUMMARY OF EQUILIBRIUM TYPES

Correct misunderstandings by clarifying the difference between static and dynamic equilibrium.

Static equilibrium is a balance of forces—essentially the two-dimensional aspect of a chemical equation. *Dynamic equilibrium* is a balance of processes—essentially the three-dimensional aspect of a chemical equation.

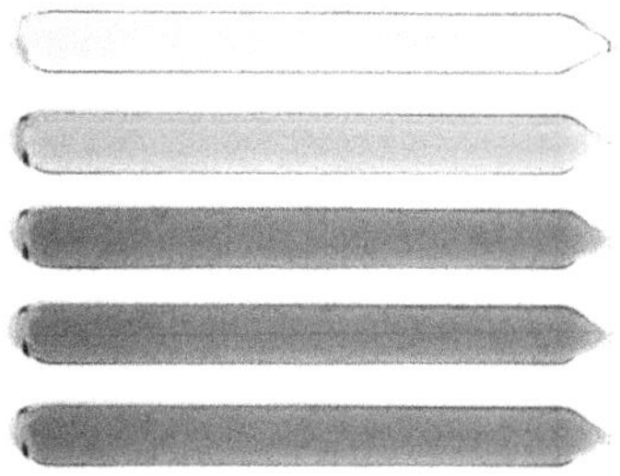

DYNAMIC EQUILIBRIUM

When you think of the term *equilibrium*, you probably picture a balanced scale or a never-ending game of tug-of-war. Yet these examples illustrate only one type of equilibrium—the static equilibrium of balanced physical forces. In chemistry, equilibrium refers to balanced changes, not balanced forces. Chemical equilibrium exists when two opposing reactions occur simultaneously at the same rate, balancing each other. Unlike the examples of balanced forces, chemical equilibria are dynamic. The particles involved constantly move and react. Particle activity continues even though no macroscopic changes seem to be happening.

Consider N_2O_4. This colorless gas can be sealed in a tube and cooled. When it warms, it changes into the brown gas NO_2. The heat energy excites the N_2O_4 particles so that they can break apart to form NO_2.

$$N_2O_4(g) \longrightarrow 2NO_2(g)$$

But not all the NO_2 molecules stay as they are. Some of them recombine to form more N_2O_4. The color changes until the rates of the forward and reverse reactions match each other and the two gases are in equilibrium.

$$2NO_2(g) \longrightarrow N_2O_4(g)$$

At varying temperatures, the gas in the tube is different colors (see above) depending on the proportions of the two gases.

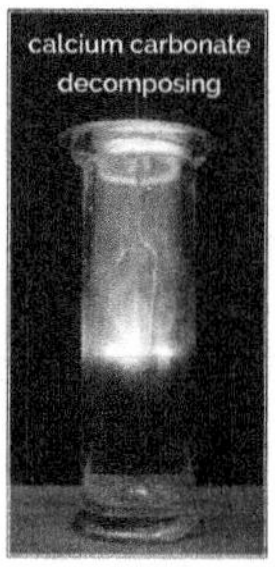

Here's another example. As molecules of calcium carbonate ($CaCO_3$) decompose, they produce calcium oxide (CaO) and carbon dioxide (CO_2). As calcium oxide and carbon dioxide are allowed to accumulate, the chance that any particle of one will collide with a particle of the other increases. Some of these collisions result in the formation of the original reactant. As more calcium oxide and carbon dioxide accumulate, more calcium carbonate is re-formed.

$$CaCO_3(s) \longrightarrow CaO(s) + CO_2(g)$$

$$CaO(s) + CO_2(g) \longrightarrow CaCO_3(s)$$

Eventually the two reactions proceed at the same rate. To an observer it appears that the amounts of calcium carbonate, calcium oxide, and carbon dioxide remain constant; yet at the particle level, the two opposing processes continue. The half-head arrows in the chemical equation below show that both the forward and reverse reactions are occurring at the same rate.

$$CaCO_3(s) \rightleftharpoons CaO(s) + CO_2(g)$$

Physical changes can also be in equilibrium, such as evaporation and dissolving. For example, water molecules in a sealed jar continue to evaporate even after the air is completely saturated. Since the air is saturated, some of the vapor molecules condense at the same rate as liquid molecules evaporate.

$$H_2O(l) \rightleftharpoons H_2O(g)$$

Dissolving processes also reach dynamic equilibria at their saturation points. Particles dissolve and precipitate at equal but opposing rates.

$$NaCl(s) \rightleftharpoons Na^+(aq) + Cl^-(aq)$$

As you can see, chemical equilibria are vitally important. Many industrial processes increase their productivity by manipulating reversible reactions. But how can equilibrium reactions be controlled?

GETTING TO
Equilibrium

To get a better understanding of equilibrium, consider the reaction of hydrogen gas with iodine gas to form another gas, hydrogen iodide. The graphs at right show the changing reaction rates and concentrations as this reaction progresses.

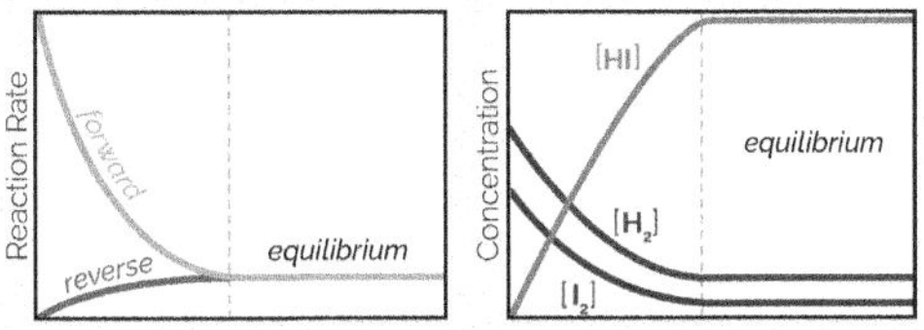

$$H_2(g) + I_2(g) \longrightarrow 2HI(g)$$

Initially the reaction vessel contains only hydrogen and iodine. The reaction can occur only in the forward direction, so the forward reaction rate is high and the reverse reaction rate is zero. As the reaction proceeds, the concentrations of hydrogen and iodine start to decrease as they are being converted to hydrogen iodide, whose concentration is thus increasing.

As hydrogen iodide is formed, some of it can decompose back into hydrogen and iodine and the equation looks slightly different.

$$H_2(g) + I_2(g) \rightleftharpoons 2HI(g)$$

Notice that there are arrows pointing in both directions, though the forward reaction arrow is longer than the reverse reaction arrow. That's because prior to equilibrium, more of the forward reaction is happening. But as the reaction proceeds, the forward rate decreases, while the reverse reaction rate increases.

Ultimately, the forward and reverse reaction rates will be equal—the reaction reaches equilibrium. To the observer the reaction appears to have stopped. In reality, the forward and reverse reactions continue, but the concentration of each reactant and product remains constant. Understand, though, that the concentration of reactants does not necessarily equal the concentration of products when equilibrium has been reached. Each chemical substance achieves its own constant concentration depending on conditions. Again, the graphs show that at equilibrium the reaction rates are equal and the concentrations are constant, but the concentrations are not necessarily equal to each other. The equation is now updated to show both the forward and reverse reaction arrows equal in length.

$$H_2(g) + I_2(g) \rightleftharpoons 2HI(g)$$

Table 17-1 shows the concentrations of hydrogen gas, iodine gas, and hydrogen iodide. The concentrations of the substances at equilibrium is called the **equilibrium position** and is dependent on the conditions at equilibrium. In Section 17.2 we will look at how changing conditions shift the equilibrium position.

TABLE 17-1

Equilibrium Concentrations of H_2, I_2, and HI

	$H_2(g)$	$I_2(g)$	$HI(g)$
Beginning Concentration (c)	0.0275	0.0175	0
Change in Concentration (c)	−0.0148	−0.0148	+0.0296
Equilibrium Concentration (c)	0.0127	0.0027	0.0296

BLUE BOTTLE REACTION

For a video demonstration of a reaction displaying a shifting equilibrium, visit TeacherToolsOnline.com. Under Additional Resources, click on Chapter 17 Web Links. Then click on *Blue Bottle Reaction*.

DANCING GUMMI BEAR

For instructions for the popular dancing gummi bear demonstration, which shows a product-favored reaction, visit TeacherToolsOnline.com. Under Additional Resources, click on Chapter 17 Web Links. Then click on *Dancing Gummi Bear*.

EQUILIBRIUM CONSTANT

Direct students to create **Sketchnotes** for the equilibrium constant. Instruct them to use the equation on page 412 to write out the equilibrium constant. Give them the following notes.

1. When $K_{eq} = 1$, there is a fifty-fifty mixture of reactants and products.
2. When $K_{eq} < 1$, there are more *reactants* than *products*, the reverse reaction predominates, and the reactant side is favored.
3. When $K_{eq} > 1$, there are more *products* than *reactants*, the forward reaction predominates, and the product side is favored.

CONSTANT CONCENTRATION

K_{eq} is calculated on the basis of concentrations in mol/L. But point out to students that as they work problems later in the chapter, the equilibrium constant is usually reported without units.

Equilibrium Constants

Chemists often describe a reaction in equilibrium using a calculated value called an *equilibrium constant.*

Consider a reaction with the generalized equation

$$aA + bB \rightleftharpoons cC + dD,$$

where A, B, C, and D are chemical substances with coefficients *a*, *b*, *c*, and *d*. The **equilibrium constant** (K_{eq}) is a constant for a reversible chemical reaction at a particular temperature and has the following form.

$$K_{eq} = \frac{[C]^c[D]^d}{[A]^a[B]^b}$$

An equilibrium constant is a numerical expression of the ratio of the product equilibrium concentrations to the reactant equilibrium concentrations. If the value of K_{eq} is greater than 1, the forward reaction predominates and the concentrations of products (in the numerator) are greater than the concentrations of the reactants (in the denominator). If the value of K_{eq} is less than 1, the reverse reaction predominates and the concentration of products is small compared with the concentration of reactants.

It is possible to determine the equilibrium constant for a reversible reaction because of the **law of chemical equilibrium**. This law states that at a specific temperature, a chemical system may reach a point at which the ratio of the concentration of the products to the reactants is constant.

CONSTANTS FOR HOMOGENEOUS EQUILIBRIA

In the equation $H_2(g) + I_2(g) \rightleftharpoons 2HI(g)$, the relationship for the equilibrium constant is written

$$K_{eq} = \frac{[HI]^2}{[H_2][I_2]}.$$

This reaction is in *homogeneous equilibrium* because all the reactants and products are in the same state.

EXAMPLE 17-1: FORMULATING HOMOGENEOUS EQUILIBRIUM CONSTANTS

Write the equilibrium constant for the formation of ammonia from its elements. The reaction is $3H_2(g) + N_2(g) \rightleftharpoons 2NH_3(g)$.

Solution

$$K_{eq} = \frac{[NH_3]^2}{[H_2]^3[N_2]}$$

CONSTANTS FOR HETEROGENEOUS EQUILIBRIA

Not all reactions that reach equilibrium are limited to substances in the same state. Some involve substances in different states. These can reach a *heterogeneous equilibrium*, that is, one in which not all the substances are in the same physical state.

412 Chapter 17

Writing equilibrium constants for heterogeneous equilibria requires an additional bit of knowledge. Pure solids and liquids don't have concentrations, so their "concentrations" for the purpose of calculating equilibrium constants are both defined as 1. The presence of a solid or liquid in a reaction thus does not affect the value of an equilibrium constant. But gases and substances in aqueous solutions are included. To see how this works in practice, consider the equilibrium between solid zinc and hydrochloric acid to produce zinc chloride and hydrogen gas.

$$Zn(s) + 2HCl(aq) \rightleftharpoons ZnCl_2(aq) + H_2(g)$$

If we include the value for solid zinc, the equilibrium constant is calculated as follows.

$$K_{eq} = \frac{[ZnCl_2][H_2]}{[Zn][HCl]^2} = \frac{[ZnCl_2][H_2]}{1\,[HCl]^2} = \frac{[ZnCl_2][H_2]}{[HCl]^2}$$

As you can see, the value of 1 for solid zinc has no effect on the calculation and can thus be omitted entirely.

The sublimation of solid iodine crystals into iodine gas in a closed system also reaches a heterogeneous equilibrium.

$$I_2(s) \rightleftharpoons I_2(g) \quad K_{eq} = [I_2]$$

Again, the equilibrium is not dependent on the amount of solid iodine that might be present, so it is not included in the expression.

When acetic acid molecules mix with water, some of them release hydrogen ions to the water to form hydronium ions, H_3O^+. Since only an insignificant amount of water is used up in the reaction, the concentration of water molecules is defined as 1 and should be left out of the equilibrium constant.

$$HC_2H_3O_2(aq) + H_2O(l) \rightleftharpoons C_2H_3O_2^-(aq) + H_3O^+(aq)$$

$$K_{eq} = \frac{[C_2H_3O_2^-][H_3O^+]}{[HC_2H_3O_2]}$$

▲ Zinc reacting with HCl to produce zinc chloride and hydrogen gas

EXAMPLE 17-2: FORMULATING HETEROGENEOUS EQUILIBRIUM CONSTANTS

Write the equilibrium constant for the reaction of sodium hydroxide and zinc chloride.

$$2NaOH(aq) + ZnCl_2(aq) \rightleftharpoons 2NaCl(aq) + Zn(OH)_2(s)$$

Solution

Since zinc hydroxide is a solid, its concentration is 1 in the equation for the equilibrium constant.

$$K_{eq} = \frac{[NaCl]^2}{[NaOH]^2[ZnCl_2]}$$

DIFFERENTIATED INSTRUCTION

Connecting Concepts

Use a research **webquest** to create connections between the equilibrium constant, rate law, and Gibbs free energy. While studying this chapter, students may have recognized the similarities between the equilibrium constant and rate laws (Ch. 16). These concepts are also related to Gibbs free energy (Ch. 15). In summary, equilibrium occurs when Gibbs free energy reaches a minimum value.

To complete their webquest, have students follow the steps below.

1. ***Task:*** Research equilibrium constant, rate law, and Gibbs free energy, and create a graphic organizer of your choosing to connect the three concepts.
2. ***Process:*** Using high-quality online resources, research equilibrium constant, rate law, and Gibbs free energy. Create a graphic organizer which combines and relates the concepts. Within the graphic organizers, include a compare/contrast component as well as an example of each concept. Be sure to document the websites used to research these concepts.
3. ***Conclusion:*** Write a brief conclusion describing why these concepts are important in the study of chemistry.

EQUILIBRIUM CONSTANT

Use the following **formative assessment** to check students' understanding.

1. At equilibrium, what must the concentration for each chemical substance be? *(constant)*
2. What kind of equilibrium is represented by a reversible reaction involving chemicals in a variety of physical states? *(heterogeneous)*
3. What is the value of the equilibrium constant for the reaction below, given that the equilibrium concentrations at a certain temperature are [NO] = 1.2 M, $[O_2]$ = 1.6 M, and $[NO_2]$ = 8.8 M?

   $2NO(g) + O_2(g) \rightleftharpoons 2NO_2(g)$

   Write what you know: [NO] = 1.2 M, $[O_2]$ = 1.6 M, and $[NO_2]$ = 8.8 M

   Write the formula and solve for the unknown.

   $$K_{eq} = \frac{[NO_2]^2}{[NO]^2[O_2]}$$

   Plug in known values and evaluate.

   $$K_{eq} = \frac{[8.8]^2}{[1.2]^2[1.6]}$$

   $$= 34$$

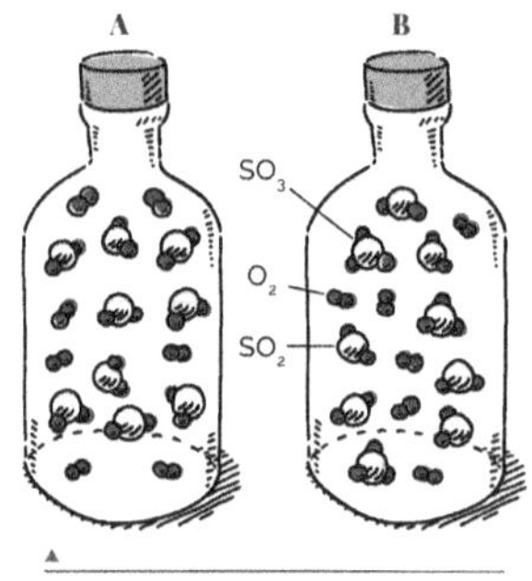

Flask A contains the reactant molecules and Flask B holds molecules of the reaction at equilibrium. Notice that all the reactants are still present with the product but in a different ratio.

DETERMINING THE VALUE OF K_{EQ}

The numerical value of an equilibrium constant must be determined experimentally. Suppose that 5 mol of sulfur dioxide and 4 mol of oxygen are placed in a 1 L container and allowed to react to form sulfur trioxide. At equilibrium, the concentrations are measured. It is found that 1.2 mol of sulfur trioxide, 3.8 mol of sulfur dioxide, and 3.4 mol of oxygen are present.

$$2SO_2(g) + O_2(g) \rightleftharpoons 2SO_3(g)$$

$$K_{eq} = \frac{[SO_3]^2}{[SO_2]^2[O_2]}$$

$$= \frac{(1.2)^2}{(3.8)^2(3.4)}$$

$$= 0.029$$

The equilibrium constant 0.029 describes the ratio between products and reactants at specific conditions.

EXAMPLE 17-3: CALCULATING THE VALUE FOR K_{EQ}

Calculate the numerical value of K_{eq} for the equilibrium involved in the formation of ammonia from nitrogen and hydrogen.

$N_2(g) + 3H_2(g) \rightleftharpoons 2NH_3(g)$

When the mixture of the gases reaches equilibrium, $[N_2]$ = 0.045 M, $[H_2]$ = 0.055 M, and $[NH_3]$ = 52 M.

Write what you know.

$[N_2]$ = 0.045 M
$[H_2]$ = 0.055 M
$[NH_3]$ = 52 M

Write the formula and solve for the unknown.

$$K_{eq} = \frac{[NH_3]^2}{[N_2][H_2]^3}$$

Plug in known values and evaluate.

$$K_{eq} = \frac{(52)^2}{(0.045)(0.055)^3}$$

$$= 3.6 \times 10^8$$

The equilibrium constant is 3.6×10^8.

SIGNIFICANCE OF THE VALUE OF K_{EQ}

Recall that the value of the equilibrium constant can tell you much about the equilibrium reaction. If the value of K_{eq} is much greater than 1, the reaction proceeds almost to completion as written, and the equilibrium lies far to the right. If the value of K_{eq} is much less than 1, the reaction does not proceed very far at all before reaching equilibrium, and the equilibrium lies to the left. In other words, the larger the value of K_{eq}, the more product-favored the reaction is; the lower the value of K_{eq}, the more reactant-favored the reaction is. If the value of K_{eq} lies between these two extremes, then significant concentrations of both reactants and products exist at equilibrium. In Example 17-3, the forward reaction is highly favored, resulting in almost exclusively products.

414 Chapter 17

MINI LAB

MIX, CHANGE, REPEAT

How can you tell whether a chemical reaction has taken place? Recall from Chapter 10 that there are different kinds of evidence that suggest that a reaction has occurred. But do they indicate whether a reaction is *finished* (i.e., reached equilibrium)?

Is it always possible to tell whether a reaction has reached equilibrium?

Procedure

Do an internet search using the keywords "Briggs-Rauscher reaction" to find videos that demonstrate the reaction. Select one to view.

1. Describe the first evidence that you observe that a reaction may have taken place.
2. Is there evidence that additional chemical changes occur? If so, describe them.

Conclusion

3. Explain what happens during the Briggs-Rauscher reaction on the basis of what you have learned in this chapter.

Going Further

4. Does the Briggs-Rauscher reaction ever reach equilibrium?
5. What is the term that chemists use to describe reactions like the Briggs-Rauscher reaction?

EQUIPMENT

- none

17.1 SECTION REVIEW

1. Why are most chemical reactions described as being reversible?
2. Under what conditions will a reversible reaction proceed to completion?
3. Explain why you don't run out of reactants if the forward reaction is still occurring at equilibrium.
4. Assuming that you start with only reactants, explain what happens to the reaction rates of forward and reverse reactions and the concentrations of products and reactants from the start of a reaction until equilibrium is reached.
5. Consider the following equation.

   $CaF_2(s) \rightleftharpoons Ca^{2+}(aq) + 2F^-(aq)$

   a. Write the equilibrium constant expression for the process.

   b. Is this an example of homogeneous or heterogeneous equilibrium?
6. Write the equilibrium constant expression for the following reaction.

   $Na_2CO_3(aq) + CaCl_2(aq) \rightleftharpoons CaCO_3(s) + 2NaCl(aq)$
7. Calculate the equilibrium constant for the chemical equation for the reaction of solid magnesium with hydrochloric acid to form magnesium chloride solution and hydrogen gas. The equilibrium position is [HCl] = 0.051 M, $[MgCl_2]$ = 0.513 M, and $[H_2]$ = 0.411 M.
8. Consider the reaction

   $2NO(g) + O_2(g) \rightleftharpoons 2NO_2(g)$.

   a. What is the value of the equilibrium constant for this reaction if the equilibrium concentrations are [NO] = 0.897 M, $[O_2]$ = 0.254 M, and $[NO_2]$ = 0.0329 M?

   b. If, under the same conditions, [NO] = 1.13 M and $[O_2]$ = 0.512 M, what will be the concentration of NO_2 in a reaction vessel?

Chemical Equilibrium 415

APPLY

MINI LAB: *MIX, CHANGE, REPEAT*

Use this **mini lab** to demonstrate the Briggs-Rauscher Reaction. Numerous videos of this reaction have been posted online. You may want to preview some of these and select one for your students to view rather than having them search for one.

1. There is a color change. The clear solution changes to an amber color.
2. Yes. The amber solution changes to a dark blue, then back to clear, and this process repeats.
3. The different colors must be because of various chemical substances being present at different times. As the concentrations of the substances change, various reactions occur.
4. Yes. The rate of color changes slows down, and the color changes eventually stop.
5. oscillating reaction

ASSESS

TICKET OUT THE DOOR

As a **summarizing activity**, have students describe how to determine the favorability of products and reactants on the basis of a reaction's K_{eq}. *(The larger the value of K_{eq}, the more product-favored the reaction is. The lower the value of K_{eq}, the more reactant-favored the reaction is.)*

17.1 REVIEW ANSWERS

* An asterisk following a question number indicates that a worked-out solution can be found on page 433A.

1. In most chemical reactions, the forward and reverse processes happen simultaneously. *(p. 409)*
2. A reversible reaction will proceed to completion if the products are removed. *(p. 410)*
3. At equilibrium the reverse reaction continues to produce more reactants so that the forward reaction can continue without using up all the reactants. *(pp. 410–11)*
4. Since there are only reactants initially, meaning that the reactant concentrations are at their maximum values, the forward reaction rate is at its maximum, and the reverse reaction rate is zero. As reactants turn into products, the concentrations of the reactants decrease and the concentrations of the products increase. The forward reaction rate decreases and the reverse reaction rate increases. At equilibrium, the reaction rates are equal. The reactant and product concentrations are all constant. *(p. 411)*
5. **a.** $K_{eq} = [Ca^{2+}][F^-]^2$

   b. heterogeneous; The substances are in different states of matter. *(all p. 412)*
6. $K_{eq} = \dfrac{[NaCl]^2}{[Na_2CO_3][CaCl_2]}$ *(pp. 412–13)*
7. * 81 *(pp. 412–14)*
8. ***a.** 0.005 30

   b. 0.0588 mol/L *(all pp. 412–14)*

SECTION 17.2 *OVERVIEW*

Essential Question

How can I produce more of the products without adding more of the reactants?

Objectives

» **17.2.1** Define *Le Châtelier's principle.*

» **17.2.2** Summarize the effects that various stresses will have on a system in equilibrium.

» **17.2.3** Predict the direction that a reaction will shift when stressed.

» **17.2.4** Formulate a biblical view of proper uses for ethanol. BWS

Resources

Worldview Investigation: Ethanol

How It Works: The Haber Process

Demonstrating Reversible Color

Web Links: Le Châtelier's Principle, Watching the Haber Process

Lab 17A: *Stressed Out*—Inquiring into Le Châtelier's principle

ENGAGE

SECTION 17.1 REVIEW

Review Section 17.1 with a two-minute **quick write** activity. Give students two minutes to write about what they learned in Section 17.1. When they have finished, select students to share their responses and then clarify any difficult concepts.

INSTRUCT

LE CHÂTELIER'S PRINCIPLE

For a video about Le Châtelier's principle, visit TeacherToolsOnline.com. Under Additional Resources, click on Chapter 17 Web Links. Then click on *Le Châtelier's Principle.*

STRESSES THAT INFLUENCE EQUILIBRIUM

Direct students to create a **graphic organizer** for the various stresses that affect a reaction's equilibrium. They may choose to do a concept map or a chart with four boxes (one for each stress covered in Section 17.2). For each stress they come across while reading the section, have them include the effect that it has on the equilibrium along with an example.

Henri Le Châtelier

QUESTIONS

» How do different kinds of stresses affect chemical reactions?

» Can I predict how a chemical reaction will shift in response to a stress?

TERMS

Le Châtelier's principle

How can I produce more product without adding more of the reactants?

17.2 LE CHÂTELIER'S PRINCIPLE

We have discussed how the concentrations of reactants and products change before they reach dynamic equilibrium. But we've also mentioned that conditions can impact the equilibrium position. How can concentrations be changed once equilibrium has been reached? Is it possible to shift an equilibrium from favoring one side of an equation to favoring the other?

In 1884, a French chemist named Henri Le Châtelier questioned how chemical systems in equilibrium would react if the conditions were changed. His findings, called **Le Châtelier's principle** in his honor, state that when a stress is placed on a reversible process, it will proceed in the direction that relieves the stress. We can put stress on a chemical system in equilibrium by changing the substance concentration, pressure, or temperature. Let's examine how each of these stresses influence equilibrium reactions.

The Effect of Concentration

Look back at Table 17-1 on page 411. What do you think would happen if the initial concentrations of H_2 and I_2 were doubled? More HI would be present at equilibrium. What would happen if HI were present initially? The reverse reaction would produce some H_2 and I_2. Changes in concentration definitely affect chemical equilibria, though not the value of K_{eq}. Consider the following equation for a reaction in equilibrium.

$$2SO_2(g) + O_2(g) \rightleftharpoons 2SO_3(g)$$

At one set of conditions, the K_{eq} has been measured to be 0.029.

$$K_{eq} = \frac{[SO_3]^2}{[SO_2]^2[O_2]} = 0.029$$

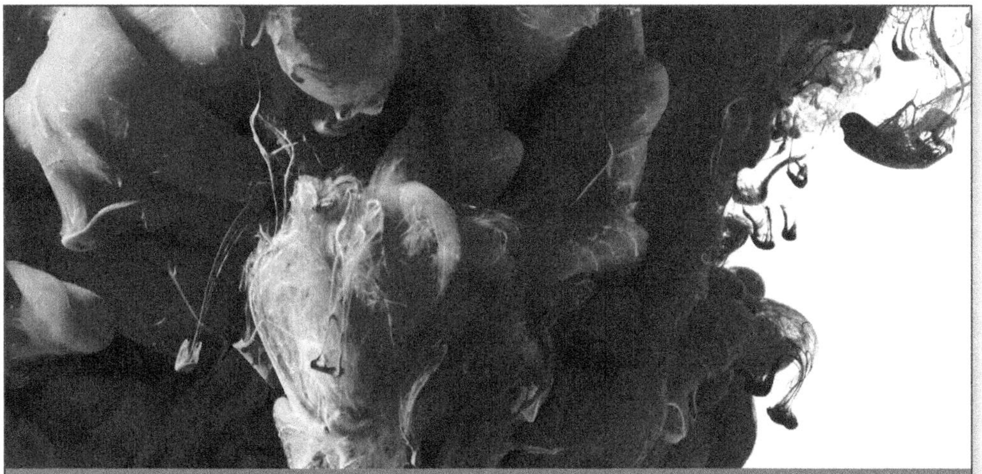

Suppose that more of the reactant sulfur dioxide were added to the container. You learned in Chapter 14 that increasing the concentration of a substance increases the rate of the reaction involving it because there are more collisions per unit of time. Thus, the system would be temporarily disturbed from equilibrium. Le Châtelier's principle predicts that the forward reaction would increase in order to reduce the extra sulfur dioxide—to reduce the stress of the additional sulfur dioxide. This reaction would not only increase the concentration of sulfur trioxide but also decrease the concentration of oxygen because it will have to react with the sulfur dioxide to form more sulfur trioxide. Despite all the changes, the equilibrium constant would remain unchanged once the rates again became equal. In other words, after adding the additional sulfur dioxide, the system would establish a new equilibrium position, again with a K_{eq} of 0.029.

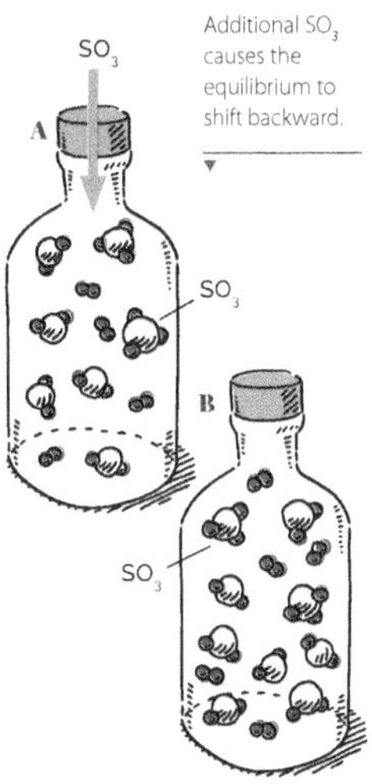

If sulfur trioxide were added, the rate of the reverse reaction would increase; the effect would appear to be the consumption of some of the added substance because of it being converted to sulfur dioxide and oxygen. If some sulfur trioxide were removed, the reverse reaction involving it would decrease; in effect, the forward reaction would work to restore some of the lost amount because it would have a greater rate. Of course, the concentrations of sulfur dioxide and oxygen would decrease when the forward reaction predominated. This action would keep the value of the equilibrium constant the same once equilibrium was reestablished.

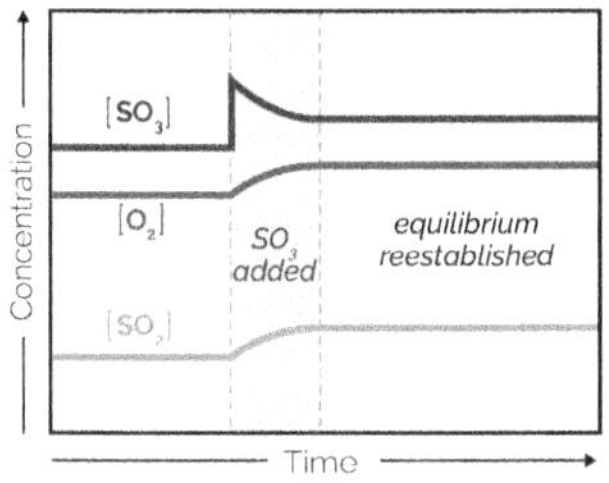

Remember that the concentrations of solids and liquids do not affect the K_{eq}, which means that adding or removing substances in those states will not place a stress on the system.

K_{eq} IS CONSTANT

Lead a quick **assessment** to check for students' understanding. Put the equilibrium constant value below on the board. Have students evaluate what will happen to the concentrations of SO_2 and O_2 if SO_3 is changed.

$$K_{eq} = \frac{[SO_3]^2}{[SO_2]^2[O_2]} = 0.029$$

(The concentrations of SO_2 and O_2 will adjust so that the K_{eq} still equals 0.029.)

Remind students that changing the concentration of reactants and products does not change the K_{eq}.

Explain that the same is true of pressure. Changing the pressure alone will not change the K_{eq}. Products and reactants will form to account for pressure changes and maintain the equilibrium, thus maintaining the K_{eq}.

DEMONSTRATING REVERSIBLE COLOR

Demonstrate Le Châtelier's principle by using the change in color between two solutions.

Materials: 100 mL graduated cylinder; 12 M HCl; water; Erlenmeyer flask; nickel(II) nitrate, $Ni(NO_3)_2$; 6 M ammonium hydroxide (NH_4OH)

Note: Since ammonia is produced, perform all parts of this demonstration in a fume hood or outside. Nickel(II) nitrate is toxic, and hydrochloric acid and ammonium hydroxide will burn skin. Gloves and goggles should be worn.

Preparation: In the graduated cylinder, add 0.9 mL of concentrated HCl (12 M) to 99.1 mL of water to prepare a 0.1 M HCl solution. Transfer this solution to the Erlenmeyer flask. Slowly add 1.83 g of nickel(II) nitrate to the 0.1 M HCl in the flask.

After you carefully rinse the graduated cylinder, prepare 100 mL of 6 M ammonium hydroxide solution by slowly adding 21.0 g of NH_4OH to 50 mL of water, dissolving it and bringing the final volume to 100 mL.

Performance/Discussion: While stirring the flask containing the green 0.1 M $Ni(NO_3)_2$ solution in 0.1 M HCl, slowly add ammonium hydroxide until the color turns blue. Add HCl until the color returns to green. The color change can be repeated.

Conclusion: Ask students what happened when ammonium hydroxide was added. *[The forward reaction was favored, producing the blue $Ni(NH_3)_6^{2+}$ ion.]* What happened when acid was added? *[The acid reduced the concentration of ammonia, favoring the reverse reaction and turning the mixture green again.]*

Aqueous nickel nitrate is green and will turn blue when an ammonium hydroxide solution (ammonia) is added. The solution will turn back to green when hydrochloric acid is added.

Cleanup: Check local regulations concerning the disposal of nickel solutions.

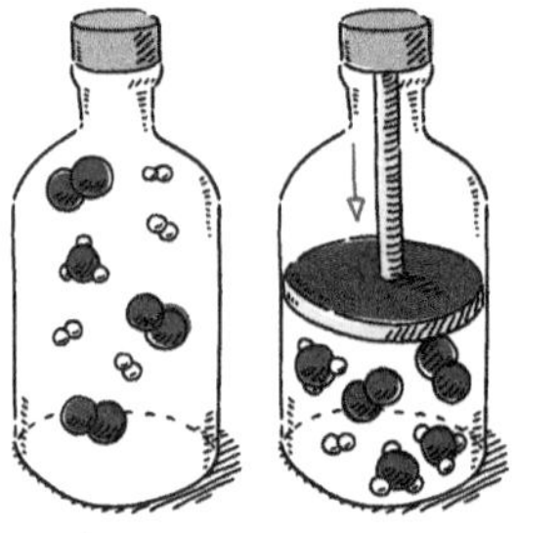

Another example: In the equation $N_2 + 3H_2 \rightleftharpoons 2NH_3$, additional pressure shifts the equilibrium forward.

The Effect of Pressure

Equilibrium reactions involving solids, liquids, and aqueous solutions are not significantly affected by a change in pressure because their particles are held more tightly, but reactions involving gases may be affected by such changes. Recall that 1 mol of any gaseous substance occupies 22.4 L at STP. In the equation

$$2SO_2(g) + O_2(g) \rightleftharpoons 2SO_3(g),$$

2 mol of sulfur trioxide are produced for every 3 mol of gaseous reactants. Since there are fewer gas molecules in the product than in the reactants, the forward reaction decreases the pressure.

But the value of K_{eq} for a reaction cannot be affected by changes in pressure alone. Suppose that the volume of a container was reduced, increasing the pressure inside it. This has the effect of increasing the *concentrations* of all the gases; thus, we can use Le Châtelier's principle to predict the effect. The reaction involving the larger number of molecules—the one whose concentrations are affected more—will increase more than the one with fewer, and the reaction will shift in the direction that produces fewer molecules. In this case, the forward reaction increases because it will reduce the total number of particles and thus counteract the increase in pressure. On the other hand, if the pressure on the reaction at equilibrium were decreased, the opposite would be true. The reverse reaction would have a greater rate and would act to fill the void—more sulfur dioxide and oxygen would be produced. In either case, the changes in reaction rates work to keep K_{eq} for the reaction constant.

Some gaseous reactions are not affected by pressure changes because there are equal numbers of gas particles in the reactants and products. For example, the reaction

$$H_2(g) + I_2(g) \rightleftharpoons 2HI(g)$$

has 2 mol of gas in the products for every 2 mol of gas in the reactants. The pressure of the entire system does not change with either the forward or the reverse reaction. Increased or reduced pressure on this equilibrium will not affect the direction of the reaction. Any reaction that has the same number of moles of *gas* product as it has *gas* reactant will be unaffected by pressure changes that result from volume changes.

EXAMPLE 17-4: PREDICTING THE EFFECT OF PRESSURE

To produce more carbon dioxide in the following reaction, should you increase or decrease the pressure? Explain.

$$O_2(g) + 2CO(g) \rightleftharpoons 2CO_2(g)$$

Solution

The balanced equation shows that 3 mol of gaseous reactants combine to form 2 mol of gaseous products. High pressure causes the reaction that produces the smallest volume to predominate. Thus, increasing the pressure will produce more carbon dioxide gas.

418 Chapter 17

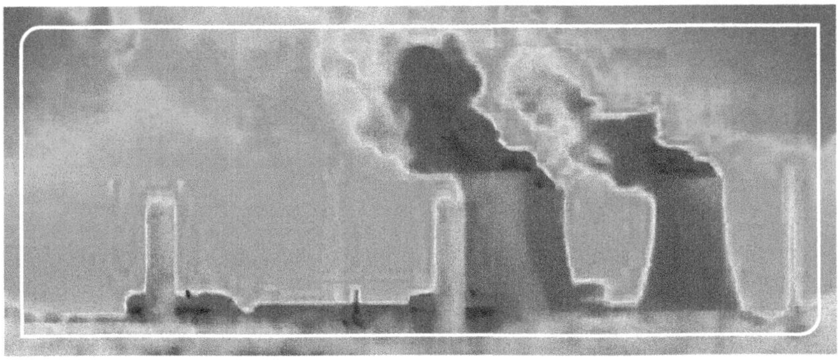

The Effect of Temperature

Recall that the equilibrium constant is a constant at a particular temperature. Therefore, temperature changes *do* change the value of K_{eq}. This is because thermal energy may be thought of as a reactant or product in chemical reactions. The exothermic reaction between sulfur dioxide and oxygen produces sulfur trioxide and thermal energy.

$$2SO_2(g) + O_2(g) \rightleftharpoons 2SO_3(g) + heat$$

If the temperature of this system is increased by adding thermal energy, the reaction will shift to the left, increasing the concentration of the reactants. Since the reactants are in the denominator, the K_{eq} value will decrease.

What would happen if you were to cool the system? If you think that the reaction would shift to the right, you are correct. This would produce more product, and since products are in the numerator of the equilibrium constant, the K_{eq} value would increase.

Le Châtelier's principle predicts how temperature affects each of these equilibria. Since thermal energy acts as a reactant in an endothermic reaction, increasing the temperature favors the forward reaction. The equilibrium of hydrogen, iodine, and hydrogen iodide—

$$H_2(g) + I_2(g) + heat \rightleftharpoons 2HI(g)$$

—will shift to produce more hydrogen iodide if heat is added to the reaction.

Additional heat shifts the equilibrium to the left in the equation $N_2(g) + 3H_2(g) \rightleftharpoons 2NH_3(g) + heat$.

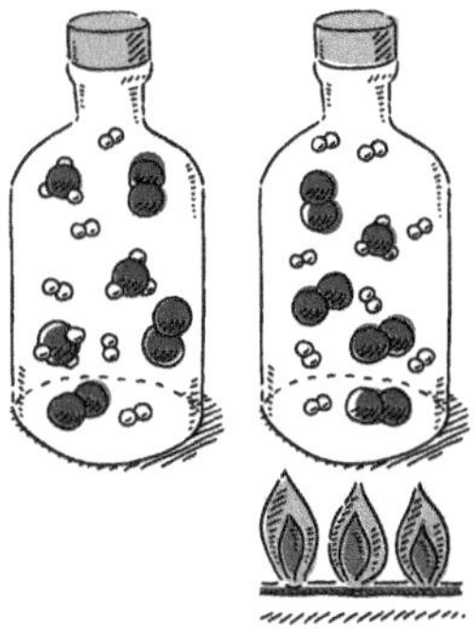

EXAMPLE 17-5:
PREDICTING THE EFFECT OF TEMPERATURE

The formation of ammonia is exothermic. Which reaction will be favored by increasing the temperature? What is the effect on the value of K_{eq}?

$$N_2(g) + 3H_2(g) \rightleftharpoons 2NH_3(g) + heat$$

Solution

Since thermal energy can be considered a product, additional heat encourages the reverse reaction and hinders the forward reaction. The value of K_{eq} decreases.

Chemical Equilibrium 419

THE CATALYST EFFECT

Stress that a catalyst is neither a reactant nor a product—it affects only the rate at which the reaction occurs. That is why a catalyst cannot change the value of K_{eq}.

EFFECTS OF STRESS ON EQUILIBRIUM CONCENTRATIONS AND K_{eq}

Direct students to create a **story** to recall the information in Table 17-2. Have them use each stress, shift, effect, and value of K_{eq} to compose a creative story. If helpful, they could bold the important words in their story and illustrate each.

Example: One day, Mr. **Catalyst** could **not shift** in his car. But this had **no effect** on his **reaction** or $\boldsymbol{K_{eq}}$. On the other hand, when Mr. **Concentration's reactants** were **increased**, his car **shifted forward and to the right**. This caused **more products** to form. Thankfully there was **not** a change in his $\boldsymbol{K_{eq}}$.

The Effect of Catalysts

As discussed in Chapter 16, catalysts are substances that change the rate of a reaction without undergoing any permanent change themselves. Since catalysts affect the rate of reaction, many people think that adding more catalyst will change the equilibrium position. However, a catalyst affects both the forward and reverse reactions, causing equilibrium to be reached sooner than if no catalyst were added. And though it causes equilibrium to be reached more quickly, the addition of a catalyst has no effect on either equilibrium concentrations or the value of K_{eq}.

Table 17-2 summarizes the effects on equilibrium reactions and K_{eq} by the addition of catalysts and by changes in concentration, pressure, and temperature.

Table 17-2
Effects of Stress on Equilibrium Concentrations and K_{eq}

Stress	Shift	Effect	Value of K_{eq}
add catalyst	none	none	no change
Increase Concentration			
of reactant	forward/toward right	more products form	no change
of product	reverse/ toward left	more reactants form	no change
Decrease Concentration			
of reactant	reverse/toward left	more reactants form	no change
of product	forward/toward right	more products form	no change
Change Pressure			
increase	toward side with fewer moles of gas		no change
decrease	toward side with more moles of gas		no change
Increase Temperature			
exothermic	reverse/toward left	more reactants form	decreases
endothermic	forward/toward right	more products form	increases
Decrease Temperature			
exothermic	forward/toward right	more products form	increases
endothermic	reverse/toward left	more reactants form	decreases

420 Chapter 17

The Haber Process

Huge quantities of ammonia (NH_3) are used every year in fertilizers, cleaning compounds, and explosives. Until World War I, industrial countries obtained nitrogen by importing saltpeter mined from Chilean *caliche* (a mineral partly composed of KNO_3 and $NaNO_3$). All countries had access to nitrogen (N_2) in the atmosphere, but no one knew how to liberate the atoms from the stable molecules. As an alternative to the expense of importing saltpeter, countries sought to form ammonia from atmospheric nitrogen.

Finding the appropriate reaction was no problem. The reaction

$$N_2(g) + 3H_2(g) \rightleftharpoons 2NH_3(g) + \textit{heat}$$

seemed perfect. The relatively large equilibrium constant of this reaction (6.4×10^2 at 25 °C) indicated that the production of ammonia was the favored direction of the reaction. The problem was that nitrogen, hydrogen, and ammonia took a very long time to reach equilibrium. In 1909, Fritz Haber found a way to manipulate the conditions to overcome this difficulty. Today the Haber process provides ammonia for use in numerous industries.

The Haber process uses the following technique. Because 2 mol of gas are formed from 4 mol of gas, the products take up less space than the reactants. Le Châtelier's principle predicts that high pressures favor the production of ammonia. Because the forward reaction is exothermic, it proceeds best at low temperatures. Thus, engineers needed a process that used high pressure and low temperatures to make ammonia manufacturing easier.

Fritz Haber

In the Haber process, the reaction takes place under high pressures, at high temperatures, and with a catalyst. However, high temperatures significantly shift the equilibrium away from the formation of ammonia (at 500 °C, $K_{eq} = 1.5 \times 10^{-5}$). To compensate, the Haber process manipulates other variables to increase the production of ammonia. A catalyst (mostly Fe_3O_4 with traces of K_2O and Al_2O_3) helps to speed up the reaction. To further increase the yield, ammonia is removed by liquefaction as it forms. This continual removal keeps the forward reaction going.

HOW IT *WORKS*

A schematic of the ammonia synthesis loop of the Haber process

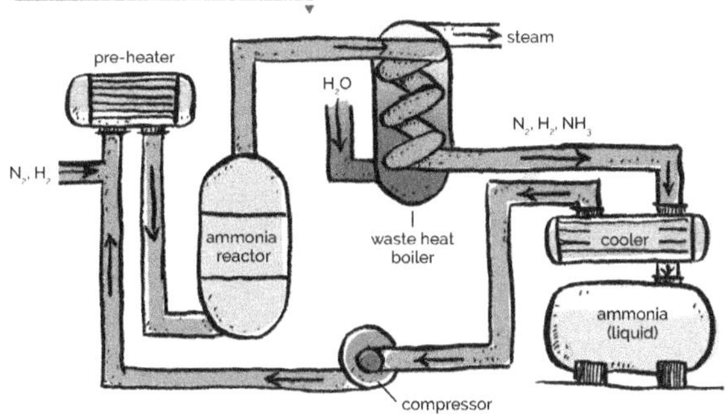

WATCHING THE HABER PROCESS

For a video that describes the Haber process, visit TeacherToolsOnline.com. Under Additional Resources, click on Chapter 17 Web Links. Then click on *The Haber Process*.

DIFFERENTIATED INSTRUCTION

The Haber Process Website

Lead students to **build a website** on the pros and cons of using the Haber process to produce fertilizer. In groups of two, have them use a free website generator such as Weebly, Google Sites, or Microsoft Sites to record their information. Before they begin creating their websites, give them some time to research the Haber process. In their websites, they will need to include photos, to list the pros and cons of the Haber process, and to state alternatives to the Haber process that would quickly and safely add nitrogen to soil.

WORLDVIEW INVESTIGATION: ETHANOL

Appendix K includes a reproducible rubric to assess the worldview investigation activity.

WORLDVIEW INVESTIGATION ANSWERS

Yes. Scientists should find ways to use ethanol. They need to use this God-given resource in ways that are wise and obedient to His commands.

If a form of ethanol, such as an alcoholic beverage, will hurt a Christian's testimony, harm his body, or allow his mind to be controlled by anything other than the Holy Spirit, he should not use it. A Christian should depend on and find his fulfillment in Christ, not in alcohol (Eph. 5:15–21; 1 Cor. 6:19–20).

God's Word should be the guide that determines ethical applications of all science, including the fermentation process.

Ethanol can be wisely used as a fuel, a medicine, or a preservative. These uses help others and thereby help us to fulfill the Creation Mandate and bring glory to God.

Equilibria and Industry

Chemical industries supply society with such diverse products as medicines, pesticides, fertilizers, paints, textiles, detergents, cosmetics, plastics, fuels, and building materials. Because the reactions used to make those products are usually reversible, the laws of equilibrium chemistry govern the processes. Methods of describing and controlling equilibria become indispensable tools in the fast, efficient, and economical production of consumer goods. The industrial production of esters illustrates this.

The characteristic flavors and odors of fruits are the results of naturally occurring compounds called *esters*. These compounds are parts of foods (left), cosmetics, and medicines. Because it is inefficient and expensive to extract esters from fruit, manufacturers of flavorings form esters artificially by reacting alcohols and organic acids.

$$\text{alcohol} + \text{organic acid} \rightleftharpoons \text{ester} + \text{water}$$

WORLDVIEW INVESTIGATION

ETHANOL

Introduction

Ethanol is an alcohol that forms naturally from the fermentation of the glucose found in fruits, vegetables, and grains. During this process, yeast breaks down glucose to form ethanol and carbon dioxide.

$$C_6H_{12}O_6 \rightleftharpoons 2C_2H_5OH + 2CO_2$$

Several factors, such as the presence of oxygen, affect the speed, progress, and direction of the reaction. This is the same process that makes bread rise. The ethanol in bread dough is decomposed by the high heat of baking, but of course the ethanol in fermented beverages is still there when they are consumed. Once in the body, ethanol has an effect on the equilibrium of the body's chemical processes.

But the modern use of ethanol isn't limited to beverages. Ethanol is used in industry for feedstock, antiseptics, paints, and personal care products like deodorant and shampoo. Ethanol is also used as a vehicle fuel. So are ethanol and the chemical processes used to make it good or evil?

Task

A chemical company plans to open a new ethanol plant in your town. Is this something that you as a Christian can or should support? Formulate a position paper on the new plant. You can kick-start your research by thinking about and answering the following questions.

Should scientists continue to find new ways to use ethanol?

Should a Christian use ethanol?

What should determine how a chemical process like fermentation is used?

How can we use the chemistry of ethanol for God's glory?

Procedure

1. Plan your position paper on the basis of your research. Cite any sources you used and note whether they display any evidence of a particular worldview regarding the topic.
2. Write your position paper and show it to another person for evaluation. Make any suggested revisions, if necessary.
3. Present your position paper to your class or family.

Conclusion

The question of whether to use a particular advancement of science is sometimes cut-and-dried for a Christian—but not always. Many times, the discoveries and products of scientific inquiry have both beneficial and detrimental applications. Christians must always be willing to be led by the Spirit and ready to apply biblical principles to questions regarding the usage of new technologies.

The general reaction works well, but it is very easily reversed. Neither the forward nor the reverse reaction dominates. Thus, efficient production of esters is difficult. Instead of going to completion, the reaction converts only a part of the reactants into the products. Rather than accept limited yields, manufacturers produce more ester per batch of reactants by forcing the forward reaction to prevail.

Manufacturers can shift the equilibrium by continually adding a reactant, removing a product, or both. If either the acid or the alcohol is inexpensive, huge quantities can be added to drive the equilibrium forward. Sometimes manufacturers can easily remove a product by boiling it off as it forms. Regardless of the technique that is used, ester production is increased.

Worldview Conflict and Equilibrium

Haber's use of equilibrium chemistry to efficiently produce ammonia on a large scale was perhaps the most significant scientific breakthrough of his century. It created a boom in agriculture and made food more plentiful and affordable. Haber's work is an example of using the earth's resources to help God's image bearers.

But as we saw with the work of Alfred Nobel in Chapter 10, chemistry can be a key to unlocking potential for both good *and* evil. The same ammonia-making process that served worldwide agriculture was also used to help create German munitions during World War I. Haber's work as director of the Kaiser Wilhelm Institute of Physical Chemistry and Electrochemistry in Berlin was also instrumental in developing gas warfare. He personally supervised the first use of poison gas at Ypres, Belgium, in 1915.

So how do we know whether we should turn the key of chemistry to unlock its potential? How can we judge whether it will bring good or evil? Chemistry itself is not the answer. Scripture gives us a moral compass and a worldview to see these issues as God sees them. We must apply the power of God's Word to the tool of science for His glory and mankind's greatest good.

▲ A soldier wearing a gas mask in World War I

17.2 SECTION REVIEW

1. Give a definition of Le Châtelier's principle in your own words.
2. Summarize how changes to the concentration of chemical substances affect a system in equilibrium.
3. Explain why changing the temperature of a system in equilibrium also changes the K_{eq} value.
4. Consider the following exothermic reaction at equilibrium.

$$CO_2(g) + 4H_2(g) \rightleftharpoons CH_4(g) + 2H_2O(g)$$

   a. What is the effect of removing some of the CH_4? Explain.
   b. What is the effect of increasing the pressure? Explain.
   c. What is the effect of increasing the temperature? Explain.
5. Predict the shift in equilibrium (to the right or to the left) under the following conditions for the following reaction.

$$CaF_2(s) \rightleftharpoons Ca^{2+}(aq) + 2F^-(aq) \quad \Delta H < 0$$

   a. CaF_2 solid is added.
   b. Ca^{2+} aqueous ions are added.
   c. F^- aqueous ions are removed.
   d. Temperature is increased.
6. How can the chemical manufacturing industry utilize Le Châtelier's principle?

APPLY

LAB 17A: *STRESSED OUT*

Once students have an understanding of the material in Section 17.2, they should be ready to work through Lab 17A.

ASSESS

TICKET OUT THE DOOR

As a **summarizing activity**, ask students to choose one stress and explain its effects on a reaction's equilibrium concentrations and K_{eq}. See Table 17-2 on page 420.

17.2 REVIEW *ANSWERS*

1. Answers will vary. *Example:* If a reversible chemical reaction is stressed, it will move in the direction that relieves the applied stress. *(p. 416)*

2. If the concentration of an aqueous or gaseous substance in a reaction vessel at equilibrium is increased, the equilibrium position will shift away from the side on which the concentration was increased. If it is decreased, the equilibrium position will shift toward the side on which the concentration was decreased. *(pp. 416–17)*

3. Temperature is changed by adding or removing thermal energy from a system. Chemical reactions are endothermic or exothermic, which means that thermal energy can be considered a reactant or a product. Changing the temperature is like changing the concentration and will shift the equilibrium position. Since thermal energy is not part of the K_{eq} equation, the changed equilibrium position causes a change in the K_{eq} value. *(p. 419)*

4. a. Removing CH_4 will shift the equilibrium position to the right (toward the products). This will produce more products and use additional reactants to reestablish equilibrium at the K_{eq} value.

b. Increasing the pressure will shift the equilibrium position to the right because this will result in fewer gas particles in the reaction vessel, reducing some of the added pressure.

c. Increasing the temperature is accomplished by adding thermal energy. Since the reaction is exothermic, adding thermal energy is like adding more product. The equilibrium position will shift to the left (reactants), which will use some of the added energy. This will result in more reactants and less products, decreasing the K_{eq} value. *(all pp. 416–20)*

5. a. no change; CaF_2 is a solid and does not appear in the equilibrium expression.

b. shift to the left

c. shift to the right

d. shift to the left *(all pp. 416–20)*

6. Industries can use Le Châtelier's principle to maximize the yield in chemical reactions. They can manipulate pressure, temperature, and concentration to drive a reaction toward the formation of a desired substance. *(p. 416)*

SECTION 17.3 *OVERVIEW*

Essential Question

Is it possible to calculate how much of a substance will dissolve?

Objectives

- » **17.3.1** Relate the solubility of a salt to its solubility product.
- » **17.3.2** Convert between solubilities and solubility products of solutes.
- » **17.3.3** Predict whether a precipitate will form when two solutions are mixed when given the solubility product.

Resources

Web Link: Solution Equilibrium

Lab 17B: *Precipitous Changes*—Exploring Solubility Products

ENGAGE

SOLUTION EQUILIBRIUM

Use a **virtual simulation** to analyze a solution's equilibrium. Visit TeacherToolsOnline.com. Under Chapter 17 Additional Resources, click on *Salts and Solubility*.

Allow students the opportunity to explore the effects of concentration on a solution. Have them analyze the reactions and record what happens when the number of ions within the solution increases and decreases.

INSTRUCT

KEEPING THE *K*s STRAIGHT

Remind students to keep K_{eq} (equilibrium constant) and K_{sp} (solubility product constant) separate in their minds—K_{sp} is a kind of K_{eq} that deals specifically with ions and salts.

17.3 SOLUTION EQUILIBRIUM

QUESTIONS

- » What does a solubility product constant tell us about the solubility of a substance?
- » Can I predict whether a mixture of two solutions will produce a precipitate?

TERMS

solubility product constant • common-ion effect

Is it possible to calculate how much of a substance will dissolve?

barium sulfate

Ionic Equilibria

Saturated solutions are a system of undissolved solids and dissolved ions in equilibrium. Some salts, such as calcium sulfate, are slightly soluble.

$$CaSO_4(s) \rightleftharpoons Ca^{2+}(aq) + SO_4^{2-}(aq)$$

Others, such as iron(III) hydroxide, dissolve so little that for all practical purposes they are insoluble.

The forward process is the dissolving process, and the reverse process is precipitation. As with all equilibria, the rate of the forward process matches the rate of the reverse process at equilibrium. Since this process is at equilibrium, the relative amounts of dissolved ions and undissolved solids can be expressed with equilibrium constants. The equilibrium constant for dissolving of $Pb_3(PO_4)_2$ is expressed as

$$K_{eq} = [Pb^{2+}]^3[PO_4^{3-}]^2.$$

As in other equilibrium expressions, solids are not included; thus, the $[Pb_3(PO_4)_2]$ is omitted in the expression of the equilibrium constant. The resulting equilibrium constant for dissolving a solute into a saturated solution is called the **solubility product constant** (K_{sp}). The equilibrium concentrations of the ions are raised to the appropriate powers as in other equilibrium constant expressions.

Solubility and Equilibria

The K_{sp} constant quantifies salt solubilities. Large numbers of ions in solution will cause the solubility product to be relatively large (much greater than 1), and the material is considered soluble. Insoluble materials will produce small numbers of ions in solution, causing the K_{sp} to be small (less than 1). Thus, the larger its K_{sp} is, the more soluble is the salt. Conversely, the smaller the value for K_{sp}, the less soluble the salt is. The K_{sp} of some slightly soluble salts are listed in Table 17-3 (p. 426).

K_{sp} values can be determined from measured solubilities. For example, barium sulfate has a solubility of 1.1×10^{-5} M. When barium sulfate dissolves, each formula unit releases one Ba^{2+} ion and one SO_4^{2-} ion.

$$1.1 \times 10^{-5} \text{ mol } BaSO_4(s) \rightleftharpoons 1.1 \times 10^{-5} \text{ mol } Ba^{2+}(aq) + 1.1 \times 10^{-5} \text{ mol } SO_4^{2-}(aq)$$

$$\begin{aligned} K_{sp} &= [Ba^{2+}][SO_4^{2-}] \\ &= (1.1 \times 10^{-5})(1.1 \times 10^{-5}) \\ &= 1.2 \times 10^{-10} \end{aligned}$$

424 Chapter 17

The K_{sp} of a substance can be used to determine the solubility in moles per liter. The K_{sp} of lead(II) phosphate is known to be 1.5×10^{-32}. The equations for its dissociation and solubility product constant can be written as follows.

$$Pb_3(PO_4)_2(s) \rightleftharpoons 3Pb^{2+}(aq) + 2PO_4^{3-}(aq)$$

$$K_{sp} = [Pb^{2+}]^3[PO_4^{3-}]^2$$

$$K_{sp} = [Pb^{2+}]^3[PO_4^{3-}]^2$$

Notice that when 1 mol of lead(II) phosphate dissolves, 3 mol of Pb^{2+} ions and 2 mol of PO_4^{3-} ions are released. The number of Pb^{2+} ions in a saturated solution must be three times the amount of $Pb_3(PO_4)_2$ units that were dissolved. Likewise, there must be twice as many PO_4^{3-} ions as the number of dissolved formula units. Suppose that S stands for the solubility of the salt, in this case $Pb_3(PO_4)_2$. The concentration of Pb^{2+} ions can be expressed as $3S$, and the concentration of PO_4^{3-} ions can be expressed as $2S$. The solubility product constant can now be expressed in terms of the solubility of the salt.

$$K_{sp} = (3S)^3(2S)^2$$

To find the solubility of the salt, we can substitute the value of K_{sp} and solve for S.

$$\begin{aligned} 1.5 \times 10^{-32} &= (3S)^3(2S)^2 \\ 1.5 \times 10^{-32} &= (27S^3)(4S^2) \\ \frac{1.5 \times 10^{-32}}{108} &= \frac{108S^5}{108} \\ \sqrt[5]{1.3888 \times 10^{-34}} &= \sqrt[5]{S^5} \\ S &= 1.7 \times 10^{-7} \end{aligned}$$

The solubility of lead(II) phosphate is 1.7×10^{-7} mol/L. This amount is so small that the salt is considered insoluble.

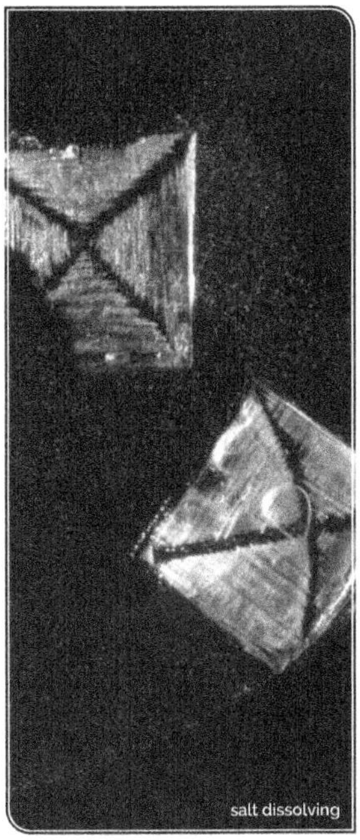

salt dissolving

EXAMPLE 17-6: DETERMINING SOLUBILITY PRODUCT CONSTANT

Given that the solubility of copper(II) hydroxide is 1.76×10^{-7} M, what is the K_{sp}?

Write what you know.

$$Cu(OH)_2(s) \rightleftharpoons Cu^{2+}(aq) + 2OH^-(aq)$$

Every mole of $Cu(OH)_2$ yields 1 mol of Cu^{2+} and 2 mol of OH^-

Solubility $Cu(OH)2 = S = 1.76 \times 10^{-7}$ mol/L

$K_{sp} = ?$

Write the formula and solve for the unknown.

$$K_{sp} = [Cu^{2+}][OH^-]^2$$

Plug in known values and evaluate.

$$\begin{aligned} K_{sp} &= (S)(2S)^2 \\ &= (1.76 \times 10^{-7})[(2)(1.76 \times 10^{-7})]^2 \\ &= (1.76 \times 10^{-7})(3.52 \times 10^{-7})^2 \\ &= (1.76 \times 10^{-7})(1.239\,04 \times 10^{-13}) \\ &= 2.18 \times 10^{-20} \end{aligned}$$

The solubility product constant is 2.18×10^{-20}.

FINDING A FIFTH ROOT

Students using TI-83 or TI-84 Plus calculators can find the fifth root by using the following method. Enter "5" and then press the "Math" key. Then scroll down to "5: x√" and press "Enter" (or simply press "5"). Enter the number, and press "Enter" to get the answer.

DIFFERENT VALUES

You may find different solubility and K_{sp} values in other sources. Solubilities are based on measurements, and K_{sp} values are derived from those measurements, so the numbers may vary depending on the method of measurement.

EXAMPLE 17-7: DETERMINING SOLUBILITY

Given that the K_{sp} of silver chloride is 1.8×10^{-10}, determine its solubility.

Write what you know.

$AgCl(s) \rightleftharpoons Ag^+(aq) + Cl^-(aq)$
$K_{sp} = 1.8 \times 10^{-10}$
$[Ag^+] = [Cl^-] = [AgCl]$
$[AgCl] = ?$

Write the formula and solve for the unknown.

$K_{sp} = [Ag^+][Cl^-]$
$K_{sp} = [AgCl][AgCl]$
$\sqrt{K_{sp}} = \sqrt{[AgCl]^2}$
$[AgCl] = \sqrt{K_{sp}}$

Plug in known values and evaluate.

$[AgCl] = \sqrt{1.8 \times 10^{-10}}$
$= 1.3 \times 10^{-5}$

The solubility of silver chloride is 1.3×10^{-5} mol/L.

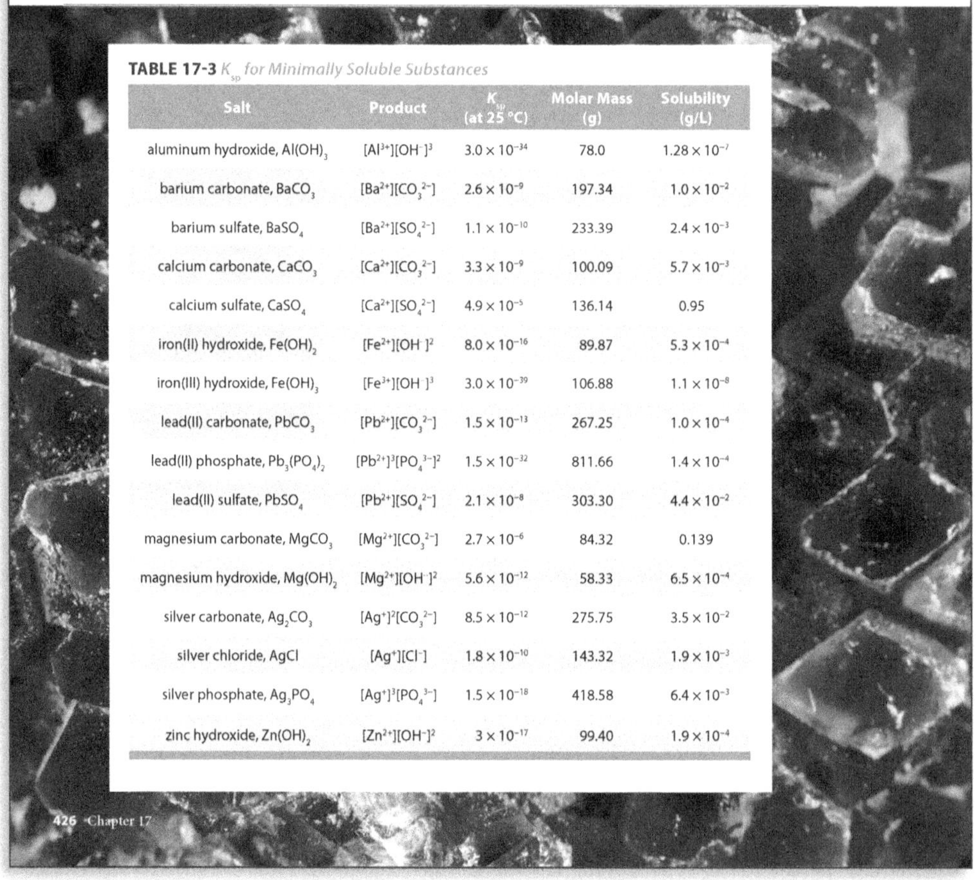

TABLE 17-3 *K_{sp} for Minimally Soluble Substances*

Salt	Product	K_{sp} (at 25 °C)	Molar Mass (g)	Solubility (g/L)
aluminum hydroxide, $Al(OH)_3$	$[Al^{3+}][OH^-]^3$	3.0×10^{-34}	78.0	1.28×10^{-7}
barium carbonate, $BaCO_3$	$[Ba^{2+}][CO_3^{2-}]$	2.6×10^{-9}	197.34	1.0×10^{-2}
barium sulfate, $BaSO_4$	$[Ba^{2+}][SO_4^{2-}]$	1.1×10^{-10}	233.39	2.4×10^{-3}
calcium carbonate, $CaCO_3$	$[Ca^{2+}][CO_3^{2-}]$	3.3×10^{-9}	100.09	5.7×10^{-3}
calcium sulfate, $CaSO_4$	$[Ca^{2+}][SO_4^{2-}]$	4.9×10^{-5}	136.14	0.95
iron(II) hydroxide, $Fe(OH)_2$	$[Fe^{2+}][OH^-]^2$	8.0×10^{-16}	89.87	5.3×10^{-4}
iron(III) hydroxide, $Fe(OH)_3$	$[Fe^{3+}][OH^-]^3$	3.0×10^{-39}	106.88	1.1×10^{-8}
lead(II) carbonate, $PbCO_3$	$[Pb^{2+}][CO_3^{2-}]$	1.5×10^{-13}	267.25	1.0×10^{-4}
lead(II) phosphate, $Pb_3(PO_4)_2$	$[Pb^{2+}]^3[PO_4^{3-}]^2$	1.5×10^{-32}	811.66	1.4×10^{-4}
lead(II) sulfate, $PbSO_4$	$[Pb^{2+}][SO_4^{2-}]$	2.1×10^{-8}	303.30	4.4×10^{-2}
magnesium carbonate, $MgCO_3$	$[Mg^{2+}][CO_3^{2-}]$	2.7×10^{-6}	84.32	0.139
magnesium hydroxide, $Mg(OH)_2$	$[Mg^{2+}][OH^-]^2$	5.6×10^{-12}	58.33	6.5×10^{-4}
silver carbonate, Ag_2CO_3	$[Ag^+]^2[CO_3^{2-}]$	8.5×10^{-12}	275.75	3.5×10^{-2}
silver chloride, AgCl	$[Ag^+][Cl^-]$	1.8×10^{-10}	143.32	1.9×10^{-3}
silver phosphate, Ag_3PO_4	$[Ag^+]^3[PO_4^{3-}]$	1.5×10^{-18}	418.58	6.4×10^{-3}
zinc hydroxide, $Zn(OH)_2$	$[Zn^{2+}][OH^-]^2$	3×10^{-17}	99.40	1.9×10^{-4}

426 Chapter 17

The K_{sp} can be used to see whether a solution is unsaturated, saturated, or supersaturated. If the product of ion concentrations equals the K_{sp}, the solution is saturated. If the product of ion concentrations is less than the K_{sp}, the solution is unsaturated. A product greater than the K_{sp} indicates a supersaturated solution. Another way to determine whether a solution is unsaturated, saturated, or supersaturated is to compare the solubility of the solute to the concentration of the solution. Be sure, however, to compare it to the concentration in mol/L, not in g/L.

EXAMPLE 17-8: DETERMINING SATURATION STATE

Calculate the product of the ion concentrations of a 2.5×10^{-6} M zinc hydroxide solution. Determine whether the solution is unsaturated, saturated, or supersaturated.

Write what you know.

$Zn(OH)_2(s) \rightleftharpoons Zn^{2+}(aq) + 2OH^-(aq)$
$[Zn(OH)_2] = 2.5 \times 10^{-6}$ M
$[Zn^{2+}] = [Zn(OH)_2] = 2.5 \times 10^{-6}$ M
$[OH^-] = 2[Zn(OH)_2] = 5.0 \times 10^{-6}$ M
$K_{sp} = 3 \times 10^{-17}$ from Table 17-3
$[Zn^{2+}][OH^-]^2 = ?$

Write the formula and solve for the unknown.

$[Zn^{2+}][OH^-]^2$

Plug in known values and evaluate.

$$(2.5 \times 10^{-6})(5.0 \times 10^{-6})^2 = (2.5 \times 10^{-6})(2.5 \times 10^{-11}) = 6.3 \times 10^{-17}$$

This product is greater than the K_{sp} of 3×10^{-17}, so the solution must be supersaturated.

Common-Ion Effect

Since salts dissociate when they dissolve, solutes that have a common ion can affect the equilibrium. For example, an unsaturated silver chloride solution has a concentration less than 1.33×10^{-5} M and an ion concentration product less than the K_{sp} of a saturated solution. What happens when sodium chloride is added to the silver chloride solution, since they both have a chloride ion in common?

Sodium chloride is very soluble. It dissolves and dissociates into sodium and chloride ions. Though the sodium ions have little or no effect on the original solution, the chloride ions do. The chloride ion is called the *common ion* because it is contained in both silver chloride and sodium chloride. The additional chloride ions from the sodium chloride cause the equilibrium to shift to the left in the reaction

$$AgCl(s) \rightleftharpoons Ag^+(aq) + Cl^-(aq).$$

In this example, AgCl is less soluble than NaCl. Adding NaCl shifts the reaction to produce more solid silver chloride. The increased concentration of chloride ions raises the ion concentration product above its K_{sp} value. The result of the **common-ion effect** is that the less soluble salt precipitates out of the solution until the K_{sp} value is reached. Remember that the K_{sp}, like any other equilibrium constant, is a particular value at a given temperature. If that value is exceeded, precipitation will occur to reestablish equilibrium conditions.

SOLUBILITY

Use the following **formative assessment** to check students' understanding.

1. What is the solubility product constant and what does it quantify? *(the equilibrium constant for dissolving a solute into a saturated solution; It quantifies salt solubilities.)*
2. If cadmium carbonate, $CdCO_3$, has a K_{sp} of 2.5×10^{-14}, what is its solubility (mol/L)?

What we know:

$CdCO_3(s) \rightleftharpoons Cd^{2+}(aq) + CO_3^{2-}(aq)$,
$K_{sp} = 2.5 \times 10^{-14}$, $[Cd^{2+}] = [CdCO_3]$,
$[CO_3^{2-}] = [CdCO_3]$

Unknown: $[CdCO_3]$

Write the formula and solve for the unknown.

$$K_{sp} = [Cd^{2+}][CO_3^{2-}]$$
$$K_{sp} = [CdCO_3][CdCO_3]$$
$$\sqrt{K_{sp}} = \sqrt{[CdCO_3]^2}$$
$$[CdCO_3] = \sqrt{K_{sp}}$$

Evaluate.

$$[CdCO_3] = \sqrt{2.5 \times 10^{-14}} = 1.6 \times 10^{-7}\ M$$

THE (SPEED) LIMIT OF K_{sp}

Use an **analogy** to help explain K_{sp}. The K_{sp} is the maximum concentration of substances that can be dissolved in a solution at a given temperature. This can be compared to a speed limit. If you increase your speed, then you will eventually be over the speed limit. At that point, you need to slow down. Similarly, if more substances are added to a solution, then the amount is over the K_{sp} limit and some must precipitate out.

SATURATED, UNSATURATED, OR SUPERSATURATED?

Direct students to write **Sketchnotes** for the following ways to determine whether a solution is saturated, unsaturated, or supersaturated.

If the product of ion concentrations is equal to the K_{sp}, the solution is *saturated.*

If the product of ion concentrations is less than the K_{sp}, the solution is *unsaturated.*

If the product of ion concentrations is greater than the K_{sp}, the solution is *supersaturated.*

PRECIPITATION REACTIONS

Lead a quick **review** of precipitation.

1. Precipitation is common with what type of reaction? *(a double-replacement reaction)*
2. What determines whether a reaction will form a precipitate? *(solubility)*

To clarify, use the following example. If compound *AB* is mixed with compound *CD*, compounds *AD* and *BC* will be formed in the reaction. Explain that if the ion concentration product of either of these new compounds exceeds their K_{sp} values, that compound will precipitate out until equilibrium is reached at the K_{sp}.

silver chloride precipitate

Precipitation Reactions

As we have seen, mixing two solutions can sometimes cause a precipitate to form. For instance, suppose that hydrochloric acid (HCl) and silver nitrate ($AgNO_3$) are mixed together. The resulting solution contains H^+, Cl^-, Ag^+, and NO_3^- ions. Hydrogen chloride and silver nitrate are quite soluble. But an alternate combination of ions, AgCl, is not. A silver chloride precipitate will form if enough silver and chloride ions are in the solution. How much is enough? That depends on the K_{sp} of silver chloride. If the value of $[Ag^+][Cl^-]$ in the solution exceeds the K_{sp} for silver chloride, a precipitate will form. How much precipitate will be deposited? Enough precipitate will form to lower the value of $[Ag^+][Cl^-]$ to the K_{sp} for silver chloride. Thus, the K_{sp} of a salt can be used to predict whether a precipitate will form and how much will form.

EXAMPLE 17-9: PREDICTING PRECIPITATION

Will a precipitate form when equal volumes of a 5.0×10^{-5} M barium nitrate solution and a 1.0×10^{-3} M sodium carbonate solution are mixed?

Write what you know.

Both barium nitrate and sodium carbonate are soluble salts. At this low concentration, they will both be completely dissolved. The first step is to calculate the theoretical concentration of each ion after both salts completely dissolve. Divide their molarities in half since the combined solution has twice the volume.

$$Ba(NO_3)_2(s) \longrightarrow Ba^{2+}(aq) + 2NO_3^-(aq)$$
$$[Ba^{2+}] = 5.0 \times 10^{-5}\ M/2 = 2.5 \times 10^{-5}\ M$$
$$[NO_3^-] = 2(5.0 \times 10^{-5}\ M)/2 = 5.0 \times 10^{-5}\ M$$

$$Na_2CO_3(s) \longrightarrow 2Na^+(aq) + CO_3^{2-}(aq)$$
$$[Na^+] = 2(1.0 \times 10^{-3}\ M)/2 = 1.0 \times 10^{-3}\ M$$
$$[CO_3^{2-}] = 1.0 \times 10^{-3}\ M/2 = 5.0 \times 10^{-4}\ M$$

Plug in known values and evaluate.

The next step is to check Table 17-3 to determine which combination of ions is most likely to precipitate. Both original combinations are very soluble, and so is sodium nitrate. Barium carbonate is the only salt formed by a combination of the ions in this solution that appears in Table 17-3 ($K_{sp} = 2.6 \times 10^{-9}$). The final step is to determine whether the value of $[Ba^{2+}][CO_3^{2-}]$ exceeds the given K_{sp}.

$$[Ba^{2+}][CO_3^{2-}] = (2.5 \times 10^{-5})(5.0 \times 10^{-4}) = 1.25 \times 10^{-8}$$

Since 1.25×10^{-8} is larger than the K_{sp} of 2.6×10^{-9}, a precipitate will form.

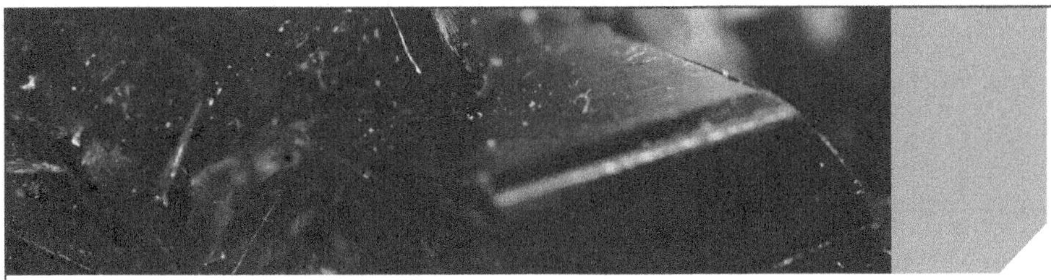

EXAMPLE 17-10: PREDICTING THE AMOUNT OF PRECIPITATE

In Example 17-9, a precipitate forms. If the total volume in the reaction vessel is 1.00 L, how many grams of barium carbonate will precipitate out of solution?

Write what you know.

$[Ba^{2+}] = 2.5 \times 10^{-5}$ M
$[CO_3^{2-}] = 5.0 \times 10^{-4}$ M
$K_{sp} = 2.6 \times 10^{-9}$

$Ba^{2+}(aq) + CO_3^{2-}(aq) \longrightarrow BaCO_3(s)$

Plug in known values and evaluate.

The ion concentrations must be reduced so that the ion concentration product equals the K_{sp}. Since one barium ion combines with one carbonate ion, each concentration will be reduced by the same amount (x).

$$[Ba^{2+}][CO_3^{2-}] = 2.6 \times 10^{-9}$$

$$(2.5 \times 10^{-5} - x)(5.0 \times 10^{-4} - x) = 2.6 \times 10^{-9}$$
$$1.25 \times 10^{-8} - 5.25 \times 10^{-4}x + x^2 - 2.6 \times 10^{-9} = 0$$
$$9.9 \times 10^{-9} - 5.25 \times 10^{-4}x + x^2 = 0$$

$$x = 5.05 \times 10^{-4} \text{ or } 1.95 \times 10^{-5}$$

Exclude the first solution because it is more than the starting amount.

Convert volume of solution to mass of precipitate.

$$1.00\ \cancel{L}\left(\frac{1.95 \times 10^{-5}\ \cancel{\text{mol BaCO}_3}}{1\ \cancel{L}}\right)\left(\frac{197.34\text{ g BaCO}_3}{1\ \cancel{\text{mol BaCO}_3}}\right)$$
$$= 3.85 \times 10^{-3}\text{ g BaCO}_3$$

Therefore, 3.85×10^{-3} g of $BaCO_3$ will precipitate.

17.3 SECTION REVIEW

1. Define *solubility product constant*.
2. The solubility of copper(I) chloride is 1.08×10^{-2} g per 100 mL of solution. Find the K_{sp} value.
3. What is the solubility of lithium phosphate in mol/L if its K_{sp} value is 3.48×10^{-9}?
4. An experimental solution has an ion concentration product of 2.5×10^{-12}. That same solution has a known K_{sp} of 3.2×10^{-10}. Is the experimental solution saturated, unsaturated, or supersaturated? Explain your answer.
5. Is a 4.72×10^{-6} M $Fe(OH)_2$ solution unsaturated, saturated, or supersaturated? ($K_{sp} = 8.0 \times 10^{-16}$)
6. What is the common ion in a mixture of Na_2CO_3 and $MgCO_3$?
7. Define *common-ion effect*.
8. Suppose you mix equal volumes of 3.50×10^{-3} M sodium hydroxide with 2.76×10^{-4} M magnesium nitrate. Does a precipitate form? If so, what is it?

17.3 REVIEW ANSWERS

* An asterisk following a question number indicates that a worked-out solution can be found on pages 433A–33B.

1. The solubility product constant is the equilibrium constant for dissolving a solute into a saturated solution. *(p. 424)*
2.* 1.19×10^{-6} *(p. 425)*
3.* 0.003 37 M *(p. 426)*
4. The experimental solution is unsaturated because its K_{sp} is less than the known K_{sp} for that solute. *(p. 427)*
5.* Because the ion concentration product is higher than the K_{sp} value, this is a supersaturated solution. *(p. 427)*
6. CO_3^{2+} *(p. 427)*
7. When a mixture of solutions contains substances with a common ion, the common ion from both solutions must be considered in solubility calculations. *(p. 427)*
8.* A $Mg(OH)_2$ precipitate forms. *(p. 428)*

APPLY

LAB 17B: *PRECIPITOUS CHANGES*

Once students have an understanding of the material in Section 17.3, they should be ready to work through Lab 17B.

ASSESS

TICKET OUT THE DOOR

As a **summarizing activity**, assess students' understanding by asking them to describe the common ion effect. *(The common ion effect is an occurrence that happens when two salts contain a common ion in the same solution, resulting in the less soluble salt precipitating out of the solution.)*

17 CHAPTER REVIEW

Chapter Summary

17.1 EQUILIBRIUM

- Many chemical reactions are reversible. The reactants and products can reach a state of dynamic equilibrium at which point the reaction rates of the forward and reverse reactions are equal.
- At equilibrium, the concentration of each chemical substance reaches a constant value even though both the forward and reverse reactions continue.
- An equilibrium constant (K_{eq}) is a numerical expression of the ratio of products to reactants and is constant for a specific temperature.
- An equilibrium-constant expression is determined from the balanced equilibrium reaction. The equilibrium constant equals the product of the concentrations of the products divided by the product of the concentrations of the reactants, all raised to the power of their stoichiometric coefficients.
- The law of chemical equilibrium states that at a fixed temperature, a chemical system may reach a point where the ratio between the concentration of the products and reactants has a constant value.
- In a homogeneous equilibrium, all the reactants and products are in the same state. In a heterogeneous equilibrium, two or more states are represented.
- The numerical value of an equilibrium constant at a specific temperature must be determined experimentally and is usually expressed without units.

TERMS

reversible reaction
chemical equilibrium
equilibrium position
equilibrium constant
law of chemical equilibrium

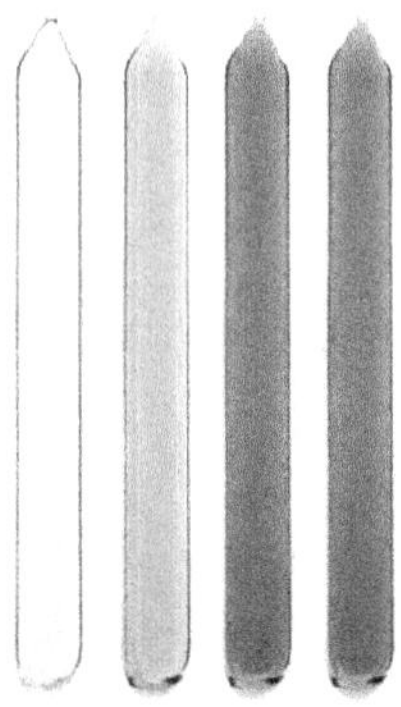

TERMS

Le Châtelier's principle

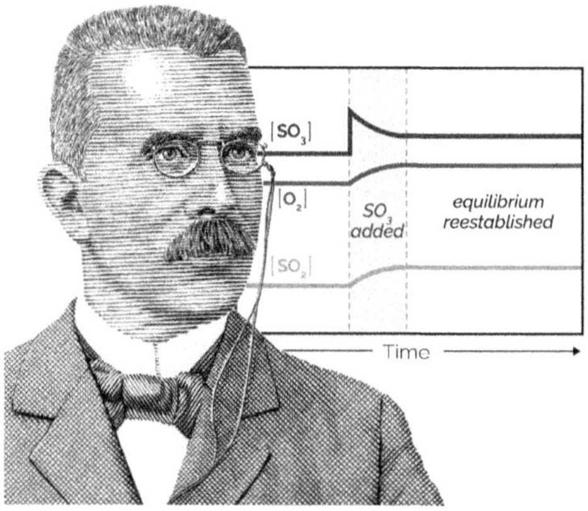

17.2 LE CHÂTELIER'S PRINCIPLE

- Le Châtelier's principle states that when a system in equilibrium is disturbed, it will shift in the direction that relieves the stress. In chemistry, the stress may be a change in concentration, pressure, or temperature.
- Pressure changes affect the equilibrium only in reactions involving gases that have unequal numbers of moles on each side of the equation.
- A catalyst speeds up both the forward and the reverse reactions, establishing equilibrium sooner. Catalysts do not affect equilibrium concentrations or the value of K_{eq}.

430 Chapter 17

TERMS
solubility product constant
common-ion effect

17.3 SOLUTION EQUILIBRIUM

- The solubility product constant (K_{sp}) is a specific K_{eq} that expresses the solubility of a salt at a specific temperature. The value of K_{sp} for a salt is for a saturated solution and can be calculated from measured solubilities.
- The K_{sp} can be compared with experimental concentration data to determine a solution's state of saturation.
- When two salts contain a common ion in the same solution, the common-ion effect can cause the less soluble salt to precipitate out of solution.

Chapter Review Questions

RECALLING FACTS

1. Define *chemical equilibrium.*
2. What is the difference between a dynamic equilibrium and a static one?
3. Define *equilibrium position.*
4. Which states of matter are included in equilibrium constant expressions? Explain.
5. What generalizations about an equilibrium constant can be made if the value for K_{eq} is large? if the value is small?
6. Name three factors that can shift equilibria.
7. Which factor(s) will change the K_{eq} as well as shift equilibria?
8. Summarize how changes to temperature affect a system in equilibrium.

UNDERSTANDING CONCEPTS

9. Your study partner says that according to the law of chemical equilibrium, in a reaction at equilibrium, the ratio between reactants and products is 1:1. Is she correct? Explain.
10. Write the equilibrium constant expression for each of the following reactions.
    a. Laughing gas can decompose into nitrogen and oxygen.
    $$2N_2O(g) \rightleftharpoons 2N_2(g) + O_2(g)$$
    b. Carbon monoxide can be converted into methane in one of the processes involved in converting coal into a gas.
    $$CO(g) + 3H_2(g) \rightleftharpoons CH_4(g) + H_2O(g)$$
    c. Methanol can be synthesized from carbon monoxide and hydrogen.
    $$CO(g) + 2H_2(g) \rightleftharpoons CH_3OH(g)$$
    d. Baking soda can extinguish fires as it decomposes to produce water vapor and carbon dioxide.
    $$2NaHCO_3(s) \rightleftharpoons Na_2CO_3(s) + H_2O(g) + CO_2(g)$$
11. A scientist experimenting with the Haber process,
    $$N_2(g) + 3H_2(g) \rightleftharpoons 2NH_3(g) + heat,$$
    seeks to determine the equilibrium constant at 450 °C.
    a. After permitting a mixture of N_2 and H_2 to react and reach equilibrium, he finds that $[N_2] = 1.00$ M, $[H_2] = 0.0769$ M, and $[NH_3] = 0.000\,200$ M. Calculate K_{eq} at this temperature.
    b. The scientist repeats the experiment under the same conditions with different initial amounts of gas in the reaction vessel. The scientist finds that $[H_2] = 0.0375$ M and $[NH_3] = 0.000\,318$ M. Use the value of K_{eq} already determined to calculate $[N_2]$.

CHAPTER 17 REVIEW ANSWERS

Recalling Facts

1. Chemical equilibrium refers to the point in a reversible reaction when the forward and reverse reactions are occurring at the same rate. *(p. 409)*
2. A dynamic equilibrium is a balance of continuously occurring, opposing processes. A static equilibrium is a balance of unchanging forces. *(p. 410)*
3. The equilibrium position is the set of reactant and product concentrations of a chemical reaction at equilibrium. *(p. 411)*
4. We use only substances in gaseous states and solutions because they have variable concentrations. Solids and liquids do not have variable concentrations. *(p. 412)*
5. If the value for K_{eq} of a reaction is large (> 1), the reaction forms mostly products. If the value for K_{eq} is small (< 1), very little product is formed, leaving mostly reactants. *(p. 414)*
6. changes in concentration, pressure, and temperature *(p. 416)*
7. temperature *(p. 419)*
8. Changing temperature affects the equilibrium position and changes the K_{eq} value. If the reaction is exothermic, increasing the temperature will shift the equilibrium position to the left and lower the K_{eq}. Decreasing the temperature for an exothermic reaction will shift the reaction toward the products and increase the K_{eq}. The effect of changing temperature on an endothermic reaction is just the opposite. *(p. 419)*

Understanding Concepts

* An asterisk following a question number indicates that a worked-out solution can be found on pages 433B–33E.

9. No. The ratio is constant, but not necessarily 1:1. *(p. 411)*
10. **a.** $K_{eq} = \dfrac{[N_2]^2[O_2]}{[N_2O]^2}$

    b. $K_{eq} = \dfrac{[CH_4][H_2O]}{[CO][H_2]^3}$

    c. $K_{eq} = \dfrac{[CH_3OH]}{[CO][H_2]^2}$

    d. $K_{eq} = [H_2O][CO_2]$ (Remember that solids are not included in the expression.) *(all pp. 412–13)*
11. ***a.** 8.80×10^{-5}

    b. 21.8 mol/L *(all p. 414)*

12.*a. 1.8×10^{-5}

b. 0.72 M

c. 5.6×10^{4} *(all p. 414)*

13.*a. 6.44×10^{-5} M

b. 6.40×10^{-5} M

c. 3.78×10^{-6} *(all p. 414)*

14. Pressure is caused by collisions between gas particles and their container. When pressure is increased, the system will shift to reduce the pressure, shifting the equilibrium position in the direction with fewer gas particles. Reducing the pressure will shift the reaction toward the side with more gas particles so that they can replace some of the pressure that was removed. *(p. 418)*

15. a. It shifts to the left.

b. It shifts to the right.

c. It shifts to the right.

d. It shifts to the left. *(all p. 418)*

16. toward the products; In an endothermic reaction, thermal energy can be considered a reactant. Supplying additional thermal energy to raise the temperature will cause the reaction to shift right to use up some of the added energy. *(p. 419)*

17. Adding catalyst will speed up both the forward and reverse reactions, bringing the system to equilibrium more quickly. The additional catalyst will not affect the equilibrium position, nor will it shift a system that is already in equilibrium. *(p. 420)*

18. a. Adding carbon dioxide (a reactant) will shift the reaction toward the right. This will lower the concentration of the products to return the system to its equilibrium constant value.

b. Decreasing the pressure will shift the reaction toward the reactant (left) side, which has more gas particles. This will replace some of the pressure decrease.

c. Decreasing the temperature is accomplished by removing thermal energy. Energy is a product in an exothermic reaction. Therefore, removing the thermal energy will shift the reaction to the right. This will produce more product and will increase the K_{eq} value. *(all pp. 416–20)*

17 CHAPTER REVIEW

12. Acetic acid ($HC_2H_3O_2$) is the compound that gives vinegar its distinctive smell and taste. When dissolved in water, it ionizes according to the reaction below.

$$HC_2H_3O_2(aq) + H_2O(l) \rightleftharpoons C_2H_3O_2^-(aq) + H_3O^+(aq)$$

a. A chemist working in a clinical research laboratory dissolves some acetic acid in water (at 25 °C) and finds that
$[H_3O^+] = 1.01 \times 10^{-5}$ M,
$[C_2H_3O_2^-] = 1.01 \times 10^{-5}$ M, and
$[HC_2H_3O_2] = 5.67 \times 10^{-6}$ M.

What is the value of K_{eq}?

b. If $[H_3O^+] = 3.6 \times 10^{-3}$ and $[C_2H_3O_2^-] = 3.6 \times 10^{-3}$, what is the concentration of un-ionized acetic acid at the same temperature?

c. What is the value of the equilibrium constant if the equation were written reversed?

13. Oxalic acid ($H_2C_2O_4$) experiences a two-step dissociation in an aqueous solution:

$H_2C_2O_4 \rightleftharpoons H^+ + HC_2O_4^-$,
where $K_{eq} = 5.90 \times 10^{-2}$ at 25 °C,

and

$HC_2O_4^- \rightleftharpoons H^+ + C_2O_4^{2-}$,
where $K_{eq} = 6.40 \times 10^{-5}$ at 25 °C.

The equilibrium concentration of $[H^+] = 1.95 \times 10^{-3}$ M and $[HC_2O_4^-] = 1.95 \times 10^{-3}$.

a. What is the equilibrium concentration of $H_2C_2O_4$?

b. What is the equilibrium concentration of $C_2O_4^{2-}$?

c. What is the equilibrium constant for the total reaction?

$$H_2C_2O_4 \rightleftharpoons 2H^+ + C_2O_4^{2-}$$

14. Explain why a change in pressure shifts a reversible reaction that is in equilibrium as it does.

15. Predict the effect of increasing the pressure on each of the four equilibria given in Question 10.

16. In an equilibrium reaction that is endothermic, will the addition of thermal energy cause the equilibrium to shift toward the reactants or toward the products? Explain.

17. How does adding more catalyst affect reversible reactions?

18. Consider the following exothermic reaction at equilibrium.

$$CO_2(g) + 4H_2(g) \rightleftharpoons CH_4(g) + 2H_2O(g)$$

a. What is the effect of adding more carbon dioxide? Explain.

b. What is the effect of decreasing the pressure? Explain.

c. What is the effect of decreasing the temperature? Explain.

19. Lithium carbonate (Li_2CO_3) is less soluble in hot water than in cold water.

a. Do you think the dissolution of Li_2CO_3 is exothermic or endothermic? Explain.

b. What will happen if a saturated solution of Li_2CO_3 at 25 °C is heated to 100 °C? Explain.

20. Write a K_{sp} expression for the dissolution of each of the following.

a. AgBr
b. MgF_2
c. Ag_2S
d. $Ba_3(PO_4)_2$
e. $PbCl_2$

432 Chapter 17

19. a. exothermic; The lower solubility at a higher temperature suggests that the addition of heat makes the dissolution process less favorable.

b. Some Li_2CO_3 will precipitate. Adding heat will drive the process toward the undissolved Li_2CO_3. *(all pp. 416–20)*

20. a. $K_{sp} = [Ag^+][Br^-]$

b. $K_{sp} = [Mg^{2+}][F^-]^2$

c. $K_{sp} = [Ag^+]^2[S^{2-}]$

d. $K_{sp} = [Ba^{2+}]^3[PO_4^{3-}]^2$

e. $K_{sp} = [Pb^{2+}][Cl^-]^2$ *(all pp. 424–25)*

21.* 1.19×10^{-11} *(p. 425)*

22.*a. 8.8×10^{-12}

b. 2.6×10^{-9}

c. 3.0×10^{-39}

d. 2.1×10^{-8} *(all p. 425)*

23.*a. 7.5×10^{-3} M

b. 1.6×10^{-7} M

c. 2.2×10^{-3} M

d. 1.4×10^{-6} M *(all pp. 425–26)*

24. The $[Li^+]$ will increase as the LiCl dissolves. This action will shift the Li_2CO_3 solubility equilibrium to the left, and some Li_2CO_3 will precipitate. *(pp. 427–28)*

21. A scientist measures the solubility of $Mg(OH)_2$. The concentration of the Mg^{2+} ions in a saturated solution at 18 °C is 1.44×10^{-4} M, and the concentration of OH^- in the same solution is 2.88×10^{-4} M. What is the value of the K_{sp} at this temperature?

22. Using the solubilities and molar masses in Table 17-3 (p. 426), calculate the K_{sp} for each of the following.
    - **a.** Ag_2CO_3
    - **b.** $BaCO_3$
    - **c.** $Fe(OH)_3$
    - **d.** $PbSO_4$

23. Calculate the solubilities (mol/L) of each of the following.
    - **a.** barium fluoride, BaF_2 ($K_{sp} = 1.7 \times 10^{-6}$)
    - **b.** cadmium carbonate, $CdCO_3$ ($K_{sp} = 2.5 \times 10^{-14}$)
    - **c.** lanthanum iodate, $La(IO_3)_3$ ($K_{sp} = 6.0 \times 10^{-10}$)
    - **d.** silver arsenate, Ag_3AsO_4 ($K_{sp} = 1.0 \times 10^{-22}$)

24. A saturated solution of Li_2CO_3 has both Li^+ and CO_3^{2-} ions in it. What will happen if some solid LiCl is added to the solution? (LiCl is much more soluble than Li_2CO_3.)

25. Will a precipitate form if equal volumes of the following solutions are mixed? If so, what substance(s) will precipitate? (*Hint*: First determine whether each substance is soluble or only minimally soluble. If a salt is minimally soluble, refer to its K_{sp}.)
    - **a.** 0.05 M NaCl and 0.05 M LiCl
    - **b.** 6.3×10^{-4} M $MgCO_3$ and 1.0×10^{-4} M $Mg(OH)_2$
    - **c.** 0.5 M NaOH and 2.0×10^{-5} M $Mg(OH)_2$

26. Summarize the process for determining whether a precipate forms in a double-replacement reaction.

CRITICAL THINKING

27. The reaction $N_2(g) + 3H_2(g) \rightleftharpoons 2NH_3(g)$ starts with the following concentrations: $[N_2] = 0.251$ M, $[H_2] = 0.653$ M, and $[NH_3] = 0.674$ M. If the K_{eq} for this reaction at the current temperature is 62.5, which reaction—the forward or the reverse—must occur to reach equilibrium?

28. The oxygen that you breathe attaches to a protein called hemoglobin (Hb) in red blood cells to form oxyhemoglobin as shown in the reaction below. This carries oxygen from your lungs to other parts of your body that need it.

$$Hb(aq) + O_2(g) \rightleftharpoons HbO_2(aq)$$

    - **a.** Is the equilibrium in the production of oxyhemoglobin homogeneous or heterogeneous? Explain.
    - **b.** Write the equilibrium constant for the production of hemoglobin.
    - **c.** Why do you think people who live at high elevations don't experience hypoxia, a lack of oxygen in the bloodstream?
    - **d.** Why do you think people with severe hypoxia receive oxygen and not hemoglobin?

29. Sickle-cell anemia is a disease in which a person's hemoglobin has a mutation that often results in misshapen blood cells. The mutation affects the blood cells' ability to deliver oxyhemoglobin and reduces their ability to carry proper hemoglobin. What kind of serious effects could this have?

30. Barium sulfate ($BaSO_4$) is administered to people when x-rays of their digestive systems are taken, despite the fact that the Ba^{2+} ion is toxic to humans. Suggest a method by which $BaSO_4$ could be administered without the danger from Ba^{2+} ions. Base your method on the common-ion effect.

25.*a. No precipitate will form.

b. $MgCO_3$ will not precipitate; $Mg(OH)_2$ will.

c. NaOH will not precipitate; $Mg(OH)_2$ will. *(all pp. 427–28)*

26. Calculate the ion concentration product of the least soluble compound. Compare the ion concentration product with the K_{sp} for that compound. If the ion concentration product is higher than the K_{sp} for that compound, some of that compound will precipitate until the ion concentration product equals the K_{sp}, meaning that the solution of that solute is saturated. *(pp. 427–28)*

Critical Thinking

27.* The forward reaction has to occur to make more product (numerator) and fewer reactants (denominator). *(p. 414)*

28. a. heterogeneous; There are two states of matter in the chemical reaction.

b. $K_{eq} = \dfrac{[HbO_2]}{[Hb][O_2]}$

c. Their bodies adjust by naturally producing more hemoglobin, shifting the equilibrium toward the production of oxyhemoglobin.

d. Answers will vary. Oxygen is easier to obtain and administer than hemoglobin and has a quicker effect. *(all pp. 413, 417)*

29. Decreased concentration of hemoglobin causes the equilibrium to shift away from oxyhemoglobin, leading to hypoxia. *(p. 417)*

30. Administer $BaSO_4$ with a soluble sulfate such as Na_2SO_4. The common ion (SO_4^{3-}) will cause the solubility of $BaSO_4$ to be shifted so that no appreciable concentration of Ba^{2+} ions will remain in solution. *(p. 427)*

Chemical Equilibrium 433

Section 17.1

7. What we know: $[HCl] = 0.051$ M, $[MgCl_2] = 0.513$ M, $[H_2] = 0.411$ M

$Mg(s) + 2HCl(aq) \rightleftharpoons MgCl_2(aq) + H_2(g)$

Unknown: K_{eq}

Write the formula and solve for the unknown.

$$K_{eq} = \frac{[MgCl_2][H_2]}{[HCl]^2}$$

Evaluate.

$$K_{eq} = \frac{(0.513)(0.411)}{(0.051)^2}$$
$$= 81$$

8. a. What we know: $[NO] = 0.897$ M, $[O_2] = 0.254$ M, $[NO_2] = 0.0329$ M

Unknown: K_{eq}

Write the formula and solve for the unknown.

$$K_{eq} = \frac{[NO_2]^2}{[NO]^2[O_2]}$$

Evaluate.

$$K_{eq} = \frac{(0.0329)^2}{(0.897)^2(0.254)}$$
$$= 0.005\,2\underline{9}6$$
$$= 0.005\,30$$

b. What we know: $K_{eq} = 0.005\,2\underline{9}6$, $[NO] = 1.13$ M, $[O_2] = 0.512$ M

Unknown: $[NO_2]$

Write the formula and solve for the unknown.

$$K_{eq} = \frac{[NO_2]^2}{[NO]^2[O_2]}$$

$$K_{eq}[NO]^2[O_2] = \frac{[NO_2]^2}{\cancel{[NO]^2[O_2]}}\cancel{[NO]^2[O_2]}$$

$$\sqrt{[NO_2]^2} = \sqrt{K_{eq}[NO]^2[O_2]}$$

$$[NO_2] = \sqrt{K_{eq}[NO]^2[O_2]}$$

Evaluate.

$$[NO_2] = \sqrt{(0.005\,2\underline{9}6)(1.13)^2(0.512)}$$
$$= 0.0588 \text{ mol/L}$$

Section 17.3

2. What we know: $CuCl(s) \rightleftharpoons Cu^+(aq) + Cl^-(aq)$

$K_{sp} = [Cu^+][Cl^-]$

$S_{CuCl} = 1.08 \times 10^{-2}$ g/100 mL

$[CuCl] = [Cu^+] = [Cl^-]$

Unknown: K_{sp}

Convert g/100 mL to mol/L.

$$\left(\frac{1.08 \times 10^{-2} \text{ g } \cancel{CuCl}}{100 \cancel{\text{ mL}}}\right)\left(\frac{1000 \cancel{\text{ mL}}}{1 \text{ L}}\right)\left(\frac{1 \text{ mol CuCl}}{99.00 \cancel{\text{ g CuCl}}}\right)$$
$$= 1.09 \times 10^{-3} \text{ M CuCl}$$

Write the formula and solve for the unknown.

$K_{sp} = [Cu^+][Cl^-]$

Evaluate.

$$K_{sp} = (1.09 \times 10^{-3})(1.09 \times 10^{-3})$$
$$= 1.19 \times 10^{-6}$$

3. What we know: $Li_3PO_4(s) \rightleftharpoons 3Li^+(aq) + PO_4^{3-}(aq)$

$K_{sp} = 3.48 \times 10^{-9}$

$[Li^+] = 3[Li_3PO_4]$

$[PO_4^{3-}] = [Li_3PO_4]$

Unknown: $[Li_3PO_4]$

Write the formula and solve for the unknown.

$$K_{sp} = [Li^+]^3[PO_4^{3-}]$$

$$K_{sp} = (3[Li_3PO_4])^3[Li_3PO_4]$$

$$\frac{K_{sp}}{27} = \frac{\cancel{27}[Li_3PO_4]^4}{\cancel{27}}$$

$$\sqrt[4]{\frac{K_{sp}}{27}} = \sqrt[4]{[Li_3PO_4]^4}$$

$$[Li_3PO_4] = \sqrt[4]{\frac{K_{sp}}{27}}$$

Evaluate.

$$[Li_3PO_4] = \sqrt[4]{\frac{3.48 \times 10^{-9}}{27}}$$
$$= 0.003\,37 \text{ M}$$

5. What we know: $Fe(OH)_2(s) \rightleftharpoons Fe^{2+}(aq) + 2OH^-(aq)$

$K_{sp} = 8.0 \times 10^{-6}$

$[Fe(OH)_2] = 4.72 \times 10^{-6}$

$[Fe^{2+}] = [Fe(OH)_2] = 4.72 \times 10^{-6}$

$[OH^-] = 2[Fe(OH)_2] = 9.44 \times 10^{-6}$

Unknown: $[Fe^{2+}][OH^-]^2$

Write the formula and solve for the unknown.

$[Fe^{2+}][OH^-]^2$

Evaluate.

$$[Fe^{2+}][OH^-]^2 = (4.72 \times 10^{-6})(9.44 \times 10^{-6})^2$$
$$= 4.20 \times 10^{-16}$$

$[Fe^{2+}][OH^-]^2 > K_{sp}$

8. What we know: $NaOH(s) \rightleftharpoons Na^+(aq) + OH^-(aq)$

$[Na^+] = [OH^-] = [NaOH] = 3.50 \times 10^{-3}$ M

$Mg(NO_3)_2(s) \rightleftharpoons Mg^{2+}(aq) + 2NO_3^-(aq)$

$[Mg^{2+}] = [Mg(NO_3)_2] = 2.76 \times 10^{-4}$ M

$[NO_3^-] = 2[Mg(NO_3)_2] = 5.52 \times 10^{-4}$ M

Evaluate.

The reactants are both quite soluble so we are concerned only with whether $NaNO_3$ or $Mg(OH)_2$ will precipitate out. We know that nitrates are soluble (Ch. 14), so we have only to compare the ion concentration product with its K_{sp} value (Table 17-3).

$Mg(OH)_2(s) \rightleftharpoons Mg^{2+}(aq) + 2OH^-(aq)$

The volume is doubled so the concentrations are cut in half.

$$[Mg^{2+}][OH^-]^2 = (1.38 \times 10^{-4})(1.75 \times 10^{-3})^2$$
$$= 4.23 \times 10^{-10}$$

The ion concentration product is higher than the K_{sp} for magnesium hydroxide (5.6×10^{-12}), so a precipitate forms.

Chapter 17 Review Questions

11. a. What we know: $[N_2] = 1.00$ M, $[H_2] = 0.0769$ M, $[NH_3] = 2.00 \times 10^{-4}$ M

Unknown: K_{eq}

Write the formula and solve for the unknown.

$$K_{eq} = \frac{[NH_3]^2}{[N_2][H_2]^3}$$

Evaluate.

$$K_{eq} = \frac{(2.00 \times 10^{-4})^2}{(1.00)(0.0769)^3}$$
$$= \frac{4.00 \times 10^{-8}}{4.547\,566\,09 \times 10^{-4}}$$
$$= 8.80 \times 10^{-5}$$

b. Use the equilibrium equation and solve for $[N_2]$.

What we know: $K_{eq} = 8.80 \times 10^{-5}$, $[H_2] = 0.0375$ M, $[NH_3] = 3.18 \times 10^{-4}$ M

Unknown: $[N_2]$

Write the formula and solve for the unknown.

$$K_{eq} = \frac{[NH_3]^2}{[N_2][H_2]^3}$$

$$K_{eq}[N_2] = \frac{[NH_3]^2}{\cancel{[N_2]}[H_2]^3}\cancel{[N_2]}$$

$$\frac{\cancel{K_{eq}}[N_2]}{\cancel{K_{eq}}} = \frac{[NH_3]^2}{[H_2]^3 K_{eq}}$$

$$[N_2] = \frac{[NH_3]^2}{[H_2]^3 K_{eq}}$$

Evaluate.

$$[N_2] = \frac{(3.18 \times 10^{-4})^2}{(0.0375)^3(8.80 \times 10^{-5})}$$

$$= \frac{1.011\,24 \times 10^{-7}}{4.640\,625 \times 10^{-9}}$$
$$= 21.8 \text{ mol/L}$$

12. a. What we know: $[H_3O^+] = 1.01 \times 10^{-5}$ M, $[C_2H_3O_2^-] = 1.01 \times 10^{-5}$ M, $[HC_2H_3O_2] = 5.67 \times 10^{-6}$ M

Unknown: K_{eq}

Write the formula and solve for the unknown.

$$K_{eq} = \frac{[C_2H_3O_2^-][H_3O^+]}{[HC_2H_3O_2]}$$

Evaluate.

$$K_{eq} = \frac{(1.01 \times 10^{-5})(1.01 \times 10^{-5})}{5.67 \times 10^{-6}}$$
$$= 1.80 \times 10^{-5}$$

b. What we know: $K_{eq} = 1.80 \times 10^{-5}$, $[H_3O^+] = 3.6 \times 10^{-3}$ M, $[C_2H_3O_2^-] = 3.6 \times 10^{-3}$ M

Unknown: $[HC_2H_3O_2]$

Write the formula and solve for the unknown.

$$K_{eq} = \frac{[C_2H_3O_2^-][H_3O^+]}{[HC_2H_3O_2]}$$

$$K_{eq}[HC_2H_3O_2] = \frac{[C_2H_3O_2^-][H_3O^+]}{\cancel{[HC_2H_3O_2]}}\cancel{[HC_2H_3O_2]}$$

$$\frac{\cancel{K_{eq}}[HC_2H_3O_2]}{\cancel{K_{eq}}} = \frac{[C_2H_3O_2^-][H_3O^+]}{K_{eq}}$$

$$[HC_2H_3O_2] = \frac{[C_2H_3O_2^-][H_3O^+]}{K_{eq}}$$

Evaluate.

$$[HC_2H_3O_2] = \frac{(3.6 \times 10^{-3})(3.6 \times 10^{-3})}{1.80 \times 10^{-5}}$$
$$= 0.72 \text{ M}$$

c. When the reaction is reversed, the left side becomes the products and the right side becomes the reactants.

What we know: $C_2H_3O_2^-(aq) + H_3O^+(aq) \rightleftharpoons HC_2H_3O_2(aq) + H_2O(l)$, $[HC_2H_3O_2] = 0.72$ M, $[H_3O^+] = 3.6 \times 10^{-3}$ M, $[C_2H_3O_2^-] = 3.6 \times 10^{-3}$ M

Unknown: K_{eq}

Write the formula and solve for the unknown.

$$K_{eq} = \frac{[HC_2H_3O_2]}{[C_2H_3O_2^-][H_3O^+]}$$

Evaluate.

$$K_{eq} = \frac{0.72}{(3.6 \times 10^{-3})(3.6 \times 10^{-3})}$$
$$= 5.6 \times 10^4$$

Students could also find the K_{eq} by using the reciprocal of the K_{eq} calculated in part a.

$$K_{eq} = \frac{1}{(1.8 \times 10^{-5})} = 5.6 \times 10^4$$

13. a. What we know: $K_{eq} = 5.90 \times 10^{-2}$, $[H^+] = 1.95 \times 10^{-3}$ M, $[HC_2O_4^-] = 1.95 \times 10^{-3}$ M

Unknown: $[H_2C_2O_4]$

Write the formula and solve for the unknown.

$$K_{eq} = \frac{[HC_2O_4^-][H^+]}{[H_2C_2O_4]}$$

$$K_{eq}[H_2C_2O_4] = \frac{[HC_2O_4^-][H^+]}{\cancel{[H_2C_2O_4]}}\cancel{[H_2C_2O_4]}$$

$$\frac{\cancel{K_{eq}}[H_2C_2O_4]}{\cancel{K_{eq}}} = \frac{[HC_2O_4^-][H^+]}{K_{eq}}$$

$$[H_2C_2O_4] = \frac{[HC_2O_4^-][H^+]}{K_{eq}}$$

Evaluate.

$$[H_2C_2O_4] = \frac{(1.95 \times 10^{-3})(1.95 \times 10^{-3})}{5.90 \times 10^{-2}}$$

$$= 6.44 \times 10^{-5}\ M$$

b. What we know: $K_{eq} = 6.40 \times 10^{-5}$, $[H^+] = 1.95 \times 10^{-3}$ M, $[HC_2O_4^-] = 1.95 \times 10^{-3}$ M

Unknown: $[C_2O_4^{2-}]$

Write the formula and solve for the unknown.

$$K_{eq} = \frac{[C_2O_4^{2-}][H^+]}{[HC_2O_4^-]}$$

$$K_{eq}\left(\frac{[HC_2O_4^-]}{[H^+]}\right) = \frac{[C_2O_4^{2-}]\cancel{[H^+]}}{\cancel{[HC_2O_4^-]}}\left(\frac{\cancel{[HC_2O_4^-]}}{\cancel{[H^+]}}\right)$$

$$[C_2O_4^{2-}] = \frac{K_{eq}[HC_2O_4^-]}{[H^+]}$$

Evaluate.

$$[C_2O_4^{2-}] = \frac{(6.40 \times 10^{-5})(1.95 \times 10^{-3})}{1.95 \times 10^{-3}}$$

$$= 6.40 \times 10^{-5}\ M$$

c. What we know: $[H^+] = 1.95 \times 10^{-3}$ M, $[H_2C_2O_4] = 6.44 \times 10^{-5}$ M, $[C_2O_4^{2-}] = 6.40 \times 10^{-5}$ M

Unknown: K_{eq}

Write the formula and solve for the unknown.

$$K_{eq} = \frac{[H^+]^2[C_2O_4^{2-}]}{[H_2C_2O_4]}$$

Evaluate.

$$[C_2O_4^{2-}] = \frac{(1.95 \times 10^{-3})(6.40 \times 10^{-5})}{6.44 \times 10^{-3}}$$

$$= 6.40 \times 10^{-5}\ M$$

$$K_{eq} = \frac{(1.95 \times 10^{-3})^2(6.40 \times 10^{-5})}{6.44 \times 10^{-5}}$$

$$= 3.78 \times 10^{-6}$$

21. What we know: $[Mg^{2+}] = 1.44 \times 10^{-4}$ M, $[OH^-] = 2.88 \times 10^{-4}$ M

Unknown: K_{sp}

Write the formula and solve for the unknown.

$$K_{sp} = [Mg^{2+}][OH^-]^2$$

Evaluate.

$$K_{sp} = (1.44 \times 10^{-4})(2.88 \times 10^{-4})^2$$

$$= 1.19 \times 10^{-11}$$

22. a. What we know: $Ag_2CO_3(s) \rightleftharpoons 2Ag^+(aq) + CO_3^-(aq)$

$\text{Solubility}_{Ag_2CO_3} = 3.6 \times 10^{-2}$ g/L

Convert solubility to concentration.

$$\left(\frac{3.6 \times 10^{-2}\ \cancel{g\ Ag_2CO_3}}{L}\right)\left(\frac{1\ mol\ Ag_2CO_3}{275.75\ \cancel{g\ Ag_2CO_3}}\right)$$

$$= 1.\underline{3}0 \times 10^{-4}\ M\ Ag_2CO_3$$

$$[Ag^+] = 2[Ag_2CO_3] = 2.\underline{6}0 \times 10^{-4}\ M$$

$$[CO_3^{2-}] = [Ag_2CO_3] = 1.\underline{3}0 \times 10^{-4}\ M$$

Unknown: K_{sp}

Write the formula and solve for the unknown.

$$K_{sp} = [Ag^+]^2[CO_3^{2-}]$$

Evaluate.

$$K_{sp} = (2.\underline{6}0 \times 10^{-4})^2(1.\underline{3}0 \times 10^{-4})$$

$$= 8.8 \times 10^{-12}$$

b. What we know: $BaCO_3(s) \rightleftharpoons Ba^{2+}(aq) + CO_3^-(aq)$

$\text{Solubility}_{BaCO_3} = 1.0 \times 10^{-2}$ g/L

Convert solubility to concentration.

$$\left(\frac{1.0 \times 10^{-2}\ \cancel{g\ BaCO_3}}{L}\right)\left(\frac{1\ mol\ BaCO_3}{197.34\ \cancel{g\ BaCO_3}}\right)$$

$$= 5.\underline{0}6 \times 10^{-5}\ M\ BaCO_3$$

$$[Ba^{2+}] = [BaCO_3] = 5.\underline{0}6 \times 10^{-5}\ M$$

$$[CO_3^{2-}] = [BaCO_3] = 5.\underline{0}6 \times 10^{-5}\ M$$

Unknown: K_{sp}

Write the formula and solve for the unknown.

$$K_{sp} = [Ba^{2+}][CO_3^{2-}]$$

Evaluate.

$$K_{sp} = (5.\underline{0}6 \times 10^{-5})(5.\underline{0}6 \times 10^{-5})$$

$$= 2.6 \times 10^{-9}$$

c. What we know: $Fe(OH)_3(s) \rightleftharpoons Fe^{3+}(aq) + 3OH^-(aq)$

$\text{Solubility}_{Fe(OH)_3} = 1.1 \times 10^{-8}$ g/L

Convert solubility to concentration.

$$\left(\frac{1.1 \times 10^{-8} \text{ g Fe(OH)}_3}{\text{L}}\right)\left(\frac{1 \text{ mol Fe(OH)}_3}{106.88 \text{ g Fe(OH)}_3}\right) = 1.02 \times 10^{-10} \text{ M Fe(OH)}_3$$

$[Fe^{3+}] = [Fe(OH)_3] = 1.02 \times 10^{-10}$ M

$[OH^-] = 3[Fe(OH)_3] = 3.06 \times 10^{-10}$ M

Unknown: K_{sp}

Write the formula and solve for the unknown.

$K_{sp} = [Fe^{3+}][OH^-]^3$

Evaluate.

$$K_{sp} = (1.02 \times 10^{-10})(3.06 \times 10^{-10})^3 = 2.9 \times 10^{-39}$$

d. What we know: $PbSO_4(s) \rightleftharpoons Pb^{2+}(aq) + SO_4^{2-}(aq)$

$\text{Solubility}_{PbSO_4} = 4.4 \times 10^{-2}$ g/L

Convert solubility to concentration.

$$\left(\frac{4.4 \times 10^{-2} \text{ g PbSO}_4}{\text{L}}\right)\left(\frac{1 \text{ mol PbSO}_4}{303.30 \text{ g PbSO}_4}\right) = 1.45 \times 10^{-4} \text{ M PbSO}_4$$

$[Pb^{2+}] = [PbSO_4] = 1.45 \times 10^{-4}$ M

$[SO_4^{2-}] = [PbSO_4] = 1.45 \times 10^{-4}$ M

Unknown: K_{sp}

Write the formula and solve for the unknown.

$K_{sp} = [Pb^{2+}][SO_4^{2-}]$

Evaluate.

$$K_{sp} = (1.45 \times 10^{-4})(1.45 \times 10^{-4}) = 2.1 \times 10^{-8}$$

23. a. What we know: $BaF_2(s) \rightleftharpoons Ba^{2+}(aq) + 2F^-(aq)$

$K_{sp} = 1.7 \times 10^{-6}$

$[Ba^{2+}] = [BaF_2]$

$[F^-] = 2[BaF_2]$

Unknown: $[BaF_2]$

Write the formula and solve for the unknown.

$$K_{sp} = [Ba^{2+}][F^-]^2$$

$$K_{sp} = [BaF_2](2[BaF_2])^2$$

$$\frac{K_{sp}}{4} = \frac{4[BaF_2]^3}{4}$$

$$\sqrt[3]{[BaF_2]^3} = \sqrt[3]{\frac{K_{sp}}{4}}$$

$$[BaF_2] = \sqrt[3]{\frac{K_{sp}}{4}}$$

Evaluate.

$$[BaF_2] = \sqrt[3]{\frac{1.7 \times 10^{-6}}{4}} = 7.5 \times 10^{-3} \text{ M}$$

b. What we know: $CdCO_3(s) \rightleftharpoons Cd^{2+}(aq) + CO_3^{2-}(aq)$

$K_{sp} = 2.5 \times 10^{-14}$

$[Cd^{2+}] = [CdCO_3]$

$[CO_3^{2-}] = [CdCO_3]$

Unknown: $[CdCO_3]$

Write the formula and solve for the unknown.

$$K_{sp} = [Cd^{2+}][CO_3^{2-}]$$

$$K_{sp} = [CdCO_3][CdCO_3]$$

$$\sqrt{K_{sp}} = \sqrt{[CdCO_3]^2}$$

$$[CdCO_3] = \sqrt{K_{sp}}$$

Evaluate.

$$[CdCO_3] = \sqrt{2.5 \times 10^{-14}} = 1.6 \times 10^{-7} \text{ M}$$

c. What we know: $La(IO_3)_3(s) \rightleftharpoons La^{3+}(aq) + 3IO_3^-(aq)$

$K_{sp} = 6.0 \times 10^{-10}$

$[La^{3+}] = [La(IO_3)_3]$

$[IO_3^-] = 3[La(IO_3)_3]$

Unknown: $[La(IO_3)_3]$

Write the formula and solve for the unknown.

$$K_{sp} = [La^{3+}][IO_3^-]^3$$

$$K_{sp} = [La(IO_3)_3](3[La(IO_3)_3])^3$$

$$\frac{K_{sp}}{27} = \frac{27[La(IO_3)_3]^4}{27}$$

$$\sqrt[4]{[La(IO_3)_3]^4} = \sqrt[4]{\frac{K_{sp}}{27}}$$

$$[La(IO_3)_3] = \sqrt[4]{\frac{K_{sp}}{27}}$$

Evaluate.

$$[La(IO_3)_3] = \sqrt[4]{\frac{6.0 \times 10^{-10}}{27}} = 2.2 \times 10^{-3} \text{ M}$$

d. What we know: $Ag_3AsO_4(s) \rightleftharpoons 3Ag^+(aq) + AsO_4^{3-}(aq)$

$K_{sp} = 1.0 \times 10^{-22}$

$[Ag^+] = 3[Ag_3AsO_4]$

$[AsO_4^{3-}] = [Ag_3AsO_4]$

Unknown: $[Ag_3AsO_4]$

(continued)

Write the formula and solve for the unknown.

$$K_{sp} = [Ag^+]^3[AsO_4^{3-}]$$

$$K_{sp} = (3[Ag_3AsO_4])^3[Ag_3AsO_4]$$

$$\frac{K_{sp}}{27} = \frac{\cancel{27}[Ag_3AsO_4]^4}{\cancel{27}}$$

$$\sqrt[4]{[Ag_3AsO_4]^4} = \sqrt[4]{\frac{K_{sp}}{27}}$$

$$[Ag_3AsO_4] = \sqrt[4]{\frac{K_{sp}}{27}}$$

Evaluate.

$$[Ag_3AsO_4] = \sqrt[4]{\frac{1.0 \times 10^{-22}}{27}}$$

$$= 1.4 \times 10^{-6}\ M$$

25. a. First, find the theoretical concentration of each ion.

$Na^+ = 0.05$ M; $Cl^- = 0.05$ M

$Li^+ = 0.05$ M; $Cl^- = 0.05$ M

Then check Table 17-3 for the most likely combination of ions to precipitate. None of the ion combinations can be found on Table 17-3; therefore, no precipitate will form because NaCl and LiCl are both very soluble.

b. The solutions have a common ion: Mg^{2+}. First, find the average of the two Mg^{2+} molarities, which is 3.7×10^{-4}. Then use this value to find the product of ion concentrations for each salt and compare them with their K_{sp} values in Table 17-3.

$[Mg^{2+}][CO_3^{2-}] = (3.65 \times 10^{-4})(3.15 \times 10^{-4}) = 1.15 \times 10^{-7}$, which is smaller than the K_{sp} of $MgCO_3$ from Table 17-3. Therefore, $MgCO_3$ will not precipitate.

$[Mg^{2+}][OH^-]^2 = (3.65 \times 10^{-4})(1.0 \times 10^{-4})^2 = 3.65 \times 10^{-12}$, which is larger than the K_{sp} of $Mg(OH)_2$ from Table 17-3. Therefore, $Mg(OH)_2$ will precipitate.

c. The solutions have a common ion, OH^-. The average molarity of the two OH^- ions is 2.5×10^{-1}.

NaOH is very soluble, so it will not precipitate.

$[Mg^{2+}][OH^-]^2 = (1.0 \times 10^{-5})[(2.25 \times 10^{-1})]^2 = 5.1 \times 10^{-7}$, which is larger than the K_{sp} of $Mg(OH)_2$ from Table 17-3. Therefore, $Mg(OH)_2$ will precipitate.

27. What we know: $[N_2] = 0.251$ M, $[H_2] = 0.653$ M, $[NH_3] = 0.674$ M, $K_{eq} = 62.5$

Write the formula and solve for the unknown.

$$K_{eq} = \frac{[NH_3]^2}{[N_2][H_2]^3}$$

Evaluate.

$$K_{eq} = \frac{(0.674)^2}{(0.251)(0.653)^3}$$

$$= 6.50$$

CHAPTER 18 *OBJECTIVES*

- Evaluate the workability of the different acid and base theories.
- Calculate the strengths of acids and bases.
- Analyze the concentration of an unknown acid or base by using titration.

OVERVIEW

Chapter 18 contains key material. Acids, bases, and salts are important industrial chemicals and play significant roles in the biochemistry of living things.

18.1 DEFINING ACIDS AND BASES
- *Observable Properties of Acids*
- *Observable Properties of Bases*

18.2 ACID-BASE EQUILIBRIA
- *The Self-Ionization of Water*
- *The pH Scale*
- *The pOH Scale*
- *Acid-Base Strength*
- *Polarity, Charge, and Acid-Base Strength*
- *Amphoteric Substances*
- *Polyprotic Acids*
- *Measuring pH*

18.3 NEUTRALIZATION
- *Salts*
- *Acid-Base Titrations*
- *Buffers*

LAB ACTIVITIES

Lab 18A: *Colorful Chemistry*—Students observe acid-base indicators and estimate the acidity of a solution.

Lab 18B: *Say Cheese!*—Students perform titrations and calculate the amount concentration of acids and bases.

Chapter 18

ACIDS, BASES, AND SALTS

Everyone knows that driving under the influence is a real problem on our highways. Deaths caused by driving under the influence are a significant percentage of all vehicular deaths. In 2016 the Centers for Disease Control reported that 10,497 deaths—28% of all auto accident fatalities—were linked to alcohol impairment. According to Federal Bureau of Investigation statistics, over a million drivers were arrested for driving under the influence in 2016. While that number seems like a lot, it is less than 1% of the 111 million people who reported that they had driven while impaired during that year. How can we keep drunk drivers off the road?

Police can measure the blood alcohol content (BAC) of people suspected of drinking and driving by using a Breathalyzer. This device works by reacting the alcohol in a person's breath with sulfuric acid. Throughout this chapter, we will learn about acids and bases and the reactions that they undergo.

Scientists have known that breath can contain trace amounts of alcohol since 1874. This knowledge led to the development of early breath analyzing methods in the 1920s. Inventor Robert Borkenstein created the first Breathalyzer unit in 1954.

18.1 DEFINING ACIDS AND BASES

We live in a world full of chemicals, and many of these chemicals are compounds called acids and bases. How can we know whether a chemical is an acid or a base? Since ancient times, people have identified acids and bases by their properties. As early as 1663, Robert Boyle classified many common substances as acids or bases on the basis of their physical properties. But it would be another two centuries before scientists began to explain what causes these properties.

Observable Properties of Acids

Aqueous solutions of acids typically have certain physical properties in common, one of which is a sour taste. For example, the characteristic sour taste of citrus fruits is caused by citric acid. Acetic acid puts the pucker in pickles. Aspirin tastes sour because of acetylsalicylic acid. Lactic acid's smell and flavor help us recognize sour milk. In fact, sourness is so closely tied to acids that their name comes from the Latin *acidus*, meaning "sour." Besides tasting sour, acidic solutions can also conduct an electric current because the acid dissociates or ionizes. For example, hydrochloric acid (HCl) ionizes into hydrogen ions and chloride ions. Any substance that produces ions, which conduct electricity in a solution, is called an **electrolyte**.

Why do we have to test the pH of pool water?

Acids can also be identified by their chemical properties. Many metals react with acids, with the metal replacing the hydrogen in the solution. Often the products of these reactions are hydrogen gas and a salt, though other products are possible. When copper metal reacts with nitric acid (see below), the copper replaces the hydrogen to produce copper(II) nitrate. A toxic reddish-brown gas—nitrogen dioxide gas—and water are also products.

$$Cu(s) + 4HNO_3(aq) \longrightarrow Cu(NO_3)_2(aq) + 2NO_2(g) + 2H_2O(l)$$

A simple test using litmus paper makes one of the chemical properties of acids observable. As litmus paper is produced, it is mixed with a chemical extracted from certain lichens. So litmus paper can be used to identify acids—an acid will turn blue litmus paper red.

QUESTIONS
- What are the characteristics of acids and bases?
- Why are there different definitions for acids and bases?
- What are conjugate acid-base pairs?

TERMS
electrolyte • neutralization reaction • Arrhenius acid • Arrhenius base • Brønsted-Lowry acid • Brønsted-Lowry base • conjugate base • conjugate acid • Lewis acid • Lewis base

TABLE 18-1
Common Acids

Name	Source	Formula
acetic acid	vinegar	$HC_2H_3O_2$
ascorbic acid	vegetables, vitamin C	$H_2C_6H_6O_6$
carbonic acid	soft drinks	H_2CO_3
citric acid	citrus fruit	$H_3C_6H_5O_7$
formic acid	bee venom	HCO_2H
lactic acid	sour milk, sore muscles	$H_2C_3H_4O_3$
oxalic acid	rhubarb	$H_2C_2O_4$
sulfuric acid	battery acid	H_2SO_4

SECTION 18.1 *OVERVIEW*

Essential Question

Why do we have to test the pH of pool water?

Objectives

» **18.1.1** Describe acids and bases according to their physical and chemical properties.

» **18.1.2** Summarize the different definitions for acids and bases.

» **18.1.3** Classify a substance as an acid or base according to the Arrhenius, Brønsted-Lowry, and Lewis definitions.

» **18.1.4** Compare the three acid-base models.

» **18.1.5** Explain the relationship between conjugate acids and bases.

Resource

Case Study: Royal Acid to the Rescue

ENGAGE

ACIDS AND BASES

Preassess prior knowledge with a two-minute **quick write** activity. Ask students to write all they know about acids and bases. While they may not be able to recall all the differences between the two, they may mention that acids taste sour and turn blue litmus paper red or that bases taste bitter and turn red litmus paper blue. They may list different foods, such as lemons and vinegar (acids) or baking soda (a base).

Explain that in this section they will learn about the unique properties of acids and bases, as well as the different models that were created to explain how we determine whether a compound is an acid or a base.

INSTRUCT

TASTE AND FEEL ACIDS AND BASES

Conduct a **hands-on activity** in which students perform a taste and feel analysis of acids and bases. Provide a small plate for each student and give each three different types of acids and bases to taste and feel. Remind students that though there normally is to be no eating in the laboratory, in this exploratory activity our sense of taste is needed and so tasting will be permitted. Examples of acids that they can try include lemon juice, lime juice, vinegar, sour apples, and salt and vinegar potato chips. For bases, use egg whites, baking soda, milk of magnesia, and soap. You may also want to provide water and explain that it is considered neutral on the pH scale.

Begin by asking students about the taste of each acidic substance. Most will mention that they are sour. As a recall of biology, ask whether anyone can remember the location of the taste buds that sense sour foods. *(on the back of the tongue at the sides)*

Now have students feel the bases. Students may mention that they are slippery. Since they are unable to taste them, explain that the bases have a bitter taste. To recall biology, ask for the location of the taste buds that sense bitter foods. *(in the central region of the back of the tongue)*

ACID BASE MODELS

Direct students to create a **graphic organizer** of the various acid-base models (pp. 436–38). A concept map would work well for highlighting these concepts, but students can use any type of graphic organizer to help organize the material. It is important that they become familiar with each model and identify the differences between acids and bases in relation to these models.

TABLE 18-2 *Common Bases*

Name	Source	Formula
ammonium hydroxide	household ammonia	NH_4OH
calcium hydroxide	lime	$Ca(OH)_2$
magnesium hydroxide	milk of magnesia	$Mg(OH)_2$
sodium hydroxide	lye	NaOH

Observable Properties of Bases

Bases, like acids, can be identified by their physical properties. Most bases have a bitter taste, which you might have experienced by accidentally tasting soap. This explains why very few foods contain strong bases. Bases also feel slippery. The soapy feeling associated with bases results from a reaction between the base and the fatty acids and oils in your skin. Bases in solution also dissociate or ionize, allowing them to conduct electric current, signifying that they are also electrolytes.

Chemical properties are also helpful in identifying bases. Litmus paper can be used to identify bases—they turn red litmus paper blue.

Acids and bases have another chemical property—they can neutralize each other in a chemical reaction. A **neutralization reaction** between an acid and a base in an aqueous solution produces a salt and water. For example, the reaction of sulfuric acid with sodium hydroxide produces sodium sulfate and water.

$$H_2SO_4(aq) + 2NaOH(aq) \longrightarrow Na_2SO_4(aq) + 2H_2O(l)$$

Svante Arrhenius

THE *Arrhenius* MODEL

We have described acids and bases, but how do we determine whether a compound is an acid or a base? Since the physical properties of acids and bases can vary so much, scientists have focused on the chemical properties of acids and bases to define them.

Acid definition: *releases H^+*

Base definition: *releases OH^-*

The earliest of the modern acid-base definitions was proposed in the 1880s by Swedish chemist Svante Arrhenius, who classified acids and bases by the ions that they produce in aqueous solution. **Arrhenius acids** ionize to release hydrogen ions (H^+) in aqueous solutions. Note that a hydrogen ion is just a proton or a hydrogen nucleus. This hydrogen ion is not stable in solution, so it bonds to a water molecule to form H_3O^+—a hydronium ion. In this and many other textbooks, the H^+ and H_3O^+ symbols are considered interchangeable. **Arrhenius bases** are substances that dissociate to release hydroxide ions (OH^-) in aqueous solutions.

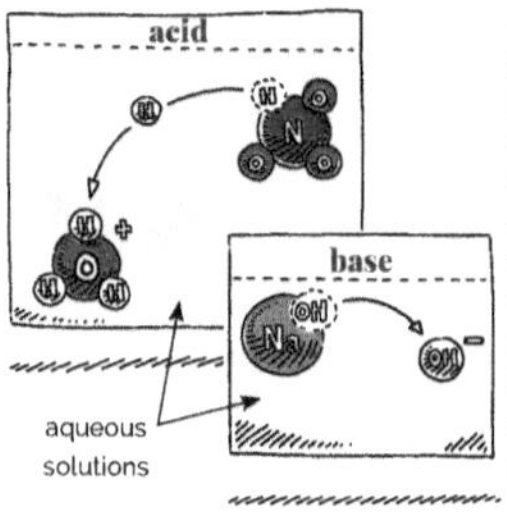

Hydrogen-containing compounds are not always acids. For example, methane (CH_4) has four hydrogen atoms, but none of these hydrogen atoms will ionize. Thus, methane is not considered an acid. Likewise, compounds with OH groups in their formulas are not always bases. Methanol (CH_3OH) does not normally release its OH group.

The Arrhenius model is useful but limited because it deals only with compounds in aqueous solutions. Normally this is not a significant limitation, but modern chemistry is pioneering research in acid-base reactions that occur in nonaqueous solvents or even without solvents. The Arrhenius definition of bases does not recognize compounds such as ammonia as being bases because these compounds do not contain an OH group. Nevertheless, ammonia exhibits properties long associated with bases. Although the Arrhenius model has some use, it is not as functional as other definitions. As we have seen often in science, continued research requires that we refine our models to explain new data.

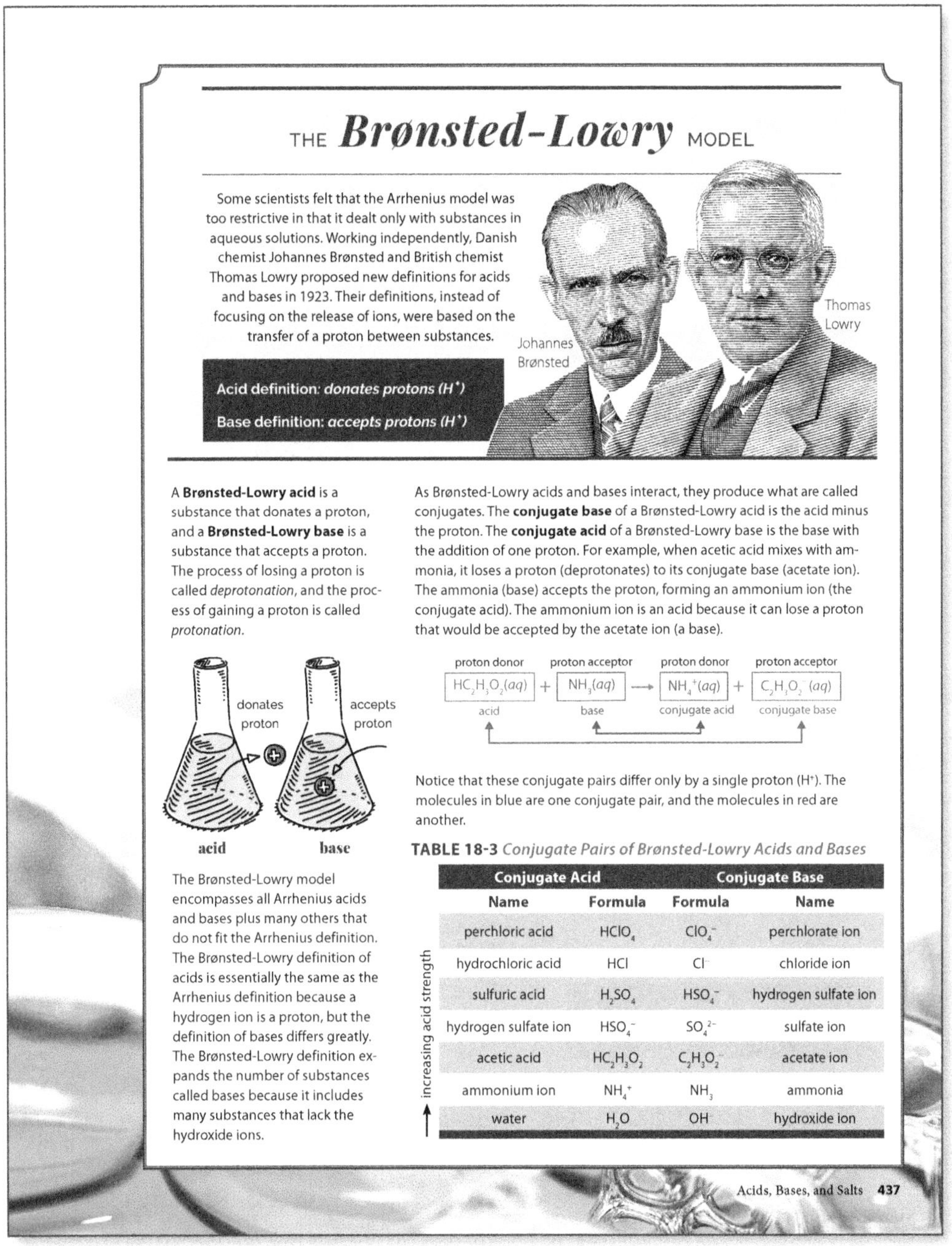

THE *Brønsted-Lowry* MODEL

Some scientists felt that the Arrhenius model was too restrictive in that it dealt only with substances in aqueous solutions. Working independently, Danish chemist Johannes Brønsted and British chemist Thomas Lowry proposed new definitions for acids and bases in 1923. Their definitions, instead of focusing on the release of ions, were based on the transfer of a proton between substances.

Acid definition: *donates protons* (H^+)

Base definition: *accepts protons* (H^+)

A **Brønsted-Lowry acid** is a substance that donates a proton, and a **Brønsted-Lowry base** is a substance that accepts a proton. The process of losing a proton is called *deprotonation*, and the process of gaining a proton is called *protonation*.

The Brønsted-Lowry model encompasses all Arrhenius acids and bases plus many others that do not fit the Arrhenius definition. The Brønsted-Lowry definition of acids is essentially the same as the Arrhenius definition because a hydrogen ion is a proton, but the definition of bases differs greatly. The Brønsted-Lowry definition expands the number of substances called bases because it includes many substances that lack the hydroxide ions.

As Brønsted-Lowry acids and bases interact, they produce what are called conjugates. The **conjugate base** of a Brønsted-Lowry acid is the acid minus the proton. The **conjugate acid** of a Brønsted-Lowry base is the base with the addition of one proton. For example, when acetic acid mixes with ammonia, it loses a proton (deprotonates) to its conjugate base (acetate ion). The ammonia (base) accepts the proton, forming an ammonium ion (the conjugate acid). The ammonium ion is an acid because it can lose a proton that would be accepted by the acetate ion (a base).

$$\underset{\text{acid}}{\overset{\text{proton donor}}{HC_2H_3O_2(aq)}} + \underset{\text{base}}{\overset{\text{proton acceptor}}{NH_3(aq)}} \longrightarrow \underset{\text{conjugate acid}}{\overset{\text{proton donor}}{NH_4^+(aq)}} + \underset{\text{conjugate base}}{\overset{\text{proton acceptor}}{C_2H_3O_2^-(aq)}}$$

Notice that these conjugate pairs differ only by a single proton (H^+). The molecules in blue are one conjugate pair, and the molecules in red are another.

TABLE 18-3 *Conjugate Pairs of Brønsted-Lowry Acids and Bases*

Conjugate Acid		Conjugate Base	
Name	**Formula**	**Formula**	**Name**
perchloric acid	$HClO_4$	ClO_4^-	perchlorate ion
hydrochloric acid	HCl	Cl^-	chloride ion
sulfuric acid	H_2SO_4	HSO_4^-	hydrogen sulfate ion
hydrogen sulfate ion	HSO_4^-	SO_4^{2-}	sulfate ion
acetic acid	$HC_2H_3O_2$	$C_2H_3O_2^-$	acetate ion
ammonium ion	NH_4^+	NH_3	ammonia
water	H_2O	OH^-	hydroxide ion

↑ increasing acid strength

Acids, Bases, and Salts 437

CONJUGATE ACIDS AND CONJUGATE BASES

In the Brønsted-Lowry model, a conjugate is a different form of an acid or base. A conjugate acid can be identified by one more H^+ that will be present because a proton was accepted. A conjugate base will have one less H^+ because the proton was released.

IS WATER AN ACID OR A BASE?

Use a **class discussion** to lead students to an understanding of one of water's unusual properties. Ask whether they think that water is an acid or a base. Select students to respond and have them explain their choices. During the ensuing discussion, point out that water is both an acid *and* a base according to all three models described in the chapter. According to the Arrhenius model, water is an acid because it releases hydrogen ions. However, since it releases an equal number of hydronium ions, it is also a base. The equal release of H^+ and OH^- makes water neutral. According to the Brønsted-Lowry model, water is an acid and a base because ionized water molecules both accept and donate protons. And according to the Lewis model, water molecules both accept and donate electron pairs.

ACIDS AND BASES

Use the following **formative assessment** to check students' understanding.

1. What type of bases are identified as substances that dissociate to release hydroxide ions in aqueous solutions? *(Arrhenius bases)*
2. Is a Brønsted-Lowry acid a proton donor or proton acceptor? *(donor)*
3. Define *Lewis acid* and *Lewis base. (A Lewis acid is a substance that accepts electron pairs; a Lewis base is a substance that donates electron pairs.)*
4. Classify each of the following as an Arrhenius, Brønsted-Lowry, or Lewis acid or base: $Ca(OH)_2$ and NH_4^+. *[$Ca(OH)_2$: Arrhenius, Brønsted-Lowry, and Lewis base; NH_4^+: Brønsted-Lowry and Lewis acid]*

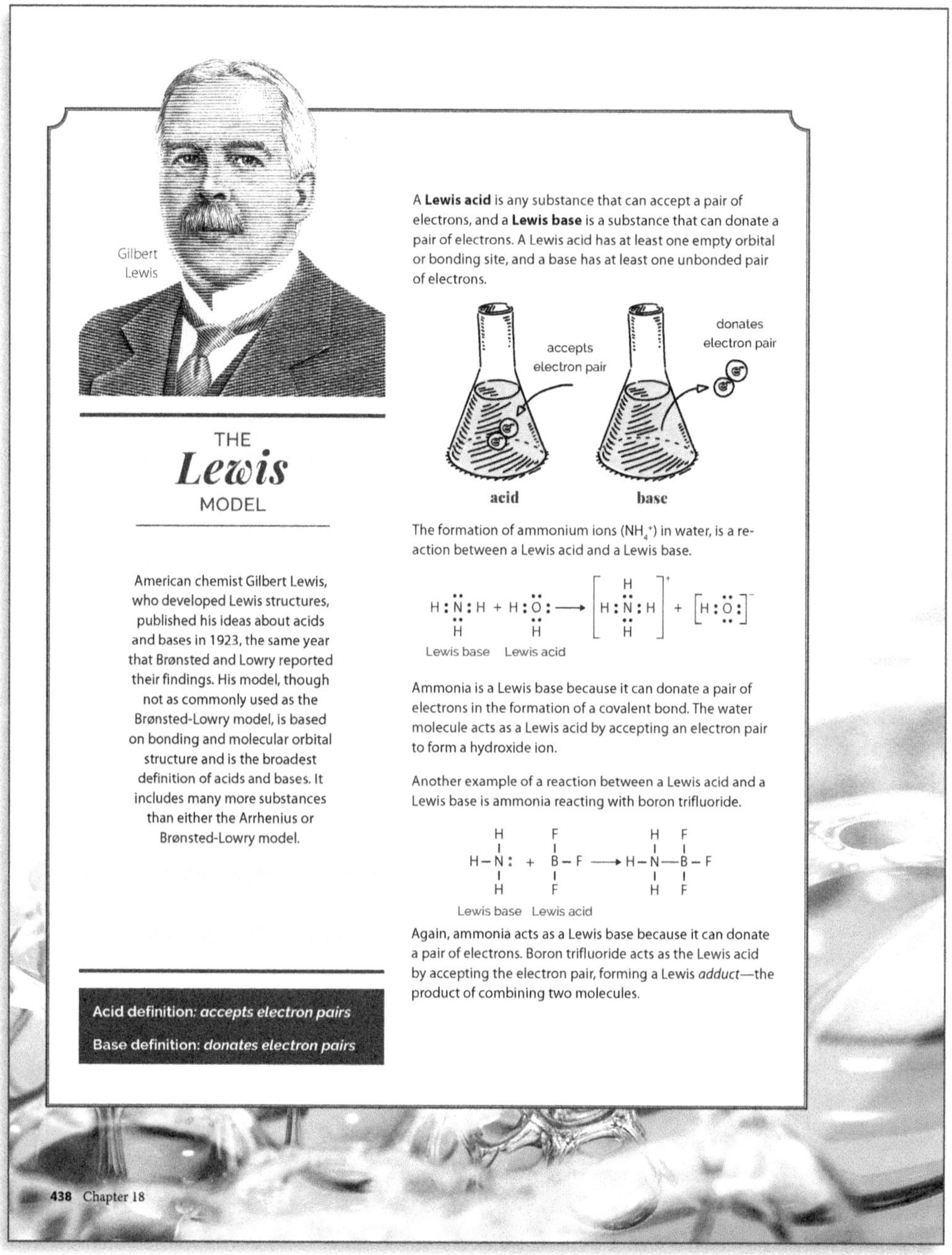
Gilbert Lewis

THE *Lewis* MODEL

American chemist Gilbert Lewis, who developed Lewis structures, published his ideas about acids and bases in 1923, the same year that Brønsted and Lowry reported their findings. His model, though not as commonly used as the Brønsted-Lowry model, is based on bonding and molecular orbital structure and is the broadest definition of acids and bases. It includes many more substances than either the Arrhenius or Brønsted-Lowry model.

Acid definition: *accepts electron pairs*

Base definition: *donates electron pairs*

A **Lewis acid** is any substance that can accept a pair of electrons, and a **Lewis base** is a substance that can donate a pair of electrons. A Lewis acid has at least one empty orbital or bonding site, and a base has at least one unbonded pair of electrons.

The formation of ammonium ions (NH_4^+) in water, is a reaction between a Lewis acid and a Lewis base.

Ammonia is a Lewis base because it can donate a pair of electrons in the formation of a covalent bond. The water molecule acts as a Lewis acid by accepting an electron pair to form a hydroxide ion.

Another example of a reaction between a Lewis acid and a Lewis base is ammonia reacting with boron trifluoride.

Again, ammonia acts as a Lewis base because it can donate a pair of electrons. Boron trifluoride acts as the Lewis acid by accepting the electron pair, forming a Lewis *adduct*—the product of combining two molecules.

438 Chapter 18

ASSESS

TICKET OUT THE DOOR

Assess students' understanding of the material with a **summarizing activity** by asking them to state how to identify a conjugate base and conjugate acid. *(A conjugate base is the acid minus the proton. A conjugate acid is the base with the addition of one proton.)*

CASE STUDY

ROYAL ACID TO THE RESCUE

In the spring of 1940, as the German army was moving through Denmark, Danish chemist Niels Bohr was in trouble. On a shelf in his laboratory sat two gold Nobel Prize medals, which had been smuggled out of Germany. Bohr was holding them for two German scientists, Max von Laue and James Franck, for safekeeping. What should he do with the medals?

George de Hevesy, a Hungarian chemist, had an idea—use chemistry. Hevesy spent the rest of the day slowly dissolving the medals in *aqua regia*, a very caustic mixture of nitric acid and hydrochloric acid. *Aqua regia* means "royal acid" and is so named because of its ability to dissolve precious metals such as gold and platinum.

When the soldiers arrived, they ransacked the laboratory. Finding nothing of value, they left, leaving behind an innocent-looking orange solution high on a shelf.

After the war, de Hevesy returned to Copenhagen and precipitated the gold out of the solution. Bohr sent the metal back to the Nobel Foundation where the medals were recast. Max von Laue and James Franck were again presented with their Nobel medals in 1952.

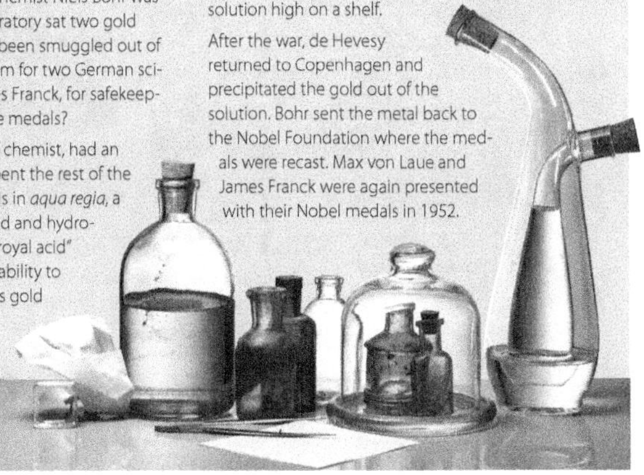

18.1 SECTION REVIEW

1. List four common properties of acids.
2. Formic acid (HCOOH) ionizes in water to form formate and hydronium ions.
   a. Write the equation for the ionization of formic acid in water.
   b. What is the acid in the forward reaction?
   c. What is the conjugate base of this acid?
   d. What is the name of the process by which formic acid loses a proton?
3. Define *acid* and *base* according to each model.
   a. Arrhenius model
   b. Brønsted-Lowry model
   c. Lewis model
4. What substance produced in aqueous solutions by H_2SO_4 makes it react strongly with many other substances? What ion is responsible for the corrosiveness of strong bases like NaOH?
5. Summarize the categories of acids and bases, especially how they are related to each other.
6. Identify each of the following as an Arrhenius acid or base, a Brønsted-Lowry acid or base, or a Lewis acid or base. Some substances may fit into more than one model.
   a. HCl
   b. Br^-
   c. CN^-
7. Write the words that complete the statements.
   a. H_2SO_4 is an Arrhenius _______ and therefore must be a Brønsted-Lowry _______.
   b. The Cl^- ion can be classified as a(n) _______ base or a(n) _______ base, but not as a(n) _______ base.

Use the case study above to answer Questions 8–9.

8. What property of acids was demonstrated in the case study?
9. Why did de Hevesy have to use the very caustic *aqua regia* to dissolve the medals?

Acids, Bases, and Salts **439**

DIFFERENTIATED INSTRUCTION

Acids and Bases

Guide students to **create a game** for identifying the differences between Arrhenius acids and bases, Brønsted-Lowry acids and bases (and their conjugate acids and bases), and Lewis acids and bases. They may set up the game any way they would like but must include the following details: the type of game, number of players, materials needed to play, game setup, and instructions on how to play and win the game.

If students would like suggestions for games, you could suggest a trivia game with categories in acids, bases, and salts. Make cards that say "acid" or "base" that students can hold up to answer questions. Or you could create a matching game with various acids and bases or a game of two corners (similar to four corners) with one corner acid and one corner base.

If time allows, have students work in pairs or as a group to play several of the student-created games.

18.1 REVIEW *ANSWERS*

1. Acids taste sour, react with active metals to produce hydrogen gas, turn blue litmus paper red, and neutralize bases. Students may list other properties. *(p. 435)*
2. a. $HCO_2H\ (aq) + H_2O\ (l) \rightleftharpoons H_3O^+\ (aq) + CO_2H^-\ (aq)$
   b. HCO_2H (formic acid)
   c. CO_2H (formate ion)
   d. deprotonation *(all p. 437)*
3. a. acid: a substance that releases hydrogen ions [H^+]; base: a substance that releases hydroxide ions [OH^-]
   b. acid: a substance that donates protons; base: a substance that accepts protons
   c. acid: a substance that can accept a pair of electrons to form a covalent bond; base: a substance that can donate a pair of electrons to form a covalent bond *(all pp. 436–38)*
4. H^+ or H_3O^+; OH^- *(pp. 436–38)*
5. The Lewis definitions of acids and bases are the broadest definitions. Lewis acids are electron-pair acceptors, while Lewis bases are electron-pair donors. These definitions are related to the bonding aspects of the substances. A subset of Lewis acids and bases are the Brønsted-Lowry acids and bases. Brønsted-Lowry acids are proton donors and Brønsted-Lowry bases are proton acceptors. The Arrhenius definitions are the most restrictive and occur only in aqueous solutions. Arrhenius acids form hydronium ions and bases form hydroxide ions in solution. *(pp. 436–38)*
6. a. Arrhenius, Brønsted-Lowry, and Lewis acid
   b. Brønsted-Lowry and Lewis base
   c. Brønsted-Lowry and Lewis base *(all pp. 436–38)*
7. a. acid; acid
   b. Brønsted-Lowry; Lewis (accept either order); Arrhenius *(all pp. 437–38)*
8. Acids react with metals. *(p. 439)*
9. Gold and platinum are not very reactive metals. Therefore, a very caustic acid was needed to react with the gold. *(p. 439)*

SECTION 18.2 *OVERVIEW*

Essential Question

If vinegar is an acid, why can we put it on foods?

Objectives

» **18.2.1** Relate self-ionization of water to pH and pOH.

» **18.2.2** Solve pH and pOH problems.

» **18.2.3** Compare the strengths of acids.

» **18.2.4** Classify acids as monoprotic, polyprotic, diprotic, or triprotic on the basis of their chemical formulas.

» **18.2.5** Summarize how indicators work.

Resources

How It Works: Breathalyzer

Demonstrating Red Cabbage and pH

Web Links: Virtual pH Meter, Acid-Base Solutions

Lab 18A: *Colorful Chemistry*—Exploring Acid-Base Indicators; Mini Lab: *Acid or Base?* (p. 452)

ENGAGE

EQUILIBRIUM CONSTANTS

Activate prior knowledge with a **think-pair-share**. Ask, "What is the difference between an equilibrium constant and a solubility product constant?" *(An equilibrium constant is the ratio of product equilibrium concentrations to reactant equilibrium concentrations. A solubility product constant is an equilibrium constant that results from the dissolving of a solute into a saturated solution.)*

Have each student discuss his answer with a partner, then select students to share their answers. Correct any misconceptions. If necessary, have students review how to calculate an equilibrium constant (see pages 412–14, 424–25).

QUESTIONS

» What does it mean to say that water is self-ionizing?

» How do we measure acidity and alkalinity?

» Are all acids and bases equally strong?

» What determines the strength of an acid or base?

» How do acid-base indicators work?

TERMS

self-ionization of water • pH • acidic solution • basic solution • neutral solution • pOH • strong acid • weak acid • weak base • strong base • acid-ionization constant • base-ionization constant • amphoteric substance • monoprotic acid • polyprotic acid • diprotic acid • triprotic acid • acid-base indicator • transition interval

If vinegar is an acid, why can we put it on foods?

18.2 ACID-BASE EQUILIBRIA

Some acids are safe to eat and drink, such as citric acid in orange juice. But other acids are dangerous, even deadly. For example, perchloric acid, which explodes on contact with cloth or wood, would wreak havoc as soon as it touched your mouth! What's the difference? Using the Brønsted-Lowry definition, the difference is the degree to which the acids release protons. Many acid-base reactions are reversible processes. Equilibrium constants describe how readily acids deprotonate and bases protonate. These equilibrium constants give scientists a way to describe the acidity or alkalinity of a solution.

The Self-Ionization of Water

In addition to all its unique physical properties, water has an intriguing chemical property—it can react with itself. The reaction is an acid-base reaction in which one water molecule donates a proton to another water molecule. Electrical conductivity experiments, which show that pure water is a weak electrolyte, verify that the reaction involves acids and bases. The two water molecules combine to form a hydroxide ion and a hydronium ion—a reaction called the **self-ionization of water**. In the reaction, one molecule acts as an acid and the other acts as a base.

proton acceptor, proton donor, proton acceptor, proton donor

$$H_2O(l) + H_2O(l) \rightleftharpoons H_3O^+(aq) + OH^-(aq)$$

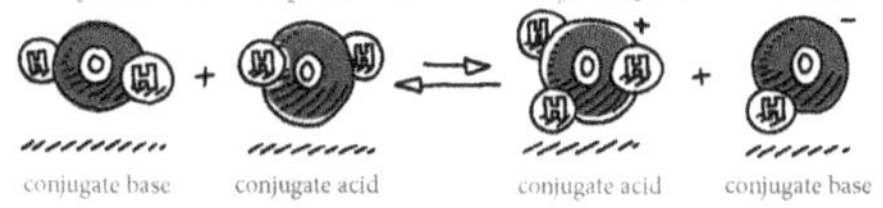

When a proton is transferred from one water molecule to another, self-ionization occurs.

The reaction is an equilibrium reaction in which the reverse reaction predominates. Only a few molecules produce ions. This reaction can be described with an equilibrium constant.

$$K_{eq} = \frac{[H_3O^+][OH^-]}{[H_2O]^2}$$

440 Chapter 18

INSTRUCT

THE SELF-IONIZATION OF WATER

Use a **video** to help explain to students the self-ionization of water. Numerous examples are hosted online, from brief illustrations to more detailed explanations. Do an internet search using the keywords "self-ionization of water," then select the video that best suits your needs.

Since water is the solvent, the water's concentration can't change; it can be considered part of K_{eq}, thus eliminating it from the equation.

$$K_{eq} = K_w = [H_3O^+][OH^-]$$

The resulting constant is called the *ionization constant of water* (K_w). Experimental evidence shows that the concentrations of hydronium and hydroxide ions are both 1.0×10^{-7} mol/L in pure water at 25 °C. Only 1 out of 555 million water molecules is ionized at any given instant. The product of these two concentrations gives K_w a value of 1.0×10^{-14} at 25 °C.

$$K_w = [H_3O^+][OH^-]$$
$$= (1.0 \times 10^{-7}\ \text{M})(1.0 \times 10^{-7}\ \text{M})$$
$$= 1.0 \times 10^{-14}$$

The value of K_w is a very important number. Whether a solution is acidic, basic, or neutral, the product of the concentration of hydronium ions and hydroxide ions always equals 1.0×10^{-14} at 25 °C.

EXAMPLE 18-1: CALCULATING AMOUNT CONCENTRATION FROM HYDRONIUM ION CONCENTRATION

The concentration of hydronium ions in a mild acid is found to be 5.2×10^{-7} mol/L. What is the concentration of hydroxide ions?

Write what you know.

$[H_3O^+] = 5.2 \times 10^{-7}$

$[OH^-] = ?$

Write the formula and solve for the unknown.

Given that $K_w = [H_3O^+][OH^-]$, solve for $[OH^-]$.

$$K_w = [H_3O^+][OH^-]$$

$$\frac{K_w}{[H_3O^+]} = \frac{\cancel{[H_3O^+]}[OH^-]}{\cancel{[H_3O^+]}}$$

$$[OH^-] = \frac{K_w}{[H_3O^+]}$$

Plug in known values and evaluate.

$$[OH^-] = \frac{1.0 \times 10^{-14}}{5.2 \times 10^{-7}}$$
$$= 1.9 \times 10^{-8}$$

The concentration of OH^- ions is 1.9×10^{-8} M.

AT 25 °C

The phrase "at 25 °C" is important because a change in temperature will cause a change in the rate of a reaction. The K_w value increases as temperature increases from 1.139×10^{-15} at 0 °C to 5.430×10^{-13} at 100 °C.

Remind students that though concentration is given in units, the units of equilibrium constants are not considered. Review from Chapter 17 how to determine an equilibrium constant (K_{eq}) and what the brackets mean (concentration).

$$K_{eq} = \frac{[\text{products}]}{[\text{reactants}]}$$

pH SCALE

Lead students to create a **T-chart** contrasting the difference between pH and pOH (presented on page 444). Be sure that they add the equations (including the antilogarithm equations) and an example of how to find the pH and pOH of a solution.

VIRTUAL pH METER

For an interactive pH meter that allows you to change the molarity and volume of a variety of acids, bases, and salts, visit TeacherToolsOnline.com. Under Additional Resources, click on Chapter 18 Web Links. Then click on *Virtual pH Meter*.

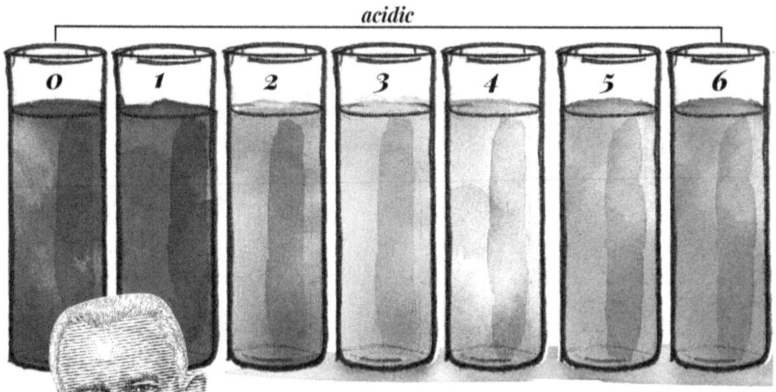

Søren P. L. Sørensen

The pH Scale

You can see that the concentrations of hydronium and hydroxide ions in aqueous solutions are very small, frequently ranging between 1 and 1×10^{-14} mol/L. Scientists find it awkward to deal regularly with such small numbers. Søren P. L. Sørensen, a Danish chemist, proposed the pH scale in 1909 to provide a clear, concise, and convenient way to describe the concentrations of these ions without using scientific notation. The **pH**, potential of hydrogen ions, is related to the concentration of the hydronium ion by the equation

$$pH = -\log[H_3O^+].$$

For example, consider a sample of pure water.

Its hydronium ion concentration is 1.0×10^{-7} mol/L. Let's calculate the pH of a sample of pure water.

$$pH = -\log[H_3O^+]$$
$$= -\log 1.0 \times 10^{-7}\ M$$
$$= -(-7.00) = 7.00$$

Thus, the pH of pure water is 7.00. Significant figures for pH calculations are a special case. The significant figures from the amount concentration determine the number of decimal places to the right of the decimal point because the digits to the left of the decimal point are related to the exponent in the amount concentration. But what does the pH tell us about the solution?

The pH value describes the acidity or alkalinity of a solution. All solutions with a pH less than 7 are called **acidic solutions** because the hydronium ion concentration is greater than the hydroxide ion concentration. All solutions with a pH greater than 7 are called **basic solutions**, or *alkaline solutions*, because the hydroxide ions outnumber the hydronium ions. A solution with a pH of 7 is a **neutral solution**. A sample of pure water is thus a neutral solution.

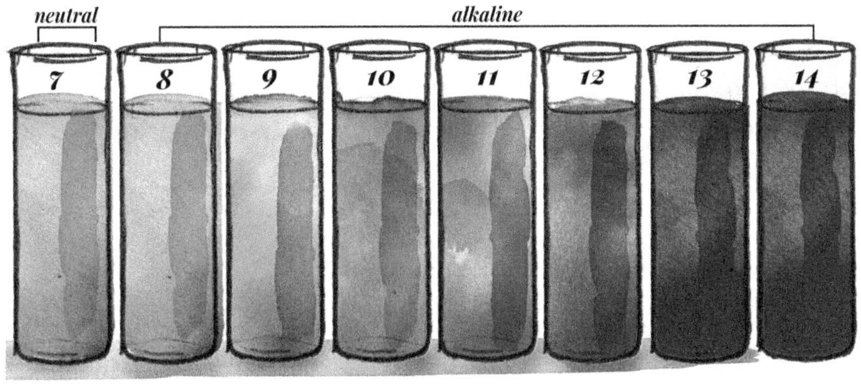

EXAMPLE 18-2: CALCULATING pH FROM HYDRONIUM ION CONCENTRATION

The hydronium ion concentration in a shampoo is 2.0×10^{-5} M. What is the pH of this shampoo?

Write what you know.

$[H_3O^+] = 2.0 \times 10^{-5}$ M
pH = ?

Write the formula and solve for the unknown.

$pH = -\log[H_3O^+]$

Plug in known values and evaluate.

$$pH = -\log 2.0 \times 10^{-5}\ M$$
$$= -(-4.70)$$
$$= 4.70$$

The pH of the shampoo is 4.70.

Calculating the concentration from the pH value is the opposite of calculating the pH from the concentration. The inverse of a logarithm is an antilogarithm, or antilog. In this case, you are taking the antilogarithm of the negative pH to get the concentration. For example, if the pH of a solution is known, the concentration of hydronium ions can be calculated. Because pH is a negative exponent, you can find $[H_3O^+]$ by raising 10 to a power given by −pH.

$$[H_3O^+] = 10^{-pH}$$

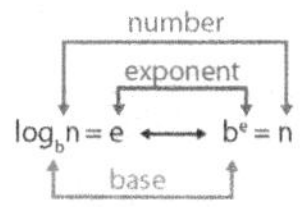

$$-\log[H_3O^+] = pH \longleftrightarrow 10^{-pH} = [H_3O^+]$$

EXAMPLE 18-3: CALCULATING HYDRONIUM ION CONCENTRATION FROM pH

What is the hydronium ion concentration in vinegar with a pH of 2.31?

Write what you know.

pH = 2.31
$[H_3O^+] = ?$

Write the formula and solve for the unknown.

$$pH = -\log[H_3O^+]$$
$$[H_3O^+] = 10^{-pH}$$

Plug in known values and evaluate.

$$[H_3O^+] = 10^{-2.31}$$
$$= 4.9 \times 10^{-3}\ M$$

The hydronium ion concentration in the vinegar is 4.9×10^{-3} M.

pH RANGE

Use a **quick check** to assess students' understanding. After working through Example 18-2, ask students what the pH of a 1.0 M HCl solution would be. *($[H_3O^+] = 1.0 \times 10^0$; the pH is 0.)* Now ask students to find the pH of a 10 M HCl solution. *($[H_3O^+] = 1.0 \times 10^1$; the pH is −1.)*

For most naturally occurring solutions, the 0–14 pH range is sufficient. When stronger lab solutions are considered (12 M HCl is commonly used), the range of pH values can expand from about −1.5 to 15.5.

pH, pOH, H^+, OH^-

Lead students to create an **illustration** of the diagram relating pH, pOH, H^+, and OH^-. Have them write in their own words a few sentences relating pH and pOH to the concentrations of H^+ and OH^- ions.

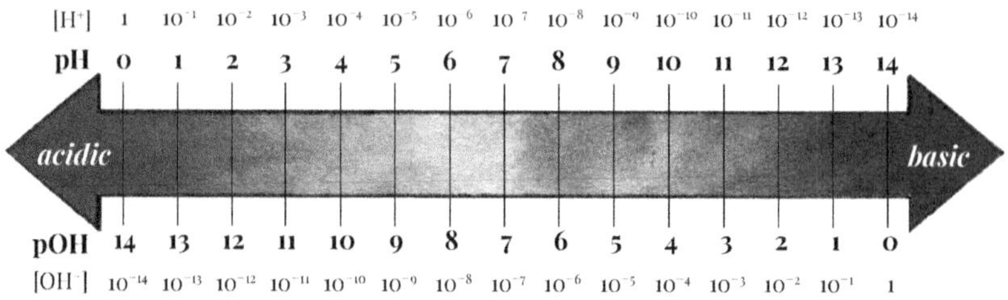

▲ This diagram can help you understand the relationships between pH, pOH, and the concentrations of H^+ and OH^- ions.

The pOH Scale

Just as pH describes hydronium ion concentration, pOH describes hydroxide ion concentration. The **pOH** of a solution is the negative logarithm of the hydroxide ion concentration.

$$pOH = -\log[OH^-]$$

Just like calculating the hydronium ion concentration in a solution from its pH, we can find the hydroxide ion concentration from the pOH value.

$$[OH^-] = 10^{-pOH}$$

Because the hydronium and hydroxide ion concentrations are related, pH and pOH are also related. For a substance at 25 °C, the sum of the pH and the pOH of a solution is 14.

$$pH + pOH = 14.0$$

Thus, $[H_3O^+]$, $[OH^-]$, pH, and pOH are all related.

Let's look at an example.

Household ammonia solutions used for cleaning are aqueous solutions of ammonia (NH_3). In water, ammonia produces ammonium hydroxide to produce a basic solution (pH = 11.7). How can the hydronium ion concentration, hydroxide ion concentration, and pOH of this solution be calculated? Because the pH of the solution is 11.7, the hydronium ion concentration can be calculated using the antilog.

$$[H_3O^+] = 10^{-11.7}$$

$$[H_3O^+] = 2 \times 10^{-12}\ M$$

The pOH can be calculated directly from the pH.

$$pOH = 14.0 - pH = 14.0 - 11.7 = 2.3$$

The hydroxide ion concentration can be calculated from the antilog of the pOH, just as the hydronium ion is calculated from the pH.

$$[OH^-] = 10^{-pOH} = 10^{-2.3} = 5 \times 10^{-3}\ M$$

EXAMPLE 18-4: CALCULATING pH AND pOH FROM CONCENTRATION

A sulfuric acid solution has a hydronium ion concentration of 3.2×10^{-2} mol/L. Calculate the pH, the pOH, and the hydroxide ion concentration of this solution. Identify the solution as acidic or basic.

Write what you know.

$[H_3O^+] = 3.2 \times 10^{-2}$ M
pH = ?
pOH = ?
$[OH^-]$ = ?

Find pH first.

Write the formula and solve for the unknown.

$pH = -\log[H_3O^+]$

Plug in known values and evaluate.

$$\begin{aligned} pH &= -\log 3.2 \times 10^{-2} \\ &= -(-1.49) \\ &= 1.49 \end{aligned}$$

Next, find the pOH.

Write the formula and solve for the unknown.

$$pH + pOH = 14.0$$
$$\cancel{pH} + pOH - \cancel{pH} = 14.0 - pH$$
$$pOH = 14.0 - pH$$

Plug in known values and evaluate.

$$\begin{aligned} pOH &= 14.00 - 1.49 \\ &= 12.51 \end{aligned}$$

The hydroxide ion concentration can now be calculated from the pOH.

Write the formula and solve for the unknown.

$[OH^-] = 10^{-pOH}$

Plug in known values and evaluate.

$$\begin{aligned} [OH^-] &= 10^{-12.51} \\ &= 3.1 \times 10^{-13}\ M \end{aligned}$$

The pH of the solution is 1.49, the pOH is 12.51, the hydroxide ion concentration is 3.1×10^{-13} M, and the solution is acidic.

Acid-Base Strength

Though pH describes the concentration of a solution, it does not describe its strength. For solutions, strong is not the same as concentrated and weak is not the same as dilute. The terms *concentrated* and *dilute* refer to the amount of acid in a given volume of aqueous solution. It is possible to have a dilute solution of a strong acid or a concentrated solution of a weak acid. **Strong acids** give up protons easily and ionize completely. The reaction in which the hydronium ions are produced is favored. Surprisingly, only six common acids are classified as strong acids: $HClO_4$, HI, HBr, HCl, H_2SO_4, and HNO_3. Notice below in the equation for the reaction that produces hydronium ions from HCl that the forward reaction is favored.

$$HCl(aq) + H_2O(l) \rightleftharpoons Cl^-(aq) + H_3O^+(aq)$$

Though the solutions look the same, testing with litmus paper demonstrates a significant difference between the two solutions.

STRENGTH VERSUS CONCENTRATION

Be sure that students don't confuse acid-base strength with concentration. Strength deals with how easily a substance releases or gains H^+ ions (the degree of ionization). Concentration is the molarity of a substance, or the number of H_3O^+ ions in solution.

For example, a 10.0 M aqueous solution of HCl is strong and concentrated. A 0.001 M HCl solution is strong (still loses H^+ ions easily) and dilute (10 000 times fewer H_3O^+ ions). A 10.0 M HCOOH solution is weak (minimal ionization) and concentrated (has many H_3O^+ ions), while a 0.001 M HCOOH solution is weak and dilute.

Acids, Bases, and Salts 445

ACID-BASE SOLUTIONS

For an interactive pH meter that allows you to change the strength of acids and bases and to vary concentrations, visit TeacherToolsOnline.com. Under Additional Resources, click on Chapter 18 Web Links. Then click on *Acid-Base Solutions*.

EXAMPLE 18-5: CALCULATING pH FROM MASS OF SOLUTE (STRONG ACID)

What is the pH of 0.500 L of solution that has 0.40 g of hydrogen iodide dissolved in it?

Write what you know.

$m_{HI} = 0.40\ g$
$V_{solution} = 0.500\ L$
$n_{HI} = ?$
$[H_3O^+] = ?$
$pH = ?$

Convert mass HI to moles.

$$0.40\ \cancel{g\ HI}\left(\frac{1\ mol\ HI}{127.91\ \cancel{g\ HI}}\right) = 0.003\underline{1}2\ mol\ HI$$

Write the formula and solve for the unknown.

$$[HI] = \frac{n_{HI}}{V_{solution}}$$

Plug in known values and evaluate.

$$[HI] = \frac{0.003\underline{1}2\ mol\ HI}{0.500\ L}$$

$$= 6.\underline{2}5 \times 10^{-3}\ \frac{mol\ HI}{L}$$

Because HI is a strong acid, we know that every mole of HI will produce a mole of hydronium ions.

Convert [HI] to $[H_3O^+]$

$$[H_3O^+] = 6.\underline{2}5 \times 10^{-3}\ \frac{\cancel{mol\ HI}}{L}\left(\frac{1\ mol\ H_3O^+}{1\ \cancel{mol\ HI}}\right)$$

$$= 6.\underline{2}5 \times 10^{-3}\ \frac{mol\ H_3O^+}{L}$$

Write the formula and solve for the unknown.

$$pH = -\log[H_3O^+]$$

Plug in known values and evaluate.

$$pH = -\log 6.\underline{2}5 \times 10^{-3}\ M$$
$$= -(-2.2)$$
$$= 2.20$$

As electrolytes, both of these acids release ions and conduct electricity. On the basis of this photo, can you tell which one is stronger?

Weak acids do not dissociate completely into ions because only a portion of their molecules loses protons. For example, only 1 in 24 molecules deprotonates in an acetic acid solution. The equilibrium reaction in which they dissociate is reactant-favored.

$$HC_2H_3O_2(aq) + H_2O(l) \rightleftharpoons C_2H_3O_2^-(aq) + H_3O^+(aq)$$

Similarly, the strength of a base depends on how easily it accepts a proton, or protonates. According to the Brønsted-Lowry model, **weak bases**, such as the Cl^- ion, are poor proton acceptors. **Strong bases**, such as the OH^- ion, accept protons readily. The hydroxides of active metals—LiOH, NaOH, KOH, RbOH, CsOH, $Mg(OH)_2$, $Ca(OH)_2$, $Sr(OH)_2$, and $Ba(OH)_2$—are the best sources of the hydroxide ion, so they are commonly called strong bases.

The conjugate of a strong acid or a strong base is always weak. For example, perchloric acid ($HClO_4$) is a strong acid that readily gives up a hydrogen ion. Once the hydrogen and the perchlorate ions are apart, they do not readily rejoin to form perchloric acid. Therefore, the perchlorate ion (ClO_4^-) is a weak conjugate base. Conversely, Cl^- is a weak base with a strong conjugate acid—HCl.

Acid and base strengths are described by the equilibrium constant of their dissociation reactions. The **acid-ionization constant** (K_a) describes the extent of the forward equilibrium reaction in the formation of the hydronium ion. In this generalized formula, *HA* represents a typical acid where *A* represents the anion.

$$HA + H_2O \rightleftharpoons H_3O^+ + A^-$$

$$K_a = \frac{[H_3O^+][A^-]}{[HA]}$$

446 Chapter 18

Similarly, the **base-ionization constant** (K_b) describes the extent of the forward equilibrium reaction in the formation of the hydroxide ion. Here, B represents a base. HB^+ represents a base that has captured a hydrogen ion from water.

$$B + H_2O \rightleftharpoons OH^- + HB^+$$

$$K_b = \frac{[OH^-][HB^+]}{[B]}$$

When dealing with acids and bases in aqueous solution, both of these constants are related to the constant for the self-ionization of water, K_w.

$$(K_a)(K_b) = K_w$$

Stronger acids and bases have higher K_a and K_b values because they ionize more readily. In fact, the forward reaction for strong acids and bases is so predominant that the reaction proceeds to completion because they completely dissociate. Table 18-4 lists conjugate pairs and their ionization constants in order from strong to weak. Because the stronger acids have weaker conjugate bases, the bases at the top of the column are the weakest. As in all equilibrium reactions, the values are specified for 25 °C, but their values change as temperature changes.

TABLE 18-4 *Relative Strengths of Some Acids and Bases**

Acid		K_a	K_b	Base	
perchloric acid	$HClO_4$	large	very small	ClO_4^-	perchlorate ion
hydriodic acid	HI	large	very small	I^-	iodide ion
hydrobromic acid	HBr	large	very small	Br^-	bromide ion
hydrochloric acid	HCl	large	very small	Cl^-	chloride ion
sulfuric acid	H_2SO_4	large	very small	HSO_4^-	hydrogen sulfate ion
nitric acid	HNO_3	large	very small	NO_3^-	nitrate ion
sulfurous acid	H_2SO_3	1.3×10^{-2}	8.3×10^{-13}	HSO_3^-	bisulfate ion
hydrogen sulfate ion	HSO_4^-	1.2×10^{-2}	8.3×10^{-13}	SO_4^{2-}	sulfate ion
phosphoric acid	H_3PO_4	6.9×10^{-3}	1.3×10^{-12}	$H_2PO_4^-$	dihydrogen phosphate ion
hydrofluoric acid	HF	6.8×10^{-4}	1.4×10^{-11}	F^-	fluoride ion
formic acid	HCO_2H	1.8×10^{-4}	5.6×10^{-11}	CO_2H^-	formate ion
acetic acid	$HC_2H_3O_2$	1.7×10^{-5}	5.6×10^{-10}	$C_2H_3O_2^-$	acetate ion
carbonic acid	H_2CO_3	4.3×10^{-7}	2.4×10^{-8}	HCO_3^-	hydrogen carbonate ion
hypochlorous acid	$HClO$	3.0×10^{-8}	2.9×10^{-7}	ClO^-	hypochlorite ion
boric acid	H_3BO_3	5.8×10^{-10}	1.4×10^{-5}	$H_2BO_3^-$	dihydrogen borate ion
ammonium ion	NH_4^+	5.7×10^{-10}	1.8×10^{-5}	NH_3	ammonia
hydrocyanic acid	HCN	4.9×10^{-10}	2.5×10^{-5}	CN^-	cyanide ion
hydrogen carbonate ion	HCO_3^-	4.8×10^{-11}	2.1×10^{-4}	CO_3^{2-}	carbonate ion
hydrogen peroxide	H_2O_2	2.6×10^{-12}	1.3×10^{-2}	HO_2^-	hydroperoxide ion
water	H_2O	1.0×10^{-14}	55.5	OH^-	hydroxide ion
ammonia	NH_3	very small	large	NH_2^-	amide ion
hydrogen	H_2	very small	large	H^-	hydride ion
methane	CH_4	very small	large	CH_3^-	methide ion

increasing acid strength ↑ (bottom to top); increasing base strength ↓ (top to bottom)

*First six acids are strong acids and last four bases are strong bases.

ALL THE *K*s

The acid-ionization and base-ionization constants are the last of the five *K*s: K_{eq} and K_{sp} from Chapter 17 and K_w, K_a and K_b from Chapter 18.

FACTORS THAT AFFECT ACID STRENGTH

Bond strength, the electronegativity of the central atom, and the number of oxygen atoms all affect the strength of an acid. For example, in the series HF, HCl, HBr, and HI, HF is the weakest acid because the bond between hydrogen and fluorine is very strong. HI is the strongest acid because iodine breaks its bond with hydrogen easily to ionize. With oxyacids, the opposite is true. The higher the electronegativity of the central atom, the stronger the acid will be. In the series HClO, HBrO, and HIO, HClO is the strongest acid because chlorine's electronegativity is higher than that of bromine and iodine. For oxyanions with different amounts of oxygen, the oxyanion with more oxygen is a stronger acid. For example, $HClO_4$ is stronger than $HClO_3$.

TABLE 18-5

Acid-Base Strength Summary

Strong Acid	Strong Base
has exposed hydrogen nuclei	has exposed electron pairs
has minimal negative charges	has possible strong negative charges

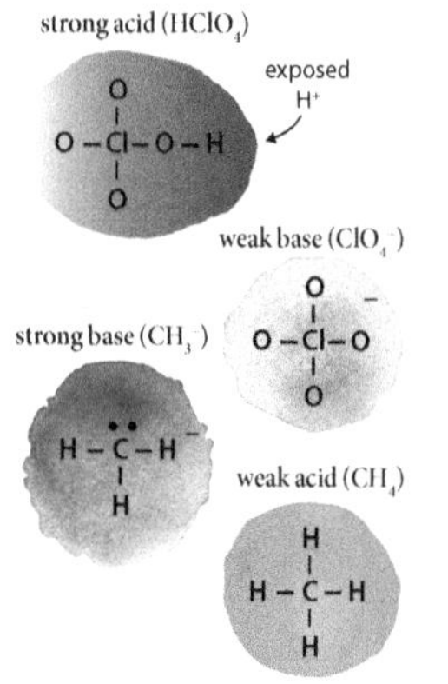

Polarity, Charge, and Acid-Base Strength

Ionization constants *describe* acid-base strengths; they do not *determine* the strengths. The location of shared electron clouds, the availability of a lone pair, and the charge on an acid or base all determine how easily a proton can be released or absorbed. In other words, the strongest acids are more polar and have lower bond energies. The strongest bases are negatively charged and have available bonding sites. Strong bases are often soluble ionic compounds of hydroxides and alkali or alkaline-earth metals, like NaOH and $Mg(OH)_2$. These ionic compounds completely dissociate in water to form hydroxide ions, which are strong proton acceptors.

The polarity of the bond between the hydrogen and the central atom is an important factor in determining acid strength. To be easily ionizable, the nucleus of a hydrogen atom must be exposed. As the polarity of the bond increases, the shared electrons are shifted away from the hydrogen toward a more electronegative atom in the center of the molecule. This creates a positive charge around the hydrogen and weakens the bond. For example, hydrofluoric acid, with its highly polar bond, is a strong acid because of the high electronegativity of fluorine. Methane on the other hand has only slightly polar bonds, making it a weak acid.

The electrical charge of a molecule also determines the strengths of acids. The sulfuric acid molecule (H_2SO_4) has a neutral charge and is a strong acid. As sulfuric acid deprotonates, it forms a hydrogen sulfate ion (HSO_4^-), which has another proton that it can donate. But due to its negative charge, it has a much lower tendency to release this proton. Similarly, H_3PO_4, $H_2PO_4^-$, and HPO_4^{2-} have decreasing acidic strengths. Anions hold protons more strongly than neutral molecules do.

Breathalyzer

The active ingredient in alcoholic beverages is ethanol, also known as ethyl alcohol or grain alcohol (CH_3CH_2OH). Ethanol is unique because it is absorbed unchanged into the bloodstream by the intestines, stomach, esophagus, and even the mouth and does not readily dissociate in the presence of digestive acids. This is why police can tell that a person has been drinking by checking the smell of his breath.

The alcohol in a person's breath is directly related to the amount in his blood—his blood alcohol content (BAC). Is there an accurate way for police officers to determine a person's BAC by measuring the ethanol in his breath? Police officers can now estimate a driver's BAC right on the side of the road using a device that tests a person's breath—a Breathalyzer. The device contains a fuel cell in which the ethanol reacts to form acetic acid and also produces an electric current. The current is proportional to the BAC of the driver. The more current produced, the greater the BAC of the driver and the more impaired he is. Through the chemistry of acids, scientists and police work to keep our roads safe.

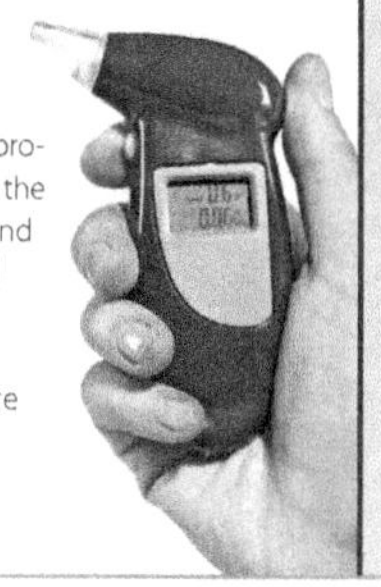

HOW IT *WORKS*

Amphoteric Substances

An **amphoteric substance** can act as both a Brønsted-Lowry acid and a Brønsted-Lowry base. Its behavior depends on reaction conditions. For example, the hydrogen carbonate ion accepts a proton (H^+ ion) when an acid is added to the solution. Under those circumstances, the hydrogen carbonate ion is a base.

$$\underset{\text{base}}{HCO_3^-(aq)} + \underset{\text{acid}}{H_3O^+(aq)} \rightleftharpoons \underset{\text{conjugate acid}}{H_2CO_3(aq)} + \underset{\text{conjugate base}}{H_2O(l)}$$

But when a base is added to the solution, the hydrogen carbonate ion acts as an acid by donating a proton.

$$\underset{\text{acid}}{HCO_3^-(aq)} + \underset{\text{base}}{OH^-(aq)} \rightleftharpoons \underset{\text{conjugate base}}{CO_3^{2-}(aq)} + \underset{\text{conjugate acid}}{H_2O(l)}$$

Water is also an amphoteric substance, as demonstrated by its reactions with ammonia and perchloric acid. In a reaction with ammonia, water acts as a Brønsted-Lowry acid, donating a proton.

$$\underset{\text{acid}}{H_2O(l)} + \underset{\text{base}}{NH_3(aq)} \rightleftharpoons \underset{\text{conjugate base}}{OH^-(aq)} + \underset{\text{conjugate acid}}{NH_4^+(aq)}$$

When reacting with perchloric acid, water acts as a base by receiving a proton.

$$\underset{\text{base}}{H_2O(l)} + \underset{\text{acid}}{HClO_4(aq)} \rightleftharpoons \underset{\text{conjugate acid}}{H_3O^+(aq)} + \underset{\text{conjugate base}}{ClO_4^-(aq)}$$

Polyprotic Acids

Some Brønsted-Lowry acids—such as perchloric acid ($HClO_4$), hydrochloric acid (HCl), and nitric acid (HNO_3)—can donate only one proton; these are called **monoprotic acids**. On the other hand, each molecule of a **polyprotic acid** can donate more than one proton. Each stage of ionization has a different equilibrium constant. A **diprotic acid** can donate two protons. For example, carbonic acid (H_2CO_3) is diprotic. The K_a for the first ionization is called K_{a1}, and that for the second ionization is called K_{a2}. (See Table 18-4 on page 447 for the K_a values of carbonic acid and the hydrogen carbonate ion.)

A proton is lost at each stage of ionization.

$$H_2CO_3(aq) + H_2O(l) \rightleftharpoons HCO_3^-(aq) + H_3O^+(aq)$$

$$K_{a1} = \frac{[H_3O^+][HCO_3^-]}{[H_2CO_3]}$$

$$= 4.3 \times 10^{-7}$$

$$HCO_3^-(aq) + H_2O(l) \rightleftharpoons CO_3^{2-}(aq) + H_3O^+(aq)$$

$$K_{a2} = \frac{[H_3O^+][CO_3^{2-}]}{[HCO_3^-]}$$

$$= 4.8 \times 10^{-11}$$

K_a AND NEGATIVE IONS

Lead a **discussion** on the K_a values of the polyprotic acids example. Point out to students that the K_a value for a first-ionization reaction is larger than the K_a for the second, which is larger than the K_a for the third. Ask students why they think this happens. *(It becomes progressively harder to remove a proton from a negatively charged ion than from a neutral particle.)*

Acids, Bases, and Salts 449

TRIPROTIC ACIDS

Use a **discussion** to lead students to identify a triprotic acid. Direct them to look at Table 18-6 for reference and have them analyze the various acids. (*Examples:* phosphoric acid [H_3PO_4] and citric acid [$C_6H_8O_7$])

DEMONSTRATING RED CABBAGE AND pH

Demonstrate a color change using a natural indicator.

Materials: ring stand and iron ring, wire gauze, laboratory burner, water, 500 mL beaker, red cabbage leaves (4), spatula, test tubes (at least 15), test tube rack, 1 mL pipette, 0.1 M HCl, 1.0 M NaOH, household substances to test (vinegar, baking powder, ammonia, coffee, soda, juice, antacids, and baking soda)

Preparation: Set up the ring stand, iron ring, and wire gauze with the burner underneath. Add 250 mL of water to the beaker and heat. While the water is heating, shred the red cabbage and add it to the water. Let the water boil for at least 5 minutes. Remove the cabbage from the liquid and let the cabbage juice cool to room temperature.

Number fourteen test tubes 1–14 and place in order in a test tube rack. Add 10 mL of water to Tube 7 and 9 mL of water to Tubes 1–6 and 8–13. Leave Tube 14 empty for now.

Tubes 1–6: With a pipette, add 10 mL of 0.1 M HCl to Tube 1. Then remove 1 mL of HCl solution from Tube 1, add it to Tube 2, and stir. Rinse the pipette and continue this procedure (1 mL from Tube 2 to Tube 3, and so on) through Tube 6.

Note: To prepare 0.1 M HCl, slowly add 0.9 mL of 12 M concentrated HCl to 99.1 mL of H_2O.

Tubes 7–14: Add 10 mL of 1.0 M NaOH to Tube 14. Remove 1 mL of NaOH solution from Tube 14, add it to Tube 13, and stir. Rinse the pipette and continue the procedure for Tubes 8–12. Do not add any NaOH to Tube 7. Now each tube has a pH value corresponding to its number (in other words, Tube 1 has a pH of 1, Tube 2 has a pH of 2, and so on).

TABLE 18-6

Ionization Constants of Polyprotic Acids

Polyprotic Acid	Acid-Base Reaction	K_a
chromic acid	$H_2CrO_4 \rightleftharpoons H^+ + HCrO_4^-$	1.8×10^{-1}
	$HCrO_4^- \rightleftharpoons H^+ + CrO_4^{2-}$	3.2×10^{-7}
hydrosulfuric acid	$H_2S \rightleftharpoons H^+ + HS^-$	1.1×10^{-7}
	$HS^- \rightleftharpoons H^+ + S^{2-}$	1.0×10^{-14}
phosphoric acid	$H_3PO_4 \rightleftharpoons H^+ + H_2PO_4^-$	6.9×10^{-3}
	$H_2PO_4^- \rightleftharpoons H^+ + HPO_4^{2-}$	6.2×10^{-8}
	$HPO_4^{2-} \rightleftharpoons H^+ + PO_4^{3-}$	4.8×10^{-13}
sulfurous acid	$H_2SO_3 \rightleftharpoons H^+ + HSO_3^-$	1.3×10^{-2}
	$HSO_3^- \rightleftharpoons H^+ + SO_3^{2-}$	6.3×10^{-8}

For any polyprotic acid, all the possible stages of ionization occur in the same solution. For instance, a solution of phosphoric acid (H_3PO_4) contains the ions $H_2PO_4^-$, HPO_4^{2-}, and PO_4^{3-} in addition to the hydronium ion H_3O^+.

All polyprotic acids have at least one amphoteric substance in their series of ionizations. In carbonic acid, the hydrogen carbonate ion is amphoteric. Furthermore, the K_{a2} is smaller than the K_{a1}. The first ionization involves separation of a proton from an uncharged carbonic acid (H_2CO_3) molecule, and the second involves separation of a proton from the negatively charged hydrogen carbonate ion (HCO_3^-). Because the strength of attraction between opposite charges depends on the magnitude of the charges, the second ionization is less favorable than the first. In general, $K_{a1} > K_{a2} > K_{a3}$. Acids with three ionizable protons are called **triprotic acids.** Can you name a triprotic acid? Several more examples of polyprotic acids are shown in Table 18-6.

Measuring pH

Acid-base indicators are substances whose colors are sensitive to pH. As a result, they change colors when the pH of a solution changes. At the beginning of this chapter you were introduced to litmus paper, a type of indicator. Indicators may be weak acids or bases whose conjugates are different colors. Typically, the anion has one color when it is combined with the hydrogen atom and a different color after ionization. Some indicators change colors at low pH values, some at high pH values. Those that change at low pH values are the stronger acids because they ionize easily. The indicators that do not change color until at the higher pH range are weaker acids. Some are polyprotic, so they may exhibit more than one color change.

Examples of indicators, their colors, and the pH range over which their colors change are given below. Notice that each indicator has a range of pH values over which the color change occurs. This is known as the **transition interval**.

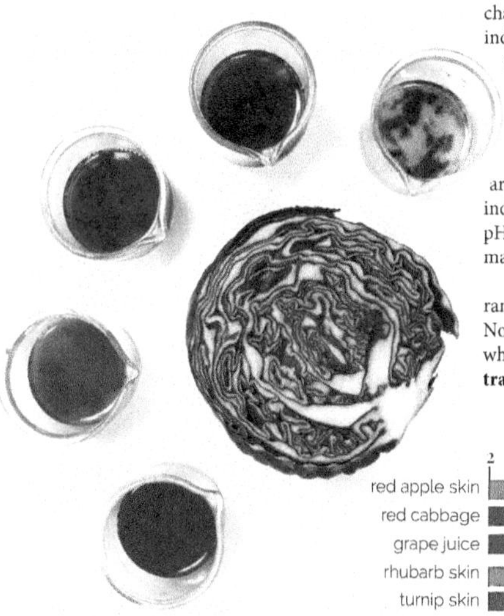

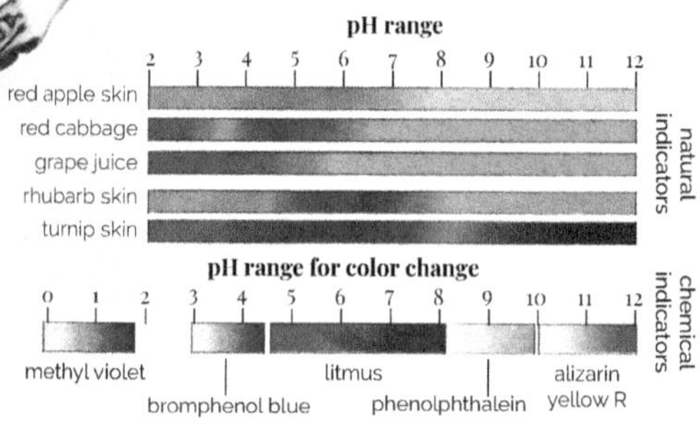

Performance/Discussion: Using a pipette, add 10 drops of cabbage juice to each test tube. You may have to add more if the cabbage juice is dilute. Compare the range of colors to those shown for red cabbage on page 450. If you have a pH meter, use it to verify. You can now use these test tubes as your standard for determining the pH of other substances.

Add 10 mL of each household solution to separate test tubes. Dissolve any solids in water. Add cabbage juice and estimate their pH by comparing them to Tubes 1–14.

Verify your results with a pH meter if one is available. If the solution is colored, such as orange juice or brown sodas, the color change of the cabbage juice may be altered.

Indicators give rough estimates of the pH value. For instance, if a solution is yellow when tested with both bromthymol blue and methyl orange, then the pH must be between 4.4 and 6.0. Methyl orange has a transition interval from a pH of 3.1 to 4.4. Once the pH is past 4.4, the color remains essentially unchanged. For example, methyl orange cannot indicate the alkalinity of a solution. This problem may be overcome by using carefully chosen combinations of indicators called *universal indicators.* More accurate values can be obtained when large numbers of indicators are used, but this process is tedious.

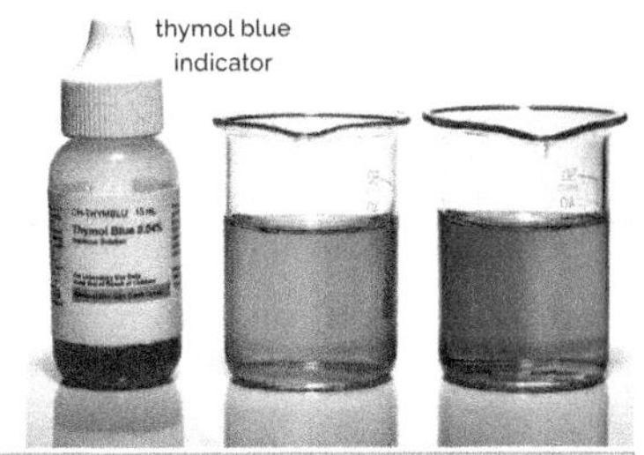

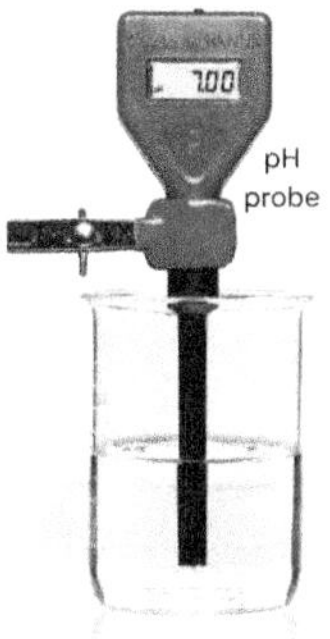

Indicators are subjective because they depend on a person's color perception and comparison. More objective pH measurements can be obtained by using a *pH meter.* A pH meter indirectly determines the concentration of the hydronium ions by measuring the voltage that they produce between two points and comparing the voltage to a standard. The instrument uses a *pH probe,* which is a sensor that responds only to hydronium ions. The meter also contains a reference probe and usually a temperature sensor or adjustment control since the measurement of pH is temperature dependent. The voltage produced by the probe is directly proportional to pH. The slope of the pH probe's output is determined by temperature. The pH instrument converts the voltage and temperature information into a digital display of pH. Before measurements are taken, these meters are standardized, using solutions of known pH, to ensure accuracy.

18.2 SECTION REVIEW

1. What does it mean that water is self-ionizing?
2. What particles are always present in pure water?
3. Using the information given, find the $[H_3O^+]$, $[OH^-]$, pH, and pOH for each solution below. Also identify the solution as acidic, neutral, or basic.
   a. orange juice, pH = 4.13
   b. $[H_3O^+] = 9.5 \times 10^{-8}$
   c. black coffee, pOH = 9.05
   d. $[OH^-] = 3.55 \times 10^{-6}$
4. Calculate the $[H_3O^+]$, pH, $[OH^-]$, and pOH of each solution. Assume that the acid completely dissociates.
   a. 1.3×10^{-5} M HCl
   b. 2.71×10^{-2} M H_2SO_4
5. Using Table 18-4, indicate the stronger acid in each pair.
   a. $HClO_4$, H_3PO_4
   b. formic acid, acetic acid
   c. hydrocyanic acid, formic acid
   d. NH_4^+, HSO_4^-
   e. NH_4^+, H_2O
6. Is the HCO_3^- ion an acid, a base, both, or neither? Explain.
7. All the following substances can undergo deprotonation reactions. Write the equations for their ionization constants. If they go through a series of ionizations, include the equation for each.
   a. H_2SO_4
   b. H_3PO_4
8. Explain how an acid-base indicator works.

18.2 REVIEW ANSWERS

* An asterisk following a question number indicates that a worked-out solution can be found on pages 461A–61B.

1. Pure water ionizes to a small degree into hydronium ions and hydroxide ions. Since the ions form from water molecules, there are always equal numbers of each ion in pure water, resulting in a neutral solution. *(p.440)*
2. H_3O^+ (H^+) and OH^- ions and, of course, H_2O molecules *(p. 440)*
3.*a. $[H_3O^+] = 7.4 \times 10^{-5}$; $[OH^-] = 1.3 \times 10^{-10}$; pOH = 9.87; acidic
   b. $[OH^-] = 1.1 \times 10^{-7}$; pH = 7.02; pOH = 6.98; basic
   c. $[H_3O^+] = 1.12 \times 10^{-5}$; $[OH^-] = 8.9 \times 10^{-10}$; pH = 4.95; acidic
   d. pOH = 2.82×10^{-9}; pH = 8.550; $[H_3O^+] = 2.82 \times 10^{-9}$; basic *(all pp. 441–45)*
4.*a. $[H_3O^+] = 1 \times 10^{-5}$; pH = 4.89; pOH = 9.11; $[OH^-] = 7.7 \times 10^{-10}$
   b. $[H_3O^+] = 5.42 \times 10^{-2}$; pH = 1.266; $[OH^-] = 1.85 \times 10^{-13}$; pOH = 12.734 *(all pp. 441–45)*
5. a. $HClO_4$
   b. formic acid
   c. formic acid
   d. HSO_4^-
   e. NH_4^+ *(all p. 447)*
6. The HCO_3^- ion acts as both an acid and a base, depending on its chemical environment. It can act as an acid, losing a proton when a base is added to it. It can also act as a base when an acid is added to it. *(p. 449)*
7.* *(pp. 449–50)*
8. An acid-base indicator is a substance whose color is sensitive to pH. As a result, it changes color when the pH of a solution changes. *(p. 450)*

WHY DO INDICATORS CREATE A COLOR CHANGE?

A substance's molecular structure determines how it will absorb or reflect light, which in turn determines its color. For example, in some substances, the tighter a molecule holds on to its electrons, the bluer it will be. When an indicator is added to the molecules, electrons and protons are either added to or taken from each molecule, and the color of each molecule changes.

APPLY

LAB 18A: *COLORFUL CHEMISTRY*

Once students have an understanding of the material in Section 18.2, they should be ready to work through Lab 18A.

ASSESS

TICKET OUT THE DOOR

As a **summarizing activity**, assess students' understanding by asking, "What is one factor in determining acid strength?" *(Students should indicate the polarity of the bond between hydrogen and the central atom or the electrical charge of a molecule.)*

MINI LAB: *ACID OR BASE?*

Use this **mini lab** to determine whether a substance is an acid or base.

1. Acids are sour, conduct electricity, and turn blue litmus paper red. Bases are bitter, conduct electricity, feel slippery, and turn red litmus paper blue.
2. An acid-base indicator is a chemical that changes color depending on the pH of its environment. It can be used to indicate the presence of an acid or base within its usable range.
3. Answers will vary. Students should recognize some solutions (e.g., juice or vinegar) as acids because of their sour taste.
4. Answers will vary. Many students may predict milk as being a base because it can feel slippery.
5. A pH meter is an electrical device. Students should conclude that the electrical conductivity of acids and bases is the property that enables pH meters to work.

MINI LAB

ACID OR BASE?

Throughout this chapter, we have been discussing acids and bases. How prevalent are these substances? What is the pH of some common substances?

Are there acids and bases around me every day?

1. What are the physical properties of acids and bases?
2. What is an acid-base indicator?

Procedure

A. Copy the table at right onto a piece of paper.

B. Consider the substances that you will be testing and predict whether each is an acid or base. Record your predictions in your table.

C. In each beaker, use a small (3 cm) strip of indicator paper to test the pH of each solution. Test each solution by dipping one end of the paper in the solution and then compare the color of the paper to the indicator paper legend. Record the color, approximate pH, and whether the solution is an acid or base in the table.

Conclusion

3. Which substances did you correctly predict? What was it about the substance that enabled you to predict whether it was an acid or base?
4. Which substances did you not correctly predict? What was it about the substance that caused you to predict it incorrectly?

Going Further

5. What property of acids and bases do you think a pH meter uses? Explain?

EQUIPMENT
- beakers, 50 mL (6)
- universal pH indicator paper
- acids and bases (6), 10 mL

Substance	Prediction	Indicator Color	pH	Conclusion: Acid or Base?

18.3 NEUTRALIZATION

The pain and discomfort of heartburn are usually associated with meals that were either too large or too spicy. But the burning sensation comes not from oregano or green peppers but from excess hydrochloric acid. This acid, which is normally confined to the stomach, irritates the tissues of the esophagus if it rises past the upper part of the stomach. To relieve the pain, a person can neutralize the acid with an antacid. Antacids react with the excess stomach acid to produce harmless products.

Salts

As mentioned in Section 18.1, a neutralization reaction is the reaction of an acid and a base to produce water and a salt. Antacids that contain magnesium hydroxide react to neutralize stomach acid as described by the following equation.

$$Mg(OH)_2(aq) + 2HCl(aq) \longrightarrow MgCl_2(aq) + 2H_2O(l)$$

Sodium hydroxide is much too corrosive to be used as an antacid, but it too neutralizes acids.

$$2NaOH(aq) + H_2SO_4(aq) \longrightarrow Na_2SO_4(aq) + 2H_2O(l)$$

A **salt** is a substance formed when the anion of an acid and the cation of a base combine. In the first reaction shown above, Cl^- (the acid's anion) combines with Mg^{2+} (the base's cation) to form $MgCl_2$ (the salt). Many different salts can be produced in neutralization reactions. Sodium chloride, zinc bromide, and potassium fluoride are all examples of salts. Most salts, like these, are composed of a metal and a nonmetal, but this is not always true. Ammonium chloride (NH_4Cl), potassium sulfate (K_2SO_4), and aluminum phosphate ($AlPO_4$) all contain polyatomic ions.

According to the Arrhenius definitions of acids and bases, neutralization reactions form water from hydronium and hydroxide ions. We can easily see this from the net ionic reaction of a neutralization reaction. The hydronium ions of acids and the hydroxide ions of bases combine to form two water molecules.

$$H_3O^+(aq) + OH^-(aq) \longrightarrow 2H_2O(l)$$

Metal cations and nonmetal anions are present, but they are not involved in the neutralization reaction. Because these ions are found in the solution of the reactant and the product, they are called *spectator ions*. If the resulting solution evaporates, the ions will crystallize into a salt.

QUESTIONS
- What are the products of a neutralization reaction?
- What is titration?
- How can I experimentally determine the concentration of an acid or base?
- How do buffers work?

TERMS
salt • acid-base titration • equivalence point • end point • buffer

How do antacids work?

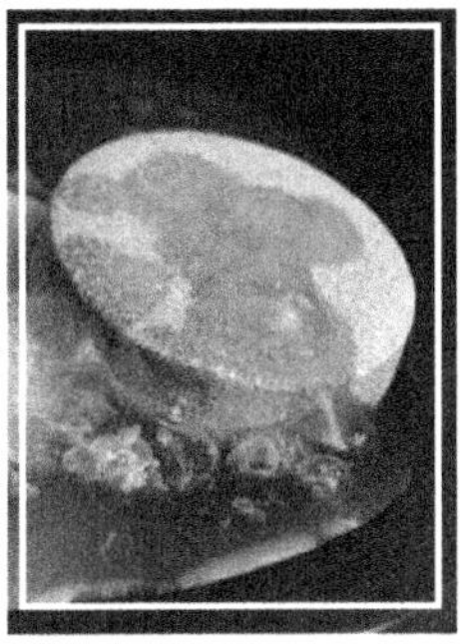

Antacid reacting with HCl acid. Antacids are effective because they react to reduce the excess hydrochloric acid in the stomach.

ENGAGE

NEUTRALIZATION REACTION

Direct students through a **review discussion** of neutralization from Section 18.1. Ask them to define the term *neutralization reaction* and give an example of a reaction that they believe may be a neutralization reaction. *(A neutralization reaction is the reaction of an acid and a base to produce water and a salt. Example: using an antacid product to neutralize stomach acid)*

After you have finished discussing the definition of a neutralization reaction, present the following video with animation on the neutralization of bee and wasp stings. Visit TeacherToolsOnline.com. Under Additional Resources, click on Chapter 18 Web Links. Then click on *Neutralization*.

SECTION 18.3 OVERVIEW

Essential Question
How do antacids work?

Objectives
- **18.3.1** Write balanced chemical equations for neutralization reactions.
- **18.3.2** Summarize the titration process.
- **18.3.3** Calculate the concentration of a solution from acid-base titration data.
- **18.3.4** Define *buffer.*
- **18.3.5** Explain how a buffer system works.
- **18.3.6** Give examples of reactions in which buffers function.
- **18.3.7** Evaluate different standards of impairment. BWS

Resources
- Worldview Investigation: Influencing Others
- Web Links: Neutralization, Buffers
- Demonstrating Acids, Antacids, and pH
- Lab 18B: *Say Cheese!*—Measuring Concentration by Titration

INSTRUCT

THE OPPOSITE OF NEUTRALIZATION

Note that neutralization is the opposite of self-ionization. Self-ionization splits water into H_3O^+ and OH^-, and neutralization combines H_3O^+ and OH^- to form water. Neutralization is the favorable reaction, making self-ionization unfavorable.

EXAMPLE 18-6: WRITING A NEUTRALIZATION REACTION

Write a neutralization reaction to produce zinc chloride ($ZnCl_2$), a salt.

Solution

Salts are made from the anions of acids and the cations of bases. In this case, the most common acid that releases the chloride ion is hydrochloric acid. Zinc hydroxide is a likely source for the zinc ion.

$$2HCl(aq) + Zn(OH)_2(aq) \longrightarrow ZnCl_2(aq) + 2H_2O(l)$$

EXAMPLE 18-7: DETERMINING SALTS

What salt is produced from the neutralization of barium hydroxide by acetic acid ($HC_2H_3O_2$)?

Solution

$$2HC_2H_3O_2(aq) + Ba(OH)_2(aq) \longrightarrow Ba(C_2H_3O_2)_2(aq) + 2H_2O(l)$$

Barium acetate forms from the barium and acetate ions.

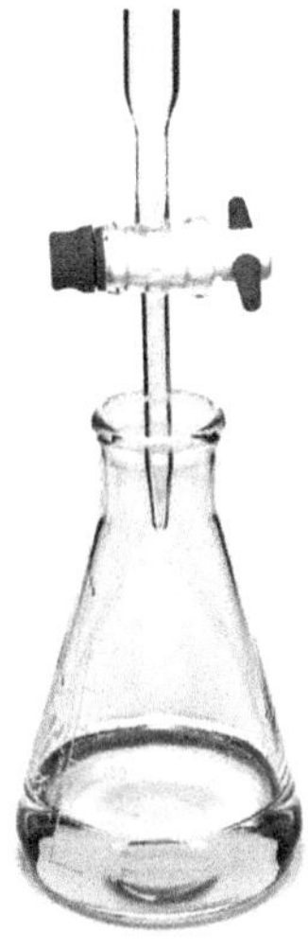

A burette is a piece of glassware that releases precise amounts of solution to allow titration calculations. Notice that the solution has just turned a slight shade of pink, indicating that the titration is at its end point.

Acid-Base Titrations

Acid-base titrations are controlled neutralization reactions. Scientists use these controlled reactions to determine the unknown concentration of a solution. Scientists use a measured volume of a solution of known concentration to react with a precisely measured volume of solution of unknown concentration. The solution with a known concentration is sometimes called the *standard solution* or *titrant*. This is all based on the concept of stoichiometry, which you studied in Chapter 11.

Suppose that a chemist has 100.0 mL of a hydrochloric acid solution, but he does not know its concentration. Because he knows that NaOH neutralizes HCl, he can find the concentration by slowly adding precisely measured volumes of the sodium hydroxide solution until the pH of the solution rises to 7.0. At this point, there are as many moles of H^+ ions from the acid (HCl) as there are OH^- ions from the base (NaOH).

A graph called a *titration curve* shows how pH changes when an acid or base is added to a solution. The graph on page 456 shows how the pH of a solution of unknown concentration changes with the addition of sodium hydroxide solution.

The chemist found that adding 50 mL of 1.00 M sodium hydroxide raised the pH of the acid to 7. So 50.0 mL of 1.00 M sodium hydroxide is chemically equivalent to 100 mL of the acid. With this information, he knows that the 1.00 M sodium hydroxide is twice as concentrated as the hydrochloric acid. He can then calculate that the hydrochloric acid has a concentration of 0.50 M. Lets see how the mathematics works on this problem.

EXAMPLE 18-8: DETERMINING A CONCENTRATION

A volume of 50.0 mL of a 1.00 M sodium hydroxide solution can neutralize 100.0 mL of a hydrochloric acid solution. What is the concentration of the hydrochloric acid?

Write what you know.

$V_{NaOH} = 50.0\ \text{mL} = 0.0500\ \text{L}$

$c_{NaOH} = 1.00\ \frac{\text{mol NaOH}}{\text{L}}$

$V_{HCl} = 100.0\ \text{mL} = 0.1000\ \text{L}$

$NaOH(aq) + HCl(aq) \longrightarrow NaCl(aq) + H_2O(l)$

Unknown: c_{HCl}

Use stoichiometry to determine moles of HCl.

$$0.0500\ \cancel{\text{L}}\left(\frac{1.00\ \cancel{\text{mol NaOH}}}{1\ \cancel{\text{L}}}\right)\left(\frac{1\ \text{mol HCl}}{1\ \cancel{\text{mol NaOH}}}\right)$$

$$= 0.0500\ \text{mol HCl}$$

Write the formula and solve for the unknown.

$$c_{solute} = \frac{n_{solute}}{V_{solution}}$$

Plug in known values and evaluate.

$$c_{HCl} = \frac{0.0500\ \text{mol HCl}}{0.1000\ \text{L}}$$

$$= 0.500\ \text{M HCl}$$

The concentration of the hydrochloric acid is 0.500 molar.

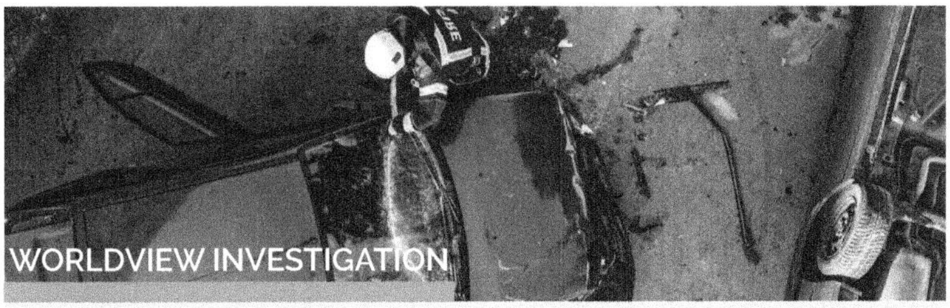

WORLDVIEW INVESTIGATION

INFLUENCING OTHERS

DUI, DWI, OUI are all acronyms for driving or operating a motor vehicle "under the influence." Looking back to the discussion in the Chapter opener, we often think of these terms as being related to driving a car, but they also apply to operating a boat or an aircraft. The federal government continues to work toward a uniform standard for what "under the influence" means.

Task

A recent accident in your community has prompted your classmates to ask you what you know about this issue. Realizing that you don't understand the topic well at all, you have decided to research the topic and write a one page summary of your findings.

Procedure

1. Research the topic of operating under the influence by doing an internet search using the keywords "driving under the influence," "driving while intoxicated," and "operating under the influence." Consider conducting research at the National Traffic Safety Board, National Highway Traffic and Safety Administration, and National Highway Institute websites.
2. Consider how biblical principles, outcomes, and motivations would apply to this issue.
3. Write your summary, citing your sources properly. Have a classmate review your summary and give you feedback.
4. Complete your summary and submit it by the deadline.

Conclusion

The number of alcohol-related accidents and deaths have been decreasing. Much of this improvement has been driven by two factors: awareness and enforcement. In the 1980s, two groups, Mothers Against Drunk Driving (MADD) and Students Against Drunk Driving (SADD), brought this issue to the public's attention. But we still have a significant way to go. Many people continue to work to protect the lives of people on the road.

WORLDVIEW INVESTIGATION: INFLUENCING OTHERS

Appendix K includes a reproducible rubric to assess the worldview investigation activity.

FINDING EQUIVALENCE POINT AND END POINT

The equivalence point is usually close to the end point. The best indicators will reach the end point at the equivalence point.

Other methods besides indicators can be used to detect end points in titrations. A pH meter indicates the end point when the digital indicator changes color. A potentiometric titration detects voltage changes instead of color changes. An isothermal titration calorimeter detects heat as end points. A spectroscope detects wavelengths of light as end points.

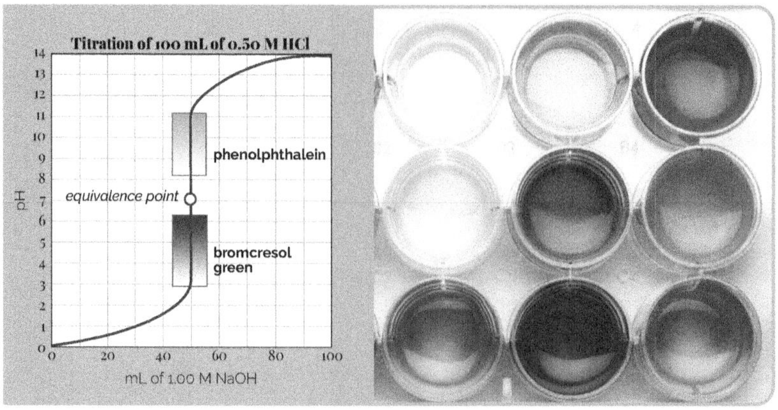

▲ Chemical indicators denote a range of values. The end point is a specific value.

The **equivalence point** is the point in a titration at which an equivalent of titrant is added, that is, the point at which the number of H_3O^+ ions equals the number of OH^- ions. The equivalence point is not always at a pH of 7. If a strong acid reacts with a strong base, the equivalence point is at a pH of 7. If a strong acid reacts with a weak base, the equivalence point will be at a pH below 7. If a strong base reacts with a weak acid, the equivalence point will be at a pH greater than 7.

The equivalence point should not be confused with the end point of a titration. The **end point** is the point at which some change in a property of the solution is detected. For example, if phenolphthalein indicator is added to a solution, it remains clear until it reaches a pH reading of 8.3, at which time a pink color appears. If a 0.1 M HCl solution is titrated with a 0.1 M NaOH solution, the equivalence point will occur at pH 7.0, but the end point will be detected at pH 8.3—the first noticeable pink tinge.

Let's look at an example of a titration problem.

EXAMPLE 18-9: DETERMINING A CONCENTRATION

A volume of 58.3 mL of a 5.00×10^{-3} M sodium hydroxide solution can neutralize 36.2 mL of a nitric acid solution. What is the concentration of the nitric acid?

Write what you know.

$V_{NaOH} = 58.3\text{ mL} = 0.0583\text{ L}$

$c_{NaOH} = 5.00 \times 10^{-3}\ \frac{\text{mol NaOH}}{\text{L}}$

$V_{HNO_3} = 36.2\text{ mL} = 0.0362\text{ L}$

$NaOH(aq) + HNO_3(aq) \longrightarrow NaNO_3(aq) + H_2O(l)$

Unknown: c_{HNO_3}

Use stoichiometry to determine moles of NO_3^-.

$$0.0583\ \cancel{\text{L}}\left(\frac{5.00 \times 10^{-3}\ \cancel{\text{mol NaOH}}}{1\ \cancel{\text{L}}}\right)\left(\frac{1\text{ mol }HNO_3}{1\ \cancel{\text{mol NaOH}}}\right)$$

$$= 2.9\underline{1}5 \times 10^{-4}\text{ mol }HNO_3$$

Write the formula and solve for the unknown.

$$c_{solute} = \frac{n_{solute}}{V_{solution}}$$

Plug in known values and evaluate.

$$c_{solute} = \frac{2.9\underline{1}5 \times 10^{-4}\text{ mol }HNO_3}{0.0362\text{ L}}$$

$$= 8.05 \times 10^{-3}\text{ M }HNO_3$$

The concentration of the nitric acid is 8.05×10^{-3} molar.

456 Chapter 18

The next example differs only in the fact that the base provides more hydroxide ions than the acid provides hydronium ions.

EXAMPLE 18-10: DETERMINING A CONCENTRATION

Adding 38.7 mL of 1.50×10^{-2} M barium hydroxide solution can neutralize 21.5 mL of a hydrochloric acid solution. What is the concentration of the hydrochloric acid?

Write what you know.

$V_{Ba(OH)_2} = 38.7 \text{ mL} = 0.0387 \text{ L}$

$c_{Ba(OH)_2} = 1.50 \times 10^{-2} \frac{\text{mol Ba(OH)}_2}{\text{L}}$

$V_{HCl} = 21.5 \text{ mL} = 0.0215 \text{ L}$

$Ba(OH)_2(aq) + 2HCl(aq) \longrightarrow BaCl_2(aq) + 2H_2O(l)$

Unknown: c_{HCl}

Use stoichiometry to determine moles of NO_3.

$$0.0387 \cancel{\text{L}} \left(\frac{1.50 \times 10^{-2} \cancel{\text{mol Ba(OH)}_2}}{1 \cancel{\text{L}}}\right)\left(\frac{2 \text{ mol HCl}}{1 \cancel{\text{mol Ba(OH)}_2}}\right)$$

$$= 1.1\underline{6} \times 10^{-3} \text{ mol HCl}$$

Write the formula and solve for the unknown.

$$c_{solute} = \frac{n_{solute}}{V_{solution}}$$

Plug in known values and evaluate.

$$c_{solute} = \frac{1.1\underline{6}1 \times 10^{-3} \text{ mol HCl}}{0.0215 \text{ L}}$$

$$= 5.40 \times 10^{-2} \text{ M HCl}$$

The concentration of the unknown acid is 5.40×10^{-2} molar.

Buffers

In the course of a single day, you probably eat foods with very different pH values. It is obvious that the human stomach can handle this wide range of pH values, but the bloodstream cannot. Its pH must stay between 7.35 and 7.45. God has designed the bloodstream with an ingenious protective feature—a buffer system.

Buffers are solutions that resist pH changes when acids or bases are added. Buffer systems usually consist of a weak acid and its conjugate base or a weak base and its conjugate acid. Water is not a buffer; a small amount of acid or base changes its pH dramatically. Adding 0.01 mol of hydrochloric acid or sodium hydroxide to 1 L of pure water changes its pH by 5 units. Due to the blood buffers, the same substances added to 1 L of blood change its pH by only 0.1 unit.

Buffers can be found regulating the pH in many living things. Scientists have also harnessed the benefits of buffers to control chemical reactions for industry and to make safer medicines, such as buffered aspirin. By properly selecting the acid-base pair, buffers can be used in almost any pH range. A given buffer acts to keep the pH relatively constant within its working range. You can see several examples of buffers and their usable ranges in Table 18-7.

TABLE 18-7 *Common Buffer Systems*

Components	Usable pH Range
formic acid + sodium formate	2.6–4.8
citric acid + sodium citrate	3.0–6.2
acetic acid + sodium acetate	3.4–5.9
sodium bicarbonate + sodium carbonate	9.2–10.6
sodium bicarbonate + sodium hydroxide	9.6–11.0

BUFFERS

For a video with an animation that explains buffers, visit TeacherToolsOnline.com. Under Additional Resources, click on Chapter 18 Web Links. Then click on *Buffers*.

DEMONSTRATING ACIDS, ANTACIDS, AND pH

Demonstrate the buffering effect of two brands of antacid tablets

Materials: 500 mL beakers (3), water, 50 mL burette, ring stand and burette holder, 1 M HCl, pH meter, crushed antacid tablets (two different brands, 0.5 g each)

Preparation: Number the beakers 1–3 and add 150 mL of water to each. Set up the burette on the ring stand and holder. Fill the burette with 1 M HCl.

Performance/Discussion: Measure the pH of the water in Beaker 1. Keeping the pH meter in the beaker, titrate the beaker with HCl. Stop titrating when the pH reaches 3. Note the amount of HCl added.

Drop the crushed Brand A antacid tablet in Beaker 2 and the crushed Brand B tablet in Beaker 3. Titrate Beakers 2 and 3 with HCl until a pH of 3 is reached. Note the amount of HCl added.

Note: When the CO_2 in the tablet dissolves in water, H_2CO_3 (carbonic acid) forms. This may slightly skew your pH results. If you feel it is necessary, gently heat the solutions to drive off the CO_2.

Compare the amounts of HCl needed to obtain a pH of 3 when titrating the water and the Brand A and Brand B solutions. Students should notice that the solutions with tablets took much more HCl to change the pH than for water. Ask them whether they can tell which antacid worked better and why. *(Since an antacid's job is to keep pH constant, the better antacid would require a greater amount of acid to change its pH.)*

Cleanup: Slowly mix the beakers' contents. Unless local regulations prohibit, dispose of the solutions down the drain with running water.

Buffers are most effective in regulating slight pH changes. If an enormous amount of acid or base is added to a buffered solution, the buffer will be depleted and the pH will change drastically. Keep in mind that the buffer does not keep the solution neutral (pH of 7.0) but rather maintains a constant pH for the given solution. For example, suppose that the pH of a given solution containing a buffer is 4.7. As a base is added to this solution, the buffer will maintain the pH at 4.7 until the buffer has been depleted. Only then will the pH begin to rise as more of the base is added.

For example, blood is buffered by a mixture of carbonic acid (H_2CO_3), which is a weak acid, and hydrogen carbonate (HCO_3^-), which is its conjugate base. This combination of solutes keeps the pH relatively constant by reacting with hydronium or hydroxide ions. When an acid intrudes on this blood buffer system, hydrogen carbonate ions snare the hydronium ions.

$$H_3O^+(aq) + HCO_3^-(aq) \rightleftharpoons H_2CO_3(aq) + H_2O(l)$$

When a base disturbs the equilibrium of the same buffer system, carbonic acid molecules spring into action and remove the hydroxide ions.

$$H_2CO_3(aq) + OH^-(aq) \rightleftharpoons H_2O(l) + HCO_3^-(aq)$$

Blood has a second buffer system that utilizes hydrogen phosphate ions (HPO_4^{2-}) and dihydrogen phosphate ions ($H_2PO_4^-$). If excess acid enters the bloodstream, it reacts with HPO_4^{2-} to form $H_2PO_4^-$. Bases react with $H_2PO_4^-$ to form HPO_4^{2-}. In this reaction, the H^+ ions released by $H_2PO_4^-$ react with hydroxide from the base. Thus, the pH is stabilized in either direction.

18.3 SECTION REVIEW

1. Write the chemical equation for each of the following neutralization reactions.
   a. An acid and a base react to produce K_2SO_4 salt.
   b. Calcium hydroxide is neutralized by hydrobromic acid.
2. Define *titration*.
3. Summarize the acid-base titration process.
4. In a titration reaction, 33.6 mL of 0.302 M RbOH neutralizes 20.0 mL of HF. Calculate the amount concentration of the acid solution.
5. A 1.000 molar potassium hydroxide solution is used to neutralize phosphoric acid. If 25.00 mL of the base neutralizes 27.00 mL of the acid, what is the amount concentration of the acid?
6. A solution has a buffer that is effective in the 3.0–6.2 pH range. If the system is overloaded with acid, what will be the effect on the buffer system?
7. What happens to excess H_3O^+ ions when an acid is added to a solution buffered by a combination of acetic acid and sodium acetate?
8. Write the two equations for the buffer reactions involving carbonic acid and the hydrogen carbonate ion in our blood. Identify the conjugate acid-base pairs and explain how it manages the pH in the blood.

458 Chapter 18

APPLY

LAB 18B: *SAY CHEESE!*

Once students have an understanding of the material in Section 18.1, they should be ready to work through Lab 18B.

ASSESS

TICKET OUT THE DOOR

Assess students' understanding of Section 18.3 with a **summarizing activity** asking them to state the difference between the equivalence point and the end point in a titration. *(The equivalence point is the point in a titration at which the number of H_3O^+ ions equals the number of OH^- ions. The end point is the point at which some change in a property of the solution is detected.)*

18.3 REVIEW ANSWERS

* An asterisk following a question number indicates that a worked-out solution can be found on page 461B.

1. a. $H_2SO_4(aq) + 2KOH(aq) \longrightarrow K_2SO_4(aq) + 2H_2O(l)$

b. $Ca(OH)_2(aq) + 2HBr(aq) \longrightarrow CaBr_2(aq) + 2H_2O(l)$ *(all p. 453)*

2. A titration is a controlled neutralization reaction that is used to determine the unknown concentration of a solution. *(p. 454)*

3. In an acid-base titration, a scientist neutralizes an acid (or base) of unknown concentration with a base (or acid) of known concentration. By using the precisely measured volumes of the acid and base and the known concentration, he can then calculate the concentration of the unknown solution. *(pp. 454, 456)*

4.* 0.507 M HF *(pp. 455–57)*

5.* 3.086×10^{-1} M H_3PO_4 *(pp. 455–57)*

6. Initially the buffer system will resist a change in the pH. But once the buffer is depleted, the pH will rapidly drop as more acid is introduced into the system. *(pp. 457–58)*

7. H_3O^+ ions combine with acetate ions from the sodium acetate buffer to form acetic acid molecules and water. *(pp. 457–58)*

8. When an acid enters the blood stream, the buffer system neutralizes the acid with hydrogen carbonate ions according to the reaction shown below.

$$H_3O^+(aq) + HCO_3^-(aq) \rightleftharpoons H_2CO_3(aq) + H_2O(l)$$

When a base disturbs the blood's equilibrium, the base is neutralized by carbonic acid according to the equation shown below.

$$H_2CO_3(aq) + OH^-(aq) \rightleftharpoons H_2O(l) + HCO_3^-(aq)$$ *(p. 458)*

18 CHAPTER REVIEW

Chapter Summary

TERMS

electrolyte
neutralization reaction
Arrhenius acid
Arrhenius base
Brønsted-Lowry acid
Brønsted-Lowry base
conjugate base
conjugate acid
Lewis acid
Lewis base

18.1 DEFINING ACIDS AND BASES

- Acids taste sour, turn blue litmus paper red, react with active metals to produce hydrogen and a salt, conduct an electrical current in solution, and neutralize bases.
- Bases taste bitter, turn red litmus paper blue, neutralize acids to form a salt and water, conduct an electrical current in solution, and feel slippery.
- Arrhenius defined acids as substances that ionize to release hydrogen ions into solutions and bases as those that release hydroxide ions into solutions.
- Brønsted and Lowry defined acids as substances that donate protons and bases as those that accept protons. These substances exist as conjugate pairs. A conjugate acid is formed when the base protonates, and the conjugate base forms when the acid deprotonates.
- Lewis defined acids as substances that can accept a pair of electrons. Bases can donate a pair of electrons. His is the broadest definition of acids and bases.

18.2 ACID-BASE EQUILIBRIA

- In self-ionization, water molecules react to form hydronium and hydroxide ions. The equilibrium constant of water (K_w) is the product of the two concentrations of these ions. It is 1.0×10^{-14} at 25 °C.
- The pH of a solution is the negative logarithm of the hydronium ion concentration. The pOH is the negative logarithm of the hydroxide ion concentration. Solutions can be acidic ($pH < 7$), basic ($pH > 7$), or neutral ($pH = 7$).
- The strength of an acid or base is not related to its concentration but instead to its ability to ionize in solution. Ionization constants quantify the degree to which these reactions proceed in the forward direction.
- Amphoteric substances can act as either Brønsted-Lowry acids or bases, depending on the reaction.
- Monoprotic Brønsted-Lowry acids can donate only one proton; polyprotic Brønsted-Lowry acids can donate more than one proton. Donations occur in steps of ionization, but all ions are found in the same solution.
- Indicators are substances whose color is sensitive to pH changes.

TERMS

self-ionization of water
pH
acidic solution
basic solution
neutral solution
pOH
strong acid
weak acid
weak base
strong base
acid-ionization constant
base-ionization constant
amphoteric substance
monoprotic acid
polyprotic acid
diprotic acid
triprotic acid
acid-base indicator
transition interval

Acids, Bases, and Salts 459

CHAPTER 18 REVIEW ANSWERS

Recalling Facts

1. Bases taste bitter, often feel slippery, turn red litmus paper blue, and neutralize acids. Students may list other properties. *(p. 436)*
2. A neutralization reaction is a reaction between an acid and a base in an aqueous solution that produces a salt and water. *(p. 436)*
3. the acid with one proton (H^+) removed *(p. 437)*
4. $H_2O\,(l) + H_2O\,(l) \rightleftharpoons H_3O^+\,(aq) + OH^-\,(aq)$ *(p. 440)*
5. $K_w = [H_3O^+][OH^-] = 1.0 \times 10^{-14}$ *(p. 441)*
6. **a.** weak

   b. strong

   c. bases

   d. weak *(all pp. 445–46)*
7. A buffer is a solution that resists pH changes when acids or bases are added. Buffer systems usually consist of a weak acid and its conjugate base or a weak base and its conjugate acid. *(p. 457)*

Understanding Concepts

* An asterisk following a question number indicates that a worked-out solution can be found on pages 461B–61E.

8. The Arrhenius model was limited to aqueous solutions, so it did not classify some substances as acids or bases. *(p. 436)*
9. He is incorrect. Conjugate acid-base pairs differ only by one H^+ ion. While these two substances are related by the sulfate ion, they are not an acid-base pair, which differ by two H^+ ions. *(p. 437)*
10. **a.** H_2SO_4

    b. HSO_4^-

    c. HSO_4^-

    d. SO_4^{2-} *(all p. 437)*
11. * *(all p. 437)*
12. **a.** Arrhenius, Brønsted-Lowry, and Lewis base

    b. both acid and base in all three models

    c. Brønsted-Lowry and Lewis acid *(all pp. 436–38)*

18 CHAPTER REVIEW

Chapter Summary

TERMS
salt
acid-base titration
equivalence point
end point
buffer

18.3 NEUTRALIZATION

- A strong acid and a strong base neutralize to form a salt and water.
- Titrations are controlled reactions in which the unknown concentration of a measured volume of a substance is determined by adding a known volume of a reactive substance of known concentration.
- In a titration, the system is neutralized at the equivalence point, when the concentration of hydronium and hydroxide ions are equal. The titration continues until the end point, when there is a distinct change in a physical property, such as color.
- Buffers are solutions that resist pH changes despite the addition of acids or bases. Many reactions in living things are possible because of buffer systems.

Chapter Review Questions

RECALLING FACTS

1. List four common properties of bases.
2. What is a neutralization reaction?
3. What is the conjugate base of a Brønsted-Lowry acid?
4. Write the chemical equation for self-ionization of water.
5. Write the equation for the equilibrium constant that describes the reaction of water with itself. What is the numerical value of this constant?
6. Choose the correct answer for each statement.

   a. (Strong/Weak) acids ionize incompletely.

   b. (Strong/Weak) acids have large K_a values.

   c. Strong (acids/bases) accept protons easily.

   d. The conjugate base of a strong acid is a (strong/weak) base.
7. What is a buffer?

UNDERSTANDING CONCEPTS

8. Explain why the Arrhenius model was limited.
9. A classmate tells you that H_2SO_4 and SO_4^{2-} are a conjugate acid-base pair. Is he correct? Explain.
10. Two reactions describe the two-step ionization of H_2SO_4.

    $H_2SO_4(aq) + H_2O(l) \rightleftharpoons HSO_4^-(aq) + H_3O^+(aq)$

    $HSO_4^-(aq) + H_2O(l) \rightleftharpoons SO_4^{2-}(aq) + H_3O^+(aq)$

    a. What is the acid in the forward direction of the first reaction?

    b. What is the conjugate base of this acid?

    c. What is the acid in the forward direction of the second reaction?

    d. What is the conjugate base of this acid?
11. For each of the following reactions, label which substance is the Brønsted-Lowry acid and which is the Brønsted-Lowry base. Also indicate the conjugate pairs.

    a. $H_2C_2O_4 + ClO^- \rightleftharpoons HC_2O_4^- + HClO$

    b. $HPO_4^{2-} + NH_4^+ \rightleftharpoons NH_3 + H_2PO_4^-$

    c. $SO_4^{2-} + H_2O \rightleftharpoons HSO_4^- + OH^-$
12. Identify each of the following as an Arrhenius acid or base, a Brønsted-Lowry acid or base, or a Lewis acid or base. Some substances may fit into more than one model.

    a. $Ca(OH)_2$

    b. H_2O

    c. NH_4^+
13. Write the words that complete each statement.

    a. $Al(OH)_3$ is an Arrhenius _______ and therefore must be a Brønsted-Lowry _______.

    b. NH_3 can be classified as a(n) _______ base and a(n) _______ base, but not as a(n) _______ base.

460 Chapter 18

13. **a.** base; base

    b. Brønsted-Lowry; Lewis; Arrhenius (either order for first two answers) *(all pp. 436–38)*
14. *Arrhenius:* a substance that releases OH^- ions when it ionizes in water; *Brønsted-Lowry:* accepts a proton (H^+); *Lewis:* donates a pair of electrons to form a covalent bond *(pp. 436–38)*
15. * *(pp. 435–38)*
16. According to the chemist's measurements, $K_w = [H_3O^+][OH^-] = 1 \times 10^{-16}$. Her data is inaccurate because for pure water K_w should be 1×10^{-14}. *(p. 441)*
17. An *acidic solution* has a hydronium ion concentration greater than 10^{-7}, a hydroxide ion concentration less than 10^{-7}, a pH less than 7, and a pOH greater than 7. A *basic solution* has a hydronium ion concentration less than 10^{-7}, a hydroxide ion concentration greater than 10^{-7}, a pH greater than 7, and a pOH less than 7. A *neutral solution* has both a hydronium ion concentration and a hydroxide ion concentration equal to 10^{-7}, and its pH and pOH both equal 7. *(p. 442)*
18. ***a.** $[H_3O^+] = 3.02 \times 10^{-4}$; $[OH^-] = 3.3 \times 10^{-11}$; pH = 3.52; pOH = 10.48; acidic

    b. $[H_3O^+] = 1.1 \times 10^{-8}$; $[OH^-] = 9.1 \times 10^{-7}$; pH = 7.96; pOH = 6.04; basic

14. Summarize the different definitions of bases according to the three models in Section 18.1.

15. Create a graphic organizer using the following terms as a minimum: *acid, Arrhenius model, base, Brønsted-Lowry model, conjugate acid, conjugate base, hydronium ion, hydroxide ion, Lewis model.*

16. A young chemist measures $[H_3O^+]$ and $[OH^-]$ in an aqueous solution at 25 °C. She reports that $[H_3O^+] = 1 \times 10^{-8}$ M and $[OH^-] = 1 \times 10^{-8}$ M. Her lab instructor tells her to go back to the laboratory and make the measurements again. Why?

17. Describe acidic, basic, and neutral solutions on the basis of concentration of hydronium ion, concentration of hydroxide ions, pH, and pOH.

18. Given the information below, find the $[H_3O^+]$, $[OH^-]$, pH, and pOH. Also identify the solution as acidic, neutral, or basic.
   a. seawater, $[H_3O^+] = 1.1 \times 10^{-8}$
   b. pH = 3.52
   c. phosphate detergent solution, pOH = 4.51
   d. $[OH^-] = 1.6 \times 10^{-3}$

19. Calculate the $[H_3O^+]$, pH, $[OH^-]$, and pOH of each solution. Assume that the acid completely dissociates.
   a. 6.54×10^{-2} M HCl
   b. 3.9×10^{-5} M H_2CO_3
   c. 9.54×10^{-1} M H_3PO_4

20. Using Table 18-4, indicate the stronger acid in each pair.
   a. HI, H_2SO_4
   b. HF, HCN
   c. H_2O_2, $HCHO_2$
   d. H_3BO_3, H_3PO_4
   e. HCl, $HClO_4$

21. From each pair, choose the stronger acid and then write a brief justification for your choice.
   a. $HBrO_4$, HBr
   b. PH_3, H_2S

22. All the following substances undergo deprotonation reactions. Write the equations for their ionization constants. If they go through a series of ionizations, include the equation for each.
   a. $HClO_4$
   b. H_3BO_3

23. Compare monoprotic, diprotic, and triprotic acids.

24. A water sample shows a blue color when tested with bromphenol blue and a red color when tested with litmus. What is the approximate pH of the sample? Is it acidic, basic, or neutral?

25. Write the chemical equation for the neutralization reaction
   a. showing how ions from an acid act to neutralize ions in a base.
   b. showing chromic acid neutralizing potassium hydroxide.

26. How could you determine the point at which a chemical reaction raises the pH of a solution past 8.8?

27. In titrations, what is the difference between the equivalence point and the end point?

28. The addition of 37.9 mL of 4.21×10^{-2} M HCl solution neutralizes 65.0 mL of NaOH solution. What is the concentration of NaOH?

29. How many milliliters of 2.00 M H_2SO_4 are required to neutralize 45.0 mL of 3.00 M NaOH?

30. A salad-dressing manufacturer wants to make a tangy salad dressing by using vinegar with an acetic acid concentration of at least 1 molar. The quality control department examines a sample of vinegar and determines that 295.7 mL of 0.1000 M sodium hydroxide neutralizes the acetic acid in 25.00 mL of the vinegar. Calculate the amount concentration of the acetic acid to determine whether the vinegar meets the manufacturer's requirements.

31. What happens to excess OH^- ions when a base is added to a solution buffered by a combination of acetic acid and sodium acetate?

32. Explain the purpose of the buffer systems in our blood.

CRITICAL THINKING

33. K_w depends on temperature. We know that since K_w is 1.0×10^{-14} at 25 °C, the pH of pure water is 7 (neutral). If the K_w is 2.0×10^{-13} at 75 °C, what is the pH of pure water at that temperature?

34. Starting with K_w at 25 °C, derive the equation pH + pOH = 14.

35. Explain the relationship between the self-ionization of water and the pH and pOH scales.

36. How many grams of calcium carbonate would be needed to neutralize 75.7 mL of 0.200 molar sulfuric acid?

c. $[H_3O^+] = 3.24 \times 10^{10}$; $[OH^-] = 3.1 \times 10^{-5}$; pH = 9.49; pOH = 4.51; basic

d. $[H_3O^+] = 6.3 \times 10^{-12}$; pOH = 2.80; pH = 11.20; basic *(all pp. 441–45)*

19.*a. $[H_3O^+] = [HCl] = 6.54 \times 10^{-2}$; pH = 1.18; $[OH^-] = 1.51 \times 10^{-13}$; pOH = 12.82

b. $[H_3O^+] = 2[H_2CO_3] = 7.8 \times 10^{-5}$; pH = 4.11; $[OH^-] = 1.28 \times 10^{-10}$; pOH = 9.89

c. $[H_3O^+] = 3[H_3PO_4] = 1.96 \times 10^{-1}$; pH = 0.708; $[OH^-] = 5.10 \times 10^{-14}$; pOH = 13.292 *(all pp. 441–45)*

20. a. HI

b. HF

c. $HCHO_2$

d. H_3PO_4

e. $HClO_4$ *(all p. 447)*

21. a. HBr; The hydrogen nucleus in HBr is much more exposed, making it more likely to leave. Also, Br^- is smaller than $(BrO_4)^-$, making Br^- more likely to dissociate.

b. H_2S; Sulfur has a higher electronegativity than phosphorus. *(all pp. 446–47)*

22.* *(all pp. 446–47)*

23. In the Brønsted-Lowry model, acids are proton donors. Depending on their structure, some acids can donate differing numbers of protons. A monoprotic acid can donate only one proton, while diprotic and triprotic acids can donate two and three respectively. *(p. 449)*

24. The approximate pH range is 4–6. It is acidic. *(p. 449)*

25.* *(all pp. 453–54)*

26. You could add an indicator such as phenolphthalein and note when the solution went from clear to pink. You could also monitor the solution with a pH meter. *(p. 456)*

27. The equivalence point is the point at which the $[H_3O^+]$ and the $[OH^-]$ are equivalent in a solution—the solution is neutral. The end point is the point where a change in a property of the solution is first noticed (typically the color change of an indicator). *(p. 456)*

28.* 2.45×10^{-2} M NaOH *(pp. 456–57)*

29.* 33.8 mL H_2SO_4 *(pp. 456–57)*

30.* 1.183 M $HC_2H_3O_2$; The acetic acid exceeds the 1 M requirement. *(pp. 456–57)*

31. OH^- ions react with acetic acid molecules to form water and acetate ions. *(p. 457)*

32. The buffer systems in our blood are designed to maintain the pH in the range 7.35 to 7.45. As we interact with our environment, we encounter both acidic and basic solutions. The buffer system neutralizes those solutions in order to maintain the required pH. *(p. 458)*

Critical Thinking

33.* 6.35 *(pp. 441-42)*

34.* 14 *(pp. 441–42)*

35. We know that pH and pOH are related to the concentration of hydronium ions and hydroxide ions. The value for a neutral solution on both scales is 7 because of the self-ionization of water. As acids or bases are added to water, the concentration of each ion changes. The concentrations can then be used to find pH and pOH. *(pp. 441–42)*

36.* 1.52 g $CaCO_3$ *(pp. 456–57)*

Section 18.2

3. a. What we know: pH = 4.13

Unknown: $[H_3O^+]$, $[OH^-]$, and pOH

Write the formula and solve for the unknown.

$[H_3O^+] = 10^{-pH}$

Evaluate.

$[H_3O^+] = 10^{-4.13}$

$= 7.4 \times 10^{-5}$

Write the formula and solve for the unknown.

$[H_3O^+][OH^-] = 1.0 \times 10^{-14}$

$\frac{\cancel{[H_3O^+]}[OH^-]}{\cancel{[H_3O^+]}} = \frac{1.0 \times 10^{-14}}{[H_3O^+]}$

$[OH^-] = \frac{1.0 \times 10^{-14}}{[H_3O^+]}$

Evaluate.

$[OH^-] = \frac{1.0 \times 10^{-14}}{7.41 \times 10^{-5}}$

$= 1.3 \times 10^{-10}$

Write the formula and solve for the unknown.

pH + pOH = 14

pOH = 14 – pH

Evaluate.

pOH = 14 – 4.13

= 9.87

b. What we know: $[H_3O^+] = 9.5 \times 10^{-8}$

Unknown: $[OH^-]$, pH, and pOH

Write the formula and solve for the unknown.

$[OH^-] = \frac{1.0 \times 10^{-14}}{[H_3O^+]}$ (from 3a)

Evaluate.

$[OH^-] = \frac{1.0 \times 10^{-14}}{9.5 \times 10^{-8}}$

$= 1.1 \times 10^{-7}$

Write the formula and solve for the unknown.

$pH = -\log[H_3O^+]$

Evaluate.

$pH = -\log 9.5 \times 10^{-8}$

= 7.02

Write the formula and solve for the unknown.

pOH = 14 – pH

Evaluate.

pOH = 14 – 7.02

= 6.98

c. What we know: pOH = 9.05

Unknown: $[H_3O^+]$, $[OH^-]$, and pH

Write the formula and solve for the unknown.

$[H_3O^+] = 10^{-pH}$

Evaluate.

$[H_3O^+] = 10^{-4.95}$

$= 1.12 \times 10^{-5}$

Write the formula and solve for the unknown.

$[OH^-] = 10^{-pOH}$

Evaluate.

$[OH^-] = 10^{-9.05}$

$= 8.9 \times 10^{-10}$

Write the formula and solve for the unknown.

pH + pOH = 14

pH = 14 – pOH

Evaluate.

pH = 14 – 9.05

= 4.95

d. What we know: $[OH^-] = 3.55 \times 10^{-6}$

Unknown: pOH, pH, and $[H_3O^+]$

Write the formula and solve for the unknown.

$pOH = -\log[OH^-]$

Evaluate.

$pOH = -\log 3.55 \times 10^{-6}$

= 5.450

Write the formula and solve for the unknown.

pH = 14 – pOH

Evaluate.

pH = 14 – 5.450

= 8.550

Write the formula and solve for the unknown.

$[H_3O^+] = 10^{-pH}$

Evaluate.

$[H_3O^+] = 10^{-8.550}$

$= 2.82 \times 10^{-9}$

4. a. What we know: $[HCl] = 1.3 \times 10^{-5}$ M

Each HCl donates one proton; therefore, the $[H_3O^+] = [HCl]$.

$[H_3O^+] = 1.3 \times 10^{-5}$

Unknown: pH, $[OH^-]$, and pOH

Write the formula and solve for the unknown.

$pH = -\log[H_3O^+]$

Evaluate.

$pH = -\log 1.3 \times 10^{-5}$

$= 4.89$

Write the formula and solve for the unknown.

$pH + pOH = 14$

$pOH = 14 - pH$

Evaluate.

$pOH = 14 - 4.89$

$= 9.11$

Write the formula and solve for the unknown.

$[OH^-] = 10^{-pOH}$

Evaluate.

$[OH^-] = 10^{-9.11}$

$= 7.7 \times 10^{-10}$

b. What we know: $[H_2SO_4] = 2.71 \times 10^{-2}$ M

Each H_2SO_4 donates two protons; therefore, $[H_3O^+] = 2[H_2SO_4]$ and $[H_3O^+] = 5.42 \times 10^{-2}$.

Unknown: pH, $[OH^-]$, and pOH

Write the formula and solve for the unknown.

$pH = -\log[H_3O^+]$

Evaluate.

$pH = -\log 5.42 \times 10^{-2}$

$= 1.266$

Write the formula and solve for the unknown.

$[OH^-] = 10^{-pOH}$

Evaluate.

$[OH^-] = 10^{-12.733\,999\,29}$

$= 1.85 \times 10^{-13}$

Write the formula and solve for the unknown.

$pOH = 14 - pH$

Evaluate.

$pOH = 14 - 1.266$

$= 12.734$

7. a. $K_{a1} = \dfrac{[HSO_4^-][H_3O^+]}{[H_2SO_4]}$

$K_{a2} = \dfrac{[SO_4^{2-}][H_3O^+]}{[HSO_4^-]}$

b. $K_{a1} = \dfrac{[H_2PO_4^-][H_3O^+]}{[H_3PO_4]}$

$K_{a2} = \dfrac{[HPO_4^{2-}][H_3O^+]}{[H_2PO_4^-]}$

$K_{a3} = \dfrac{[PO_4^{3-}][H_3O^+]}{[HPO_4^{2-}]}$

Section 18.3

4. What we know: $V_{RbOH} = 33.6$ mL $= 0.0336$ L, $c_{RbOH} = 0.302$ M, $V_{HF} = 20.0$ mL $= 0.0200$ L

$RbOH\ (aq) + HF\ (aq) \longrightarrow RbF\ (aq) + H_2O\ (l)$

Unknown: n_{HF} c_{HF}

Use stoichiometry to convert volume of RbOH to moles HF.

$$0.0336\ \cancel{L}\left(\frac{0.302\ \cancel{mol\ RbOH}}{1\ \cancel{L}}\right)\left(\frac{1\ mol\ HF}{1\ \cancel{mol\ RbOH}}\right) = 0.01\underline{0}\,147\,2\ mol\ HF$$

Write the formula and solve for the unknown.

$c_{solute} = \dfrac{n_{solute}}{V_{solution}}$

Evaluate.

$c_{solute} = \dfrac{0.010\,147\,2\ mol\ HF}{.0200\ L}$

$= 0.507$ M HF

5. What we know: $c_{KOH} = 1.000$ M, $V_{KOH} = 25.00$ mL $= 0.025\,00$ L, $V_{H_3PO_4} = 27.00$ mL $= 0.027\,00$ L

$3KOH\ (aq) + H_3PO_4\ (aq) \longrightarrow K_3PO_4\ (aq) + 3H_2O\ (l)$

Unknown: $n_{H_3PO_4}$, $c_{H_3PO_4}$

Use stoichiometry to convert volume of KOH to moles H_3PO_4.

$$0.025\,00\ \cancel{L}\left(\frac{1.000\ \cancel{mol\ KOH}}{1\ \cancel{L}}\right)\left(\frac{1\ mol\ H_3PO_4}{3\ \cancel{mol\ KOH}}\right)$$
$$= 0.008\,33\underline{3}\,333\ mol\ H_3PO_4$$

Write the formula and solve for the unknown.

$c_{solute} = \dfrac{n_{solute}}{V_{solution}}$

Evaluate.

$c_{solute} = \dfrac{0.008\,33\underline{3}\,333\ mol\ H_3PO_4}{0.027\,00\ L}$

$= 3.086 \times 10^{-1}$ M H_3PO_4

Chapter 18 Review Questions

11. a. $H_2C_2O_4 + ClO^- \rightleftharpoons HC_2O_4^- + HClO$

acid base conjugate base conjugate acid

$H_2C_2O_4$ and $HC_2O_4^-$ are conjugate pairs; ClO^- and HClO are conjugate pairs.

b. $HPO_4^{2-} + NH_4^+ \rightleftharpoons NH_3 + H_2PO_4^-$

base acid conjugate base conjugate acid

HPO_4^{2-} and $H_2PO_4^-$ are conjugate pairs; NH_4^+ and NH_3 are conjugate pairs.

c. $SO_4^{2-} + H_2O \rightleftharpoons HSO_4^- + OH^-$

base acid conjugate acid conjugate base

SO_4^{2-} and HSO_4^- are conjugate pairs; H_2O and OH^- are conjugate pairs.

15.

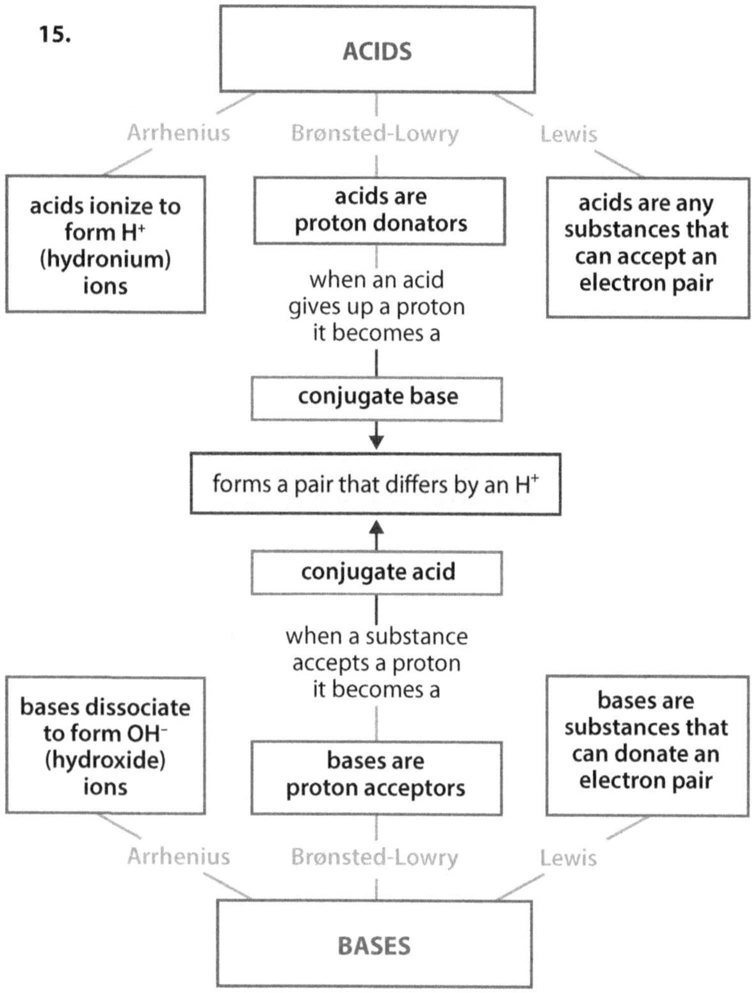

18. a. What we know: $[H_3O^+] = 1.1 \times 10^{-8}$

Unknown: $[OH^-]$, pH, pOH

Write the formula and solve for the unknown.

$$[OH^-] = \frac{1.0 \times 10^{-14}}{[H_3O^+]}$$

Evaluate.

$$[OH^-] = \frac{1.0 \times 10^{-14}}{1.1 \times 10^{-8}}$$

$$= 9.1 \times 10^{-7}$$

Write the formula and solve for the unknown.

$$pH = -\log[H_3O^+]$$

Evaluate.

$$pH = -\log 1.1 \times 10^{-8}$$

$$= 7.96$$

Write the formula and solve for the unknown.

$$pOH = 14 - pH$$

Evaluate.

$$pOH = 14 - 7.96$$

$$= 6.04$$

b. What we know: pH = 3.52

Unknown: $[H_3O^+]$, $[OH^-]$, pOH

Write the formula and solve for the unknown.

$$[H_3O^+] = 10^{-pH}$$

Evaluate.

$$[H_3O^+] = 10^{-3.52}$$

$$= 3.02 \times 10^{-4}$$

Write the formula and solve for the unknown.

$$[H_3O^+][OH^-] = 1.0 \times 10^{-14}$$

$$\frac{\cancel{[H_3O^+]}[OH^-]}{\cancel{[H_3O^+]}} = \frac{1.0 \times 10^{-14}}{[H_3O^+]}$$

$$[OH^-] = \frac{1.0 \times 10^{-14}}{[H_3O^+]}$$

Evaluate.

$$[OH^-] = \frac{1.0 \times 10^{-14}}{3.\underline{0}1995172 \times 10^{-4}}$$

$$= 3.3 \times 10^{-11}$$

Write the formula and solve for the unknown.

$$pH + pOH = 14$$

$$pOH = 14 - pH$$

Evaluate.

$$pOH = 14 - 3.52$$

$$= 10.48$$

c. What we know: pOH = 4.51

Unknown: $[H_3O^+]$, $[OH^-]$, pH

Write the formula and solve for the unknown.

$$[OH^-] = 10^{-pOH}$$

Evaluate.

$$[OH^-] = 10^{-4.51}$$

$$= 3.1 \times 10^{-5}$$

Write the formula and solve for the unknown.

$$pH + pOH = 14$$

$$pH = 14 - pOH$$

Evaluate.

$$pH = 14 - 4.51$$

$$= 9.49$$

Write the formula and solve for the unknown.

$$[H_3O^+] = 10^{-pH}$$

Evaluate.

$$[H_3O^+] = 10^{-9.49}$$

$$= 3.24 \times 10^{-10}$$

d. What we know: $[OH^-] = 1.6 \times 10^{-3}$

Unknown: $[H_3O^+]$, pOH, pH

Write the formula and solve for the unknown.

$pOH = -\log[OH^-]$

Evaluate.

$pOH = -\log 1.6 \times 10^{-3}$

$= 2.80$

Write the formula and solve for the unknown.

$pH = 14 - pOH$

Evaluate.

$pH = 14 - 2.80$

$= 11.20$

Write the formula and solve for the unknown.

$[H_3O^+] = 10^{-pH}$

Evaluate.

$[H_3O^+] = 10^{-11.20}$

$= 6.3 \times 10^{-12}$

19. a. What we know: $[HCl] = 6.54 \times 10^{-2}$ M

Each HCl donates one proton; therefore, $[H_3O^+] = [HCl]$ and $[H_3O^+] = 6.54 \times 10^{-2}$.

Unknown: pH, $[OH^-]$, and pOH

Write the formula and solve for the unknown.

$pH = -\log[H_3O^+]$

Evaluate.

$pH = -\log 6.54 \times 10^{-2}$

$= 1.18$

Write the formula and solve for the unknown.

$pH + pOH = 14$

$pOH = 14 - pH$

Evaluate.

$pOH = 14 - 1.18$

$= 12.82$

Write the formula and solve for the unknown.

$[OH^-] = 10^{-pOH}$

Evaluate.

$[OH^-] = 10^{-12.82}$

$= 1.51 \times 10^{-13}$

b. What we know: $[H_2CO_3] = 3.9 \times 10^{-5}$ M

Each H_2CO_3 donates two protons; therefore, $[H_3O^+] = 2[H_2CO_3] = 7.8 \times 10^{-5}$.

Unknown: pH, $[OH^-]$, pOH

Write the formula and solve for the unknown.

$pH = -\log[H_3O^+]$

Evaluate.

$pH = -\log 7.8 \times 10^{-5}$

$= 4.11$

Write the formula and solve for the unknown.

$pH + pOH = 14$

$pOH = 14 - pH$

Evaluate.

$pOH = 14 - 4.11$

$= 9.89$

Write the formula and solve for the unknown.

$[OH^-] = 10^{-pOH}$

Evaluate.

$[OH^-] = 10^{-9.89}$

$= 1.28 \times 10^{-10}$

c. What we know: $[H_3PO_4] = 9.54 \times 10^{-1}$ M

Each H_3PO_4 donates three protons; therefore, $[H_3O^+] = 3[H_3PO_4] = 2.86$.

Unknown: pH, $[OH^-]$, and pOH

Write the formula and solve for the unknown.

$pH = -\log[H_3O^+]$

Evaluate.

$pH = -\log 2.86$

$= -0.46$

Write the formula and solve for the unknown.

$pOH = 14 - (-0.46)$

Evaluate.

$pOH = 14 - 0.708$

$= 14.46$

Write the formula and solve for the unknown.

$[OH^-] = 10^{-pOH}$

Evaluate.

$[OH^-] = 10^{0.46}$

$= 2.88$

22. a. $K_a = \dfrac{[ClO_4^-][H_3O^+]}{[HClO_4]}$

b. $K_{a1} = \dfrac{[H_2BO_3^-][H_3O^+]}{[H_3BO_3]}$

$K_{a2} = \dfrac{[HBO_3^{2-}][H_3O^+]}{[H_2BO_3^-]}$

$K_{a3} = \dfrac{[BO_3^{3-}][H_3O^+]}{[HBO_3^{2-}]}$

25. a. $H_3O^+ (aq) + OH^- (aq) \longrightarrow 2H_2O (l)$ or
$H^+ (aq) + OH^- (aq) \longrightarrow 2H_2O (l)$

b. $2H_2CrO_4 (aq) + 2KOH (aq) \longrightarrow K_2Cr_2O_7 (aq) + 3H_2O (l)$

28. What we know: $V_{HCl} = 37.9$ mL $= 0.0379$ L, $c_{HCl} = 4.21 \times 10^{-2}$ M, $V_{NaOH} = 65.0$ mL $= 0.0650$ L

$NaOH (aq) + HCl (aq) \longrightarrow NaCl (aq) + H_2O (l)$

Unknown: n_{NaOH} c_{NaOH}

Use stoichiometry to convert volume of HCl to moles NaOH.

$$0.0379 \cancel{L} \left(\frac{4.21 \times 10^{-2} \cancel{mol\ HCl}}{1 \cancel{L}}\right)\left(\frac{1 \text{ mol NaOH}}{1 \cancel{mol\ HCl}}\right)$$
$$= 0.001\,5\underline{9}5\,59 \text{ mol NaOH}$$

Write the formula and solve for the unknown.

$$c_{solute} = \frac{n_{solute}}{V_{solution}}$$

Evaluate.

$$c_{solute} = \frac{0.001\,5\underline{9}5\,59 \text{ mol NaOH}}{.0650 \text{ L}}$$
$$= 2.45 \times 10^{-2} \text{ M NaOH}$$

29. What we know: $c_{H_2SO_4} = 2.00$ M, $V_{NaOH} = 45.0$ mL $= 0.0450$ L,

$c_{NaOH} = 3.00$ M

$2NaOH (aq) + H_2SO_4 (aq) \longrightarrow Na_2SO_4 (aq) + 2H_2O (l)$

Unknown: $V_{H_2SO_4}$

Use stoichiometry to convert volume of NaOH to volume H_2SO_4.

$$0.04500 \cancel{L} \left(\frac{3.00 \cancel{mol\ NaOH}}{1 \cancel{L}}\right)\left(\frac{1 \cancel{mol\ H_2SO_4}}{2 \cancel{mol\ NaOH}}\right)\left(\frac{1 \text{ L}}{2 \cancel{mol\ H_2SO_4}}\right)$$
$$= 0.0338 \text{ L } H_2SO_4$$
$$= 33.8 \text{ mL } H_2SO_4$$

30. What we know: $V_{NaOH} = 295.7$ mL $= 0.2957$ L, $c_{NaOH} = 0.1000$ M,

$V_{HC_2H_3O_2} = 25.00$ mL $= 0.025\,00$ L

$NaOH (aq) + HC_2H_3O_2 (aq) \longrightarrow NaC_2H_3O_2 (aq) + H_2O (l)$

Unknown: $n_{HC_2H_3O_2}$, $c_{HC_2H_3O_2}$

Use stoichiometry to convert volume of NaOH to moles $HC_2H_3O_2$.

$$0.2957 \cancel{L} \left(\frac{0.1000 \cancel{mol\ NaOH}}{1 \cancel{L}}\right)\left(\frac{1 \text{ mol } HC_2H_3O_2}{1 \cancel{mol\ NaOH}}\right)$$
$$= 0.029\,57 \text{ mol } HC_2H_3O_2$$

Write the formula and solve for the unknown.

$$c_{solute} = \frac{n_{solute}}{V_{solution}}$$

Evaluate.

$$c_{solute} = \frac{0.029\,57 \text{ mol } HC_2H_3O_2}{0.0250 \text{ L}}$$
$$= 1.183 \text{ M } HC_2H_3O_2$$

33. What we know: $K_w = 2.0 \times 10^{-13}$ (at 75 °C), $K_w = [H_3O^+][OH^-]$,

$[H_3O^+] = [OH^-]$ (for a neutral solution)

$K_w = [H_3O^+][OH^-] = 2.0 \times 10^{-13}$

Substitute $[H_3O^+]$ for $[OH^-]$ since they are equal.

$[H_3O^+][H_3O^+] = 2.0 \times 10^{-13}$

$$\sqrt{[H_3O^+]^2} = \sqrt{2.0 \times 10^{-13}}$$
$$[H_3O^+] = 4.4\underline{7}2\,135\,955 \times 10^{-7}$$
$$pH = -\log[H_3O^+]$$
$$= -\log 4.4\underline{7}2\,135\,955 \times 10^{-7}$$
$$= 6.35$$

34. $K_w = [H_3O^+][OH^-] = 1.0 \times 10^{-14}$

Take the negative log of both sides.

$-\log([H_3O^+][OH^-]) = -\log 1.0 \times 10^{-14}$

Using the log of a product rule, rewrite the left side.

$-\log[H_3O^+] + -\log[OH^-] = -\log 1.0 \times 10^{-14}$

We can substitute pH and pOH on the left and simplify the right side.

$pH + pOH = 14$

36. What we know: $V_{H_2SO_4} = 75.7$ mL $= 0.0757$ L, $c_{H_2SO_4} = 0.200$ M,

$CaCO_3 (s) + H_2SO_4 (aq) \longrightarrow CaSO_4 (s) + CO_2 (g) + H_2O (l)$

Unknown: m_{CaCO_3}

Use stoichiometry to convert volume of H_2SO_4 to mass $CaCO_3$.

$$0.0757 \cancel{L} \left(\frac{0.200 \cancel{mol\ H_2SO_4}}{1 \cancel{L}}\right)\left(\frac{1 \cancel{mol\ CaCO_3}}{1 \cancel{mol\ H_2SO_4}}\right)\left(\frac{100.09 \text{ g } CaCO_3}{1 \cancel{mol\ CaCO_3}}\right)$$
$$= 1.52 \text{ g } CaCO_3$$

CHAPTER 19 *OBJECTIVES*

- Analyze oxidation-reduction.
- Describe how electrochemical processes produce energy.
- Analyze voltaic cells.

OVERVIEW

Chapter 19 has key material that explores the many different redox reactions that are used to provide power to our world. Redox chemistry is a different way of analyzing many of the reactions covered thus far. In this chapter the focus is on the flow of electrons from one atom to another, describing how energy is used and generated. For application, students will examine practical ways to harness and use common redox reactions.

19.1 REDOX REACTIONS

- *Oxidation: Loss of Electrons*
- *Reduction: Gain of Electrons*
- *Oxidizing and Reducing Agents*
- *Balancing Redox Reactions*

19.2 ELECTROCHEMICAL REACTIONS

- *Electrochemical Cells*
- *Using Electrolytic Cells*
- *Using Voltaic Cells*

LAB ACTIVITIES

Lab 19A: *The Dead, Twitching Frog Mystery*—Students construct a voltaic cell and use it to study redox reactions.

Lab 19B: *Danger Under the Sink*—Students track the movement of electrons in a redox titration.

Chapter 19

REDOX REACTIONS

When someone mentions the Nobel prizes for science, people think of cutting-edge research. So when the 2019 prize in chemistry was announced, people were mystified that work on batteries could be the winner. Batteries have been around for over two hundred years! What is cutting-edge about them?

The current interest in batteries stems from how many devices we power with them every day. Many people today think that all of today's fields of technology will be limited by how far we can advance battery technology. Can we make them smaller, lighter, more powerful, and longer-lasting?

The 2019 Nobel prize in chemistry was awarded to the developers of the lithium ion battery. Advanced lithium ion batteries could literally power the next round of advances in technology, including long-range electric cars. Throughout this chapter, we will learn about electrochemistry and how chemical reactions can produce electricity.

The Chapter opener shows a photo of a lithium ion battery. Though lightweight, a lithium ion battery is able to produce a large amount of energy. But it does have several drawbacks. Disposal is posing a challenge since the toxic chemicals from the batteries can leach into the ground and affect nearby waterways and agriculture. As with all batteries, recycling is the best solution to help resolve this important issue.

19.1 REDOX REACTIONS

In Chapter 10 you learned about different types of reactions, such as synthesis, decomposition, composition, single-replacement, and double-replacement. Some of these can be grouped together because they are reactions that involve the transfer or shifting of electrons from one atom to another. All single-replacement reactions and combustion reactions as well as some synthesis and decomposition reactions fall into this group. Reactions that involve transferring electrons are called **oxidation-reduction reactions**, or *redox reactions*.

QUESTIONS

- » What is a redox reaction?
- » How are oxidation and reduction related to electrons?
- » How can I tell what was oxidized or reduced in a redox reaction?
- » How can I balance a redox reaction equation?

TERMS

oxidation-reduction reaction • oxidation • reduction • reducing agent • oxidizing agent

How can I prevent my car from rusting?

Oxidation: Loss of Electrons

Redox reactions occur in the formation of both ionic and covalent compounds. For example, when magnesium burns to form magnesium oxide, two magnesium atoms each transfer two electrons to the two oxygen atoms that compose an oxygen molecule. Reactions between covalent compounds often end up shifting electrons toward or away from atoms, depending on their electronegativities. When sulfur dioxide forms from sulfur and oxygen, oxygen attracts the shared electrons closer to itself than sulfur does, thus gaining electrons. In both of these cases, one of the reactants loses electrons and the other gains electrons.

Oxidation occurs when an atom loses electrons. In the reaction between magnesium and oxygen previously mentioned, magnesium atoms are oxidized.

$$Mg \longrightarrow Mg^{2+} + 2e^-$$

Lost electrons (e) in the reaction above are shown as products. Because neutral magnesium loses electrons, it becomes a cation. When an atom is oxidized, its oxidation number always becomes more positive. Notice the small number above the magnesium in the equation shown below, which is a common system of notation to keep track of the oxidation numbers of the elements (see Chapter 9).

$$2\overset{0}{Mg} + O_2 \longrightarrow 2\overset{+2}{Mg}O$$

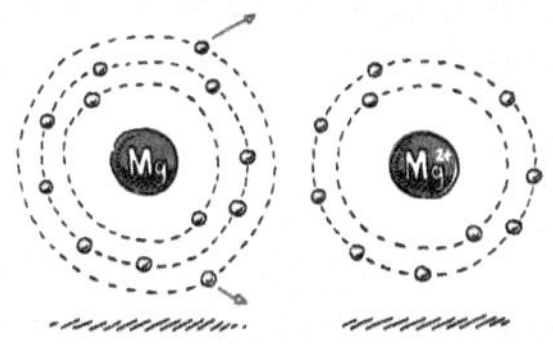

lost electrons = oxidation

At this point it may seem logical to assume that all oxidation reactions involve oxygen. While oxygen usually causes atoms to oxidize because of its high electronegativity, other atoms can do the same thing. For example, when sodium reacts with chlorine, chlorine causes the sodium atoms to oxidize.

$$2\overset{0}{Na} + \overset{0}{Cl_2} \longrightarrow 2\overset{+1}{Na^+} + 2\overset{-1}{Cl^-} \longrightarrow 2\overset{+1}{Na}\overset{-1}{Cl}$$

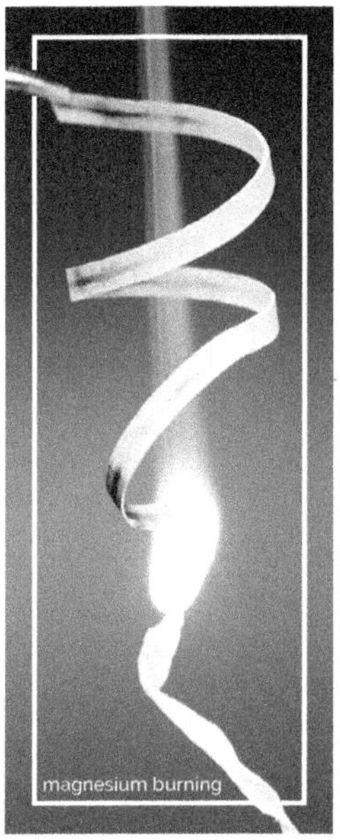

magnesium burning

SECTION 19.1 *OVERVIEW*

Essential Question

How can I prevent my car from rusting?

Objectives

» **19.1.1** Define *oxidation-reduction reaction.*

» **19.1.2** Relate oxidation and reduction to the exchange of electrons.

» **19.1.3** Identify the oxidized and reduced substances in a redox reaction.

» **19.1.4** Balance redox reaction equations.

Resources

Web Links: Redox Reaction, Screaming Gummy Reaction

Lab 19A: *The Dead, Twitching Frog Mystery*—Investigating a Voltaic Cell

ENGAGE

EXAMPLES OF REDOX REACTIONS

Lead a **visual analysis** of real-life examples of redox reactions. Before class meets, print several photos of the following redox reaction examples:

1. an apple slice when it is first cut and the slice after it has been sitting out in the air for a while
2. an article of stained clothing before it is bleached and the article after it has been decolorized by bleach
3. a new nail and the nail after being exposed to water over a long period of time

Ask students to look at the photos and write down their observations. Instruct them to draw conclusions about what has happened. Why have these items changed? What do they think caused these changes?

Explain that all the above reactions are examples of redox reactions, which they will be learning about throughout this chapter.

INSTRUCT

OXIDATION REDUCTION

Direct students to create **Sketchnotes** on the vocabulary and concepts throughout the chapter. Be sure that they understand the difference between oxidation and reduction and the structures and uses of electrochemical cells.

OXIDATION NUMBERS

Lead a **review** of the rules of oxidation numbers (Ch. 8). You may opt to play a game of popcorn or around-the-world, or simply select students to explain each rule and how it applies to assigning oxidation numbers.

Reduction: Gain of Electrons

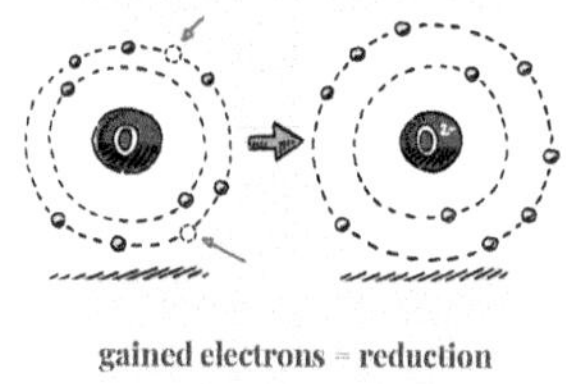

Electrons lost by atoms must go somewhere; in fact, they are gained by other atoms. An atom that gains electrons undergoes a process called **reduction**. In the reaction between magnesium and oxygen, for example, each oxygen atom is reduced because it gains two electrons. Reduction makes oxidation numbers smaller (*reducing* the oxidation number) as more negative charges join atoms. The oxidation number of oxygen reduces from 0 to −2.

$$2Mg + \overset{0}{O_2} \longrightarrow 2Mg\overset{-2}{O}$$

Is the reaction that forms magnesium oxide a reduction reaction? Or is it an oxidation reaction? Actually, it is both. Oxygen atoms gain electrons and are reduced, while the magnesium atoms lose electrons and are oxidized. Oxidation and reduction *always* occur simultaneously. The electrons that leave one atom join another.

Recall the rules for oxidation numbers from Chapter 9. (See page 199 for the oxidation numbers of some common atoms.)

Rule 1	free elements = 0
Rule 2	monatomic ion charge = oxidation number
Rule 3	compound sum = 0
Rule 4A	Group 1 = +1
Rule 4B	Group 2 = +2
Rule 4C	hydrogen = +1 or −1 (if with a metal)
Rule 4D	oxygen = −2, −1 (in a peroxide), or +2 (when with fluorine)
Rule 4E	Group 17 = −1 (when with a metal)
Rule 5	sum of oxidation numbers in polyatomic ion = charge

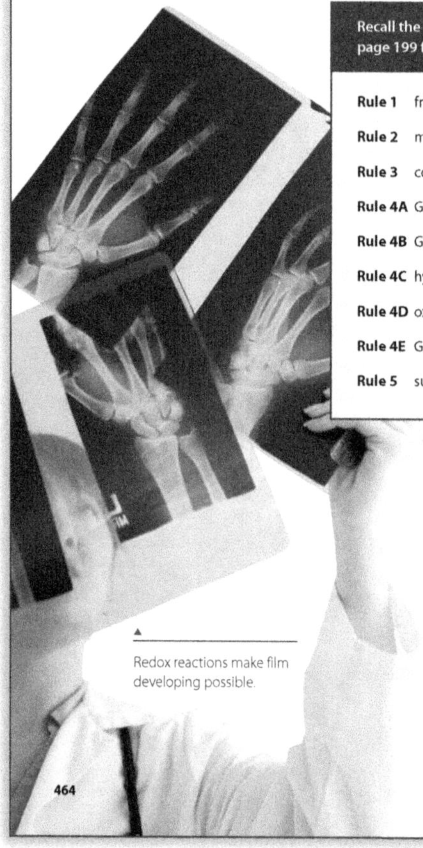

▲ Redox reactions make film developing possible.

Today we are all used to the instant results of digital photography. In the not too distant past, however, we had to wait as film was developed before we could see our pictures. The process of film developing is still currently used to produce x-rays. The processing of x-ray film involves a redox reaction in which silver ions are reduced to silver atoms. The unexposed x-ray film contains grains of a silver halide such as silver bromide (AgBr). When exposed to x-rays, silver ions in the silver bromide grains are energized. The activated ions are more prone to being reduced during the developing process than those in areas that were not struck by light.

$$\overset{+1}{Ag^+} + e^- \longrightarrow \overset{0}{Ag}$$

464

The film is developed in a solution that contains substances that cause the sensitized silver ions to gain electrons.

Only those reactions in which oxidation numbers change are considered redox reactions. If oxidation numbers do not change, neither oxidation nor reduction has occurred.

EXAMPLE 19-1: IDENTIFYING REDOX REACTIONS

Is either of the following reactions a redox reaction?

a. $HCl + H_2O \rightleftharpoons H_3O^+ + Cl^-$

b. $2KClO_3 \longrightarrow 2KCl + 3O_2$

Solution

a. After assigning oxidation numbers to each atom, we notice that the oxidation numbers of all the atoms remain the same before and after the reaction. Therefore, the reaction is not a redox reaction.

$$\overset{+1}{H}\overset{-1}{Cl} + \overset{+1}{H_2}\overset{-2}{O} \rightleftharpoons \overset{+1}{H_3}\overset{-2}{O^+} + \overset{-1}{Cl^-}$$

b. The oxidation numbers for both oxygen and chlorine change during the reaction. This reaction involves both oxidation and reduction.

$$2\overset{+1}{K}\overset{+5}{Cl}\overset{-2}{O_3} \longrightarrow 2\overset{+1}{K}\overset{-1}{Cl} + 3\overset{0}{O_2}$$

CAREERS

SERVING AS AN ELECTROCHEMIST:
POWER THE FUTURE

How many battery-powered devices have you used today? Our modern lifestyle relies on batteries, such as those found in our digital gadgets and cars. The future of technologies such as fuel cell vehicles and lighter, smaller, and better digital devices depends on improving battery technology. Scientists today are reaching into the future, developing the batteries that you will be carrying around in your pocket in the decades ahead. These scientists are electrochemists doing battery research. At this point, digital technology is growing faster than battery technology, making innovation in this field even more crucial.

Some electrochemists, such as 2019 Nobel prize winners John B. Goodenough, M. Stanley Whittingham, and Akira Yoshino, focus on battery research to find ways to improve the components of batteries so that they can be smaller, lighter, more efficient, longer-lasting, more powerful, and more environmentally friendly. These scientists focus on specific parts of the battery such as the anode or cathode. They work with materials scientists to pick the best materials for batteries. They create working prototypes, then test and analyze them in the laboratory. They study and analyze oxidation-reduction reactions that could be used in batteries. Through their work, some believe that they can solve many of our future energy needs.

REDOX REACTION

For a video demonstrating a redox reaction between copper and silver nitrate, visit TeacherToolsOnline.com. Under Additional Resources, click on Chapter 19 Web Links. Then click on *Redox Reaction*.

WHAT IS REDUCED?

Students may wonder how a reduced substance *gains* electrons. Remind them that it is the oxidation number of the substance that is reduced, not the number of electrons. For example, in the reaction

$$Cl_2 + 2e^- \longrightarrow 2Cl^-,$$

the oxidation number of chlorine on the left side is 0, which is then reduced to −1 on the right side.

ELECTRONEGATIVITY, ELECTRONS, AND REDUCING/OXIDIZING AGENTS

Lead a **review** of electronegativities by asking students the following questions.

1. Do substances with low electronegativity tend to lose or gain electrons? *(lose)*
2. Knowing that substances with low electronegativities lose electrons, what relationship between electronegativities and reducing agents can you formulate? *(Reducing agents are able to lose electrons easily.)*
3. Explain the relationship between oxidizing agents and electronegativities. *(Oxidizing agents are able to take electrons because they have high electronegativities.)*

CHARGES OR OXIDATION NUMBERS?

Remind students that oxidation numbers are written with the charge first and then the number (Ch. 9). Charges are written with the number first and then the charge. This will allow students to understand whether they are looking at an oxidation number or a charge.

Oxidizing and Reducing Agents

In a redox reaction, one substance is reduced by another substance, called a **reducing agent**. In the film-developing process, one or more reducing agents cause silver ions to be reduced to silver atoms. Because reduction cannot occur without oxidation, reducing agents contain atoms that donate electrons. Since magnesium donates electrons, it is a reducing agent in the reaction between magnesium and oxygen.

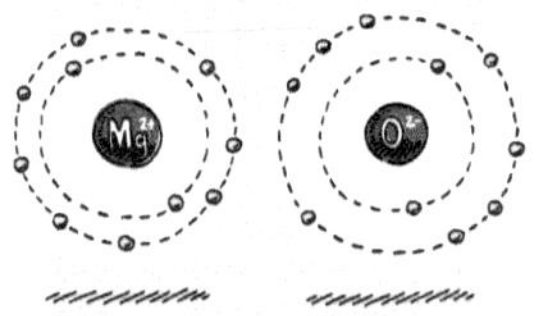

Reducing agents are always oxidized and oxidizing agents are always reduced.

$$Mg \longrightarrow Mg^{2+} + 2e^-$$

Remember that oxidation and reduction always occur simultaneously. If magnesium acts as a reducing agent, it donates electrons and is oxidized. *Reducing agents are always oxidized in redox reactions.*

An **oxidizing agent** is a substance that oxidizes other substances. Oxidizing agents are commonly used as cleaners and disinfectants. Chlorine, for instance, is an oxidizing agent added to swimming pools to kill bacteria, algae, and fungi. Chlorine acts as an oxidizing agent by taking electrons from these microbes. In the process, chlorine atoms are reduced to chloride ions.

$$Cl_2 + 2e^- \longrightarrow 2Cl^-$$

Because chlorine gains electrons in this reaction, it is reduced. Oxidizing agents are always reduced in redox reactions.

EXAMPLE 19-2: IDENTIFYING OXIDIZING AND REDUCING AGENTS

Which substance in the following reaction is a reducing agent? Which is an oxidizing agent?

$$2Na + 2H_2O \longrightarrow 2NaOH + H_2$$

Solution

$$2\overset{0}{Na} + 2\overset{+1}{H}_2O \longrightarrow 2\overset{+1}{Na}OH + \overset{0}{H}_2$$

The oxidation number of sodium goes from 0 in sodium to +1 in sodium hydroxide. The oxidation number of hydrogen goes from +1 in water to 0 in hydrogen gas. Sodium was oxidized (lost electrons), and hydrogen was reduced (gained electrons). The hydrogen in water, therefore, is acting as an oxidizing agent, and sodium is acting as a reducing agent.

When considering a redox reaction, it is sometimes easier to look at the oxidation number on an entire ion. See the example below.

EXAMPLE 19-3: IDENTIFYING OXIDIZING AND REDUCING AGENTS

Identify which substance is oxidized and which is reduced. Also indicate which substance is the reducing agent and which is the oxidizing agent.

$$2S_2O_3^{2-} + OCl^- + 2H^+ \longrightarrow Cl^- + S_4O_6^{2-} + H_2O$$

Solution

The charge on thiosulfate ($S_2O_3^{2-}$) is 2− and the charge on tetrathionate ($S_4O_6^{2-}$) is also 2−. Since there are two thiosulfate ions on the left (total charge of 4−), one of these elements must be oxidized to keep the charge at 2−. The chlorine in the hypochlorite changes from an oxidation number of +1 to a −1 in the chloride ion.

$$2S_2\overset{-2}{O}_3^{2-} + O\overset{+1}{Cl}^- + 2H^+ \longrightarrow \overset{-1}{Cl}^- + S_4\overset{-2}{O}_6^{2-} + H_2O$$

The thiosulfate is oxidized and the chlorine in the hypochlorite ion is reduced. This means that hypochlorite is the oxidizing agent and thiosulfate is the reducing agent.

466 Chapter 19

Household bleach is a 5% aqueous solution of sodium hypochlorite (NaOCl). Sodium hypochlorite is an effective oxidizing agent. It is reduced in redox reactions according to the equation below.

$$NaOCl + H_2O + 2e^- \longrightarrow NaCl + 2OH^-$$

Bleach is normally used to eliminate stains and make dirty white clothes clean and white again. The molecules in stains possess very mobile electrons. These molecules are colored because they absorb visible light energy, energizing their electrons. When a dirty article of clothing is bleached, the sodium hypochlorite in the bleach grabs the less-tightly-bonded electrons from the molecules in the stains. When these electrons are removed, the molecules no longer absorb visible light. Consequently, the color disappears and the cloth is once again white. In reality, bleach does not remove stains; it merely decolorizes them.

LEO the lion goes **GER**
Lost **E**lectrons = **O**xidation;
Gained **E**lectrons = **R**eduction.

This mnemonic device can help you remember the relationship between reduction, oxidation, and the movement of electrons.

Using Oxidation TO SOLVE PROBLEMS

We all understand that many metals, especially iron, rust. Rusting is another redox reaction, albeit a complex one. Water reacts with the iron in steel, causing the iron to lose two electrons. The hydrogen from the water gains those two electrons as it forms hydrogen gas and hydroxide ions, which combine with iron(II) ions to form iron(II) hydroxide.

$$Fe(s) + 2H_2O(l) \longrightarrow H_2(g) + Fe(OH)_2(s)$$

The iron(II) hydroxide then reacts in a second redox reaction with oxygen to produce the more familiar rust, or iron(III) oxide (Fe_2O_3).

$$4Fe(OH)_2(s) + O_2(g) \longrightarrow 2Fe_2O_3(s) + 4H_2O(l)$$

The formation of rust is much slower—about one hundred times slower—if no oxygen is present. Anything that pits or creates cracks, divots, and bends in the iron can aid the corrosion process. Another contributing factor is the presence of chloride ions, such as those found in salt. Knowing the conditions that encourage rusting can lead to its prevention. If iron can be coated to avoid contact with water and oxygen, rusting can be prevented.

The process of rust formation occurs in the presence of iron, water, and oxygen. It is very similar to the processes occurring in a battery.

Stainless steel is an iron-chromium alloy that is rust-resistant. It contains 10.5%–28% chromium, which oxidizes in atmospheric oxygen to form a very thin layer of chromium(III) oxide (Cr_2O_3) on the surface of the alloy. This layer, which is thin enough to maintain the luster of the alloy, is impervious to water and oxygen. The layer is added in a process known as *passivation*. Stainless steel has many uses in jewelry, cookware, surgical instruments, and building materials for skyscrapers and industrial machinery. However, even stainless steel can rust in extreme conditions, such as when it is gouged, pitted, stressed, or exposed to high concentrations of chloride ions.

LEO GER

Direct students to create an **illustration** of the acronym LEO GER given in the Student Edition. At times students may get confused with the electron differences between oxidation and reduction. Knowing this acronym will allow them to quickly recall and differentiate between the two.

SCREAMING GUMMY REACTION

For a video demonstrating a redox reaction between sodium chlorate and potassium permanganate, visit TeacherToolsOnline .com. Under Additional Resources, click on Chapter 19 Web Links. Then click on *Screaming Gummy Reaction*.

OXIDATION-NUMBER METHOD

This page in the Student Edition shows one of the simpler methods used for balancing the equations of some, but not all, redox reactions. This method is called the *oxidation-number,* or *oxidation-state, method.*

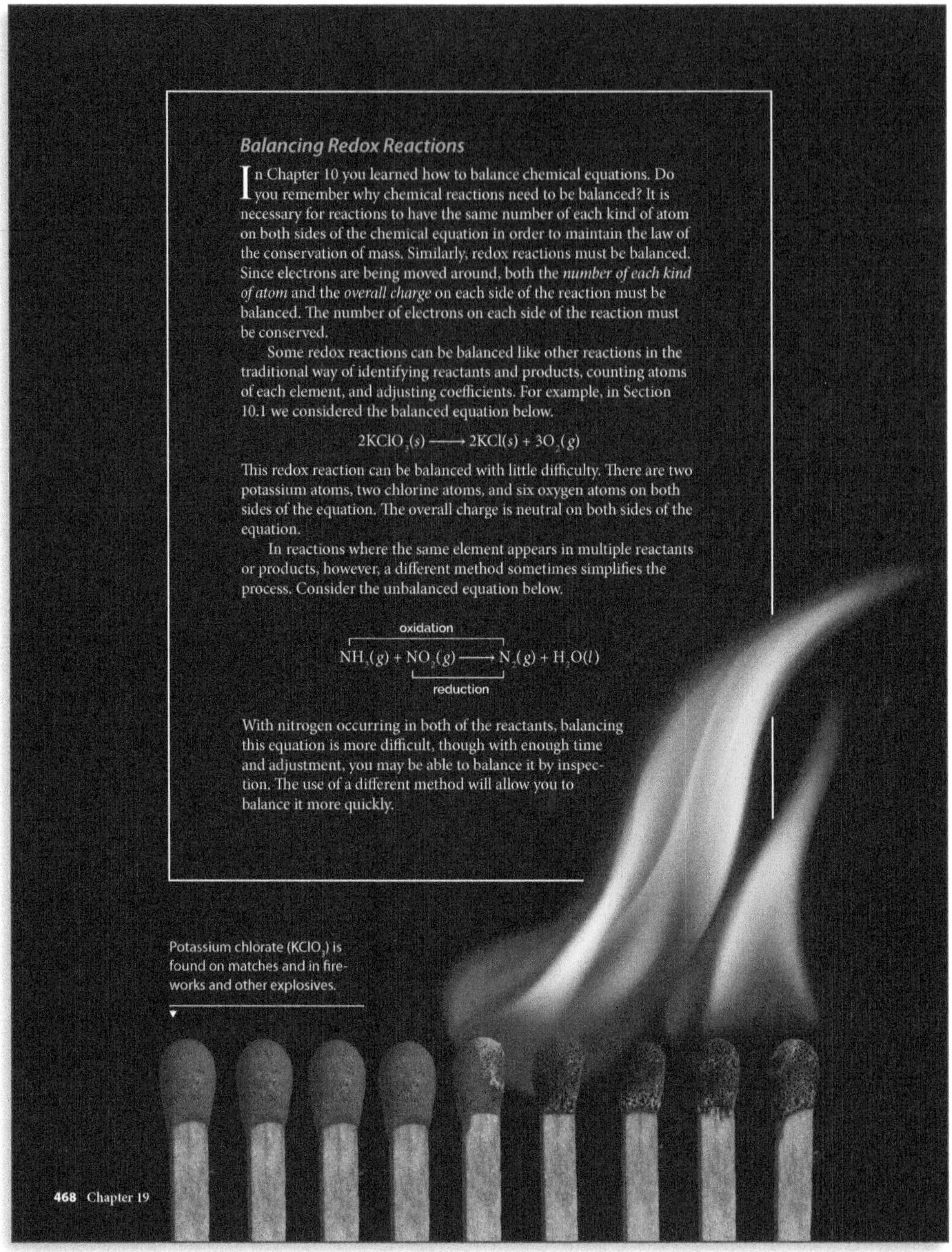

Balancing Redox Reactions

In Chapter 10 you learned how to balance chemical equations. Do you remember why chemical reactions need to be balanced? It is necessary for reactions to have the same number of each kind of atom on both sides of the chemical equation in order to maintain the law of the conservation of mass. Similarly, redox reactions must be balanced. Since electrons are being moved around, both the *number of each kind of atom* and the *overall charge* on each side of the reaction must be balanced. The number of electrons on each side of the reaction must be conserved.

Some redox reactions can be balanced like other reactions in the traditional way of identifying reactants and products, counting atoms of each element, and adjusting coefficients. For example, in Section 10.1 we considered the balanced equation below.

$$2KClO_3(s) \longrightarrow 2KCl(s) + 3O_2(g)$$

This redox reaction can be balanced with little difficulty. There are two potassium atoms, two chlorine atoms, and six oxygen atoms on both sides of the equation. The overall charge is neutral on both sides of the equation.

In reactions where the same element appears in multiple reactants or products, however, a different method sometimes simplifies the process. Consider the unbalanced equation below.

oxidation

$$NH_3(g) + NO_2(g) \longrightarrow N_2(g) + H_2O(l)$$

reduction

With nitrogen occurring in both of the reactants, balancing this equation is more difficult, though with enough time and adjustment, you may be able to balance it by inspection. The use of a different method will allow you to balance it more quickly.

Potassium chlorate ($KClO_3$) is found on matches and in fireworks and other explosives.

468 Chapter 19

Steps TO BALANCE A REDOX REACTION

Step 1

Assign oxidation numbers to all atoms, and determine which atoms are oxidized and which ones are reduced.

$$\overset{-3\,+1}{NH_3} + \overset{+4\,-2}{NO_2} \longrightarrow \overset{0}{N_2} + \overset{+1\,-2}{H_2O}$$

Since the oxidation numbers of hydrogen and oxygen remain unchanged in this particular reaction, ignore them for now and focus on the other atoms.

$$\overset{-3}{N}H_3 + \overset{+4}{N}O_2 \longrightarrow \overset{0}{N_2} + H_2O$$

Step 2

Determine which atoms have been oxidized and which have been reduced. In this case, the nitrogen from the reactants is both oxidized and reduced. Nitrogen from the ammonia (NH_3) is oxidized because its oxidation number increases from −3 to 0. The nitrogen in nitrogen dioxide (NO_2) is reduced from +4 to 0. The oxidation numbers for the hydrogen and oxygen atoms do not change.

oxidation

$$\overset{-3}{N}H_3 + \overset{+4}{N}O_2 \longrightarrow \overset{0}{N_2} + H_2O$$

reduction

Step 3

To help keep track of the oxidation and reduction halves of the reaction, draw a line connecting the atoms involved in reduction and those involved in oxidation. You should also write the net change in oxidation number along each line.

+3

$$NH_3 + NO_2 \longrightarrow N_2 + H_2O$$

−4

Step 4

Balance the magnitude of the oxidation number changes by multiplying both reactant-product pairs by a single coefficient for the reduction change and another coefficient for the oxidation change. In some cases, you may need to multiply only one of the changes to balance the change in oxidation number. In this reaction, both changes must be multiplied to reach the least common multiple of 12. Notice that the N_2 on the product side has been multiplied by both 4 *and* 3. We add these multiples to get a coefficient of 7 on the right side of the equation.

+3 × 4 = 12

$$4NH_3 + 3NO_2 \longrightarrow (4+3)N_2 + H_2O$$

−4 × 3 = −12

Step 5

Now you can use the conventional inspection method to finish balancing the equation. Notice that you have 14 nitrogen atoms on the right. There are half as many nitrogen atoms on the reactant side.

$$4NH_3 + 3NO_2 \longrightarrow 7N_2 + H_2O$$

Doubling the coefficients of each of the reactants would give you the right number of nitrogen atoms. But now you should recognize that the hydrogen and oxygen are still unbalanced.

$$8NH_3 + 6NO_2 \longrightarrow 7N_2 + H_2O$$

Since there are 24 hydrogen atoms and 12 oxygen atoms on the reactant side, the equation balances by simply changing the coefficient on water to a 12.

$$8NH_3 + 6NO_2 \longrightarrow 7N_2 + 12H_2O$$

Redox Reactions 469

BALANCING REDOX REACTIONS STEPS

Prompt students to create a **sequence chart** for the steps to balancing redox reactions.

1. Assign oxidation numbers to all the atoms.
2. Determine which atoms are oxidized or reduced and be sure that the charges are balanced.
3. Draw lines connecting the atoms involved in reduction and oxidation. Write the net charges along each line.
4. Balance the oxidation number changes by multiplying both reactant-product pairs by a coefficient.
5. Balance the equation by the conventional inspection method.

DIFFERENTIATED INSTRUCTION

Another Option: The Half-Reaction Method

Apply an **alternative method** to balancing redox reactions using the half-reaction method. Students may prefer this approach.

1. Write separate equations for oxidation and reduction half-reactions.
2. For each half-reaction, balance all the elements except H and O. Then, balance oxygen by adding H_2O, hydrogen by adding H^+, and the charge using electrons.
3. If needed, multiply balanced half-reactions by an integer to make the number of electrons in both half-reactions equal.
4. Add half-reactions and check that charges are balanced.

Electricity and Aluminum

Lead students to do a **research project** on aluminum can production and recycling. To demonstrate their knowledge on the topic, they may choose to write a paper, create a project board, design a visual or video presentation, or create a webpage.

Inform students that the amount of electricity required to produce one aluminum soda can is about the same as needed to power a 300-watt light bulb for an hour. Students should use this information, together with knowing that aluminum can be recycled repeatedly, to devise an aluminum recycling plan that is based on their research. To present their research, students should give a brief description of how aluminum is produced, why and how it is recycled, and steps that could be taken to implement aluminum recycling.

APPLY

LAB 19A: *THE DEAD, TWITCHING FROG MYSTERY*

Once students have an understanding of the material in Section 19.1, they should be ready to work through Lab 19A.

ASSESS

TICKET OUT THE DOOR

As a **summarizing activity**, ask students to write the steps to balancing redox reactions. (See page 469.)

19.1 REVIEW *ANSWERS*

* An asterisk following a question number indicates that a worked-out solution can be found on page 483B.

1. A redox reaction is one in which oxidation and reduction occurs; that is, there is a transfer of electrons between substances in the reaction. *(p. 463)*

2. Oxidation is the process by which a chemical substance loses electrons. *(p. 463)*

3. a. 0

b. Cu = +2, NO_3 = −1

c. Cr^- = −1 *(all p. 464)*

4. a. Fe = +2, OH = −1

b. H = +1, S = −2

c. C = +2, H = +1, O = −2 *(all p. 464)*

5. False *(p. 466)*

6. a. a redox reaction; Bromine is oxidized and chlorine is reduced.

b. This is not a redox reaction since no atoms have changed oxidation numbers.

c. a redox reaction; Magnesium is oxidized and iodine is reduced.

d. a redox reaction; Carbon is oxidized and oxygen is reduced. *(all pp. 465–66)*

EXAMPLE 19-4: BALANCING REDOX REACTIONS

Balance the equation for the redox reaction below.

$$HCl + HNO_3 \longrightarrow HOCl + NO + H_2O$$

Solution

Step 1. Assign oxidation numbers to all atoms whose charges have changed. In this reaction, hydrogen and oxygen atoms do not undergo oxidation or reduction.

$$H\overset{-1}{Cl} + H\overset{+5}{N}O_3 \longrightarrow HO\overset{+1}{Cl} + \overset{+2}{N}O + H_2O$$

Step 2. Determine which atoms have been oxidized and which have been reduced.

$$\overbrace{H\overset{-1}{Cl} + H\overset{+5}{N}O_3 \longrightarrow HO\overset{+1}{Cl}}^{\text{oxidation}} + \overset{+2}{N}O + H_2O \qquad (\text{reduction}: \overset{+5}{N} \rightarrow \overset{+2}{N})$$

Step 3. Write the net change in oxidation number along each line.

$$\overbrace{H\overset{-1}{Cl} + H\overset{+5}{N}O_3 \longrightarrow HO\overset{+1}{Cl}}^{+2} + \overset{+2}{N}O + H_2O \qquad (N: -3)$$

Step 4. Balance the magnitude of the oxidation number changes by multiplying both reactant-product pairs by an appropriate coefficient for each oxidation number change.

$$\overbrace{3H\overset{-1}{Cl} + 2H\overset{+5}{N}O_3 \longrightarrow 3HO\overset{+1}{Cl}}^{+2 \times 3 = +6} + 2\overset{+2}{N}O + H_2O \qquad (N: -3 \times 2 = -6)$$

Step 5. Now you can use the conventional inspection method to finish balancing the equation. In this case, the equation is balanced, so no further coefficient changes are necessary.

$$3HCl + 2HNO_3 \longrightarrow 3HOCl + 2NO + H_2O$$

19.1 SECTION REVIEW

1. What is a redox reaction?
2. Define *oxidation*.
3. Write the oxidation number for each element or polyatomic ion in each of the following compounds.
   a. F_2
   b. $Cu(NO_3)_2$
   c. Cr^-
4. Write the oxidation number for each element or polyatomic ion in each of the following compounds.
   a. $Fe(OH)_2$
   b. H_2S
   c. CH_2O_2
5. (True or False) Oxidation always occurs before reduction.
6. For each of the following equations, determine whether the reaction is a redox reaction. For each redox reaction, tell which element is oxidized and which is reduced.
   a. $2KBr(aq) + Cl_2(g) \longrightarrow 2KCl(aq) + Br_2(l)$
   b. $2NaOH(aq) + CuCl_2(aq) \longrightarrow Cu(OH)_2(s) + 2NaCl(aq)$
   c. $Mg(s) + I_2(g) \longrightarrow MgI_2(s)$
   d. $CH_4(g) + 2O_2(g) \longrightarrow CO_2(g) + 2H_2O(g)$
7. In the redox equation $2K + Br_2 \longrightarrow 2KBr$,
   a. which element is reduced?
   b. which element is oxidized?
   c. what is the reducing agent?
   d. what is the oxidizing agent?
   e. which element loses an electron or electrons?
   f. which element gains an electron or electrons?
   g. how many electrons are exchanged between each potassium and bromine atom? how many in total for the reaction?
8. Balance each of these equations using the oxidation-number method.
   a. $SnCl_4 + Fe \longrightarrow SnCl_2 + FeCl_3$
   b. $SO_2 + Br_2 + H_2O \longrightarrow HBr + H_2SO_4$
   c. $CO + I_2O_5 \longrightarrow I_2 + CO_2$

470 Chapter 19

7. a. bromine

b. potassium

c. potassium

d. bromine

e. potassium

f. bromine

g. one electron; two electrons *(all pp. 465–66)*

8.* *(all pp. 467–70)*

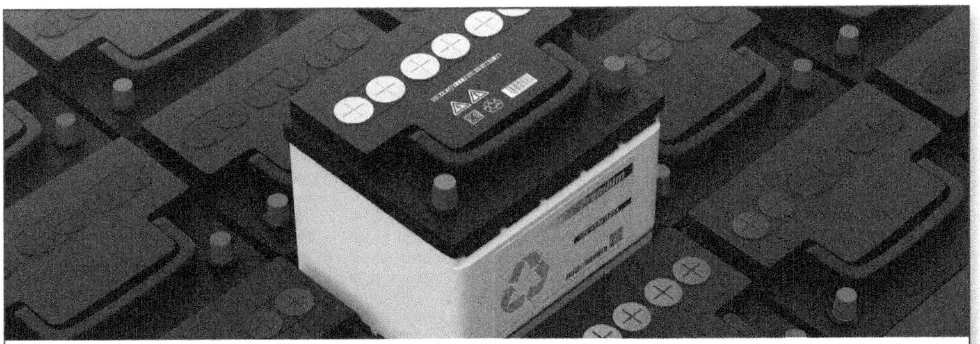

19.2 ELECTROCHEMICAL REACTIONS

With the movement of electrons being required in redox reactions, we can see a definite connection between these chemical reactions and electricity. **Electrochemistry** is the field of chemistry that studies how electricity and redox reactions are related. Today we use redox reactions to produce electricity, as in batteries, or we use electricity to cause a redox reaction, as in the electroplating of metal objects.

QUESTIONS
- » What is electrochemistry?
- » What different types of electrochemical cells are there?
- » How can we use electrochemistry?
- » How do different electrochemical cells compare?

TERMS
electrochemistry • electrochemical cell • electrolytic cell • voltaic cell • electrolysis • cathode • anode • electroplating • battery • half-cell • half-reaction • salt bridge • fuel cell

Electrochemical Cells

Metals can conduct electricity because their bonds allow electrons to be mobile in a metal lattice. Some solutions can conduct electricity, but for a different reason. Water conducts electricity only when a sufficient number of ions are present. An electrolyte is any substance that, when dissolved in water, allows the resulting solution to conduct electricity. When an electrolyte dissolves in water, anions and cations form. The ions move freely in the solution and therefore may carry a charge.

A substance's ability to act as an electrolyte depends on its ability to form ions. Solutions of strong electrolytes conduct electricity well because they produce many ions in the solution. Most salts, strong acids, and strong bases are strong electrolytes (e.g., NaCl, HCl, H_2SO_4, HNO_3, and NaOH). Substances that do not readily form ions, such as weak acids, weak bases, and less soluble salts, are weak electrolytes. Solutions of weak electrolytes do not conduct electricity as well as those of strong electrolytes. Covalent substances such as sugar, alcohol, and oxygen might dissolve in water, but they cannot conduct electricity. For this reason, such substances are called *nonelectrolytes*.

How do batteries transform chemical energy to electrical energy?

▲ Solutions of a strong electrolyte (HCl), a weak electrolyte ($HC_2H_3O_2$), and a nonelectrolyte ($C_{12}H_{22}O_{11}$) have different electrical conductivities.

All electrochemical techniques rely on the electrical conductivity of metals and electrolyte solutions. But to be useful, these substances must be assembled in just the right way. The **electrochemical cell** is the fundamental apparatus used in electrochemistry and either uses a spontaneous chemical reaction to produce electricity or uses electricity to drive a nonspontaneous chemical reaction.

There are two types of electrochemical cells—electrolytic and voltaic. **Electrolytic cells** use electrical energy to force a nonspontaneous chemical reaction to occur. A **voltaic cell** uses a spontaneous redox reaction to produce electrical energy.

ENGAGE

OXIDATION, REDUCTION, AND ELECTRICITY

Lead students to participate in a **think-pair-share** by asking the question, "What do oxidation and reduction have to do with electricity?" Have students think about the answer to this question, choose partners, and share their thoughts with one another. After they have finished discussing answers with their peers, select students to share their group's response with the class and dispel any misunderstandings.

Explain that oxidation and reduction deal with the flow and transfer of electrons. During reactions electrons are exchanged between atoms. Energy from these reactions may generate or release energy. The generated energy can then be directed and used to produce electricity.

SECTION 19.2 OVERVIEW

Essential Question

How do batteries transform chemical energy to electrical energy?

Objectives

- » **19.2.1** Define *electrochemistry.*
- » **19.2.2** Compare electrolytic and voltaic cells.
- » **19.2.3** List (or explain) several practical applications of electrochemistry.
- » **19.2.4** Compare rechargeable cells, fuel cells, and conventional voltaic cells.
- » **19.2.5** Evaluate the need for battery recycling on the basis of a biblical worldview. BWS
- » **19.2.6** Argue for or against using electric cars to be better stewards of God's creation. BWS

Resources

- Worldview Investigation: Battery Recycling
- Demonstrating The Golden Touch, Demonstrating Electric Metal
- Web Links: Electroplating, Aluminum Smelting, How Batteries Work
- Mini-Lab: *Observing a Voltaic Cell;* Lab 19B: *Danger Under the Sink*—Using Redox Titration

Redox Reactions 471

INSTRUCT

ELECTROLYTIC CELLS

Lead students to record the following **mnemonic device** to help them recall what happens in an electrolytic cell.

Red **Cat**: reduction at cathode

An Ox: oxidation at anode

Anode to **C**athode electron flow (in alphabetical order)

ELECTROPLATING

For an animation with information about electroplating, visit TeacherToolsOnline .com. Under Additional Resources, click on Chapter 14 Web Links. Then click on *Electroplating*.

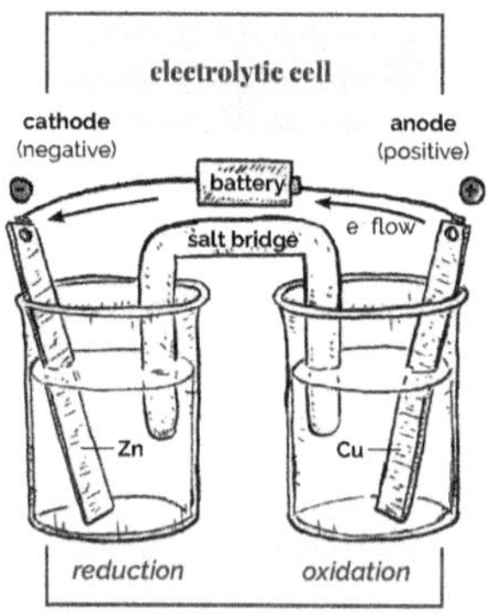

Reduction occurs at the cathode. Oxidation occurs at the anode.

Using Electrolytic Cells

Electrolysis is the process of forcing an otherwise nonspontaneous redox reaction to occur with the aid of an electrical current in an electrochemical cell. For example, normally stable water molecules can be decomposed by an electric current to produce hydrogen and oxygen gases. Current can be passed through an electrolytic cell when a source of electricity is connected to two electrodes immersed in an electrolyte solution. Electrodes are nothing more than rods or wires. They are commonly made of metals such as zinc, platinum, or copper.

What happens when electrons flow through the cell? First, electrons flow from the source of the electrical energy into one of the electrodes. These electrons are available to cause reduction reactions in the solution. The electrode where reduction occurs is called the **cathode**, and in the case of an electrolytic cell this electrode is negatively charged. Remember that a redox reaction cannot occur unless oxidation and reduction reactions occur simultaneously. The oxidation occurs at the **anode**, which in electrolytic cells is the positively charged electrode. The electrons freed in the oxidation flow back to the source of electrical energy. Since any anions in the solution are negatively charged, they migrate to the positively charged anode. Similarly, positively charged cations migrate to the negatively charged cathode. As long as the electric potential difference (voltage) between the two electrodes is large enough, the redox reaction will occur.

Electrolytic Cells

Electrodeposition

Sterling silver is at least 92.5% silver. Less expensive silverware is made of some common metal that is covered with a thin layer of silver. How is the thin silver layer put onto the inexpensive metal? You could pound, melt, or glue the silver onto the metal, but there is a better way. Metallic ions in solution can be forced to cling to another metal through an electrochemical process called electroplating, which is one form of *electrodeposition*—any process that deposits one substance onto another by an electrochemical reaction.

Electroplating is a type of electrolysis in which the metal object to be plated is the cathode and the metal that is to cover the object is the anode. For example, we use a silver anode to do silver plating. The electrolyte solution contains silver ions. When current flows in the cell, electrons leave the anode, liberating more silver ions to maintain an adequate level of silver ions in the electrolyte solution. These silver ions migrate to the cathode and are reduced to metallic silver with the electrons from within the circuit. The silver then plates onto the item being electroplated.

$$Ag^+ + e^- \longrightarrow Ag$$

We make galvanized steel by electroplating zinc onto steel to prevent the steel from rusting. While zinc also corrodes, the product of this reaction actually protects the zinc from further oxidation. Therefore, the layer of zinc also protects the iron in the steel from being oxidized. Even if a small crack forms in the zinc plating, the iron is still protected because zinc is more easily oxidized than iron. Any oxidation that occurs will be the oxidation of zinc, which serves as a *sacrificial anode*.

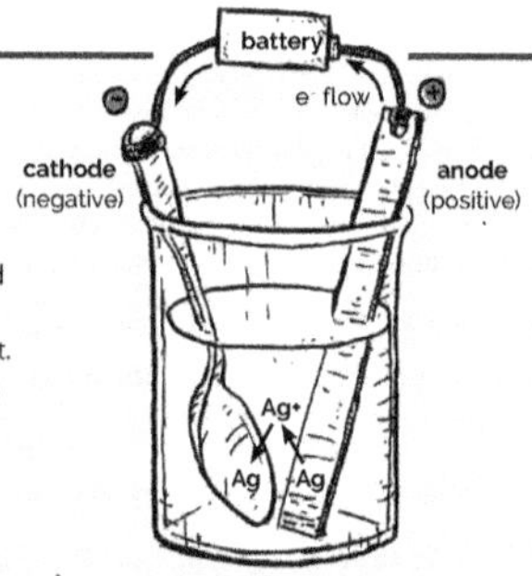

An electrolytic cell is used to electroplate metals.

Nonmetals can also be electrodeposited onto metal surfaces. The automotive industry uses an electrodeposition process to paint car bodies. Positively charged paints are deposited onto the negatively charged sheet metal. This technique more effectively covers the metal and gives better corrosion resistance than conventional spray painting.

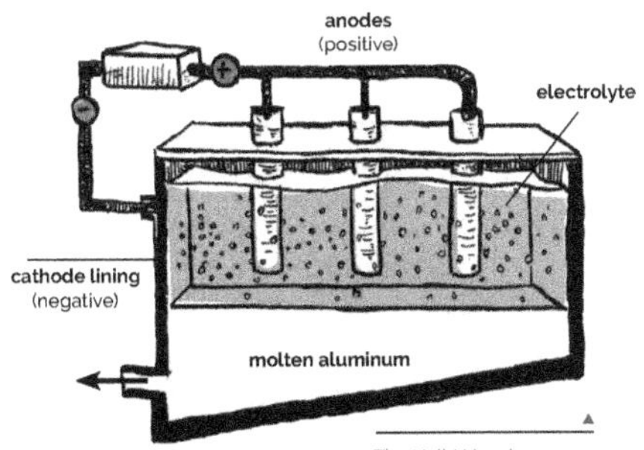

The Hall-Héroult process

Aluminum Smelting

Metals such as copper, tin, and iron, which are low on the activity series (see table on page 232), can be freed from their naturally occurring compounds by chemical means. But active metals such as sodium, lithium, and aluminum bond too strongly for those "mild" techniques to work, so engineers must separate their ores in electrolytic cells. In nature, aluminum atoms are oxidized by oxygen atoms in an ore commonly known as *bauxite*. To get pure aluminum metal from the very stable aluminum oxide (Al_2O_3), the natural oxidation reaction must be reversed—electrons must be *forced* back into the aluminum ions.

The electrolysis process used to produce aluminum in industry is called the *Hall-Héroult process*. This process is named after American chemist Charles Hall and French chemist Paul Héroult, who each developed the process independently in 1886. Until the discovery of this process, aluminum was more precious than gold because there was no practical way to extract the otherwise abundant metal from its ores. In the Hall-Héroult process, aluminum oxide is dissolved in molten cryolite (Na_3AlF_6) and electrolyzed with carbon anodes.

$$3C + 2Al_2O_3 \longrightarrow 4Al + 3CO_2$$

The molten elemental aluminum falls to the bottom and is extracted. The oxygen reacts with the carbon of the anode and forms carbon dioxide.

Melting cryolite and bauxite requires great amounts of electricity. Although less than 6 volts of electricity are needed, the electric current must be between 100 000 and 150 000 amps. To lower operating costs, aluminum refineries are often located close to hydroelectric power stations, where energy is abundant and less expensive. (It's worth noting that it takes only one-twentieth as much energy to recycle aluminum as it does to extract it from its ores, which is why aluminum is commonly recycled, despite the fact that it is abundant in the earth's crust.)

Electrolysis of Brine

Sodium hydroxide, chlorine gas, and hydrogen gas are produced by an electrolytic process from a concentrated sodium chloride solution called *brine*. These chemicals are valuable in industry. The most common type of cell used for this process uses a graphite anode and a steel cathode placed in the brine that are separated by a membrane. Although the membrane will allow cations to pass through it, it prevents substances produced at each electrode to mix. Oxidation at the anode produces chlorine gas from chloride ions.

$$2Cl^-(aq) \longrightarrow Cl_2(g) + 2e^-$$

Reduction at the cathode produces pure sodium from sodium ions and hydrogen gas from water molecules.

$$2H_2O(l) + 2e^- \longrightarrow H_2(g) + 2OH^-(aq)$$

The membrane allows the sodium cations to move toward the cathode side of the device where there are hydroxide anions.

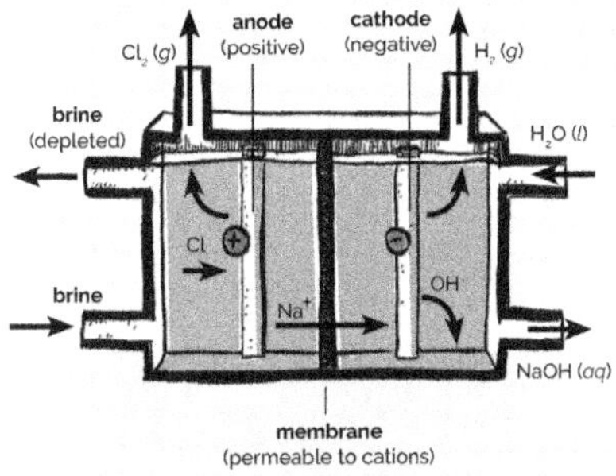

Many very useful elements and compounds can be separated from brine by electrolysis.

REDUCING ALUMINUM

Ask **discussion questions** to help students consider the reaction involved in the Hall-Héroult process. Which substance is oxidized? *(carbon)* Which is reduced? *(aluminum)*

ALUMINUM SMELTING

For an animation showing how aluminum is made, visit TeacherToolsOnline.com. Under Additional Resources, click on Chapter 14 Web Links. Then click on *Aluminum Smelting*.

WORLDVIEW INVESTIGATION: BATTERY RECYCLING

Appendix K includes a reproducible rubric to assess the worldview investigation activity.

DEMONSTRATING THE GOLDEN TOUCH

Demonstrate the reduction and oxidation processes involved in metal plating.

Materials: pennies or other copper coins, steel wool, 250 mL beaker, distilled water (100 mL), ring stand and ring, wire gauze, laboratory burner or hot plate, tongs or forceps, glass stirring rod, sodium hydroxide pellets (24 g), zinc powder (5 g)

Note: ***Sodium hydroxide is caustic and may splatter when heated, so be careful!*** The pellets are corrosive, and zinc powder is highly flammable. Wear gloves and goggles and be cautious with the laboratory burner. Because hydrogen gas is produced, perform this demonstration in a well-ventilated area.

Preparation: Polish the copper coins with steel wool until they are shiny. Dissolve sodium hydroxide pellets in 100 mL of distilled water. Carefully heat the solution over the laboratory burner until it has just started to boil, and then turn the burner off. Then add zinc powder to the solution. The solution will fizz and give off hydrogen gas. You may have to filter the solution if it is too cloudy to see into the beaker.

Performance/Discussion: Drop the coins into the solution. Make sure that they are in contact with the glob of zinc at the bottom of the beaker. Move the coins around with tongs or a stirring rod, making sure that all sides of the coins touch the zinc. After 2–3 minutes, the copper coins will be plated with zinc and turn a silver color.

As soon as the coins are plated, remove them with tongs and rinse them in running water (tap water is fine). Pat the coins dry.

Light the burner again. Pick up each coin with tongs and wave them over the top part of the flame. (They should not be placed directly in the flame.) After a few seconds the side over the flame will turn a gold color, which is the result of copper and zinc atoms forming an alloy of brass. The brass will tarnish if overheated.

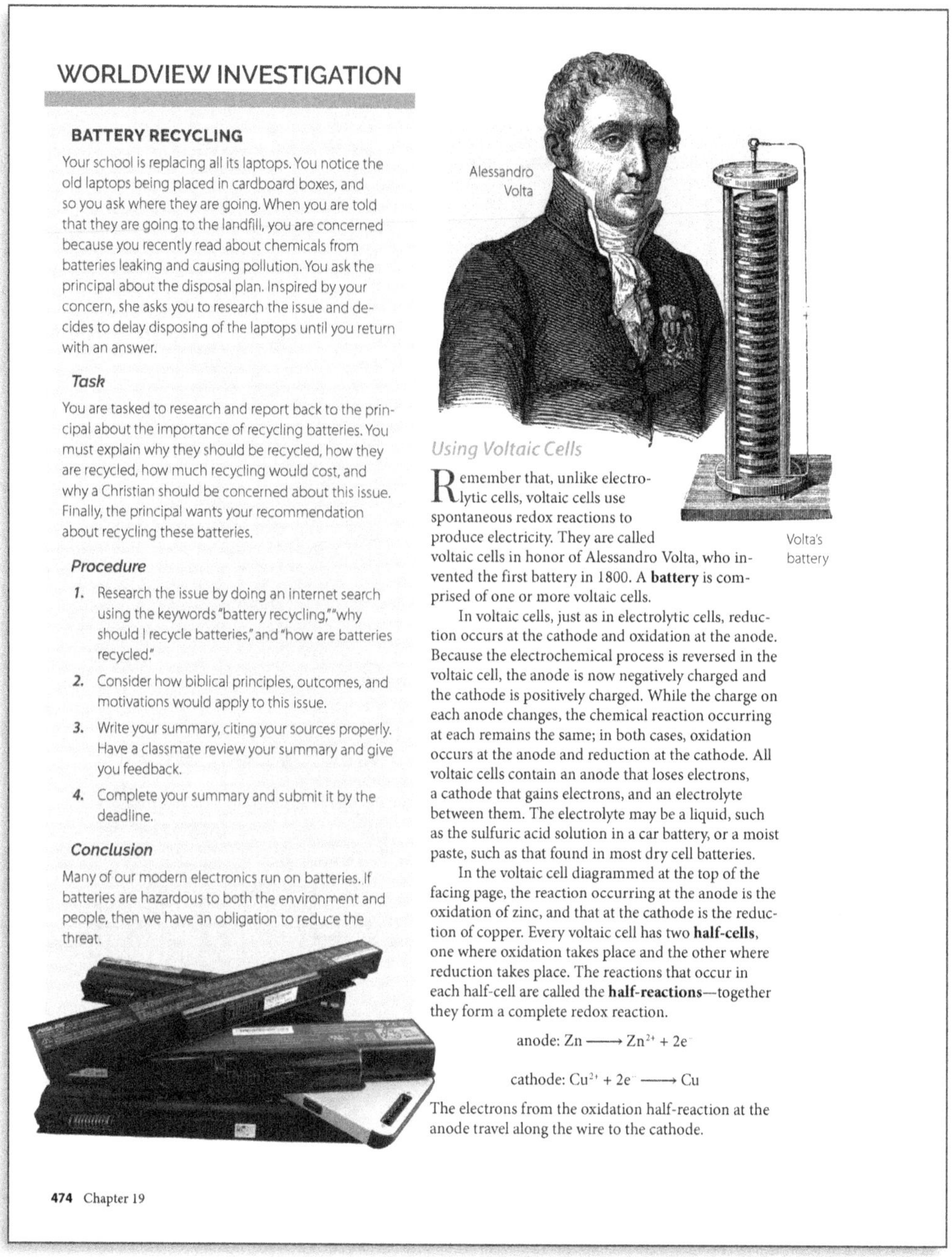

WORLDVIEW INVESTIGATION

BATTERY RECYCLING

Your school is replacing all its laptops. You notice the old laptops being placed in cardboard boxes, and so you ask where they are going. When you are told that they are going to the landfill, you are concerned because you recently read about chemicals from batteries leaking and causing pollution. You ask the principal about the disposal plan. Inspired by your concern, she asks you to research the issue and decides to delay disposing of the laptops until you return with an answer.

Task

You are tasked to research and report back to the principal about the importance of recycling batteries. You must explain why they should be recycled, how they are recycled, how much recycling would cost, and why a Christian should be concerned about this issue. Finally, the principal wants your recommendation about recycling these batteries.

Procedure

1. Research the issue by doing an internet search using the keywords "battery recycling," "why should I recycle batteries," and "how are batteries recycled."
2. Consider how biblical principles, outcomes, and motivations would apply to this issue.
3. Write your summary, citing your sources properly. Have a classmate review your summary and give you feedback.
4. Complete your summary and submit it by the deadline.

Conclusion

Many of our modern electronics run on batteries. If batteries are hazardous to both the environment and people, then we have an obligation to reduce the threat.

Alessandro Volta

Volta's battery

Using Voltaic Cells

Remember that, unlike electrolytic cells, voltaic cells use spontaneous redox reactions to produce electricity. They are called voltaic cells in honor of Alessandro Volta, who invented the first battery in 1800. A **battery** is comprised of one or more voltaic cells.

In voltaic cells, just as in electrolytic cells, reduction occurs at the cathode and oxidation at the anode. Because the electrochemical process is reversed in the voltaic cell, the anode is now negatively charged and the cathode is positively charged. While the charge on each anode changes, the chemical reaction occurring at each remains the same; in both cases, oxidation occurs at the anode and reduction at the cathode. All voltaic cells contain an anode that loses electrons, a cathode that gains electrons, and an electrolyte between them. The electrolyte may be a liquid, such as the sulfuric acid solution in a car battery, or a moist paste, such as that found in most dry cell batteries.

In the voltaic cell diagrammed at the top of the facing page, the reaction occurring at the anode is the oxidation of zinc, and that at the cathode is the reduction of copper. Every voltaic cell has two **half-cells**, one where oxidation takes place and the other where reduction takes place. The reactions that occur in each half-cell are called the **half-reactions**—together they form a complete redox reaction.

$$\text{anode: } Zn \longrightarrow Zn^{2+} + 2e^-$$

$$\text{cathode: } Cu^{2+} + 2e^- \longrightarrow Cu$$

The electrons from the oxidation half-reaction at the anode travel along the wire to the cathode.

474 Chapter 19

Conclusion: In the copper-to-zinc reaction, ask students which substance acts as the cathode and which acts as the anode. *(The copper is the cathode; it is the metal receiving the plating. The zinc is the anode; it is the metal plated onto the cathode.)*

This kind of plating, known as *electroless plating*, does not require an electrical source. It uses a chemical catalyst, in this case sodium hydroxide and zinc ions, to deposit the zinc on the copper coins.

As an alternative, try using granulated tin instead of zinc. It will deposit onto a copper coin just like zinc, but it will create an alloy of bronze instead of brass.

Cleanup: Check your local waste regulations for disposing of sodium hydroxide and zinc powder. Do *not* rinse zinc powder down the drain.

MAKING GOLD PENNIES

As an alternative to performing this demonstration in class, you may show a video of the activity. To find videos, do an internet search using the keywords "make gold pennies."

At the cathode, copper(II) ions are reduced to metallic copper by the electrons from the anode. The steady flow of electrons from the anode to the cathode can be harnessed to produce electrical energy. As the reactions in each half-cell continue, the zinc solution builds up a positive charge from the accumulation of zinc ions. As the copper ions plate out as copper, that solution builds up a negative charge. The reactions will stop unless there is a mechanism to prevent the buildup of charges in the solutions. Electrochemists accomplish this with a **salt bridge**—a tube of electrolytic gel that connects the two half-cells of a voltaic cell. The salt bridge allows the flow of ions but prevents the mixing of the solutions.

A salt bridge is illustrated in the image at right. Current flows between the solutions as ions migrate. As zinc is oxidized, excess zinc ions accumulate in the solution around the anode. Chloride ions migrate from the salt bridge toward the concentration of positive charges and keep the solution close to neutral. As copper(II) is reduced to metallic copper at the cathode, positive charges are removed from the solution around the cathode. Potassium ions migrate from the salt bridge into the solution in order to keep the solution electrically neutral. If the salt bridge were removed, current would stop.

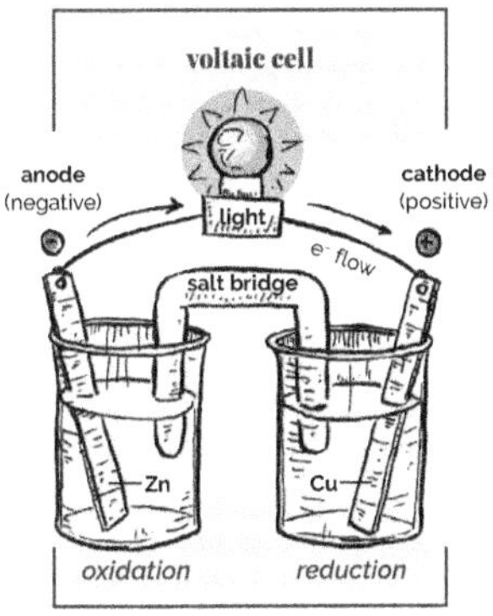

A voltaic cell. The salt bridge allows K^+ and Cl^- ions to flow between the beakers, propagating the redox reaction that generates an electrical current.

TABLE 19-1 *Electrode Conventions*

Properties	Cathode	Anode
ions attracted	cations	anions
electron movement	into cell	out of cell
half-reaction	reduction	oxidation
sign in electrolytic cell	negative	positive
sign in voltaic cell	positive	negative

Sign conventions of the electrodes are a common source of confusion. The confusion can be avoided if we remember that the electrode that emits the electrons is always negative. Recall that oxidation always occurs at the anode. In a voltaic cell, the anode is negative (−) because it is where a metal is *spontaneously* losing electrons. But in an electrolytic cell, the anode is positive (+) because its electrons are being *forcibly* removed by an external power supply. The cathode in a voltaic cell is positive as the reduction of the metal uses electrons. The cathode in an electrolytic cell is negative as the electrons move into solution to reduce ions in the solution. Reduction always occurs at the cathode.

EXAMPLE 19-5: WRITING HALF-REACTIONS

Write the half-reactions and the redox reaction for the oxidation of calcium and the reduction of iron(III) ions into iron atoms.

Solution

LEO GER reminds us that oxidation is the losing of electrons. Calcium in Group 2 has two valence electrons, which it will lose.

$$Ca \longrightarrow Ca^{2+} + 2e^-$$

LEO GER reminds us that reduction is the gaining of electrons. Iron(III) needs to gain three electrons to become neutral iron atoms.

$$Fe^{3+} + 3e^- \longrightarrow Fe$$

To write the balanced redox reaction we have to balance the electrons on either side of the equation.

$$3(Ca \longrightarrow Ca^{2+} + 2e^-)$$
$$2(Fe^{3+} + 3e^- \longrightarrow Fe)$$

We can now cancel the electrons and add the two equations together.

$$3Ca \longrightarrow 3Ca^{2+} + \cancel{6e^-}$$
$$2Fe^{3+} + \cancel{6e^-} \longrightarrow 2Fe$$
$$3Ca + 2Fe^{3+} \longrightarrow 3Ca^{2+} + 2Fe$$

DEMONSTRATING ELECTRIC METAL

Demonstrate how the reactivity series of metals relates to spontaneous redox reactions.

Materials: petri dish or other small dish; filter paper; 0.1 M potassium nitrate (KNO_3); pipettes or eye droppers (5); chloride or nitrate salt solutions that contain Mg^{2+}, Zn^{2+}, Sn^{2+}, and Cu^{2+} ions; magnesium, zinc, tin, and copper strips (1–2 cm); wires with alligator clips (2); voltmeter

Preparation: Cut the filter paper into an X shape that will fit inside the petri dish.

Performance/Discussion: Using a pipette, place enough drops of KNO_3 on the filter paper to thoroughly saturate the paper. Then place 1–2 drops of each of the four salt solutions on each end of the X.

If not already attached, attach the wires to the voltmeter. Then attach a metal strip to each alligator clip. These will act as electrodes. The red wire will be the cathode and the black wire the anode. Turn on the voltmeter, and then touch one metal strip to its corresponding metal salt and the other metal strip to its metal salt. For example, touch the magnesium strip to the drop of magnesium salt. If you receive a negative voltage reading, simply switch the metal strips on the wires.

Several combinations will produce a positive voltage. One example is when the zinc strip on the black wire touches zinc salt while the copper strip on the red wire touches copper salt.

Each combination may produce a single-replacement reaction. Using the reactivity series (p. 232), see whether students can determine why some metals reacted and some didn't. They should notice that if the anode metal was higher in the reactivity series than the cathode metal, a reaction occurred, which was measured by the voltmeter.

Cleanup: Check your local regulations for disposing of metal-salt solutions.

A BATTERY OR A CELL?

A cell, or electrochemical cell, consists of an anode and a cathode joined together in an electrolyte solution. A collection of these cells is a battery. AAA, AA, C, and D batteries are actually individual cells. No matter what the size of the cell, it has a voltage of 1.5 V. But larger cells, such as D, have a larger current. Examples of true batteries are 6V and 9V batteries. They consist of four to six 1.5 V cells joined in a series so that their voltages combine.

HOW BATTERIES WORK

For a video which gives information on how batteries work, visit TeacherToolsOnline.com. Under Additional Resources, click on Chapter 14 Web Links. Then click on *How Batteries Work*.

VOLTAIC CELLS

Direct students to create a **graphic organizer** for the various voltaic cells described on pages 476–78. For each type of battery, have students illustrate, label, and show the flow of electrons; describe anodes, cathodes, and electrodes; and list the battery's uses.

Voltaic Cells

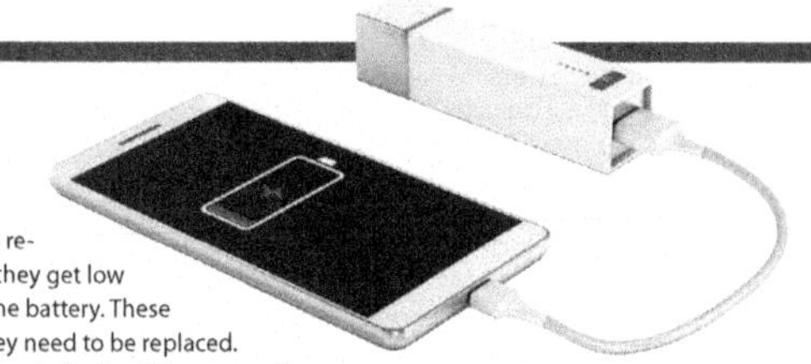

Rechargeable Batteries

We all know the frustration of turning on a battery-operated device only to find that the batteries are dead. Happily, many devices have rechargeable batteries, which means that when they get low on power, we can plug them in and recharge the battery. These batteries can be used multiple times before they need to be replaced. Reversing the polarity of the electrodes recharges batteries. This reverses the redox reaction and regenerates the cell.

The most common uses for rechargeable batteries, also known as *secondary batteries*, are cars, laptops, tablets, and cellphones. Interestingly, as we use a rechargeable battery, it acts as a voltaic cell, but when it is recharging, it acts as an electrolytic cell.

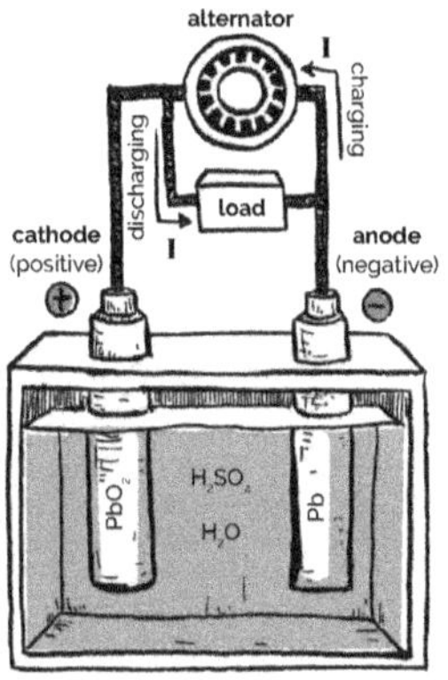

LEAD-ACID STORAGE BATTERIES

Cars and trucks start by cranking the engine from energy stored in a series of six lead storage cells linked together so that their voltages add to each other. These are called *lead-acid storage batteries*. The cathode is a series of lead-antimony alloy plates permeated with lead(IV) oxide (PbO_2). The anode is a series of lead-antimony alloy plates filled with spongy lead. The cathode and anode are immersed in sulfuric acid.

The oxidation half-reaction is

$$Pb + SO_4^{2-} \longrightarrow PbSO_4 + 2e^-.$$

The reduction half-reaction is

$$PbO_2 + 4H^+ + SO_4^{2-} + 2e^- \longrightarrow PbSO_4 + 2H_2O.$$

As strange as it seems, lead atoms are oxidized from 0 to +2 on one plate and reduced from +4 to +2 on another. As the battery discharges, the concentration of the sulfuric acid decreases as H_2SO_4 is consumed at both electrodes.

LITHIUM ION BATTERIES

As mentioned in the Chapter opener, *lithium ion batteries* are the cutting edge of battery technology. They are the newer, lighter, longer-lasting, more powerful batteries that many feel will power our technology-based society for decades to come. These batteries power most of our laptop computers, cellphones, tablets, and electric vehicles.

The specific design of a lithium ion battery depends on the specific application for which it will be used. In general, one electrode is made of carbon and the other is a metal oxide. The electrolyte is a lithium compound in an organic solvent. The lithium ions move between the electrodes during the operation of the battery.

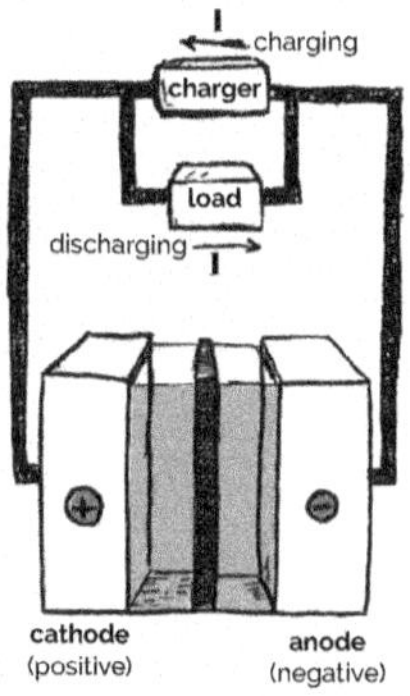

The oxidation half-reaction is

$$LiC_6 \longrightarrow C_6 + Li^+ + e^-.$$

The reduction half-reaction is

$$CoO_2 + Li^+ + e^- \longrightarrow LiCoO_2.$$

One of the most important aspects of the lithium ion battery is that it is rechargeable.

Nonrechargeable Batteries

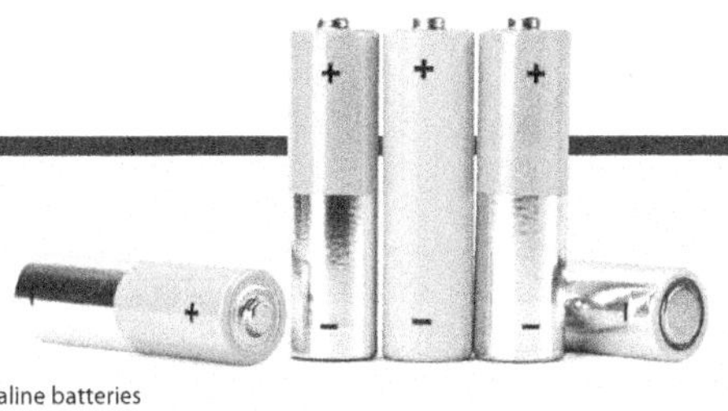

Some cells cannot or should not be recharged. Manufacturers will often put a label on their alkaline batteries and other *primary* (nonrechargeable) batteries to warn customers against recharging the batteries. It's not that alkaline batteries *cannot* be recharged; rather, they *should not* be recharged because to do so would be dangerous. Even though the redox reaction in an alkaline cell is reversible, recharging produces some gases. Since many alkaline cells have no vents to release gases, they could explode if an attempt is made to recharge them.

ZINC-CARBON DRY CELLS

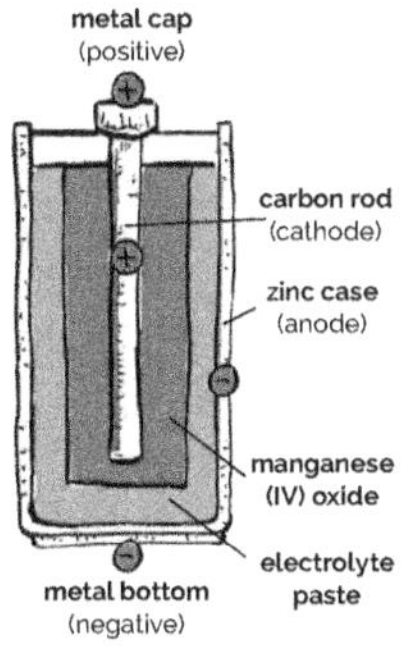

One common type of battery is the *zinc-carbon dry cell*. A dry cell consists of a zinc container filled with an electrolyte paste made of MnO_2 and $ZnCl_2$ or NH_4Cl in a binder that keeps it all together. The zinc cylinder acts as the anode and loses electrons. Inserted into the electrolyte paste is a graphite rod that acts as the cathode. A coated paper separator acts as an insulator and prevents a short circuit.

Although the reactions occurring at these electrodes are complicated, they can be summarized as shown here.

$$\text{anode: } Zn + 2Cl^- \longrightarrow ZnCl_2 + 2e^-$$

$$\text{cathode: } 2NH_4Cl + 2MnO_2 + 2e^- \longrightarrow Mn_2O_3 + H_2O + 2NH_3 + 2Cl^-$$

In these half-reactions, zinc is oxidized from a charge of 0 to +2, and manganese is reduced from +4 to +3.

ALKALINE BATTERIES

The most popular batteries in consumer products today are *alkaline batteries*, which are based on the alkaline substance potassium hydroxide. These batteries are a type of dry cell battery but have some chemical and structural differences. During the operation of an alkaline battery, a reaction takes place in a paste of zinc metal and potassium hydroxide. The battery does not have a carbon rod cathode, nor does it have a solid metal liner serving as an anode.

The following reactions occur at each electrode.

$$\text{anode: } Zn + 2OH^- \longrightarrow ZnO + H_2O + 2e^-$$

$$\text{cathode: } 2MnO_2 + H_2O + 2e^- \longrightarrow Mn_2O_3 + 2OH^-$$

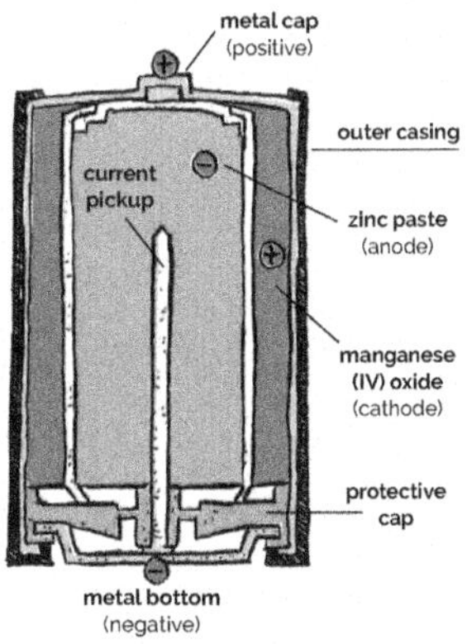

ELECTROCHEMICAL REACTIONS

Use this **formative assessment** to check for students' understanding.

1. What is the process of forcing an otherwise nonspontaneous redox reaction to occur with the aid of an electrical current in an electrochemical cell? *(electrolysis)*
2. What is the charge of the cathode in an electrolytic cell? *(negative)*
3. When can a redox reaction occur in an electrolytic cell? *(when the electric potential difference [voltage] between the two electrodes is large enough)*
4. Name one example of an electrolytic process. *(Accept any one: electroplating, aluminum smelting, or electrolysis of brine.)*
5. Name one example of a voltaic cell. *(Accept any one: lead storage batteries, lithium ion batteries, zinc-ion dry cells, or alkaline batteries.)*
6. Describe half-cells. *(Every voltaic cell has two half-cells: oxidation occurs in one half-cell and reduction occurs in the other.)*

Redox Reactions 477

THE FUTURE OF FUEL CELLS

Lead students to write a **research report** on one of the up-and-coming fuel cell technologies. Because of their efficiency and long life, fuel cells have been the center of energy research for several decades. Scientists imagine using all kinds of materials as their electrodes in fuel cells: hydrogen, ceramics, chlorine, propane, and even microbes. Some scientists are researching ways to create a personal fuel cell, which could be used to power and heat a home and help people become less dependent on power companies.

For their research reports, students should include the potential uses, both good and bad, for this new way to provide energy. Be sure that they cite all sources used.

ELECTROLYTIC VERSUS VOLTAIC

Direct students to create a **T-Chart** that outlines the differences between electrolytic and voltaic cells. Shown below is one example.

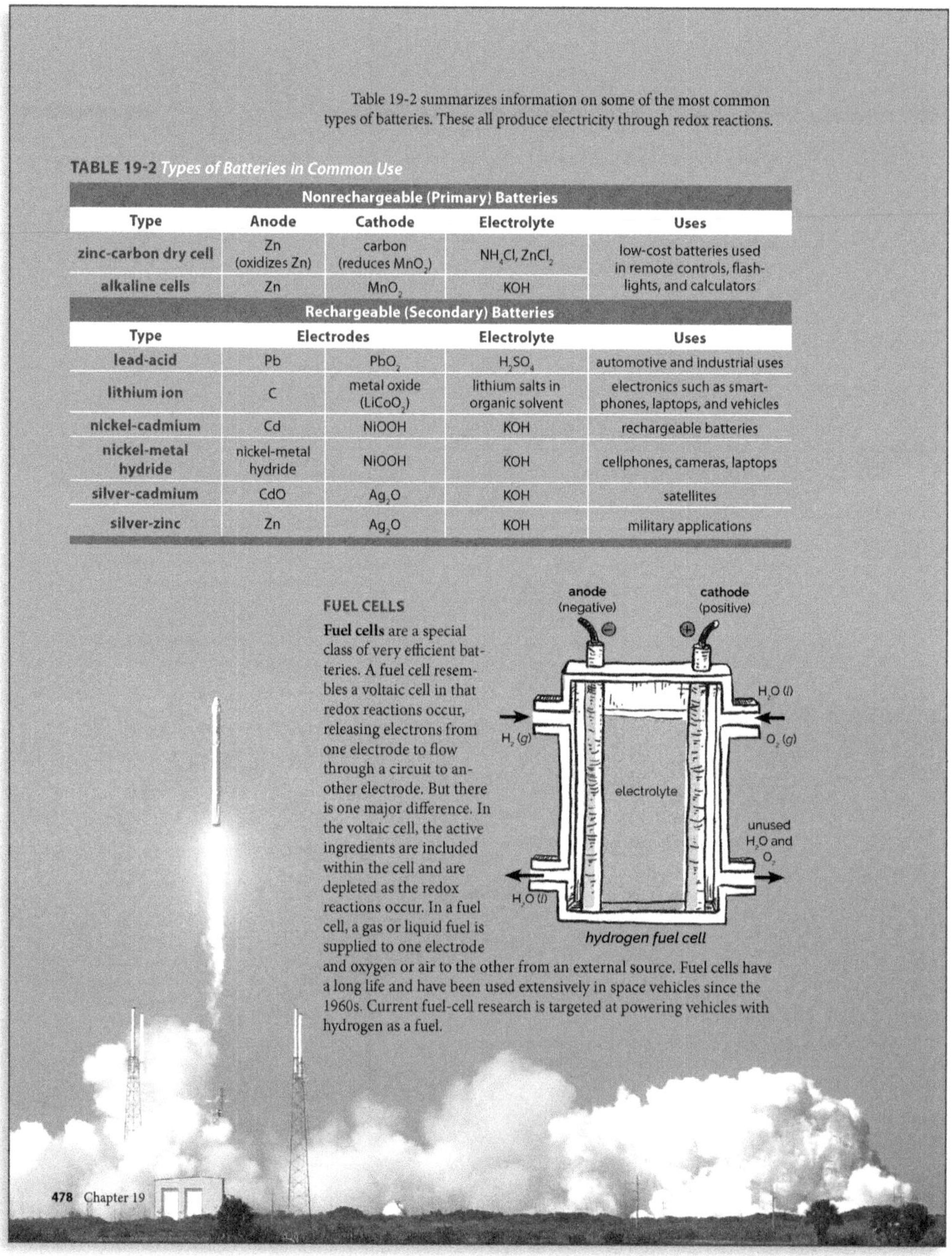

Table 19-2 summarizes information on some of the most common types of batteries. These all produce electricity through redox reactions.

TABLE 19-2 *Types of Batteries in Common Use*

Nonrechargeable (Primary) Batteries				
Type	**Anode**	**Cathode**	**Electrolyte**	**Uses**
zinc-carbon dry cell	Zn (oxidizes Zn)	carbon (reduces MnO_2)	NH_4Cl, $ZnCl_2$	low-cost batteries used in remote controls, flashlights, and calculators
alkaline cells	Zn	MnO_2	KOH	
Rechargeable (Secondary) Batteries				
Type	**Electrodes**		**Electrolyte**	**Uses**
lead-acid	Pb	PbO_2	H_2SO_4	automotive and industrial uses
lithium ion	C	metal oxide ($LiCoO_2$)	lithium salts in organic solvent	electronics such as smartphones, laptops, and vehicles
nickel-cadmium	Cd	NiOOH	KOH	rechargeable batteries
nickel-metal hydride	nickel-metal hydride	NiOOH	KOH	cellphones, cameras, laptops
silver-cadmium	CdO	Ag_2O	KOH	satellites
silver-zinc	Zn	Ag_2O	KOH	military applications

FUEL CELLS

Fuel cells are a special class of very efficient batteries. A fuel cell resembles a voltaic cell in that redox reactions occur, releasing electrons from one electrode to flow through a circuit to another electrode. But there is one major difference. In the voltaic cell, the active ingredients are included within the cell and are depleted as the redox reactions occur. In a fuel cell, a gas or liquid fuel is supplied to one electrode and oxygen or air to the other from an external source. Fuel cells have a long life and have been used extensively in space vehicles since the 1960s. Current fuel-cell research is targeted at powering vehicles with hydrogen as a fuel.

hydrogen fuel cell

478 Chapter 19

ELECTROLYTIC VERSUS VOLTAIC

Electrolytic Cell	Voltaic Cell
converts electrical energy to chemical energy	converts chemical energy to electrical energy
does not react spontaneously	reacts spontaneously
positive anode, negative cathode	negative anode, positive cathode
oxidation at the anode, reduction at the cathode	oxidation at the anode, reduction at the cathode

MINILAB

OBSERVING A VOLTAIC CELL

We use voltaic cells in the form of batteries all the time. Voltaic cells work as two half-reactions (oxidation and reduction) as part of an overall redox reaction. This lab activity will allow you to observe each half-cell of the reaction. Zinc metal will be oxidized in one half-cell, while copper(II) ions are reduced in the other half-cell.

How can I make a simple battery?

1. What is oxidation? What is reduction?

Procedure

A Fill one beaker with approximately 75 mL of copper(II) sulfate solution and the other with approximately 75 mL of zinc sulfate solution.

B Connect one of the wires between one end of the copper strip and the positive terminal of the voltmeter. Connect the other wire between one end of the zinc strip and the negative terminal of the voltmeter.

C Place the end of the copper strip in the copper(II) sulfate solution and the end of the zinc strip in the zinc sulfate.

D Turn on the voltmeter.

2. What is the voltmeter reading? Explain why you think it is what it is.

E Put the two ends of the salt bridge strip in each one of the solutions.

3. What is the voltmeter reading? Explain why you think this is what it is.
4. Write the half-reaction occurring in each half-cell. Write the redox reaction equation from the two half-reactions.

Going Further

5. How could we produce a different voltage?

EQUIPMENT

- voltmeter
- beakers, 100 mL (2)
- 1 M copper(II) sulfate solution, 75 mL
- 1 M zinc sulfate solution, 75 mL
- connecting wires (2)
- copper strip, 6 cm
- zinc strip, 6 cm
- salt bridge strip

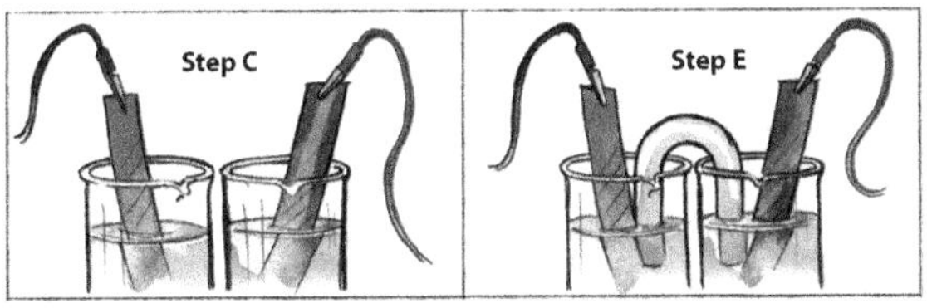

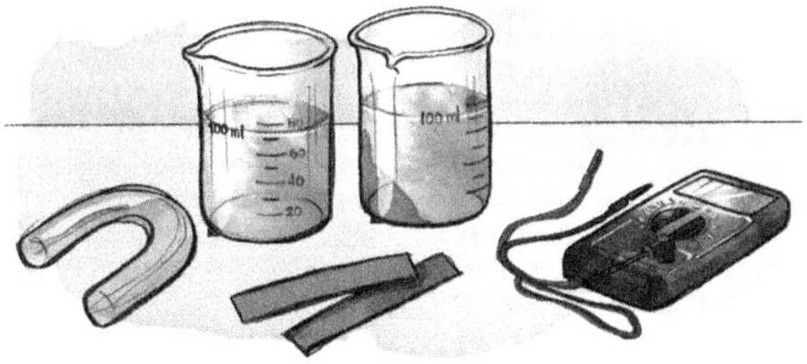

MINI-LAB: *OBSERVING A VOLTAIC CELL*

Use this **mini lab** to observe a redox reaction and identify the half-reactions in a voltaic cell.

1. Oxidation is the chemical process by which electrons are removed from a substance. Reduction is the process by which electrons are added to a substance.
2. The voltmeter reading is zero because the two half-cells are not connected.
3. Answers will vary. Because of the particular elements being used, the voltage should read close to the theoretical value of 1.1 V.
4. oxidation: $Zn \longrightarrow Zn^{+2} + 2e^-$
   reduction: $Cu^{+2} + 2e^- \longrightarrow Cu$

   $Zn \longrightarrow Zn^{+2} + \cancel{2e^-}$
   $Cu^{+2} + \cancel{2e^-} \longrightarrow Cu$
   $Zn + Cu^{+2} \longrightarrow Zn^{+2} + Cu$
5. Answers will vary. Students may suggest changing the concentration of the solutions (which would not work). Others may suggest changing the metals and composition of the solutions (which could work).

APPLY

LAB 19B: *DANGER UNDER THE SINK*

Once students have an understanding of the material in Section 19.2, they should be ready to work through Lab 19B.

ASSESS

TICKET OUT THE DOOR

As a **summarizing activity**, ask students to explain one difference between electrolytic and voltaic cells. (See pages 472–77.)

19.2 REVIEW *ANSWERS*

1. Electrochemistry is the field of chemistry that studies two related processes, one in which a spontaneous redox reaction is used to produce electricity and another in which electricity is used to cause a nonspontaneous redox reaction to occur. *(p. 471)*
2. electrolytic and voltaic cells; The redox reaction in an electrolytic cell is nonspontaneous and requires electricity to occur. In a voltaic cell the reaction occurs spontaneously and produces electricity. *(p. 471)*
3. The atoms of active metals are held in stronger chemical bonds than other metals. Also, there are fewer elements active enough to replace these elements in the compounds in which they are found. *(p. 473)*
4. The anode has a negative charge. Anions move toward the anode. Oxidation occurs at the anode. *(pp. 472–74)*
5. As the two half-reactions occur, ions will accumulate in the solutions. The accumulation of ions will stop the reaction from occurring. A salt bridge allows the flow of ions between the two electrolytic solutions but prevents the solutions from mixing. *(p. 475)*
6. In these reactions zinc and cadmium would not work together in a battery because both are being oxidized. For a working battery there must be an oxidation reaction and a reduction reaction. *(pp. 474–75)*

CASE STUDY

SMALLER, SAFER BATTERIES

In 2016 there were numerous news reports of electronic devices igniting. We learned from these incidents that lithium ion batteries had a significant drawback—the electrolyte was a flammable liquid. To address this issue, scientists at both Penn State and Cornell Universities worked on developing batteries with a solid electrolyte.

Both teams worked through the challenges of establishing a reliable interface between the electrodes and the electrolyte. The fluid property of liquids naturally allows them to change shape and remain in contact with electrodes. Researchers worked to establish the same level of contact between the electrodes and a solid electrolyte. Through nanotechnology and polymer chemistry, they achieved their goal.

In addition to solving the safety issue, both teams identified other advantages of a solid electrolyte.

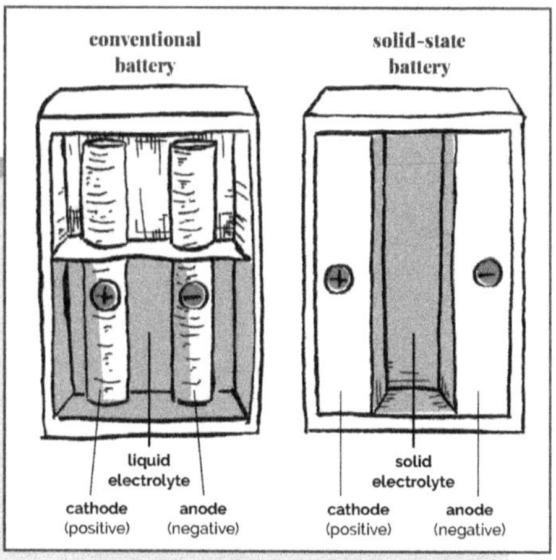

They found that batteries with a solid-state electrolyte also have a high energy density (they can store more energy), they are longer-lasting, and they can be made smaller than their liquid-electrolyte counterparts. Scientists love it when they can solve multiple problems at the same time!

19.2 SECTION REVIEW

1. What is electrochemistry?
2. Name the two types of electrochemical cells and explain the difference between them.
3. Why is a special process necessary to purify active metals such as aluminum and sodium when other metals can be more easily purified from their ores?
4. In a voltaic cell, what is the electric charge on the anode? What type of ion migrates toward the anode? What process (oxidation or reduction) occurs at the surface of the anode?
5. Why is a salt bridge used in voltaic cells?
6. Would the electrodes in the half-reactions represented below make a functional battery? Explain your answer.

$$Zn \longrightarrow Zn^{2+} + 2e^-$$

$$Cd \longrightarrow Cd^{2+} + 2e^-$$

7. Write the half reactions and redox reaction for lithium being oxidized and gold(III) ions being reduced to gold atoms.

Use the case study above to answer Questions 8–10.

8. Summarize how a lithium ion battery works.
9. What was the primary issue that the research teams were trying to solve?
10. What is the challenge of using a solid-state electrolyte?

7. oxidation: $Li \longrightarrow Li^+ + e^-$

reduction: $Au^{3+} + 3\,e^- \longrightarrow Au$

Balance electrons.

$3(Li \longrightarrow Li^+ + e^-)$

$Au^{3+} + 3\,e^- \longrightarrow Au$

Add half-reactions.

$3Li \longrightarrow 3Li^+ + \cancel{3e^-}$

$Au^{3+} + \cancel{3e^-} \longrightarrow Au$

$3Li + Au^{3+} \longrightarrow 3Li^+ + Au$

(pp. 474–75)

8. A lithium ion battery has a carbon electrode and a metal oxide electrode where the half-reactions of a redox reaction take place. Lithium ions travel through a liquid electrolyte during the reaction, in which electric current is produced.
9. They were trying to improve a safety issue arising from use of a flammable liquid electrolyte.
10. All chemical reactions require that the reactants come in contact with each other. Because solids can't flow, it is more difficult to ensure that contact is made all around the electrodes.

19 CHAPTER REVIEW

Chapter Summary

TERMS
oxidation-reduction reaction
oxidation
reduction
reducing agent
oxidizing agent

19.1 REDOX REACTIONS

- Oxidation-reduction, or redox, reactions are chemical changes in which electrons are transferred from one atom or molecule to another.
- Oxidation involves the loss of one or more electrons (LEO). Reduction involves the gain of one or more electrons (GER). These processes occur simultaneously.
- A reducing agent causes another substance to be reduced and is itself oxidized in the process. An oxidizing agent causes another substance to be oxidized and is itself reduced in the process.
- Equations of redox reactions must be balanced to maintain the laws of the conservation of mass and charge.

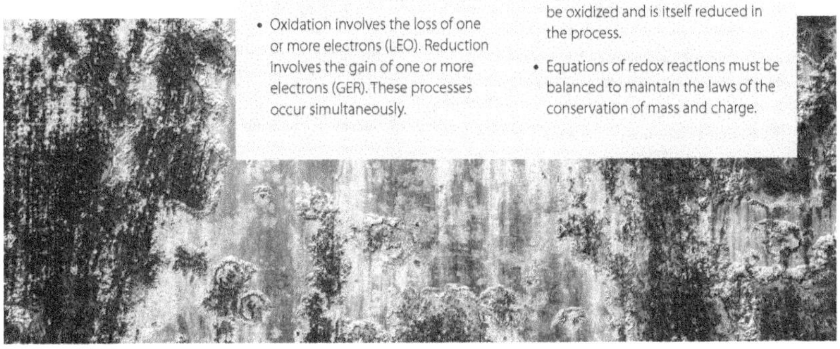

19.2 ELECTROCHEMICAL REACTIONS

- Electrochemistry is the study of chemical reactions that can produce electricity and reactions that require electricity to occur.
- An electrolyte is any substance that releases ions when dissolved in water, allowing the resulting solution to conduct electricity.
- An electrochemical cell has two electrodes (electrical contacts) immersed in an electrolyte, with a wire joining the electrodes. The two main groups of electrochemical cells are electrolytic cells and voltaic cells.
- Electrolysis, a process occurring in electrolytic cells, requires electrical current to cause an otherwise nonspontaneous redox reaction to occur.
- Electrolytic cells use electricity to cause a nonspontaneous chemical reaction to occur. Reduction occurs at the negatively charged cathode and oxidation occurs at the positively charged anode.
- In voltaic cells, spontaneous redox reactions produce electricity by causing electrons to flow. Reduction occurs at the positively charged cathode and oxidation occurs at the negatively charged anode. Batteries are collections of voltaic cells.

TERMS
electrochemistry
electrochemical cell
electrolytic cell
voltaic cell
electrolysis
cathode
anode
electroplating
battery
half-cell
half-reaction
salt bridge
fuel cell

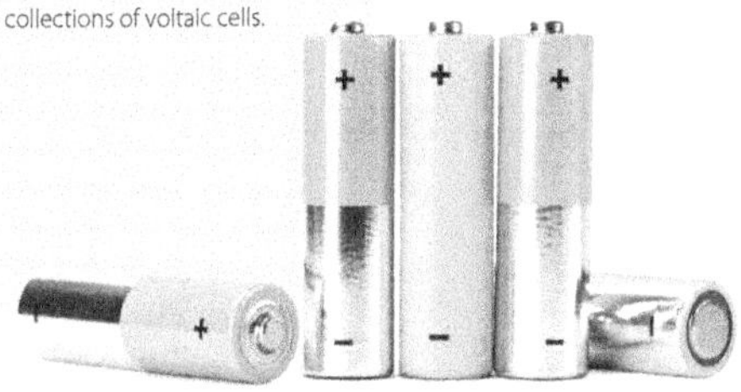

Redox Reactions 481

CHAPTER 19 *REVIEW ANSWERS*

Recalling Facts

1. Single-replacement and combustion reactions are always redox reactions, while synthesis and decomposition reactions can be redox reactions. *(p. 463)*
2. No. Any atom that causes other atoms to lose electrons can cause oxidation. *(p. 463)*
3. Reduction is the process by which a chemical substance gains electrons. *(p. 464)*
4. True *(p. 468)*
5. The number of ions that an electrolyte forms in a solution, that is, its ability to dissociate, indicates its strength. *(p. 468)*
6. Pure water will not conduct electricity because it does not contain an electrolyte. *(p. 471)*
7. An electrochemical cell uses either a chemical reaction to produce a voltage difference between two electrical contacts, called electrodes, or uses the voltage difference to drive a chemical reaction. *(p. 471)*
8. oxidation (for both) *(p. 472)*
9. True *(p. 472)*
10. The smelting of aluminum, electrolysis of brine, and electrodepositing are all mentioned in the chapter. *(p. 473)*
11. The reactants in a voltaic cell are contained within the cell and are depleted as the reactions occur. The fuel cell's reactants are supplied from an external source. *(pp. 471–78)*

19 CHAPTER REVIEW

Chapter Review Questions

RECALLING FACTS

1. Which types of reactions are or can be redox reactions?
2. Does oxidation require that oxygen atoms be present? Explain your answer.
3. Define *reduction.*
4. (True or False) In some redox reactions, the same element is both reduced and oxidized.
5. What determines the strength of an electrolyte?
6. Why is pure water a poor conductor of electricity?
7. Define *electrochemical cell.*
8. What type of reaction occurs at the anode of an electrolytic cell? of a voltaic cell?
9. (True or False) In every type of electrochemical cell, oxidation always takes place at the anode and reduction always takes place at the cathode.
10. What are some useful applications of electrolytic cells?
11. What is the main difference between a voltaic cell and a fuel cell?

UNDERSTANDING CONCEPTS

12. Indicate whether each reaction is a redox reaction.
    - **a.** $2Fe(s) + 3Cl_2(g) \longrightarrow 2FeCl_3(s)$
    - **b.** $CaO(s) + 2HCl(g) \longrightarrow CaCl_2(s) + H_2O(l)$
    - **c.** $2C_2H_6(g) + 7O_2(g) \longrightarrow 4CO_2(g) + 6H_2O(l)$
    - **d.** $Zn(s) + CuSO_4(aq) \longrightarrow Cu(s) + ZnSO_4(aq)$
    - **e.** $H_2SO_4(aq) + 2KOH(aq) \longrightarrow K_2SO_4(s) + 2H_2O(l)$
    - **f.** $Pb(s) + H_2SO_4(aq) \longrightarrow PbSO_4(s) + H_2(g)$
    - **g.** $AgNO_3(aq) + HCl(aq) \longrightarrow AgCl(s) + HNO_3(aq)$
13. Create a graphic organizer using the terms *electrons, oxidation, oxidizing agent, redox reaction, reducing agent,* and *reduction.*

For Questions 14–17, refer to the following redox reactions.

- **a.** $2KClO_3(s) \longrightarrow 2KCl(s) + 3O_2(g)$
- **b.** $Zn(s) + 2HCl(aq) \longrightarrow ZnCl_2(aq) + H_2(g)$
- **c.** $Fe_2O_3(s) + 3CO(g) \longrightarrow 2Fe(s) + 3CO_2(g)$
- **d.** $Mg(s) + Cu_2SO_4(aq) \longrightarrow 2Cu(s) + MgSO_4(aq)$
- **e.** $H_2(g) + Cl_2(g) \longrightarrow 2HCl(g)$
- **f.** $4NH_3(g) + 3O_2(g) \longrightarrow 2N_2(g) + 6H_2O(g)$
- **g.** $Cu(s) + 4HNO_3(aq) \longrightarrow Cu(NO_3)_2(aq) + 2NO_2(g) + 2H_2O(l)$
- **h.** $MnO_4^- + 5Fe^{2+} + 8H^+ \longrightarrow Mn^{2+} + 5Fe^{3+} + 4H_2O$
- **i.** $2SO_4^{2-} + C + 4H^+ \longrightarrow CO_2 + 2SO_2 + 2H_2O$

14. Identify the substance being oxidized in each reaction.
15. Identify the substance being reduced in each reaction.
16. Identify the oxidizing agent in each reaction.
17. Identify the reducing agent in each reaction.
18. Identify what is being oxidized and reduced in the reaction below.

$$2H_2O_2(l) \longrightarrow 2H_2O(l) + O_2(g)$$

19. Balance each of the following equations.
    - **a.** $Cu^+(aq) + Fe(s) \longrightarrow Fe^{3+}(aq) + Cu(s)$
    - **b.** $Fe(OH)_2 + H_2O_2 \longrightarrow Fe(OH)_3$
    - **c.** $Cu + HNO_3 \longrightarrow Cu(NO_3)_2 + NO_2 + H_2O$
20. Explain why zinc plating will protect steel from corroding even if the plating is cracked.
21. Describe how the Hall-Héroult process uses electrons to free aluminum atoms from bauxite.
22. Compare electrolytic cells and voltaic cells.
23. What do we mean when we speak of half-reactions and half-cells?
24. Write the half-reactions and redox reaction for aluminum being oxidized and copper(II) being reduced to copper atoms.
25. In a voltaic cell, what is the electrical charge on the cathode? What type of ion migrates toward the cathode? What process (oxidation or reduction) occurs at the surface of the cathode?

Understanding Concepts

* An asterisk following a question number indicates that a worked-out solution can be found on page 483B.

12. **a.** yes
    b. no
    c. yes
    d. yes
    e. no
    f. yes
    g. no *(all p. 465)*

13.* *(pp. 463–66)*

14. **a.** oxygen
    b. zinc
    c. carbon
    d. magnesium
    e. hydrogen
    f. nitrogen
    g. copper
    h. iron(II) ion
    i. carbon *(all p. 466)*

15. **a.** chlorine
    b. hydrogen
    c. iron
    d. copper
    e. chlorine
    f. oxygen
    g. nitrogen
    h. permanganate ion
    i. sulfate ion *(all p. 466)*

16. **a.** chlorine
    b. hydrogen
    c. iron
    d. copper
    e. chlorine
    f. oxygen
    g. nitrogen
    h. permanganate ion
    i. sulfate ion *(all p. 466)*

26. Why do battery manufacturers recommend not charging some batteries even though they are based on the same reversible redox reactions as those in rechargeable batteries?

27. In the lead-acid storage battery of a vehicle, the degree to which the power has been discharged can be determined by using a hydrometer to measure the density of the sulfuric acid solution. Explain why this is possible.

28. Compare the types of batteries listed in the chapter (zinc-carbon, alkaline, lead acid, and lithium ion).

29. Describe how rechargeable batteries are both voltaic and electrolytic cells.

CRITICAL THINKING

30. Oxidation and reduction involve the losing or gaining of electrons. While this is easily understood in reactions with ionic compounds, how does oxidation and reduction work with covalently bonded substances?

31. Explain why sodium is a strong reducer and fluorine is a strong oxidizer.

32. Consider the list of nitrogen compounds below. Determine the oxidation number for nitrogen in each one. How does this explain the variety of nitrogen-containing compounds?

NO, NO_2, N_2O, N_2O_5, HNO_2, HNO_3, HNO_4

Use the ethics box below to answer Question 33.

33. How should a Christian respond to the claim that a good steward of our planet's resources and environment should drive only electric vehicles?

ethics

ELECTRIC CARS

Watch almost any news program and you are likely to hear a segment on global warming, air pollution, and fossil fuels. Many people are concerned about our dependence on fossil fuels, the condition in which we are leaving our environment, and even whether we are going to destroy the planet through global warming. Some claim that electric cars are the answer to these issues. Electric cars do not burn fossil fuels and do not produce gases that pollute or contribute to global warming. Others say that electric cars solve none of these issues because the electricity required to operate them still needs to be produced, and it may be produced in a fossil fuel plant that emits polluting greenhouse gases.

17. **a.** oxygen
    b. zinc
    c. carbon
    d. magnesium
    e. hydrogen
    f. nitrogen
    g. copper
    h. iron(II) ion
    i. carbon *(all p. 466)*

18. Oxygen is being both oxidized and reduced. *(pp. 466, 468)*

19.* *(all pp. 468–70)*

20. Zinc plating isolates the steel from the conditions that cause corrosion. Even if the plating is cracked, zinc is more easily oxidized than iron is. Therefore, any oxidation that occurs will involve the zinc rather than the steel (until all the zinc is oxidized). *(p. 472)*

21. The Hall-Héroult process uses a very high current of electricity to force electrons to join aluminum ions. *(p. 473)*

22. Both types of cells are electrochemical cells. Electrolytic cells use electrical energy to force a nonspontaneous chemical reaction to occur, while voltaic cells use a redox reaction that spontaneously occurs to produce electrical energy. *(pp. 471, 474)*

23. In a voltaic cell, the oxidation and reduction reactions happen in two separate vessels; these are considered the half-cells that make up the voltaic cell. The reaction that occurs in each half-cell is a half-reaction. When the two half-reactions are added together, the balanced equation for the redox reaction is obtained. *(p.475)*

24.* *(p. 475)*

25. The cathode has a positive charge. Cations move toward the cathode. Reduction occurs at the cathode. *(p. 476)*

26. Gases are produced during the recharging. Rechargeable batteries are designed to let this gas escape, but nonrechargeable batteries lack this design element. *(p. 477)*

27. As the battery is discharged, H_2SO_4 is converted to H_2O and SO_4^{2-} ions. A hydrometer can measure the amount of H_2O that has been converted. *(p. 476)*

28. All four batteries work in the same manner in that all involve a redox reaction occurring to produce an electric current. The differences between these batteries are in the specific design and the half-reactions occurring. Zinc-carbon and alkaline batteries are dry cells in which zinc is oxidized at the anode and manganese is reduced. Both zinc-carbon and alkaline batteries are single-use, nonrecyclable batteries. Lead acid and lithium ion batteries are both rechargeable batteries. A lead acid battery is a wet cell in which the lead compound electrodes are in a sulfuric acid solution. Lead is both oxidized and reduced in the lead acid battery. In a lithium ion battery, lithium ions move between a carbon electrode and a metal ion electrode. *(pp. 476–77)*

29. When a rechargeable battery is discharging, it carries on a spontaneous reaction, supplying electricity like a voltaic cell. When it is recharged, the reaction is reversed and the electrical energy forces a reaction like an electrolytic cell. *(p. 476)*

Critical Thinking

30. Most covalent bonds are polar, with one atom pulling on the shared electrons more than the other atom. The atom that is pulling the electrons closer is considered to be reduced and the other atom is oxidized.

31. Sodium has one valence electron that it gives up easily, meaning that other elements can easily be reduced by sodium. Fluorine has seven valence electrons and is eager to take one more. It is likely to remove an electron from another element by oxidizing it.

32. $\overset{+2}{N}O$, $\overset{+4}{N}O_2$, $\overset{+1}{N}_2O$, $\overset{+5}{N}_2O_5$, $H\overset{+3}{N}O_2$, $H\overset{+5}{N}O_3$, $H\overset{+7}{N}O_4$

Nitrogen can form many different compounds because it can take on many oxidation numbers. *(pp. 464–66)*

Appendix L includes a reproducible rubric to assess the ethics essay.

33. There are two aspects of biblical principles that apply to the Creation Mandate. We are commanded to take care of people and the world that God has created for us. Therefore, according to ethical relevance, Christians should make all decisions on the basis of what protects human life, what protects the environment, and what best manages resources.

All three aspects of biblical outcomes should be considered when addressing this issue. The issues of pollution, global warming, and resource use will all have an impact on human prospering, a thriving creation, and glorifying God. One possible outcome would be to avoid trying to understand and investigate the claim, perhaps resulting in being apathetic to possible issues involving the use of our resources. Another option would be to endorse electric vehicle usage and not worry about whether the electric cars actually improve the issues involved. A balanced approach would be to investigate the claims of electric car proponents and detractors.

Again, all three aspects of biblical motivations are involved in this problem. God is clear about how the world will be destroyed, but that doesn't mean that we can damage the earth without regard for consequences before that time. We must make our decisions on the basis of our faith in God and on the promises that He has made in the Bible. We must always demonstrate our love for God and others.

There are many considerations when it comes to purchasing a vehicle. It would be difficult to come to a conclusion that everyone must drive electric cars or that no one should. That decision would depend on environmental risks and dangers associated with electric batteries, the amount of travel required, the source of electricity for the cars, and the efficiency of both gasoline- and electric-powered vehicles. Each person needs to make an informed decision that glorifies God and protects life and the environment.

Section 19.1

8. a. -2×1

$\overset{+4}{Sn}Cl_4 + \overset{+2}{Fe} \longrightarrow \overset{+2}{Sn}Cl_2 + \overset{+3}{Fe}Cl_3$

$+1 \times 2$

$SnCl_4 + 2Fe \longrightarrow SnCl_2 + 2FeCl_3$

Balance the rest by inspection.

$3SnCl_4 + 2Fe \longrightarrow 3SnCl_2 + 2FeCl_3$

$+2 \times 1$

b. $\overset{+4}{S}O_2 + \overset{0}{Br_2} + H_2O \longrightarrow H\overset{-1}{Br} + H_2\overset{+6}{S}O_4$

-1×2

$SO_2 + 2Br_2 + H_2O \longrightarrow 2HBr + H_2SO_4$

Balance the rest by inspection.

$SO_2 + Br_2 + 2H_2O \longrightarrow 2HBr + H_2SO_4$

$+2 \times 5$

c. $\overset{+2}{C}O + \overset{+5}{I_2}O_5 \longrightarrow \overset{0}{I_2} + \overset{+4}{C}O_2$

-5×2

$5CO + 2I_2O_5 \longrightarrow 2I_2 + 5CO_2$

Balance the rest by inspection.

$5CO + I_2O_5 \longrightarrow I_2 + 5CO_2$

Chapter 19 Review

13.

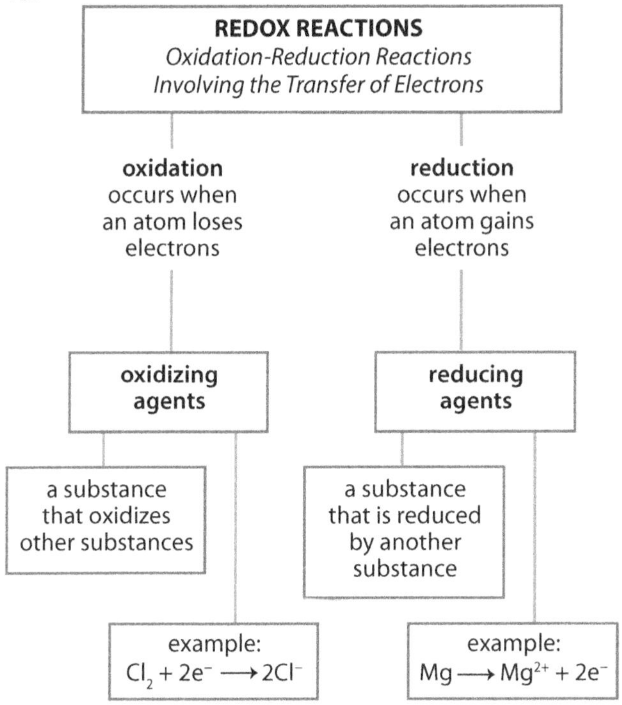

19. a. -1×3

$\overset{+1}{Cu^+} + \overset{0}{Fe} \longrightarrow \overset{+3}{Fe^{3+}} + \overset{0}{Cu}$

$+3 \times 1$

$3Cu^+ (aq) + Fe (s) \longrightarrow Fe^{3+} (aq) + 3Cu (s)$

Balance the rest by inspection.

$3Cu^+ + Fe \longrightarrow Fe^{3+} + 3Cu$

$+1 \times 1$

b. $\overset{+2}{Fe}(OH)_2 + H_2\overset{-1}{O_2} \longrightarrow \overset{+3}{Fe}(\overset{-2}{O}H)_3$

-1×1

$Fe(OH)_2 + H_2O_2 \longrightarrow Fe(OH)_3$

$Cu + 2HNO_3 \longrightarrow Cu(NO_3)_2 + 2NO_2 + H_2O$

Balance the rest by inspection.

$2Fe(OH)_2 + H_2O_2 \longrightarrow 2Fe(OH)_3$

$+2 \times 1$

c. $\overset{0}{Cu} + H\overset{+5}{N}O_3 \longrightarrow \overset{+2}{Cu}(NO_3)_2 + \overset{+4}{N}O_2 + H_2O$

-1×2

Balance the rest by inspection.

$Cu + 4HNO_3 \longrightarrow Cu(NO_3)_2 + 2NO_2 + 2H_2O$

24. oxidation: $Al \longrightarrow Al^{3+} + 3e^-$

reduction: $Cu^{2+} + 2e^- \longrightarrow Cu$

Balance electrons.

$2(Al \longrightarrow Al^{3+} + 3e^-)$

$3(Cu^{2+} + 2e^- \longrightarrow Cu)$

Add half-reactions.

$2Al \longrightarrow 2Al^{3+} + \cancel{6e^-}$

$3Cu^{2+} + \cancel{6e^-} \longrightarrow 3Cu$

$2Al + 3Cu^{2+} \longrightarrow 2Al^{3+} + 3Cu$

CHAPTER 20 *OBJECTIVES*

- Evaluate the statement, "Properties of compounds are a result of their internal structure."
- Classify organic compounds.
- Complete chemical equations for different organic reactions.
- Synthesize organic compounds in the laboratory.

OVERVIEW

Chapter 20 has key material that is used in the study of organic chemistry. Because some of our most innovative and common products are the results of organic chemistry, it is easy to relate these concepts to students' daily lives. The most important material in this chapter that they should master is the nomenclature and the structure of organic molecules.

20.1 ORGANIC COMPOUNDS

- *Classification*

20.2 HYDROCARBONS

- *Aliphatic Hydrocarbons*
- *Cyclic Aliphatic Hydrocarbons*
- *Aromatic Hydrocarbons*

20.3 SUBSTITUTED HYDROCARBONS

- *Halocarbons*
- *Alcohols*
- *Ethers*
- *Aldehydes and Ketones*
- *Carboxylic Acids*
- *Esters*
- *Amines and Amides*

20.4 ORGANIC REACTIONS

- *Oxidation-Reduction*
- *Substitution*
- *Addition*
- *Elimination*
- *Condensation*

LAB ACTIVITIES

Lab 20A: *Makes Scents!*—Students synthesize esters.

Lab 20B: *Squeaky Clean*—Students investigate hard water and the effects of using soaps and detergents.

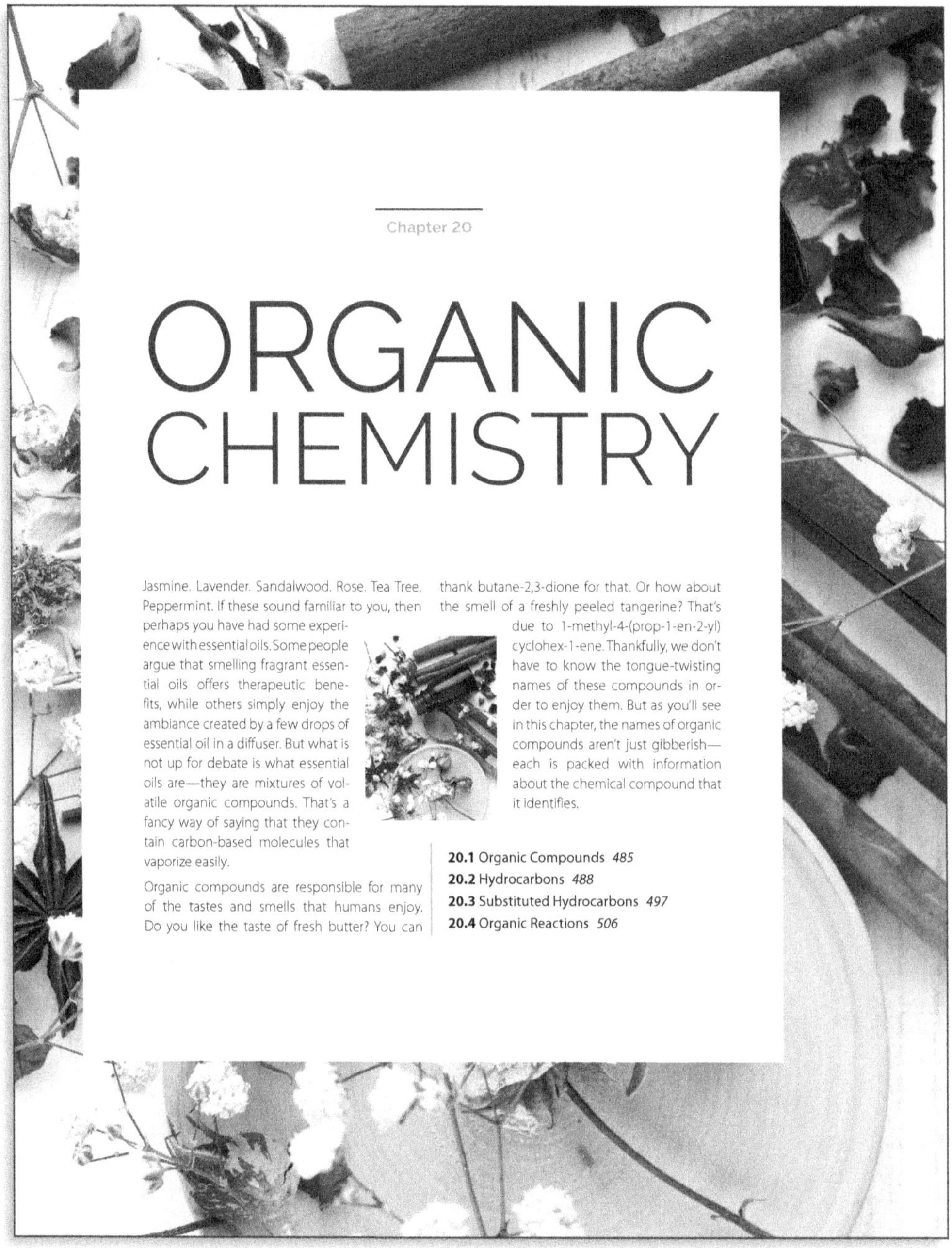
Chapter 20

ORGANIC CHEMISTRY

Jasmine. Lavender. Sandalwood. Rose. Tea Tree. Peppermint. If these sound familiar to you, then perhaps you have had some experience with essential oils. Some people argue that smelling fragrant essential oils offers therapeutic benefits, while others simply enjoy the ambiance created by a few drops of essential oil in a diffuser. But what is not up for debate is what essential oils are—they are mixtures of volatile organic compounds. That's a fancy way of saying that they contain carbon-based molecules that vaporize easily.

Organic compounds are responsible for many of the tastes and smells that humans enjoy. Do you like the taste of fresh butter? You can thank butane-2,3-dione for that. Or how about the smell of a freshly peeled tangerine? That's due to 1-methyl-4-(prop-1-en-2-yl)cyclohex-1-ene. Thankfully, we don't have to know the tongue-twisting names of these compounds in order to enjoy them. But as you'll see in this chapter, the names of organic compounds aren't just gibberish—each is packed with information about the chemical compound that it identifies.

The photo in the Chapter opener displays several examples of aroma-producing plants found in nature. Students may wonder how they produce such sweet fragrances. The answer to this question lies within the study of organic chemistry.

20.1 ORGANIC COMPOUNDS

Carbon is a common element that is found in nature both as a pure element and in compounds. It can be found in all living matter. In fact, without carbon, there would be no life. Carbon is also often in the news these days since it is a major component of both fossil fuels, such as petroleum and natural gas, and the carbon dioxide—a greenhouse gas—that is produced by the combustion of those fuels.

Organic compounds were so named because for many years it was believed that only living things could produce them. But in 1828, Friedrich Wöhler, a German chemist, unintentionally synthesized urea (NH_2CONH_2) in the laboratory. This compound was previously known only from the urine of humans and animals—a compound clearly linked to living things. Beginning with this breakthrough, a new field of study emerged—organic chemistry. Scientists can now synthesize many **organic compounds**, which they define as covalently bonded carbon compounds, with the exception of carbonates, carbon oxides, and carbides. The branch of chemistry that focuses specifically on these carbon compounds is called **organic chemistry**.

QUESTIONS

- When did organic chemistry become a recognized field?
- What makes carbon so special compared with other elements?
- What information can be seen in a structural formula?
- What is the difference between aromatic and aliphatic compounds?

TERMS

organic compound • organic chemistry • condensed structural formula • aromatic compound • aliphatic compound

How does organic chemistry fit within the broader study of chemistry in general?

THE UNIQUE
Carbon Atom

Carbon is an element unparalleled in its ability to form a variety of compounds. Other elements can form several hundred thousand compounds, but carbon can form more than fifty million compounds! What makes the carbon atom so versatile? Carbon atoms have unique bonding abilities.

Three important properties of carbon enable it to form large, stable molecules.

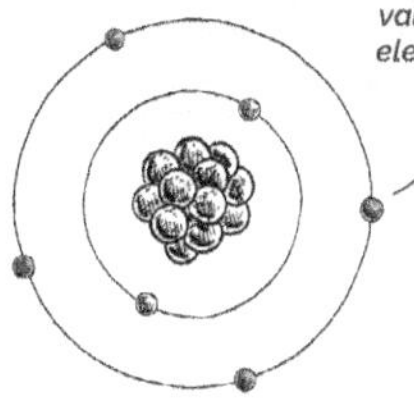

❶ Carbon has four valence electrons, allowing it to form four bonds to obtain a full valence shell.

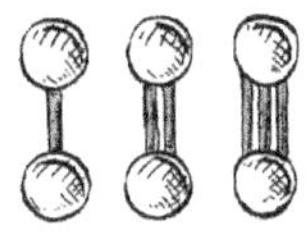

❷ Carbon forms strong chemical bonds with other carbon atoms.

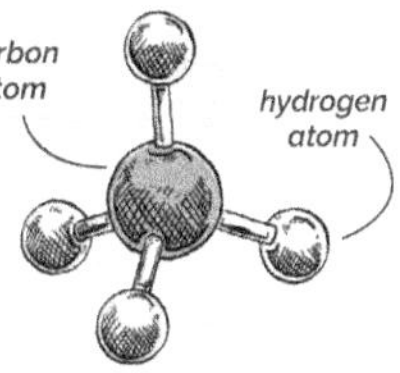

❸ Carbon forms stable, essentially nonpolar bonds with hydrogen. The electronegativity difference between carbon (2.6) and hydrogen (2.2) is small.

Carbon atoms can bond to a wide variety of other atoms, including hydrogen, phosphorus, oxygen, nitrogen, sulfur, the halogens, and even metal atoms. Carbon atoms can bond with one another to form linear or branched chains of various lengths, and they can even form rings. Carbon atoms can form double and triple bonds, further adding to the almost endless possibilities.

Organic Chemistry **485**

SECTION 20.1 *OVERVIEW*

Essential Question

How does organic chemistry fit within the broader study of chemistry in general?

Objectives

» **20.1.1** Define *organic compound.*

» **20.1.2** Explain why carbon forms so many compounds.

» **20.1.3** Describe the basic features of a structural formula.

» **20.1.4** Distinguish between aliphatic and aromatic organic compounds.

Resource

Careers: Serving as an Odor Tester

ENGAGE

RECALLING INORGANIC CHEMISTRY

Lead students in a **collaborative mind review warm-up** by asking them to individually record the definition and general concepts of inorganic chemistry.

1. What is studied in the field of inorganic chemistry? *(Inorganic chemistry is the study of chemical compounds and processes of substances with nonliving origins.)*
2. What types of reactions are involved with inorganic chemical reactions? *(synthesis, single- and double-replacement, decomposition, combustion, and redox reactions)*
3. What element is typically missing from many inorganic chemical reactions? *(carbon, except the oxides and carbonates)*

Once students have finished answering the questions, select several to read their answers to the class. Explain away any misunderstandings and clarify difficult concepts. Explain that inorganic chemistry deals with chemical processes that do not contain carbon-hydrogen bonds.

In this chapter, students explore chemistry involving carbon-based molecules, which are essential for life.

INSTRUCT

INORGANIC CARBON

Carbonates, carbon oxides, and carbides are considered inorganic because they come from minerals and ores.

CARBON AND ELECTRONEGATIVITY

Conduct a **review** by asking the following questions.

1. What determines an atom's tendency to attract electrons within a molecule? *(electronegativity)*
2. What type of bond occurs between carbon and hydrogen? *(covalent)* Why is this type of bond present? *(They have similar electronegativities.)*

COMPLETE STRUCTURAL FORMULAS

Because this is an introductory course, the Student Edition shows complete structural formulas, rather than condensed or skeletal formulas. Introduce the latter conventions at your discretion.

FINDING THE DIFFERENCE

Lead a **visual analysis** of a molecular formula that has several structural formulas, such as $C_4H_8O_4$, by displaying each structure on a board or screen. Have students analyze the structures and try to find the differences. For example, one arrangement of $C_4H_8O_4$, erythrose, has an OH group on one side of the structural formula. Another arrangement, threose, has the same OH group on the other side. The difference will be more readily apparent if you use physical models of both compounds.

Structural formulas are important because internal structure determines the physical and chemical properties of compounds. Molecules with the same number and types of atoms may have hundreds of different arrangements of their atoms.

MODELS IN YOUR CLASSROOM

Molecular models are essential in this chapter because they show the three-dimensional nature of molecules. If possible, purchase a large ball-and-stick teacher set so that you have enough parts for students to build models at the same time. Space-filling

Structural Formulas

AND MODELS

Organic chemists study more than just the types of atoms in molecules. They also study how these atoms are arranged. If an analytical chemist were to announce that he had isolated a compound with the molecular formula C_2H_6O, there might be some confusion about what exactly the compound was. Let's look at why this is so.

Ethanol is an alcohol with the formula C_2H_6O. Its two carbon atoms are bonded together in a short chain with the oxygen atom on one end. Shown below is ethanol's structural formula and a ball-and-stick model. Sometimes you might also see a **condensed structural formula**, which is a way of modeling a compound's molecular structure in a single line of text. Ethanol's condensed structural formula is CH_3CH_2OH.

Methoxymethane has the same molecular formula, C_2H_6O, but as shown below, its structural formula and model look quite different. The arrangement of the atoms in the molecule makes the difference. In methoxymethane's case, the oxygen atom is located between the two carbon atoms. It might seem like a minor difference, but this change in structure causes methoxymethane and ethanol to have very different physical and chemical properties. Methoxymethane's condensed structural formula is CH_3OCH_3.

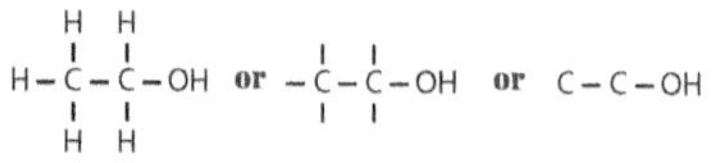

ethanol

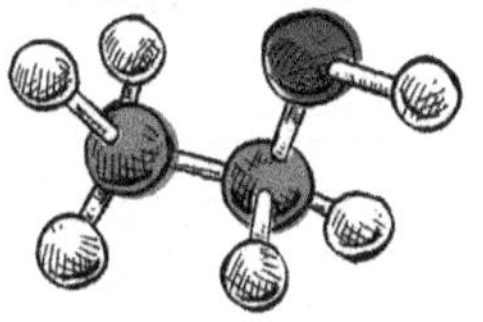

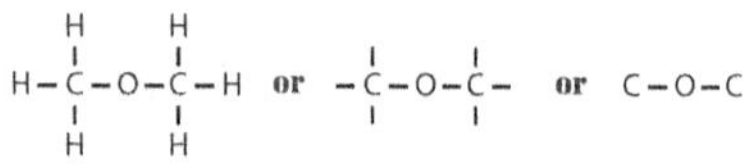

methoxymethane

By now you may have noticed that some organic compounds contain a lot of hydrogen atoms. It's commonplace to see these hydrogen atoms omitted in structural formulas. In such instances, it's understood by consensus that the "missing" atoms are hydrogens. In some cases where hydrogen forms part of a functional group, such as a hydroxyl group (OH), it remains shown.

ethanol

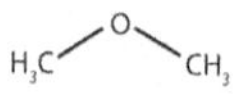

methoxymethane

To further reduce the visual clutter in a structural formula, chemists will often use a form known as a *skeletal formula* that omits the carbon atoms as well. In skeletal formulas, it is understood that each unlabeled bend in the structure, along with any "empty" end of a bond, is occupied by a carbon atom and its bonded hydrogens, if any.

ethanol

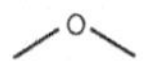

methoxymethane

models are not that useful since they hide the bonds in the molecule. In the infographic on this page, note the zigzag shape of the carbon backbone in methoxymethane. Linear alkane molecules also have this zigzag shape because of the tetrahedral bonding angles between carbon atoms. This is a common feature of organic molecules that is illustrated well by a modeling set. If you do not have access to a molecular modeling kit or would like to do both, consider downloading free molecular modeling software. To find such models, do an internet search using the keywords "3D molecular modeling app."

ASSESS

TICKET OUT THE DOOR

As a **summarizing activity**, ask students to write the three unique properties of the carbon atom. *([1] It has four valence electrons, [2] allowing it to obtain a full valence shell by forming strong chemical bonds with other carbon atoms. [3] It forms stable bonds with hydrogen.)*

Classification

Every year, many new organic compounds are synthesized for the first time. If a person wants to find his way through this ever-growing field, he must use some guidelines. What's needed is a classification scheme that organizes compounds into easily identifiable groups.

Organic compounds can be divided into two large groups: aromatic compounds and aliphatic compounds. **Aromatic compounds** are organic compounds that contain highly stable ringed structures. The highly stable nature of these rings is due to their electrons not being associated with a specific bond or atom—they are delocalized. This is similar to the way that metal atoms bound by metallic bonds share electrons, as you learned in Chapter 7. Not surprisingly, aromatic compounds are so named because many of the first ones to be identified had distinctive smells. Today, though, the word is applied to compounds with a particular kind of chemical structure without regard to odor. You'll learn more about aromatic compounds and their special structure in the next section. **Aliphatic compounds** consist of open-chain compounds, either branched or unbranched, such as ethanol, or rings that can be formed by bending a straight chain and connecting its ends together. Aliphatic rings do not have delocalized electrons and are less stable than aromatic rings. Cyclohexane is an example of a ring-shaped aliphatic compound.

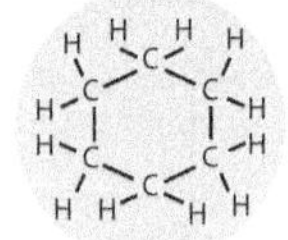

cyclohexane

CAREERS

SERVING AS AN ODOR TESTER: ***IMPROVING LIFE ONE SMELL AT A TIME***

Some people are more sensitive to smells than others. Some of those sensitive people make their livings with their discerning sniffers. Think about the many everyday products that have distinctive scents—everything from foodstuffs to personal hygiene products. The makers of those products know that pleasant smells make potential customers more likely to buy their wares. The opposite is also true—foul smells are far less likely to tempt buyers! That's where odor testers come in. An odor tester is a person with a keen sense of smell who is able to detect minute differences in smells that most people wouldn't notice. Chances are, your favorite coffee blend, body spray, or air freshener has been approved by a panel of odor testers. Because people are made in God's image, they can use their creative talents to devise a vast array of products that improve people's quality of life. Odor testers help ensure that pleasant smells contribute to that improvement.

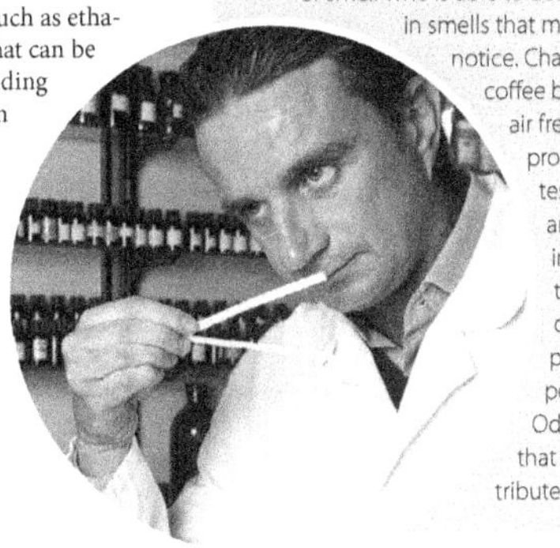

20.1 SECTION REVIEW

1. What is an organic compound?
2. What characteristics of carbon enable it to be found in millions of compounds?
3. Why are structural formulas important to organic chemists?
4. List and define the two large groups into which organic compounds are divided.
5. Cyclohexane has a distinctive smell (like that of detergent), just as many aromatic compounds do. Why is cyclohexane not classified as an aromatic hydrocarbon?

20.1 Review Answers

1. An organic compound is one that contains covalently bonded carbon atoms, excluding carbonates, carbon oxides, and carbides. *(p. 485)*
2. Carbon has four valence electrons, and so four bonds can be formed. It forms strong bonds to other carbon atoms. It forms stable, unreactive bonds with hydrogen. *(p. 485)*
3. Structural formulas show the number of atoms of each element in a compound, as chemical formulas do, but also show how the atoms are arranged. The internal structure of a compound determines its physical and chemical properties. *(p. 486)*
4. *Aromatic compounds* are ring-shaped compounds whose electrons are delocalized—not held to a specific bond or atom. *Aliphatic compounds* are either linear compounds or rings that can be formed from straight chains; they do not have delocalized electrons. *(p. 487)*
5. Cyclohexane contains only single-bonded carbon atoms, therefore it is an aliphatic hydrocarbon. *(p. 487)*

DIFFERENTIATED INSTRUCTION

Make Your Own Models

Guide students to **create models** of organic structures. Small molecular modeling sets can be used for this activity. Alternatively, toothpicks with foam balls or modeling clay also work well. Have students paint and assemble the various molecules and create a name plate for each compound they create. Some suggested models are shown below.

Hydrocarbons:

alkanes: C_3H_8, C_4H_{10}

alkenes: C_2H_4, C_4H_8 straight isomer, C_4H_8 branched isomer

alkyne: C_2H_2

Organic compounds that contain oxygen:

alcohol: C_2H_6O

aldehyde: C_2H_4O

carboxylic acid: $C_2H_4O_2$

ester: $C_2H_4O_2$

ether: C_2H_6O

ketone: C_3H_6O

Organic compounds that contain nitrogen:

amide: C_2H_5NO

amine: CH_5N

amino acid: $C_2H_5NO_2$

The following list includes elements commonly used in models along with the colors that typically represent them.

carbon: gray

chlorine: green

hydrogen: white

nitrogen: blue

oxygen: red

phosphorus: orange

sulfur: yellow

If you are homeschooling, any younger children at home could benefit from being included in this activity, giving them an early opportunity to become familiar with the appearances of compounds.

SECTION 20.2 *OVERVIEW*

Essential Question

What chemicals are in my shampoo?

Objectives

» **20.2.1** Identify alkanes, alkenes, and alkynes from their names or formulas.

» **20.2.2** Draw structural formulas for compounds in common organic families.

» **20.2.3** Name alkanes, alkenes, and alkynes in accordance with IUPAC rules.

» **20.2.4** Relate the differences in physical and chemical properties to isomerism.

» **20.2.5** Contrast cyclic aliphatic compounds and aromatic substances.

Resource

Web Link: Interactive Molecular Structures

ENGAGE

REVIEW SECTION 20.1

Lead students to do a **turn and talk** by asking them to turn to their neighbor and tell them two things they learned in Section 20.1. Each student will have one minute to respond. Once they have finished, select several students to share some of their responses with the class. Clear up any misunderstandings and review additional material as needed.

INSTRUCT

THE MEANINGS OF SATURATED

Note that the meaning of the word *saturated* used here (referring to a carbon atom surrounded by four other atoms) is different from the meaning of *saturated* in Chapter 14 (referring to a solution with a maximum amount of solute). Have students observe the structural formulas in Table 20-2 (p. 492) to see examples of saturation, in which every carbon is bonded to four atoms.

20.2 HYDROCARBONS

QUESTIONS

» What are the different kinds of hydrocarbons?

» What do the names of organic compounds tell us about their structures?

» How does isomerism affect the physical and chemical properties of compounds?

TERMS

hydrocarbon • alkane • saturated hydrocarbon • alkyl group • isomer • alkene • unsaturated hydrocarbon • alkyne • cyclic aliphatic compound • benzene

What chemicals are in my shampoo?

If you have ever taken the time to read the list of ingredients in your shampoo, you were probably mystified by the list of unpronounceable names. Take *methylisothiazolinone* (MIT), for example. It's used to prevent the growth of germs in cosmetics and personal care products. After all, no one wants to wash with germs, right? The IUPAC name of MIT is 2-methyl-1,2-thiazol-3(2H)-one, and as we have hinted, this name tells a trained chemist about the structure of the compound. In this textbook, we won't handle anything as complex as MIT, but we will examine how to name simpler organic compounds, starting with the simplest of all—hydrocarbons.

As their name implies, **hydrocarbons** are organic compounds that contain only hydrogen and carbon. Hydrocarbons can contain single, double, or triple carbon-carbon bonds. The classification and naming of hydrocarbons is based on the number of carbons in the compound, the number and type(s) of bonds present, and the arrangement of the carbons within a molecule of the compound.

Aliphatic Hydrocarbons

ALKANES

The simplest aliphatic hydrocarbons are **alkanes**, which contain only single bonds between carbon atoms. Just keep in mind that the word "simple" in this case is relative. Some alkanes consist of many carbon and hydrogen atoms and can have relatively complex structures, but they're still made from only two elements. Their general formula is C_nH_{2n+2}. Because they are energy-dense, our society relies on alkanes for fuel. Natural gas—used to heat homes—contains mainly methane (CH_4). Portable gas barbecue grills use bottles of pressurized propane, and gasoline-powered vehicles burn a mixture composed mostly of alkanes. All these compounds contain only carbon and hydrogen. They have structural formulas that resemble open chains, and they contain only single bonds between their carbons.

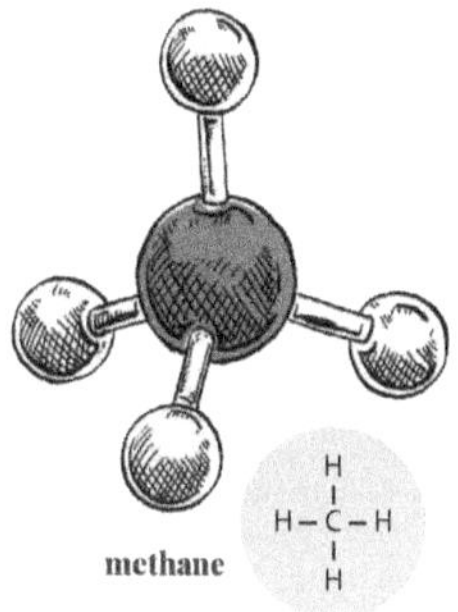

methane

Methane (CH_4) is the simplest alkane. Its one carbon atom is bonded to four hydrogen atoms. Other alkanes are formed as additional carbons lengthen the chain. Ethane (C_2H_6) has two carbons, propane (C_3H_8) has three, and butane (C_4H_{10}) has four. Each carbon atom has only single bonds and is therefore surrounded by four other atoms—the maximum number possible. For this reason, an alkane molecule is said to be a **saturated hydrocarbon**.

488 Chapter 20

HYDROCARBONS

Direct students to begin creating a **concept map** of the hydrocarbons mentioned throughout this section. They should use the term *hydrocarbon* as the main central term and then draw lines extending out for the terms *alkane*, *alkene*, and *alkyne*. As you cover each type of hydrocarbon, have students list the bond types and the suffix used, and be sure to give examples.

IUPAC has devised and manages a system to accurately name organic compounds. This system relies on a series of prefixes (shown in Table 20-1) to indicate the number of carbon atoms present in the compound's longest chain. A substance's suffix identifies the type of compound it is. All alkanes have an *-ane* ending. The names and some properties of the first five alkanes are listed in Table 20-2 (p. 492).

The simplest hydrocarbons have a single continuous chain of carbons atoms from end to end and are called *straight* or *linear chains*. *Branched hydrocarbons*, as their name implies, have carbon chains that branch off a main chain. Branched alkanes are named on the basis of the longest carbon chain in the molecule. For example, the compound commonly known as isobutane has the structure shown below. Though there are four carbons in this molecule, the longest possible *chain* of carbons is only three, so its IUPAC name is based on a three-carbon alkane—propane. The additional hydrocarbon side chain is an **alkyl group,** an alkane with one hydrogen missing, allowing it to bond to a larger molecule. An alkyl group takes its name from its parent alkane molecule with the *-ane* ending changed to *-yl*. Because this alkyl group has only one carbon atom, its parent molecule is methane, and it is referred to as a methyl group (CH_3). Note that the methyl group is attached to the second carbon of the carbon chain, which makes the IUPAC name of this molecule *2-methylpropane*.

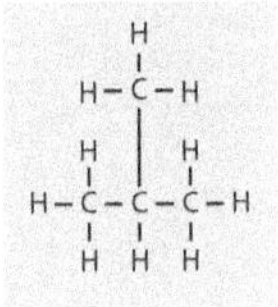

isobutane
(2-methylpropane)

We can also do this process in reverse to derive a compound's structural formula from its name. A close examination of the name 2-methylpropane tells us how a molecule of the compound is configured. Propane is the base structure of the hydrocarbon. Since the name *propane* contains the prefix *prop-*, the main hydrocarbon structure is identified as a three-carbon chain. The *-ane* ending tells us that all the bonds between carbons are single bonds. The *2-methyl-* indicates that there is a branch, or side chain, with the *2-* indicating that the branch is attached to the second carbon of the propane base. *Methyl* is made up of two parts—the *-yl* ending tells us that the branch is an alkyl group and *meth-* indicates that the branch has one carbon.

TABLE 20-1
Numerical Prefixes

Number of Carbon Atoms	Prefix
1	meth-
2	eth-
3	prop-
4	but-
5	pent-
6	hex-
7	hept-
8	oct-
9	non-
10	dec-

HYDROCARBON PREFIXES

Direct students to create **flashcards with** the information from Table 20-1. They may choose to make these as digital flashcards or use an app such as Quizlet to generate questions and answers. Students should memorize these prefixes since they are used throughout the chapter.

The first four prefixes were assigned before scientists realized how high the numbers would go. After that they began using numerical root words.

DIFFERENTIATED INSTRUCTION

Hydrocarbon Naming Rules

Lead students to create a **graphic organizer** that organizes the rules for naming hydrocarbons. Students should structure their creation in any manner that would help them recall the information, or they can choose to create a flow chart or sequence chart. Have them read through the text to deduce these rules. The following example can be used as a reference.

Rule 1: Find the longest continuous chain of carbon atoms and use the name of this chain as the base name of the compound.

Rule 2: Number the longest chain, beginning with the end of the chain nearest a functional group (substituent).

Rule 3: Name the groups attached to the longest chain as the alkyl groups. Give the location of each alkyl group by the number of the main chain carbon atom to which it is attached. Write the alkyl groups in alphabetical order regardless of their position in the chain.

Let students know that alkenes, alkynes, cyclic and aromatic hydrocarbons, halocarbons, alcohols, ethers, aldehydes, ketones, carboxylic acids, esters, amines, and amides will use naming conventions that vary according to their composition and structure. As students learn different organic compounds, they should record how to name them as well.

INTERACTIVE MOLECULAR STRUCTURES

For practice in drawing the molecular structures of many different types of organic compounds, visit TeacherToolsOnline.com. Under Additional Resources, click on Chapter 20 Web Links. Then click on *Interactive Molecular Structures*.

From these examples, it should be apparent that once you understand how the IUPAC names of organic compounds are put together, you can quickly deduce the structural formula of an organic compound from its name and vice versa.

EXAMPLE 20-1: WRITING A STRUCTURAL FORMULA FROM A COMPOUND'S NAME

Write the structural formulas for each of the following.

a. 2-methylhexane

b. 2,3-dimethylpentane

c. 3-ethyl-2-methylheptane

Solution:

a. The root *hexane* tells us that the molecule is based on a six-carbon chain containing only single bonds (identified by the *-ane* ending). The next part, *2-methyl-*, tells us that a one-carbon alkyl group is bonded to the second carbon of the hexane molecule; the carbons are numbered from the end nearer the branch. The structural formula is shown below.

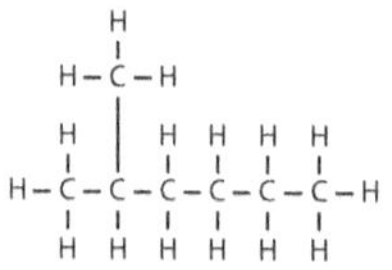

b. When we look at the end of the compound's name, we see that *pentane*, a five-carbon chain with only single bonds, is the parent molecule. *Dimethyl-* indicates that two methyl groups are connected to the pentane molecule. The *2,3-* tells us that one methyl group is bonded to the second carbon, while the other methyl group is bonded to the third carbon in the longest chain.

The structural formula is shown below.

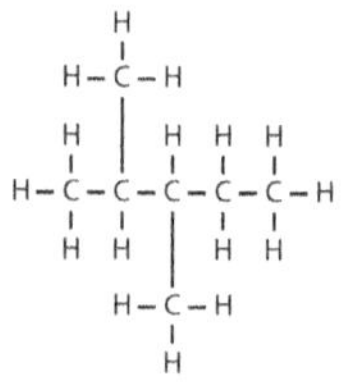

c. Again, look to the end of the name to identify the parent molecule, in this case *heptane*, a seven-carbon chain. Our molecule has two alkyl groups bonded to it, a one-carbon group (*methyl*) and a two-carbon group (*ethyl*). The alkyl groups are placed in alphabetical order, so ethyl is named first, and *3-* tells us that it is bonded to the third carbon of the chain. The methyl group is bonded to the second carbon. The finished structural formula is shown below.

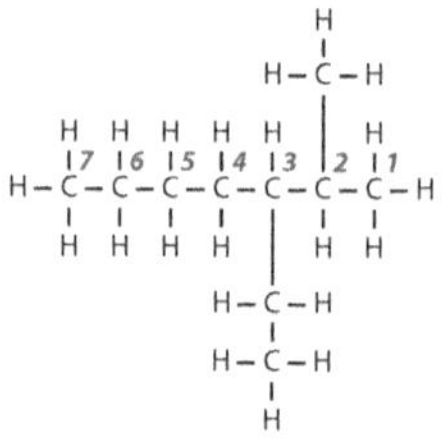

Take note that even though the alkyl groups are placed in alphabetical order in the name, the carbons in the chain are still numbered starting at the end closer to the nearest branching.

490 Chapter 20

EXAMPLE 20-2: NAMING A HYDROCARBON FROM ITS STRUCTURAL FORMULA

Name each of the following branched hydrocarbons.

a.

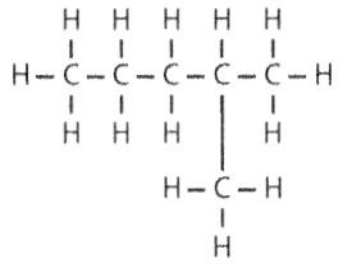

b.

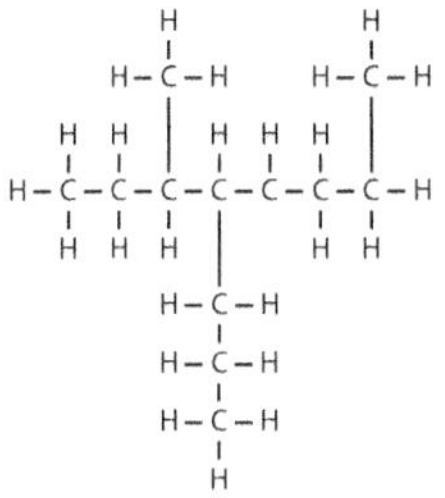

c.

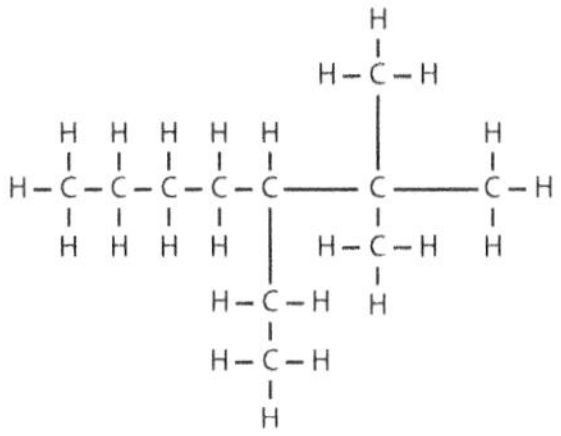

Solution:

a. Locate the longest chain and number the carbons in the chain, starting from the end closer to a branch.

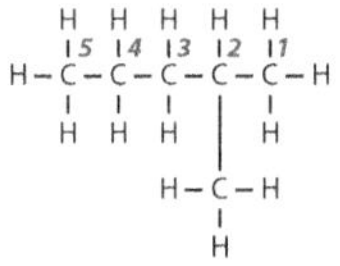

Name the parent molecule. A five-carbon chain with only single bonds is pentane. Add prefixes to indicate any branches, including their locations. In this case, a methyl group is bonded to the second carbon, so it is identified using the prefix 2-methyl. The name is therefore *2-methylpentane.*

b. Locate the longest chain and number the carbons in the chain, starting from the end closer to a branch.

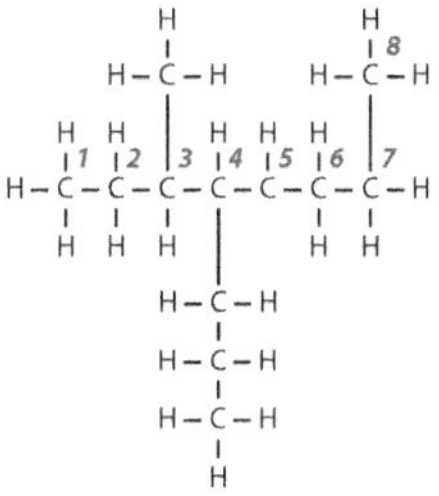

Name the parent molecule. An eight-carbon chain with only single bonds is octane. Add prefixes for any branches, including their locations. The branches on this molecule consist of a one-carbon group (methyl) and a three-carbon-group (propyl). Remember, the alkyl groups are listed in alphabetical order, so this is *3-methyl-4-propyloctane.*

c. Locate the longest chain and number the carbons in the chain, starting from the end closer to a branch.

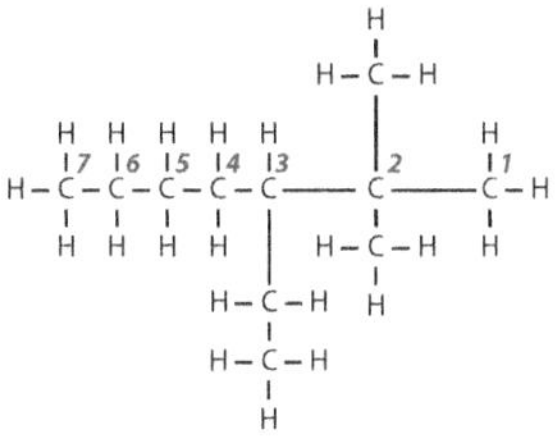

Name the parent molecule. A seven-carbon chain with only single bonds is heptane. Add prefixes for any branches, including their locations. This molecule includes an ethyl group and two methyl groups, both of which are bonded to the number two carbon. Each alkyl group requires its own position identifier, so the two methyl groups will be identified together as 2,2-dimethyl. Listing the alkyl groups in alphabetical order makes this *3-ethyl-2,2-dimethylheptane.* Note that the numerical prefix *di-* is not considered when alphabetizing the alkyl groups.

Organic Chemistry 491

PROPERTIES OF CARBON CHAINS

Using Table 20-2 as reference, lead students in answering a **discussion question** by asking why they believe the melting and boiling points tend to increase as the carbon chains increase in length. *(The more atoms in the chain, the stronger the intermolecular forces. And the stronger the intermolecular forces, the higher the melting and boiling points.)*

Are alkanes polar or nonpolar? Bonds between two carbon atoms are not polar because both atoms have the same electronegativity. Bonds between carbon and hydrogen are slightly polar, but these bonds are arranged so that the resulting positive charge of the hydrogen atoms is evenly distributed over the exterior of the molecule. As a result, the molecule has no localized accumulation of charge and is therefore nonpolar. Alkanes dissolve well in nonpolar solvents such as carbon tetrachloride. But in polar substances, such as water, liquid alkanes are immiscible and form a layer on top of water.

Crude oil contains several types of alkanes. Chains from four carbons up to twenty carbons form naturally and are combined into one seemingly inseparable mixture. Chemical engineers take advantage of the properties of these alkanes to separate them so that they can be used as lubricating oils, gasoline, and kerosene. How do chemical engineers separate the individual compounds? The boiling points of alkanes rise as additional carbons are added to the chain, so petroleum engineers can separate the alkanes in a process called *fractional distillation*.

TABLE 20-2 *Linear Alkanes*

Name	Structural Formula	Melting Point (°C)	Boiling Point (°C)
methane	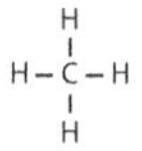	−183	−162
ethane	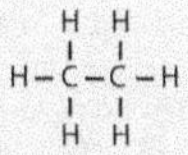	−183	−89
propane	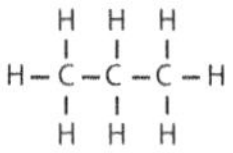	−188	−42
butane	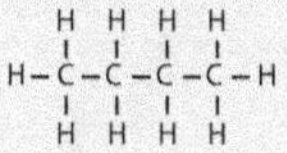	−138	−1
pentane	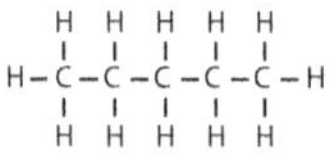	−130	36

ISOMERS

You may recall from a course in physical science that there is an issue that arises with longer hydrocarbon chains. Hydrocarbons with four or more carbons can be configured in multiple ways yet still have the same chemical formula. The number of possible configurations increases as the number of carbon atoms increases. These compounds with the same molecular formula but different structural formulas are called **isomers**. Normal butane (*n*-butane, the linear form) and its isomer, 2-methylpropane, have slightly different physical properties. Their melting and boiling points, density, and solubility reflect their different structures. Such differences in physical properties are typical of isomers.

TABLE 20-3 *Comparison of Butane Isomers*

Isomer	Melting Point (°C)	Density (g/mL)	Solubility (mg/L water at 25 °C)
n-butane	−138	0.002 48	61.2
2-methylpropane (isobutane)	−159	0.002 51	48.9

492 Chapter 20

EXAMPLE 20-3: DRAWING ISOMERS

Draw structural formulas for all the isomers of pentane (C_5H_{12}).

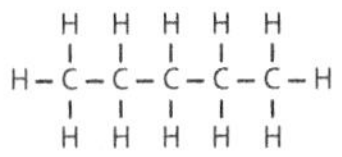

Solution

For each isomer, we need to move one or more of pentane's end carbons to an internal carbon on the chain. By moving one end carbon to an internal carbon, we arrive at 2-methylbutane (a.). Note that there is no "3-methylbutane" possible; moving an end carbon to butane's "third" carbon makes it necessary to renumber the carbons from the other end of the chain, the end nearer the branch, resulting in that carbon being identified as number two again.

The only other possible isomer of pentane results from moving both end carbons to the internal carbon of a propane chain, producing 2,2-dimethylpropane (b.).

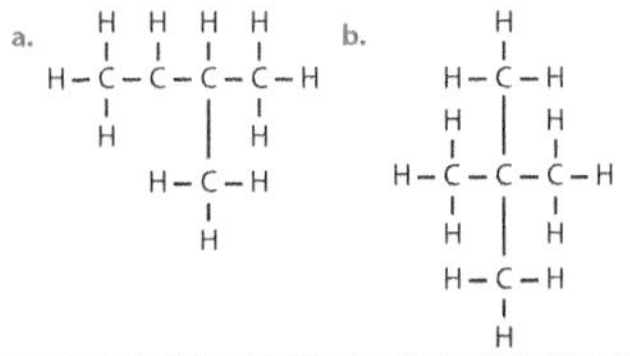

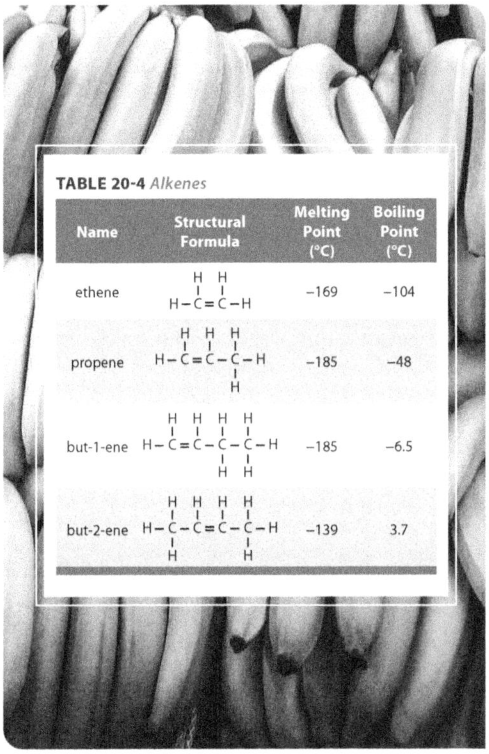

TABLE 20-4 *Alkenes*

Name	Structural Formula	Melting Point (°C)	Boiling Point (°C)
ethene	H H I I H−C=C−H	−169	−104
propene	H H H I I I H−C=C−C−H I H	−185	−48
but-1-ene	H H H H I I I I H−C=C−C−C−H I I H H	−185	−6.5
but-2-ene	H H H H I I I I H−C−C=C−C−H I I H H	−139	3.7

◄ Ethene speeds up ripening. These bananas were picked and shipped green. Before sale, they were exposed to ethene for quick ripening.

ALKENES

Carbons can form double bonds quite easily. Hydrocarbons that contain double bonds between carbon atoms are called **alkenes**. Alkenes use the same prefixes as alkanes but end with the suffix *-ene*. The simplest alkene is ethene. Because double bonds reduce the number of hydrogen atoms in their structures, all alkenes are said to be **unsaturated hydrocarbons**. Ethene contains only two carbons, but when the carbon chain is longer than three carbons, the double bond could be in several locations. As in branched alkanes, an alkene's name pinpoints the location of the double bond by specifying which carbon in the parent chain is the first carbon that is doubly bonded. The number is not placed at the front of the name, but instead is located between the numbering prefix and the *-ene* suffix as shown in Table 20-4.

The physical properties of alkenes are very much like those of alkanes. The first few are gases at room temperature. Pentene and larger compounds are liquids at room temperature because of their greater intermolecular attractions. Alkenes are relatively nonpolar. Alkenes are slightly more reactive than alkanes.

Organic Chemistry 493

THE ABSENCE OF METHENE

Using Tables 20-4 and 20-5 for reference, guide students to answer a **discussion question** by asking why methene and methyne are not listed in the tables. *(Double and triple bonds require the presence of a second carbon atom.)*

HYDROCARBON MNEMONIC

Direct students to record a **mnemonic** for recalling the bond type for each hydrocarbon. Explain to them that *alkane, alkene,* and *alkyne* are in alphabetical order, corresponding to the numerical order of their bonds—single, double, and triple.

BOND STRENGTH IN ALIPHATIC RINGS

Bending carbon chains to form rings of less than five carbons brings the electron clouds of each carbon very close together, increasing their repulsion and weakening the bonds between each carbon.

TABLE 20-5 *Alkynes*

Name	Structural Formula	Melting Point (°C)	Boiling Point (°C)
ethyne	H−C≡C−H	−84	−81
propyne	H H−C≡C−C−H H	−102.7	−23
but-1-yne	H H H−C≡C−C−C−H H H	−126	8
but-2-yne	H H H−C−C≡C−C−H H H	−32	27
pent-1-yne	H H H H−C≡C−C−C−C−H H H H	−106	40
pent-2-yne	H H H H−C−C≡C−C−C−H H H H	−109	56

ALKYNES

A triple bond between two carbon atoms identifies a member of the **alkyne** family. Alkynes use prefixes to indicate the number of carbons and end with the suffix *-yne*. In the same manner as you saw for alkenes, a number is used to tell where the triple bond occurs within the carbon chain, when necessary. The most common alkyne is also the simplest. Ethyne, commonly called *acetylene*, consists of two carbons joined by a triple bond. This compound is often used as a fuel for welding torches and as an ingredient for plastics.

Physically, alkynes are similar to other hydrocarbons. They are practically nonpolar, so they are insoluble in water and very soluble in nonpolar solvents. Their boiling points rise as the carbon chains get longer.

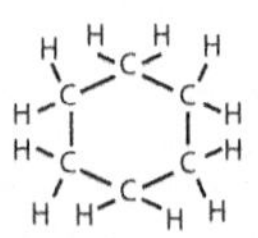
cyclohexane

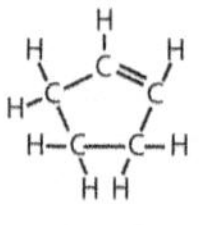
cyclopentene

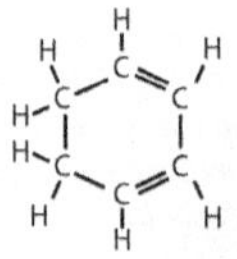
cyclohexa-1,3-diene

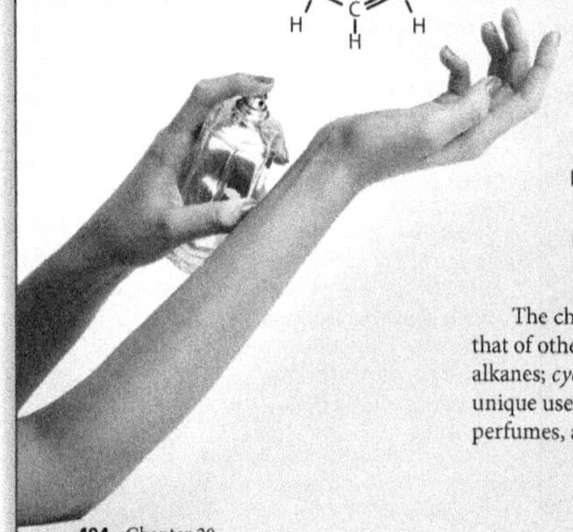

Cyclic Aliphatic Hydrocarbons

As stated in Section 20.1, not all aliphatic hydrocarbons consist only of open chains of carbon atoms. Some form rings. Such compounds are called **cyclic aliphatic compounds**. Though many rings are possible, five- and six-carbon rings are the most abundant. Simple alkenes and alkenes with more than one double bond multiply the number of possible structures. Three structures and their names are shown at left.

Some very unusual structures are possible when several rings combine as shown below.

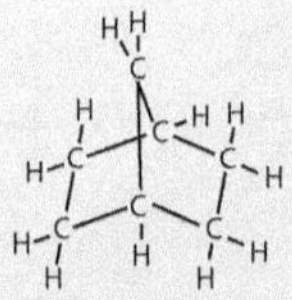
bicyclo[2.2.1] heptane

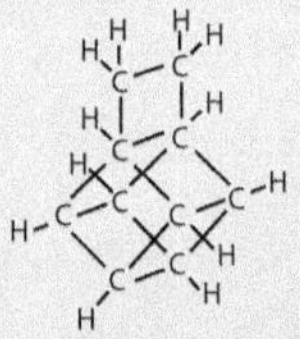
pentacyclo[4.4.0.0^{2,5}.0^{3,8}.0^{4,7}] decane (basketane)

The chemical activity of cyclic compounds is about the same as that of other members of their parent families. *Cycloalkanes* act like alkanes; *cycloalkenes* act like alkenes. Cyclic compounds have several unique uses and are found in anesthetics, car maintenance products, perfumes, and paint removers.

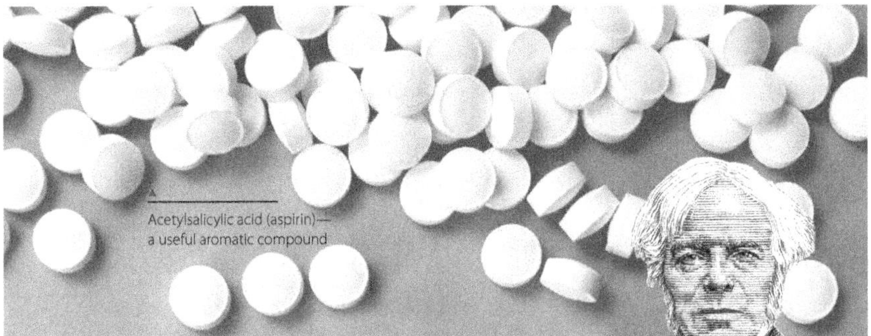

Acetylsalicylic acid (aspirin)—a useful aromatic compound

Aromatic Hydrocarbons

Aromatic hydrocarbons, so named because of the often pleasant-smelling odors that the first-identified aromatic compounds produced, are an entirely different category of hydrocarbons. The most common of these is **benzene**. Benzene was isolated in 1825 by Michael Faraday. An analysis of the elements in benzene and a determination of its molecular weight showed its molecular formula to be C_6H_6. In its unsubstituted form, benzene is the simplest aromatic compound known. Today it is one of industry's most important compounds, most often extracted from petroleum.

Michael Faraday

The structural formula of benzene puzzled scientists for thirty years after Faraday discovered the compound. Many clues were gathered, but they did not seem to fit together. The molecular formula C_6H_6 led chemists to believe that the molecule must have several double or triple bonds. Yet the chemical reactions of benzene did not support this idea; it behaved like an alkane, not an alkene or alkyne. When scientists determined the bond lengths between the carbon atoms, they found that the distances were not those of single or double bonds—they were in between. It was as if benzene used one-and-a-half bonds. Furthermore, scientists found that the carbons were arranged in a ring and that all the carbon atoms had identical bonds.

In 1865 August Kekulé proposed a structure that could account for most of the observations. He described benzene in terms of two symmetrical resonance structures.

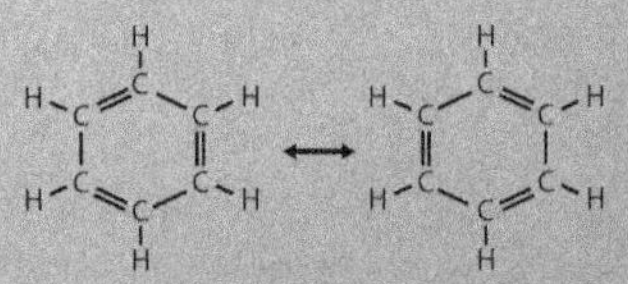

August Kekulé

The actual structure of a benzene molecule was thought to be a dynamic equilibrium of these two structures. Thus, the electrons in the double bonds were mobile and not tied down to specific locations. But the development of the valence bond theory modified this concept. The single bonds between the carbon atoms—sigma bonds—were due to head-on overlap of the carbon atom's hybridized orbitals. The double bond included the additional components of pi bonds—side-to-side overlap of additional orbitals between pairs of carbon atoms.

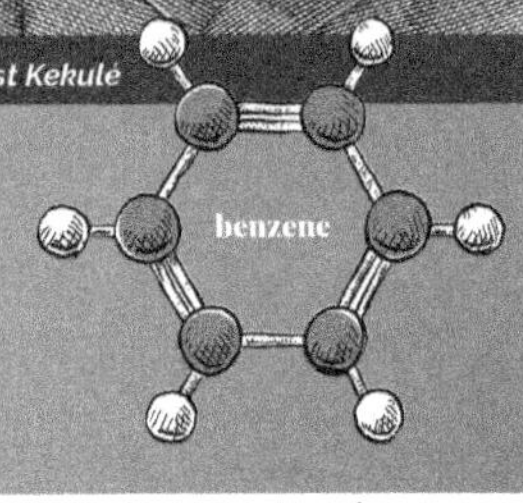

HYDROCARBONS

Use the following **formative assessment** to check students' understanding.

1. What type of hydrocarbon contains a double bond between carbon atoms? *(alkene)*
2. List the numerical prefixes according to the number of carbon atoms (1–10) indicated by each. *(1, meth-; 2, eth-; 3, prop-; 4, but-; 5, pent-; 6, hex-; 7, hept-; 8, oct-; 9, non-; 10, dec-)*
3. Define the term *alkyl group*. *(An alkyl group is an alkane with one hydrogen missing, allowing it to bond to a larger molecule.)*
4. What name is given to compounds with the same molecular formulas but different structural formulas? *(isomers)*
5. Explain why alkenes are said to be unsaturated hydrocarbons. *(They have double bonds that reduce the number of hydrogen atoms in their structures.)*

ASSESS

TICKET OUT THE DOOR

As a **summarizing activity**, ask students to state the difference between cyclic aliphatic hydrocarbons and aromatic hydrocarbons. *(The bonds between carbons in cyclic aliphatic hydrocarbons contain localized electrons. The bonds between carbons in aromatic hydrocarbons contain delocalized electrons.)*

20.2 REVIEW ANSWERS

* An asterisk following a question number indicates that a worked-out solution can be found on page 513A.

1. Hydrocarbons contain only hydrogen and carbon. A few sources of hydrocarbons are propane, gasoline, crude oil, plastic, and perfume. Other sources are possible. *(p. 488)*

2. The two compounds must be isomers of hexane. Isomerism results in compounds that have different physical and chemical properties. *(p. 492)*

3. They are nonpolar. *(p. 492)*

4. Saturated hydrocarbons contain carbons that are surrounded by the maximum possible number of atoms (four). Unsaturated molecules contain carbons linked with multiple bonds that are surrounded by fewer than four atoms. *(pp. 488, 493)*

5. *Alkanes* have single bonds and can be saturated. *Alkenes* have at least one double bond. *Alkynes* have at least one triple bond. Both alkenes and alkynes are unsaturated. *(pp. 488–94)*

6. a. alkyne

b. alkane

c. alkyne

d. alkyne

e. alkene *(all pp. 488–94)*

7. cyclic *(p. 494)*

8. Their bond lengths are between those of single and double bonds. The bonds contain mobile or delocalized pi electrons that are shared by all the carbon atoms in the ring, as well as sigma electrons that are shared between each pair of carbon atoms. *(p. 495)*

9.* *(all pp. 488–94)*

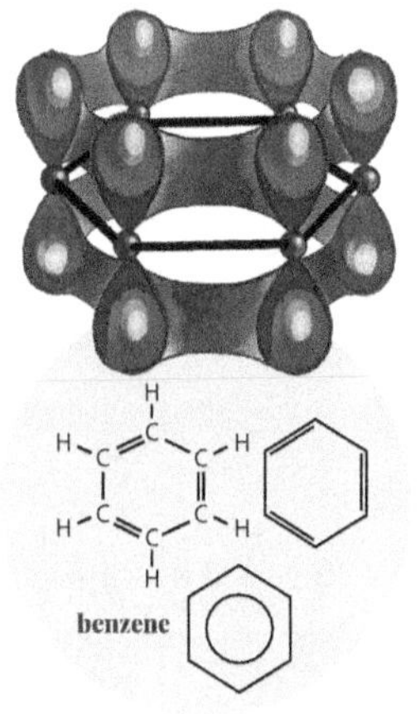

benzene

These pi clouds overlap in the molecule to form doughnut-shaped areas of electron concentration above and below the plane of the ring. Therefore, the electrons are free to move throughout the entire "doughnut." For this reason, they are called *delocalized electrons*. All aromatic compounds have cyclic clouds of delocalized electrons.

Because the pi electrons in the double bonds are not bound between any two carbon atoms, chemists often draw the structure of benzene as shown at left, either with or without the single-bonded hydrogens. They are understood to be there if they are not shown.

Today other non-benzene-based aromatics are known. One example is *furan*, which contains one oxygen atom bonded in a ring with four carbon atoms. One of the oxygen's unbonded pairs of electrons is delocalized into the ring structure. Furan serves as the starting point for the synthesis of a host of other compounds, called *furans*, many of which are used as medicines to treat a variety of conditions. One naturally occurring furan, 1-(3-hydroxyfuran-2-yl) ethan-1-one, contributes to the characteristic taste of bread crust.

20.2 SECTION REVIEW

1. What do hydrocarbons contain? Name some sources of hydrocarbons.
2. A chemist is given two samples of clear liquid, each labeled as C_6H_{14}. When tested, one sample boils at 68.5 °C, while the other does so at 62.9 °C. Explain how this is possible.
3. Why are hydrocarbons mainly insoluble in water?
4. Explain the differences between saturated and unsaturated hydrocarbons.
5. Compare the structures of alkanes, alkenes, and alkynes.
6. Identify each molecular formula as an alkane, alkene, or alkyne.
   a. C_2H_2 d. C_4H_6
   b. $C_{10}H_{22}$ e. C_2H_4
   c. C_5H_8
7. What term describes aliphatic compounds whose chains have been bonded into rings?
8. Describe the nature of the bonds between carbon atoms in aromatic compounds.
9. Draw structural formulas for each of the following.
   a. hexane c. 2-methylhexane
   b. hex-1-ene d. hex-3-yne
10. Name the compounds indicated by each of the following structural formulas.

a.
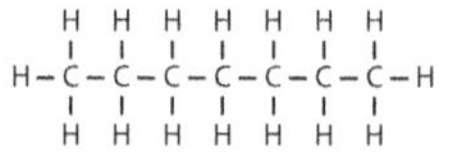

b.
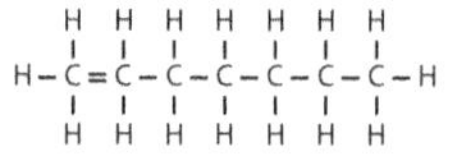

c.
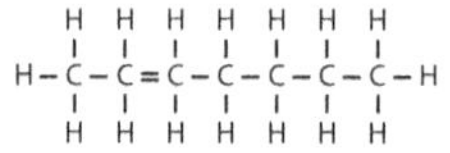

d.
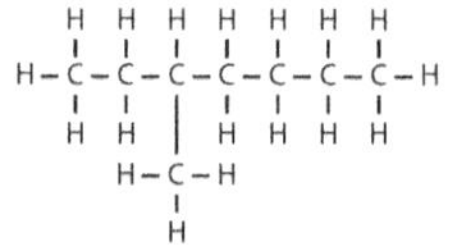

11. Your study partner says that the following structural formulas are both acceptable forms for showing toluene (C_7H_8). Is he correct? Explain.

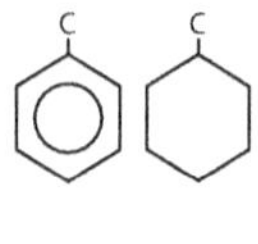

12. Since the two compounds shown in Question 11 both have six-carbon rings, would you expect them to have similar physical and chemical properties? Explain.

496 Chapter 20

10. a. heptane

b. hept-1-ene

c. hept-2-ene

d. 3-methylheptane *(all pp. 488–94)*

11. No. The first diagram indicates the presence of a benzene ring, making it a structural formula for an aromatic hydrocarbon. The second formula shows a cyclic aliphatic hydrocarbon. Therefore, they cannot both be toluene. *(pp. 494–96)*

12. No. The aromatic compound contains delocalized electrons, making it more stable than the other compound, which is a cyclic aliphatic compound. *(pp. 494–96)*

20.3 SUBSTITUTED HYDROCARBONS

QUESTIONS
- What are substituted hydrocarbons?
- Do all substituted hydrocarbons have similar properties?
- What makes one group of substituted hydrocarbons distinct from another?
- How do I name and write structural formulas for substituted hydrocarbons?

TERMS
functional group • halocarbon • haloaromatic • hydroxyl group • alcohol • ether • carbonyl group • aldehyde • ketone • carboxylic acid • carboxyl group • fatty acid • ester • amine • amide

Functional groups are the hot spots of chemical activity on an organic molecule. A **functional group**, also called a *substituent*, is an atom or group of atoms that can substitute for a hydrogen atom in a hydrocarbon. It greatly modifies the behavior of the hydrocarbon. Hydrocarbons that contain a functional group are often called *substituted hydrocarbons*.

Does substituting one kind of atom for another in a hydrocarbon really make that much of a difference?

There are many kinds of functional groups. Most functional groups in organic chemistry contain arrangements of oxygen or nitrogen atoms. Some even contain sulfur or halogens. Since the composition and structure of a molecule determine its physical and chemical properties, functional groups partly determine a molecule's properties.

Halocarbons

When a halogen and a hydrocarbon combine, a **halocarbon** forms. The simplest halocarbons are haloalkanes, which are a combination of an alkane and one or more fluorine, chlorine, bromine, or iodine atoms in place of one or more of the alkane's hydrogen atoms. The general formula for haloalkanes is R–X, where R represents an alkyl group (derived from the parent alkane) and X represents a halide. *Haloalkenes* and *haloalkynes* are also possible. When a halogen is attached to an aromatic ring, it forms a **haloaromatic**. Polytetrafluoroethylene (a nonstick coating for pans) and polyvinyl chloride (PVC plastic) are two halocarbon polymers that you have likely used. Many other halides serve as intermediates in the synthesis of other compounds.

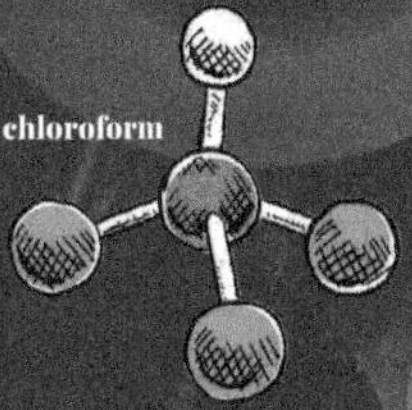
chloroform

TABLE 20-6 ***Industrial Uses of Halocarbons***

Name	Structural Formula	Application
trichloromethane (chloroform)	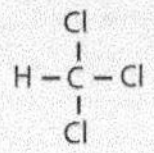	early anesthetic
tetrachloroethene	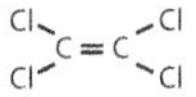	nonpolar solvent (dry-cleaning agent)
triiodomethane (iodoform)	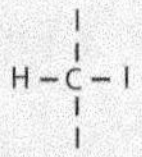	veterinary antiseptic

INSTRUCT

SUBSTITUTED HYDROCARBONS

Prompt students to create a **cluster diagram** on the different substituted hydrocarbons. As you teach through the section, have them write the term, definition, naming convention, and examples for each type of molecule.

SECTION 20.3 OVERVIEW

Essential Question

Does substituting one kind of atom for another in a hydrocarbon really make that big of a difference?

Objectives

- **20.3.1** Explain how functional groups affect a compound's properties.
- **20.3.2** Identify the functional group associated with each substituted organic compound.
- **20.3.3** Name substituted organic compounds using IUPAC rules.
- **20.3.4** Draw structural formulas for compounds with functional groups when given the IUPAC name.

Resources

Mini Lab: *Isomerism in Substituted Hydrocarbons*; Lab 20A: *Makes Scents!*—Synthesizing Esters

ENGAGE

REVIEWING HYDROCARBONS

Lead a **review** of Section 20.2. Select one alkane, alkene, and alkyne structure from the section and have students name it. Once they have finished, have them check their answers. If they did not name the compound correctly, have them assess what was incorrect and write a short description stating how to name it correctly.

MINI LAB: *ISOMERISM IN SUBSTITUTED HYDROCARBONS*

Use this **mini lab** to give students an opportunity to discover how the structures of isomers affect their physical properties.

1. No
2. No. Exchanging the position of the chlorine atom with any hydrogen atom in the molecule produces a molecule with the same configuration.
3. Yes. Two isomers are possible: one with both chlorines on the same side of the imaginary plane and the other with the chlorine atoms on opposite sides.
4. *cis*-1,2-dichloroethene

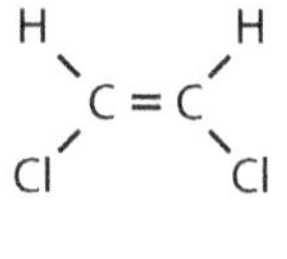

trans-1,2-dichloroethene

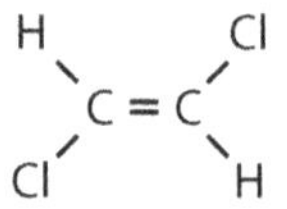

5. Answers will vary. The two isomers have different physical properties. Chlorine is highly electronegative. By having both chlorine atoms on the same side, the cis isomer has a dipole moment, whereas the trans isomer does not.
6. Yes

1,1-dichloroethene

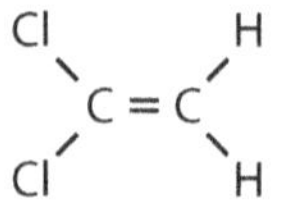

7. Answers will vary. The proteins in living things are made only from left-handed amino acids, but experimental attempts to produce amino acids from their precursors produce both left- and right-handed forms in equal measure. Any theory of origins must be able to explain how living things came to be homochiral, that is, having only left-handed amino acids. Naturalistic theories do not account for this phenomenon, but of course it poses no difficulty at all for someone with a biblical view of origins.

MINI LAB

ISOMERISM IN SUBSTITUTED HYDROCARBONS

Modeling is an essential skill in science. Three-dimensional models of molecules give us a much better understanding of their structures. In this lab activity, you will model isomers and think about how their differences in structure might affect their physical properties.

How does adding substituents to a hydrocarbon affect isomerism?

EQUIPMENT
- molecular modeling set

Procedure

A Build a model of ethene. Refer back to Table 20-4 if you need help.

1. Are any isomers of ethene possible?

B Create a model of chloroethene by removing one hydrogen atom from your ethene model and replacing it with an atom of chlorine.

2. Are any isomers of chloroethene possible? Explain. (*Hint*: To check your answer, move the chlorine atom from one carbon atom to the other. Does that affect the structure of the molecule in any chemically significant way?)

C Create a model of 1,2-dichloroethene by adding a chlorine atom to the other carbon atom in your chloroethene molecule. You should now have one chlorine atom bonded to each carbon atom.

D Examine your 1,2-dichloroethene model by imagining a plane running through both carbon atoms in a way that causes the hydrogen and chlorine atoms to lie either above or below the plane.

3. Are any isomers of 1,2-dichloroethene possible? Explain.

What you have just observed is an example of what chemists call *cis-trans isomerism*. The prefixes *cis-* and *trans-* come from Latin and mean "this side of" and "the other side of."

4. Draw and label the structural formulas for the *cis* and *trans* versions of 1,2-dichlorethene.

Conclusion

5. Would you expect the two isomers of 1,2-dichloroethene to have the same or different physical properties? Explain.

Going Further

6. Is it possible to create a third isomer of dichloroethene? If so, draw and label its structural formula.

Amino acids, the building blocks of proteins, exhibit a characteristic called *chirality* that is similar to cis-trans isomerism. Chirality results when a carbon atom is bonded to four different groups; the molecule and its mirror-image form cannot be superimposed on one another. The two forms, known as *enantiomers*, are often designated as either left- or right-handed.

7. Go to the website of Creation Ministries International and do a search using the keyword "chirality." Why is chirality significant when evaluating theories of the origin of life?

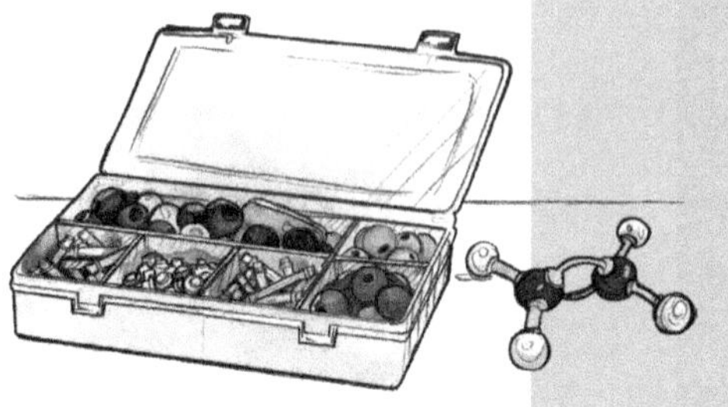

Alcohols

Compounds that have a covalently bonded OH group, called a **hydroxyl group**, attached to an alkyl group are classified as **alcohols**. The general formula for the whole family is R–OH, where R represents an alkyl group. The simplest alcohol is methanol. In this case the R group is the smallest one possible, which is CH_3 (methyl).

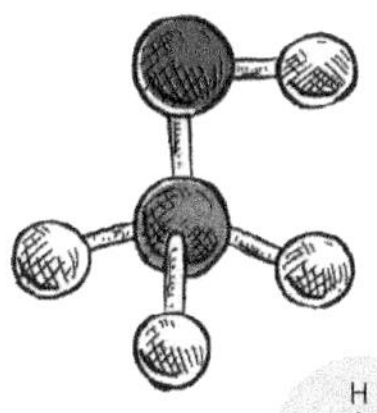

methanol (alcohol)

H
H–C–OH
H

Alcohol names consist of the standard prefixes that tell how long the carbon chain is plus an *-ol* ending in place of the *-e* ending. For instance, what is commonly called *rubbing alcohol* is a three-carbon chain with the OH group attached to the middle carbon. The IUPAC name is propan-2-ol. Note that the numeric indicator is inserted between the name of the parent alkane and the *-ol* suffix. This is done even if the hydroxyl group is bonded to an end carbon, as for instance for propan-1-ol.

The physical properties of alcohols are a result of two factors—a polar OH group and a nonpolar alkyl group. The combination of these two opposites determines the behavior of each specific molecule. If the hydrocarbon chain is relatively short, the OH group dominates the molecule. As a result, it behaves as a polar molecule. As the hydrocarbon chain becomes longer, the chain begins to dominate and imparts nonpolar characteristics to the molecule. Alcohols, under the influence of one or more OH groups, form hydrogen bonds and thus have higher boiling points than their parent molecules. Small alcohols, with their polar nature, are soluble in water. Larger alcohols, under the influence of their hydrocarbon chains, are insoluble in water and soluble in nonpolar solvents.

Alcohols that contain more than one OH group are called *polyhydroxy alcohols*. One common polyhydroxy alcohol is ethane-1,2-diol (commonly called ethylene glycol), which is used as an antifreeze in car radiators. Another common alcohol—propane-1,2,3-triol (glycerol)—serves as a moisturizer in cosmetics.

Industries use alcohols as solvents, paint thinners, antifreezes, and ingredients in aftershave lotions. In the United States, most gasoline is 10%–15% ethanol. Some vehicle engines are designed to run on E85 fuel, which is 85% ethanol and 15% gasoline.

TABLE 20-7 *Alcohols*

Name	Structural Formula	Application
methanol (wood alcohol)	H H–C–OH H	solvent, fuel
ethanol (grain alcohol)	H H H–C–C–OH H H	alcoholic beverages, engine fuel, solvent
propan-1-ol	H H H H–C–C–C–OH H H H	solvent for making pharmaceuticals, resins
propan-2-ol (rubbing alcohol)	H OH H H–C–C–C–H H H H	sterilizing pads, solvent, gasoline additive
butan-1-ol	H H H H H–C–C–C–C–OH H H H H	solvent, shellac, varnish

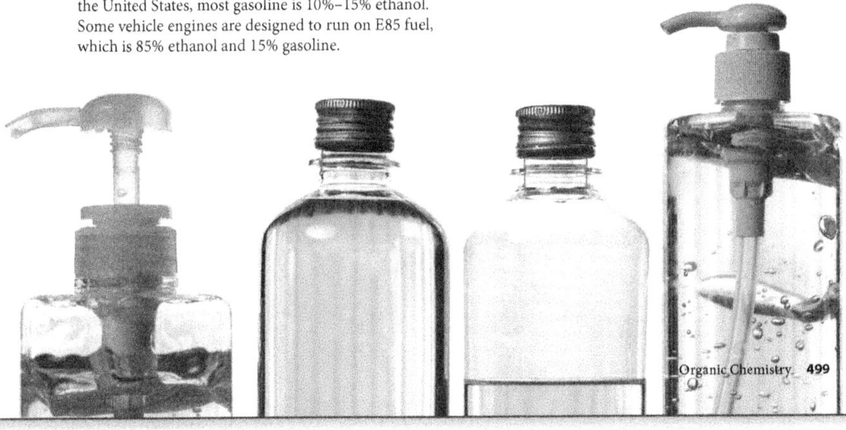

Organic Chemistry 499

THE POLARITY OF ALCOHOLS

Use Table 20-7 to compare the polarities of alcohols. In methanol, the OH group and carbon chain are the same size, making the molecule polar overall. But with increasing chain length, as seen in butan-1-ol, the OH group is increasingly outnumbered by the nonpolar carbon chain with the result that larger alcohols are nonpolar.

REPRESENTING ETHERS

The placement of specific alkyl groups on each end of an ether's structural formula doesn't affect the naming of the ether. For example, the structural formulas

C–O–C–C–C and C–C–C–O–C

both represent methoxypropane since the one molecule can simply be rotated to produce the other.

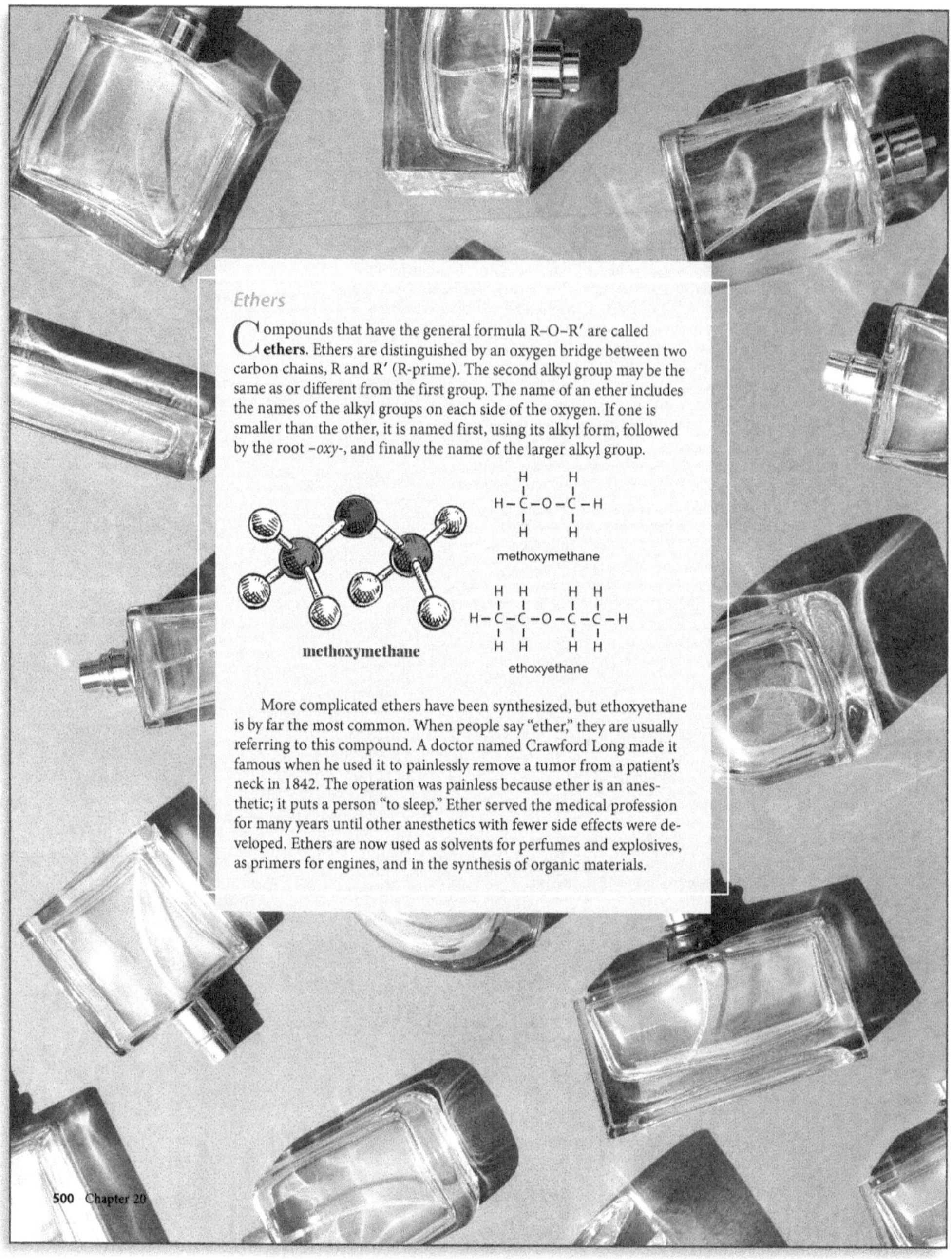

Ethers

Compounds that have the general formula R–O–R′ are called **ethers**. Ethers are distinguished by an oxygen bridge between two carbon chains, R and R′ (R-prime). The second alkyl group may be the same as or different from the first group. The name of an ether includes the names of the alkyl groups on each side of the oxygen. If one is smaller than the other, it is named first, using its alkyl form, followed by the root *-oxy-*, and finally the name of the larger alkyl group.

More complicated ethers have been synthesized, but ethoxyethane is by far the most common. When people say "ether," they are usually referring to this compound. A doctor named Crawford Long made it famous when he used it to painlessly remove a tumor from a patient's neck in 1842. The operation was painless because ether is an anesthetic; it puts a person "to sleep." Ether served the medical profession for many years until other anesthetics with fewer side effects were developed. Ethers are now used as solvents for perfumes and explosives, as primers for engines, and in the synthesis of organic materials.

500 Chapter 20

Aldehydes and Ketones

When an oxygen atom forms a double bond with a carbon atom, it forms a **carbonyl group**. (C=O) The location of carbonyl groups is a key feature for distinguishing between two major groups of organic compounds.

ALDEHYDES

Aldehydes are organic compounds that contain an oxygen held with a double bond to an end carbon. Their general structure looks like the structural formula shown below.

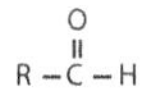

According to the IUPAC rules, the name of an aldehyde is formed with an *-al* ending on the name of the corresponding alkane. Other substituents may be bonded to the aldehyde as well, as is shown by 2-methylpentanal.

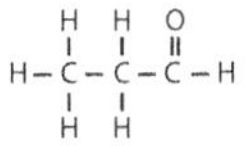

propanal

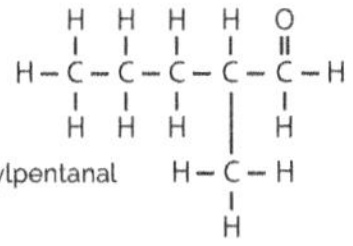

2-methylpentanal

The simplest aldehyde and one of the most important ones in industry is known by its common name of formaldehyde. Its systematic IUPAC name is methanal. This colorless gas with a piercing odor is often dissolved in water to make a 37% solution called *formalin*. It has been used in the past to preserve frogs, fetal pigs, and other creatures for dissection in biology laboratories. But because of health concerns about its possible link to cancer and allergic reactions, the use of formalin as a preserving fluid has declined. But not all aldehydes are potentially harmful. Some are responsible for the unique smells and tastes associated with certain foods. The pleasant aroma and taste of cinnamon is produced by (2*E*)-3-phenylprop-2-enal, better known as cinnamaldehyde. The root *phenyl* in the name indicates that a benzene ring is attached to the propene chain.

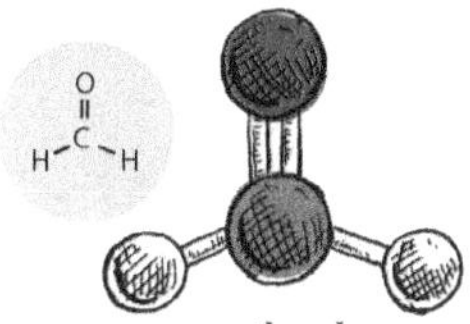

methanal

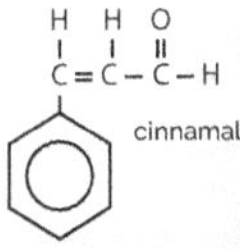

cinnamaldehyde

NO NUMBERS FOR ALDEHYDES

Since the carbonyl group of an aldehyde is always on the end carbon, it doesn't need to be numbered. In other words, *propanal* is correct, not *propan-1-al*. Numbers are included in aldehyde names only to show the position of other groups, such as the *2* in *2-methylpentanal*, which marks the position of an extra carbon branching from the main carbon chain.

NO SUCH THING AS METHANONE

Guide students to answer a **discussion question** by asking why there is no such thing as methanone or ethanone. *(The carbonyl group [CO] in a ketone can occur only between two other carbons, so there needs to be a minimum of three carbons in the chain.)*

LEFT-HANDED ACIDS

When a carboxyl group is attached to the left side of a molecular structure, it is often written as HOOC instead of COOH. Amino acids, the building blocks of proteins, contain carboxylic acids and can exhibit this left-handed tendency. (See answer to Question 7 on page 498.)

KETONES

A carbonyl group within a carbon chain—not on an end carbon—is a key feature of compounds called **ketones**. The general formula of ketones is shown here.

$$R-\overset{\overset{\displaystyle O}{\|}}{C}-R'$$

The simplest ketone is commonly called acetone. The word *ketone* itself is derived from the German word for acetone. The IUPAC name for acetone is *propanone*—the *-e* ending of the alkane is changed to *-one*. For chains over four carbons long, the location of the carbonyl group is indicated by a number placed between the name of the parent alkyl group and the *-one* suffix as shown below for pentan-2-one.

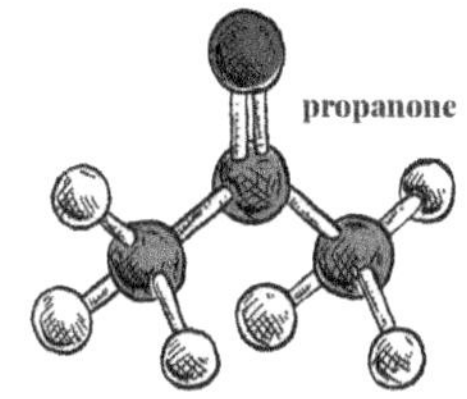

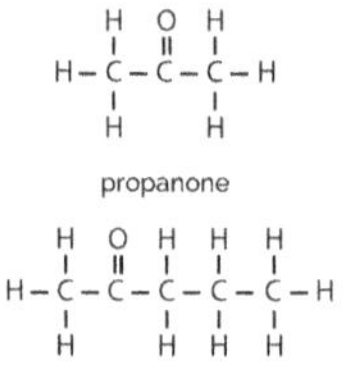

propanone

pentan-2-one

Acetone is an excellent solvent. While the molecule's methyl groups are nonpolar, the carbonyl group is polar. As a result, acetone dissolves most organic compounds but still mixes well with water. Acetone is widely used as a solvent for lacquers, paint removers, explosives, plastics, and disinfectants. It is also the active ingredient in some nail polish removers. Remember MIT from the introduction to Section 20.2? Both its common name and its IUPAC name end in *-one*, so it's a ketone too. Perhaps now it will seem less alien to you when you see it in a list of ingredients.

Since both ketones and aldehydes have carbonyl groups, it is not surprising that they have similar physical and chemical properties. As a rule, though, aldehydes are more reactive because their functional group is exposed on the end of the carbon chain.

Carboxylic Acids

Because of their abundance in nature, carboxylic acids were among the first organic compounds to be studied in detail. As a result, many of these acids acquired common names from their most familiar sources. For example, the Latin word for vinegar is *acetum*, so the acid in vinegar was called *acetic acid*. The Latin word for ant is *formica*. Consequently, the stinging acid of ants was called *formic acid*.

Carboxylic acids derive their name from the presence of a **carboxyl group**, which consists of both a carbonyl group and a hydroxyl group. The chemical formula for a carboxyl group is written as COOH. The generalized structural formula for a carboxylic acid is shown here.

$$R-C\overset{\large O}{\underset{\large OH}{\lessgtr}}$$

502 Chapter 20

According to IUPAC nomenclature, the *-e* ending of a carboxylic acid's corresponding alkane is changed to *-oic*, and the word *acid* is added to form the name of a carboxylic acid. Thus, formic acid, which is the simplest carboxylic acid, is called *methanoic acid* in the IUPAC system. Acetic acid's IUPAC name is *ethanoic acid*.

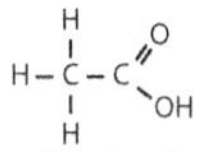

ethanoic acid

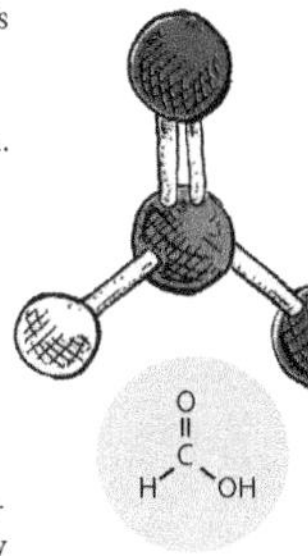

methanoic acid

Carboxylic acids with shorter alkyl groups are liquids at room temperature and have sharp or unpleasant odors. Acids with longer carbon chains are usually waxy solids. When the carbon chains are between twelve and twenty carbon atoms long, they are often called **fatty acids**. They can form hydrogen bonds between themselves and other molecules. These hydrogen bonds keep even the smallest fatty acids solid at room temperature. One such acid, octadecanoic acid (commonly known as stearic acid) is a significant ingredient in a popular food item—chocolate!

Carboxylic acids are called acids because they contain an ionizable hydrogen. The ionizable hydrogen in these acids is the hydrogen in the carboxyl group. Since only a small fraction of carboxylic acid molecules ionize (a mere 4%), these acids are weak. Although they are weak acids, carboxylic acids react quickly with strong bases to form salts. Many of these salts are commercially useful, such as sodium or potassium salts of fatty acids used to make soaps.

Esters

If the hydrogen of a carboxylic acid's carboxyl group is replaced with an alkyl group, an **ester** forms. Esters have the general formula shown below.

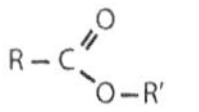

Unlike their cousins the carboxylic acids, esters generally have appealing smells. These compounds are responsible for the flavors of many fruits and the fragrances of many flowers. In the naming of an ester, the R′ group is indicated with its alkyl name and the carboxylic acid part is given an *-oate* ending.

TABLE 20-8: *Esters*

Name	Structural Formula	Flavor or Scent
ethyl butanoate	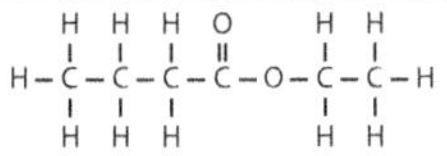	pineapple
pentyl ethanoate	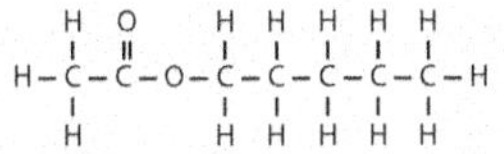	banana
ethyl heptanoate	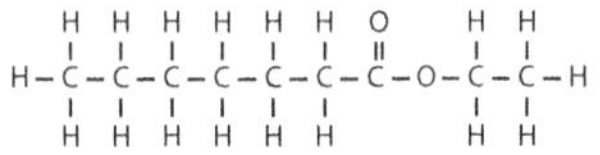	grape
2-methylpropyl formate	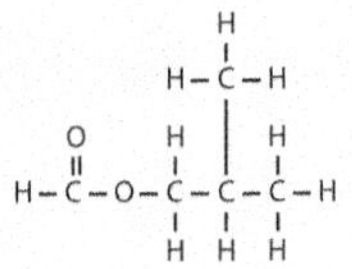	raspberry

Organic Chemistry 503

SUBSTITUTED HYDROCARBONS

Use the following **formative assessment** to check students' understanding.

1. Which hydrocarbon forms when a halogen and a hydrocarbon combine? *(a halocarbon)*
2. What two factors create the physical properties of alcohols? *(a polar OH group and a nonpolar alkyl group)*
3. Describe an ether's general formula. *(R–O–R' [R-prime])*
4. Explain the difference between aldehydes and ketones. *(Aldehydes contain an oxygen held with a double bond to an end carbon. Ketones contain a carbonyl group within the carbon chain, not on an end carbon.)*
5. Which hydrocarbon is known for its production of sweet scents? *(an ester)*

Amines and Amides

Nitrogen can bond in organic molecules in several different ways. **Amines** are a family of organic compounds with ammonia (NH_3) as the parent molecule. Derivatives are formed when one or more of the hydrogen atoms in the ammonia molecule is replaced with an organic group, such as an alkyl group. The names of the compounds that result commonly have the word *amine* as a suffix after the names of the alkyl groups.

methanamine

N-ethylethanamine

Another group of compounds that contain nitrogen is called **amides**. Amides are produced when an amine group takes the place of an OH group in a carboxylic acid. All the members of this group have the structure shown below in common. This structure is especially important because it holds the amino acids in proteins together.

An amide compound that you might be familiar with is *N,N*-diethyl-3-methylbenzamide, better known as DEET. It's the active ingredient in mosquito repellents. Appendix J presents a summary of the families of organic compounds that we have discussed in this chapter.

504 Chapter 20

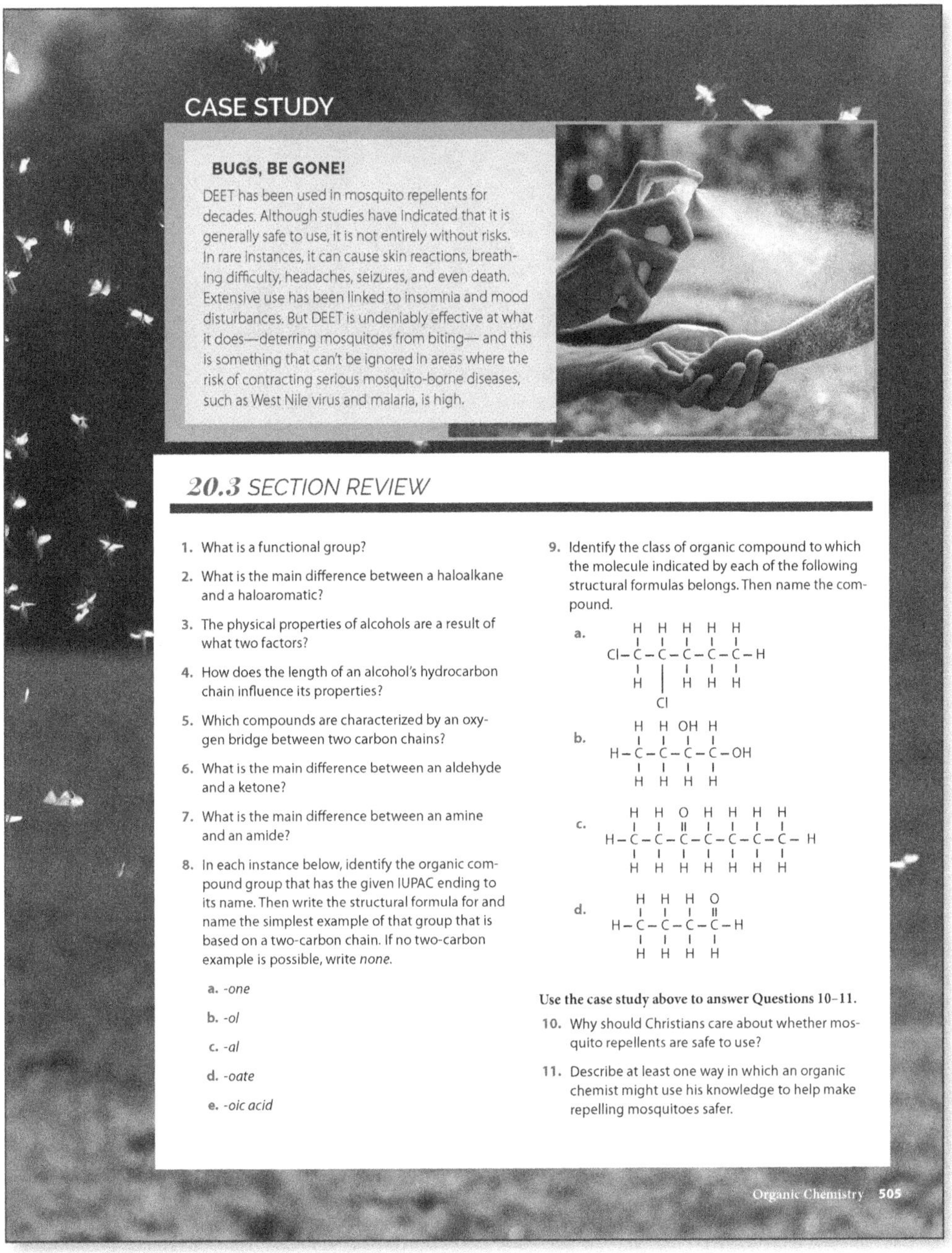

CASE STUDY

BUGS, BE GONE!

DEET has been used in mosquito repellents for decades. Although studies have indicated that it is generally safe to use, it is not entirely without risks. In rare instances, it can cause skin reactions, breathing difficulty, headaches, seizures, and even death. Extensive use has been linked to insomnia and mood disturbances. But DEET is undeniably effective at what it does—deterring mosquitoes from biting—and this is something that can't be ignored in areas where the risk of contracting serious mosquito-borne diseases, such as West Nile virus and malaria, is high.

20.3 SECTION REVIEW

1. What is a functional group?
2. What is the main difference between a haloalkane and a haloaromatic?
3. The physical properties of alcohols are a result of what two factors?
4. How does the length of an alcohol's hydrocarbon chain influence its properties?
5. Which compounds are characterized by an oxygen bridge between two carbon chains?
6. What is the main difference between an aldehyde and a ketone?
7. What is the main difference between an amine and an amide?
8. In each instance below, identify the organic compound group that has the given IUPAC ending to its name. Then write the structural formula for and name the simplest example of that group that is based on a two-carbon chain. If no two-carbon example is possible, write *none.*
   a. *-one*
   b. *-ol*
   c. *-al*
   d. *-oate*
   e. *-oic acid*
9. Identify the class of organic compound to which the molecule indicated by each of the following structural formulas belongs. Then name the compound.

```
a.     H   H   H   H   H
       |   |   |   |   |
   Cl— C — C — C — C — C — H
       |   |   |   |   |
       H   |   H   H   H
           Cl

b.     H   H   OH  H
       |   |   |   |
    H— C — C — C — C —OH
       |   |   |   |
       H   H   H   H

c.     H   H   O   H   H   H   H
       |   |   ||  |   |   |   |
    H— C — C — C — C — C — C — C — H
       |   |       |   |   |   |
       H   H   H   H   H   H   H

d.     H   H   H   O
       |   |   |   ||
    H— C — C — C — C — H
       |   |   |
       H   H   H   H
```

Use the case study above to answer Questions 10–11.

10. Why should Christians care about whether mosquito repellents are safe to use?
11. Describe at least one way in which an organic chemist might use his knowledge to help make repelling mosquitoes safer.

Organic Chemistry 505

APPLY

LAB 20A: *MAKES SCENTS!*

Once students have an understanding of the material in Section 20.3, they should be ready to work through Lab 20A.

ASSESS

TICKET OUT THE DOOR

As a **summarizing activity**, ask students to explain the general structure and name ending of two types of substituted hydrocarbons.

20.3 REVIEW *ANSWERS*

* An asterisk following a question number indicates that a worked-out solution can be found on page 513A.

1. A functional group is an atom or group of atoms that replaces a hydrogen in a hydrocarbon. *(p. 497)*

2. A haloalkane is a halogen bonded to an alkane (an aliphatic hydrocarbon), whereas a haloaromatic is a halogen bonded to an aromatic hydrocarbon, such as benzene. *(p. 497)*

3. a polar OH group and a nonpolar alkyl group *(p. 499)*

4. The length of the hydrocarbon chain determines whether the alcohol exhibits polar or nonpolar characteristics. This in turn determines solubility and boiling point. The longer the alcohol, the less polar it is. *(p. 499)*

5. ethers *(p. 500)*

6. An aldehyde has a carbonyl group attached on the end of a carbon chain, whereas a ketone has a carbonyl group attached to a carbon that is not on the end of the chain. *(pp. 501–2)*

7. An amine is derived from ammonia, with an alkyl group replacing a hydrogen atom of ammonia. An amide is derived from a carboxylic acid by replacing the OH group with an amine group. *(p. 504)*

8.* a. ketone; none

b. alcohol; ethanol

c. aldehyde; ethanal

d. ester; methyl ethanoate

e. carboxylic acid; ethanoic acid *(all pp. 502–3)*

9. a. halocarbon (also accept haloalkane); 1,2-dichloropentane

b. alcohol; butan-1,2-diol

c. ketone; heptan-3-one

d. aldehyde; butanal *(all pp. 497–504)*

10. Answers will vary. Christians are commanded in Scripture to exercise wise dominion over God's creation and to love and serve others. The use of repellents in areas where the risk of mosquito-borne disease is high allows humans to exercise dominion in areas where it might otherwise be difficult to do so. Making repellents safer to use also demonstrates concern for others.

11. Answers will vary. Organic chemists can study ways to make DEET safer to use, such as in formulating repellents with lower concentrations but equal effectiveness. They might also do research on possible substitutes for DEET that have fewer possible side effects or study compounds that might safely eliminate mosquitoes in the environment.

SECTION 20.4 *OVERVIEW*

Essential Question

How are organic reactions classified?

Objectives

» **20.4.1** Identify reactions as redox, substitution, addition, or condensation.

» **20.4.2** Give examples of substitution, addition, and condensation reactions.

» **20.4.3** Summarize the different reactions involving organic compounds.

» **20.4.4** Predict the products from different organic reactions.

Resources

Worldview Investigation: Aromatherapy

Lab 20B: *Squeaky Clean*—Investigating Soaps and Detergents

ENGAGE

REVIEW ORGANIC COMPOUNDS

Activate prior knowledge with a **mingle-pair-share**. Begin your lesson with the following question written on the board: "What do you recall about organic compounds?" Give students some time to think about the question and write down a few concepts that they can recall regarding organic compounds. Next, direct them to quickly mingle around the room and ask three peers to share their responses. Be sure that they write down those answers. After everyone has finished, have pairs of students share their answers with one another. If time allows, discuss students' answers with the class.

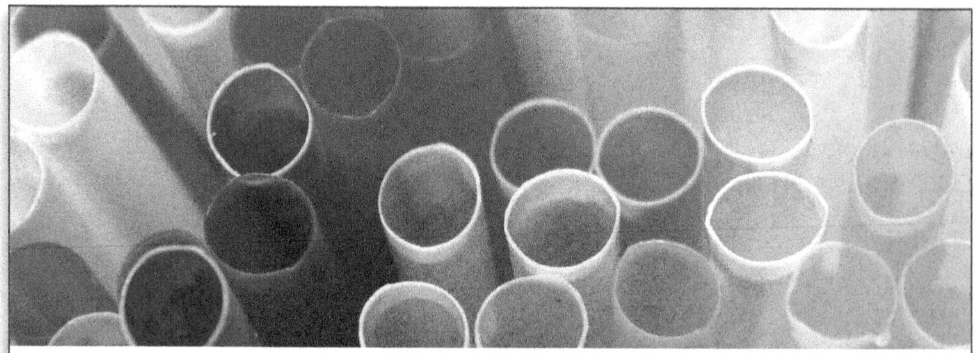

QUESTIONS

» What kinds of chemical reactions do organic compounds participate in?

» How can I determine the kind of reaction that an organic compound is involved in?

» Is it possible to predict the products in a reaction involving organic compounds?

TERMS

substitution reaction • addition reaction • elimination reaction • condensation reaction

How are organic reactions classified?

20.4 ORGANIC REACTIONS

The number of synthesized organic compounds is continually growing because these compounds can participate in many kinds of chemical reactions. Most biological processes rely on chemical reactions between organic molecules. Such reactions are responsible for the movement of muscles, the digestion of food, the transmission of nerve impulses, and the sensing of light on the retina. Industrial chemists also manipulate organic molecules to make flavorings, plastics, fuels, synthetic fabrics, and a host of other products. Some of the reactions involving organic compounds are quite complicated. This section will survey a few of the basic kinds of reactions in which organic compounds participate.

Oxidation-Reduction

Think back on what you read in Chapter 19 about redox reactions. When oxygen and carbon atoms bond, carbon atoms are oxidized and oxygen atoms are reduced. Since oxygen atoms have high electronegativities, they pull shared electrons away from carbon. This means that adding oxygen always makes the oxidation number of carbon more positive. Adding hydrogen atoms, on the other hand, reduces carbon atoms.

Recall that all combustion reactions are redox reactions. Combustion oxidizes all the carbon atoms in an organic molecule to form carbon dioxide. All hydrocarbons burn in oxygen to form carbon dioxide and water, releasing thermal energy in the process. The energy from these combustion reactions is used to produce motion, heat, and light. The burning of methane gas, a simple alkane, is a combustion reaction.

$$CH_4 + 2O_2 \longrightarrow CO_2 + 2H_2O$$

We can see in the equation below that the carbon is oxidized in the combustion reaction and oxygen is reduced.

$$\overset{-4}{C}H_4 + 2\overset{0}{O}_2 \longrightarrow \overset{+4}{C}\overset{-2}{O}_2 + 2H_2\overset{-2}{O}$$

Fatty acid chains in food are oxidized by the human body in a way that is similar to how other hydrocarbons are burned. The body is designed to control the oxidation precisely so that only small amounts of energy are released at any instant. This regulation keeps the temperatures during oxidation tolerable and allows the body to capture and use most of the released energy.

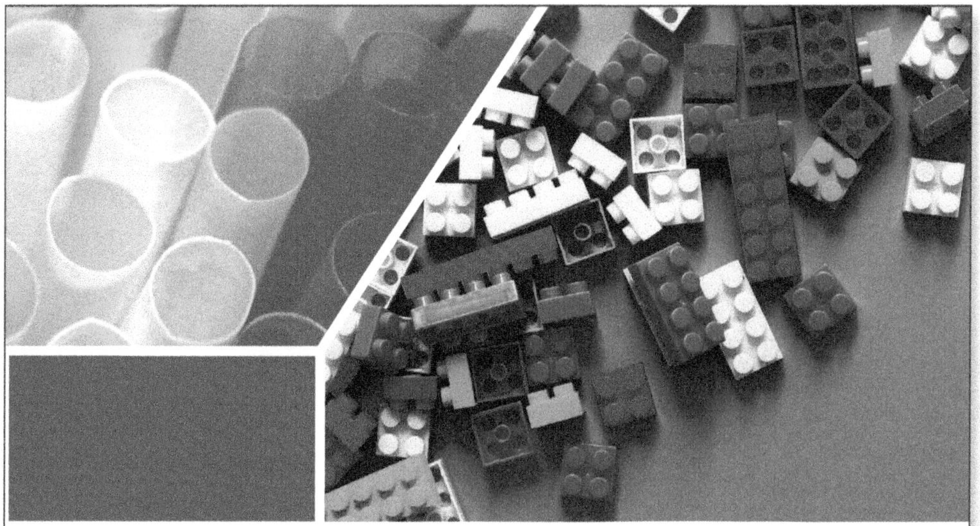

Substitution

Substitution reactions replace one part of a molecule with another part. Typically, most of the reactions of chemically inactive compounds are substitution reactions. Alkanes are not very reactive, but when heated to high temperatures or exposed to energetic ultraviolet light, their hydrogen atoms can be replaced by other atoms. For example, methane and chlorine can react to form a variety of substitution products. In the example below, a chlorine atom replaces a hydrogen atom when a mixture of the two gases is exposed to heat or certain types of light.

$$CH_4 + Cl_2 \xrightarrow{\text{heat or light}} CH_3Cl + HCl$$

Various groups can replace one or more of the hydrogens of aromatic compounds. Benzene can be nitrated, halogenated, or even alkylated. The simplest alkylated benzene compound, consisting of a methyl group bonded to a benzene ring, is toluene. It is a common solvent and produces the characteristic smell of paint thinner.

Addition

Compared with carbon-carbon single bonds, double and triple bonds are very reactive. Consequently, the carbons with double and triple bonds react first and determine the molecule's behavior. An **addition reaction** is a reaction in which a multiple bond of a molecule is broken and two atoms or groups of atoms are added. This is a characteristic reaction of unsaturated molecules. Some of the most common addition reactions involve water (called a *hydration reaction*), hydrogen gas (called a *hydrogenation reaction*), halogens, and hydrogen halides. In the example below, hydrogen converts an alkene (ethene) to an alkane (ethane).

$$C_2H_4 + H_2 \longrightarrow C_2H_6$$

INSTRUCT

ORGANIC REACTIONS

Lead students to create a **concept map** for the types of organic reactions covered in this section. As you cover the material, have students add in the five types of reactions, definitions, and examples.

REACTIONS AND BONDS

Alkanes are less reactive because of their single bonds. The double and triple bonds of alkenes and alkynes make them more reactive because the extra electrons crowded between their carbon atoms are ready to leave as soon as a more electronegative atom comes by.

HYDROGENATION

The hydrogenation process that converts oils to solid fats is an example of an addition reaction.

WORLDVIEW INVESTIGATION: AROMATHERAPY

Appendix K includes a reproducible rubric to assess the worldview investigation activity.

TYPES OF REACTIONS

Direct students to do a **compare and contrast** activity with the reactions in Section 20.4 and those in Section 10.2 (pp. 229–34). Have them determine how the reactions are related and record their answers on a separate sheet of paper. Some of the relationships are listed below.

- oxidation-reduction—synthesis, decomposition, or single-replacement reaction
- combustion—synthesis reaction
- substitution—single- or double-replacement reaction
- addition—synthesis reaction
- condensation—synthesis reaction

WORLDVIEW INVESTIGATION

AROMATHERAPY

Essential oils have been popularized through the practice of *aromatherapy*—the use of essential oils to help improve mental and physical well-being. Some people firmly believe in the therapeutic value of essential oils; others claim that aromatherapy is pseudoscience. Where does the truth lie?

Task

The manager of the store where you work asks you for an opinion on whether the store should stock essential oils, but you don't know much about them. You want to give your manager an informed opinion, so you'll need to do some research and then get back to her.

Procedure

1. Research aromatherapy by doing an internet search using the keywords "aromatherapy" and "essential oils."
2. To get a biblical perspective, do an internet search using the keywords "biblical view of essential oils."
3. Write an opinion paper to present to your manager, citing your sources properly. Have a classmate review your paper and give you feedback.
4. Complete your paper and submit it by the deadline.

Conclusion

In the world that He created, God has given us many compounds that are useful to humans. At the very least, the pleasant scent of essential oils can improve our mood. But like the claims of therapeutic effectiveness made for other substances, those made on behalf of essential oils should be rigorously and scientifically tested.

Elimination

We can think of elimination reactions as the opposite of addition reactions. In an **elimination reaction**, two atoms are removed from the organic compound. For example, 2-chlorobutane can react with a sodium hydroxide solution, undergoing an elimination reaction to produce but-2-ene, water, and dissolved sodium chloride.

$$CH_3CClHCH_2CH_3(aq) + NaOH(aq) \longrightarrow$$
$$CH_3CH{=}CHCH_3(aq) + NaCl(aq) + H_2O(l)$$

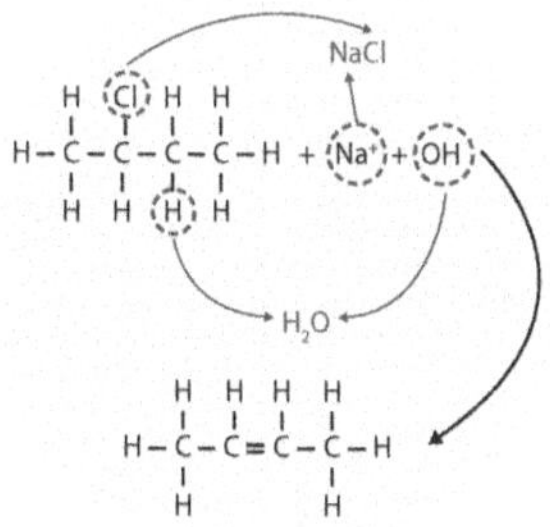

2-chlorobutane reacting with NaOH in solution to form but-2-ene, water, and NaCl

This reaction forms unsaturated molecules. Some of the most common elimination reactions involve water (called a *dehydration reaction*), hydrogen (called a *dehydrogenation reaction*), and halogens. The example below shows the dehydration of ethanol to ethylene.

$$CH_3CH_2OH \longrightarrow CH_2{=}CH_2 + H_2O(l)$$

Condensation

Reactions in which molecules combine to form a larger molecule are called **condensation reactions** and are a type of addition reaction. A water molecule is also produced during some condensation reactions. Under the proper conditions, two identical alcohol molecules can be made to join together to form an ether.

$$R\text{-}OH + R\text{-}OH \xrightarrow{H_2SO_4} R\text{-}O\text{-}R + H_2O$$

For example, two methanol molecules can be condensed to form methoxymethane and water. As you can see, this is also a dehydration reaction.

$$2CH_3OH \longrightarrow CH_3OCH_3 + H_2O$$

Esters form when carboxylic acids and alcohols go through a condensation reaction. This condensation reaction is called *esterification*. For example, an artificial banana flavoring, pentyl ethanoate, can be made by mixing ethanoic acid and pentanol.

A condensation reaction is responsible for much of the clothing that people wear. Polymers are substances that consist of huge molecules that have repeating structural units. Polyester, one of the more common polymers, forms when ethylene glycol and terephthalic acid condense. We will discuss polymers more in Chapter 21.

▲ A condensation reaction occurs at the interface between layers of two organic compounds. Above, nylon 6-10 is being formed.

20.4 SECTION REVIEW

For Questions 1–7, determine the most specific organic reaction that is taking place.

1. Hydrogen atoms are replaced by chlorine atoms when an alkane is heated with chlorine.
2. Unsaturated molecules react.
3. Chloroethane reacts with potassium hydroxide to form ethane, potassium chloride, and water.
4. Carbon and oxygen atoms bond.
5. A hydrocarbon reacts with oxygen to form water and carbon dioxide.
6. A reaction between an acid and an alcohol forms an ester and water.
7. Molecules combine and a water molecule is lost.
8. Give one example each of a substitution reaction, an addition reaction, and a condensation reaction.
9. Copy the table below. Fill in the table to summarize and compare different kinds of organic reactions.
10. Predict the compound that will result if propan-1-ol and butan-1-ol undergo a condensation reaction.

Type of Reaction	Key Feature	Example
redox		combustion
	One part of a molecule is replaced with another part.	replacing a hydrogen in a hydrocarbon with a functional group
		breaking a double bond and adding H_2 to convert an alkene to an alkane
	A multiple bond is formed when two groups of atoms are removed.	
condensation		

ASSESS

Ticket Out the Door

As a **summarizing activity**, ask students to describe two types of organic reactions.

20.4 REVIEW *ANSWERS*

1. substitution *(p. 507)*
2. addition *(p. 507)*
3. elimination *(p. 508)*
4. redox *(p. 506)*
5. combustion and redox *(p. 506)*
6. esterification *(p. 509)*
7. condensation (Also accept dehydration.) *(p. 509)*
8. Answers will vary. Examples described in the Student Edition include the formation of chloromethane from methane and chlorine (substitution), the formation of ethane from ethene and hydrogen (addition), and the production of an ester and water from the combining of two alcohols (condensation). Other examples are possible. *(pp. 507, 509)*
9. See table below. *(pp. 506–9)*
10. propoxybutane (More correctly, this is 1-propoxybutane, but the simpler name is acceptable for this course.) *(p. 509)*

MAKING A POLYMER ROPE

Nylon and polyester are both condensation polymers. Purchase nylon synthesis kits (sometimes called nylon rope trick kits) and show students polymerization in action.

APPLY

LAB 20B: *SQUEAKY CLEAN*

Once students have an understanding of the material in Section 20.4, they should be ready to work through Lab 20B.

Type of Reaction	Key Feature	Example
redox	One bonded atom gains electrons; the other loses them.	combustion
substitution	One part of a molecule is replaced with another part.	replacing a hydrogen in a hydrocarbon with a functional group
addition	A multiple bond is broken and replaced with two groups of atoms.	breaking a double bond and adding H_2 to convert an alkene to an alkane
elimination	A multiple bond is formed when two groups of atoms are removed.	removing two hydrogen atoms from an alkene to form an alkyne
condensation	Two groups combine and release a water molecule in the process.	esterification

20 CHAPTER REVIEW

Chapter Summary

TERMS

organic compound
organic chemistry
condensed structural formula
aromatic compound
aliphatic compound

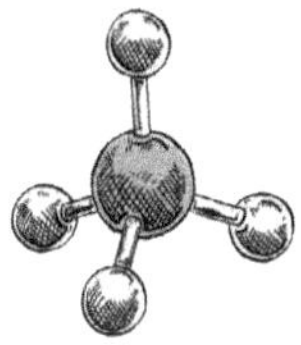

20.1 ORGANIC COMPOUNDS

- All organic compounds contain carbon. They were thought at first to be produced only by living things, hence the name. Many organic compounds can now be synthesized.
- Carbon has four valence electrons and forms strong bonds with other carbon atoms and atoms of many other elements. It can form chains, rings, and other shapes with single, double, and triple bonds.
- Organic compounds are divided into two main groups: aromatic compounds, which have ringed shapes with delocalized electrons, and aliphatic compounds, which include those with linear chains or ring structures that can be formed by closing a chain.

20.2 HYDROCARBONS

- Hydrocarbons are a class of compounds containing only hydrogen and carbon. Some common hydrocarbon types are alkanes, which have only single bonds; alkenes, which include at least one double bond; and alkynes, which have at least one triple bond.
- The IUPAC names of organic compounds are based on their molecular structures. The structure of an organic compound can be determined from its IUPAC name.
- Isomers are compounds with identical molecular formulas but different structures. Because of their different structures, isomers have different properties.
- The key feature that distinguishes aromatic compounds from similarly shaped cyclic aliphatic compounds is the presence of a highly stable ring structure, often a benzene ring. The electrons in the ring are delocalized, meaning that they are shared by all the carbons in the ring.

TERMS

hydrocarbon
alkane
saturated hydrocarbon
alkyl group
isomer
alkene
unsaturated hydrocarbon
alkyne
cyclic aliphatic compound
benzene

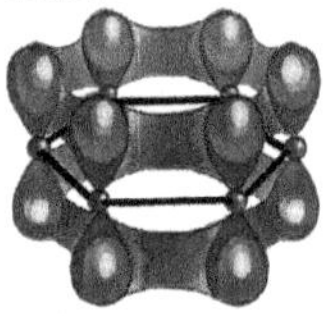

TERMS

functional group
halocarbon
haloaromatic
hydroxyl group
alcohol
ether
carbonyl group
aldehyde
ketone
carboxylic acid
carboxyl group
fatty acid
ester
amine
amide

20.3 SUBSTITUTED HYDROCARBONS

- Functional groups are atoms or groups of atoms that replace hydrogens within organic compounds. The type, number, and location of functional groups partly determine the physical and chemical properties of substituted hydrocarbons. IUPAC names are based on the nature and location of these functional groups.
- Some common functional groups are halides, hydroxyl groups, carbonyl groups, carboxyl groups, amine groups, and amide groups.
- Some of the types of organic compounds that contain functional groups are halocarbons, alcohols, ethers, aldehydes, ketones, carboxylic acids, esters, amines, and amides. Each of these is identified by the presence of one or more specific functional groups.

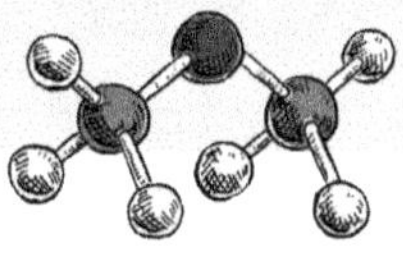

TERMS
substitution reaction
addition reaction
elimination reaction
condensation reaction

20.4 ORGANIC REACTIONS

- Many reactions between organic compounds are redox reactions. Combustion is a common type of hydrocarbon redox reaction.
- Both substitution and addition reactions add atoms to a molecule. In substitution reactions, part of the original molecule is replaced. In addition reactions, a multiple bond is broken and new atoms or groups of atoms are added.
- Elimination reactions remove atoms or groups of atoms from a molecule.
- Condensation reactions join two molecules or two parts of the same molecule, often releasing a water molecule.

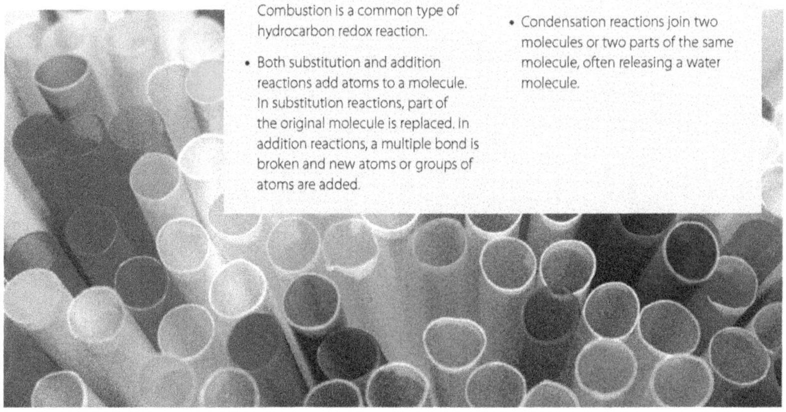

Chapter Review Questions

RECALLING FACTS

1. What is the modern definition of *organic chemistry*?
2. How can you tell when two compounds are isomers? Why is this important?
3. What is unique about the carbon-carbon bonds in benzene and other aromatic compounds?
4. Alcohols and metallic hydroxides both have OH groups in their structural formulas. Explain why metallic hydroxides such as NaOH are caustic but alcohols are not.
5. What is similar about the functions of HCl and CH_3COOH? How are they different?
6. In most substitution reactions of organic compounds, what atom is usually replaced by another atom or group of atoms?

UNDERSTANDING CONCEPTS

7. Compare aliphatic and aromatic compounds.
8. Methane (CH_4) is a gas at room temperature, whereas methanol (CH_3OH) is a liquid. Aside from the difference in molecular masses, suggest an explanation for their different boiling points.
9. Methanol is soluble in water, but larger alcohols such as octanol are not. Why is this?

CHAPTER 20 REVIEW ANSWERS

Recalling Facts

1. Organic chemistry is the branch of chemistry that focuses on those compounds that are covalently bonded carbon compounds, excluding carbonates, carbon oxides, and carbides. *(p. 485)*
2. Compounds are isomers if their molecular formulas are identical but their structural formulas are different. While the molecular formula tells us the components in the compound, the structural formula tells how the components are arranged. The different internal structures of isomers produce different physical and chemical properties. *(p. 492)*
3. The electrons in the bonds between carbon atoms in benzene rings are delocalized, meaning that they move between the carbons that form the ring, producing a highly stable ring structure. *(pp. 495–96)*
4. Metallic hydroxides, such as NaOH, easily release their OH^- ions in solution because of their ionic bonds. Alcohols do not release OH^- ions because they are covalently bonded to a carbon atom. *(p. 499)*
5. They are both acids. HCl is a strong inorganic acid and CH_3COOH is a weak organic acid. *(pp. 502–3)*
6. hydrogen *(p. 507)*

Understanding Concepts

* An asterisk following a question number indicates that a worked-out solution can be found on pages 513A–13B.

7. Aliphatic compounds are made of chains or single-bonded rings. Aromatic compounds contain ring structures that contain both single and multiple bonds. The bonding electrons in the rings are delocalized. *(p. 495)*
8. A short-chained alkane like methane (CH_4) has a low boiling point because its bonds are easily broken. A small alcohol like methanol (CH_3OH) is polar and forms strong hydrogen bonds, giving it a high boiling point. *(p. 492)*
9. The long hydrocarbon chains of larger alcohols make them less polar than small alcohols such as methanol. Therefore, methanol is soluble in polar solvents such as water, and larger alcohols are soluble in nonpolar solvents. *(p. 499)*

10.* *(all pp. 497–504)*

11. a. haloalkane (also accept halocarbon)

b. ketone

c. carboxylic acid

d. amide

e. alkane

f. amine

g. alkane

h. ester

i. alcohol

j. alkene

k. haloaromatic

l. ether *(all pp. 497–504)*

20 CHAPTER REVIEW

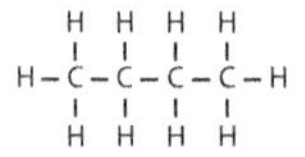

10. Modify the structural formula of butane (left) to create the compounds listed below. Remember that carbon atoms always have four bonds. Add or delete hydrogens when necessary.

a. but-1-ene
b. but-1-yne
c. 2-iodobutane
d. butan-1-ol
e. butan-2-one
f. butoxybutane
g. butanal
h. butanoic acid
i. methyl butanoate

11. Classify each of the following compounds according to its general family.

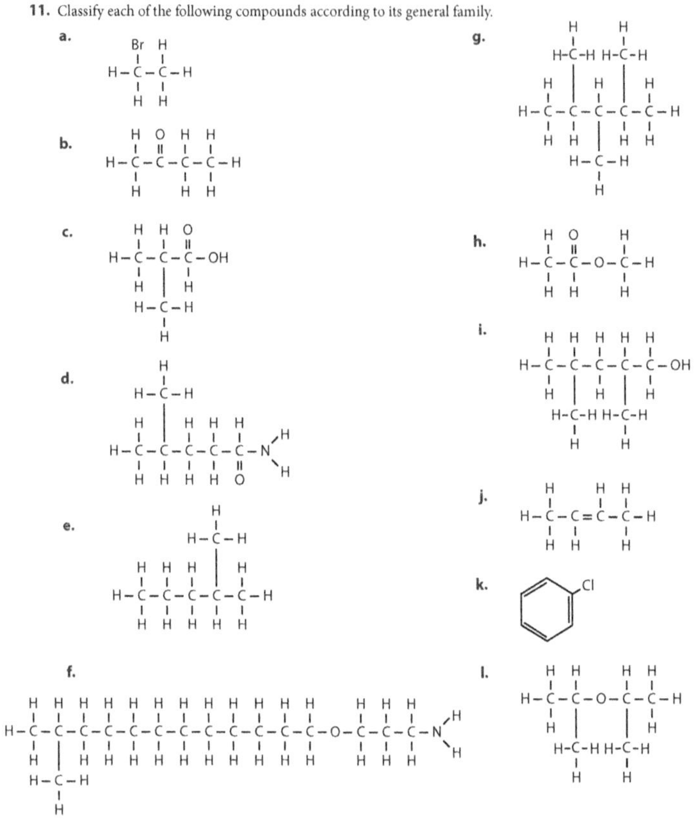

512 Chapter 20

12. Draw the structural formula for each of the following compounds. Assume that the carbon chain is straight in each case.

a. hexane
b. hept-1-ene
c. oct-2-yne
d. pentan-1-ol
e. butan-2-ol
f. 1-chloropropane
g. ethyl butanoate
h. hexanoic acid
i. octan-3-one
j. 2,2-dimethylbutane

13. Name each of the following compounds.

a. 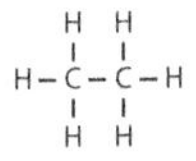

b. 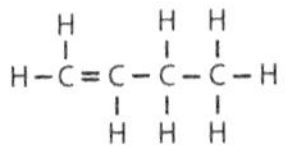

c. 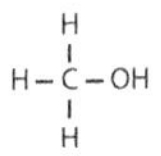

d. 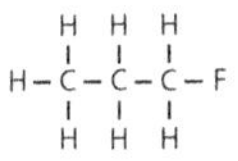

e. 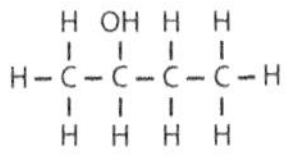

f. 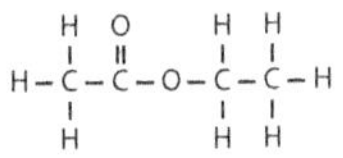

g. 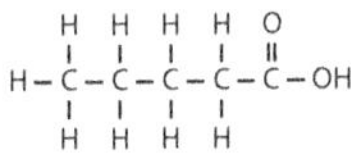

h. 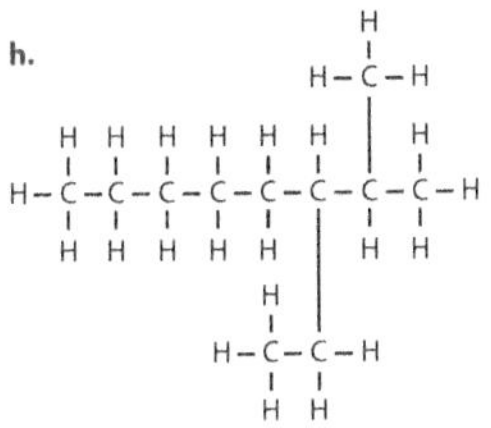

i. 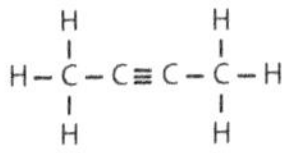

j. 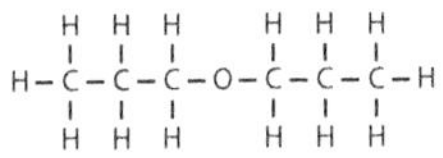

k. 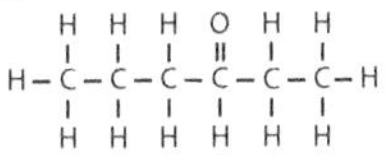

14. Predict the specific products of each of the following reactions. In some cases, more than one product may be possible.

a. a condensation reaction between butanoic acid and ethanol
b. the combustion of octane
c. a reaction between propyne and hydrogen
d. a reaction between methane and bromine

CRITICAL THINKING

15. On a piece of paper, draw an electron-dot structure for propyne. Would you expect this molecule to be polar or nonpolar? Why?

16. What is the name of the compound shown at right?

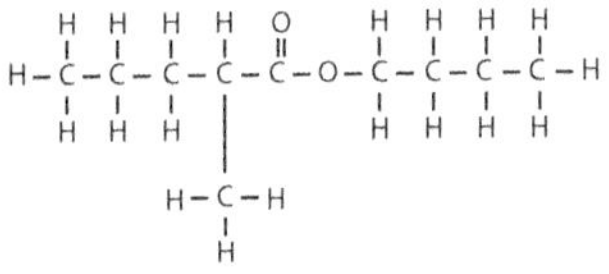

17. Write the structural formula for each of the following compounds.

a. 3-ethyl-2,2-dimethyl-4-phenyloctane
b. 3-bromo-2-fluoro-1-methylbenzene

12.* *(all pp. 489–504)*

13. a. ethane

b. but-1-ene

c. ethanol

d. 1-fluoropropane

e. butan-2-ol

f. ethyl ethanoate

g. pentanoic acid

h. 3-ethyl-2-methyloctane

i. but-2-yne

j. propoxypropane

k. hexan-3-one *(all pp. 489–504)*

14. a. ethyl butanoate and water

b. carbon dioxide and water

c. either propene or propane

d. either bromomethane, dibromomethane, tribromomethane, or tetrabromomethane *(all pp. 506–9)*

Critical Thinking

15.* Propyne would be slightly polar with a partial negative charge at the end of each molecule where the electrons are concentrated, that is, the end closest to the triple bond. *(p. 494)*

16. butyl-2-methylpentanoate *(p. 503)*

17.* *(all pp. 490–96)*

20.2 Review Answers

9. a. 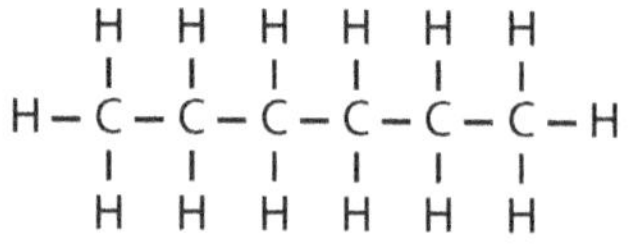

b. 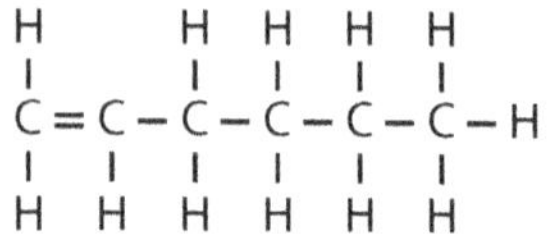

c. 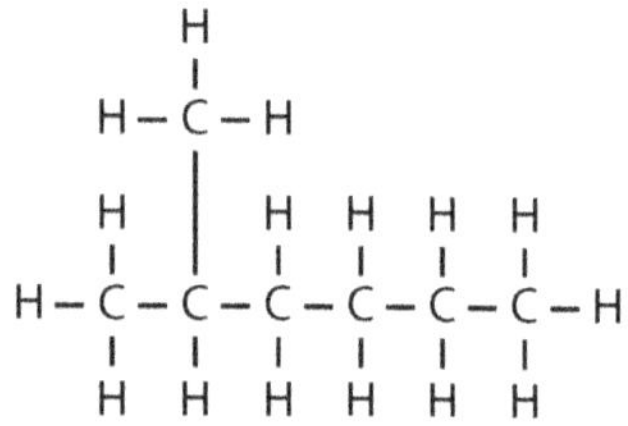

d. 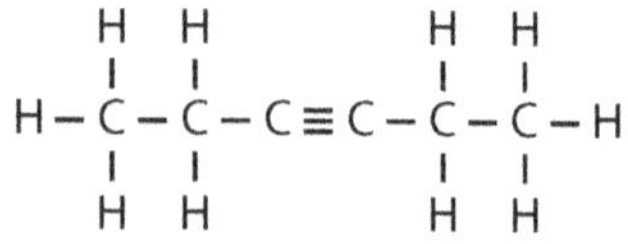

20.3 Review Answers

8. b. 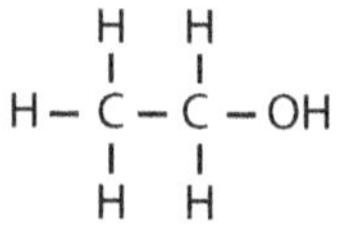

c. 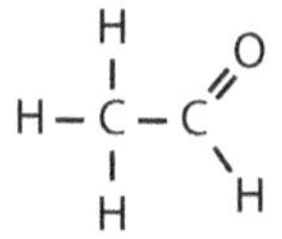

d. 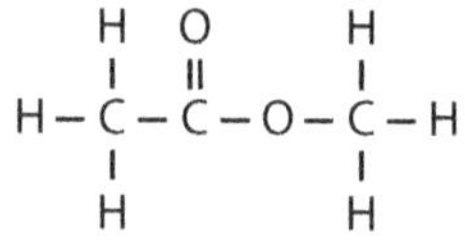

e. 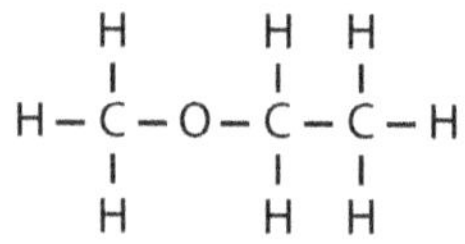

Chapter Review Answers

10. a. 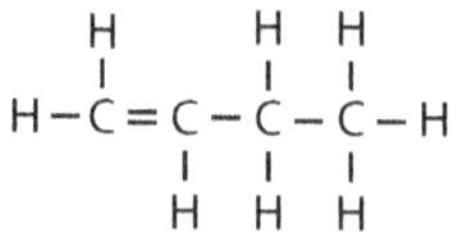

b. 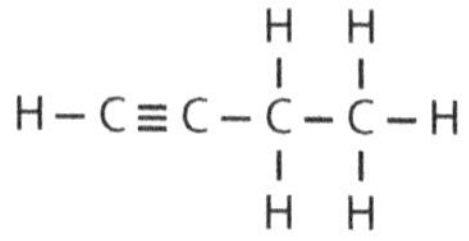

c. 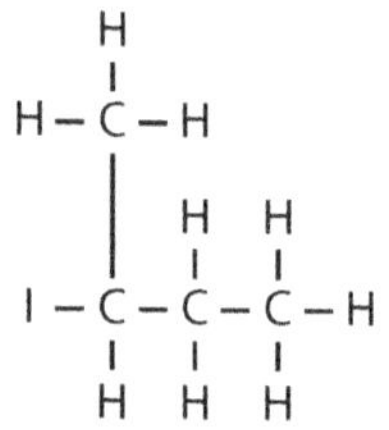

d. 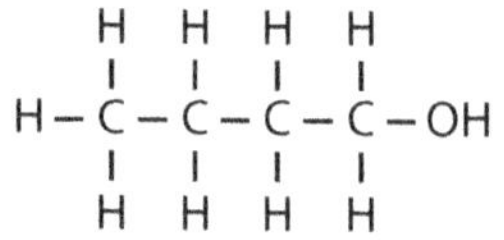

e. 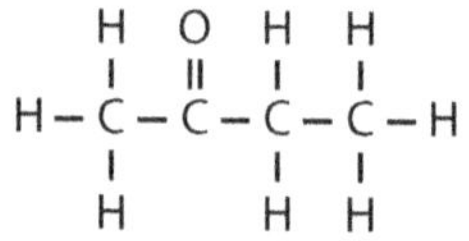

f. 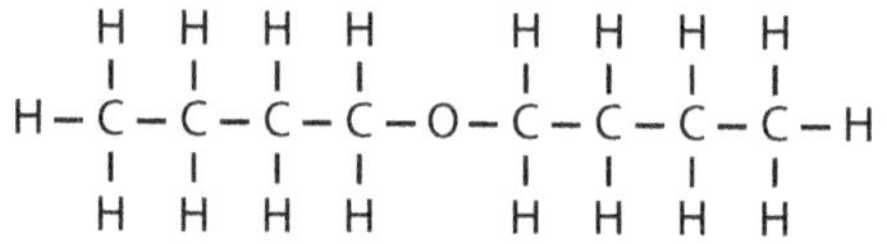

g. 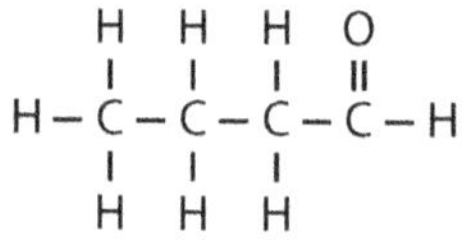

h. 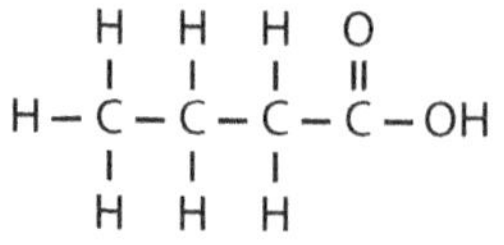

i. 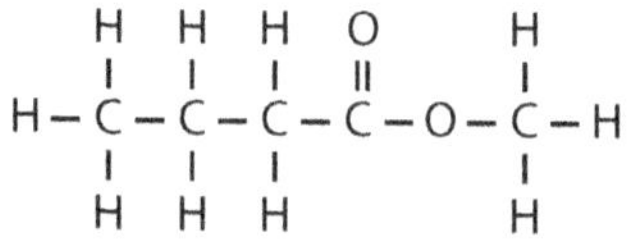

12. a. 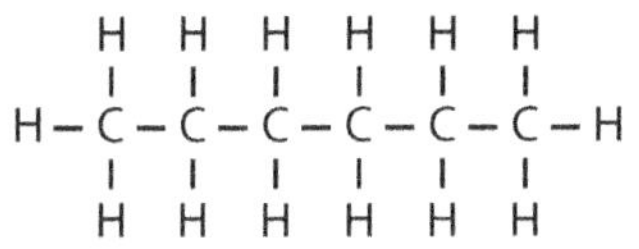

b. 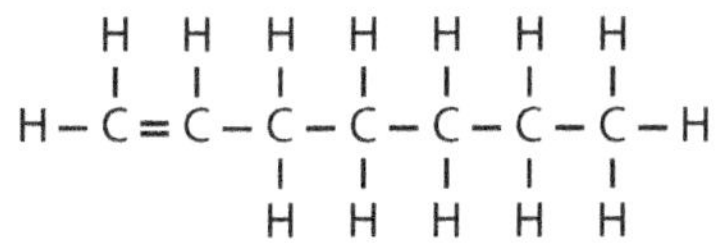

c. 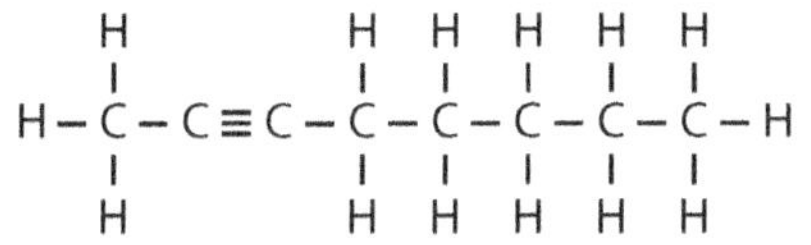

d. 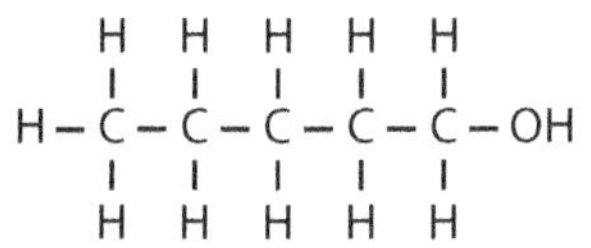

e. 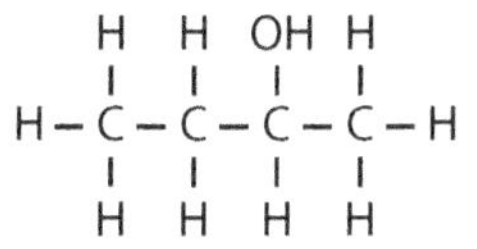

f. 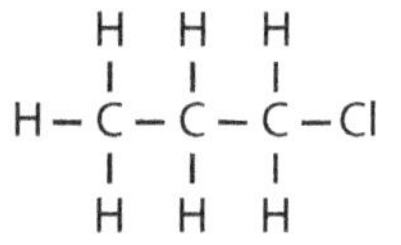

g. 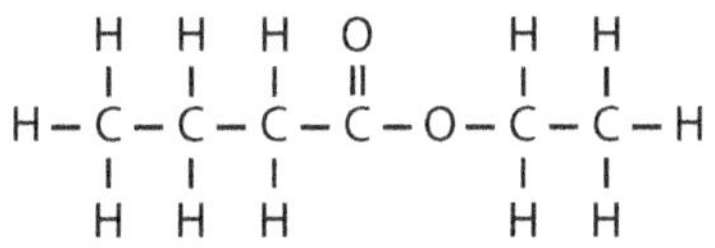

h. 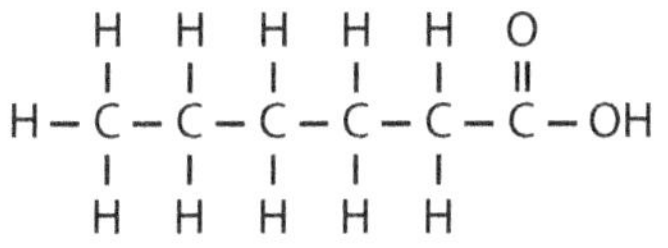

i. 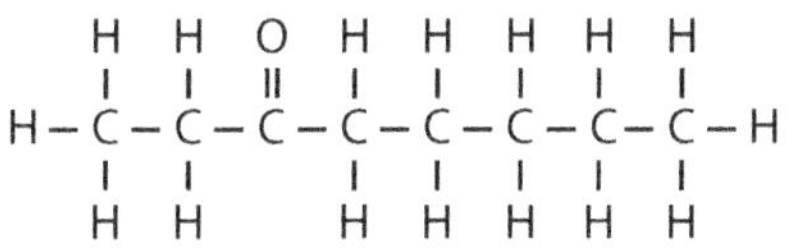

j. 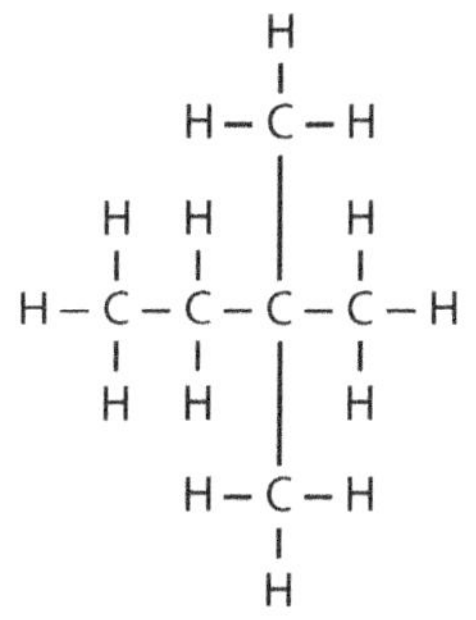

15. 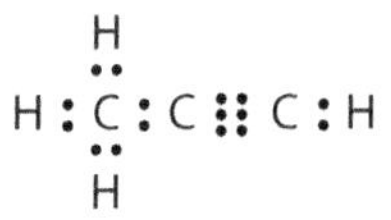

17. a. 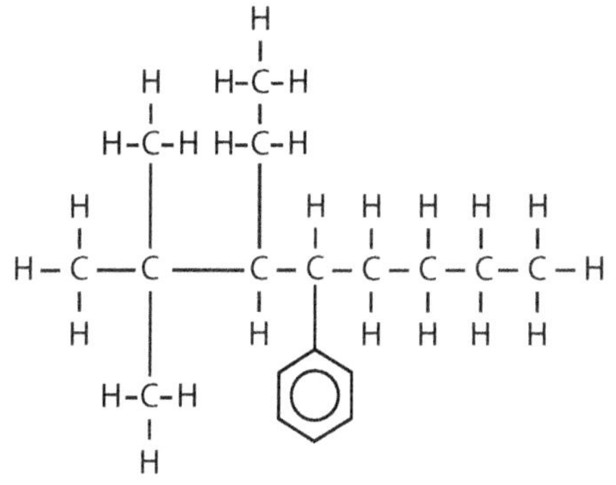

b. 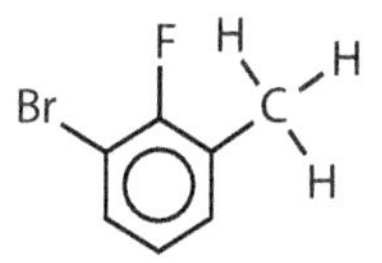

CHAPTER 21 *OBJECTIVES*

- Describe the key processes of metabolism.
- Classify the key biochemical compounds.
- Explain the importance of carbohydrates in our diets.
- Justify the need for a moderate amount of lipids in our diets.
- Justify the study of biochemistry on the basis of the Creation Mandate.
- Determine the biochemical compounds in foods.

OVERVIEW

Chapter 21 has key material that brings together the fields of biology and chemistry. In this chapter students explore the functions and structures of carbohydrates, lipids, proteins, and nucleic acids. Understanding these concepts is important for connecting the importance of inorganic and organic compounds, which are essential for all living things.

21.1 CHEMISTRY OF LIFE
- *Chemical Reactions in Cells*
- *Biochemistry and Ultimate Questions*

21.2 CARBOHYDRATES
- *Carbohydrate Structure*
- *Monosaccharides*
- *Disaccharides*
- *Polysaccharides*

21.3 LIPIDS
- *Fats and Oils*
- *Steroids*
- *Phospholipids*

21.4 PROTEINS
- *Amino Acids*
- *Polypeptide Chains*
- *Enzymes*
- *Denaturing*

21.5 NUCLEIC ACIDS
- *Worldview Conflict in Biochemistry*

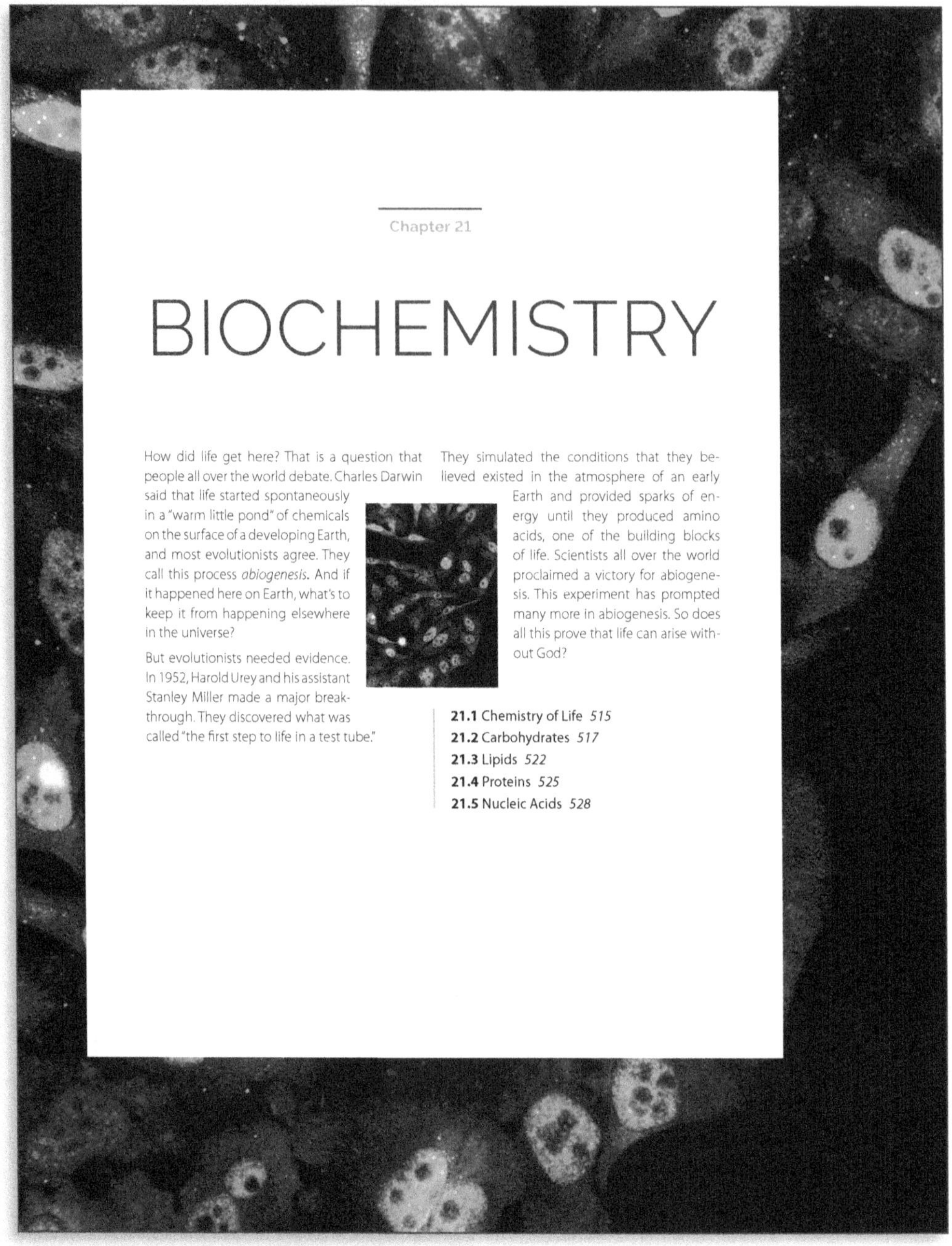

Chapter 21

BIOCHEMISTRY

How did life get here? That is a question that people all over the world debate. Charles Darwin said that life started spontaneously in a "warm little pond" of chemicals on the surface of a developing Earth, and most evolutionists agree. They call this process *abiogenesis*. And if it happened here on Earth, what's to keep it from happening elsewhere in the universe?

But evolutionists needed evidence. In 1952, Harold Urey and his assistant Stanley Miller made a major breakthrough. They discovered what was called "the first step to life in a test tube." They simulated the conditions that they believed existed in the atmosphere of an early Earth and provided sparks of energy until they produced amino acids, one of the building blocks of life. Scientists all over the world proclaimed a victory for abiogenesis. This experiment has prompted many more in abiogenesis. So does all this prove that life can arise without God?

LAB ACTIVITIES

Lab 21A: *A Balancing Act*—Students explore ways to test for macronutrients in foods.

Lab 21B: *The Proof Is in the Jell-O®*—Students investigate the effect of enzymes and factors that contribute to enzyme activity.

The Chapter opener features an image of cells undergoing heat shock response. In response to the stress of increased temperature, cells can produce additional heat shock proteins, a type of molecular chaperone, that help the cell continue the proper folding of proteins that might otherwise begin to denature in response to the stress.

21.1 CHEMISTRY OF LIFE

In Chapter 20 you learned about organic chemistry, which at one time was thought to be the chemistry of living things. Today, though, this narrower focus on living things within the broader context of organic chemistry is known as **biochemistry**. The chemistry of genetics and cellular processes falls within this field of study. Much of this field deals with organic compounds, but living things depend on many inorganic compounds as well. The overlaps between the various fields of chemistry and biology illustrate the fact that the marvelous complexities of life cannot be studied within the confines of a single subject area.

QUESTIONS

- What is biochemistry?
- What chemical reactions occur within cells?

TERMS

biochemistry • metabolism • catabolism • anabolism • polymer

Is biochemistry another name for organic chemistry?

Chemical Reactions in Cells

It's tempting to think of cells as "simple"—they are, after all, the basic building blocks from which living things are made. But individual cells are only *relatively* simple when compared with the extraordinary complexity of multicellular organisms. In truth, every living cell is, by itself, incredibly complex. Each one depends on *thousands* of different chemical processes to live, grow, and reproduce. We use the term **metabolism** as a collective noun for all the chemical reactions that take place within cells. We can break down this very large group of chemical processes into *catabolism* and *anabolism*.

Catabolism & Anabolism

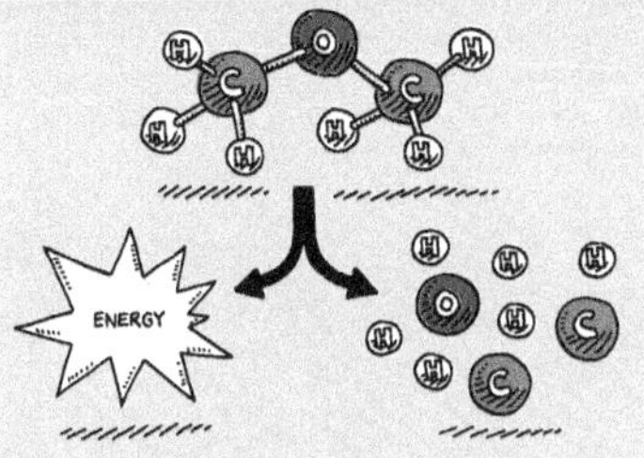

Catabolism

Catabolism includes all the cell's chemical reactions that break molecules into smaller particles. Catabolism provides cells with two very important raw materials—the starting substances needed to build macromolecules and the energy needed for their manufacture.

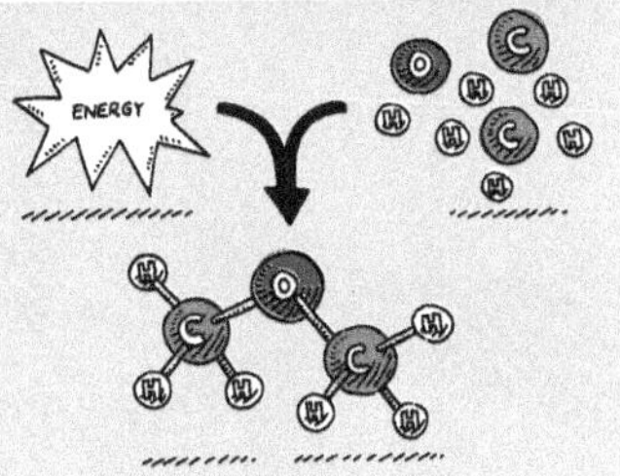

Anabolism

Anabolism can be thought of as the reverse of catabolism—it includes those processes by which cells assemble small particles into larger ones—often *much* larger. Some of the compounds produced by anabolic processes are organic **polymers**, very large molecules built from repeating subunits called *monomers*. The bonding of monomers together is called *polymerization*. Starch, protein, and DNA are examples of organic polymers.

SECTION 21.1 *OVERVIEW*

Essential Question

Is biochemistry another name for organic chemistry?

Objectives

- **21.1.1** Define *biochemistry*.
- **21.1.2** Explain the relationship between anabolism, catabolism, and metabolism.

Resource

Web Link: Metabolism

ENGAGE

ORGANIC AND INORGANIC CHEMISTRY

Lead students to participate in a **think-pair-share** to connect organic and inorganic chemistry. Have them think about the differences and similarities of organic and inorganic chemistry and pair together to create a Venn diagram which displays their information. Once they have finished, select students to share their responses with the class. Be sure to address any misconceptions and clarify any information as needed.

INSTRUCT

METABOLISM: CATABOLISM AND ANABOLISM

Have students create a **T-chart** that compares catabolism and anabolism. Challenge students to teach the difference between these two terms to someone at school or in their home.

DIFFERENTIATED INSTRUCTION

Carbohydrate Structure

Lead students to pair up with a peer in creating a **student-generated assessment** for the concepts covered in this chapter. Give them a few minutes at the end of each class or section and have them generate several test questions and answers that they think would be good as assessment items. Once the chapter is complete, you may opt to have them use their generated assessments as a review or pretest, or you may choose to use some of them for the Chapter 21 assessment.

METABOLISM

For a video with information about the metabolic processes that occur in the body, visit TeacherToolsOnline.com. Under Additional Resources, click on Chapter 21 Web Links. Then click on *Metabolism*.

ASSESS

TICKET OUT THE DOOR

As a **summarizing activity**, ask students to describe the term *metabolism*. *(Metabolism is all the reactions that a cell undergoes in order to live, grow, and reproduce. It includes the processes of catabolism and anabolism.)*

21.1 REVIEW *ANSWERS*

1. Biochemistry is the area of study within general chemistry that focuses on the chemistry of life. There is overlap between the fields of biochemistry and organic chemistry, but biochemical processes also involve many inorganic substances. Organic chemistry is the study of carbon-containing compounds, some of which are necessary for life but many that are involved in nonbiological processes. *(p. 515)*
2. Catabolism and anabolism are subsets of metabolism, which is a collective term for all the chemical reactions within cells. Catabolism breaks large molecules into smaller ones; anabolism builds larger molecules from smaller ones. *(p. 515)*
3. A polymer is a macromolecule made up of many repeated units called monomers. *(p. 515)*
4. Many catabolic and anabolic processes work together in cyclical processes, such as the ATP cycle. *(pp. 515–16)*
5. There are thousands of different processes that take place within cells. Many of these processes involve the assembly or breaking down of very large molecules, such as starch, protein, and DNA. (Other examples are possible.) *(p. 516)*

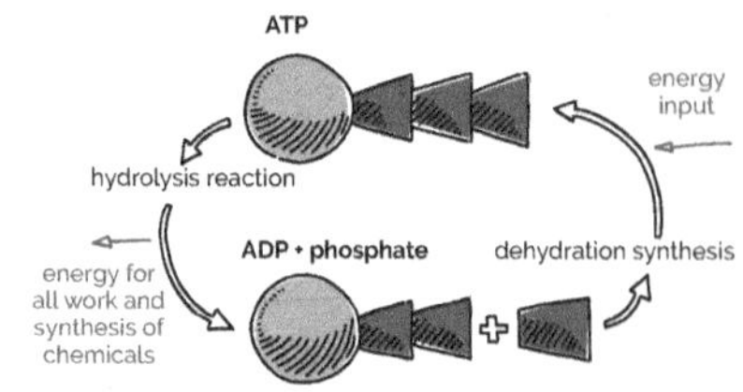

Catabolism and anabolism often go hand in hand. Many cellular processes are cyclical—the products of a catabolic process are used during an anabolic process, whose products are again used by the catabolic process. A good example of this should be familiar to you from biology. Adenosine triphosphate (ATP), the molecule that cells use for energy, is made by bonding a phosphate group to a molecule of adenosine diphosphate (ADP) through an anabolic process. The splitting off of a phosphate group from ATP to release energy is a catabolic process. The product of this process, ADP, is recycled to make ATP once again. Other familiar examples include photosynthesis (anabolic) and cellular respiration (catabolic).

Biochemistry and Ultimate Questions

Because biochemistry deals with life, it particularly leads to philosophical and spiritual issues. As technology develops, scientists encounter perplexing ethical predicaments. Should humans be cloned? Is it right to use stem cells? Is it ever right to harvest human embryos for their stem cells? When does a legal drug become illegal, and vice versa? The Bible, not science, contains the answers to these questions. For this reason, Christians must engage in the field of biochemistry.

Ultimately, the study of biochemistry reveals further levels of complexity in creation, and this shouts out the infinite wisdom of the Creator. Every molecule bears witness to the power, ingenuity, and foresight of God. This flies in the face of what most scientists believe—that life got here through abiogenesis. We'll embark on our study of biochemistry by studying some of the basic molecules of life—carbohydrates, lipids, proteins, and nucleic acids.

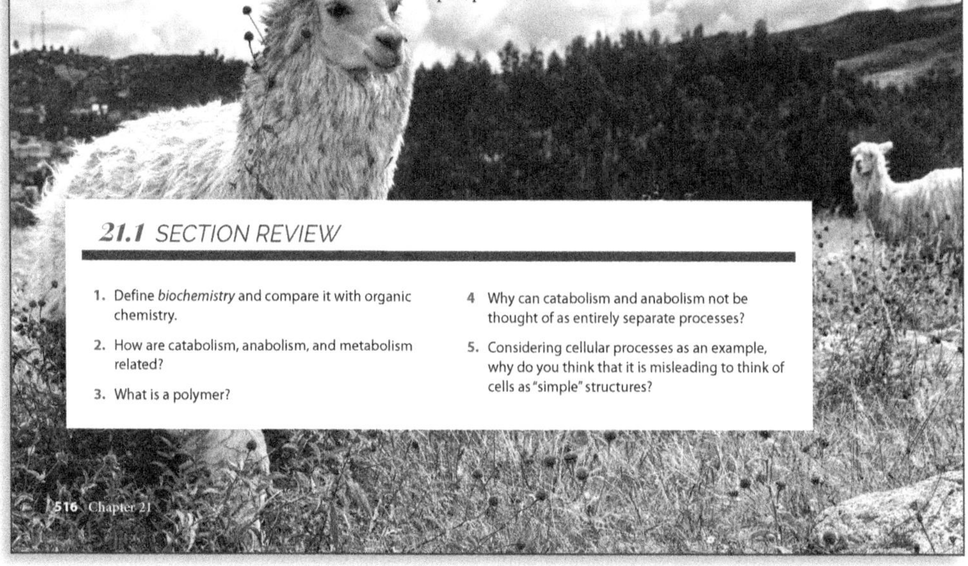

21.1 SECTION REVIEW

1. Define *biochemistry* and compare it with organic chemistry.
2. How are catabolism, anabolism, and metabolism related?
3. What is a polymer?
4. Why can catabolism and anabolism not be thought of as entirely separate processes?
5. Considering cellular processes as an example, why do you think that it is misleading to think of cells as "simple" structures?

21.2 CARBOHYDRATES

QUESTIONS

- » What is a carbohydrate?
- » How are carbohydrates classified?
- » How are carbohydrates used by living things?

TERMS

carbohydrate • monosaccharide • disaccharide • polysaccharide

Low-carb diets are popular these days. Considering how many people that you might know who are trying to cut grains and cereals from their diets, you might think that carbohydrates are bad. As usual, context is the key. At the cellular level, living things absolutely depend on carbohydrates for energy and often for structure as well. Simple sugars make up part of the human diet, as do starches, which consist of long chains of one simple sugar—glucose—bonded together. A slight change to the manner in which individual glucose molecules are bonded together produces cellulose, the stuff of which plant cell walls are made. The exoskeletons of insects and crustaceans are made of chitin, a derivative of glucose.

Are carbohydrates good or bad?

The name *carbohydrate* itself tells us something about the compounds in the group. The word means "water of carbon," since at one time all carbohydrates were thought to be hydrates of carbon, containing only carbon, hydrogen, and oxygen in a ratio of 1:2:1. In biochemistry, the term **carbohydrate** is used to collectively refer to sugars, starches, and cellulose. These organic compounds are also known as *saccharides*, from the Latin word for sugar.

Carbohydrate Structure

When you hear the word *sugar*, you probably think right away of granulated table sugar. But there are actually many different kinds of sugars, some of which can be easily spotted on food labels by their ending in *-ose*. You probably already know something about glucose. Granulated table sugar is sucrose. Other sugars that you may have come across are lactose, fructose, and maltose. How do the structures of these sugars compare? Sugars differ from one another on the basis of how many carbon atoms they contain, how their oxygen atoms are bonded within their structure, and whether they exist as open chains or rings. The simplest sugars are **monosaccharides**, and as their name implies, they consist of a single sugar unit. Let's look at D-altrose to get a better view of carbohydrate structure.

SECTION 21.2 *OVERVIEW*

Essential Question

Are carbohydrates good or bad?

Objectives

» **21.2.1** Define *carbohydrate.*

» **21.2.2** Explain the relationship between monosaccharides, disaccharides, and polysaccharides.

» **21.2.3** Explain the role of carbohydrates in living things.

Resources

Demonstrating the Presence of Starch

Mini Lab: *Simple Sugars?*

ENGAGE

CARBOHYDRATES

Check students' knowledge of carbohydrates with a **preassessment**. Have each student write down three things they know about carbohydrates. Once they have finished, select students to share their responses as you write some of them on the board. Explain that in Section 21.2 we will take a closer look at the structure of carbohydrates and how our bodies use them as a source of energy.

INSTRUCT

CARBOHYDRATE STRUCTURE

Lead students to create a **graphic organizer** or **Sketchnotes** of the structures for carbohydrates, lipids, proteins, and nucleic acids covered in this chapter. They may want to create a concept map or just do simple illustrations with Sketchnotes depicting the different structures. Have students add in brief descriptions for the structures drawn.

D AND L CHIRALITY

The different structures of D- and L-glucose are not readily grasped when looking at their structural formulas. If possible, show students physical models of the two versions to make the differences more apparent.

Carbohydrates

D-altrose and other carbohydrates are built on a chain of single-bonded carbon atoms. Each internal carbon atom and one end carbon of the chain is bonded to a hydrogen atom and one substituent. The other end carbon is bonded to two hydrogens and a substituent.

The substituent on one end of D-altrose is a double-bonded oxygen atom. Recall from Chapter 20 that this is an identifying feature of aldehydes. This and the presence of multiple hydroxyl groups makes glucose an example of a *polyhydroxy aldehyde*, also referred to as an *aldose*.

D-altrose has six carbon atoms, but not all sugars do. Because it is a six-carbon sugar, D-altrose can be classified as a *hexose*. Because it is also an aldose, these terms are sometimes combined to form *aldohexose*.

D-ALTROSE

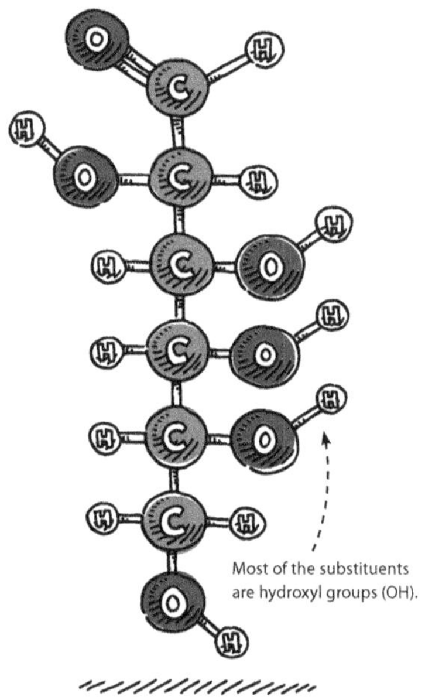

Most of the substituents are hydroxyl groups (OH).

If you did the mini lab in Chapter 20, you may recall that many organic compounds exhibit *chirality*—having left- and right-handed forms called *enantiomers*. D-altrose, as well as many other sugars, exhibit this type of isomerism. The *D-* and *L-* in the names of the enantiomers stand for *dexter* and *laevus*—Latin for "right" and "left."

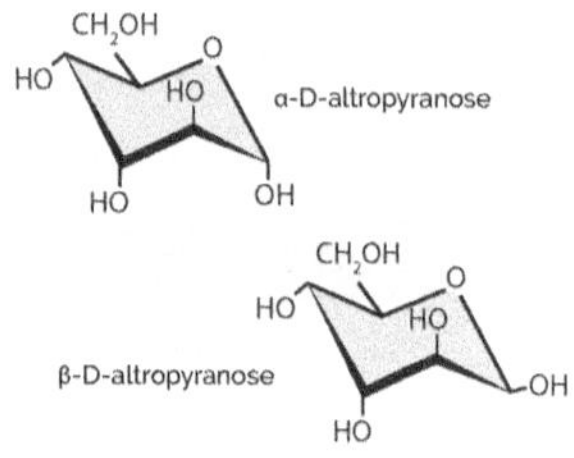

If one of the bonds on D-altrose's double-bonded oxygen atom is broken, the chain can fold back on itself, and the oxygen can bond to the fifth carbon atom of the chain, forming D-altropyranose. The word *pyranose* refers to the six-member ring comprised of five carbons and one oxygen. Because this ring has several possible configurations, two of which can be seen in the *chair conformations* at left, pyranoses have many isomers.

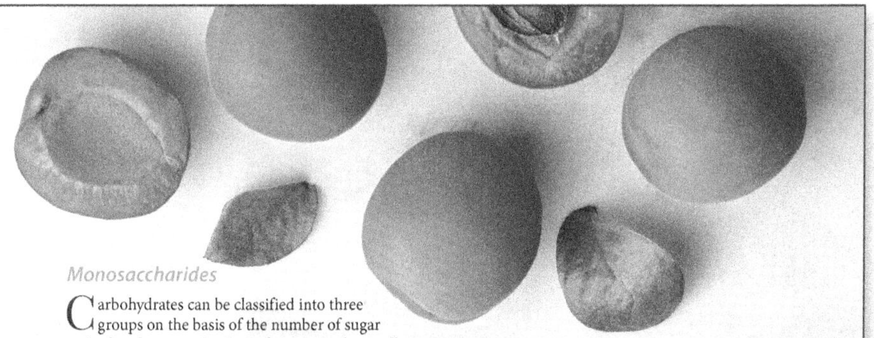

Monosaccharides

Carbohydrates can be classified into three groups on the basis of the number of sugar units that they contain. As we have seen, the smallest possible sugars consist of a single unit. These are the monosaccharides. When purified and dried, monosaccharides—and there are many—are white, water-soluble, crystalline solids. Most have a sweet taste. They rarely occur in nature as free molecules but are usually bonded to a protein, a fat, or another carbohydrate. Two significant exceptions are glucose and fructose.

Glucose is the most abundant sugar in nature. Ripe berries, grapes, and oranges are 20% to 30% glucose in composition. The human body maintains a fairly constant level of 80 to 120 mg of glucose per 100 mL of blood. Hence, it is often called *blood sugar*. Glucose is also the fundamental building block of the most common long-chain carbohydrates: starch and cellulose.

Although monosaccharides are often drawn as open-chain molecules, they most often exist in their ring form. Glucose in an aqueous solution exists in an equilibrium between the ring and open-chain forms. The equilibrium lies strongly in favor of the ring form. Fructose also forms ring structures when it is in solution. In its open-chain form, fructose's carbonyl group is not at the end of the carbon chain. It is thus based on a ketone and is classified as a *polyhydroxy ketone* or *ketose*. Its ring form has only five atoms in its ring, compared with the six in glucose.

fructose

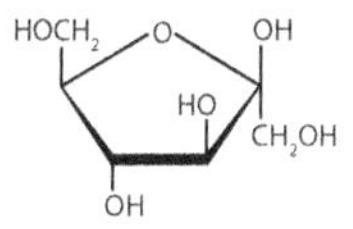

Disaccharides

As their name implies, **disaccharides** consist of two monosaccharide units. Typically, two monosaccharides can join in a condensation reaction to release a water molecule and form a disaccharide. An oxygen bridge between the two monosaccharides holds the two units together. While many monosaccharides exist, an even larger number of disaccharides can be formed from combinations of monosaccharides.

Three disaccharides play an important part in the human diet—maltose, lactose, and sucrose. Maltose consists of two bonded glucose molecules. The bond forms between the first carbon of one molecule and the fourth carbon of the other. Maltose is found in germinating grain and is produced during the digestion of starches. Lactose is a disaccharide found only in milk. It consists of an isomer of glucose (galactose) joined to a glucose molecule. This sugar is not very sweet, but it is an important ingredient in milk. Milk sours when lactose breaks down into lactic acid. A glucose and a fructose molecule can bond in a condensation reaction, releasing a water molecule and forming the disaccharide sucrose (table sugar). Sucrose is abundant in fruits, sugar cane, sugar beets, and nectar.

lactose

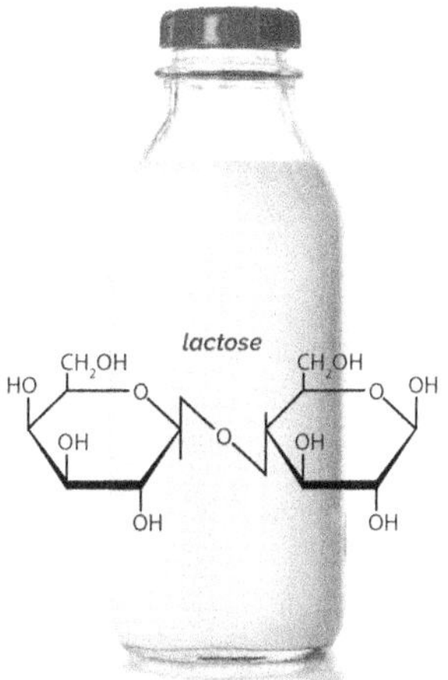

MONOSACCHARIDES, DISACCHARIDES, AND POLYSACCHARIDES

Direct students through a **review** of prefixes by having them analyze the words *monosaccharide, disaccharide*, and *polysaccharide*.

Monosaccharides (*mono-* meaning "one") consist of one saccharide molecule.

Disaccharides (*di-* meaning "two") consist of two saccharide molecules.

Polysaccharides (*poly-* meaning "many") consist of many saccharide molecules.

Have students write **Sketchnotes** on the differences between the three types of carbohydrates as you cover them in the section.

DEMONSTRATING THE PRESENCE OF STARCH

Demonstrate whether a substance contains starch using an iodine test.

Materials: items to test (e.g., orange, green banana, ripe banana, lettuce leaf, onion, potato chip, bean), small containers for each item, mortar and pestle (or some other way to crush each item), tincture of iodine (should be a brown solution, not clear), eyedropper or pipette

Preparation: Crush each test item well and place in separate containers. You will need only small samples for the test. Be careful not to cross-contaminate the samples that you will be testing.

Performance/Discussion: Place one or two drops of iodine on each sample. If the sample contains starch, the iodine will turn a bluish black. If it does not contain starch, the color of the iodine will not change. Of the items listed above, the green banana, lettuce leaf, potato chip, and bean contain starch. The orange, ripe banana, and onion do not because they store excess energy as sugars.

If you have time, you can set up two samples that look identical, such as flour mixed with water (contains starch) and flour mixed with milk (contains no starch). Have a student test them to determine which contains starch. You can also use the iodine test to detect cellulose in paper.

Cleanup: Dispose of the samples in the trash.

ASSESS

TICKET OUT THE DOOR

As a **summarizing activity**, ask students to state the differences between the three different types of carbohydrates discussed in this section (see pages 519–20).

HOW IT WORKS

New Bone from Sugar?

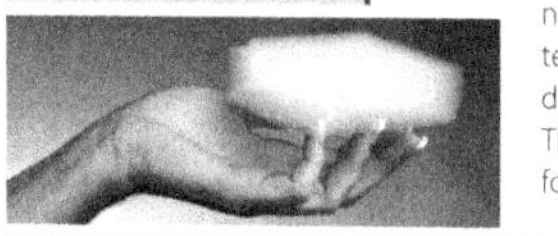

If you've ever taken a wilderness first aid course, you may have learned how to make a splint for a broken bone by using a tree branch. But medical researchers are taking this idea one step further—they are helping bones heal with help from a surprising source. Researchers in Canada have recently had much success in quickening new bone growth by injecting test subjects with an aerogel derived from plant cellulose. The nanocrystals of the cellulose form a scaffolded structure in which osteoblasts can deposit new bone. And unlike commonly used ceramic implant materials, which are hard and brittle, the new aerogel is soft enough to flex and completely fill all the gaps in a host bone. Those gaps hinder the growth of new bone when using ceramic implants; the new aerogel has demonstrated 50% more bone growth after twelve weeks compared with ceramic. Our God-given ability to think of creative ways to use the resources around us is part of exercising godly dominion over His world.

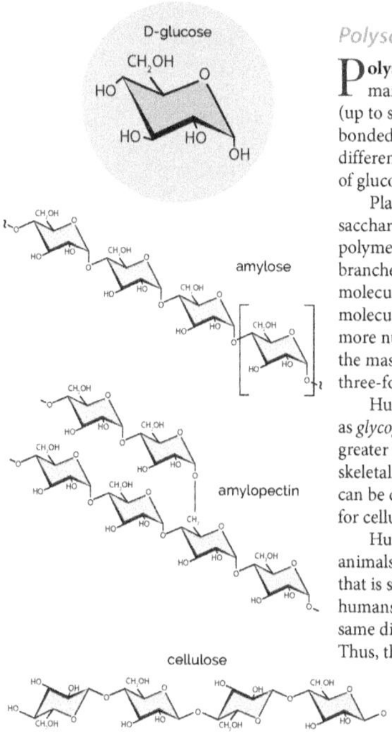

Polysaccharides

Polysaccharides, literally "many sugars," are molecules that contain many sugar units. This is evident from their large molecular masses (up to several million atomic mass units). Multitudes of sugar units are bonded into long chains. Polysaccharides may be built from several different monosaccharides, but we will concentrate on the polymers of glucose.

Plants such as rice, potatoes, wheat, and oats store food in polysaccharide deposits called starch. *Starch* exists as one of two glucose polymers. Most of the mass of starch found in plants exists as the branched isomer called *amylopectin*. But most of the actual starch molecules are the linear form known as *amylose*. Because the amylose molecules are very much smaller than amylopectin molecules, the more numerous amylose molecules make up only about a quarter of the mass of starch. Together, these two polysaccharides supply nearly three-fourths of the world's food energy.

Humans and animals also store glucose as a polysaccharide known as *glycogen*. Like amylopectin, glycogen is branched, but to an even greater degree. In humans, most glycogen is stored in the liver and skeletal muscles. It serves as a readily accessible energy reserve since it can be quickly broken down and converted into the molecules needed for cellular respiration.

Humans can't digest much of the plant matter that herbivorous animals can because plants contain lots of *cellulose*, a polysaccharide that is similar to starch and glycogen. In the polysaccharides that humans can digest, such as starch, each glucose unit is oriented in the same direction. But the glucose units in cellulose alternate directions. Thus, the difference between the starch in a tasty potato and the cellulose in grass, cotton, or a splintery piece of wood is the manner in which the glucose units are arranged. This may seem like a minor difference at first, but it isn't. Humans can digest the uniformly oriented starch, but they lack the enzyme needed to digest cellulose. Cows and other herbivores can't actually digest cellulose either—but symbiotic bacteria that live in their guts can. This mutualistic relationship allows both bacteria and herbivores to thrive.

APPLY

MINI LAB: *SIMPLE SUGARS?*

Use this **mini lab** to demonstrate the complexity of simple sugars.

1. No
2. See bottom margin of next page.
3. fifteen
4. No. Counting only aldohexoses, there are eight possible D configurations. Since each of these can exist as either a right-handed or left-handed molecule, the total number of open-chain aldohexoses is sixteen.
5. See bottom margin of next page.

MINILAB

SIMPLE SUGARS?

You've seen that the ring forms of simple sugars have many isomers, but what about the open-chain forms? Can they also exist as many isomers?

Are simple sugars, you know, like, really simple?

Procedure

A Use your molecular modeling set to build a model of D-glucose as shown at right. When finished, you should be able to view your model from above in a manner that places the hydroxyl (-OH) groups on either the left or right side of the carbon backbone. Keep the double-bonded oxygen of the carboxyl group to the right to help you maintain your orientation when viewing.

B Swap the positions of the hydroxyl group and hydrogen atom on any internal carbon. When viewed from above, that hydroxyl group should now appear to be on the opposite side of the carbon backbone from its original position. Make sure that all the other substituents on the model remain in their original locations.

1. Can the affected carbon atom be rotated so that the hydroxyl group and hydrogen atom are returned to their original positions?

C The affected carbon atom in Step B is an example of a *stereocenter*. Isomers created around a stereocenter are called *stereoisomers*. The three remaining internal carbons are also stereocenters. Repeat Step B for each of those carbons. The resulting model is L-glucose.

D Try to make as many different aldohexoses as you can by continuing to swap substituents on the internal carbons, either individually or in various combinations.

2. Write the structural formula for each aldohexose you come up with for Step D.
3. How many different aldohexoses are possible in addition to D-glucose?

Conclusion

4. So, are open-chain simple sugars simple? Defend your answer.

Going Further

5. Search the internet to find the names of the stereoisomers that you created for Question 2. Label each of your structural formulas with the appropriate name.

EQUIPMENT
- molecular modeling set

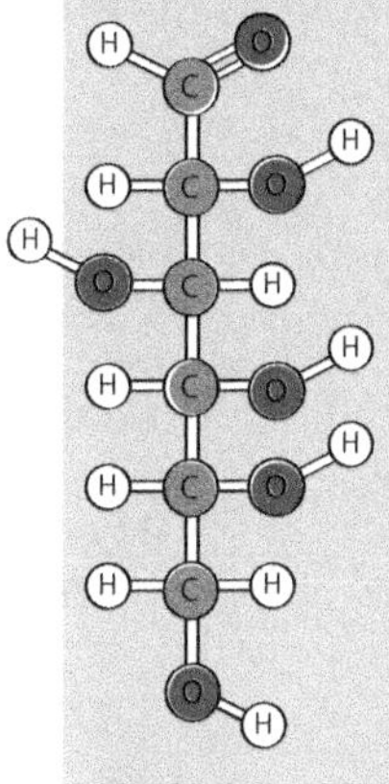

D-glucose

21.2 SECTION REVIEW

1. What are carbohydrates?
2. How does the structure of one kind of monosaccharide differ from another?
3. What can we know about a compound when told that it is an aldohexose?
4. What products result from a condensation reaction between glucose and fructose?
5. How are monosaccharides, disaccharides, and polysaccharides related?
6. Describe at least two roles of carbohydrates in living things.

21.2 REVIEW ANSWERS

1. Carbohydrates are organic compounds that include sugars, starches, and cellulose. *(p. 517)*
2. Monosaccharides differ in the number of carbon atoms each has, how and where their oxygen atoms are bonded, and whether they exist as open chains or rings. *(p. 518)*
3. The prefix *aldo-* alerts us to the fact that the compound is a polyhydroxy aldehyde. *Hex* indicates that it has six carbon atoms, and the suffix *-ose* indicates that the compound is a sugar. *(p. 518)*
4. water and sucrose *(p. 519)*
5. All three are made of sugar molecules. Monosaccharides consist of individual sugar units. Disaccharides consist of bonded pairs of monosaccharides. Polysaccharides are large molecules made of many sugar units. *(pp. 517, 519–20)*
6. Answers will vary. Carbohydrates store energy, serve as an energy source for cellular functions, and supply structural elements in plants and animals. (Accept any two.) *(p. 520)*

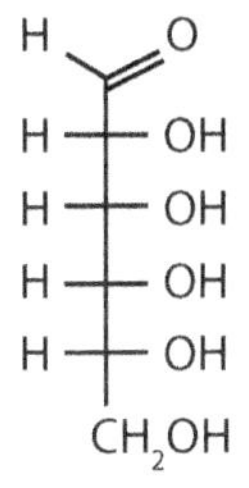

D-Allose

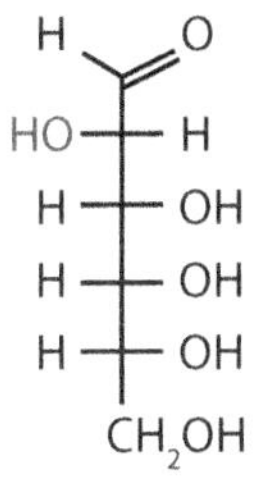

D-Altrose

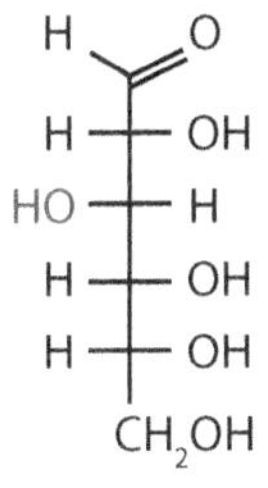

D-Glucose

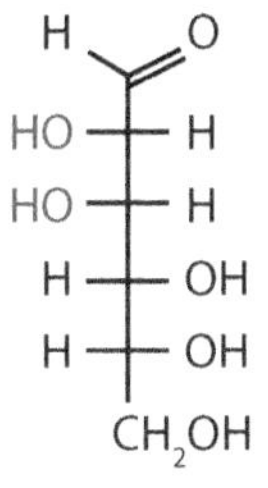

D-Mannose

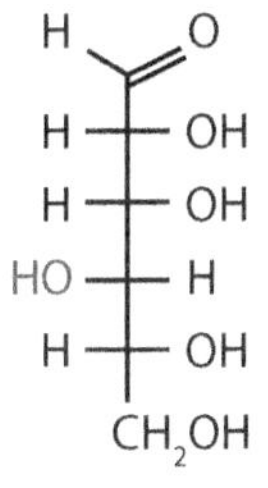

D-Gulose

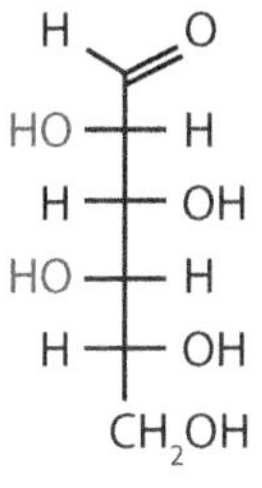

D-Idose

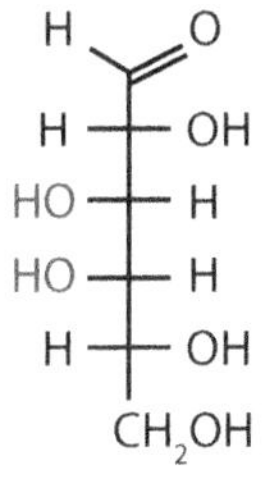

D-Galactose

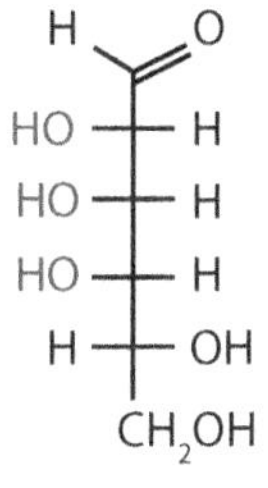

D-Talose

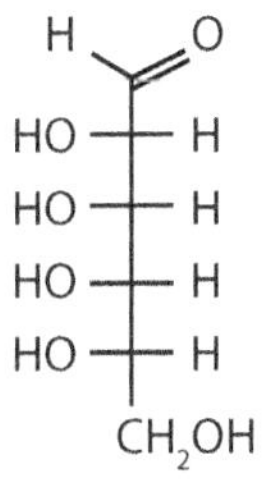

L-Allose

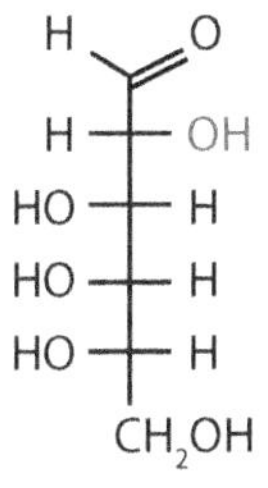

L-Altose

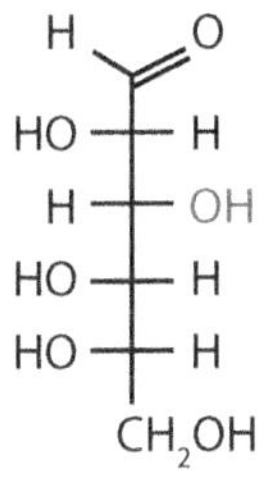

L-Glucose

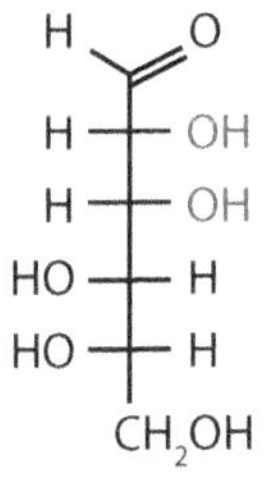

L-Mannose

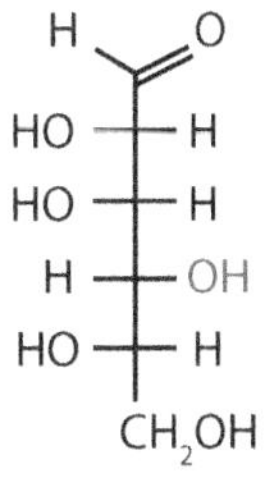

L-Gulose

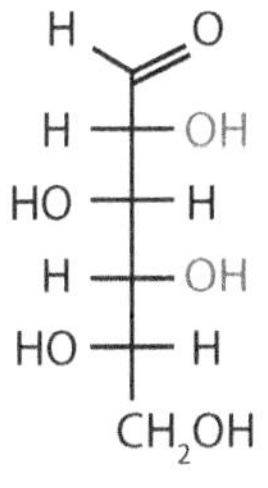

L-Idose

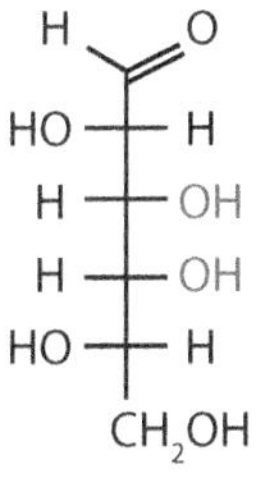

L-Galactose

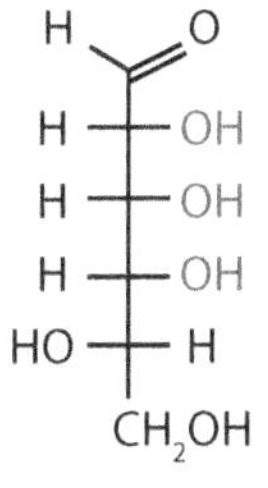

L-Talose

SECTION 21.3 *OVERVIEW*

Essential Question

Why can't I live without fats?

Objectives

» **21.3.1** Define *lipids.*

» **21.3.2** Compare saturated and unsaturated fats.

» **21.3.3** Explain the role of lipids in living things.

Resource

Lab 21A: *A Balancing Act*—Testing Macronutrients in Food

ENGAGE

LIPID INTRODUCTION

Guide students through a **visual analysis** of lipids. Using a sample of olive oil and lard or butter (one being liquid and one being solid at room temperature), have students analyze and make inferences to the composition of these samples. Have them write down their observations and conclusions. They should note that the sample of oil is liquid and the sample of lard or butter is solid. Ask, "If they both are fats, why is one a liquid and one a solid?" Help them to recall intermolecular forces (Ch. 13) and form a conclusion as to why one would be solid and one would be liquid. *(The solid lard has stronger intermolecular forces and has molecules more closely packed together than the liquid oil.)*

Ask students to state any additional observations and properties that these two samples have in common. *(insoluble in water, slippery, essential for living things)*

21.3 LIPIDS

QUESTIONS
» What are lipids?
» How are saturated fats different from unsaturated fats?
» What functions do lipids serve in living things?

TERMS
lipid • fat • oil • steroid • phospholipid

Why can't I live without fats?

Although water is sometimes called the universal solvent, it does not mix with all the compounds in the human body. An entire class of biomolecules (those molecules necessary for cellular processes) called lipids cannot dissolve in water. They are characterized by a high proportion of C–H bonds, making them nonpolar. As energy storage molecules and as an integral part of cell membranes, **lipids** serve vital roles in living things. Fatty acids, fats, oils, waxes, and steroids are examples of lipids.

Fats and Oils

Propane-1,2,3-triol, commonly known as *glycerol*, is a three-carbon molecule that has three hydroxyl groups on separate carbons. Fats and oils are esters of glycerol and fatty acids, which in turn are carboxylic acids with long hydrocarbon tails. Ester linkages join the carboxyl (COOH) groups of fatty acids to the hydroxyl groups of glycerol to construct a fat or oil molecule and water. Fatty acids rarely occur alone in living things. Typically, three of them bond with a glycerol molecule to form a *triglyceride*.

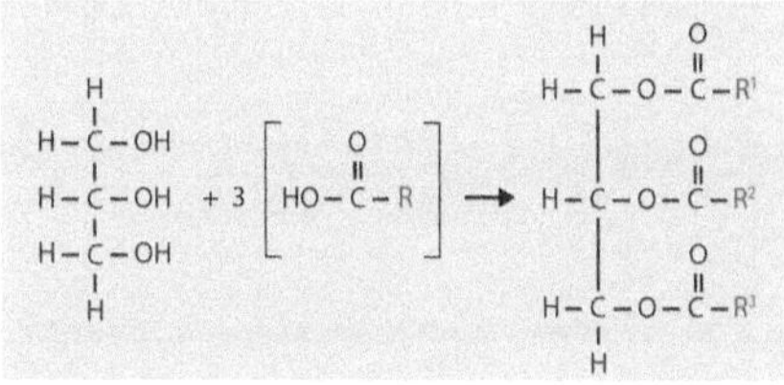

glycerol fatty acid triglyceride

▲ Three fatty acids and a glycerol molecule can combine to form a triglyceride.

The fatty acids that bond to glycerol usually contain a large hydrocarbon chain (chains of twelve to eighteen carbons are common) that most often contains an even number of carbons (the chains are made in two-carbon units). Some chains contain only single carbon-carbon bonds, and some contain a few double bonds. This difference leads to the distinction between fats and oils.

Fats are triglycerides that often exist as solids at room temperature. Most of their fatty acid chains are saturated. Saturated chains tend to extend in straight lines from the glycerol backbone. This particular structure allows saturated fat molecules to pack closely together. Moreover, saturated fats have stronger intermolecular forces, so their melting points are higher.

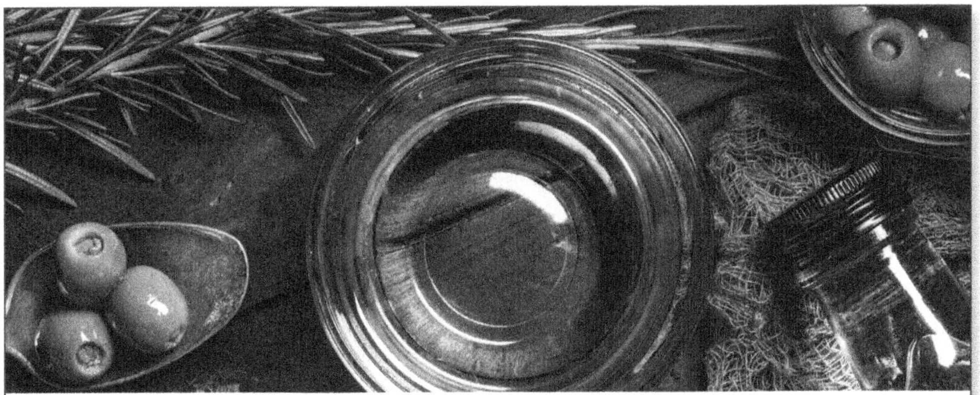

Triglycerides that have one double bond somewhere within their fatty acid chains are said to be *monounsaturated*. Those with multiple double bonds are classified as *polyunsaturated*. The greater a triglyceride's degree of unsaturation, the more bent its chains become. The molecules can't pack as tightly, reducing their intermolecular forces, which lowers their melting point. Unsaturated fats that remain liquid at room temperature are referred to as **oils**.

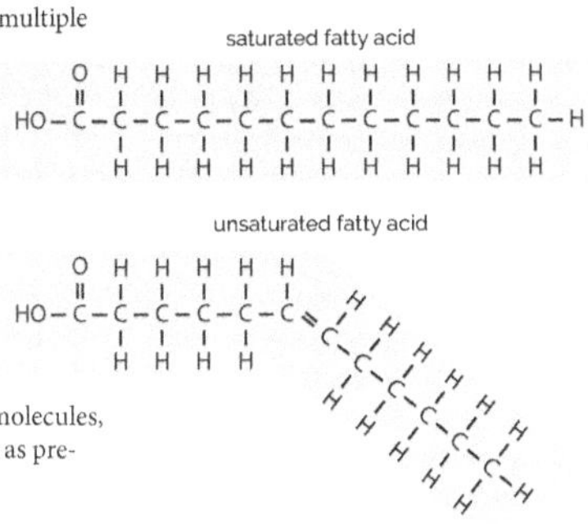

Dietary fat is a vital nutrient for a healthful lifestyle, especially as a source of energy for the body. It is the most concentrated source of energy in one's diet, providing nine calories per gram compared with only four calories per gram from either carbohydrates or protein. Fats also carry vitamins, cushion the body, insulate nerves, act as signaling molecules, regulate immune response, and can act as hormones or serve as precursors for the production of hormones.

Steroids

Steroids are lipids, but their structures do not resemble triglycerides in any way. They are the non-ester lipids. The basic structure of a steroid (shown at right) is a combination of three six-carbon rings and one five-carbon ring. Functional groups attached to various points on the rings result in a wide variety of steroids. Cholesterol, vitamin D, cortisone, testosterone, and estrogen all use this common "chicken wire" frame that you see at right. In living things, steroids serve as important components of cell membranes and as chemical-signaling molecules.

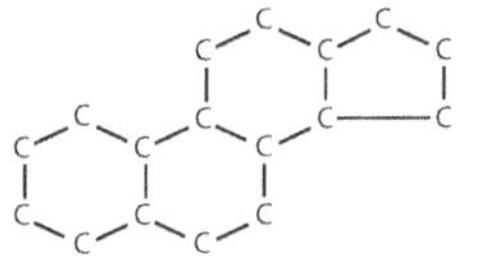

The study of steroids ranks as one of the most active areas of biochemical research. One steroid that has been studied much in recent years is *cholesterol*—a compound that, although vital to good health, some believe can increase the risk of heart disease if excessive amounts are present in the blood. Routine blood panels, such as you might have done for an annual physical, will test for the concentration of cholesterol. Contrary to popular belief that cholesterol levels are controlled by diet, most of the cholesterol found in the body is manufactured by the body itself. The average total blood cholesterol in Americans is 203 milligrams per deciliter (mg/dL). The National Institutes for Health considers less than 200 mg/dL desirable and greater than 240 mg/dL to be too high.

STEROIDS: GOOD CHOLESTEROL, BAD CHOLESTEROL

The *kind* of cholesterol in the body is just as important as *how much*. Some people can have high levels of high-density lipoprotein (HDL) cholesterol yet little arterial blockage because HDLs tend to scavenge arteries for deposits of low-density lipoprotein (LDL) cholesterol and take them to the liver to be recycled. To remember the difference between the two types of cholesterol, use the mnemonic device "Healthy HDL, Lethal LDL."

CLARIFYING TRIGLYCERIDES

Be sure that students understand the difference between monounsaturated and polyunsaturated fats. If only one bond in an unsaturated fat is a double bond, it is monounsaturated; if two or more are double bonds, it is polyunsaturated.

SATURATED AND UNSATURATED LIPIDS

Use a **quick check** to assess students' understanding by asking them to state how saturated fats are different from unsaturated fats. *(Saturated fats are long, fatty acid chains with high intermolecular forces that exist as solids at room temperature. Unsaturated fats have one or more double bonds within their fatty acid chains, have lower intermolecular forces, and exist as liquids at room temperature.)*

APPLY

LAB 21A: *A BALANCING ACT*

Once students have an understanding of the material in Section 21.3, they should be ready to work through Lab 21A.

ASSESS

TICKET OUT THE DOOR

As a **summarizing activity**, ask students to illustrate and describe the phospholipid bilayer. *(The phospholipids in the bilayer have hydrophilic (water-loving) polar heads that face outward from both sides of the bilayer and hydrophobic (water-fearing) tails that face in toward the interior of the bilayer.)*

21.3 REVIEW *ANSWERS*

1. Lipids are biomolecules that are involved in numerous biochemical processes. They are nonpolar, making them insoluble in water. Lipids are the class of biomolecules that includes fats, oils, waxes, and steroids. *(p. 522)*
2. The carbon-carbon bonds in saturated fats are single bonds, whereas unsaturated fats contain one or more double bonds. *(pp. 522–23)*
3. The chains of saturated fats extend in almost straight lines from the glycerol backbone. As a result, they are able to fit together closely. The double bonds in unsaturated fats cause bends in the chains, preventing a close fit of the chains. The intermolecular forces are stronger in the closely packed chains of saturated fats; therefore, they tend to be solid at room temperature, whereas unsaturated fats tend to be liquid. *(pp. 522–23)*
4. A steroid has a combination of three six-carbon rings and one five-carbon ring, and each ring has functional groups attached at various points. *(p. 523)*
5. Answers will vary. *Fats and oils* provide energy, carry vitamins, produce hormones, cushion the body, and insulate nerves. *Steroids* form part of the cell membrane structure and act as chemical-signaling molecules. *Phospholipids* form the lipid bilayer of cell membranes. *(pp. 522–24)*

CAREERS

SERVING AS A BIOMEDICAL RESEARCHER:
MAKING A MIRACLE MOLECULE

Dr. Percy Julian

In 1929 Dr. Philip Hench of the Mayo Clinic discovered that a chemical called *cortisone*, a type of steroid, had an amazing ability to relieve the pain of rheumatoid arthritis. It was a miracle molecule. But producing cortisone was extraordinarily difficult. The only known way to make it was from cattle bile using a chemical process that required thirty-six separate steps. The bile from a whopping 14,600 cattle was needed to produce enough cortisone to treat a single patient for one year! Not surprisingly, cortisone was also expensive. The cost for a single dose in 1949 was $200—equivalent to $2162 in 2019.

A solution to producing large quantities of cortisone inexpensively was discovered by Dr. Percy Julian, the grandson of slaves and a chemist working for a chemical company. Julian had experience in synthesizing steroids from chemicals found in plants. In 1949 Julian used his knowledge of steroids to improve the process for making cortisone. His process did not require the use of osmium tetroxide, the rare and expensive compound that made the earlier production method so costly. Other chemists later discovered that a mold could produce cortisone from progesterone, a hormone readily synthesized from a chemical found in a plant, the Mexican yam. Julian eventually decided to work full time for his own company that made progesterone for other businesses to produce cortisone.

Born and raised in Alabama, Dr. Julian lived and worked in an era of institutionalized racism, but he didn't allow the problems he faced to keep him from helping people. Through his work, he was able to save and improve the lives of millions of people around the world. He never lost sight of the potential of chemistry to help people.

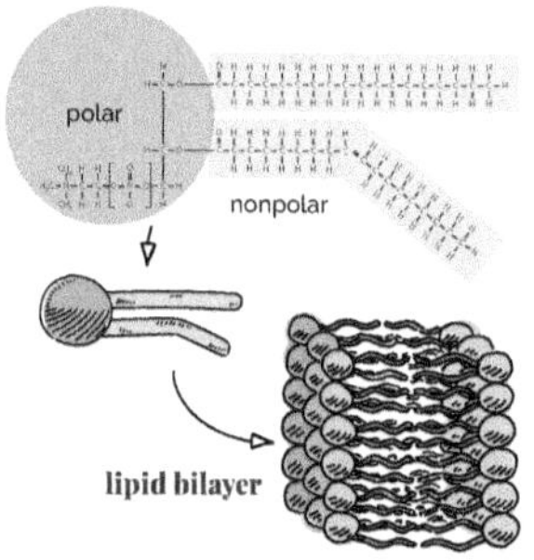

Phospholipids

Phospholipids are structurally similar to triglycerides. But instead of a glycerol head, the head of a phospholipid is a phosphate group. Instead of three fatty acid tails, it has only two. Most importantly though, unlike triglycerides, phospholipids are not completely nonpolar. The fatty acid tails are nonpolar, but the phosphate head is polar. This makes phospholipids *amphiphilic*, meaning that one end (the phosphate head) is attracted to water, but the other (the fatty acid tails) is not. This peculiar physical characteristic is what allows phospholipids to form lipid bilayer cell membranes (see left). The hydrophilic ("water loving") polar heads face outward from both sides of the bilayer, while the hydrophobic ("water fearing") tails face in toward the interior of the bilayer. As you can see, even something as "simple" as the boundary that separates a cell's insides from its environment is incredibly complex.

21.3 SECTION REVIEW

1. What are lipids?
2. Explain the difference between saturated and unsaturated fats.
3. How does the difference in saturation affect physical properties?
4. What is the basic structure of a steroid?
5. Describe at least one function for each of the three kinds of lipids described in this section.
6. Define *amphiphilic*.

524 Chapter 21

6. The term *amphiphilic* describes a molecule as being both "water loving" and "water hating." This characteristic occurs in a large molecule that has both a polar and a nonpolar end. *(p. 524)*

21.4 PROTEINS

Protein powders, protein bars, protein shakes—these are products that you can easily find in the health food section of your local grocery. But what exactly is protein, and why is it important? Proteins are versatile molecules in all living organisms. Various proteins form the basis for muscle, hair, blood cells, skin, spider webs, silk, enzymes, insulin, and even snake venom. They are essential nutrients, and they have many life-sustaining functions. Each protein polymer exhibits a unique and intricate three-dimensional architecture custom-made for its function.

What do proteins do for me?

QUESTIONS
- » What is a protein?
- » What is tertiary structure?
- » What is quaternary structure?
- » Why is the shape of a protein important?

TERMS
protein • amino acid • peptide bond

Amino Acids

Proteins are organic polymers made from hundreds, even thousands, of amino acids. Each **amino acid** molecule consists of a carbon atom bonded to an amine group (NH_2), a carboxyl group (COOH), a hydrogen atom, and a side chain, or *R-group*. It is the side chain that determines the identity of each amino acid. Though there are about five hundred naturally occurring amino acids, fewer than 5% have so far been found to make proteins.

The human body can synthesize twelve of the twenty amino acids that it needs. The other eight must come from a proper diet. The amino acids that cannot be manufactured by the body are called *essential amino acids*.

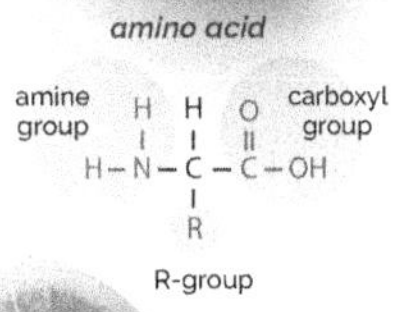

Polypeptide Chains

Amino acids join together when a hydrogen in the amine group of one amino acid reacts with the carboxyl group in another. It is a dehydration reaction and releases water. The bond that links the two amino acids is called a **peptide bond** (see below). Two amino acids bond to form a *dipeptide*. Aspartame (aspartyl-phenylalanine), a popular artificial sweetener, is a dipeptide. *Polypeptides* occur when three or more amino acids bond together in an unbranched chain.

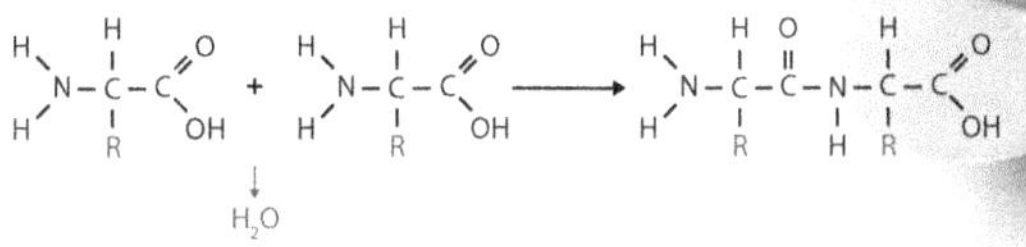

A finished protein molecule is much more than simply a chain of amino acids. In addition to this basic level of complexity, polypeptide chains can be folded, twisted, and combined with other chains to produce a fantastic variety of forms. Let's examine how this variety is produced.

Biochemistry 525

DIFFERENTIATED INSTRUCTION

Protein Structures

Direct students to create an **infographic** on the structures of proteins. They can draw the structures by hand, model them with modeling clay, or use a free 3D design website to create their illustrations. For more information on free 3D design websites, perform an internet search using the keywords "free 3D design."

SECTION 21.4 OVERVIEW

Essential Question

What do proteins do for me?

Objectives

» **21.4.1** Define *protein.*

» **21.4.2** Describe the formation and structure of proteins.

» **21.4.3** Explain the importance of the structure and shape of a protein molecule.

Resources

Web Link: Proteins

Lab 21B: *The Proof Is in the Jell-O*—Investigating Enzymes

ENGAGE

METABOLISM, CARBOHYDRATES, AND LIPIDS REVIEW

Lead students to do a two-minute **quick write** as a review of Sections 21.1–21.3. Have students write down all they can recall from the sections regarding the concepts of metabolism, carbohydrates, and lipids. Once they have finished, have them take turns sharing their response with a nearby peer. If time allows, select students to read their summary; then lead a quick review on the material, and dispel any misunderstandings.

INSTRUCT

FUNCTIONS OF PROTEINS

Guide students in creating a **graphic organizer** or **Sketchnotes** for Section 21.4. Write the following statements on the board and instruct students to create a graphic organizer or Sketchnotes that will indicate their responses.

1. What are the functions of proteins?
2. What determines a protein's function?
3. What are proteins made of?
4. Draw the main structure or backbone of a protein.
5. State and sketch the differences between the primary, secondary, tertiary, and quaternary structures of proteins.
6. What are enzymes and why are they important?
7. Why does denaturing of proteins occur?

PROTEINS

For a video with an animation about proteins and their structures and uses, visit TeacherToolsOnline.com. Under Additional Resources, click on Chapter 21 Web Links. Then click on *Proteins*.

PROTEIN STRUCTURE

Primary Structure

Any particular protein may consist of one or more polypeptide chains. The basic order of the amino acids in a polypeptide chain is called its *primary structure*.

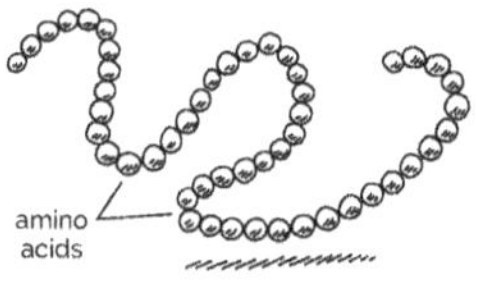

Even with a comparatively short chain, the number of possible different proteins is staggering. Using only the twenty amino acids typically found in living things, 1.1×10^{65} unique sequences of fifty amino acids can be formed.

Secondary Structure

The *secondary structure* of a protein is determined by the shape and polarity of its amino acids. Amino acids in one part of the chain can bond with other amino acids in another part. The most common secondary structures are *turns* (the chain bends back on itself), *alpha helixes* (α-helix), and *beta-sheets* (β-sheet).

An α-helix is a tight spiral of amino acids held in place by hydrogen bonds. A hydrogen in one amino acid forms a hydrogen bond with an oxygen of an amino acid four positions away. The side chains of each amino acid extend like spokes from the surface of the helix.

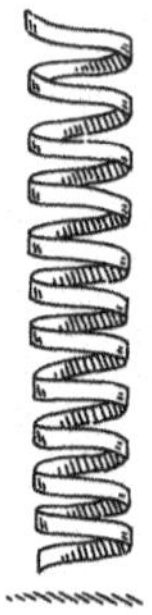

Another form of secondary structure, the β-sheet, results when hydrogen bonding occurs between adjacent polypeptide strands. These sheets have a slightly folded appearance, so they are sometimes referred to as β-pleated sheets.

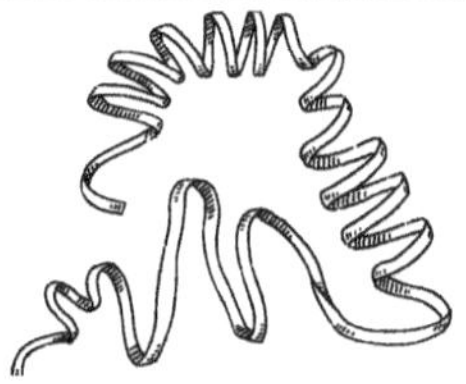

Tertiary Structure

An individual polypeptide may consist of many turns, helixes, and sheets, as well as regions with no specific structure, known as *random coils*, giving it a complex three-dimensional shape. This is known as its *tertiary structure*. At this point, the protein may be complete, or it may only be part of a larger structure, in which case it is called *a protein subunit*.

Quaternary Structure

Many proteins consist of two or more protein subunits fitted together to form a *protein complex*. Such a complex exhibits *quaternary structure*.

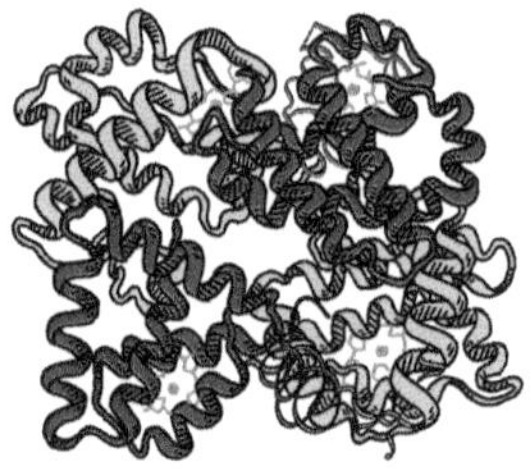

It is amazing that these intricate molecules derive most of their form from ordinary, but carefully arranged, hydrogen bonds. The structure truly is a masterpiece of art and engineering. Even more amazing, each protein's distinctive shape equips it to perform a unique function. For example, hemoglobin, the protein that carries oxygen in the bloodstream, consists of four interwoven chains. The shape of the protein provides perfectly formed crevices for oxygen molecules to nestle into.

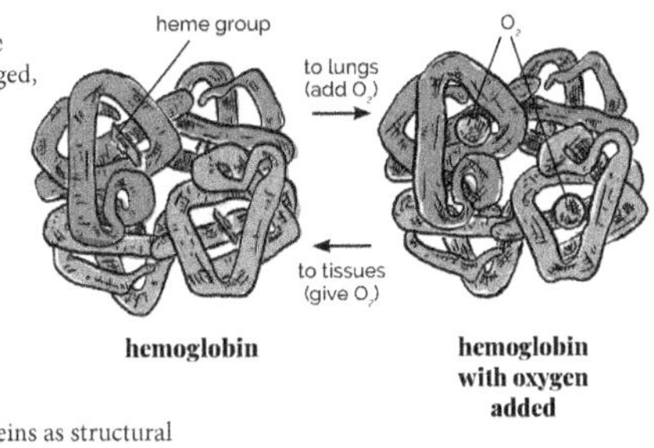

Enzymes

We've already mentioned the importance of proteins as structural molecules. Another critical role of proteins in living things is their function as organic catalysts called *enzymes*. Most cellular processes involve chemical reactions that would happen far too slowly without the assistance of enzymes. The exact shape of each enzyme normally allows it to catalyze only one specific reaction, so every cell requires an enormous number of enzymes just to maintain everyday function. Scientists know of thousands of enzyme-catalyzed reactions in cells. Without the assistance of these intricately designed chemical machines, life could not exist.

Denaturing Structure

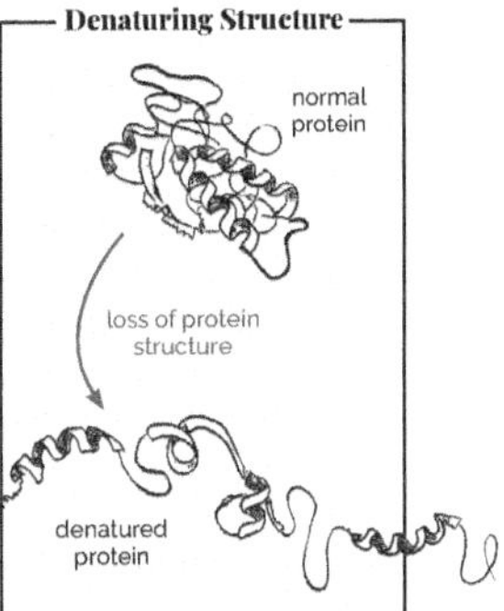

Denaturing

Considering their complexity and the relative weakness of hydrogen bonds compared with either covalent or ionic bonds, you might not be surprised to learn that proteins are not especially durable. Like radioactive elements, the duration of their existence is measured in half-lives, which can range anywhere from a few minutes to many years but averages only a few days. In living things, old, worn-out proteins are constantly being broken down and replaced in a process called *protein turnover*. A decrease in the rate of protein turnover is thought to be a contributing factor of the aging process.

Proteins can also "unwind" in the face of stresses, such as high heat, radiation, extreme salt concentrations, or the presence of particular chemicals. These stress agents cause proteins to lose their proper structure and thus the function that goes with it. Such a loss of protein structure is called *denaturing*. You can see the effect of denaturing when you grill a steak. As the meat cooks, its proteins unravel and its color changes from bright red to brown. As the steak cooks, its denaturing proteins absorb and reflect different wavelengths of visible light compared with the raw meat. Denaturing affects living things too. Stress agents can cause cellular proteins to work inefficiently or not at all. Left untreated, such conditions can lead to the death of an organism.

21.4 SECTION REVIEW

1. Define *protein*.
2. How are amino acids bonded together? What is this bond called?
3. In order from least to most complex, describe the types of structure found in proteins.
4. Why is the shape of a protein important?

21.4 REVIEW *ANSWERS*

1. A protein is an organic polymer consisting of one or more amino acid (polypeptide) chains. *(p. 525)*
2. Amino acids join when a hydrogen in the amine group of one amino acid reacts with the carboxyl group in another—a dehydration reaction. The resulting bond is a peptide bond. *(p. 525)*
3. Primary structure consists of the order of amino acids in a polypeptide chain. Secondary structure describes the turns, helixes, and sheets formed by the polypeptide. The three-dimensional sum of all the turns, helixes, sheets, and random coils is a polypeptide's tertiary structure. Quaternary structure describes the three-dimensional structure that results from combining two or more subunits. *(p. 526)*
4. The shape of a protein determines its function. A loss of proper shape (denaturing) can result in a loss of the protein's function. *(p. 527)*

FORCES THAT HOLD POLYPEPTIDES TOGETHER

Lead a **review** by asking students to state the types of bonds or forces that hold polypeptide chains in their distinctive shapes.

1. peptide bonds between amino acids
2. hydrogen bonds between atoms within a polypeptide chain
3. dipole-dipole forces between oppositely charged regions within a protein
4. dispersion forces

APPLY

LAB 21B: *THE PROOF IS IN THE JELL-O*

Once students have an understanding of the material in Section 21.4, they should be ready to work through Lab 21B.

ASSESS

TICKET OUT THE DOOR

As a **summarizing activity**, ask students to illustrate and briefly describe the four types of protein structures (see page 526).

SECTION 21.5 *OVERVIEW*

Essential Question

How do cells know how to do things?

Objectives

» **21.5.1** List the three parts of a nucleotide and describe their arrangement.

» **21.5.2** Describe how nucleic acids store information in cells.

» **21.5.3** Explain how information is transferred from the nucleus to other parts of cells.

» **21.5.4** Formulate a response to the theory of abiogenesis from a biblical worldview perspective. BWS

» **21.5.5** Apply an understanding of biochemistry to decide whether to follow a paleo diet. BWS

Resources

Ethics: Paleo Diets—Ancient Key to Modern Health? (p. 535)

Worldview Investigation: Abiogenesis

Web Link: Replication, Transcription, and Translation

ENGAGE

CHROMOSOMES, DNA, NUCLEIC ACIDS

Lead students through a review of biology with a **class discussion** and **concept map**. Put a picture of a chromosome on the board and have students recall what the image is. As you begin the lesson, create a concept map on the board with "chromosome" as the main topic, then select students to fill in the details. Ask the following questions to open the discussion on nucleic acids.

1. What is a chromosome made of? *(protein and DNA)*
2. What does a chromosome do? *(It carries hereditary information in the form of genes.)*
3. What is DNA? *(deoxyribonucleic acid)*
4. What makes up a strand of DNA? *(thousands of nucleotides)*
5. What is in a nucleotide? *(deoxyribose sugar, phosphate, and a nitrogenous base bonded together)*

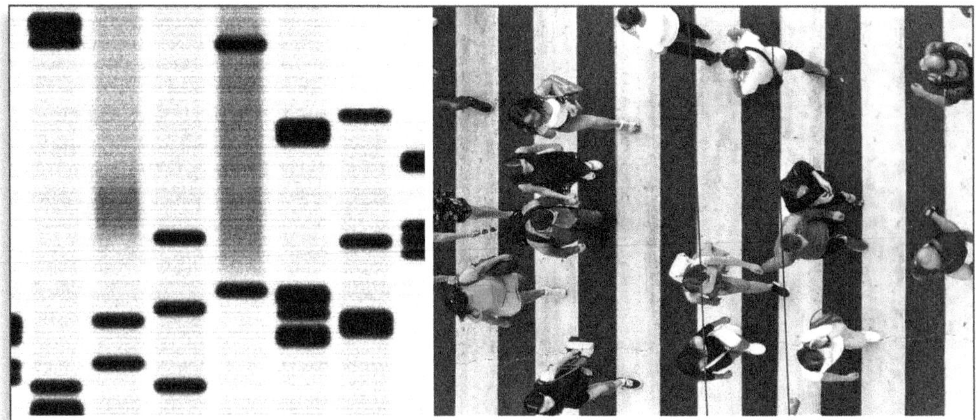

QUESTIONS

» What are nucleotides?

» How do nucleic acids store information?

» How does a cell's nucleus transmit information to other parts of the cell?

TERMS

nucleic acid • nucleotide

21.5 NUCLEIC ACIDS

When cells reproduce, genetic information is passed from the parent cell to the daughter cells on *chromosomes*. Human body cells contain forty-six of these long structures in their nuclei. A segment of a chromosome that carries the information that directs the production of specific polypeptide chain is called a *gene*. Each gene, in turn, is constructed of many *nucleotides*. A chain of nucleotides forms a **nucleic acid**.

How do cells know how to do things?

Each **nucleotide** in a nucleic acid consists of three parts: a five-carbon sugar, a phosphate group, and a ring-shaped, nitrogenous (nitrogen-containing) base (see left, below). Sugars and phosphate groups alternate to form a long chain that supports the bases much like the sides of a ladder support its rungs. In RNA (ribonucleic acid), the sugar is ribose, while in DNA (deoxyribonucleic acid), it is deoxyribose, which is a ribose with one less hydroxyl group.

There are five possible nitrogenous bases: adenine, cytosine, guanine, thymine, and uracil (often abbreviated as A, C, G, T, and U). DNA strands contain only adenine, cytosine, guanine, and thymine bases, while RNA strands have adenine, cytosine, guanine, and uracil. Of these bases, cytosine, thymine, and uracil are small, single-ringed structures; adenine and guanine are larger, double-ringed structures. It is the sequence of nucleotides in a nucleic acid that encodes information. Each amino acid in a protein is coded for by a sequence of three nucleotides known as a *codon*.

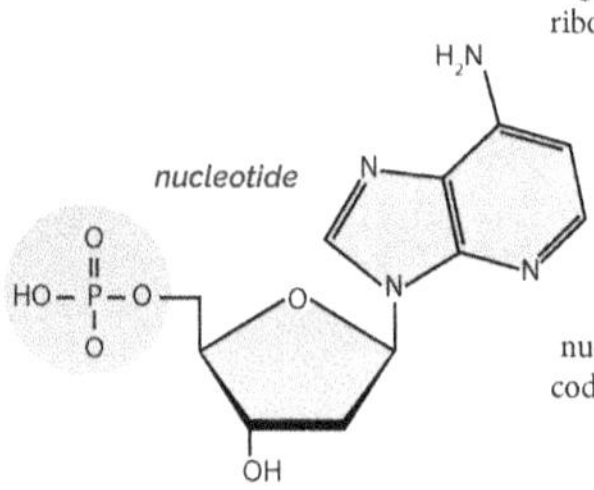

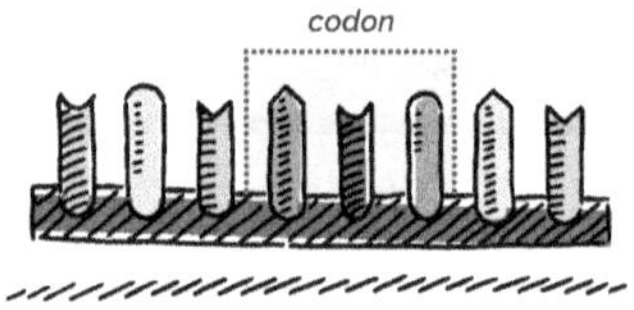

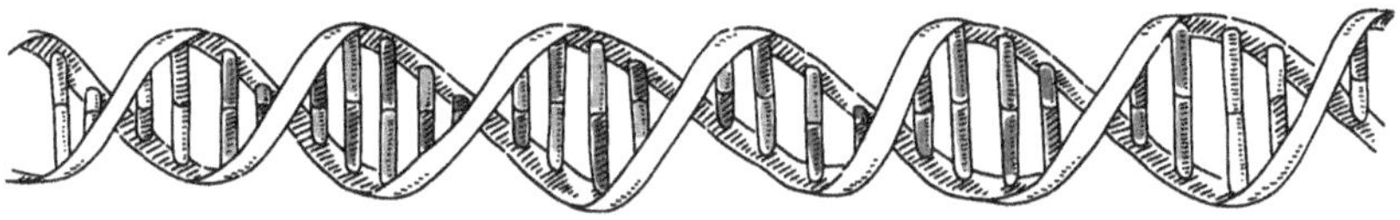

The nucleic acid DNA has been designed so that two strands coil around each other in a double helix. The backbones circle around the outside, and the bases pair together inside the coil. Large, double-ringed adenine bases pair with smaller thymine bases, while large guanine bases fit neatly next to smaller cytosine bases. Hydrogen bonds hold the complementary bases snugly in position.

double helix

When cells divide, a DNA strand reproduces by first unraveling with the help of enzymes. Each of the two resulting strands serves as a template, or pattern, for a new complementary chain. Complementary bases on the newly forming strand match the now-exposed bases of the old strand. When the process of replication is completed, two identical double-stranded DNA molecules result. One strand goes to each half of the dividing cell.

replication

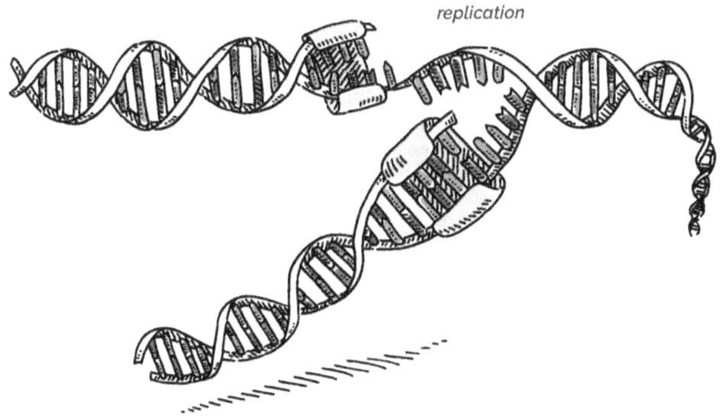

DIFFERENTIATED INSTRUCTION

DNA Design Project

Prompt students to create a **model** of DNA. They may choose the method by which to model (using an illustration, a clay model, or a molecular modeling program), but they must include the information regarding its composition (base pairs, bonds, and double helix). Additionally, have students illustrate or model the replication process of DNA.

TRANSCRIPTION AND TRANSLATION

Direct students to create a **comic strip** illustrating the activity occurring in transcription and translation. Be sure that students illustrate the process of both transcription and translation and show the molecules and structures involved.

REPLICATION, TRANSCRIPTION, AND TRANSLATION

For a video describing replication, transcription, and translation in further detail, visit TeacherToolsOnline.com. Under Additional Resources, click on Chapter 21 Web Links. Then click on *Replication, Transcription, and Translation*.

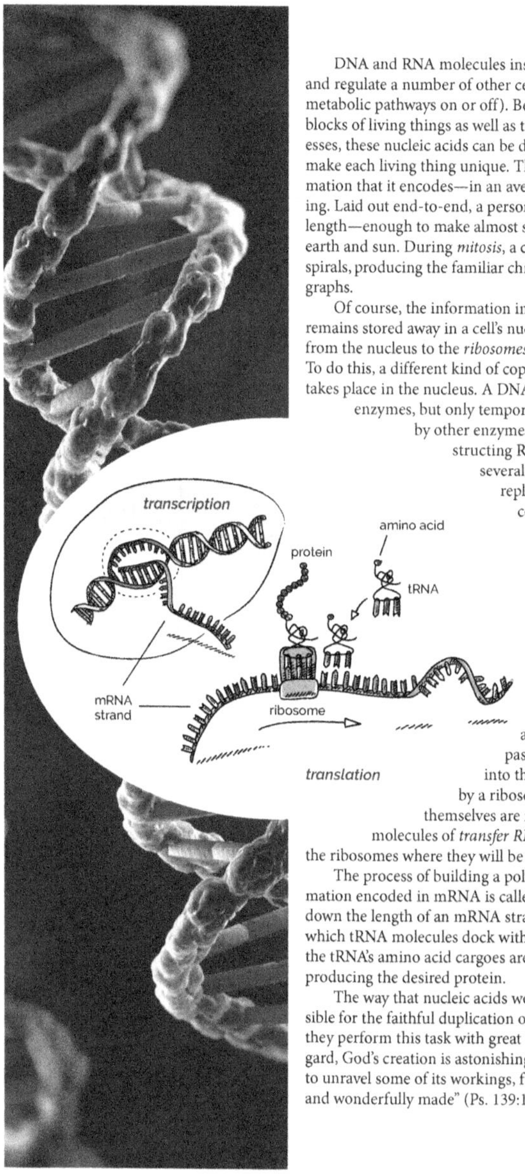

DNA and RNA molecules instruct cells on how to make proteins and regulate a number of other cell functions (such as turning certain metabolic pathways on or off). Because proteins are the building blocks of living things as well as the controllers of all biological processes, these nucleic acids can be described as sets of "blueprints" that make each living thing unique. The amount of DNA—and the information that it encodes—in an average adult human is truly astonishing. Laid out end-to-end, a person's DNA is roughly 2.0×10^{13} m in length—enough to make almost sixty-seven round trips between the earth and sun. During *mitosis*, a cell's DNA condenses into a series of spirals, producing the familiar chromosome structure seen in micrographs.

Of course, the information in DNA is not useful to a cell if it remains stored away in a cell's nucleus. The information must get from the nucleus to the *ribosomes*, where proteins are actually built. To do this, a different kind of copying process, called *transcription*, takes place in the nucleus. A DNA strand is once again "unzipped" by enzymes, but only temporarily. The unzipped portion is read by other enzymes and used as a template for constructing RNA. RNA is different from DNA in several ways. First, the thymine of DNA is replaced by uracil in RNA. Second, RNA consists of a single strand of nucleotides, unlike DNA's double helix, and it is not a copy of an entire chromosome. Instead, a strand of RNA carries a single gene—the information for building a particular protein. Third, RNA exists in multiple forms, and each form has a different function. *Messenger RNA* (mRNA) is the form that is transcribed in a cell's nucleus. It's a working copy of a gene. The mRNA passes through the nuclear membrane into the *cytoplasm* where it can be "read" by a ribosome. The protein-building ribosomes themselves are made of *ribosomal RNA* (rRNA). And molecules of *transfer RNA* (tRNA) transport amino acids to the ribosomes where they will be bonded to form a polypeptide.

The process of building a polypeptide on the basis of the information encoded in mRNA is called *translation*. As a ribosome moves down the length of an mRNA strand, its codons direct the order in which tRNA molecules dock with the ribosome. This ensures that the tRNA's amino acid cargoes are bonded in the correct sequence for producing the desired protein.

The way that nucleic acids work is marvelous. They are responsible for the faithful duplication of an organism's characteristics, and they perform this task with great precision and accuracy. In this regard, God's creation is astonishingly complex. We have been privileged to unravel some of its workings, further verifying that we are "fearfully and wonderfully made" (Ps. 139:14).

Worldview Conflict in Biochemistry

Scientists have conducted experiments in which they were able to produce amino acids under conditions thought to be those that existed on an ancient Earth. But does that prove that life got here without God? It takes much more than amino acids to make something alive. In fact, some people say, with good reason, that such experiments only show that intelligence and purposeful design are needed to synthesize even the most basic organic compounds.

The origin of the first cell is one of the biggest obstacles to the story of abiogenesis—the creation of living things from nonliving substances. As you read earlier, cells are incredibly complex. Each contains many thousands of complex chemicals, structures, and processes. The early experiments that produced amino acids did not, for example, produce nucleotides, and all life on Earth stores information in nucleic acids. Amino acids alone don't equal life.

Through the years, the difficulties inherent in the prevailing abiogenesis story caused some scientists to seek alternatives. One competing idea to help explain the origins of life is called *panspermia*. The panspermia hypothesis suggests that organic compounds are common throughout the universe and can travel between planets on comets and other space objects. You might be surprised to learn that some of the famous scientists mentioned in this textbook, such as Jöns Jacob Berzelius, Svante Arrhenius, and even Lord Kelvin have put some stock in this idea. But speculation about life arising from somewhere else other than Earth doesn't answer the question of ultimate origins—it just pushes it further back into "deep time."

The Bible tells us that God's creation of the world was a miracle. How would you answer someone who claims that experiments have proven that life got here without God? Use the worldview investigation box on the next page to gather some information and form your own response.

Biochemistry 531

WORLDVIEWS IN CONFLICT

The Miller-Urey experiment is an example of the many ways that a scientific model can be interpreted through the lens of a worldview. To the evolutionist, this experiment was a triumph of evolutionary theory and a step toward understanding how life came to be. To the creationist, it proved that delicately balanced conditions and a high degree of intelligence are required to create just a small component of life. If a similar experiment were to one day create life in a test tube, it would show that it takes decades of research, hours of thinking and planning, billions of dollars, and the genius of generations of scientists to do what God did with His spoken Word alone.

WORLDVIEW INVESTIGATION: ABIOGENESIS

Appendix K includes a reproducible rubric to assess the worldview investigation activity.

ASSESS

TICKET OUT THE DOOR

As a **summarizing activity**, ask students to contrast nucleotides, DNA, and RNA using a table. Areas of comparison would be repeating units and the function of the compound in living things along with its general shape.

21.5 REVIEW *ANSWERS*

1. A DNA nucleotide consists of a sugar (deoxyribose), a phosphate group, and a nitrogenous base (either cytosine, guanine, adenine, or thymine). Alternating sugars and phosphates form the sides of a DNA strand, and paired nitrogenous bases form the "rungs." *(p. 528)*
2. DNA nucleotides contain deoxyribose sugar, while RNA nucleotides contain ribose sugar. In addition, DNA nucleotides can contain thymine, but RNA nucleotides contain uracil instead of thymine. *(p. 528)*
3. Each sequence of three nucleotides in a nucleic acid, that is, a codon, codes for a specific amino acid, and the order of the codons determines the sequence of amino acids in a protein. *(p. 528)*

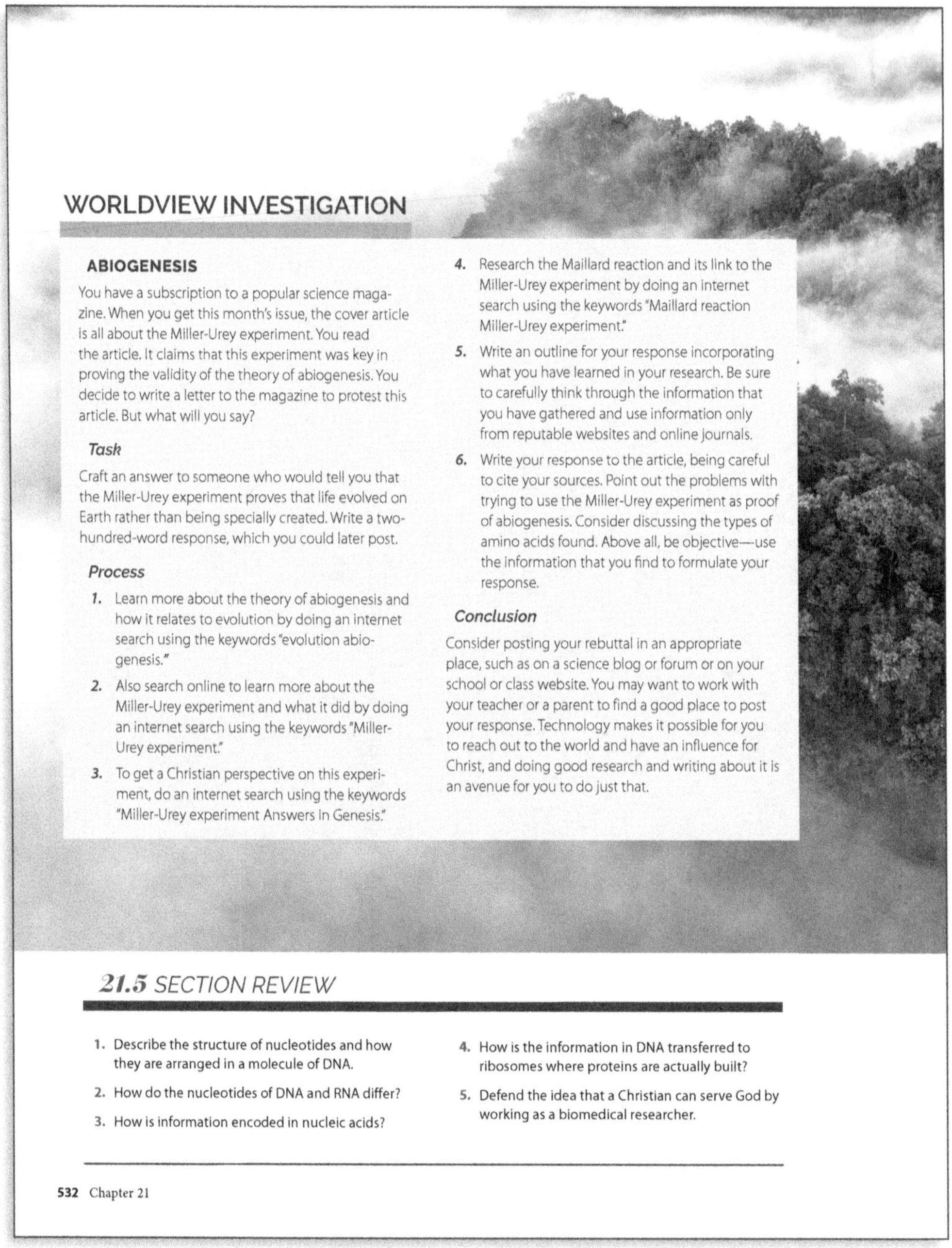

WORLDVIEW INVESTIGATION

ABIOGENESIS

You have a subscription to a popular science magazine. When you get this month's issue, the cover article is all about the Miller-Urey experiment. You read the article. It claims that this experiment was key in proving the validity of the theory of abiogenesis. You decide to write a letter to the magazine to protest this article. But what will you say?

Task

Craft an answer to someone who would tell you that the Miller-Urey experiment proves that life evolved on Earth rather than being specially created. Write a two-hundred-word response, which you could later post.

Process

1. Learn more about the theory of abiogenesis and how it relates to evolution by doing an internet search using the keywords "evolution abiogenesis."
2. Also search online to learn more about the Miller-Urey experiment and what it did by doing an internet search using the keywords "Miller-Urey experiment."
3. To get a Christian perspective on this experiment, do an internet search using the keywords "Miller-Urey experiment Answers in Genesis."
4. Research the Maillard reaction and its link to the Miller-Urey experiment by doing an internet search using the keywords "Maillard reaction Miller-Urey experiment."
5. Write an outline for your response incorporating what you have learned in your research. Be sure to carefully think through the information that you have gathered and use information only from reputable websites and online journals.
6. Write your response to the article, being careful to cite your sources. Point out the problems with trying to use the Miller-Urey experiment as proof of abiogenesis. Consider discussing the types of amino acids found. Above all, be objective—use the information that you find to formulate your response.

Conclusion

Consider posting your rebuttal in an appropriate place, such as on a science blog or forum or on your school or class website. You may want to work with your teacher or a parent to find a good place to post your response. Technology makes it possible for you to reach out to the world and have an influence for Christ, and doing good research and writing about it is an avenue for you to do just that.

21.5 SECTION REVIEW

1. Describe the structure of nucleotides and how they are arranged in a molecule of DNA.
2. How do the nucleotides of DNA and RNA differ?
3. How is information encoded in nucleic acids?
4. How is the information in DNA transferred to ribosomes where proteins are actually built?
5. Defend the idea that a Christian can serve God by working as a biomedical researcher.

532 Chapter 21

4. The information in DNA is first transcribed to a molecule of mRNA. The mRNA passes through the nuclear membrane into the cytoplasm where it can be read by a ribosome. *(p. 530)*
5. The Bible commands us to love others as ourselves (Mark 12:31). Researching new ways to relieve pain or treat disease demonstrates compassion for others and concern for alleviating their suffering, just as Christ demonstrated compassion and healed people in need.

21 CHAPTER REVIEW

Chapter Summary

TERMS
biochemistry
metabolism
catabolism
anabolism
polymer

21.1 CHEMISTRY OF LIFE

- Biochemistry is an area of study within general chemistry that focuses on the chemistry of life, including genetics, metabolism, cellular respiration, and other cellular functions.
- Metabolism includes all the chemical processes that take place within cells, both catabolic and anabolic.
- Catabolic processes break larger molecules into smaller particles. Anabolic processes build larger molecules from smaller particles. Often these both occur in cyclical cellular processes.
- Some compounds produced by anabolic processes are polymers, large molecules made of repeating smaller subunits.

21.2 CARBOHYDRATES

- Carbohydrates are macromolecules consisting of carbon, hydrogen, and oxygen and are categorized as sugar, starch, or fiber.
- Carbohydrates are sources of energy and structure in living things.
- Carbohydrates may be simple sugars (monosaccharides), two simple sugars combined (disaccharides), or polymers of many sugars (polysaccharides).
- Starch and glycogen are important polysaccharides found in plants and animals, respectively.

TERMS
carbohydrate
monosaccharide
disaccharide
polysaccharide

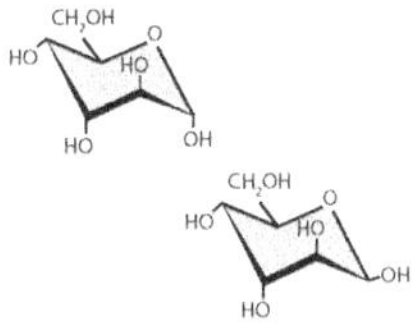

TERMS
lipid
fat
oil
steroid
phospholipid

21.3 LIPIDS

- Lipids are a group of compounds that are insoluble in water, including fats, oils, waxes, and steroids.
- Fatty acids are the simplest lipids. Three of these long-chain carboxylic acids can link to a glycerol backbone to form a triglyceride.
- Fats are saturated lipids with high intermolecular forces that exist as solids at room temperature. Oils remain in the liquid state because they are unsaturated and have lower intermolecular forces than saturated fats.
- Steroids are lipids that contain carbon ring structures. Cholesterol is a well-known steroid.
- Phospholipids are amphiphilic lipids with two fatty acid tails. The lipid bilayer of cell membranes is built in large measure from phospholipids.

CHAPTER 21 REVIEW ANSWERS

Recalling Facts

1. catabolism; anabolism *(p. 515)*
2. Chirality indicates the left- or right-handedness of a molecule. It indicates variations in the structure of the molecule. *(p. 518)*
3. energy storage, energy source, and structural support *(p. 520)*
4. energy, vitamin transport, hormone production, body cushioning, nerve insulation, formation of cell membranes, chemical signaling (Accept any three.) *(p. 523)*
5. an amine group, a carboxyl group, and a side chain (or R-group) *(p. 525)*
6. An enzyme is an organic catalyst that is critical for most biochemical processes. *(p. 527)*
7. A nucleotide is the building block of a nucleic acid. Each nucleotide consists of a five-carbon sugar, a phosphate group, and a nitrogenous base. *(p. 528)*
8. DNA stores the information needed for making proteins in cells. *(pp. 529–30)*

Understanding Concepts

9. It is both. Since the mouse's cells, which are living tissue, synthesize the protein, the study of the process is an example of biochemistry. Many of the chemical substances involved in these processes are organic compounds, and so it is also an example of organic chemistry. *(p. 515)*
10. Unlike alkanes, carbohydrates contain oxygen in addition to carbon and hydrogen. *(p. 517)*

11. a. a sugar composed of only one sugar unit; glucose, fructose (Accept one.)

b. a sugar composed of two sugar units; maltose, lactose, sucrose (Accept one.)

c. a sugar composed of three or more sugar units; starch, glycogen, cellulose (Accept one.) *(all pp. 517, 519–20)*

12. Cellulose and glycogen are both polymers of glucose, but the bonds that connect their glucose units are oriented differently. The glucose units in glycogen are aligned with each other, while in cellulose the glucose units alternate directions. Humans cannot derive nutritional value from cellulose because of its bond orientation. *(p. 520)*

13. Glycogen is a highly branched polysaccharide that forms an energy reserve in humans and animals. *(p. 520)*

14. Termites can eat wood because they have the enzymes needed to break the bonds of cellulose. (The enzymes are supplied by microorganisms in their gut.) *(p. 520)*

15. A fat has saturated (single-bond) chains with relatively high intermolecular forces and is solid at room temperature. An oil has unsaturated (double-bond) chains with relatively low intermolecular forces and is liquid at room temperature. *(pp. 522–23)*

16. Esters form when the single-bonded oxygen of a carboxyl group in a carboxylic acid bonds with the hydroxyl group of an alcohol. Fats and oils form when the carboxyl group of a fatty acid combines with one of the hydroxyl groups of glycerol. *(pp. 522–23)*

17. Steroids are not esters like other lipids, and they all have three six-carbon rings and one five-carbon ring instead of chains like other lipids. *(p. 523)*

18. A peptide bond forms when a hydrogen in the amine group of one amino acid reacts with the –OH group of a carboxyl group in another. It is a dehydration reaction and releases water. *(p. 525)*

19. Polysaccharides are polymers of sugar units; polypeptides are polymers of amino acids. *(pp. 520, 525)*

20. amino acid, alpha helix, protein subunit *(p. 526)*

21. Yes. The polypeptide chains can be folded and clustered together to form a protein. *(p. 526)*

21 CHAPTER REVIEW

Chapter Summary

21.4 AMINO ACIDS AND PROTEINS

- Proteins are large, organic polymers built from amino acids. They are essential for life because they provide structure, act as hormones, and serve as enzymes to control the rate of biochemical reactions.
- Amino acids link through peptide bonds to form polypeptide chains. A finished protein consists of one or more of these chains.
- The function of a protein is determined by its composition and resulting shape, which is determined by bonding between different amino acids within its polypeptide chains. A protein subunit normally contains turns, alpha helixes, beta sheets, and random coils.
- Heat, radiation, toxic chemicals, or other stresses can cause proteins to lose their shape, or denature.

TERMS
protein
amino acid
peptide bond

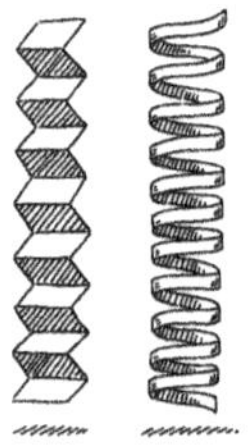

TERMS
nucleic acid
nucleotide

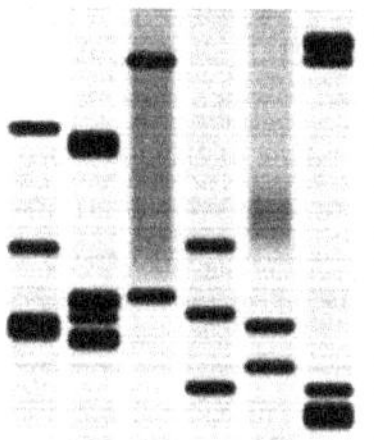

21.5 NUCLEIC ACIDS

- The nucleic acids DNA and RNA are similar in structure and play related but unique roles in living things. DNA stores hereditary information, and RNA uses that code to assemble proteins.
- A chromosome is a long strand of DNA within a cell's nucleus that contains genes. Each gene, constructed of many nucleotides, directs the production of a particular polypeptide.
- RNA exists in multiple forms: mRNA carries genetic information from the nucleus to the cytoplasm, rRNA forms the structure of ribosomes, and tRNA transfers amino acids to the ribosome-mRNA complex for the purpose of synthesizing proteins.

Chapter Review Questions

RECALLING FACTS

1. Which type of metabolic process breaks down substances? Which process builds larger molecules from smaller substances?
2. What does the term *chirality* describe about molecules?
3. List three major functions of carbohydrates.
4. List three functions of lipids in living things.
5. What are the three parts of an amino acid bonded to a central carbon atom?
6. What are enzymes, and why are they important?
7. What is a nucleotide, and what is it composed of?
8. What is the function of DNA?

UNDERSTANDING CONCEPTS

9. A scientist is studying the synthesis of a particular protein in laboratory mice. Is this an example of organic chemistry or biochemistry? Explain.
10. Like many alkanes, carbohydrates serve as an important fuel source. Why are alkanes and carbohydrates not classified together?
11. Describe what is meant by each of the following terms, and give one example of each.
    a. monosaccharide
    b. disaccharide
    c. polysaccharide

22. Yes. The information given is correct for DNA. In RNA, however, thymine is replaced by uracil. *(p. 528)*

23. 333; A codon, the code for a particular amino acid, consists of three nucleotides, thus the maximum possible number of amino acids is $999 \div 3 = 333$. *(p. 528)*

24. a. lipid

b. carbohydrate

c. protein

d. nucleic acid

e. carbohydrate *(all pp. 517–30)*

Critical Thinking

25. No. Photosynthesis and digestion are not part of a metabolic cycle because they take place in different organisms. Photosynthesis and cellular respiration, not digestion, can be thought of as parts of a metabolic cycle. *(p. 516)*

26. Choice *d*; A mature oak tree, including its trunk, branches, and leaves, is made in large measure of cellulose. Wood fibers are an excellent fuel source—just not for humans. *(p. 520)*

27. The secondary and tertiary structures of polypeptides are a result of bonding between different parts of the molecule. The longer the polypeptide, the greater its potential for having a variety of structures. *(p. 526)*

12. How are cellulose and glycogen similar? How are they different? How does the difference between cellulose and glycogen affect their nutritional value to humans?
13. Briefly describe the structure and function of glycogen.
14. Why can termites eat wood but humans cannot?
15. What is the difference between a fat and an oil molecule?
16. Explain how fats and oils are esters.
17. What distinguishes steroids from other lipids?
18. Describe how a peptide bond forms.
19. Polysaccharides and polypeptides are both polymers. What is the difference between them?
20. Rank the following in order from least to most complex: alpha helix, amino acid, protein subunit.
21. Can a protein consist of more than one polypeptide? Explain.
22. You're proofreading a friend's report on nucleic acids. The report states that nucleic acids contain the nucleotides adenine, thymine, guanine, and cytosine. Does the report need correction? Defend your answer.
23. A gene consists of 999 nucleotides, not including those that tell a ribosome when to start and stop synthesizing a polypeptide. What is the maximum number of amino acids that could be found in the corresponding polypeptide? Explain.
24. Classify each of the following compounds as either a carbohydrate, lipid, protein, or nucleic acid.
    a. cholesterol
    b. gulose
    c. hemoglobin
    d. tRNA
    e. starch

CRITICAL THINKING

25. Your study partner says that photosynthesis and digestion are both part of a metabolic cycle. Is he correct? Explain.
26. Which of the following is the best source for carbohydrates? Defend your answer.
    a. sugar beet
    b. lean cut of beef
    c. stalk of wheat
    d. mature oak tree
27. Why would you expect the complexity of a protein's shape to be a function of the length(s) of its subunits?
28. As in humans, fish transport oxygen in their blood via a carrier molecule called hemoglobin—a protein. Well-oxygenated fish blood appears bright red. In the presence of elevated levels of toxic nitrite, fish blood takes on a dark-brown color. The condition is known as "brown blood disease" in the aquaculture industry. On the basis of what you have learned in this chapter, suggest a mechanism by which brown blood disease occurs.
29. During DNA replication, several nucleotides are removed from a particular sequence. Assuming that this mutation is passed on to an organism's offspring, how might the organism be affected?

Use the ethics box below to answer Question 30.

30. Use the ethics triad from Chapter 1 and the strategy modeled for you in Chapter 3 to formulate a four-paragraph biblical position on the question of paleo diets. Be sure to address each leg of the triad: biblical principles, biblical outcomes, and biblical motivations. In the last paragraph, formulate your own position on the issue.

ethics

PALEO DIETS—ANCIENT KEY TO MODERN HEALTH?

Paleo dieting is currently very popular. Paleo diets are typically based primarily on eating lean meat, fish, fruits, and vegetables while excluding carbohydrates, dairy, and processed foods. But why exactly is a paleo diet called *paleo* in the first place? And is there a biblical justification for eating paleo?

BROWN BLOOD DISEASE

Brown blood disease is the colloquial name for nitrite poisoning, an ever-present danger in the crowded conditions found in aquaculture facilities. For more information, conduct an internet search using the keywords "brown blood disease."

28. Since well-oxygenated fish blood is red, brown blood must indicate a lack of oxygen. Certain chemicals are known to denature proteins. It is likely, then, that in the presence of nitrite, hemoglobin in the fish's blood denatures, hindering its ability to carry oxygen, resulting in the brown appearance. *(p. 527)*

DELETION MUTATIONS (QUESTION 29)

The mutation described in Question 29 is a deletion mutation, a type of frameshift mutation, which students should be familiar with from their study of biology. For more information on frameshift mutations, see page 163 of BJU Press *Biology* 5th Edition.

29. If nucleotides are removed from a sequence, a different amino acid will likely be coded for, affecting the sequence of amino acids in a polypeptide. The new polypeptide may not have the same function as the original. If the affected polypeptide serves a critical function, the organism may be adversely affected or even killed.

ETHICS: PALEO DIETS—ANCIENT KEY TO MODERN HEALTH?

Appendix L includes a reproducible rubric to assess the ethics essay.

30. Answers will vary. The Creation Mandate of Genesis 1:28 can be considered to extend to our own bodies, just as it does to the rest of creation. Our bodies should be recognized as a gift from God, useful for service both to Him and for loving our neighbor. Seen in that context, it should be recognized that healthy eating is desirable for keeping our bodies as fit as possible. A paleo diet can include the essential nutrients described in Chapter 21, and the health hazards of some foods proscribed by paleo dieting are in some instances well documented.

If the biblical principle just cited is ignored, our bodies can be adversely affected by a broad range of food-related disorders that can lead to our being less useful for service. Obedience to the Creation Mandate and the command to love my neighbor should lead the believer to actively engage in healthy eating habits. A paleo dieting plan can be included as part of an overall health and fitness regimen.

By following a paleo diet as part of a strategy for maintaining good health, I can demonstrate a reverence for God as shown by my obedience to His commands. I can also show love and concern for my neighbor by looking to keep myself healthy for useful service. It should be recognized, however, that the concept of paleo dieting, sometimes called the "caveman diet," is based on a naturalistic interpretation of history, not on any biblical grounds. So while Christians may choose to eat a paleo diet, it is probably unwise to be dogmatic about any particular eating strategy, especially since our ideas about what constitutes a "healthy diet" tend to change over time. Paleo may be "in" today but may be "out" tomorrow and replaced by a newer dietary fad.

CHAPTER 22 *OBJECTIVES*

- Explain what determines the stability of atomic nuclei.
- Analyze the nuclear decay of various nuclei.
- Evaluate nuclear reactions as a source of electrical energy.
- Model radioactive decay.

OVERVIEW

Chapter 22 has enrichment material that will challenge students to think on a different level of chemistry. Nuclear chemistry is different from other branches of chemistry because of the transformation of one element into another. This area of chemistry overlaps significantly with nuclear physics. Radon detection, radiation therapy, x-rays, nuclear power plants, and nuclear waste disposal are just a few examples of how nuclear chemistry affects modern life.

22.1 INSIDE THE NUCLEUS

- *Discovery in the Dark*
- *Nuclear Stability*
- *Energy Changes and Nuclear Changes*
- *Measuring Radiation*

22.2 NUCLEAR DECAY

- *Radioactive Decay*
- *Predicting Types of Decay*
- *Radioactive Decay Series*
- *Half-Life*

22.3 USING NUCLEAR CHEMISTRY

- *Nuclear Reactions*
- *Fission*
- *Fusion*
- *Using Nuclear Chemistry to Solve Problems*

LAB ACTIVITIES

Lab 22A: *It's Only a Matter of Time*—Students determine the half-life and decay of radioactive materials.

Lab 22B: *Atomic Asteroids*—Students investigate mass defect and the energy released in a nuclear reaction.

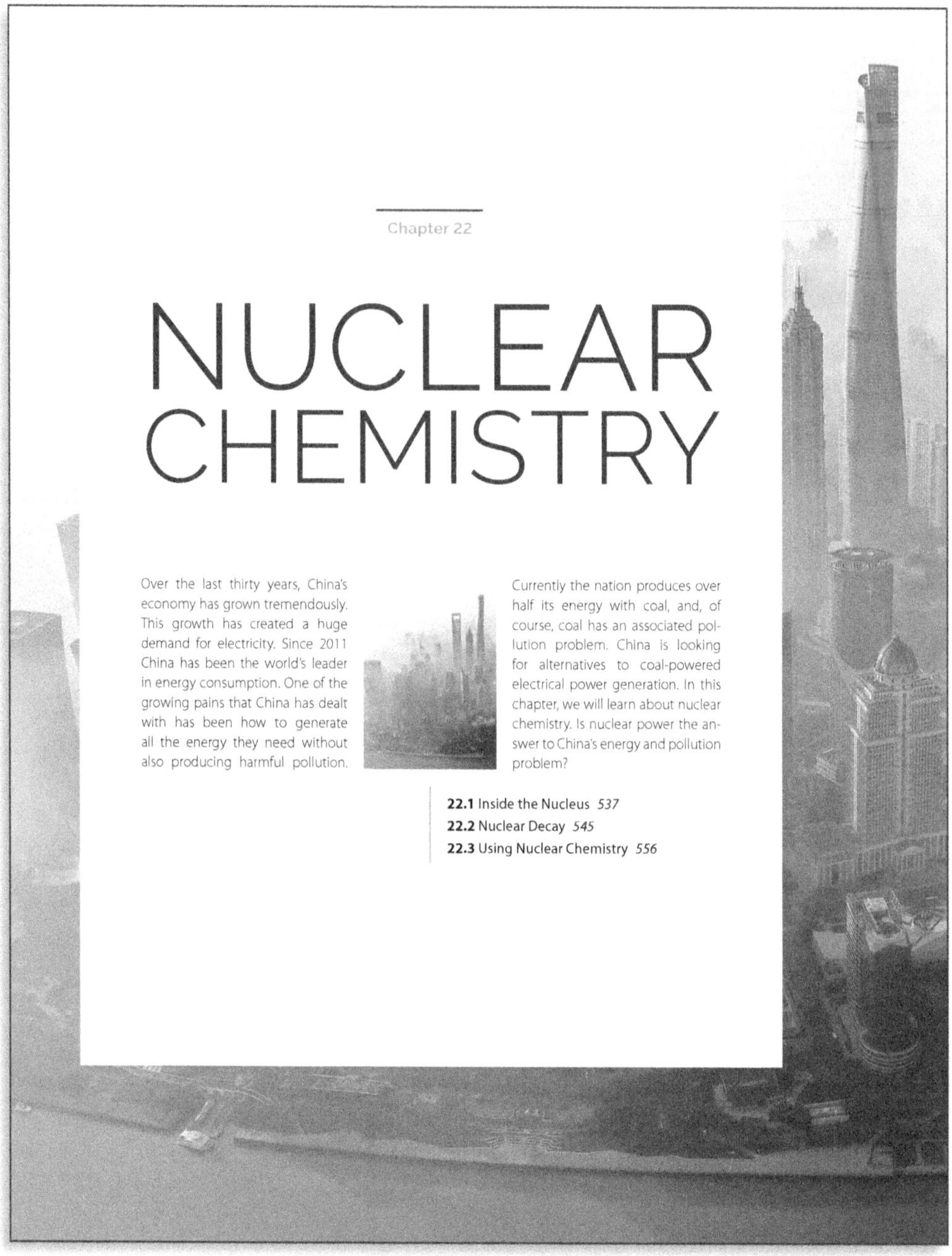

Chapter 22

NUCLEAR CHEMISTRY

Over the last thirty years, China's economy has grown tremendously. This growth has created a huge demand for electricity. Since 2011 China has been the world's leader in energy consumption. One of the growing pains that China has dealt with has been how to generate all the energy they need without also producing harmful pollution. Currently the nation produces over half its energy with coal, and, of course, coal has an associated pollution problem. China is looking for alternatives to coal-powered electrical power generation. In this chapter, we will learn about nuclear chemistry. Is nuclear power the answer to China's energy and pollution problem?

All around the world major cities such as Shanghai, China, shown in the Chapter opener, are covered with a blanket of pollution. With increasing populations, scientists are continually challenged with creating solutions for eradicating pollution while still providing the energy necessary to run densely populated cities.

22.1 INSIDE THE NUCLEUS

Discovery in the Dark

In the previous chapters, the chemistry you studied involved only the atom's valence electrons. But *nuclear chemistry* is concerned with changes in an atom's nucleus—its protons and neutrons—that affect the atom's identity and release radiation. But what causes radiation? How are nuclear changes different from the ones that happen in chemical reactions? Could these mysterious rays hold the key to addressing China's energy and pollution problems? The answers to all these questions lie inside the nucleus.

Why do some atoms decay?

QUESTIONS

- What is radioactivity?
- Why are some atoms stable, but not others?
- How can we measure amounts of radiation?

TERMS

nuclear radiation • radioactivity • nuclide • nucleon • radioisotope • strong nuclear force • band of stability • magic number • mass defect • nuclear binding energy

THE DISCOVERY OF

Radioactivity

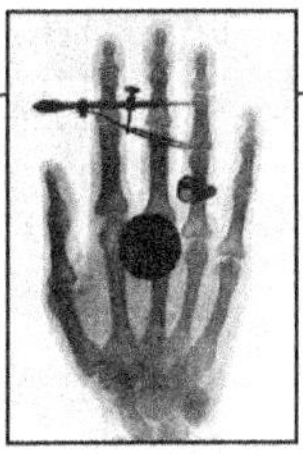

In 1895 German physicist Wilhelm Röntgen discovered x-rays while working with vacuum tubes. Röntgen was awarded the 1901 Nobel Prize in Physics for his discovery.

In 1896 French physicist Henri Becquerel made an unexpected and remarkable discovery. While researching how certain crystals phosphoresce, or glow, after being exposed to light, he wondered whether uranium salts would emit x-rays after being exposed to sunlight. He discovered that uranium salts naturally emitted x-rays even without being exposed to sunlight. Other scientists went on to discover that these atoms emitted energy and particles in order to become more stable. The energy and particles emitted from unstable nuclei are called **nuclear radiation**.

SECTION 22.1 OVERVIEW

Essential Question

Why do some atoms decay?

Objectives

» **22.1.1** Define *radioactivity.*

» **22.1.2** Summarize the progression of scientists' understanding of radioactivity.

» **22.1.3** Determine whether a given nuclide is stable.

» **22.1.4** Relate the mass defect of a nucleus to its binding energy.

» **22.1.5** List instruments used to measure radiation.

Resource

Serving as a Nuclear Engineer: Harnessing the Power of the Atom

ENGAGE

NUCLEAR CHEMISTRY

Open the chapter with a **class poll** by asking, "Do you think that there is more silver or uranium in the earth's crust?" (Uranium is actually forty times more abundant than silver!)

Use **discussion questions** to activate prior learning.

1. Can you recall the location of uranium on the periodic table? *(the f block; see Chapter 6)*
2. In what series is it located? *(the actinide series; see Chapter 6)*
3. What are some properties of elements in the actinide series? *(Elements in this series consist of many radioactive isotopes that are produced artificially and are very unstable and radioactive. See Chapter 6.)*
4. Considering the word *nuclear*, what part of the atom do you think nuclear chemistry involves? *(the nucleus—specifically the protons and neutrons)*

INSTRUCT

THE DISCOVERY OF RADIOACTIVITY

Guide students in creating a **graphic organizer** for the scientists responsible for the discoveries of radioactivity (pp. 537–38). Be sure that students state the year for each discovery and describe what each scientist discovered and how he did it.

THE DISCOVERY OF

Radioactivity

Polish physicist Marie Sklodowska Curie and her husband Pierre Curie, a French chemist, used Becquerel's findings to explore radiation. All three shared a Nobel Prize in Physics in 1903 for the discovery of radioactivity. It was the Curies who later coined the term **radioactivity** to describe the process by which unstable nuclei emit nuclear radiation to become more stable. Radioactivity is also referred to as *radioactive decay*. The Curies worked with uranium ore to discover the elements polonium and radium. Marie Curie was awarded a second Nobel Prize, this time in Chemistry for this work, making her the first person to earn two Nobel Prizes.

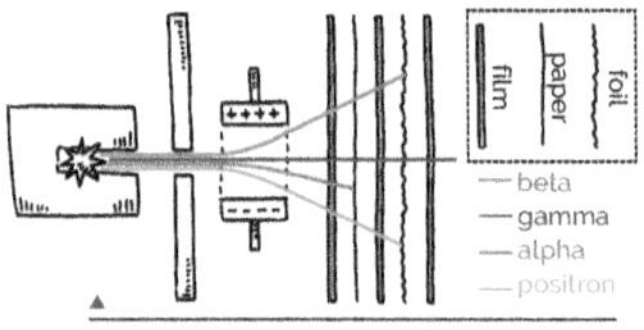

Experiments displayed the charges and relative masses of the particles produced by nuclear radiation.

British physicist Ernest Rutherford continued the research in the field by analyzing the energy and particles emitted during radioactivity. He passed these emissions through powerful electric and magnetic fields. By charting the deflections of the radiation, he came to conclusions about the masses and charges of the different types of radiation. He and later scientists who investigated radiation discovered four types: two that consisted of positively charged particles (alpha particles and positrons), one with a negative charge (beta particles), and one with no charge at all (gamma rays).

538 Chapter 22

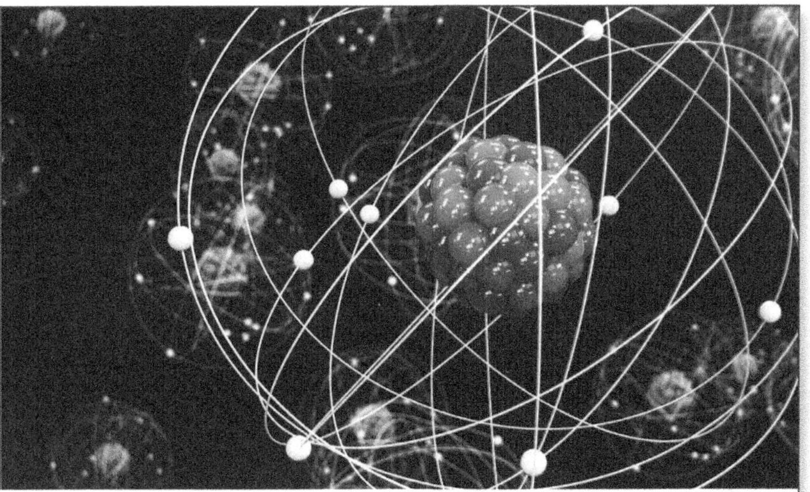

Nuclear Stability

As you learned in Chapter 4, an atom's incredibly dense nucleus contains most of the atom's mass. It is so dense that a sphere of nuclear material the size of a golf ball would have a mass of over 9.3 *trillion* kilograms!

Also in Chapter 4 you learned that atoms with identical atomic numbers but different mass numbers are called isotopes. When discussing nuclear characteristics of isotopes, we call them nuclides. Isotopes and nuclides are identical, but the term *nuclide* emphasizes the composition of the nucleus, while *isotope* emphasizes the entire atom. Therefore a **nuclide** is a unique atom of an element with a specific set of protons and neutrons and a specific energy state. Since they are found in the nucleus, protons and neutrons are collectively called **nucleons**. We represent nuclides using isotope notation, which you used in Chapter 4. An isotope that emits nuclear radiation is called a **radioisotope**.

$$^{A}_{Z}X$$

Nuclei contain protons packed close together. Since protons are positively charged, they repel each other, and one would expect them to fly apart. Yet most nuclei are stable and exist for millennia without changing. At the same time, other nuclei are so unstable that they last for only a fraction of a second before changing into another element entirely.

So what determines whether a nucleus will stay together or not? During the development of the quantum model, physicists discovered that the **strong nuclear force** holds nucleons together. This force is a field force that is effective only over small distances (less than 10^{-15} m). Neutrons, having a neutral charge, do not repel each other, nor do they repel the positively charged protons. The strong nuclear force allows neutrons and protons to interact in a way that balances the electrostatic repulsion between the protons. If the strong nuclear force is strong enough, the nucleus will be stable.

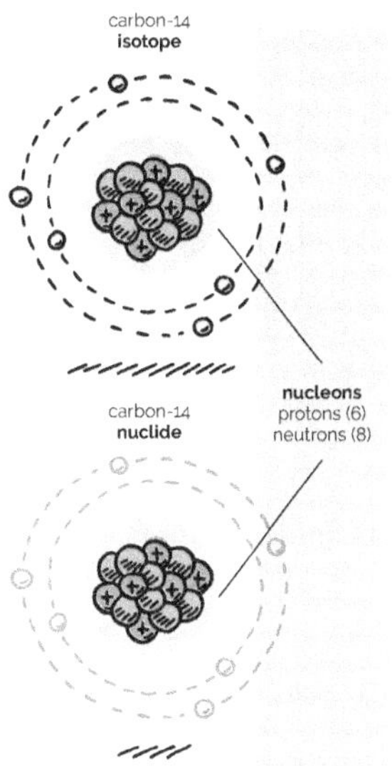

ELECTRONS DON'T MATTER

Emphasize that nuclear reactions occur independently of electron configuration. This fact separates Chapter 22 from the ideas discussed in other chapters in this book.

WHAT IS A FIELD FORCE?

A field force is a force vector that exists at every point in a field. A vector is simply a quantity that requires two pieces of information to describe it—a magnitude and a direction. For example, think of the force of gravity, which on Earth acts on objects in a downward direction at a magnitude of 9.81 m/s^2. Gravity acts on your body at every possible point; there is no point on your body that escapes its effect!

UNIVERSAL FORCES

The strong nuclear force is one of four foundational forces in the universe. The other three are the weak nuclear force, gravity, and electromagnetism. The strong nuclear force holds matter together, and the weak nuclear force is involved in nuclear decay.

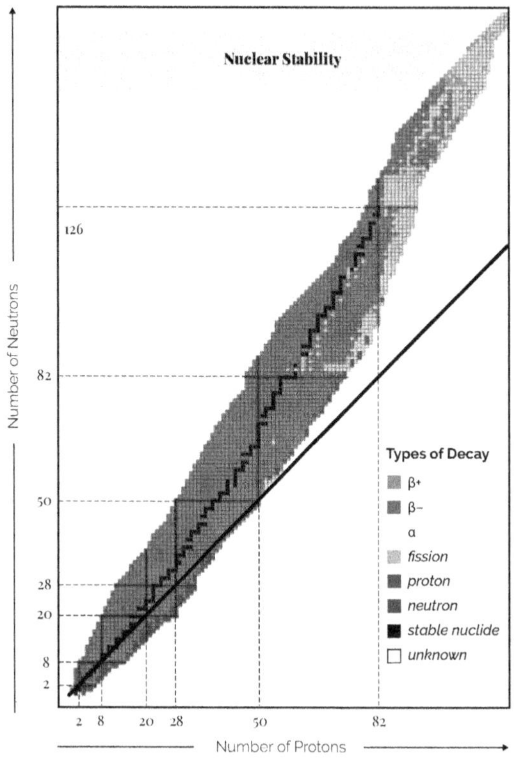

This graph relates the stablility of all known nuclides to the numbers of protons and neutrons. The colors represent the types of decay that will occur.

To a certain extent, we can predict nuclear stability on the basis of the ratio of neutrons to protons within the nucleus. For smaller atoms ($Z < 20$), the most stable nuclei have a 1:1 ratio between neutrons and protons. As the number of nucleons increases, additional neutrons, with their strong nuclear forces, are required to balance the repulsive forces between the protons. In some very large nuclei, the ratio may be as high as 1.5:1. The nuclide $^{206}_{82}Pb$ is one such example. With 124 neutrons and 82 protons, its ratio is 1.5:1. The graph at left relates the stability of all known nuclides to their neutron-to-proton ratio. The band of black points is called the **band of stability** because it identifies the most stable nuclides.

The graph of nuclear stability can be used to predict how an unstable nuclide will spontaneously change to form a more stable one—radioactive decay. Nuclides with atomic numbers less than 83 that fall above the band of stability have more neutrons than their stable isotopes. It is thus reasonable that they will decay in a way that will decrease the number of neutrons and increase the number of protons. Nuclides with 83 or more protons frequently decay in a way that makes them lose both protons and neutrons. All the most common isotopes of elements beyond bismuth on the periodic table are radioactive. We will look more closely at the types of radioactive decay in Section 22.2.

EXAMPLE 22-1: NUCLEAR STABILITY PREDICTION

Are $^{60}_{27}Co$ atoms radioactive or stable?

Solution

Cobalt-60 atoms have 27 protons and 33 neutrons. According to the graph of nuclear stability, the point on the graph corresponding to the intersection of 27 protons and 33 neutrons does not represent a stable atom, meaning that that cobalt-60 is an unstable, radioactive nuclide.

540 Chapter 22

NUCLEAR SHELL MODEL

The nuclear shell model works well for stable nuclei but not so well for unstable nuclei. Other models—the liquid drop model and the collective model (a combination of the nuclear shell and liquid drop models)—have been proposed to account for nuclear structures that the shell model cannot fully explain.

The protons and neutrons in a nucleus seem to have energy levels similar to the energy levels in the electron shells. The *nuclear shell model* is a nuclear model in which nucleons exist in levels, or shells, that are analogous to the energy levels that exist for electrons. Just as "full" electron shells are more stable than those that are not full, there are "full" nuclear shells that appear to be more stable. The number of nucleons in a full shell is called the **magic number** for that shell. For protons, the magic numbers are 2, 8, 20, 28, 50, and 82. That explains why tin ($Z = 50$) has ten different stable nuclides, while the elements on either side of it, indium and antimony, have only one and two, respectively. Neutrons have the magic numbers 2, 8, 20, 28, 50, 82, and 126. The nuclide iron-54 is stable because it has a magic number of 28 neutrons, even though it doesn't have a magic number of protons. A few nuclides have stable numbers of both neutrons and protons and are considered very stable, such as calcium-40 with 20 protons and 20 neutrons. Scientists have more complicated rules that govern magic numbers to help predict the stability of nuclides, but these give you an idea of how they work.

Nuclear Shell Model

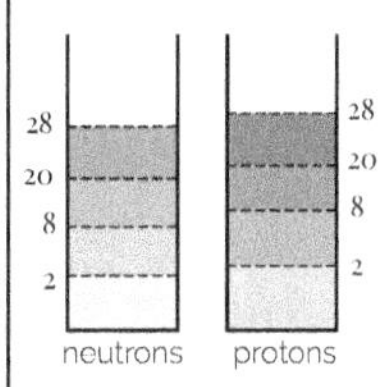

- Similar to atomic shells
- Nuclei are particularly stable if either protons or neutrons are a magic number and very stable if both are magic numbers.
- Shells for protons are more widely spaced due to the repulsive force between protons.

▲ Nitrogen-15 has 7 protons and 8 neutrons. The 8 neutrons is a magic number, so nitrogen-15 is stable.

Nitrogen-13 has 7 protons and 6 neutrons. Since neither is a magic number, nitrogen-13 is unstable.

Oxygen-16 has 8 protons and 8 neutrons. Since both are magic numbers, oxygen-16 is very stable.

If we were to extend the graph of nuclear stability to 180 neutrons or more, we would see that there is a theoretical *island of stability* that is separate from the band of stability. This island could be a future destination for nuclear chemistry research and experimentation. In Chapter 6, we discussed the fact that most of the elements created artificially don't last very long. It is possible that in the future, chemists and physicists may be able to produce a new element with magic numbers that will allow it to be very stable. This could produce exciting new opportunities for exploration and application in nuclear chemistry.

CAREERS

SERVING AS A NUCLEAR ENGINEER: *HARNESSING THE POWER OF THE ATOM*

Many scientists have spent their careers learning about atomic nuclei. They have learned about the structure of the nucleus and how nuclei can change. As with most discoveries in science, technologists have sought to use these discoveries to help people. Almost immediately following the discovery of x-rays, doctors began using them to view bones within the body.

Today, nuclear engineers continue to investigate how to harness the energy and particles that can be released from the nuclei of atoms. A nuclear engineer develops new processes and devices that will put nuclear energy to good use. As you can imagine, a major task for nuclear engineers is to harness this energy while avoiding the risks of nuclear radiation. If you like the challenge of working on cutting-edge applications of science and energy, you too may be interested in a career as a nuclear engineer.

DIFFERENTIATED INSTRUCTION

Nuclear Shell Model

Lead students to create their own nuclear shell model. Have them pair up to create a unique model for relating the magic numbers of nucleons to their position on the shells. Have them practice predicting the stability of nuclides by using their nuclear shell models.

MASS DEFECT AND BINDING ENERGY

Lead students to create **Sketchnotes** to record the following equations. These equations will help them understand mass defect and its relationship to binding energy.

1. Mass defect equals the mass of an atom's nucleus minus the total mass of its nucleons.
2. The energy of the nucleus equals the energy of its nucleons minus its binding energy.

THE MOST STABLE NUCLEUS

Iron, with a mass number of 56, has the most stable nucleus.

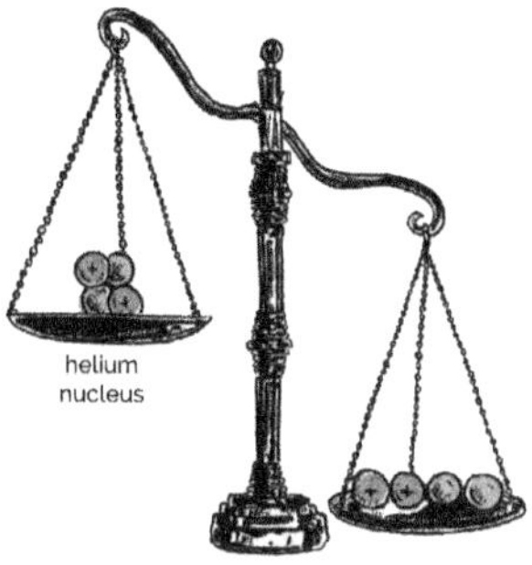

When the nucleons combine to form a nucleus some of their mass gets converted to binding energy. The mass of the nucleus is less than the mass of the nucleons that make it up. We call this the *mass defect.*

Energy Changes and Nuclear Changes

A nucleus has slightly less mass than the protons and neutrons that make up that nucleus. The difference between the mass of an atom's nucleus and the total mass of its nucleons in a free state is called the **mass defect** of the nucleus. The idea that energy and mass are interconvertible explains this phenomenon. According to Albert Einstein's theory of special relativity, mass and energy are equivalent, as indicated by the equation $E = mc^2$, where E is energy, m is mass, and c is the speed of light. Since the speed of light is an astounding 3×10^8 m/s, the energy released by the conversion of even a small amount of mass into energy is huge.

If it were possible, a certain amount of energy would have to be absorbed to separate all the protons and neutrons in a nucleus far from each other. You can think of this like the heat of vaporization when boiling water, which is the energy needed to move liquid particles far away from each other. The energy to separate the nucleons is the same as the energy that is released when a nucleus forms from its nucleons. Scientists call this energy the **nuclear binding energy**. The unit for the nuclear binding energy is a *megaelectronvolt* (MeV). For the purpose of comparing the stability of nuclides, researchers have determined the nuclear binding energies of various nuclei. They then divide these values by the total number of nucleons to obtain the *binding energy per nucleon*. The graph below shows the binding energy per nucleon plotted as a function of mass number. It shows that nuclei with mass numbers near 56 have the most binding energy per nuclear particle.

Binding energy per nucleon peaks near an atomic mass of 56 u.

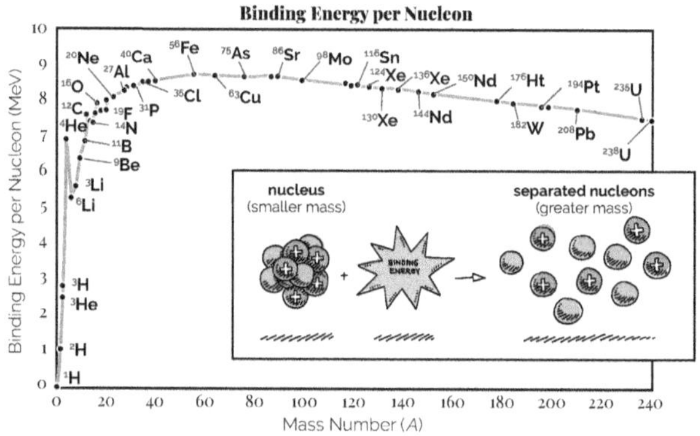

Nuclei with high binding energies per nucleon are more stable than those with lower binding energies per nucleon. As expected, the observed mass defects for the various elements match the observed binding energies. Nuclei with mass numbers near 56 have the most mass defect per nuclear particle. The mass that has "disappeared" (transformed into energy) serves as the nuclear binding energy. These elements have more energy per nucleon holding their nuclei together, so they are more stable.

542 Chapter 22

Geiger counters detect radiation by the tendency of radiation to ionize gases, allowing them to conduct electricity. This change in electrical conductivity indicates the level of radioactivity.

Measuring Radiation

SI UNITS FOR RADIATION

Soon after the discovery of radiation—the matter and energy spontaneously emitted by unstable nuclides—scientists recognized that they could use this technology to "look" inside the human body. Within a year of the first use of x-rays on a human being came reports of injuries from the radiation exposure. Today we have a good understanding of how damaging this radiation can be, and scientists have established safe limits for our exposure.

Scientists recognized that they could measure different aspects of radiation. They could measure radioactivity itself, the absorption of radiation, or the biological effect caused by radiation. Physical radiation units measure the activity of the radiation source, that is, the number of particles or rays produced per unit of time. This measurement is usually expressed using an SI unit called a *becquerel* (Bq). A radiation source with an activity of 1 Bq has one nuclear transformation per second. Another unit for activity which is older but still used is the *curie* (Ci), which is a non-SI unit. Radiation equal to 1 Ci has 3.7×10^{10} transformations per second, or 3.7×10^{10} Bq.

While it is important to understand how much radiation is emitted by its source, it may be more vital in certain instances to understand how much radiation is absorbed by objects. Scientists use an SI unit called the *gray* (Gy) to measure the absorption of *ionizing radiation*. A measure of 1 Gy is equivalent to 1 joule of energy absorbed per kilogram of material. This unit is important in radiotherapy and food irradiation.

These units are important for scientists and technicians, but most of us are more concerned with the effect that the radiation has on living things, especially people. Doctors have devised a unit that factors in the differences in energy, penetrating ability, and ionization capability of differing types of radiation. This unit, which considers both the absorbed dose and its impact on the tissue, is called a *sievert* (Sv). This SI unit is named for Rolf Sievert, a Swedish medical physicist who studied the biological effects of radiation. Table 22-1 shows the health effects of various doses of radiation measured in millisieverts (mSv). But how do we measure how much radiation is present, not just the amount that is absorbed?

TABLE 22-1 *Health Effects of Radiation*

Dose (mSv)	Health Effect
0–250	no detectable clinical effect in humans
250–1000	slight short-term reduction in the number of some types of red blood cells; severe sickness uncommon
1000–2000	fatigue, nausea; vomiting if > 1500 mSv; longer-term decrease in some types of blood cells
2000–3000	nausea, vomiting first day of exposure; a two-week latent period followed by malaise, appetite loss, sore throat, and diarrhea; recovery usually in three months unless complicated by infection
3000–6000	nausea, vomiting, and diarrhea in first few hours; after one week, fever, appetite loss, and malaise; inflammation of the mouth and throat, diarrhea, and emaciation follow, some deaths in two to six weeks; death likely for 50% if exposure was above 4500 mSv; recovery for others in about six months
> 6000	nausea, vomiting, and diarrhea in the first few hours, followed by rapid emaciation and death, possibly within two weeks; death probable in all cases

SI UNITS FOR RADIATION

Lead students to create a **graphic organizer** or **Sketchnotes** for the SI units for radiation. Be sure that they include the abbreviation for and use of each unit.

1 Bq (becquerel)—physical radiation unit that measures the activity of the radiation source (the number of particles or rays produced per unit of time)

1 Gy (gray)—measures the absorption of ionizing radiation (energy absorbed per kilogram of material)

1 Sv (sievert) or 1 mSv (millisievert)—unit considered the absorbed dose of radiation in tissue

DIFFERENTIATED INSTRUCTION

Radiation Project

Instruct students to create an **informational graphic** that informs the public about the effects of radiation and lists several activities or objects that release radiation and the amount that each one releases. To complete this activity, students may opt to create a poster or website (Weebly, Google Sites, or Microsoft Sites). Have them research recent documentation of the effects of radiation and the common amounts of radiation found in everyday activities and objects. Suggest that they visit the United States Nuclear Regulatory Commission website for updated information.

The following list contains activities and objects that release radiation and the amount of radiation that is absorbed with each.

Note: Students will not see cellphones or Wi-Fi exposure in this list since these are forms of nonionizing radiation (covered in Section 22.2.

one cancer treatment: 50 000 mSv to the tumor

smoking ten cigarettes per day: 26.5 mSv to a smoker's lungs

CT scan: 25 mSv

natural radon in air: 2 mSv

food and water: 400 µSv

soil: 350 µSv

sun/cosmic rays: 300 µSv

chest x-ray: 80 µSv

building materials: 40 µSv

five-hour plane ride: 30 µSv

watching TV: 10 µSv

ongoing fallout from the era of nuclear weapons testing: 10 µSv

living near a coal-fired power plant: 0.3 µSv

living within 50 miles of a nuclear power plant: 0.09 µSv

Nuclear Chemistry 543

ASSESS

TICKET OUT THE DOOR

As a **summarizing activity**, ask students to state why some atoms decay. *(Unstable nuclides spontaneously change to form more stable ones.)*

22.1 REVIEW *ANSWERS*

1. the waves and particles emitted from unstable nuclei *(p. 537)*
2. the particles in the nucleus (protons and neutrons) of a nuclide *(p. 539)*
3. Though essentially the same thing, nuclides emphasize the nucleus and what it contains, while isotopes emphasize the entire atom. Both are identified using isotope notation. *(p. 539)*
4. Neutrons stabilize the nucleus. Since the nucleus contains protons and neutrons, we would expect that the protons would repel each other. In stable nuclei, the neutrons separate the protons enough so that the attractive force between the neutrons and protons from the strong nuclear force is sufficiently large to balance the electrostatic repulsion between the protons. *(p. 539)*
5. **a.** stable
   b. unstable; The ratio of neutrons to protons is too low.
   c. stable
   d. unstable; The ratio of neutrons to protons is too high. *(all p. 540)*
6. **a.** xenon-124
   b. magnesium-24 (Though Mg-24 is not shown on the graph on page 542, its binding energy can be inferred to fall between Ne-20 and Al-27.)
   c. calcium-40
   d. copper-63 *(all p. 542)*
7. Each of the SI units measures a particular aspect of radioactivity. A *becquerel* measures the emission of the nuclear material in transformations per second. A *gray* measures the amount of radiant energy absorbed per kilogram of material. A *sievert* measures the effect that radiation has on living things by factoring in its energy, penetrating ability, and ionizing ability. *(p. 543)*
8. Accept any two: Geiger counters, scintillation counters, dosimeters. *(p. 544)*

DEVICES FOR MEASURING RADIATION

A number of different devices can measure radiation. The *Geiger counter* is one. This instrument contains a tube filled with gas that is ionized when exposed to certain kinds of radiation. The ions cause an electric current that is displayed as a series of pulses on a meter. The meter is often connected to an amplifier so that the user can hear the pulses. Another kind of radiation detector, called a *scintillation counter*, works similarly but produces flashes of light. These counters indicate the amount of radiation by the frequency and intensity of pulses in the Geiger counter or flashes in the scintillation counter. People who do work that might expose them to radioactive sources must be able to monitor their exposure to radiation. They can carry pocket instruments called *dosimeters* that monitor their exposure. Modern day dosimeters work on the premise that ionizing radiation alters some characteristic of a material in the dosimeter. The internal circuit monitors both the rate and the total number of those alterations. The dosimeter can then warn the user when either the rate or cumulative limit is approached.

22.1 SECTION REVIEW

1. What is nuclear radiation?
2. What is a nucleon?
3. Compare nuclides and isotopes.
4. What seems to be the main function of neutrons in the nucleus? Explain.
5. Use the nuclear stability graph on page 540 to determine whether the following nuclides are stable. If the nuclide is unstable, explain why this is so.
   a. $^{36}_{18}Ar$
   b. $^{122}_{55}Cs$
   c. $^{166}_{68}Er$
   d. $^{184}_{72}Hf$
6. Using the nuclear binding energy per nucleon graph on page 542, indicate which isotope in each pair will be more stable.
   a. xenon-124, tungsten-182
   b. magnesium-24, carbon-12
   c. calcium-40, lead-208
   d. boron-11, copper-63
7. Why are there different SI units related to radioactivity?
8. Name two types of radiation detectors.

544 Chapter 22

22.2 NUCLEAR DECAY

Radioactive Decay

Recall that in Section 22.1 we defined radioactivity as the spontaneous process that emitted nuclear radiation—particles and energy—from the nuclei of unstable atoms. This process is a naturally occurring nuclear change in which an original unstable nuclide, called the *parent nuclide*, changes to become a more stable *daughter nuclide*. But what do we know about these particles and energy that are emitted?

How long will radioactive waste be around?

The particles and waves that a parent nuclide emits have enough kinetic energy to knock electrons out of neighboring atoms. Those atoms could be in any substance. When this happens, the affected atom ionizes, so these kinds of particles and waves are called **ionizing radiation**. Radiation that doesn't have enough kinetic energy to knock out electrons is called *nonionizing radiation*. We will learn about five forms of radioactive decay below, including three that you might remember from a physical science course: alpha decay, beta decay, and gamma decay.

Nuclear equations describe nuclear changes that release radiation during radioactive decay processes. In some cases, the number of protons changes, so the atom becomes a different element. Nuclear equations are similar to chemical equations with reactants on the left and products on the right. But nuclear equations are not written with chemical formulas; rather, they are written with each element's isotope notation. By using isotope notation, we can track changes to the nucleons during nuclear transformations. To balance the nuclear equation, both the mass number and atomic number have to be balanced across the equation.

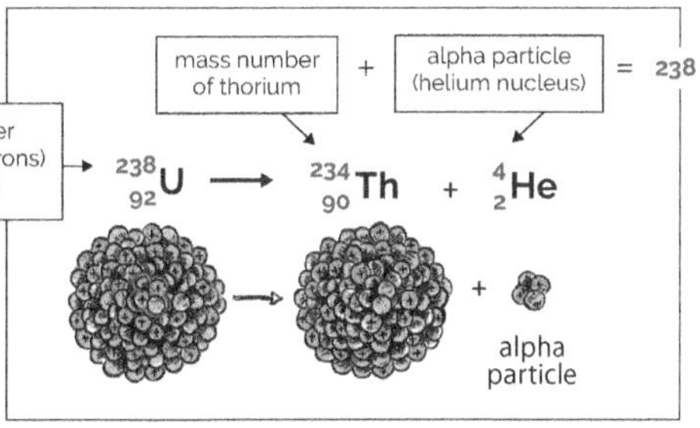

QUESTIONS
- Is all radioactivity the same?
- How can I determine the type of decay that an isotope will undergo?
- How can I represent decay events?
- How can I solve half-life problems?

TERMS
ionizing radiation • nuclear equation • alpha decay • beta decay • positron emission • electron capture • gamma decay • radioactive decay series • half-life

ENGAGE

STRONG NUCLEAR FORCE AND REPULSION

Direct a **review discussion** by asking the following questions.

1. What is the strong nuclear force? *(the force that holds nucleons together)*
2. What else does this force do for neutrons and protons? *(It allows their interactions to balance the electrostatic repulsion between protons.)*
3. What happens if the strong nuclear force is strong enough? *(The nucleus will be stable.)*
4. What happens if the nuclide is unstable? *(It will spontaneously change to form a more stable nuclide [radioactive decay].)*

INSTRUCT

MICROWAVES AND RADIATION

Some people are concerned that the waves their microwave ovens use to heat food are ionizing radiation, making their food dangerous after cooking it. That doesn't happen. Microwaves fall in the part of the electromagnetic spectrum that includes nonionizing radiation, so microwave ovens can't make something radioactive. A neutron has to be absorbed to make something radioactive.

SECTION 22.2 *OVERVIEW*

Essential Question

How long will radioactive waste be around?

Objectives

- **22.2.1** Compare the types of radioactive decay products.
- **22.2.2** Predict the type of decay that will occur for a particular isotope.
- **22.2.3** Write balanced equations for radioactive decay.
- **22.2.4** Solve half-life problems.

Resources

- Worldview Investigation: Radiometric Dating (p. 555)
- Lab 22A: *It's Only a Matter of Time*—Investigating Half-Life

DECAY TABLE

Guide students in creating a **table** that outlines the different types of decay covered in this section (alpha decay, beta decay, positron emission, electron capture, and gamma decay). Students should include a definition and an example for each type of decay.

CHANGES FROM ALPHA DECAY

When an atom releases an alpha particle, its identity changes due to the release of the two protons. The element's identity shifts to that of the element whose atomic number is two less than that of the parent nuclide.

TYPES OF

Radioactive Decay

ALPHA DECAY

Alpha decay is radioactivity that produces positively charged *alpha particles* (α, or ${}^{4}_{2}He$). Ernest Rutherford detected alpha particles as a stream of positively charged particles deflected slightly toward a negative electrical plate (see image below). The small deflection indicated that they must be more massive than other types of radiation. It was later determined that alpha particles contained two protons and two neutrons. Nuclides with 83 or more protons frequently decay in a way that releases alpha particles.

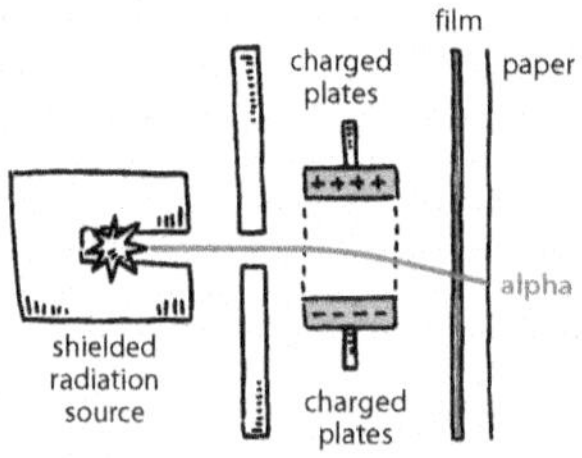

For example, uranium-238 emits alpha particles and forms thorium.

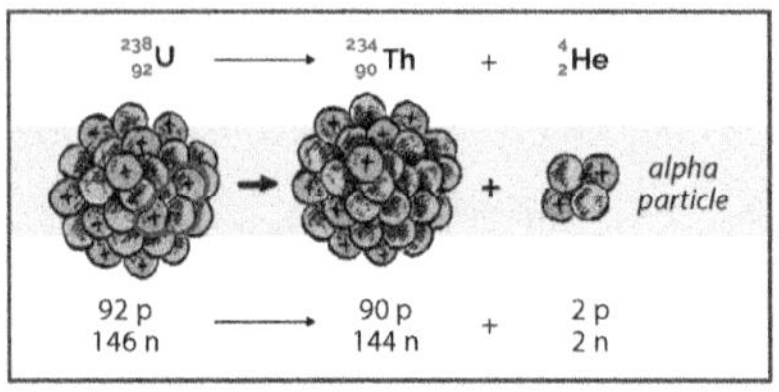

Notice how the mass and atomic numbers are balanced in the equation.

Alpha particles have the greatest ability to ionize atoms with which they collide. But due to their relatively large size and low speed, alpha particles are easily stopped by matter and don't penetrate deeply. For instance, alpha particles cannot go through a piece of paper.

EXAMPLE 22-2: ALPHA DECAY

Radon-222 is a radioactive gas found in buildings. Write the nuclear equation that describes the alpha decay of radon-222.

Solution

Alpha decay implies that an alpha particle is one of the products. Radon-222 is the parent nuclide.

$$^{222}_{86}Rn \longrightarrow {}^{A}_{Z}X + {}^{4}_{2}He$$

X is the unknown element, A is its mass number, and Z is its atomic number.

To balance the equation, the mass numbers and the atomic numbers of the products must equal the mass number and the atomic number of the parent nuclide. From the equation above, $222 = A + 4$ and $86 = Z + 2$. Therefore, the mass number must be 218 and the atomic number must be 84. With an atomic number of 84, the daughter nuclide must be polonium, or ${}^{218}_{84}Po$. Thus, the final equation is

$$^{222}_{86}Rn \longrightarrow {}^{218}_{84}Po + {}^{4}_{2}He.$$

546 Chapter 22

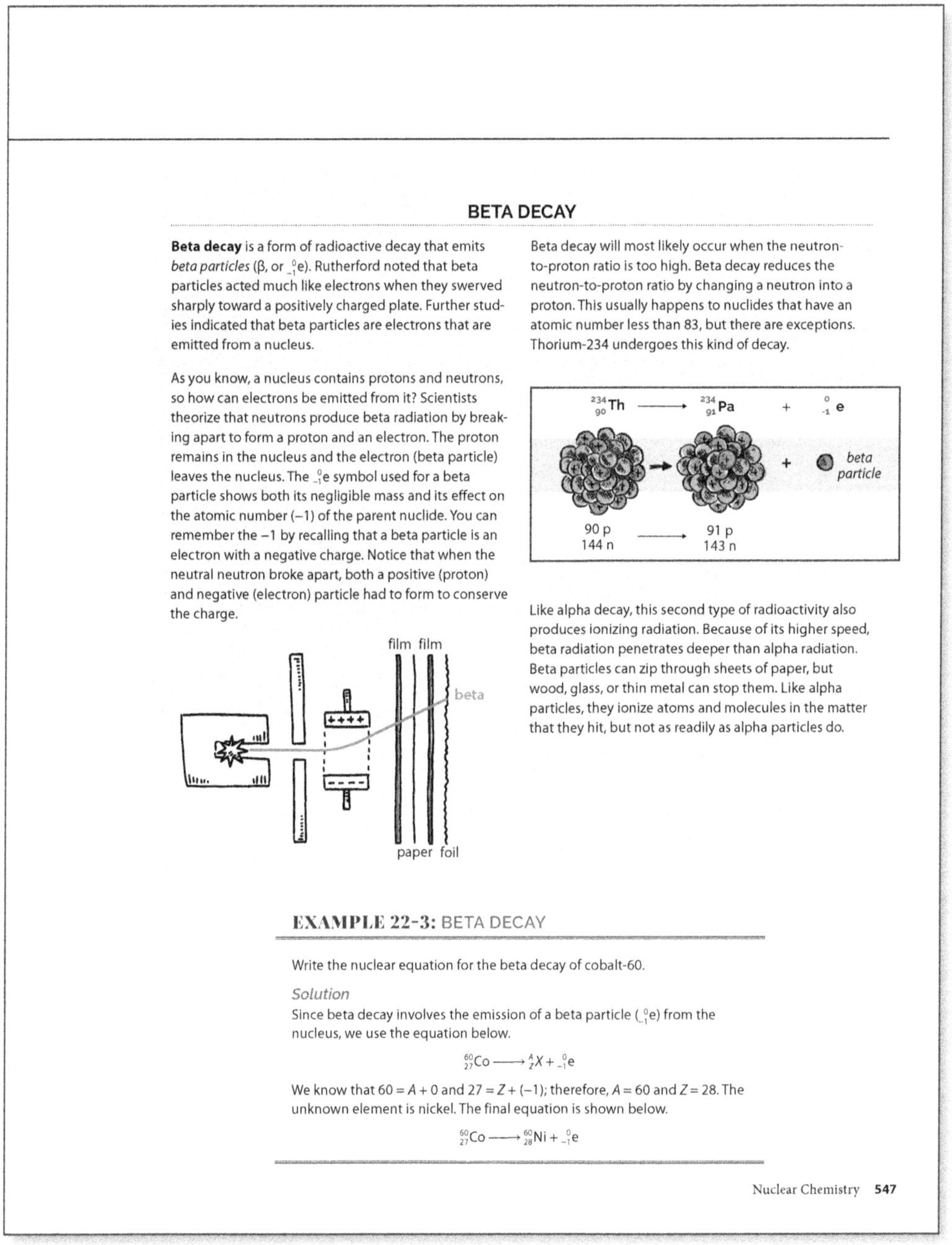

BETA DECAY

Beta decay is a form of radioactive decay that emits *beta particles* (β, or ${}_{-1}^{0}e$). Rutherford noted that beta particles acted much like electrons when they swerved sharply toward a positively charged plate. Further studies indicated that beta particles are electrons that are emitted from a nucleus.

As you know, a nucleus contains protons and neutrons, so how can electrons be emitted from it? Scientists theorize that neutrons produce beta radiation by breaking apart to form a proton and an electron. The proton remains in the nucleus and the electron (beta particle) leaves the nucleus. The ${}_{-1}^{0}e$ symbol used for a beta particle shows both its negligible mass and its effect on the atomic number (−1) of the parent nuclide. You can remember the −1 by recalling that a beta particle is an electron with a negative charge. Notice that when the neutral neutron broke apart, both a positive (proton) and negative (electron) particle had to form to conserve the charge.

Beta decay will most likely occur when the neutron-to-proton ratio is too high. Beta decay reduces the neutron-to-proton ratio by changing a neutron into a proton. This usually happens to nuclides that have an atomic number less than 83, but there are exceptions. Thorium-234 undergoes this kind of decay.

Like alpha decay, this second type of radioactivity also produces ionizing radiation. Because of its higher speed, beta radiation penetrates deeper than alpha radiation. Beta particles can zip through sheets of paper, but wood, glass, or thin metal can stop them. Like alpha particles, they ionize atoms and molecules in the matter that they hit, but not as readily as alpha particles do.

EXAMPLE 22-3: BETA DECAY

Write the nuclear equation for the beta decay of cobalt-60.

Solution

Since beta decay involves the emission of a beta particle (${}_{-1}^{0}e$) from the nucleus, we use the equation below.

$${}_{27}^{60}Co \longrightarrow {}_{Z}^{A}X + {}_{-1}^{0}e$$

We know that $60 = A + 0$ and $27 = Z + (-1)$; therefore, $A = 60$ and $Z = 28$. The unknown element is nickel. The final equation is shown below.

$${}_{27}^{60}Co \longrightarrow {}_{28}^{60}Ni + {}_{-1}^{0}e$$

Nuclear Chemistry 547

COMPARING ALPHA AND BETA PARTICLES

Beta particles penetrate about 100 times farther than alpha particles. Alpha particles are about 7000 times more massive than beta particles.

PAIR PRODUCTION

Sometimes during a nuclear decay, a positron and an electron are both produced when a photon (particle of light) interacts with the nucleus. This kind of decay occurs in space and in the air around a bolt of lightning.

TYPES OF

Radioactive Decay

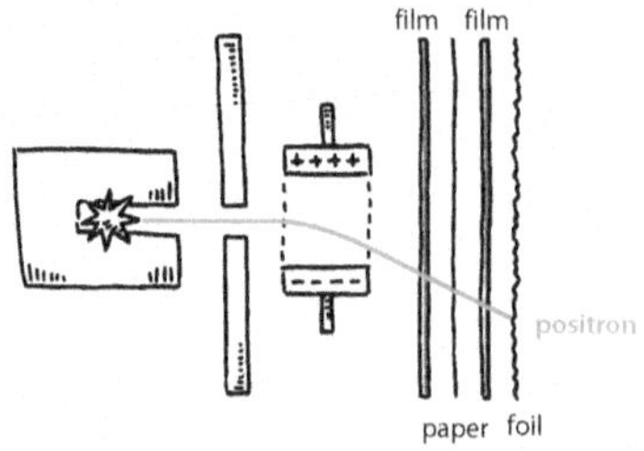

POSITRON EMISSION

In some cases, a nuclide may be unstable because the neutron-to-proton ratio is too low. Positron emission is one decay process that can alleviate this problem by reducing the number of protons in a nucleus by one. During **positron emission**, a proton changes into a neutron and a *positron* (${}^{0}_{+1}e$), a particle with positive charge but the same low mass as an electron. Again you can see that charge is conserved as the positive proton breaks into a neutron and a positron. Positron emission is also known as *beta plus decay*. You can remember the +1 by recalling that a positron is like an electron but with a positive charge.

For example, potassium-38 undergoes positron emission as follows.

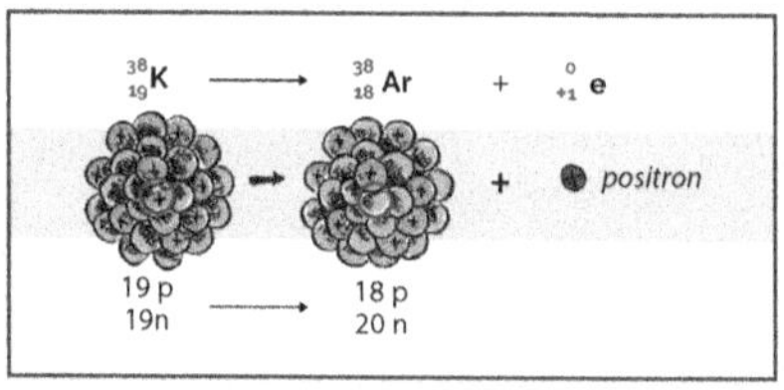

Notice that the atomic number decreased by one, but the mass number didn't change. This occurred because a proton changed into a neutron.

EXAMPLE 22-4: POSITRON EMISSION

Write the nuclear equation for the positron emission of magnesium-23.

Solution

Since positron emission involves the emission of a positron (${}^{0}_{+1}e$) from a nucleus, we use the equation below.

$${}^{23}_{12}Mg \longrightarrow {}^{A}_{Z}X + {}^{0}_{+1}e$$

We know that $23 = A + 0$ and $12 = Z + (+1)$; therefore, $A = 23$ and $Z = 11$. The unknown element is sodium. The final equation is shown below.

$${}^{23}_{12}Mg \longrightarrow {}^{23}_{11}Na + {}^{0}_{+1}e$$

ELECTRON CAPTURE

Another process that can lower the number of protons in the nucleus is electron capture. **Electron capture** is a nuclear change that occurs when a nucleus pulls in one of its closest electrons (usually from the 1s sublevel) and combines it with a proton to form a neutron. The resulting daughter isotope is in an excited state and may emit a gamma ray as electrons fall into now partially vacated lower energy levels. Silver-106 undergoes electron capture in the following equation.

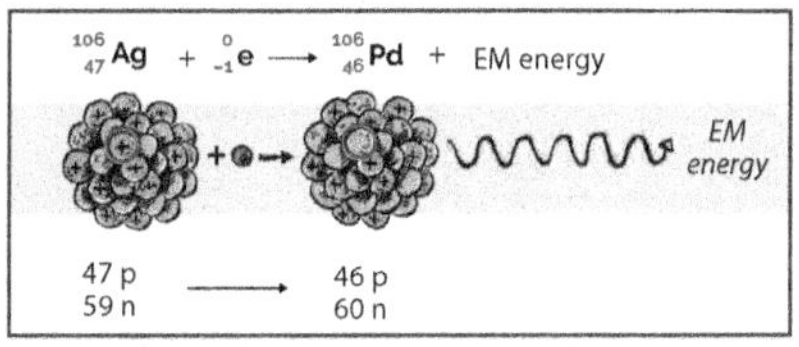

In electron capture, the mass number again remains the same, but the atomic number is reduced by one as a proton becomes a neutron. This process increases the neutron-to-proton ratio to make the daughter nuclide more stable.

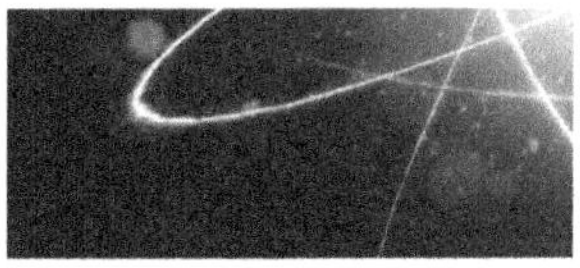

EXAMPLE 22-5: ELECTRON CAPTURE

Write the nuclear equation for potassium-40 undergoing electron capture.

Solution

Since electron capture involves the absorption of an electron (${}^{0}_{-1}\text{e}$) by a nucleus, we use the equation below.

$${}^{40}_{19}\text{K} + {}^{0}_{-1}\text{e} \longrightarrow {}^{A}_{Z}X$$

We know that $40 + 0 = A$ and $19 + (-1) = Z$; therefore, $A = 40$ and $Z = 18$. The unknown element is argon. The final equation is shown below.

$${}^{40}_{19}\text{K} + {}^{0}_{-1}\text{e} \longrightarrow {}^{40}_{18}\text{Ar}$$

GAMMA DECAY

Unlike the decay processes outlined above, gamma decay doesn't emit particles. **Gamma decay** is a process that emits high-energy electromagnetic waves called *gamma rays* (${}^{0}_{0}\gamma$). These rays are uncharged and thus not deflected by electrical fields, as you can see in the image below. Any nuclear change can produce gamma radiation and most do.

If gamma emission produces no particles, how then are gamma rays produced? As a nucleus changes from an excited state to a lower energy state, it emits gamma rays, similar to electrons changing from higher energy levels to lower energy levels. In an example of gamma decay, an excited technetium-99 nucleus emits a gamma ray to form an unexcited technetium-99 nucleus.

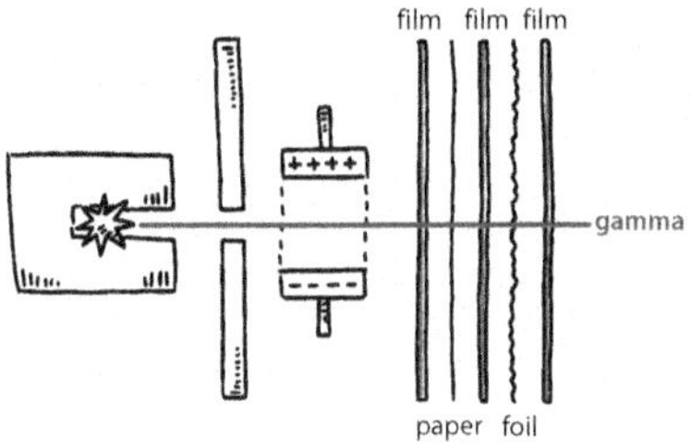

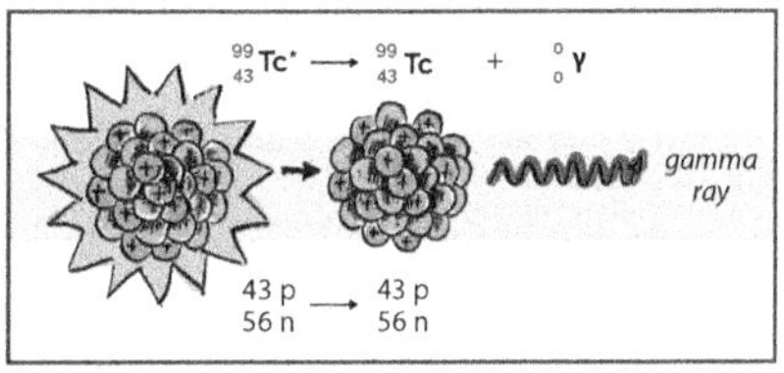

The asterisk on the technetium on the reactant side is used to indicate an isotope in an excited state. As an excited nucleus returns to its ground state, it releases energy in the form of gamma rays.

COMPARING PARTICLES

Lead a **visual analysis** of the decay illustrations on pages 546–49. Ask students what they notice about the illustrations. What are the similarities and differences? What conclusions can they make on the basis of their observations?

Point out the different particles in the decay illustrations and how they react to different charges. Negative beta particles are attracted to positively charged plates, and positive alpha particles and positrons are attracted to negatively charged plates. Gamma rays have no charge and are therefore unaffected by charged plates.

DIFFERENT LEVELS OF EXCITEMENT

When you tell students that excited nuclei emit gamma rays, remind them that excited electrons give off light energy (Ch. 4). Since the forces holding a nucleus together are greater than the forces that hold electrons in orbit, nuclei must vibrate faster to emit a gamma ray. Because of this, gamma rays on the electromagnetic spectrum have shorter wavelengths and are more energetic than visible light.

Nuclear Chemistry 549

PREDICTING TYPES OF DECAY

Using the nuclear stability graph on page 540, guide students in creating a **memory strategy prompt** for predicting the type of decay that a nuclide may experience. They may create a function, illustration, or mnemonic device.

An example of a function is shown below.

If $Z > 82$ (heavy), then this is predicted to be alpha decay.

If nuclide < 82 protons and falls above band of stability, then this is predicted to be beta decay.

If nuclide < 82 protons and falls below band of stability, then this is predicted to be positron emission or electron capture.

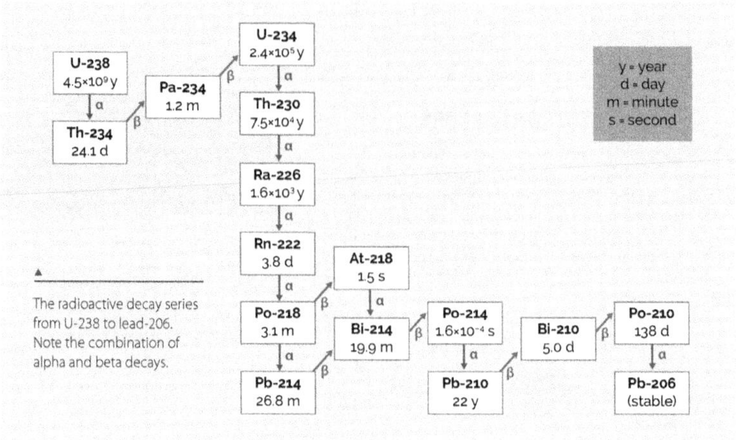

The radioactive decay series from U-238 to lead-206. Note the combination of alpha and beta decays.

Predicting Types of Decay

The nuclear stability graph on page 540 can be used to predict the type of decay that a nuclide might experience. Keep in mind that nuclear stability depends on the neutron-to-proton ratio. Let's look at a few examples.

EXAMPLE 22-6: RADIOACTIVE DECAY PREDICTIONS

Use the graph on page 540 to predict the type of decay that the following nuclides are most likely to undergo: alpha decay, beta decay, or positron emission. Then write the equation for the decay.

a. $^{35}_{13}Al$

b. $^{138}_{60}Nd$

c. $^{220}_{90}Th$

Solution

a. Beta decay is most likely because the nuclide has less than 82 protons, and it falls above the band of stability.

$$^{35}_{13}Al \longrightarrow ^{35}_{14}Si + ^{0}_{-1}e$$

b. Positron emission is most likely because the nuclide has less than 82 protons, and it falls below the band of stability.

$$^{138}_{60}Nd \longrightarrow ^{138}_{59}Pr + ^{0}_{+1}e$$

c. Alpha decay is most likely because the atomic number is greater than 82.

$$^{220}_{90}Th \longrightarrow ^{216}_{88}Ra + ^{4}_{2}He$$

Radioactive Decay Series

Unstable nuclides become more stable by emitting various types of radiation. Some release alpha particles, and some release beta particles or positrons. Some radioactive nuclides, such as uranium-238, are not stable after just one alpha emission.

$$^{234}_{90}Th \longrightarrow ^{234}_{91}Pa + ^{0}_{-1}e$$

Thorium's daughter nuclide protactinium-234 is still unstable, and it also decays by beta emission.

$$^{234}_{91}\mathrm{Pa} \longrightarrow {}^{234}_{92}\mathrm{U} + {}^{0}_{-1}\mathrm{e}$$

Uranium-234 is *also* unstable, and it too decays, emitting an alpha particle in this case.

$$^{234}_{92}\mathrm{U} \longrightarrow {}^{230}_{90}\mathrm{Th} + {}^{4}_{2}\mathrm{He}$$

Do these decay reactions ever stop? Yes, but not until a stable nuclide forms! In each step, the daughter nuclide from one decay becomes the parent nuclide of the next decay.

When the product of nuclear decay is at last stable, the radiation emissions stop for that specific nuclide, although other atoms in the same sample will continue to decay until they also reach a stable product. Nuclear scientists have identified several series of predictable alpha and beta decays for a given parent nuclide that result in a single stable daughter nuclide. Sequential alpha and beta emissions often form a long series of nuclear decay events called **radioactive decay series**, though they are statistical models of nuclear decay behavior and not definite decay paths. When uranium-238 decays, nuclear decay reactions proceed until stable lead-206 forms. The image below shows the possible radioactive decay series of uranium-238 in red. The other colors represent the other decay paths for different nuclides. Depending on the pathway of the decay series, as many as fourteen decays may occur involving nine different elements.

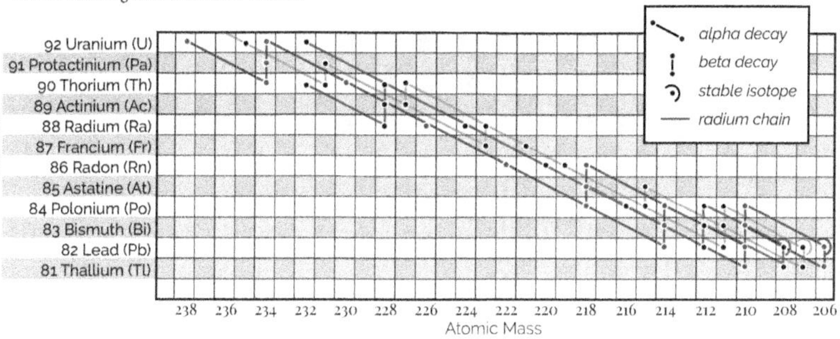

All nuclides for elements with more than 83 protons are radioactive, though every element has some radioisotopes. They all decay according to one of four radioactive decay series: the uranium (or radium) series, the thorium series, the actinium series, or the neptunium series. The first three series can occur naturally. The uranium series begins with the parent nuclide uranium-238 and ends with lead-206. The actinium series begins with plutonium-239 and ends with lead-207. The thorium series begins with uranium-232 or thorium-232 and ends with lead-208. The fourth series, the neptunium series, occurs artificially. It begins with plutonium-241 and ends with thallium-205. Scientists refer to this as the neptunium series instead of plutonium since neptunium is the longest-lived member of the series.

Nuclear Chemistry **551**

SANDWICH HALF-LIFE

Use the following **analogy** to help students understand half-life. Compare the rate of decay and half-lives to someone eating a sandwich. The sandwich is analogous to an element: eating the sandwich is the decay of that element, and the speed at which the person eats the sandwich is the rate of decay. After one half-life has passed, one-half of the sandwich is gone. If he eats the sandwich slowly, then the half-life happens at a slow rate. The faster he eats the sandwich, the faster the rate of decay. One thing to remember is that when an element decays, it is transmuting into another substance, not disappearing.

Large Hadron Collider in Geneva, Switzerland

Half-Life

How quickly does nuclear decay occur? Scientists describe the rate of nuclear decay by measuring the **half-life** ($t_{1/2}$) of a parent nuclide, that is, the time it takes for half the atoms of a parent nuclide to decay to a daughter nuclide. Each radioactive nuclide has a unique half-life. For any specific atom, there is a fifty-fifty chance that it will decay in one half-life, similar to your chance of getting heads when you flip a coin. Shorter half-lives indicate that the nuclei tend to quickly decay, while longer half-lives show that radioactive decay usually proceeds more slowly.

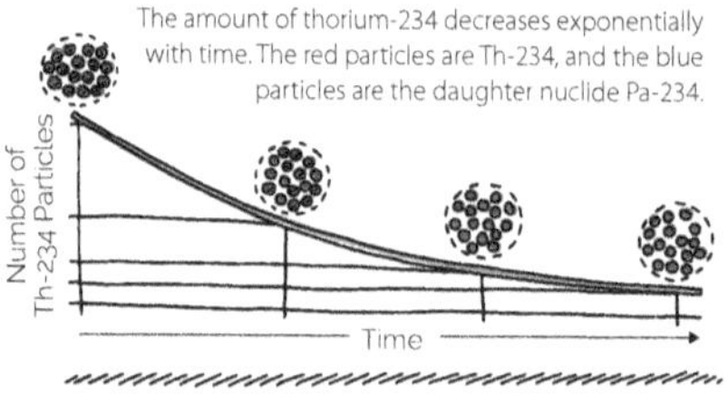

The amount of thorium-234 decreases exponentially with time. The red particles are Th-234, and the blue particles are the daughter nuclide Pa-234.

For example, the half-life of thorium-234 is 24.1 d. If you had a sample of 40 g of thorium-234, in 24.1 d, that is, in one half-life, half of the thorium, or 20 g, will decay into protactinium-234. How much thorium-234 remains after two half-lives? It might seem logical to say none, but that is not correct. During each half-life, half of the *remaining* thorium-234 nuclides decay. There will be 20 g of Th-234 when the second half-life begins, of which 10 g will decay during the second half-life, leaving 10 g after 48.2 d. After

552 Chapter 22

another 24.1 d, half of the 10 g will decay, leaving 5 g. In this example, the conservation of mass requires that there will always be 40 g of matter—it's just changing from one nuclide to another.

The above example is a great starting point, but we were only considering the sample at the end of each half-life. Real-world science is never so clear-cut. Scientists need to be able to analyze decay after any amount of elapsed time. To accomplish this, scientists model half-life with the exponential decay equation

$$N = N_0(0.5)^{\frac{t}{t_{1/2}}},$$

where N is the remaining amount of a radioisotope in grams or particles, N_0 is the original amount, t is the elapsed time, and $t_{1/2}$ is the radioisotope's half-life. Let's look at a few example problems dealing with radioactive decay and half-life.

TABLE 22-2 *Half-Lives*

Nucleus	Half-Life
oxygen-13	8.9 ms
bromine-80	17.7 min
magnesium-28	21.0 h
radon-222	3.8 d
thorium-234	24.1 d
hydrogen-3	12.33 y
carbon-14	5.73×10^3 y
uranium-238	4.47×10^9 y

EXAMPLE 22-7: CALCULATING AMOUNT REMAINING

A 192 g sample of thorium-234 decays for 17.9 d. At the end of this time, how much thorium-234 remains?

Write what you know.

$N_0 = 192$ g
$t = 17.9$ d
$t = 24.1$ d (from Table 22-2)
$N = ?$

Write the formula and solve for the unknown.

$N = N_0(0.5)^{\frac{t}{t_{1/2}}}$

Plug in known values and evaluate.

$$N = 192\text{ g}\,(0.5)^{\frac{17.9\text{ d}}{24.1\text{ d}}}$$
$$= 192\text{ g}\,(0.5)^{0.7427}$$
$$= (192\text{ g})(0.5976)$$
$$= 115\text{ g}$$

There would still be 115 g of thorium-234 remaining after 17.9 d.

EXAMPLE 22-8: CALCULATING INITIAL AMOUNT

You order a sample that contains magnesium-24. When you receive the sample, it contains 34.5 g of magnesium-24. If the sample was shipped 45.3 h ago, what was the mass of magnesium-24 in the sample when it was shipped?

Write what you know.

$N = 34.5$ g
$t = 45.3$ h
$t_{1/2} = 21.0$ h (from Table 22-2)
$N_0 = ?$

Write the formula and solve for the unknown.

$$N = N_0(0.5)^{\frac{t}{t_{1/2}}}$$
$$\frac{N}{(0.5)^{\frac{t}{t_{1/2}}}} = \frac{N_0(0.5)^{\frac{t}{t_{1/2}}}}{(0.5)^{\frac{t}{t_{1/2}}}}$$
$$N_0 = \frac{N}{(0.5)^{\frac{t}{t_{1/2}}}}$$

Plug in known values and evaluate.

$$N_0 = \frac{34.5\text{ g}}{(0.5)^{\frac{45.3\text{ h}}{21.0\text{ h}}}}$$
$$= \frac{34.5\text{ g}}{(0.5)^{2.157}}$$
$$= \frac{34.5\text{ g}}{0.2242}$$
$$= 154\text{ g}$$

The sample originally contained 154 g of magnesium-24.

DECAY

Use the following **formative assessment** to check students' understanding.

1. What is the name for the particles and waves that parent nuclides emit that have enough kinetic energy to knock electrons out of neighboring atoms? *(ionizing radiation)*
2. What is the charge of an alpha particle? *(+2)*
3. Which type of decay has the greatest power of penetration? *(gamma rays)*
4. Predict the type of decay that $^{37}_{18}Ar$ will undergo. *(positron emission or electron capture)*
5. Write the nuclear equation for the beta decay of $^{210}_{83}Bi$.

   ($^{210}_{83}Bi \longrightarrow {}^{210}_{84}Po + {}^{0}_{-1}e$)

EXPONENTIAL VERSUS LINEAR

Use the following **illustration** to demonstrate how quickly exponential sequences grow. Ask, "Would you rather have a million dollars or a penny on day one, $.02 on day 2, and so on, the amount doubled every day until day 30?" If students say that they would rather have a million dollars, explain how doubling the amount every day would actually result in their having $5,368,709.12 on day 30.

APPLY

LAB 22A: *IT'S ONLY A MATTER OF TIME*

Once students have an understanding of the material in Section 22.2, they should be ready to work through Lab 22A.

ASSESS

TICKET OUT THE DOOR

As a **summarizing activity**, ask students to explain half-life. *(A half-life is the time it takes for half a sample of a parent nuclide to decay to a daughter nuclide.)*

22.2 REVIEW *ANSWERS*

* An asterisk following a question number indicates that a worked-out solution can be found on page 569A.

1. Ionizing radiation is any electromagnetic energy or particle that has sufficient energy to ionize an atom that it collides with. *(p. 545)*

2. gamma decay, beta decay, alpha decay *(pp. 546–49)*

3. a. alpha

b. positron emission or electron capture

c. beta

d. alpha

e. positron emission or electron capture *(all pp. 546–48)*

4. a. $^{217}_{86}Rn \longrightarrow ^{213}_{84}Po + ^{4}_{2}He$

b. $^{238}_{94}Pu \longrightarrow ^{234}_{92}U + ^{4}_{2}He$

c. $^{214}_{83}Bi \longrightarrow ^{214}_{84}Po + ^{0}_{-1}e$

d. $^{234}_{91}Pa \longrightarrow ^{234}_{92}U + ^{0}_{-1}e$

e. $^{18}_{9}F \longrightarrow ^{18}_{8}O + ^{0}_{+1}e$

f. $^{22}_{11}Na \longrightarrow ^{22}_{10}Ne + ^{0}_{+1}e$

g. $^{26}_{13}Al + ^{0}_{-1}e \longrightarrow ^{26}_{12}Mg$

h. $^{59}_{28}Ni + ^{0}_{-1}e \longrightarrow ^{59}_{27}Co$

i. $^{152}_{63}Eu^* \longrightarrow ^{152}_{63}Eu + ^{0}_{0}\gamma$

j. $^{165}_{66}Dy^* \longrightarrow ^{165}_{66}Dy + ^{0}_{0}\gamma$ *(all pp. 546–49)*

5. a. alpha decay and beta decay

b. polonium; 164.3 μs

c. lead; stable (no half-life) *(all p. 550)*

6. Answers will vary. A scientist with a biblical worldview would know that dating a rock sample containing U-238 on the basis of its 4.5 billion year half-life would lead to results that are incompatible with the biblical narrative. *(pp. 552–53)*

7.*a. 1.67 g

b. 109.1 g

c. 3.03×10^5 y *(all pp. 552–53)*

EXAMPLE 22-9: CALCULATING DECAY TIME

A scientist starts with a 15.4 mg sample of radon-222. How many days will it take for the sample to decay so that there is less than 1.00 mg remaining?

Write what you know.

$N_0 = 15.4$ mg
$N = 1.00$ mg
$t_{½} = 3.8$ d (from Table 22-2)
$t = ?$

Write the formula and solve for the unknown.

$$N = N_0(0.5)^{\frac{t}{t_{½}}}$$

$$\frac{N}{N_0} = \frac{\cancel{N_0}(0.5)^{\frac{t}{t_{½}}}}{\cancel{N_0}}$$

$$\log_{0.5}\left(\frac{N}{N_0}\right) = \log_{0.5}(0.5)^{\frac{t}{t_{½}}}$$

$$t_{½}\frac{t}{\cancel{t_{½}}} = t_{½}\left(\log_{0.5}\left(\frac{N}{N_0}\right)\right)$$

$$t = t_{½}\left(\log_{0.5}\left(\frac{N}{N_0}\right)\right)$$

Plug in known values and evaluate.

$$t = (3.8\text{ d})\left(\log_{0.5}\left(\frac{1.00\ \cancel{\text{mg}}}{15.4\ \cancel{\text{mg}}}\right)\right)$$
$$= (3.8\text{ d})(\log_{0.5}(0.064\underline{9}3))$$
$$= (3.8\text{ d})(3.9\underline{4}4)$$
$$= 15\text{ d}$$

It will take 15 d for the sample to decay to the point of having less than a milligram of radon-222 remaining.

22.2 SECTION REVIEW

1. What is ionizing radiation?
2. Rank alpha, beta, and gamma decay according to decreasing penetrating power of their products.
3. Use the nuclear stability graph on page 540 to predict the type of decay that each of the following nuclides will undergo.
   a. $^{154}_{66}Dy$
   b. $^{83}_{38}Sr$
   c. $^{61}_{26}Fe$
   d. $^{232}_{94}Pu$
   e. $^{11}_{6}C$
4. Write the equation for each of the following.
   a. alpha decay of $^{217}_{86}Rn$
   b. alpha decay of $^{238}_{94}Pu$
   c. beta decay of $^{214}_{83}Bi$
   d. beta decay of $^{234}_{91}Pa$
   e. positron emission of $^{18}_{9}F$
   f. positron emission of $^{22}_{11}Na$
   g. electron capture of $^{26}_{13}Al$
   h. electron capture of $^{59}_{28}Ni$
   i. gamma decay of $^{152}_{63}Eu$
   j. gamma decay of $^{165}_{66}Dy$
5. Use the uranium decay series shown on page 550 to answer the following questions.
   a. What two kinds of decays does this chain show?
   b. What is the most short-lived nuclide on the chart? Give its half-life.
   c. What is the most stable nuclide on the chart? Give its half-life.
6. How could your worldview affect the way that you would date rocks containing U-238, given its half-life?
7. Solve the following half-life problems.
   a. Oxygen-15 has a half-life of 2.04 min. If you prepare for an experiment by obtaining a 301.75 g sample of pure oxygen-15 and it takes 15.3 min for additional preparations, how much oxygen-15 remains when the experiment begins?
   b. The half-life of hydrogen-3 is 12.32 y. If you have 35.86 g of hydrogen-3 after it is allowed to decay for 19.78 y, with what mass of hydrogen-3 did you start?
   c. The half-life of thorium-230 is 7.538×10^4 y. How long will it take for a 16.2 g sample to decay to less than 1.00 g?

WORLDVIEW INVESTIGATION

RADIOMETRIC DATING

Radiometric dating is a scientific technique in which the radioactive isotopes in a sample are compared with amounts of the decay products in the sample. On the basis of the half-life of the specific isotope, the age of the sample can be estimated. There are many different isotopes that are used for radiometric dating. Radiocarbon dating uses the decay of carbon-14 to estimate the date of formerly living material such as trees.

On the day that you learned about radiometric dating in chemistry, your history teacher told you about the remains of a wooden ship that was said to be 15,000 years old. As a young-earth creationist, you wonder about the age of that ship.

The Oseberg Ship in the Viking Ship Museum, Bygdøy, Oslo, Norway

Task

You have decided to learn more about radiometric dating so that you will have a better understanding of the topic. Prepare a one-page outline of the current research from both secular and creationist sources on the subject of radiometric dating.

Process

1. Conduct research on a biblical view at the website for the Institute for Creation Research and Answers in Genesis. Use the keywords "RATE Project," "Carbon Dating Undercuts Evolution's Long Ages," and "Measurable 14C in Fossilized Organic Materials."
2. Conduct research on a secular view at the website for the American Chemical Society. Use the keywords "Carbon-14 dating," "Carbon Dating Undercuts Evolution's Long Ages," and "Discovery of Radiocarbon Dating."
3. Prepare your outline of radiometric dating and share it with a classmate for review.
4. Finalize your outline and turn it in.

Conclusion

Radiocarbon dating is a scientific tool. As with all things in science, it is affected by worldview. We must assess scientific models and theories with the correct lens of a biblical worldview.

WORLDVIEW INVESTIGATION: RADIOMETRIC DATING

Appendix K includes a reproducible rubric to assess the worldview investigation activity.

SECTION 22.3 *OVERVIEW*

Essential Question

Are nuclear power plants worth the risk?

Objectives

» **22.3.1** Compare nuclear decay, nuclear reactions, and chemical reactions.

» **22.3.2** Distinguish between nuclear fission and fusion.

» **22.3.3** Write the nuclear equation for fission reactions.

» **22.3.4** Explain the relationship between the mass of a fissionable substance and a chain reaction.

» **22.3.5** Calculate the energy released in a nuclear reaction.

» **22.3.6** Explain how worldview impacts assumptions about and conclusions drawn from radiometric dating. BWS

» **22.3.7** Construct a position on whether to support or oppose building a nuclear plant near the local community. BWS

Resources

Ethics: Nuclear Power (p. 569)

Web Links: Nuclear Fission Simulation; How Do Nuclear Power Plants Work?

Mini Lab: *Inquiring into Chain Reactions*; Lab 22B: *Atomic Asteroids*—Determining Mass Defect and Binding Energy

ENGAGE

NUCLEAR CHEMISTRY REVIEW

Prompt students to do a **turn and talk** as a review of Sections 22.1 and 22.2. Students should take two minutes to write down all they can recall from these sections. Once time is up, have them turn to a peer and take turns sharing information with one another.

When students have finished, select several to share their responses with the class. Be sure to correct any misunderstandings and discuss any difficult concepts.

QUESTIONS

» How is a nuclear reaction different from nuclear decay or chemical reactions?

» What is the difference between fission and fusion?

» How can nuclear reactions sustain themselves?

» How much energy is released in a nuclear reaction?

TERMS

transmutation • nuclear fission • chain reaction • critical mass • nuclear fusion

Are nuclear power plants worth the risk?

22.3 USING NUCLEAR CHEMISTRY

Nuclear Reactions

Alchemists dreamed of changing base metals such as lead into gold. We've seen that radioactive decay can naturally change parent nuclides into very different daughter nuclides. But what about changing lead into gold? This can't happen spontaneously through a nuclear decay process—it requires a nuclear reaction. Nuclear reactions are different from radioactive decay because they typically do not occur spontaneously and usually involve more than one particle. One such kind of nuclear reaction is called a *nuclear bombardment reaction*, in which a nucleus is struck by a high-energy particle.

So what are some differences between a nuclear reaction and a chemical reaction? A few of the differences are obvious. In chemical reactions, bonds are broken and formed between atoms, but the atomic nuclei remain unchanged. Chemical reactions involve only electrons, while nuclear reactions affect entire atoms, including their nuclei.

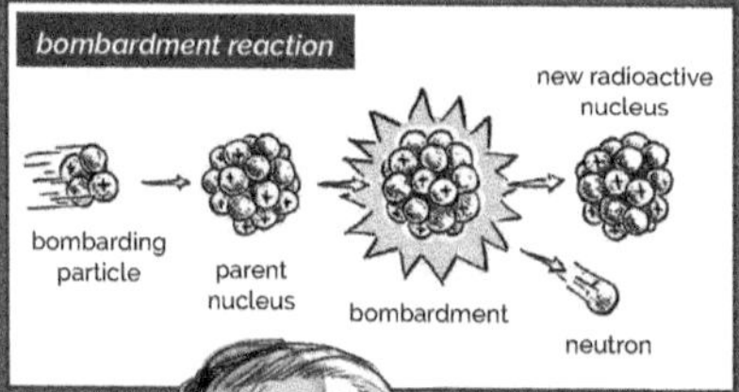

Ernest Rutherford

The rates of chemical reactions can be affected by pressure, concentration, temperature, and catalysts, and such reactions usually involve relatively modest changes in energy. But that all changes in a nuclear reaction, where atoms can send out particles and rays, changing their identity in the process and releasing huge amounts of energy. Nuclear reactions are generally unaffected by pressures and temperatures associated with chemical reactions, but some can occur only at extreme pressures and temperatures.

A **transmutation** is the process by which an atom of one element changes into another element by changing the number of protons in the atom's nucleus. Transmutations can occur naturally, as in nuclear decay or solar fusion, but can also be caused by humans, as in some nuclear reactions. Scientists have used this process to create artificial elements.

Before the atomic age began, scientists knew of no elements with atomic numbers higher than that of uranium ($Z = 92$). In 1919 Ernest Rutherford, who theorized the existence of atomic nuclei from his gold foil experiment, bombarded nitrogen with alpha particles and found that it produced protons and an isotope of oxygen.

$$^{14}_{7}\text{N} + ^{4}_{2}\text{He} \longrightarrow ^{17}_{8}\text{O} + ^{1}_{1}\text{p}$$

His experiment was the first known induced transmutation.

In 1934 Italian physicist Enrico Fermi sent shock waves through the scientific world. Theorizing that if uranium could be forced to emit an electron from one of its neutrons, then the remaining part of the neutron would become a proton. If this were to happen, he could produce an element beyond uranium. Fermi succeeded in producing several elements with atomic numbers higher than uranium, though he couldn't verify their existence. Neptunium was first produced in 1940 when uranium-239 atoms underwent beta decay.

$$^{239}_{92}U \longrightarrow ^{239}_{93}Np + ^{0}_{-1}e$$

Presently, scientists have produced elements up to atomic number 118. The elements following uranium on the periodic table were all produced with nuclear bombardment reactions. As you learned back in Chapter 6, scientists call elements with atomic numbers higher than 92 transuranium elements.

Fission

As scientists continued their work to produce heavier elements, some were surprised when their bombardment reactions produced lighter elements. Austrian physicist Lise Meitner was the first to correctly identify the process of fission after observing its products. **Nuclear fission** is the process in which some very heavy nuclei are split apart into smaller, more stable nuclei. Fission reactions are usually triggered by bombardment of heavy nuclei with high-energy particles, though some fission reactions occur spontaneously. For instance, uranium-235 can be bombarded with neutrons ($^{1}_{0}n$) to split the nucleus and release various fragments, some free neutrons, and a tremendous amount of energy. There may be more than one way for the nucleus to split. The equations below show two of the ways that uranium-235 can split.

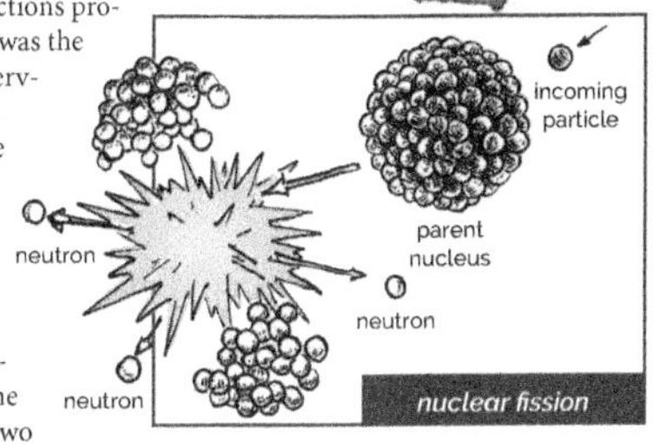

$$^{235}_{92}U + ^{1}_{0}n \longrightarrow ^{141}_{56}Ba + ^{92}_{36}Kr + 3^{1}_{0}n + \text{energy}$$

$$^{235}_{92}U + ^{1}_{0}n \longrightarrow ^{139}_{52}Te + ^{94}_{40}Zr + 3^{1}_{0}n + \text{energy}$$

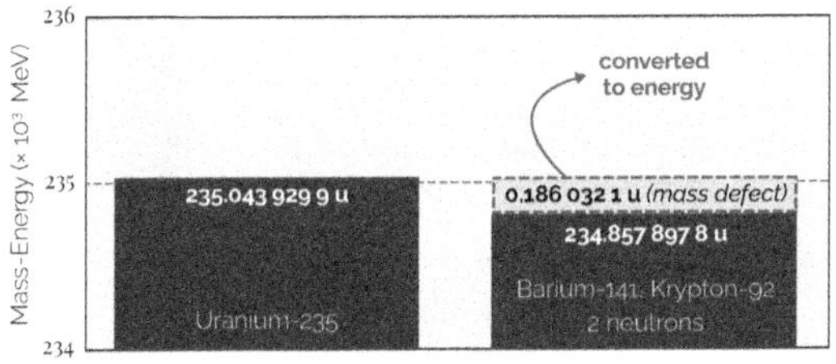

The difference between the binding energy per nucleon of the parent nuclide U-235 and the daughter nuclides Ba-141 and Kr-92 is the energy released in the nuclear reaction, or the mass defect.

Writing equations for nuclear reactions is similar to writing an equation for nuclear decay. Once again, the mass numbers and atomic numbers must balance on each side of the equation. Let's look at an example.

NUCLEAR FISSION SIMULATION

To see a fun way for students to manipulate their own chain reactions by changing the concentrations of U-235 and U-238, visit TeacherToolsOnline.com. Under Additional Resources, click on Chapter 22 Web Links. Then click on *Nuclear Fission Simulation*.

INSTRUCT

TRANSMUTATION

Help students to understand that transmutations can occur in two ways: by radioactive decay and by induced transmutation, where high energy particles (protons, neutrons, or alpha particles) bombard a nucleus.

TRANSURANIUM ELEMENTS

Transuranium elements have been synthesized in nuclear reactors and nuclear accelerators, which make bombarding particles accelerate to very high speeds. Only two transuranium elements are found in nature—neptunium and plutonium—and only in trace amounts. All transuranium elements are unstable and radioactive.

EXAMPLE 22-10:
WRITING THE EQUATION FOR A NUCLEAR REACTION

By bombarding a plutonium-239 nucleus with a neutron, we can trigger a fission reaction. The reaction produces two nuclei and three neutrons. One of the nuclei is zirconium-103. Write the nuclear equation.

Solution

To finish the equation, we need to balance the mass numbers and atomic numbers.

$$239 + 1 = A + 103 + 3$$
$$A = 134$$
$$94 + 0 = Z + 40 + 0$$
$$Z = 54$$

The element with atomic number 54 is xenon. The nuclear equation is

$$^{239}_{94}\text{Pu} + ^{1}_{0}\text{n} \longrightarrow ^{134}_{54}\text{Xe} + ^{103}_{40}\text{Zr} + 3\,^{1}_{0}\text{n} + \text{energy.}$$

Even though the atomic and mass numbers balance, empirical measurement of the products and reactants reveals that there is a small change in mass between the two sides of the equation. Recall from Section 22.1 that mass defect is the difference in the mass of a nucleus and the sum of the masses of all the nucleons. A nucleus with a high mass defect needs more energy to hold it together. In the example above, the plutonium nucleus has a higher mass defect than the combined mass defects of the products; in other words the products are more stable than the reactant. The change in energy required to hold the nuclei together is equal to the energy released in the nuclear reaction.

The energy released in a nuclear reaction can also be calculated by calculating the overall change in mass between the two sides of the equation. This "missing" mass can then be converted to its energy equivalence by using Einstein's equation, $E = mc^2$. The nuclear reaction converts the "missing" mass to energy. So how much energy does the fission of uranium-235 into barium-141 and krypton-92 produce?

558 Chapter 22

EXAMPLE 22-11: CALCULATING ENERGY FROM A NUCLEAR REACTION

Given the isotope masses of uranium-235 (235.053 9299 u), barium-141 (140.914 411 9 u), krypton-92 (91.926 156 1 u), and a free neutron (1.008 664 9 u), calculate the energy released by the fission of uranium-235.

$$^{235}_{92}\text{U} + ^{1}_{0}\text{n} \longrightarrow ^{141}_{56}\text{Ba} + ^{92}_{36}\text{Kr} + 3^{1}_{0}\text{n} + \text{energy}$$

Calculate the mass of the reactants.

$$235.043\,9299 \text{ u} + 1.008\,664\,9 \text{ u} = 236.052\,594\,8 \text{ u}$$

Calculate the mass of the products.

$$140.914\,411\,9 \text{ u} + 91.926\,156\,1 \text{ u} + 3(1.008\,664\,9 \text{ u}) = 235.866\,562\,7 \text{ u}$$

Calculate the mass defect.

$$m_{\text{defect}} = m_{\text{product}} - m_{\text{reactants}} = 235.866\,562\,7 \text{ u} - 236.052\,594\,8 \text{ u} = -0.186\,032\,1 \text{ u}$$

Convert the mass defect from daltons to kilograms.

$$-0.186\,032\,1 \text{ u}\left(\frac{1 \text{ g}}{6.022 \times 10^{23} \text{ u}}\right)\left(\frac{1 \text{ kg}}{1000 \text{ g}}\right) = -3.089\,207\,9 \times 10^{-28} \text{ kg}$$

Write the formula and solve for the unknown.

$$E = mc^2$$

Plug in known values and evaluate.

$$E = (-3.089\,207\,9 \times 10^{-28} \text{ kg})(3.0 \times 10^{8} \text{m/s})^2 = -2.78 \times 10^{-11} \text{ J for every nucleus.}$$

To put the energy released in a nuclear reaction in perspective, the energy released in the fusion of 1 kg of uranium-235 would require burning over 2 *billion* kilograms of coal!

In the binding energy per nucleon graph (p. 542), as expected, the observed mass defects for the various elements match the observed binding energies. Nuclei with mass numbers near 56 have the highest binding energy per nuclear particle. This means that they are the most stable. The energy released is the result of the mass defect produced when these more stable nuclei form.

EXAMPLE 22-12: NUCLEAR BINDING ENERGY COMPARISON

Using the binding energy per nucleon graph, determine which of the following nuclei is the most stable on the basis of its nuclear binding energy: hydrogen-2, arsenic-75, or uranium-235.

Solution

From the binding energy per nucleon graph, you can see that of the three nuclei mentioned, arsenic-75 has the highest binding energy per nucleon. Therefore, it is the most stable—it is closest to 56 u.

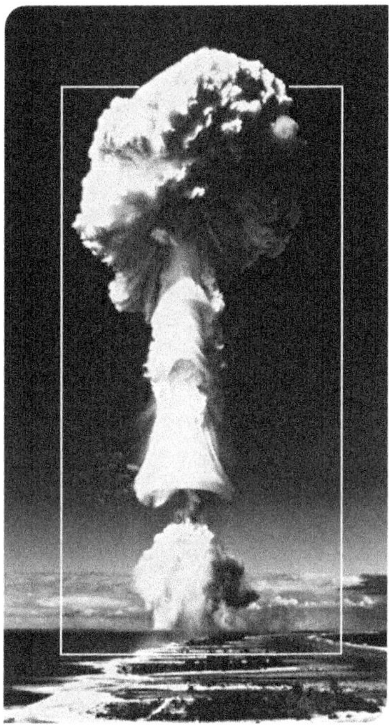

This picture taken in 1970 shows a French nuclear test at Mururoa, French Polynesia.

CONTAMINATED FISSION

The elements Ba, Kr, Cs, and Rb shown in the reaction of U-235 are just some of the hundreds of particles, known as *contaminants*, produced during the fission process. When these contaminants are removed, the concentration of U-235 increases. This is known as *enrichment*. Nuclear reactors tend to use enriched fuel that has a low concentration of U-235 to help control the fission reaction. The enriched fuel used in nuclear weapons contains a high concentration of U-235.

KEEPING REACTIONS IN CHECK

Nuclear reactors use control rods, which are made of a material that absorbs neutrons and which moderates the reaction. Even if the control rods are removed, the concentration of fissionable uranium in the fuel is too low to cause an explosion like a nuclear bomb.

HOW DO NUCLEAR POWER PLANTS WORK?

For an animation that describes how nuclear power plants work to provide energy to the public, visit TeacherToolsOnline.com. Under Additional Resources, click on Chapter 22 Web Links. Then click on *How Nuclear Power Plants Work*.

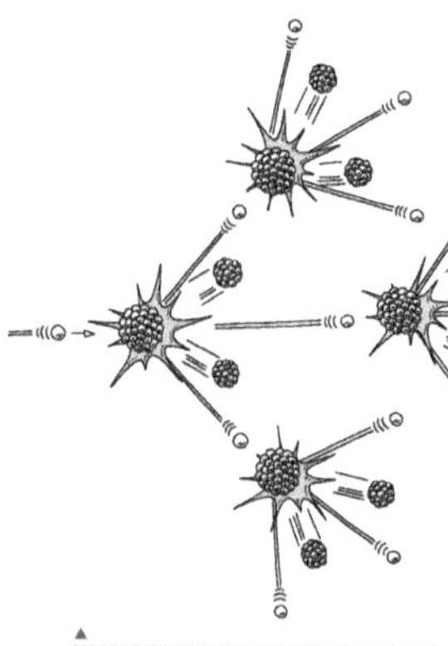

The fission of U-235 can trigger a chain reaction if a critical mass of uranium is present.

CHAIN REACTIONS

The fission of a uranium-235 nuclide produces, among other things, an average of between 2 and 3 neutrons. What happens to these neutrons? They can either escape from the sample of uranium or they can collide with other uranium-235 atoms. If three neutrons are released and hit three other uranium-235 nuclei, the impacted nuclei may immediately undergo fission themselves, releasing up to 9 more neutrons. These neutrons can, in turn, initiate more nuclear fission reactions, and so on. This ongoing fission process, in which the neutrons from one reaction trigger additional reactions, is called a **chain reaction**. It can occur only if the sample of uranium is large and dense enough to intercept many of the released neutrons. If the mass of uranium is too small or too spread out, a condition known as a *subcritical mass* exists and many neutrons will escape without initiating more nuclear fission reactions—and a chain reaction does not occur. The smallest mass of a fissionable substance that can sustain a chain reaction is called the **critical mass** of the substance. If the mass of fissionable material is larger or more compact than the critical mass, the mass produces many neutrons and the chain reaction proceeds out of control, as happens in the detonation of a nuclear bomb.

While each reaction converts only a small amount of mass into energy, chain reactions release vast amounts of thermal energy because they involve unimaginably large numbers of nuclei. This is the energy that technology has enabled us to harness to generate electricity in nuclear power plants. But the chain reaction in a power plant has to be closely monitored and controlled. Perhaps nuclear power plants could be one way that nuclear chemistry helps people in China who live in unhealthy environments caused by coal-fired power plants.

560 Chapter 22

MINI LAB

INQUIRING INTO CHAIN REACTIONS

Nuclear reactions convert mass into energy. Each individual reaction generates only a small amount of energy, but nuclear power plants produce vast amounts of energy because many fission reactions occur in a short amount of time. This is possible because nuclear engineers design the reactors to take advantage of chain reactions. In this inquiry lab activity, you will try to model a chain reaction and then see whether you can modify the process to speed it up.

How can we alter a chain reaction?

EQUIPMENT

- dominoes (30)
- stopwatch

1. What is a chain reaction?

Procedure

A. Standing each domino on its narrow end, arrange all thirty in such a way as to make all the dominoes fall by pushing on only one domino.

B. Using the stopwatch, time how long it takes for all thirty dominoes to fall when you push over the first one.

2. What does a domino represent?
3. What does the domino falling represent?

C. Rearrange the dominoes to decrease the time needed for all the dominoes to fall.

Conclusion

4. How does this exercise model a chain reaction?
5. What arrangement resulted in the shortest time for all the dominoes to fall?

Going Further

6. How does your answer to Question 5 represent the concept of critical mass?

MINI LAB: *INQUIRING INTO CHAIN REACTIONS*

Use this **mini lab** as an inquiry into modeling and modifying chain reactions.

1. A chain reaction is one in which a product of one reaction starts another reaction.
2. an atom that can undergo fission
3. an atom undergoing fission
4. The falling of each domino triggers the next one or two dominoes to fall. This is similar to the neutrons from a fission reaction starting the next reaction(s).
5. Answers will vary. Students should find that placing the dominoes close together and having each falling domino strike multiple dominoes will result in the fastest fall time.
6. Critical mass is the smallest amount of matter in sufficient concentration to maintain a chain reaction. More dominoes closer together produces more events.

NATURALLY OCCURRING FISSION AND FUSION

Natural fission is very rare; it must usually be induced. Fusion, on the other hand, is common throughout the universe.

Fusion

Nuclear fusion is the transmutation process of combining several light nuclei to form more massive nuclei. You can think of it as the opposite of fission. You might expect fusion to absorb energy, but instead, it releases even more energy than fission does. To understand why this is, look back at the binding energy per nucleon graph on the opposite page. Notice how the left side of the graph is very steep, especially at low mass numbers. Fusion reactions will move us toward the right on the graph, and the change in nuclear binding energy is released as we move toward the most stable atomic mass (56). Both fission and fusion result in more stable materials and are *exergonic*, meaning that they release energy.

Fusion in the sun is a multistep process. It starts with two hydrogen (H-1) nuclei colliding to form deuterium (H-2). The deuterium nucleus collides with another hydrogen nucleus to form helium-3. Two helium-3 nuclei collide to form a helium-4 nucleus and two hydrogen atoms that can continue the process.

$$^{1}_{1}\text{H} + {}^{1}_{1}\text{H} \longrightarrow {}^{2}_{1}\text{H} + {}^{0}_{+1}\text{e (occurs twice)}$$

$$^{1}_{1}\text{H} + {}^{2}_{1}\text{H} \longrightarrow {}^{3}_{2}\text{He (occurs twice)}$$

$$^{3}_{2}\text{He} + {}^{3}_{2}\text{He} \longrightarrow {}^{4}_{2}\text{He} + 2\,{}^{1}_{1}\text{H (occurs once)}$$

The net reaction is shown below.

$$4\,{}^{1}_{1}\text{H} \longrightarrow {}^{4}_{2}\text{He} + 2\,{}^{0}_{+1}\text{e}$$

As with fission, there is a discrepancy of mass between the parent and daughter nuclides of fusion. The nuclei that form a larger nucleus have more mass than the product of the reaction. The nuclear mass of helium is 4.003 u. However, the combined masses of the two protons (2 × 1.0073 u) and the two neutrons (2 × 1.0087 u) equal 4.0320 u—a 0.029 u difference. Just as in fission, this lost mass is transformed into an enormous amount of energy.

Again refer to the graph of binding energy per nucleon on the facing page. Nuclides to the left of the peak could potentially undergo fusion, and nuclides to the right of the peak could potentially undergo fission. The graph peaks at a mass number of 56, demonstrating that the greater the binding energy per nucleon, the more stable the nucleus will be and the less likely that it will experience fusion or fission. Any element with a mass number of 56 will achieve the greatest stability

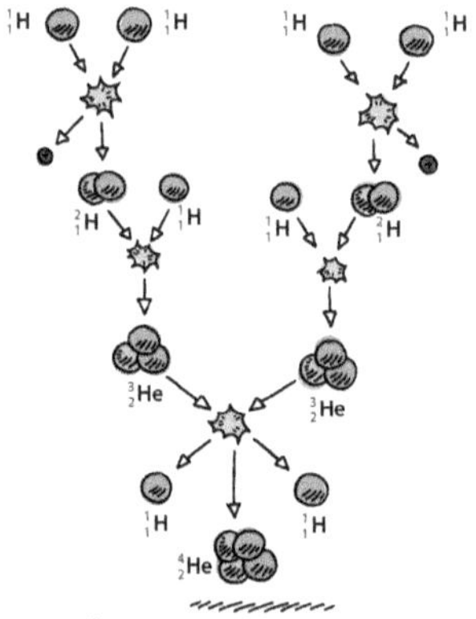

Nuclear fusion is important to all living things because it fuels our sun and other stars. The reaction forms a helium nucleus and an immense amount of energy. This is the most common form of fusion.

possible. Thus, when bombarded by nuclear particles, elements higher than 56 can fission into smaller elements to become more stable. Elements lower than 56 can fuse to become more stable. Both processes produce vast amounts of energy.

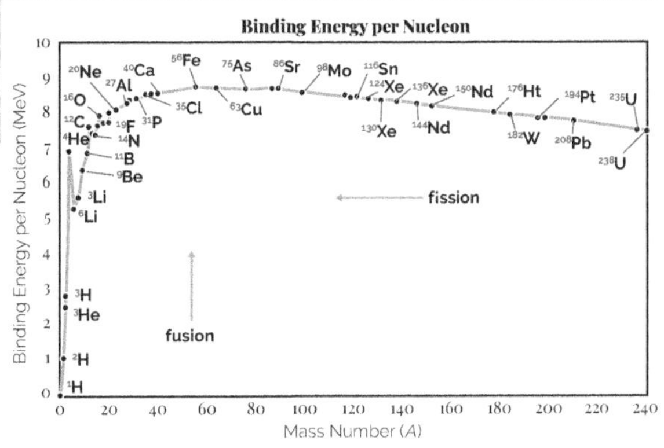

Binding energy per nucleon peaks near an atomic mass of 56 u. Notice how fission and fusion processes are related to binding energy in this diagram.

EXAMPLE 22-13: FUSION OR FISSION PREDICTION

Using the graph above, predict which of the following candidates are more likely to undergo fusion or fission: hydrogen-3, technetium-97, beryllium-7, or plutonium-239.

Solution

Because hydrogen-3 and beryllium-7 are to the left of iron-56 on the graph, they are more likely to undergo fusion. The nuclides technetium-97 and plutonium-239 are strong candidates for fission because they are to the right of iron-56.

Although the concept of fusing two atoms may appear simple, light nuclei must collide with enough kinetic energy to overcome the natural repulsion between nuclei before nuclear fusion can occur. Temperatures close to 100 000 000 K are required before nuclei have enough energy for fusion to proceed. Because so much thermal energy is required, scientists call fusion reactions *thermonuclear reactions.* Large amounts of energy must be expended to heat atoms to this temperature. In fact, in the first fusion reactions (hydrogen bombs), atomic fission bombs had to be used to supply the vast amount of energy required to initiate the fusion process. Such extreme conditions also exist within the sun, where fusion is an ongoing process. There, hydrogen nuclei are fused together to form helium nuclei. The vast amount of energy produced is emitted from the sun as electromagnetic radiation. Most of the energy that we use on Earth originates in the nuclear reactions within the sun.

USING NUCLEAR CHEMISTRY

Use the following formative assessment to check students' understanding.

1. Describe a nuclear bombardment reaction. *(It is a reaction in which a nucleus is struck by a high-energy particle.)*
2. Explain the concept of transmutation. *(It is the process by which an atom of one type of element changes into another by changing the number of protons in the atom's nucleus.)*
3. What usually triggers a fission reaction? *(the bombardment of heavy nuclei with high-energy particles)*
4. Can a chain reaction start if the uranium sample is too small or too spread out? *(No. A chain reaction will not occur because the uranium is at subcritical mass.)*
5. If 100.0 g of carbon-14 decays until only 25.0 g of carbon-14 is left after 11 460 y, what is the half-life of carbon-14?

What we know: $N_0 = 100.0$ g, $N = 25.0$ g, $t = 11\,460$ y

Unknown: $t_{½}$

Write the formula and solve for the unknown.

$$N = N_0(0.5)^{t/t_{½}}$$

$$\frac{N}{N_0} = \frac{\cancel{N_0}(0.5)^{t/t_{½}}}{\cancel{N_0}}$$

$$\log_{0.5}\left(\frac{N}{N_0}\right) = \log_{0.5}(0.5)^{t/t_{½}}$$

$$\log_{0.5}\left(\frac{N}{N_0}\right)t_{½} = \frac{t}{\cancel{t_{½}}}\cancel{t_{½}}$$

$$\frac{\cancel{\log_{0.5}\left(\frac{N}{N_0}\right)}t_{½}}{\cancel{\log_{0.5}\left(\frac{N}{N_0}\right)}} = \frac{t}{\log_{0.5}\left(\frac{N}{N_0}\right)}$$

$$t_{½} = \frac{t}{\log_{0.5}\left(\frac{N}{N_0}\right)}$$

Evaluate.

$$t_{½} = \frac{11\,460 \text{ y}}{\log_{0.5}\left(\frac{25.0\ \cancel{g}}{100.0\ \cancel{g}}\right)}$$

$$= \frac{11\,460 \text{ y}}{\log_{0.5}(0.25)}$$

$$= \frac{11\,460 \text{ y}}{2}$$

$$= 5730 \text{ y}$$

COSMIC RADIATION

Human activity is not the only source of radiation. Cosmic rays coming to the earth from the sun and other stars consist of alpha and beta radiation, protons, and gamma rays. Once cosmic rays reach the earth's atmosphere, they induce reactions in the atmosphere that release gamma radiation. These processes create a significant amount of radiation in the environment.

Aerial view of Grenoble's polygon scientifique, syncrotron ring, and nuclear reactor

Using Nuclear Chemistry to Solve Problems

Over 3 million people in China will be diagnosed with cancer this year. Many of their cancers can be traced back to polluted water and air. And much of the air pollution is from coal-powered electric plants throughout the country. As China continues to develop, its need for electrical power increases. How can they provide this additional power without exacerbating the pollution problem that they already have? Could further decreasing their reliance on coal-burning power plants and increasing their already significant use of nuclear-powered plants solve some of these problems?

Nuclear chemistry can be used to irradiate water by exposing it to ionizing radiation in wastewater treatment plants, removing toxins such as hydrocarbons, nitrogen oxides, heavy metals, and pesticides. Also, many industrialized countries have mastered the technology to harness the fission energy released in nuclear power plants. Using nuclear power plants eliminates the toxic and sometimes radioactive pollutants created by coal-fired power plants. Some reactors even use repurposed nuclear weapons as fuel for generating electricity. Nuclear power produces almost 20% of the electricity generated in the United States. Other countries make even greater use of nuclear power for their energy needs. For example, France provides almost 80% of its electricity using nuclear reactors.

Nuclear chemists and physicists also hope to one day control nuclear fusion reactions and to convert their energy into electricity. This would have the added benefit of avoiding the high-level radioactive nuclear waste products that fission nuclear power plants generate. But the promise of fusion power is not without its challenges. Scientists are currently trying to address the greatest challenge to Earth-based fusion: the necessary containment for the enormous temperatures required for fusion. Researchers are experimenting with various methods of containment, such as magnetic, inertial, and electrostatic confinement. Many nations are spending huge sums of money for the research and development of this almost limitless energy source.

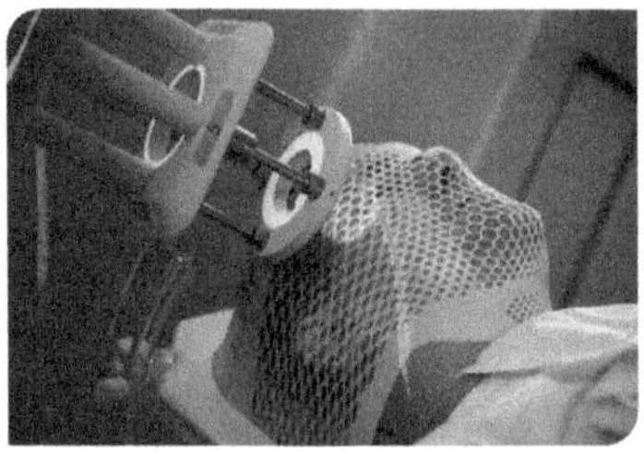

A cancer patient receiving radiotherapy

Nuclear chemistry offers further hope for China and other countries to help treat cancer. We've seen that cobalt-60 undergoes beta decay to release beta particles and gamma rays that can be used to treat cancerous brain tumors. Radiation treatment in a variety of forms is used to treat other cancers as well.

564 Chapter 22

But nuclear chemistry is not limited to producing electricity and treating cancer. Nuclear chemistry helps us explore the outer reaches of space and the depths of the ocean, thanks to the energy density of nuclear fuels. Radiation is used in agriculture as well. It has helped researchers develop new seeds with higher production rates and pest and disease resistance. Radiation is used to control pests by sterilizing them, thereby reducing their numbers. It is a useful tool for sterilizing medical instruments. Radiation also lets us see the invisible by giving us the ability to image the body's systems, defects in bridges, the levels of liquids in tanks and oil wells, and even the atmosphere of Jupiter.

But, as with any area in science, we need to consider the risks along with the benefits of nuclear chemistry. Newsworthy accidents, such as the ones that occurred at Chernobyl and Fukushima, highlight the risks of nuclear power. In the Nuclear Power ethics box on page 569, you'll be tasked with developing a position on the use of nuclear energy for power production. Part of your decision making must include assessing the risks of nuclear power. Using God's world in ways that please Him involves minimizing the risks and maximizing the benefits of our efforts to exercise dominion. This means that we should develop a mindset of safety that evaluates and minimizes risk.

In your journey through chemistry this year, you've seen how the Bible's account of Creation, the Fall, and Redemption encapsulates a biblical worldview that gives us a framework for all of life. As you looked at chemistry through the lens of Scripture, you have found that the best reasons to study and practice chemistry are biblical ones. We can use the tool of chemistry to help find solutions to the challenges of malaria, cancer villages, electricity generation, and so much more for God's glory and mankind's good.

Inner Radiation Belts of Jupiter

22.3 SECTION REVIEW

1. What is a bombardment reaction?
2. State two ways in which nuclear fission and nuclear fusion are similar and one way in which they are dissimilar.
3. Complete the nuclear equation for the fission of uranium-233 using the partial equation below.

$$^{233}_{92}\text{U} + ^{1}_{0}\text{n} \longrightarrow ^{A}_{Z}\text{X} + ^{137}_{54}\text{Xe} + 3\,^{1}_{0}\text{n} + \text{energy}$$

4. What happens to the missing mass in a nuclear reaction represented by the mass defect?
5. Explain the relationship between the terms *critical mass* and *chain reaction*.
6. Given the isotope masses of plutonium-239 (239.052 163 4 u), xenon-134 (133.905 394 5 u), zirconium-103 (102.926 601 2 u), and a free neutron (1.008 664 9 u), calculate the energy released by the fission of plutonium-239.

$$^{239}_{94}\text{Pu} + ^{1}_{0}\text{n} \longrightarrow ^{134}_{54}\text{Xe} + ^{103}_{40}\text{Zr} + 3\,^{1}_{0}\text{n} + \text{energy}$$

7. Would each of the following nuclides be more likely to undergo fusion or fission? (Use the graph on page 563.)
   a. carbon-12
   b. uranium-235
   c. neon-20

DIFFERENTIATED INSTRUCTION

Nuclear Energy Devices

Direct students to **create an advertisement** for a device that uses nuclear energy. One of the best uses of nuclear energy is as a long-term source of fuel. A nuclear power supply can generate energy for decades without needing to be refueled, so it is ideal for remote devices such as spacecraft, weather stations, navigation buoys, and submarines in the middle of the ocean.

To create their advertisements, students may promote a nuclear-powered device that is currently used or create one that could be used in the future. Their advertisements should include the fuel source's uses, effectiveness, safety, efficiency, cost, environmental impact, health risks, and disposal.

APPLY

LAB 22B: *ATOMIC ASTEROIDS*

Once students have an understanding of the material in Section 22.3, they should be ready to work through Lab 22B.

ASSESS

TICKET OUT THE DOOR

As a **summarizing activity**, ask students to state the difference between fission and fusion. *(Fission is the splitting of heavy nuclei into smaller, more stable nuclei. Fusion is the combining of several light nuclei to form more massive nuclei.)*

22.3 REVIEW *ANSWERS*

* An asterisk following a question number indicates that a worked-out solution can be found on page 569A.

1. A bombardment reaction is a nuclear reaction in which the nucleus is struck by a high-energy particle, perhaps even another nucleus. *(p. 556)*
2. *Similar:* Both are transmutation processes and both release energy. *Dissimilar:* Nuclear fission splits a nucleus into two smaller nuclei; nuclear fusion forms a larger nucleus from two smaller ones. *(pp. 557, 562)*
3. $^{233}_{92}\text{U} + ^{1}_{0}\text{n} \longrightarrow ^{94}_{38}\text{Sr} + ^{137}_{54}\text{Xe} + 3\,^{1}_{0}\text{n} + \text{energy}$ *(pp. 557–58)*
4. This matter changes into energy in the reaction. *(p. 558)*
5. The smallest mass of a fissionable substance that can sustain a chain reaction is called the critical mass of the substance. *(p. 560)*
6. * 3.03×10^{-11} J for every nucleus *(p. 559)*
7. **a.** fusion
   b. fission
   c. fusion *(all p. 563)*

22 CHAPTER REVIEW

Chapter Summary

TERMS

nuclear radiation
radioactivity
nuclide
nucleon
radioisotope
strong nuclear force
band of stability
magic number
mass defect
nuclear binding energy

22.1 INSIDE THE NUCLEUS

- Nuclear chemistry studies the changes that can occur in an atom's nucleus.
- Nuclear radiation, or radioactivity, is the spontaneous emission of particles and energy from an unstable nucleus in order to become more stable.
- The stability of the nucleus depends on the ratio of neutrons to protons. Nuclear shells model nuclear stability well, including the specific numbers of neutrons or protons, or magic numbers, associated with stable nuclei.
- The difference between the mass of an atom's nucleus and the total mass of all the individual nucleons is called the mass defect. Mass defect is related to the energy that binds the nucleus together.
- The SI unit for measuring emitted radiation is the becquerel. The gray is the SI unit that quantifies radiation absorption. A sievert is the measure of the biological effects of absorbed radiation.

22.2 NUCLEAR DECAY

- Nuclear equations use isotope notation to represent the nuclides involved in a nuclear event. Nuclear equations are balanced by accounting for both mass numbers and atomic numbers.
- Alpha decay, beta decay, positron emission, electron capture, and gamma emission all cause predictable changes to the charge and mass of an atom.
- Alpha particles are composed of two protons and two neutrons, giving them a +2 charge. They easily ionize atoms that they collide with and have little penetrating power.
- Beta particles are electrons that form in and are released from the nucleus. They have lower ionizing potential than alpha particles but greater penetrating ability. Beta decay changes a neutron to a proton.
- Positron emission is a form of beta decay, except that a positron (positive electron) is emitted from the nucleus. Positron emission changes a proton to a neutron.
- Electron capture occurs when an inner orbital electron is absorbed by the nucleus. Electron capture changes a proton to a neutron.
- Gamma rays are the most energetic type of radiation and are uncharged electromagnetic waves. They have the greatest power of penetration.
- Many nuclides undergo a series of nuclear reactions that culminate in a stable form. These changes can be represented as a radioactive decay series.
- Half-lives measure the amount of time that it takes for half of a sample of a nuclide to decay.

TERMS

ionizing radiation
nuclear equation
alpha decay
beta decay
positron emission
electron capture
gamma decay
radioactive decay series
half-life

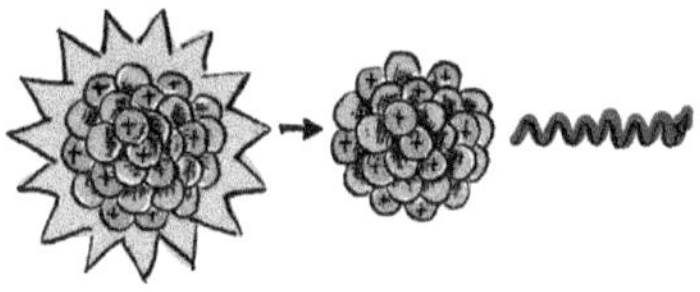

566 Chapter 22

22.3 USING NUCLEAR CHEMISTRY

- Nuclear reactions can be triggered through nuclear bombardment with particles or even other nuclei. This process can be used to create synthetic transuranium elements.
- In nuclear fission, a nucleus splits to produce more stable nuclides.
- A chain reaction of controlled fission is produced when particles emitted from one reaction trigger additional reactions. There must be sufficient mass—the critical mass—to sustain a chain reaction.
- In nuclear fusion, nuclei are fused to form larger, more stable nuclei. Both fission and fusion release great amounts of energy.

TERMS
transmutation
nuclear fission
chain reaction
critical mass
nuclear fusion

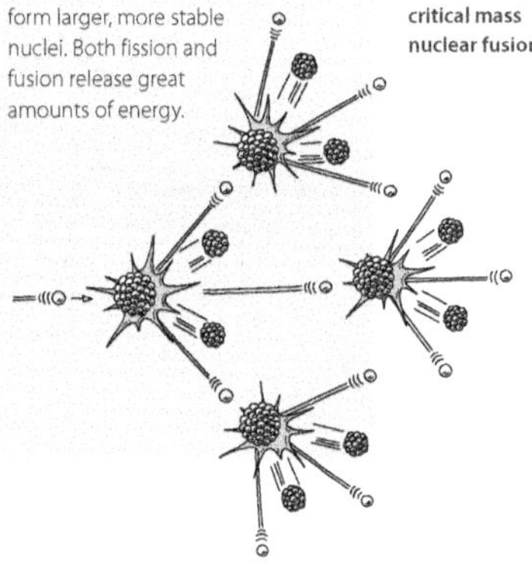

Chapter Review Questions

RECALLING FACTS

1. What is radioactivity?
2. What is the band of stability?
3. Define *binding energy per nucleon*.
4. What are the three SI units related to radioactivity?
5. How are nuclear equations balanced?
6. (True or False) Alpha particles have more mass but less penetrating power than beta particles.
7. Which types of radiation consist of particles? Which consist of only waves?
8. Explain the relationship between ionizing power and the depth of penetration of particles emitted as nuclear radiation.
9. Make a table for the five different types of radioactive decay. Make columns for the name, symbol, nuclear notation, charge, mass number, effect on atomic number, and penetration power. Rate penetration power as low, medium, or high.
10. Make a table that compares nuclear decay, a nuclear reaction, and a chemical reaction.
11. (True or False) The mass needed to sustain a nuclear chain reaction is known as the critical mass.
12. Where does the energy released by fission and fusion come from?
13. Why do some nuclei undergo fission but not fusion?

UNDERSTANDING CONCEPTS

14. Summarize the discoveries of scientists and their impact on our understanding of radioactivity.
15. What determines the stability of a nucleus? Explain.
16. Use the nuclear stability graph on page 540 to predict whether the following nuclides are stable. Explain each prediction.
    a. $^{160}_{70}Yb$
    b. $^{200}_{80}Hg$
    c. $^{55}_{25}Mn$
    d. $^{107}_{42}Mo$
17. Using the nuclear binding energy per nucleon graph on page 542, determine which nuclide in each pair will be more stable.
    a. oxygen-16, tin-119
    b. helium-4, lithium-6
    c. uranium-238, neon-20
    d. tin-119, helium-4
18. Gamma radiation, visible light, and radio waves are all forms of electromagnetic radiation. Why are gamma rays much more dangerous than visible light and radio waves?

Nuclear Chemistry 567

CHAPTER 22 REVIEW ANSWERS

* An asterisk following a question number indicates that a worked-out solution can be found on pages 569B–69C.

Recalling Facts

1. the spontaneous emission of nuclear radiation from the nuclei of unstable atoms *(p. 538)*
2. On a graph of neutrons versus protons that shows all known isotopes, there exists a band of stable isotopes through the middle of plotted data. *(p. 540)*
3. Binding energy is the energy released as nucleons are brought together in a nucleus. The binding energy is related to the mass defect—the mass difference between the sum of the nucleon masses and the mass of the nucleus itself. By dividing the binding energy of each isotope by its number of nucleons, scientists have determined a relationship between mass defect and atomic number. *(p. 542)*
4. becquerel (Bq), gray (Gy), and seivert (Sv) *(p. 543)*
5. Nuclear equations are written with isotope notation instead of chemical formulas. To balance a nuclear equation, both the mass numbers and the atomic numbers on each side of the equation must be balanced. *(p. 545)*
6. True *(p. 546)*
7. alpha, beta, and positron emission radiation; electron capture and gamma radiation *(pp. 546–49)*
8. Radiation with high ionizing power does not penetrate matter very deeply because it interacts with matter quickly. Radiation with low ionizing power penetrates deeply into the matter because it does *not* interact quickly. *(pp. 546–47)*
9.* Tables may vary. *(pp. 546–49)*
10.* *(pp. 546–49, 556)*
11. True *(p. 560)*
12. the transformation of a small amount of matter *(pp. 557, 562)*
13. A substance that undergoes fission readily will not undergo fusion because the product of such a fusion process would be a far larger nuclide and thus less stable than the reactants. *(pp. 562–63)*

Understanding Concepts

14. In 1895 Wilhelm Röntgen accidentally discovered x-rays (a form of nuclear radiation). Henri Becquerel discovered that some elements (uranium) spontaneously emitted radiation. Marie and Pierre Curie continued the research into radiation and coined the term *radioactivity* for the spontaneous emission of particles and energy from unstable nuclei. Ernest Rutherford studied the types of radiation (alpha particles, positrons, beta particles, and gamma rays). *(pp. 537–38)*
15. the ratio of neutrons to protons; In small nuclei ($Z < 20$) a ratio of 1:1 is most stable. As the nuclei get larger and the repulsive force of the protons increases, more neutrons are needed to spread the protons apart. The ratio on larger nuclei increases to about 1.5:1. *(pp. 539–40)*
16. **a.** unstable; The ratio of neutrons to protons is too low.
    b. stable; The ratio of neutrons to protons is sufficient.
    c. stable; The ratio of neutrons to protons is sufficient.
    d. unstable; The ratio of neutrons to protons is too high. *(all p. 540)*
17. **a.** tin-119 (Though Sn-119 is not shown on the graph, its binding energy can be inferred from Sn-116 to be higher than O-16.)
    b. helium-4
    c. neon-20
    d. tin-119 *(all p. 542)*
18. Gamma rays have much higher energy. *(p. 549)*

19. a. beta

b. positron emission or electron capture

c. positron emission or electron capture

d. alpha

e. beta *(all pp. 546–49)*

20. a. ${}^{180}_{74}\text{W} \longrightarrow {}^{176}_{72}\text{Hf} + {}^{4}_{2}\text{He}$

b. ${}^{223}_{88}\text{Ra} \longrightarrow {}^{219}_{86}\text{Rn} + {}^{4}_{2}\text{He}$

c. ${}^{210}_{83}\text{Bi} \longrightarrow {}^{210}_{84}\text{Po} + {}^{0}_{-1}\text{e}$

d. ${}^{225}_{88}\text{Ra} \longrightarrow {}^{225}_{89}\text{Ac} + {}^{0}_{-1}\text{e}$

e. ${}^{126}_{53}\text{I} \longrightarrow {}^{126}_{52}\text{Te} + {}^{0}_{+1}\text{e}$

f. ${}^{13}_{7}\text{N} \longrightarrow {}^{13}_{6}\text{C} + {}^{0}_{+1}\text{e}$

g. ${}^{7}_{4}\text{Be} + {}^{0}_{-1}\text{e} \longrightarrow {}^{7}_{3}\text{Li}$

h. ${}^{53}_{25}\text{Mn} + {}^{0}_{-1}\text{e} \longrightarrow {}^{53}_{24}\text{Cr}$

i. ${}^{60}_{28}\text{Ni}^{*} \longrightarrow {}^{60}_{28}\text{Ni} + {}^{0}_{0}\gamma$

j. ${}^{237}_{93}\text{Np}^{*} \longrightarrow {}^{237}_{93}\text{Np} + {}^{0}_{0}\gamma$ *(all pp. 546–49)*

21. Unstable nuclei decay to become more stable. The process ends once the nucleus becomes stable. *(p. 551)*

22. Br-80 (because it has a shorter half-life) *(p. 553)*

23.*a. 34.2 g

b. 1.06×10^{3} g

c. 2.33 min *(all p. 553)*

24. Fission is the splitting of a nucleus into smaller nuclei, producing energy. Fusion is the combining of two smaller nuclei into a larger nucleus, also producing energy. *(pp. 557, 562)*

25. ${}^{239}_{94}\text{Pu} + {}^{1}_{0}\text{n} \longrightarrow {}^{98}_{43}\text{Tc} + {}^{139}_{51}\text{Sb} + 3\,{}^{1}_{0}\text{n} + \text{energy}$ *(p. 557)*

26. The products of both processes are more stable (have lower energy) than the reactants. Both processes also convert mass to energy. *(pp. 557, 562)*

27.* -3.16×10^{-11} J for every nucleus *(p. 559)*

28. a. Mg-24 (beside Ne-20)

b. Fe-56

c. U-235 *(all p. 563)*

29. Answers will vary. Some areas of chemistry that require a balance of safety and risk include pharmaceutical trials, chemotherapy, mining, and other industries that deal with dangerous chemicals and processes. *(pp. 564–65)*

22 CHAPTER REVIEW

19. Using the nuclear stability graph on page 540, predict the type of decay that each nuclide will undergo.

a. ${}^{143}_{58}\text{Ce}$

b. ${}^{37}_{18}\text{Ar}$

c. ${}^{15}_{8}\text{O}$

d. ${}^{286}_{111}\text{Rg}$

e. ${}^{106}_{44}\text{Ru}$

20. Write the nuclear equation for each of the following.

a. alpha decay of ${}^{180}_{74}\text{W}$

b. alpha decay of ${}^{223}_{88}\text{Ra}$

c. beta decay of ${}^{210}_{83}\text{Bi}$

d. beta decay of ${}^{225}_{88}\text{Ra}$

e. positron emission of ${}^{126}_{53}\text{I}$

f. positron emission of ${}^{13}_{7}\text{N}$

g. electron capture of ${}^{7}_{4}\text{Be}$

h. electron capture of ${}^{53}_{25}\text{Mn}$

i. gamma decay of ${}^{60}_{28}\text{Ni}$

j. gamma decay of ${}^{237}_{93}\text{Np}$

21. Why do the decay processes in a radioactive decay series not continue indefinitely?

22. Using Table 22-2, determine which nuclide decays more quickly: bromine-80 or magnesium-28.

23. Solve the following half-life problems.

a. Iodine-131 is used to treat a hyperactive thyroid gland. The half-life of iodine-131 is 8.02 d. If a hospital receives a 215.25 g shipment of iodine-131, how much will be left after 21.3 d?

b. The half-life of copper-62 is 9.67 min. If you need 10.0 g to conduct an experiment and it will take 65 min to set up the experiment once the sample arrives, how much must be in the sample when it arrives?

c. Carbon-10 has a half-life of 19.29 s. If you have 1.53 kg, how long will it take until you have less than 10.0 g?

24. Explain the difference between nuclear fission and fusion.

25. Given the partial equation below, complete the nuclear equation for the fission of plutonium-239.

$${}^{239}_{94}\text{Pu} + {}^{1}_{0}\text{n} \longrightarrow {}^{A}_{Z}\text{X} + {}^{140}_{51}\text{Sb} + 3\,{}^{1}_{0}\text{n} + \text{energy}$$

26. Why do nuclear fission and nuclear fusion both release energy?

27. Given the isotope masses of plutonium-239 (239.052 1634 u), niobium-104 (103.922 4647 u), iodine-134 (133.909 7449 u), and a free neutron (1.008 6649 u), calculate the energy released by the fission of plutonium-239.

$${}^{239}_{94}\text{Pu} + {}^{1}_{0}\text{n} \longrightarrow {}^{104}_{41}\text{Nb} + {}^{134}_{53}\text{I} + 2\,{}^{1}_{0}\text{n} + \text{energy}$$

28. In the following pairs, determine which nucleus is more stable by referring to the graph on page 563.

a. lithium-6 or magnesium-24

b. uranium-235 or iron-56

c. helium-4 or uranium-235

29. Write a paragraph about another area in chemistry in which safety and risk are an important part of using this field for God's glory and mankind's good. Include in your paragraph uses, risks, and safety considerations in this field of chemistry.

CRITICAL THINKING

30. Why do scientists suspect that there is an island of stability beyond the band of stability?

31. As you are working on a nuclear decay lab activity, you get to the point of having one atom remaining. Your lab partner says, "Just one more half-life and they will all have decayed." Is he correct? Explain.

32. You are working in the laboratory with carbon-11. Your sample has gone from 13.58 g to 8.074 g in 15.25 min. What is the half-life of carbon-11?

33. Iodine-131 experiences beta decay with a half-life of 8.02 d. You start an experiment with a 10.0 g sample. Answer the following questions.

a. How many beta particles will be emitted in the first half-life? Iodine-131 has a molar mass of 130.906 g/mol.

b. Is the number of beta particles emitted per second a constant? Explain.

c. How many beta particles will be emitted per second, on average?

Critical Thinking

30. According to the nuclear shell model, there are magic numbers of nucleons that produce stable nuclei. If the pattern established by the model holds true, there should be elements near atomic number 126 that are stable. *(p. 540)*

31. He may be correct but we can't be sure. Half-life is a statistical function. In one half-life each atom has a 50% chance of decaying. There is no way of knowing whether one particular atom will decay or not. It is very much like flipping a coin: you can't predict the outcome of a single coin flip. *(p. 552)*

32.* 20.33 min *(p. 553)*

33.* a. 2.30×10^{22}

b. No. The rate of decays per second will decrease throughout the half-life. We know this because there is a decrease in the number of decays in each successive half-life, so a change in decays per second must occur throughout each half-life also.

c. 3.32×10^{16} decays/s *(all p. 553)*

34. Suppose that a uranium-238 nucleus were bombarded with a high-energy neutron to fission into iodine-135 and krypton-96, also emitting both neutrons and protons in the process. Write the nuclear equation for this event and determine how many protons and neutrons would be emitted.

$$^{238}_{92}\text{U} + ^{1}_{0}\text{n} \longrightarrow ^{135}_{53}\text{I} + ^{96}_{36}\text{Kr} + X^{1}_{0}\text{n} + Y^{1}_{1} + \text{energy}$$

35. Given the isotope masses of uranium-233 (233.039 u), strontium-94 (93.915 361 u), xenon-137 (136.911 562 1 u), and a free neutron (1.008 664 9 u), calculate the energy released by the fission of 1.75 g of uranium-233.

$$^{233}_{92}\text{U} + ^{1}_{0}\text{n} \longrightarrow ^{94}_{38}\text{Sr} + ^{137}_{54}\text{Xe} + 3^{1}_{0}\text{n} + \text{energy}$$

ethics

NUCLEAR POWER

Introduction

We live in a technology-driven society, and most technology requires electrical energy—lots of electrical energy. We are also living in a time when the environment is a major concern. Many are advocating decreasing our dependence on fossil fuels and increasing our electricity generation from clean sources. Many green technologies are expensive. So how do we balance our energy needs, our obligation to protect the world that God gave us, and the economic reality that solutions are expensive and we have limited resources?

Task

You are a representative in your state legislature. Your state is facing a significant increase in the demand for electrical power. At the same time, numerous groups have approached you about pollution and the environment. Advocates for green power have proposed new, cleaner sources for electrical power generation. One of the proposals is to increase power production from nuclear sources. In the upcoming weeks, you will have to decide on a proposal to build nuclear power plants in the state.

Process

1. Search online for information on nuclear power generation. Include research on safety and security, benefits and risks, cleanliness of nuclear power, and nuclear waste issues.
2. Research biblical principles, outcomes, and motivations for electrical power generation from nuclear sources.
3. Organize your research into evidence that would argue either for or against the use of nuclear power.
4. Prepare for a debate on the topic of whether your state should increase electrical power production by building five new nuclear power plants. Be prepared to argue for or against the proposal.
5. Participate in a debate with your classmates, arguing the side assigned by your teacher.

Conclusion

We constantly face the challenge of deciding between conflicting demands. As a society, we want cheap, clean, and safe electrical power. We also want to leave our descendants a livable world. We have to be knowledgeable about the issues around us so that we can make informed decisions. We must always strive for our decisions to glorify God and benefit other people.

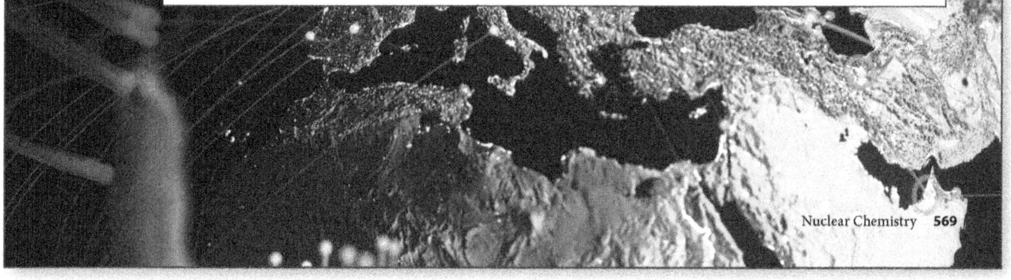

ETHICS: NUCLEAR POWER

Appendix L includes a reproducible rubric to assess the ethics debate.

34.* $^{238}_{92}\text{U} + ^{1}_{0}\text{n} \longrightarrow$

$^{135}_{53}\text{I} + ^{96}_{36}\text{Kr} + 5^{1}_{0}\text{n} + 3^{1}_{1} + \text{energy}$ *(p. 558)*

35.* -1.32×10^{11} J *(p. 559)*

Section 22.2

7. a. What we know: $t_{½} = 2.04$ min, $N_0 = 301.75$ g, $t = 15.3$ min

Unknown: N

Write the formula and solve for the unknown.

$N = N_0(0.5)^{t/t_{½}}$

Evaluate.

$N = 301.75\text{ g}(0.5)^{\frac{15.3\text{ min}}{2.04\text{ min}}}$

$= 301.75\text{ g}(0.5)^{7.50}$

$= (301.75\text{ g})(0.005\,524)$

$= 1.67$ g

b. What we know: $t_{½} = 12.32$ y, $N = 35.86$ g, $t = 19.78$ y

Unknown: N_0

Write the formula and solve for the unknown.

$N = N_0(0.5)^{t/t_{½}}$

$\frac{N}{(0.5)^{t/t_{½}}} = \frac{N_0(0.5)^{t/t_{½}}}{(0.5)^{t/t_{½}}}$

$N_0 = \frac{N}{(0.5)^{t/t_{½}}}$

Evaluate.

$N_0 = \frac{35.86\text{ g}}{(0.5)^{\frac{19.78\text{ y}}{12.32\text{ y}}}}$

$= \frac{35.86\text{ g}}{(0.5)^{1.6055}}$

$= \frac{35.86\text{ g}}{0.328\,62}$

$= 109.1$ g

c. What we know: $t_{½} = 7.538 \times 10^4$ y, $N_0 = 16.2$ g, $N = 1.00$ g

Unknown: t

Write the formula and solve for the unknown.

$N = N_0(0.5)^{t/t_{½}}$

$\frac{N}{N_0} = \frac{N_0(0.5)^{t/t_{½}}}{N_0}$

$\log_{0.5}\left(\frac{N}{N_0}\right) = \log_{0.5}(0.5)^{t/t_{½}}$

$t_{½}\frac{t}{t_{½}} = t_{½}\left[\log_{0.5}\left(\frac{N}{N_0}\right)\right]$

$t = t_{½}\left[\log_{0.5}\left(\frac{N}{N_0}\right)\right]$

Evaluate.

$t = (7.538 \times 10^4\text{ y})\left[\log_{0.5}\left(\frac{1.00\text{ g}}{16.2\text{ g}}\right)\right]$

$= (7.538 \times 10^4\text{ y})[\log_{0.5}(0.061\,72)]$

$= (7.538 \times 10^4\text{ y})(4.018)$

$= 3.03 \times 10^5$ y

Section 22.3

6. Calculate the mass of the reactants.

$239.052\,163\,4\text{ u} + 1.008\,664\,9\text{ u} = 240.060\,828\,3\text{ u}$

Calculate the mass of the products.

$133.905\,394\,5\text{ u} + 102.926\,601\,2\text{ u} + 3(1.008\,664\,9\text{ u})$

$= 239.857\,990\,4\text{ u}$

Calculate the mass defect.

$m_{defect} = m_{products} - m_{reactants}$

$m_{defect} = 240.060\,828\,3\text{ u} - 239.857\,990\,4\text{ u} = 0.202\,837\,9\text{ u}$

Convert the mass defect from daltons to kilograms.

$0.202\,837\,9\text{ u}\left(\frac{1\text{ g}}{6.022 \times 10^{23}\text{ u}}\right)\left(\frac{1\text{ kg}}{1000\text{ g}}\right) = 3.368 \times 10^{-28}\text{ kg}$

Write the formula and solve for the unknown.

$E = mc^2$

Evaluate.

$E = (3.368 \times 10^{-28}\text{ kg})(3.0 \times 10^8\text{ m/s})^2$

$= 3.03 \times 10^{-11}$ J for every nucleus

Chapter 22 Review Questions

9.

Name	Symbol	Isotope Notation	Charge	Mass Number	Effect on Atomic Number	Penetration Power
Alpha Decay	α	${}^{4}_{2}He$	2+	−4	−2	low
Beta Decay	β^-	${}^{0}_{-1}e$	1−	0	+1	medium
Positron Emission	β^+	${}^{0}_{+1}e$	1+	0	−1	medium
Electron Capture	e^-	${}^{0}_{-1}e$	1−	0	−1	high
Gamma Decay	γ	${}^{0}_{0}\gamma$	0	0	0	high

10.

Nuclear Decay	Nuclear Reaction	Chemical Reaction
involves one kind of particle	involves the whole atom	involves electrons
involves small and large energy changes	involves large energy changes	involves small energy changes
is relatively unaffected by pressure and temperature	is relatively unaffected by pressure and temperature	is affected by pressure and temperature
occurs spontaneously	may or may not occur spontaneously	may or may not occur spontaneously

23. a. What we know: $t_{1/2} = 8.02$ d, $N_0 = 215.25$ g, $t = 21.3$ d

Unknown: N

Write the formula and solve for the unknown.

$$N = N_0(0.5)^{t/t_{1/2}}$$

Evaluate.

$$N = 215.25\text{ g}(0.5)^{\frac{21.3\cancel{d}}{8.02\cancel{d}}}$$

$$= 215.25\text{ g}(0.5)^{2.655\,860\,349}$$

$$= (215.25\text{ g})(0.158\,674\,219\,5)$$

$$= 34.2\text{ g}$$

b. What we know: $t_{1/2} = 9.67$ min, $N = 10.0$ g, $t = 65.0$ min

Unknown: N_0

Write the formula and solve for the unknown.

$$N = N_0(0.5)^{t/t_{1/2}}$$

$$\frac{N}{(0.5)^{t/t_{1/2}}} = \frac{N_0\cancel{(0.5)^{t/t_{1/2}}}}{\cancel{(0.5)^{t/t_{1/2}}}}$$

$$N_0 = \frac{N}{(0.5)^{t/t_{1/2}}}$$

Evaluate.

$$N_0 = \frac{10.0\text{ g}}{(0.5)^{\frac{65.0\cancel{min}}{9.67\cancel{min}}}}$$

$$= \frac{10.0\text{ g}}{(0.5)^{6.721\,820\,062}}$$

$$= \frac{10.0\text{ g}}{0.009\,473\,937\,9}$$

$$= 1055.527\,285\text{ g} = 1.06 \times 10^3\text{ g}$$

c. What we know: $t_{1/2} = 19.29$ s, $N_0 = 1.53$ kg, $N = 10.0$ g

Unknown: t

Write the formula and solve for the unknown.

$$N = N_0(0.5)^{t/t_{1/2}}$$

$$\frac{N}{N_0} = \frac{\cancel{N_0}(0.5)^{t/t_{1/2}}}{\cancel{N_0}}$$

$$\log_{0.5}\left(\frac{N}{N_0}\right) = \log_{0.5}(0.5)^{t/t_{1/2}}$$

$$\cancel{t_{1/2}}\frac{t}{\cancel{t_{1/2}}} = t_{1/2}\left[\log_{0.5}\left(\frac{N}{N_0}\right)\right]$$

$$t = t_{1/2}\left[\log_{0.5}\left(\frac{N}{N_0}\right)\right]$$

Evaluate.

$$t = (19.29\text{ s})\left[\log_{0.5}\left(\frac{1.00 \times 10^{-2}\cancel{kg}}{1.53\cancel{kg}}\right)\right]$$

$$= (19.29\text{ s})\left[\log_{0.5}(0.006\,535\,947\,7)\right]$$

$$= (19.29\text{ s})(7.257\,387\,843)$$

$$= 140\text{ s} = 2.33\text{ min}$$

27. Calculate the mass of the reactants.

239.052 163 4 u + 1.008 664 9 u = 240.060 828 3 u

Calculate the mass of the products.

103.922 464 7 u + 133.909 744 9 u + 2(1.008 664 9 u)

= 239.849 539 4 u

Calculate the mass defect.

$m_{defect} = m_{products} - m_{reactants}$

$m_{defect} = 239.849\,539\,4 \text{ u} - 240.060\,828\,3 \text{ u} = -0.211\,288\,9 \text{ u}$

Convert the mass defect from daltons to kilograms.

$$-0.211\,288\,9 \cancel{\text{u}}\left(\frac{1 \cancel{\text{g}}}{6.022 \times 10^{23} \cancel{\text{u}}}\right)\left(\frac{1 \text{ kg}}{1000 \cancel{\text{g}}}\right) = -3.509 \times 10^{-28} \text{ kg}$$

Write the formula and solve for the unknown.

$E = mc^2$

Evaluate.

$E = (-3.509 \times 10^{-28} \text{ kg})(3.0 \times 10^8 \text{ m/s})^2$

$= -3.16 \times 10^{-11}$ J for every nucleus

32. What we know: $N_0 = 13.58$ g, $N = 8.074$ g, $t = 15.25$ min

Unknown: $t_{½}$

Write the formula and solve for the unknown.

$$N = N_0(0.5)^{t/t_{½}}$$

$$\frac{N}{N_0} = \frac{\cancel{N_0}(0.5)^{t/t_{½}}}{\cancel{N_0}}$$

$$\log_{0.5}\left(\frac{N}{N_0}\right) = \log_{0.5}(0.5)^{t/t_{½}}$$

$$\log_{0.5}\left(\frac{N}{N_0}\right)t_{½} = \frac{t}{\cancel{t_{½}}}\cancel{t_{½}}$$

$$\frac{\cancel{\log_{0.5}\left(\frac{N}{N_0}\right)}t_{½}}{\cancel{\log_{0.5}\left(\frac{N}{N_0}\right)}} = \frac{t}{\log_{0.5}\left(\frac{N}{N_0}\right)}$$

$$t_{½} = \frac{t}{\log_{0.5}\left(\frac{N}{N_0}\right)}$$

Evaluate.

$$t_{½} = \frac{15.25 \text{ min}}{\log_{0.5}\left(\frac{8.074 \cancel{\text{g}}}{13.58 \cancel{\text{g}}}\right)}$$

$$= \frac{15.25 \text{ min}}{\log_{0.5}(0.594\,550\,81)}$$

$$= \frac{15.25 \text{ min}}{0.750\,127\,987\,7}$$

$= 20.33$ min

33. What we know: $t_{½} = 8.02$ d, $N_0 = 10.0$ g

Unknown: decay events

a. Since we know that the sample has gone through one half-life, half of the atoms would have decayed, emitting beta particles. Convert the mass into particles.

$$10.0 \cancel{\text{g I-131}}\left(\frac{1 \cancel{\text{mol I-131}}}{130.906 \cancel{\text{g I-131}}}\right)\left(\frac{6.022 \times 10^{23} \text{ atoms I-131}}{1 \cancel{\text{mol I-131}}}\right)$$

$= 4.60 \times 10^{22}$ atoms I-131

Half of these (2.30×10^{22}) have decayed and have emitted beta particles.

c. One half-life is 8.02 d. If we find the number of seconds per half-life and divide the number of decays by the number of seconds, we will have the average decays per second.

$$8.02 \cancel{\text{d}}\left(\frac{24 \cancel{\text{h}}}{1 \cancel{\text{d}}}\right)\left(\frac{3600 \text{ s}}{1 \cancel{\text{h}}}\right) = 692\,928 \text{ s}$$

$$\frac{2.30 \times 10^{22} \text{ decays}}{692\,928 \text{ s}} = 3.32 \times 10^{16} \text{ decays/s}$$

34. Atomic number equation: $92 + 0 = 53 + 36 + 0 + Y$

Solve the atomic number equation for the number of protons.
$Y = 3$

Mass number equation: $238 + 1 = 135 + 96 + X + Y$

Plug in value for Y and solve for number of neutrons.

$238 + 1 = 135 + 96 + X + 3$

$X = 5$

$${}^{238}_{92}\text{U} + {}^{1}_{0}\text{n} \longrightarrow {}^{135}_{53}\text{I} + {}^{96}_{36}\text{Kr} + 5\,{}^{1}_{0}\text{n} + 3\,{}^{1}_{1} + \text{energy}$$

35. Calculate the mass of the reactants.

233.039 u + 1.008 664 9 u = 234.047 664 9 u

Calculate the mass of the products.

93.915 361 u + 136.911 562 1 u + 3(1.008 664 9 u)

= 233.852 917 8 u

Calculate the mass defect.

$m_{defect} = m_{products} - m_{reactants}$

$m_{defect} = 233.852\,917\,8 \text{ u} - 234.047\,664\,9 \text{ u} = -0.194\,747\,1 \text{ u}$

Convert the mass defect from daltons to kilograms.

$$-0.194\,747\,1 \cancel{\text{u}}\left(\frac{1 \cancel{\text{g}}}{6.022 \times 10^{23} \cancel{\text{u}}}\right)\left(\frac{1 \text{ kg}}{1000 \cancel{\text{g}}}\right) = -3.234 \times 10^{-28} \text{ kg}$$

Write the formula and solve for the unknown.

$E = mc^2$

Evaluate.

$E = (-3.234 \times 10^{-28} \text{ kg})(3.0 \times 10^8 \text{ m/s})^2$

$= -2.91 \times 10^{-11}$ J for every nucleus

Convert grams to particles and then to energy.

$$1.75 \cancel{\text{g U-233}}\left(\frac{1 \cancel{\text{mol U-233}}}{233.039 \cancel{\text{g U-233}}}\right)\left(\frac{6.022 \times 10^{23} \cancel{\text{atoms U-233}}}{1 \cancel{\text{mol U-233}}}\right)$$

$$\left(\frac{-2.91 \times 10^{-11} \text{ J}}{1 \cancel{\text{atoms U-233}}}\right) = -1.32 \times 10^{11} \text{ J}$$

Appendix A

UNDERSTANDING SCIENTIFIC TERMS

You may find science a little intimidating because of all the long, unfamiliar words that scientists use. But you can often unravel the meanings of these words by breaking them down into simple parts that do have meaning to you. When you see a difficult scientific word, look at the entries in this appendix to help you understand that term. These word parts may come at the beginning, at the end, or in the middle of the term, depending on their meaning.

For example, if you ran into the word *heterogeneous equilibrium*, you could separate it into four parts—*hetero-*, *-gen*, *equi-*, and *-libra*. *Hetero-* means "other, different," *-gen* means "kind," *equi-* means "equal," and *-libra* means "balance." So heterogeneous equilibrium has to do with different kinds of substances being in equal balance.

a, **an** (Gk.)—not, without

ab (L.)—away from

ac, **ad**, **ag** (L.)—to, toward

acou (Gk.)—hearing

aer, **aero** (Gk.)—air

alter (L.)—change

amal (Gk.)—soft

amphi, **ampho** (Gk.)—on both sides

ant, **anti** (Gk.)—opposite, against

ante (L.)—before

aqua (L.)—water

ar (L.)—of or related to

audio (L.)—hear

aut, **auto** (Gk.)—self

bar, **baro** (Gk.)—weight, pressure

bi (L.)—two, twice, double

bio, **bios**, **biot** (Gk.)—life

calc, **calci** (L.)—calcium

calor (L.)—heat

centi (L.)—a hundred

centr, **centri**, **centro** (Gk.)—center

chem, **chemi**, **chemo** (Gk.)—chemistry

chrom, **chromo** (Gk.)—color

chron, **chrono** (Gk.)—time

cline (Gk.)—sloping

co, **com**, **con** (L.)—with, together

cupr (Gk.)—copper

cycl, **cyclo** (Gk.)—circle, wheel

de (L.)—loss, removal

deci (L.)—tenth

di (Gk.)—two

div (Gk.)—apart

duce, **duct** (L.)—to lead

dyna (Gk.)—power

eco (Gk.)—house

electro (L.)—electricity

en, **end**, **endo** (Gk.)—within, inner

equ, **equa**, **equi** (L.)—equal

ex, **exo** (Gk.)—out, outside, without

extra (L.)—outside, more, beyond, besides

fissi (L.)—split, divide

flam (L.)—fire

fund (L.)—basis

fusi (L.)—to join together

gen (L.)—kind

grad (L.)—step, walk, slope

graph, **grapho**, **graphy** (Gk.)—to write

grav (L.)—heavy

gyro (Gk.)—spinning

halo (Gk.)—salt

hemi (Gk.)—half

hetero (Gk.)—other, different

homeo, **homio**, **homo** (Gk.)—like, same, resembling

hydr, **hydra**, **hydro** (Gk.)—water, fluid

hyper (Gk.)—over, beyond

hypo (Gk.)—under, beneath

ic (Gk.)—of, relating to

inter (L.)—between

is, **iso** (Gk.)—equal

ism (Gk.)—belief, process of

kine, **kinema**, **kinemato**, **kines**, **kinesi**, **kinet**, **kineto** (Gk.)—move, moving, movement

libra (L.)—balance

log, **logo**, **logus**, **logy** (Gk.)—word, study of

macr, **macro** (Gk.)—large

magneto (Gk.)—magnetic

medi, **media**, **medio** (L.)—middle

met, **meta** (Gk.)—between, with, after, change

meter, **metry** (Gk.)—measure

micro (Gk.)—small

mill, **mille**, **milli**, **millo** (L.)—one thousand

mit (L.)—to send

mono (Gk.)—one

morph, **morpha**, **morpho** (Gk.)—form, shape

multi (L.)—many

nan, **nani**, **nano**, **nanus** (Gk.)—dwarf, one billionth

nomy (Gk.)—the science of

nuc, **nucle**, **nucleo** (L.)—central part

ocul, **oculi**, **oculo**, **oculus** (L.)—eye

opt, **opti**, **opto** (Gk.)—eye, vision

organ (Gk.)—living

orth, **ortho** (Gk.)—upright, perpendicular

ox, **oxy** (Gk.)—oxygen

par, **para** (Gk.)—beside

pause (Gk.)—to stop

pend (L.)—hanging

peri (Gk.)—around, near

phon, **phono** (Gk.)—sound

phos, **phot**, **photo** (Gk.)—light

phyt, **phyto**, **phytum** (Gk.)—plant

poly (Gk.)—many

post (L.)—after

pre (L.), **pro** (Gk.)—before, in front of

prot, **prote**, **proto** (Gk.)—first, original

pyro (Gk.)—fire

radi, **radia**, **radio** (L.)—spoke, ray

retro (L.)—backward

sal (L.)—salt

scientia (L.)—knowledge

scope, **scopy** (Gk.)—to see, watch

sect (L.)—to cut

seism (Gk.)—earthquake

semi (L.)—half

sol (L.)—sun

son (L.)—sound

spec (L.)—to see, look at

sphere (Gk.)—ball, globe

stasis (Gk.)—to stand still

sub (L.)—below, under

super (L.)—above, over

syn (Gk.)—together

tele (Gk.)—distant

terra (L.)—earth

tetr, **tetra** (Gk.)—four

therm, **thermo** (Gk.)—heat

top, **topo** (Gk.)—place

tran, **trans** (L.)—across, through

trop, **tropae**, **trope**, **tropo** (Gk.)—turn, change

uni (L.)—single, one

vacu (L.)—empty

vari, **vario** (L.)—difference

vect (L.)—to carry

volu (L.)—bulk, amount

Appendix B

MATH HELPS

This appendix provides you the necessary helps for solving the many kinds of chemistry problems found in this textbook. It's not intended to be all-inclusive. We assume that you understand or are learning the methods for solving single-variable algebraic equations, including using the order of operations and solving equations for an unknown quantity.

ROUNDING RULES

We round numbers all the time. Sometimes it's convenient to round, for example, the number of residents in your town to the nearest 100 people or the distance around the earth to the nearest 1000 kilometers. Rounding is useful for several reasons. It helps us grasp large numbers when the specific number is not needed but the approximate size is. Rounding also allows us to report measured scientific data correctly.

For the purposes of measuring scientific data and performing calculations, scientists have agreed on certain rounding rules. These ensure that calculation solutions are properly rounded to show the needed precision of numerical quantities. We suggest that you use the following rules for problems in this textbook to closely imitate those used by scientists.

1. Identify the place value that you are going to round to. This is the rounded place value.
2. If the digit to the right of the rounded place value is 0–4, the digit in the rounded place value remains unchanged ("rounded down"). If the digit to the right is 5–9, the digit in the rounded place value is increased by 1 ("rounded up").
   a. If the rounded place value is to the right of the decimal point, all digits to the right of the rounded place value will be dropped after rounding.

      Examples: $56.\underline{7}39$ mL → 56.7 mL

      $39.\underline{4}7$ mm → 39.5 mm

      $74.\underline{9}5$ s → 75.0 s

   b. If the rounded place value is to the left of the decimal point (or assumed decimal point), all digits between the rounded place value and the decimal point become zeros and the decimal point (if one is shown) is omitted.

      Examples: $1\underline{6}94$ m → 1700 m

      $1\underline{9}.6$ °C → 20 °C

3. Notice in two of the examples above that rounding to a particular place value may affect other digits to the left of the rounding place value. When a 9 is rounded up, the 9 rounds up to 10, so the 9 becomes a 0 and 1 is added to the digit to the left.

MATHEMATICS AND MEASUREMENT

When measured quantities appear in equations as terms or factors, follow the same arithmetic principles that you have learned for solving any equation. But acting as a scientist, you have to think about some extra things before arriving at a solution to a problem.

Measured quantities include units. Units, such as meters (m), seconds (s), and meters per second (m/s), are treated as parts of a measurement. So any arithmetic operation applies to both the number and the unit factors in a measurement.

Measured quantities also have precision (see page 60). Precision is the exactness of a measurement. Scientists exert a lot of effort to ensure that their data properly represents the exactness that their instruments can read. Scientists alert other scientists to the precision of their measurements by the number of significant figures (SF) they include in their reported data.

On the following pages you will find some rules for doing basic arithmetic operations using measurements.

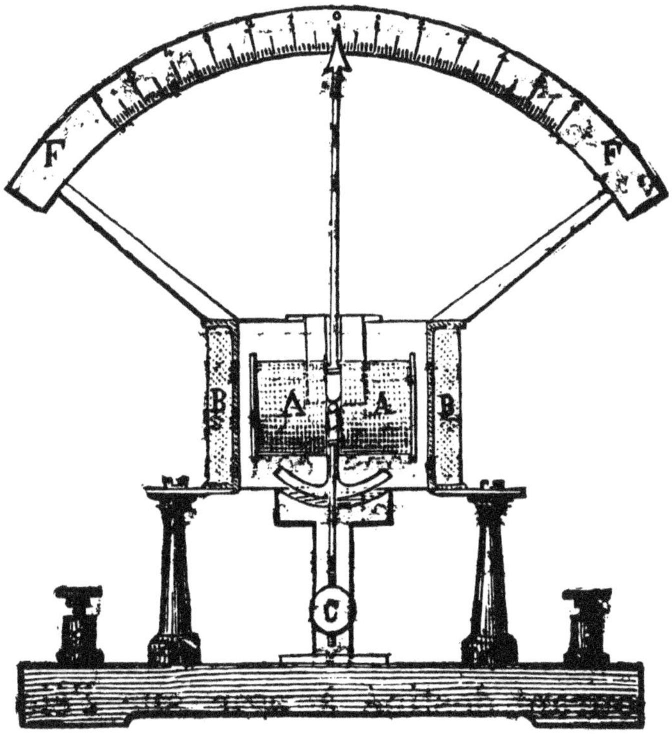

DETERMINING SIGNIFICANT FIGURES

When we are reading measured data collected by someone else, we have to be able to identify the significant figures. (Significant figures do not apply to counts or definitions—only to measured data.) Scientists follow an established set of rules to determine which digits in a measurement are significant.

Rule 1: All nonzero digits are significant.

Rule 2: All zeros between significant figures are significant.

Rule 3: All ending zeros to the right of the decimal point are significant.

Examples:

a. 1.694 mL → 4 SF (all four digits are nonzero—Rule 1)

b. 51.021 m → 5 SF (four nonzero digits and a zero between SF—Rule 2)

c. 22.7500 g → 6 SF (four nonzero digits and two ending zeros to the right of the decimal point—Rule 3)

d. 0.097 mL → 2 SF (Rule 1 [Since the zero in the tenths place is not an ending zero, Rule 3 does not apply.])

The fourth example can be confusing, but it is much easier to understand if you change the number to scientific notation.

$$0.097\ \text{N} = 9.7 \times 10^{-2}\ \text{N} \rightarrow \text{only 2 SF}$$

One other case in which determining SF can be difficult is when ending zeros occur to the left of the decimal point.

Example:

How many SF does the measurement 7600 m have? You know that two of the digits must be significant, but you as the reader cannot determine which, if either, of the zeros are significant. Does this number have two, three, or four SF? Again, the person reporting the value can use scientific notation to avoid confusion.

7600 m → 7.6×10^3 m (two SF)

7600 m → 7.60×10^3 m (three SF)

7600 m → 7.600×10^3 m (four SF)

Appendix B

MATH HELPS

ADDING AND SUBTRACTING CHEMISTRY DATA

Math Rule 1: Added or subtracted data must have the same units. Even if the kinds of data are the same, if their units are not the same, then you are adding apples and oranges. For example, you can't add the lengths 3.1 m and 45 cm together without first converting one of the measurements to the other's units.

Math Rule 2: The result of adding or subtracting data can't be more precise than the least precisely measured data used in the calculation. After adding or subtracting, round the result to the decimal place of the estimated digit in the least precise measurement.

EXAMPLE 1: ADDING DATA: LENGTH

Add 3.1 m and 45 cm.

Unit Conversion:

$$45\ \cancel{\text{cm}}\left(\frac{1\ \text{m}}{100\ \cancel{\text{cm}}}\right) = 0.45\ \text{m}$$

Add data:

$$3.\underline{1}\ \text{m} + 0.4\underline{5}\ \text{m} = 3.\underline{55}\ \text{m} = 3.6\ \text{m}$$

The estimated digits in each piece of data and the sum are underlined. The sum contains two underlined digits that result from the summing operation. These must be rounded to the place having the least precise estimated value, in this case the 0.1 m place.

MULTIPLYING AND DIVIDING CHEMISTRY DATA

Math Rule 3: The result of multiplying or dividing data can't have more SF than the data with the fewest SF used in the calculation. After multiplying or dividing, round the results to the same number of significant figures as the data with the fewest SF.

EXAMPLE 2: DIVIDING DATA: DENSITY

Calculate the density of a sample of quartz with a mass of 27.55 g and a volume of 10.4 cm^3.

Given data: $m = 27.55$ g (four SF), $V = 10.4\ \text{cm}^3$ (three SF)
Calculation:

$$d = \frac{m}{V}$$

$$= \frac{27.55\ \text{g}}{10.4\ \text{cm}^3}$$

$$= 2.6\underline{4}9\ \frac{\text{g}}{\text{cm}^3}$$

$$= 2.65\ \frac{\text{g}}{\text{cm}^3}\ \text{(three SF allowed)}$$

Since 10.4 cm^3 has only three SF, only three SF are allowed in the quotient.

Math Rule 4: The result of multiplying or dividing a measured quantity and a pure number has the same number of decimal places, or the same precision, as the measured quantity used in the calculation.

Examples:

a. (7)(2.35 cm) = 16.45 cm (not 16.5 cm)

b. 2.63 cm ÷ 5 = 0.53 cm (not 0.526 cm)

Notice that the number of SF in the measured data do not determine the number of SF in the result when multiplying or dividing by pure numbers. Math Rule 4 ensures that you preserve the precision of the original measurement, even if you change the number by multiplying or dividing by a pure number.

PROPORTIONALITIES IN CHEMISTRY

As you study chemistry, you will discover that many measurable quantities change or vary in a reliable, predictable way with other quantities. For example, the pressure of a gas in a rigid container changes as the absolute temperature of the gas varies. Double its temperature and the pressure doubles too. Similarly, if you double the volume of the container (at a constant temperature), the pressure will be cut in half. These kinds of relationships are called *proportionalities.*

Direct Proportionality

If two numbers, A and B, are directly proportional, they can be set equal to each other by including a proportionality constant factor—k. The equation is

$$A = kB,$$

which means that

$$\frac{A}{B} = k$$

and k is a constant for all ratios of these two quantities. For an example, let A equal time in minutes and B time in seconds. Then the proportionality constant k is equal to 1 min/60 s as shown below.

$$A = \left(\frac{1\ \text{min}}{60\ \text{s}}\right)B$$

In this textbook, you will use direct proportions in Charles's law, Gay-Lussac's law, and Avogadro's law.

Inverse Proportionality

You'll also find that other pairs of quantities are *inversely proportional.* If the value of one increases, the other decreases in proportion. The equations for these proportions set up as shown below.

$$A = \frac{k}{B}$$

If you multiply both sides of the equation by B, you end up with

$$AB = k.$$

So if k is a constant, as A increases, B must decrease in the same proportion to maintain the equality.

In chemistry, Boyle's law uses the inverse proportion concept.

Other Proportionalities

Lastly, there are other kinds of proportionalities that are neither entirely direct nor inverse relationships. For example, the combined gas law is a joint variation with some variables that vary directly and others that vary inversely. In another case, the kinetic energy of particles changes directly with the mass of the particles but according to a square of the particles' velocity.

Exponentials and Logarithms

Two other relationships that are common in chemistry are exponential and logarithmic relationships. These two functions are inverses of each other and are needed when studying acids, bases, and nuclear chemistry. The independent variable in an exponential function is an exponent. The general form is

$$y = Ab^x,$$

where A is a coefficient and b is the base of a power. In chemistry, we see this function used in three different calculations. To calculate the concentration of hydronium from pH, we use the equation $[H_3O^+] = 10^{-pH}$. When calculating the concentration of hydroxide from pOH, the equation is $[OH^-] = 10^{-pOH}$. In nuclear chemistry, the half-life formula involves an exponential.

$$N = N_0(0.5)^{\frac{t}{t_{1/2}}}$$

As mentioned above, the logarithmic function is the inverse of the exponential. The general form of a logarithmic function is $y = A\log_b x$. Again A is the coefficient and b is the base of the logarithm. In chemistry, we use logarithmic functions to solve for pH and pOH. We also use logarithms to solve half-life problems to determine elapsed time or the half-life of an isotope.

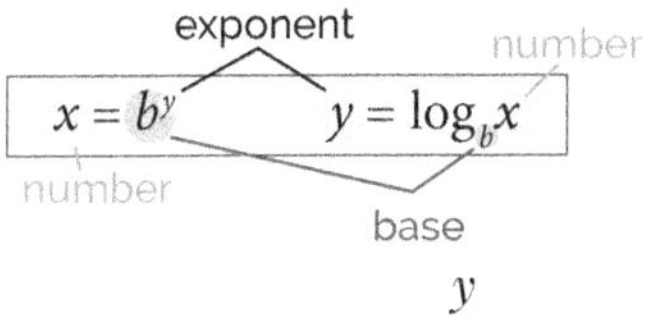

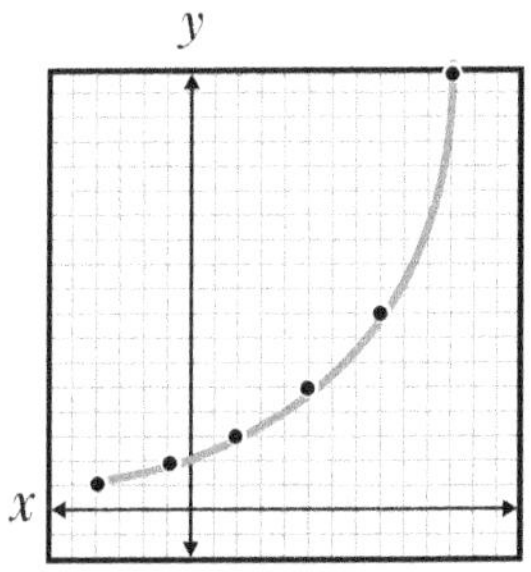

Exponential Function

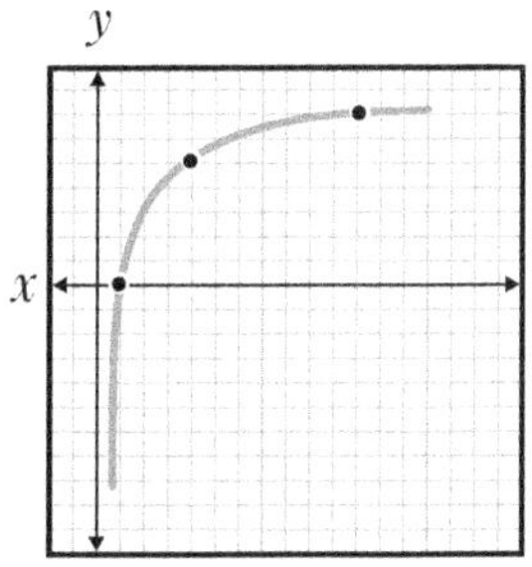

Logarithmic Function

Appendix B

GRAPHING

Scientists often like to compare two or more groups of numbers visually to see whether they are related in some way. When scientists plot data to compare different quantities, they make a graph. The simplest graphs compare two changing quantities, called *variables*. Usually, one of the variables is determined by the scientist or else changes in a regular way (e.g., time). This is called an *independent variable*. Its value doesn't depend on anything in the data. The other variable is expected to change in some way related to the independent variable. Its value depends on the first variable, so it is called the *dependent variable*. The values of the independent and dependent variables are called the *coordinates of the data*. To plot the data, an ordered pair of coordinates is used. You have graphed ordered pairs in the form (x, y) in a math class.

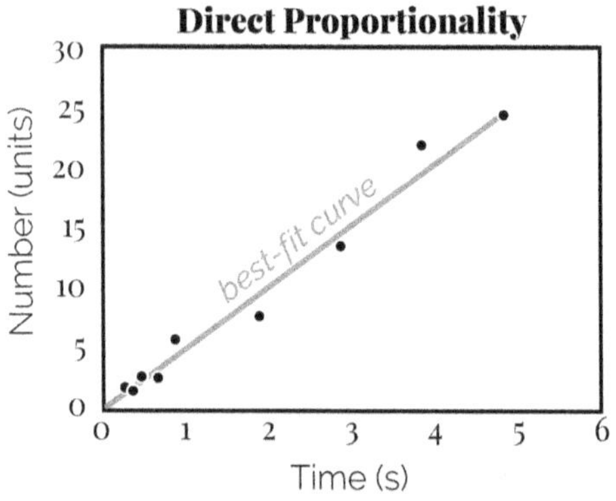

Scientists usually plot the independent variable on the horizontal axis (x-axis), with increasing values to the right. The dependent variable is typically plotted on the vertical axis (y-axis), increasing upward. These are not hard and fast rules, and many graphs are arranged differently to more clearly see the relationships in the plotted data. Useful graphs include a title describing the graph's purpose and labels identifying the quantities and units used on each axis. Graphs are often depicted on a scaled grid with the x- and y-axis scales shown so that estimates of the values of the plotted variables can be made.

SCATTERPLOTS

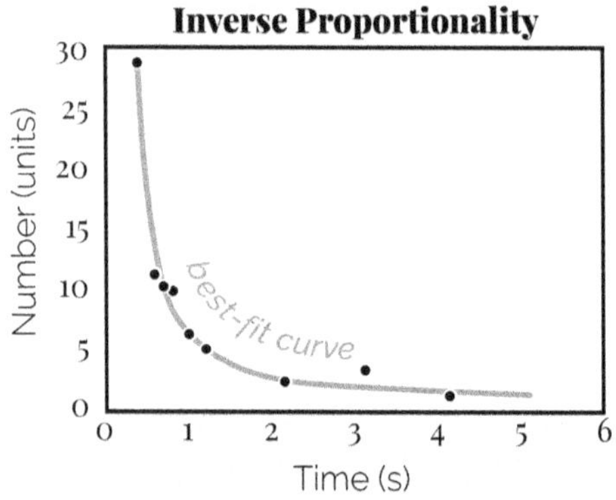

Graphs come in different forms. A simple plot of points on a graph is called a *scatterplot*. This is the starting point for many graphs. Scientists like to detect trends in the data and then create a mathematical equation (model) that describes the trend. They draw a *best-fit curve* through the pattern of dots. The kind of curve drawn depends on how the data changes. We still call it a best-fit curve even if it doesn't curve. Curves that are straight lines are called *linear graphs*. These are fairly rare in nature. Most trends in nature range from slightly curved to really wavy! These graphs, logically enough, are called *nonlinear graphs*.

SLOPE

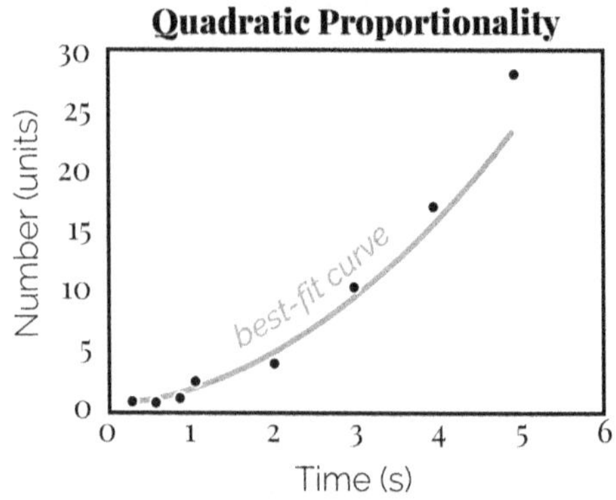

One of the most important things to be learned from a graph is the rate at which the dependent variable changes in comparison to the independent variable. This rate is indicated by the *slope* of the graph. A graph with a steep slope shows that things are changing quickly. One with a horizontal slope shows that the dependent variable is not changing at all. A graph that rises from left to right has a positive slope; a dropping curve has a negative slope.

To calculate the slope (m) of a curve, use the slope formula,

$$m = \frac{\Delta y}{\Delta x} = \frac{y_f - y_i}{x_f - x_i},$$

where m is the slope, Δy is the change in the y variable, and Δx is the change in the x variable.

ESTIMATING DATA

You can sometimes use scatterplots and trend lines to obtain information that is not in the measured data set. If you follow the trend line between two data points, these values are estimated—not measured. Obtaining unmeasured data this way is called *interpolation*. Scientists also often try to predict the values of the dependent variable beyond the range of the measured independent variable data points. This method of analysis is called *extrapolation*. Extrapolating data assumes that the trend will continue in the same fashion as observed within the measured data.

OTHER TYPES OF GRAPHS

In a bar graph, dependent data is plotted as vertical bars at each independent data value. Area graphs fill in the area of a graph. When several dependent variables are plotted on a single graph, the areas can be compared to show their relationships visually. Pie charts are another type of area graph. They are especially useful for showing percentages of a whole.

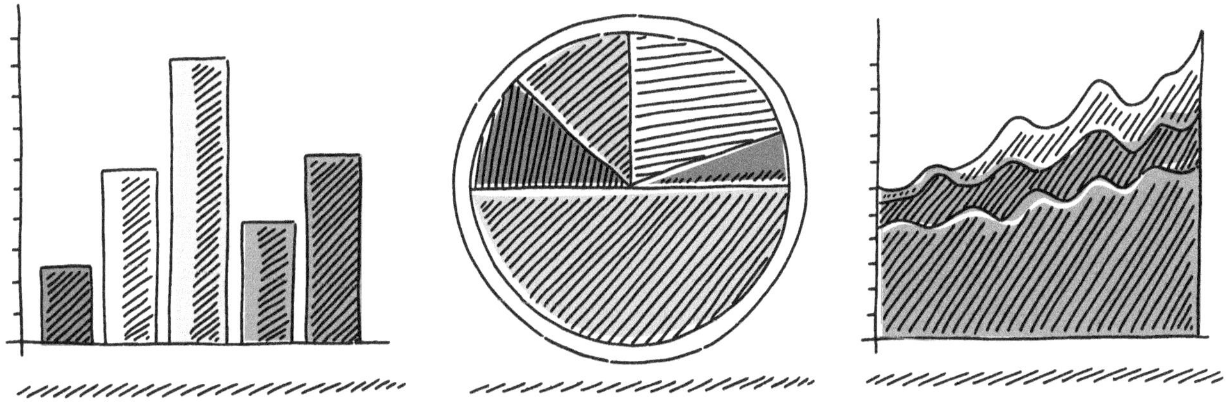

A bar graph (left), pie chart (center), and an area graph (right)

Appendix C

FUNDAMENTAL AND DERIVED UNITS OF THE SI

FUNDAMENTAL UNITS

Dimension	Name	Symbol	Definition
length	meter	m	The meter is the length of the path traveled by light in a vacuum during a time interval of 1/299 792 458 of a second.
mass	kilogram	kg	The kilogram is the unit of mass. It is defined on the basis of the Planck constant ($6.626\,070\,15 \times 10^{-34}$ J·s), the meter, and the second.
time	second	s	The second is the duration of 9 192 631 770 cycles of the radiation associated with a specific transition of the cesium-133 atom.
electric current	ampere	A	The ampere is the current required for one coulomb of charge to pass through a conductor every second. The coulomb is defined on the basis of the elementary charge, the electric charge carried by a single proton.
temperature	kelvin	K	The kelvin, the unit of thermodynamic temperature, is defined on the basis of the Boltzmann constant ($1.380\,649 \times 10^{-23}$ J/K), the kilogram, the meter, and the second.
amount of substance	mole	mol	A mole is the amount of material that contains $6.022\,140\,76 \times 10^{23}$ entities. This value is the Avogadro constant.
luminous intensity	candela	cd	The candela is the luminous intensity, in a given direction, of a source that emits monochromatic radiation of frequency 540×10^{12} Hz and that has a radiant intensity in that direction of 1/683 watts per steradian (W/sr).

Note: The unit definitions are a contribution of the National Institute of Standards and Technology.

COMMONLY USED DERIVED UNITS

Dimension	Name	Symbol	Derivation
force	newton	N	$\frac{\text{kg} \cdot \text{m}}{\text{s}^2}$
energy, work, heat	joule	J	$\frac{\text{kg} \cdot \text{m}^2}{\text{s}^2}$
power	watt	W	$\frac{\text{J}}{\text{s}} = \frac{\text{kg} \cdot \text{m}^2}{\text{s}^3}$
pressure	pascal	Pa	$\frac{\text{N}}{\text{m}^2} = \frac{\text{kg}}{\text{m} \cdot \text{s}^2}$
electric charge	coulomb	C	A·s
voltage	volt	V	$\frac{\text{J}}{\text{C}} = \frac{\text{kg} \cdot \text{m}^2}{\text{A} \cdot \text{s}^3}$
electrical resistance	ohm	Ω	$\frac{\text{V}}{\text{A}} = \frac{\text{kg} \cdot \text{m}^2}{\text{A}^2 \cdot \text{s}^3}$
frequency	hertz	Hz	$\frac{\text{cycles}}{\text{s}} = \text{s}^{-1}$
particle mass	atomic mass unit	u	1/12 of a carbon-12 nuclide

Appendix D

METRIC PREFIXES

Prefix	Meaning (Origin)	Symbol	Factor	Example	Application
exa-	six (Gk.)	E	10^{18}	exabyte (EB)	amount of data created every second
peta-	five (Gk.)	P	10^{15}	petahertz (PHz)	frequency of ultraviolet radiation
tera-	monster (Gk.)	T	10^{12}	terawatt (TW)	average annual power generation in the United States
giga-	giant (Gk.)	G	10^{9}	gigabyte (GB)	hard-drive storage capacity
mega-	great (Gk.)	M	10^{6}	megajoule (MJ)	energy to heat 10 L of water from 0 °C to 100 °C
kilo-	thousand (Gk.)	k	10^{3}	kilometer (km)	distances on Earth
hecto-	hundred (Gk.)	h	10^{2}	hectometer (hm)	wavelength of radio waves
deca-	ten (Gk.)	da	10^{1}	decapascal (daPa)	pressure of sound
(base)			10^{0}		
deci-	tenth (L.)	d	10^{-1}	decibel (dB)	sound loudness
centi-	hundredth (L.)	c	10^{-2}	centimeter (cm)	distances in a laboratory
milli-	thousandth (L.)	m	10^{-3}	millivolt (mV)	EKG signal from heart at skin
micro-	small (Gk.)	µ	10^{-6}	microsecond (µs)	time for light to travel 1 km
nano-	dwarf (Gk.)	n	10^{-9}	nanometer (nm)	size of atoms
pico-	small (Sp.)	p	10^{-12}	picometer (pm)	long gamma ray wavelength
femto-	fifteen (Dan.)	f	10^{-15}	femtogram (fg)	mass of a virus
atto-	eighteen (Dan.)	a	10^{-18}	attosecond (as)	period required to image an orbiting electron

Appendix E

PHYSICAL CONSTANTS

Quantity	Symbol	SI Units
atomic mass unit	u	$1.660\,539 \times 10^{-27}$ kg
Avogadro's number	N_A	$6.022\,140\,76 \times 10^{23}$ particles/mol
fundamental electric charge	e	$1.602\,176\,634 \times 10^{-19}$ C
ionization constant of water	K_w	1.0×10^{-14} mol/L at 298.15 K
molar volume (STP)	V_{STP}	22.4 L/mol
normal boiling point of water	T_b	373.15 K = 100 °C
normal freezing point of water	T_f	273.15 K = 0.00 °C
speed of light	c	$2.997\,924\,58 \times 10^8$ m/s
universal gas constant	R	$8.314 \frac{J}{mol \cdot K}$

Appendix F

COMMON ABBREVIATIONS AND SYMBOLS

Unit	Abbreviation	Dimension	Unit	Abbreviation	Dimension
becquerel	Bq	nuclear activity	liter	L	volume
candela	cd	light intensity	meter	m	length/distance
coulomb	C	electric charge	millibar	mbar	pressure
dalton	Da	atomic mass	minute	min	time
day	d	time	molal	m	molality
decibel	dB	relative power	molar	M	amount concentration
degree	°	temperature or angle	mole	mol	quantity (particles)
degree (Celsius)	°C	temperature	newton	N	force
degree (Fahrenheit)	°F	temperature	ohm	Ω	electrical resistance
gram	g	mass	pascal	Pa	pressure
gray	Gy	radiation absorption	percent	%	ratio (per hundred)
hertz	Hz, s^{-1}	frequency	second	s	time
hour	h	time	sievert	Sv	biological effect of radioactivity
joule	J	energy or work	volt	V	electric potential difference
kelvin	K	temperature	watt	W	power
kilogram	kg	mass	year	y	time
kilowatt-hour	kW·h	energy			

Appendix F

FORMULA QUANTITIES AND SYMBOLS

Quantity	Symbol	Quantity	Symbol
acid-ionization constant	K_a	heat	Q
activation energy	E_a	ionization constant of water	K_w
amount concentration	c_{solute}	Kelvin temperature	T_K
amount of substance (moles)	n	kinetic energy	KE
atomic number	Z	mass	m
base-ionization constant	K_b	mass fraction	w_{solute}
boiling-point elevation	ΔT_b	mass number	A
Celsius temperature	T_C	molal boiling-point constant	K_b
constant (unspecified)	k	molal freezing-point constant	K_f
critical pressure	P_c	molality	b_{solute}
critical temperature	T_c	Planck's constant	h
density	ρ	potential energy	PE
enthalpy	H	pressure	P
enthalpy of fusion	ΔH_{fus}	principal quantum number (energy level)	n
enthalpy of reaction	ΔH_r	solubility	S
enthalpy of solution	ΔH_{soln}	solubility product	K_{sp}
enthalpy of vaporization	ΔH_{vap}	specific heat	c_{sp}
entropy	S	speed of light	c
equilibrium constant	K_{eq}	standard molar enthalpy of combustion	ΔH°_c
Fahrenheit temperature	T_F	standard molar enthalpy of formation	ΔH°_f
freezing-point depression	ΔT_f	time interval	Δt
frequency	f	universal gas constant	R
fundamental electric charge	e	volume	V
Gibbs free energy	G	volume fraction	φ_{solute}
Gibbs free-energy change	ΔG	wavelength	λ
half-life	$t_{1/2}$		

Appendix F

OTHER ABBREVIATIONS

Term	Abbreviation
acidity (potential of hydrogen)	pH
alkalinity	pOH
alpha particle	α or $^{4}_{2}He$
beta particle	β or $^{0}_{-1}e$
chemical state, aqueous	(*aq*)
chemical state, gas	(*g*)
chemical state, liquid	(*l*)
chemical state, solid	(*s*)
deoxyribonucleic acid	DNA
electron	e^-
fundamental electric charge	*e*
gamma ray	γ or $^{0}_{0}\gamma$
International Union of Pure and Applied Chemistry	IUPAC
kinetic energy	KE
National Institute of Standards and Technology	NIST
neutron	n or $^{1}_{0}n$
potential energy	PE
proton	p or $^{1}_{1}p$
ribonucleic acid	RNA
significant figure	SF
standard temperature and pressure	STP
Système International d'Unités	SI
valence shell electron pair repulsion theory	VSEPR

Appendix G

COMMON IONS

1−	2−	3−	1+
acetate, $C_2H_3O_2^-$	carbonate, CO_3^{2-}	arsenate, AsO_4^{3-}	ammonium, NH_4^+
amide, NH_2^-	chromate, CrO_4^{2-}	arsenite, AsO_3^{3-}	hydronium, H_3O^+
azide, N_3^-	dichromate, $Cr_2O_7^{2-}$	phosphate, PO_4^{3-}	
bromate, BrO_3^-	hydrogen phosphate, HPO_4^{2-}	phosphite, PO_3^{3-}	
bromite, BrO_2^-	oxalate, $C_2O_4^{2-}$		
chlorate, ClO_3^-	peroxide, O_2^{2-}		
chlorite, ClO_2^-	sulfate, SO_4^{2-}		
cyanate, OCN^-	sulfite, SO_3^{2-}		
cyanide, CN^-	thiosulfate, $S_2O_3^{2-}$		
dihydrogen phosphate, $H_2PO_4^-$			**2+**
hydrogen carbonate, HCO_3^- (bicarbonate)			mercury(I), Hg_2^{2+}
hydrogen sulfate, HSO_4^- (bisulfate)			
hydrogen sulfide, HS^-			
hydrogen sulfite, HSO_3^- (bisulfite)			
hydroxide, OH^-			
hypobromite, BrO^-			
hypochlorite, ClO^-			
hypoiodite, IO^-			
iodate, IO_3^-			
iodite, IO_2^-			
nitrate, NO_3^-			
nitrite, NO_2^-			
perbromate, BrO_4^-			
perchlorate, ClO_4^-			
periodate, IO_4^-			
permanganate, MnO_4^-			
thiocyanate, SCN^-			

Appendix H

STANDARD THERMODYNAMIC PROPERTY VALUES

Compound	ΔH°_f (kJ/mol)	S° [J/(mol · K)]	ΔG° (kJ/mol)
Ag (*s*)	0	42.6	0
AgBr (*s*)	−99.5	107.1	−96.9
AgCl (*s*)	−127.0	96.3	−109.8
AgI (*s*)	−61.8	115.5	−66.2
Ag_2O (*s*)	−31.1	121.3	−11.2
Ag_2S (*s*)	−32.6	144.0	−40.7
Al (*s*)	0	28.3	0
Al_2O_3 (*s*)	−1675.7	50.9	−1582.3
Ba (*s*)	0	62.5	0
$BaCl_2$ (*s*)	−855.0	123.7	−806.7
$BaCO_3$ (*s*)	−1213.0	112.1	−1134.4
$BaSO_4$ (*s*)	−1473.2	132.2	−1362.2
Br_2 (*l*)	0	152.2	0
C (*s*)	0	5.7	0
Ca (*s*)	0	41.6	0
$CaCl_2$ (*s*)	−795.4	108.4	−748.8
$CaCO_3$ (*s*)	−1207.6	917	−1129.1
CaO (*s*)	−634.9	38.1	−603.3
$Ca(OH)_2$ (*s*)	−985.2	83.4	−897.5
$CaSO_4$ (*s*)	−1434.5	56.5	−477.4
CCl_4 (*l*)	−128.2	214.4	−65.3
CH_4 (*g*)	−79.6	186.3	−50.5
C_2H_2 (*g*)	227.4	200.9	209.9
C_2H_4 (*g*)	52.4	219.3	68.4
C_2H_6 (*g*)	−84.0	229.2	−32.0
C_3H_8 (*g*)	−103.8	270.3	−23.4
C_6H_6 (*l*)	49.1	173.4	124.5
CH_3OH (*l*)	−239.2	126.8	−166.6
C_2H_5OH (*l*)	−277.6	160.7	−174.8
Cl_2 (*g*)	0	165.2	0
CO (*g*)	−110.5	197.7	−137.2
CO_2 (*g*)	−393.5	213.8	−394.4
Co (*s*)	0	30.1	0
Cr (*s*)	0	23.8	0
Cr_2O_3 (*s*)	−1139.7	81.2	−1058.1
Cu (*s*)	0	33.2	0
CuO (*s*)	−157.3	42.6	−129.7
Cu_2O (*s*)	−168.6	93.1	−146
CuS (*s*)	−48.5	120.9	−86.2
$CuSO_4$ (*s*)	−771.4	109.2	−662.2
F_2 (*g*)	0	158.8	0
Fe (*s*)	0	27.3	0
Fe_2O_3 (*s*)	−824.2	87.4	−742.2
H_2 (*g*)	0	130.7	0
HBr (*g*)	−36.3	198.7	−53.4
HCl (*g*)	−92.3	186.9	−95.3
HF (*g*)	−273.3	173.8	−275.4
Hg (*l*)	0	75.90	0
HgO (*s*)	−90.8	70.25	−58.5
HgS (*s*)	−58.2	82.4	−50.6
HI (*g*)	26.50	206.6	1.7
HNO_3 (*l*)	−174.1	155.6	−80.7
H_2O (*g*)	−241.8	188.8	−228.6
H_2O (*l*)	−285.8	70.0	−237.1
H_2S (*g*)	−20.6	205.8	−33.4
H_2SO_4 (*l*)	−814.0	156.9	−690.0
I_2 (*s*)	0	116.1	0
K (*s*)	0	64.7	0
KBr (*s*)	−393.8	95.9	−380.7
KCl (*s*)	−436.5	82.6	−408.5
$KClO_3$ (*s*)	−397.7	143.1	−296.3
KF (*s*)	−567.3	66.6	−537.8
KOH (*s*)	−424.6	81.2	−379.4
Mg (*s*)	0	32.7	0
$MgCl_2$ (*s*)	−641.3	89.6	−591.8
$MgCO_3$ (*s*)	−1095.8	65.7	−1012.1
MgO (*s*)	−601.6	27.0	−569.3
$Mg(OH)_2$ (*s*)	−924.5	63.2	−833.5
$MgSO_4$ (*s*)	−1284.9	91.6	−1170.6
Mn (*s*)	0	32.0	0

Compound	ΔH°_f (kJ/mol)	S° [J/(mol · K)]	ΔG° (kJ/mol)
MnO (*s*)	−385.2	59.7	−362.9
MnO_2 (*s*)	−520	53.1	−465.1
N_2 (*g*)	0	191.6	0
Na (*s*)	0	51.3	0
NaBr (*s*)	−361.1	86.8	−349.0
NaCl (*s*)	−411.2	72.1	−384.1
NaF (*s*)	−576.6	51.1	−546.3
NaI (*s*)	−287.8	98.5	−286.1
NaOH (*s*)	−425.8	64.4	−379.7
NH_3 (*g*)	−45.9	192.8	−16.4
NH_4Cl (*s*)	−314.4	94.6	−262.9
NH_4NO_3 (*s*)	−365.6	151.1	−183.9
NO (*g*)	91.3	210.8	87.6
NO_2 (*g*)	33.2	240.4	51.3
O_2 (*g*)	0	205.2	0
O_3 (*g*)	142.7	238.9	163.2
Pb (*s*)	0	51.9	0
$PbBr_2$ (*s*)	−278.7	161.5	−261.9
$PbCl_2$ (*s*)	−359.4	136.0	−314.1
PbO (*s*)	−217.3	66.5	−187.9
PbO_2 (*s*)	−277.4	68.6	−217.3
Pb_3O_4 (*s*)	−718.4	211.3	−601.2
PCl_3 (*l*)	−319.7	217.1	−272.3
S (*s*)	0	32.1	0
Si (*s*)	0	18.8	0
SiO_2 (*s*)	−859.4	41.5	−856.3
Sn (*s*)	0	51.2	0
$SnCl_4$ (*l*)	−511.3	258.6	−440.1
SnO (*s*)	−280.7	57.2	−251.9
SnO_2 (*s*)	−577.6	49.0	−515.8
SO_2 (*g*)	−296.8	248.2	−300.1
SO_3 (*g*)	−395.7	256.8	−371.1
Zn (*s*)	0	41.6	0
ZnO (*s*)	−350.5	43.7	−320.5
ZnS (*s*)	−206.0	57.7	−201.3

Appendix I

K_{SP} FOR MINIMALLY SOLUBLE SUBSTANCES

Salt	Product	K_{sp} (at 25 °C)	Molar Mass (g)	Solubility (g/L)
aluminum hydroxide, $Al(OH)_3$	$[Al^{3+}][OH^-]^3$	3.0×10^{-34}	78.0	1.28×10^{-7}
barium carbonate, $BaCO_3$	$[Ba^{2+}][CO_3^{2-}]$	2.6×10^{-9}	197.34	1.0×10^{-2}
barium sulfate, $BaSO_4$	$[Ba^{2+}][SO_4^{2-}]$	1.1×10^{-10}	233.39	2.4×10^{-3}
calcium carbonate, $CaCO_3$	$[Ca^{2+}][CO_3^{2-}]$	3.3×10^{-9}	100.09	5.7×10^{-3}
calcium sulfate, $CaSO_4$	$[Ca^{2+}][SO_4^{2-}]$	4.9×10^{-5}	136.14	0.95
iron(II) hydroxide, $Fe(OH)_2$	$[Fe^{2+}][OH^-]^2$	8.0×10^{-16}	89.87	5.3×10^{-4}
iron(III) hydroxide, $Fe(OH)_3$	$[Fe^{3+}][OH^-]^3$	3.0×10^{-39}	106.88	1.1×10^{-8}
lead(II) carbonate, $PbCO_3$	$[Pb^{2+}][CO_3^{2-}]$	1.5×10^{-13}	267.25	1.0×10^{-4}
lead(II) phosphate, $Pb_3(PO_4)_2$	$[Pb^{2+}]^3[PO_4^{3-}]^2$	1.5×10^{-32}	811.66	1.4×10^{-4}
lead(II) sulfate, $PbSO_4$	$[Pb^{2+}][SO_4^{2-}]$	2.1×10^{-8}	303.30	4.4×10^{-2}
magnesium carbonate, $MgCO_3$	$[Mg^{2+}][CO_3^{2-}]$	2.7×10^{-6}	84.32	0.139
magnesium hydroxide, $Mg(OH)_2$	$[Mg^{2+}][OH^-]^2$	5.6×10^{-12}	58.33	6.5×10^{-4}
silver carbonate, Ag_2CO_3	$[Ag^+]^2[CO_3^{2-}]$	8.5×10^{-12}	275.75	3.6×10^{-2}
silver chloride, $AgCl$	$[Ag^+][Cl^-]$	1.8×10^{-10}	143.32	1.9×10^{-3}
silver phosphate, Ag_3PO_4	$[Ag^+]^3[PO_4^{3-}]$	1.5×10^{-18}	418.58	6.4×10^{-3}
zinc hydroxide, $Zn(OH)_2$	$[Zn^{2+}][OH^{-2}]$	3×10^{-17}	99.40	1.9×10^{-4}

Appendix J

FAMILIES OF ORGANIC COMPOUNDS

Hydrocarbons				
alkane	**alkene**	**alkyne**	**cyclic**	**aromatic**
propane	propene	propyne	cyclopropane	benzene
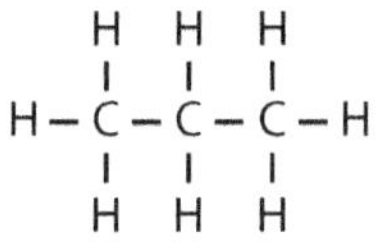	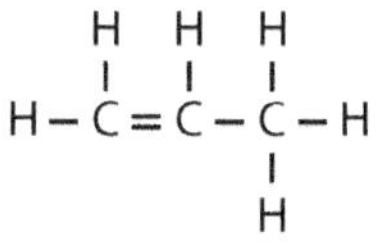	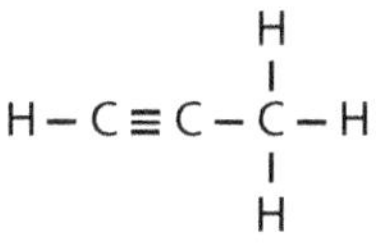	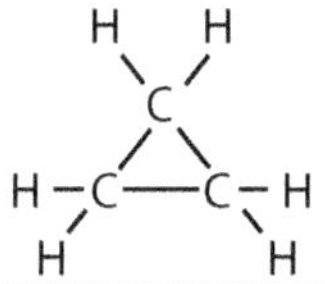	

Substituted Hydrocarbons				
Family	**General Structural Formula**	**Prefix, Suffix, or Group Name**	**Typical Compound**	
halide	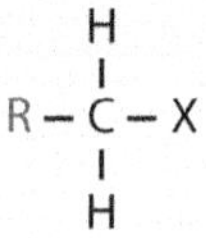	fluoro- chloro- bromo- iodo-	1-fluoropropane	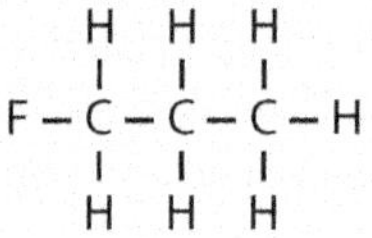
alcohol	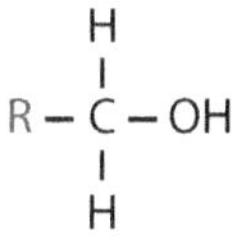	-ol	propan-1-ol	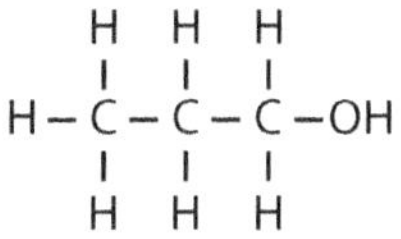
ether	R – O – R′	-oxy-	methoxymethane	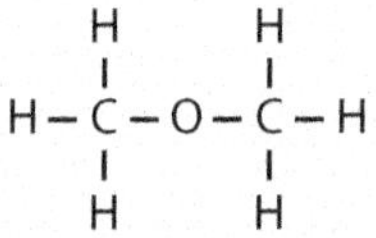
aldehyde	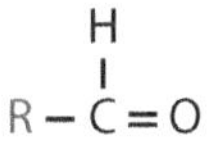	-al	propanal	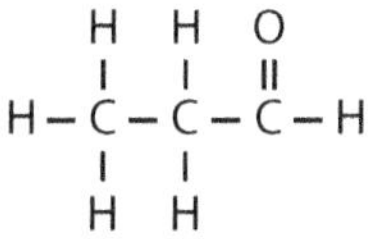
ketone	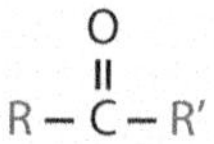	-one	propan-2-one	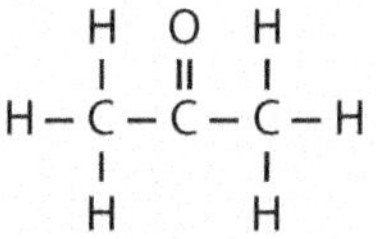
carboxylic acid	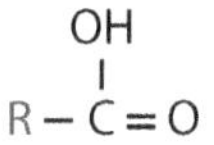	-oic acid	propanoic acid	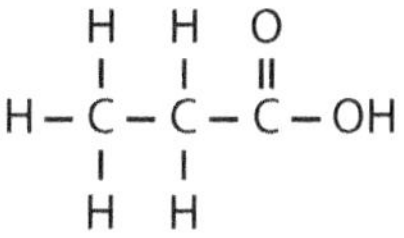
ester	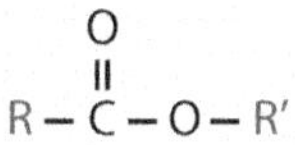	-oate	methyl propanoate	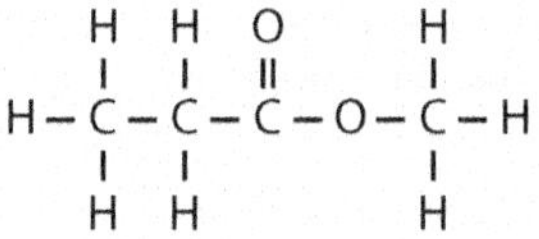
amine	R – N – R′	-amine	*N*-methylethan-1-amine	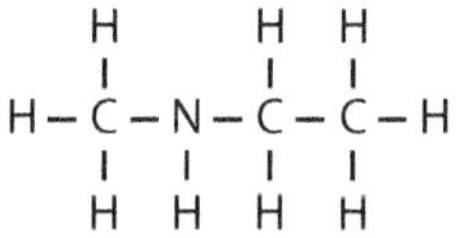
amide	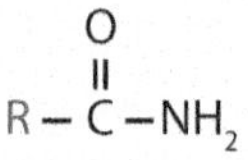	-amide	propanamide	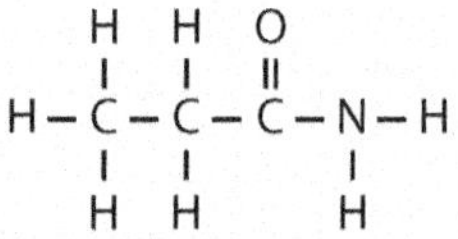

Appendix K

WORLDVIEW INVESTIGATION GRADING RUBRICS

Article/Paper

(Ch. 2, p. 32; Ch. 5, p. 97; Ch. 7, p. 169; Ch. 8, p. 186; Ch. 12, p. 292; Ch. 15, p. 380; Ch. 17, p. 422; Ch. 18, p. 455; Ch. 19, p. 474; Ch. 20, p. 508; Ch. 21, p. 532; Ch. 22, p. 555)

Use the standards below to assess the criteria listed in the left column of the rubric. Specific values are left blank to allow teachers to assign those values. Use the boxes in the rubric to take notes and provide feedback.

Excellent—Student demonstrates thorough understanding of the concept/completion of the task. Work may include minor conceptual errors that do not affect communication of understanding/completion of the task.

Good—Student demonstrates good understanding of the concept/completion of the task. Work may have some conceptual errors. Work may not communicate effectively.

Fair—Student demonstrates some understanding of the concept/completion of the task. Work may have major conceptual errors.

Poor—Student demonstrates little or no understanding of the concept/completion of the task.

	Excellent (___ pts)	Good (___ pts)	Fair (___ pts)	Poor (___ pts)
Research				
Credible Sources	__ sources	__ sources	__ sources	__ sources
Citations	clear and complete	complete but with __ minor errors	__ significant errors	not cited
Product				
Understanding of Science Issue				
Mechanics				
Grammar, Usage, and Spelling	__ minor errors	__ minor errors or __ major errors	__ minor errors or __ major errors	numerous errors throughout
Worldview				
Presentation of Opposing View				
Presentation of Biblical View				
Reflection upon the Issue				
Quality				
Timeliness	on time			late

Video Presentation

(Ch. 6, p. 126)

Use the standards below to assess the criteria listed in the left column of the rubric. Specific values are left blank to allow teachers to assign those values. Use the boxes in the rubric to take notes and provide feedback.

Excellent—Student demonstrates thorough understanding of the concept/completion of the task. Work may include minor conceptual errors that do not affect communication of understanding/completion of the task.

Good—Student demonstrates good understanding of the concept/completion of the task. Work may have some conceptual errors. Work may not communicate effectively.

Fair—Student demonstrates some understanding of the concept/completion of the task. Work may have major conceptual errors.

Poor—Student demonstrates little or no understanding of the concept/completion of the task.

	Excellent (___ pts)	Good (___ pts)	Fair (___ pts)	Poor (___ pts)
Research				
Credible Sources	__ sources	__ sources	__ sources	__ sources
Citations	clear and complete	complete but with __ minor errors	__ significant errors	not cited
Product				
Understanding of Science Issue				
Mechanics				
Grammar, Usage, and Spelling	__ minor errors	__ minor errors or __ major errors	__ minor errors or __ major errors	numerous errors throughout
Graphics and Design				
Content and Organization				
Worldview				
Presentation of Opposing View				
Presentation of Biblical View				
Reflection upon the Issue				
Quality				
Timeliness	on time			late

Appendix K

WORLDVIEW INVESTIGATION GRADING RUBRICS

Presentation

(Ch. 9, p. 206)

Use the standards below to assess the criteria listed in the left column of the rubric. Specific values are left blank to allow teachers to assign those values. Use the boxes in the rubric to take notes and provide feedback.

Excellent—Student demonstrates thorough understanding of the concept/completion of the task. Work may include minor conceptual errors that do not affect communication of understanding/completion of the task.

Good—Student demonstrates good understanding of the concept/completion of the task. Work may have some conceptual errors. Work may not communicate effectively.

Fair—Student demonstrates some understanding of the concept/completion of the task. Work may have major conceptual errors.

Poor—Student demonstrates little or no understanding of the concept/completion of the task.

	Excellent (___ pts)	Good (___ pts)	Fair (___ pts)	Poor (___ pts)
Research				
Credible Sources	__ sources	__ sources	__ sources	__ sources
Citations	clear and complete	complete but with __ minor errors	__ significant errors	not cited
Product				
Understanding of Science Issue				
Mechanics				
Grammar, Usage, and Spelling	__ minor errors	__ minor errors or __ major errors	__ minor errors or __ major errors	numerous errors throughout
Graphics and Visual Presentations				
Speaking Audience Awareness Projection Enunciation Posture				
Worldview				
Presentation of Opposing View				
Presentation of Biblical View				
Reflection upon the Issue				
Quality				
Timeliness	on time			late

Appendix L

ETHICS ESSAY GRADING RUBRICS

Use the standards below to assess the criteria listed in the left column of the rubric. Specific values are left blank to allow teachers to assign those values. Use the boxes in the rubric to take notes and provide feedback.

Excellent—Student demonstrates thorough understanding of the concept/completion of the task. Work may include minor conceptual errors that do not affect communication of understanding/completion of the task.

Good—Student demonstrates good understanding of the concept/completion of the task. Work may have some conceptual errors. Work may not communicate effectively.

Fair—Student demonstrates some understanding of the concept/completion of the task. Work may have major conceptual errors.

Poor—Student demonstrates little or no understanding of the concept/completion of the task.

	Excellent (___ pts)	Good (___ pts)	Fair (___ pts)	Poor (___ pts)
Research				
Research Sources, Information	__ sources	__ sources	__ sources	__ sources
Reference Citations	clear and complete	complete but with __ minor errors	__ significant errors	not cited
Worldview				
Biblical Principles				
Acceptable and Unacceptable Options	considered all of both	considered some of both	considered few of both	considered none or only one option
Consequences	all	at least one for each option	at least one for some options	none
Biblical Outcomes Human Flourishing, Thriving Creation, God's Glory	all three	only two	only one	none
Biblical Motivation Faith in God, Hope in God's Promises, Love for God and Others	all three	only two	only one	none
Action Urged a Feasible Action				
Product				
Grammar, Usage, Mechanics, and Spelling	__ minor errors	__ minor errors or __ major errors	__ minor errors or __ major errors	numerous errors throughout
Appearance, Neatness, and Organization				
Quality				
Timeliness	on time			late

Appendix L

ETHICS ESSAY GRADING RUBRICS

Ethics Debate Rubric

(Ch. 22, p. 569)

Use the standards below to assess the criteria listed in the left column of the rubric. Specific values are left blank to allow teachers to assign those values. Use the boxes in the rubric to take notes and provide feedback.

Excellent—Student demonstrates thorough understanding of the concept/completion of the task. Work may include minor conceptual errors that do not affect communication of understanding/completion of the task.

Good—Student demonstrates good understanding of the concept/completion of the task. Work may have some conceptual errors. Work may not communicate effectively.

Fair—Student demonstrates some understanding of the concept/completion of the task. Work may have major conceptual errors.

Poor—Student demonstrates little or no understanding of the concept/completion of the task.

	Excellent (___ pts)	Good (___ pts)	Fair (___ pts)	Poor (___ pts)
Research				
Research Sources, Information, Citations	__ sources	__ sources	__ sources	__ sources
Worldview				
Biblical Principles				
Acceptable and Unacceptable Options	considered all of both	considered some of both	considered few of both	considered none or only one option
Consequences	all	at least one for each option	at least one for some options	none
Biblical Outcomes Human Flourishing, Thriving Creation, God's Glory	all three	only two	only one	none
Biblical Motivation Faith in God, Hope in God's Promises, Love for God and Others	all three	only two	only one	none
Action Urged a Feasible Action				
Concept				
Information Research, Understanding Both Sides				
Point Focus, Statement, Support				
Counterpoint On Topic, Challenging				
Organization				
Delivery				
Language and Poise Grammar, Use of Voice, Composure, Gesticulation				
Persuasion	convinced completely	partially convinced		failed to convince
Time Usage				
Quality				
Timeliness	on time			late

Appendix M

FLOW CHARTS

Chapter 9: Nomenclature Flow Charts

Naming Compounds Flowchart

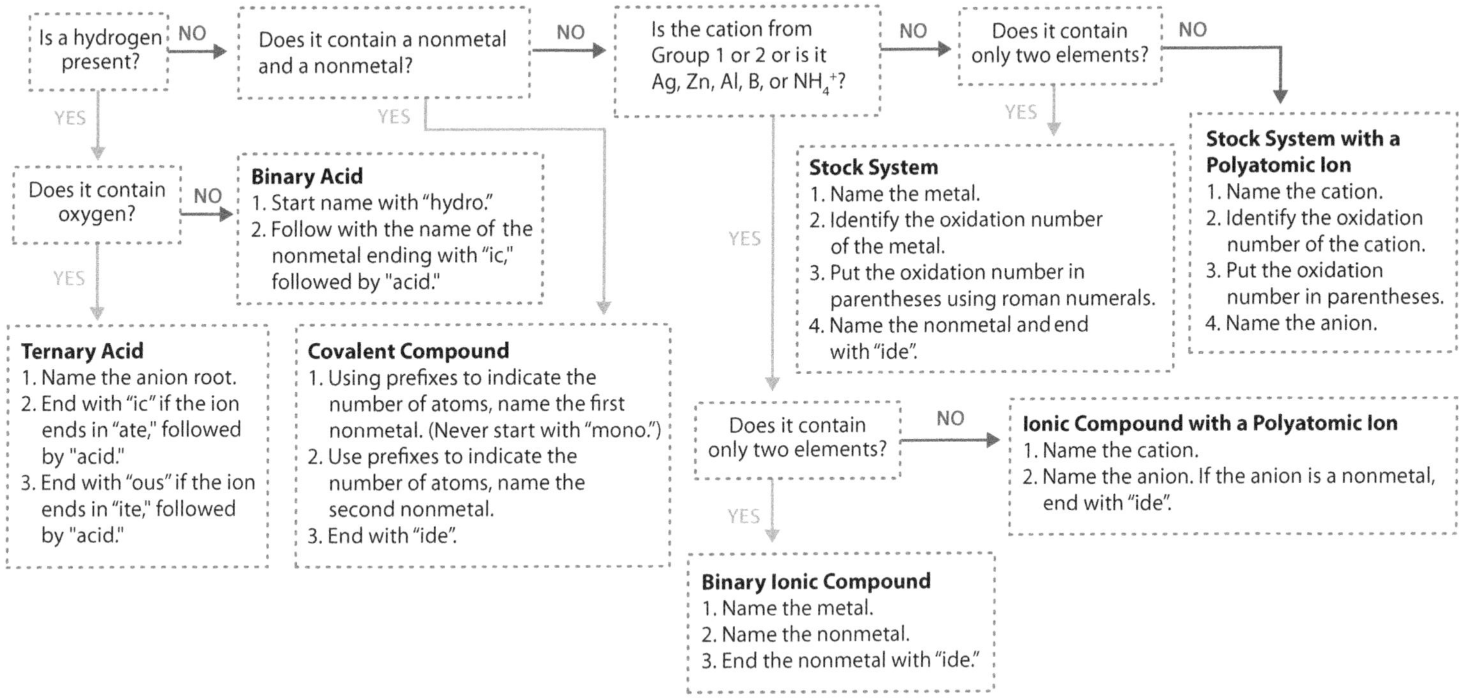

Writing Compound Formulas Flowchart

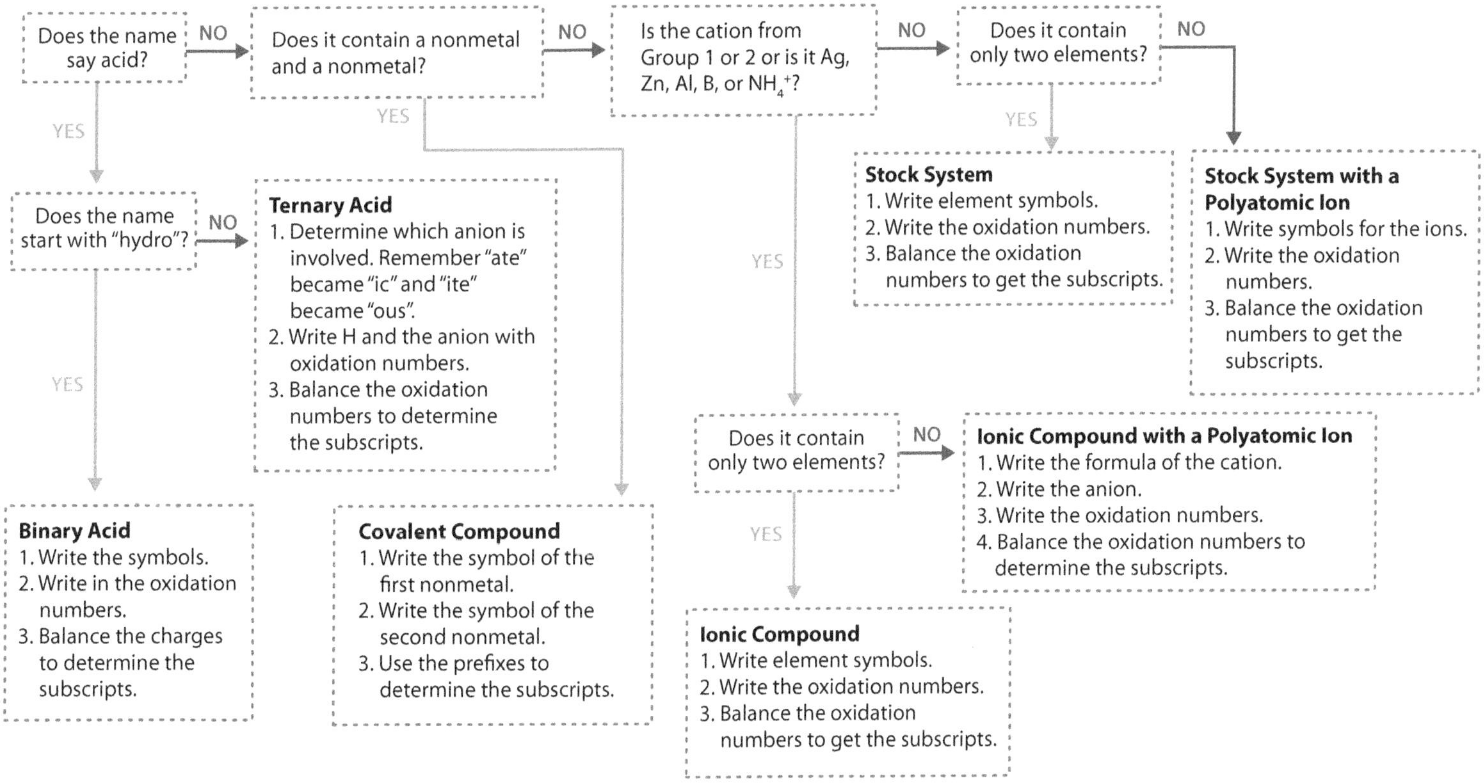

Appendix M

FLOW CHARTS

Chapter 11: Stoichiometry Map

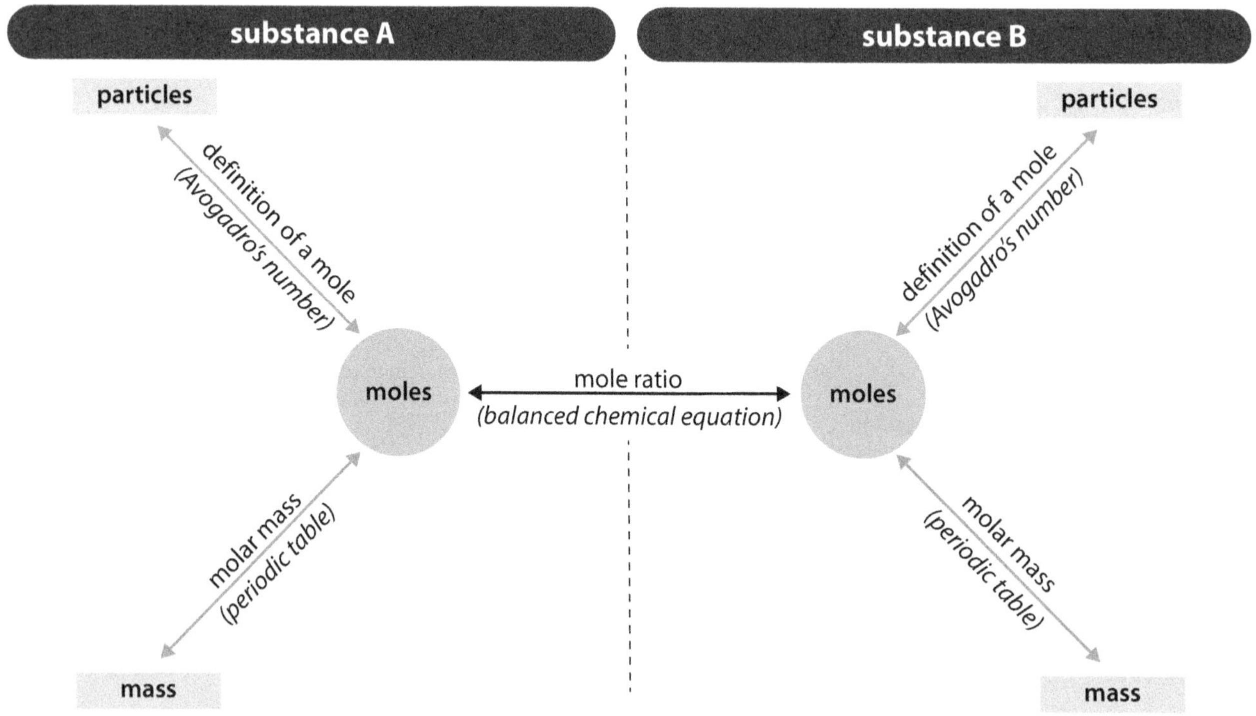

Chapter 12: Stoichiometry Map

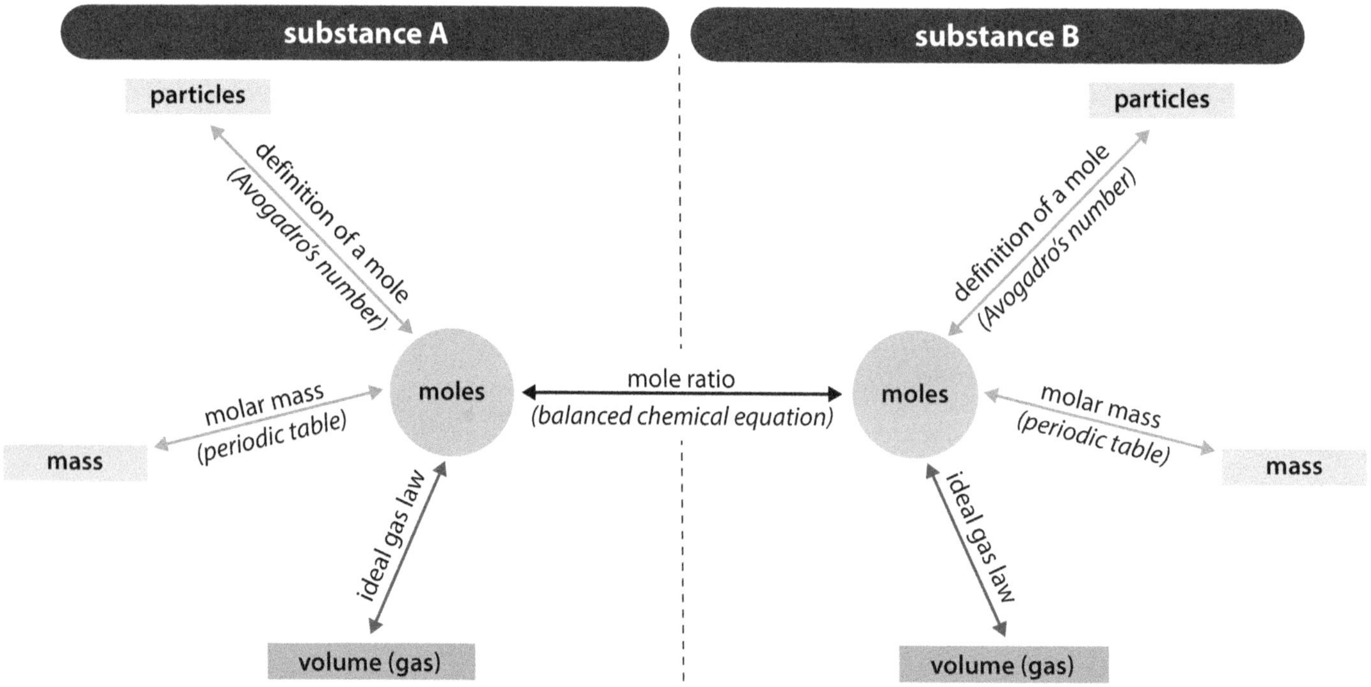

Chapter 14: Stoichiometry Map

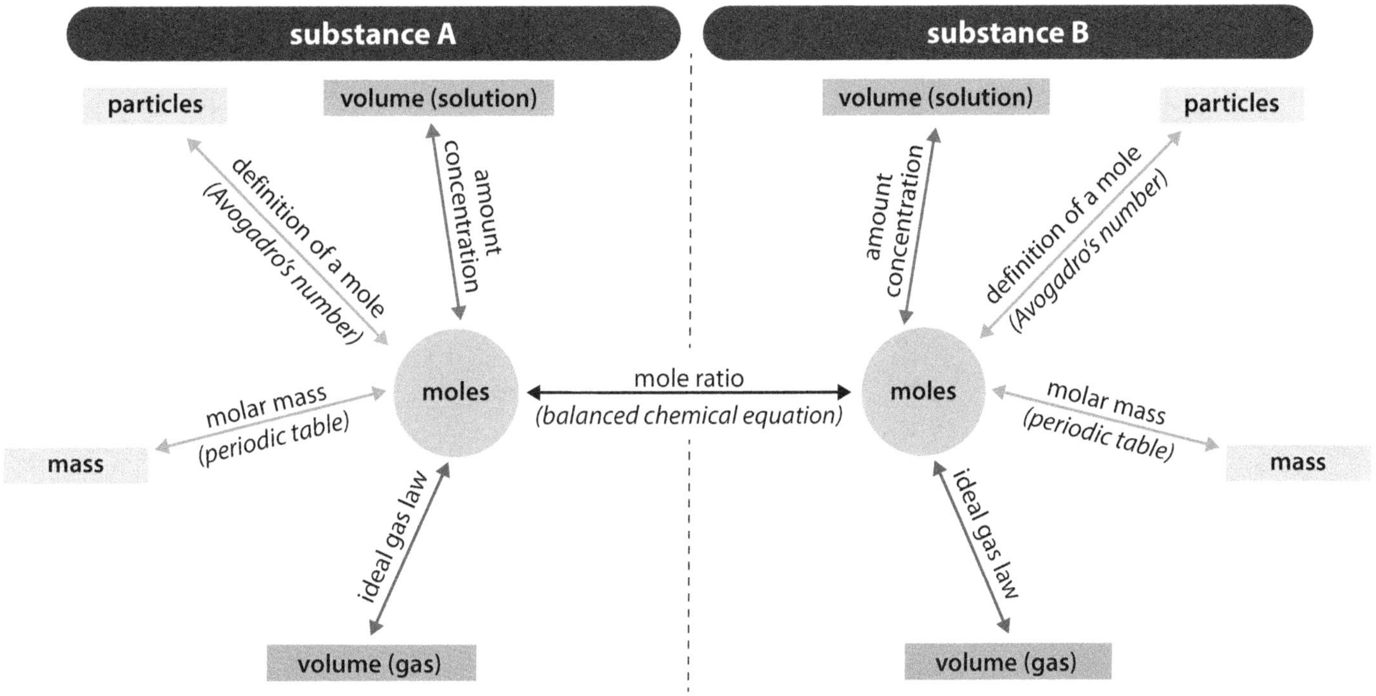

Appendix N

MINI LAB EQUIPMENT AND MATERIALS LIST (ALPHABETICALLY)

Amount required is specified for each lab group.

Item	Chapter	Size	# Req.	Remarks
acids and bases	18	10 mL	6	six different acids and/or bases, each 10 mL; suitable acids and bases are lemon juice, orange juice, coffee, milk, salt water, soapy water
baking soda	11		15 g	
balance, laboratory	11, 14		1	
balloon	11, 12		5, 1	
beaker	2	300 mL	1	
beaker	8	50 mL	2	
	18		6	
beaker	14	250 mL	4	
beaker	15	400 mL	1	
beaker	19	100 mL	2	
bromothymol blue (BTB)	13		1 drop	
bucket	12		1	
chromatography paper	2		1 pc.	
connecting wires	19		2	
copper strip	16	2 cm	1	
	19	6 cm	1	
copper(II) sulfate solution, 1 M	19		75 mL	
density cube, aluminum	15		1	
density cube, nickel	15		1	
different light sources	5			
diffraction grating	5		1	
dime	8		1	
disposable pipette	8		2	
dominoes	22		30	
Erlenmeyer flask	11	500 mL	5	
goggles	11, 15		1 pair	
graduated cylinder	16	25 mL	1	
granulated sugar	14		11 g	
hot plate	7, 15		1	
ice	12			enough to fill bucket
index card	5		1	
isopropyl alcohol	8		25 mL	
magnesium strips	16	2 cm	3	
marker	14, 16		1	
marker, permanent	7, 12		1	
marker, water-based	2		3	three different colors
molecular modeling set	9, 10, 20, 21		1	

Item	Chapter	Size	# Req.	Remarks
observation boxes	4		1 set	can be purchased under the name Ob-Scertainer from science suppliers such as Flinn Scientific
paper clip	2		1	
paper ruler	3		3	
paraffin wax	7		1	
petri dish with cover	13		1	
pie pan, aluminum	7	9 in.	1	
rubber band	5		1	
salt bridge strip	19		1	
shoebox with lid	5		1	
spoon	12		1	
stirring rod	14		1	
stopwatch	14, 22		1	
string	12	25 cm	1	
sugar	7		1 tsp	
sugar cube	14		1	
table salt	7		1 tsp	
tape, clear	5			
test tube	16		4	
test tube rack	16		1	
thermometer	15		2	
tongs	15		1	
universal pH indicator paper	18		6 pcs.	
utility knife or scissors	5		1	
vinegar	13		1 drop	
	16		55 mL	
voltmeter	19		1	
watch glass	2		1	
water	8, 16	25 mL		
water, hot	14	100 mL		
water, room temperature	14	300 mL		
weighing dish	14		4	
weighing paper	11		1 pc.	
white vinegar	11		1000 mL	
zinc strip	19	6 cm	1	
zinc sulfate solution, 1 M	19		75 mL	

Appendix N

MINI LAB EQUIPMENT AND MATERIALS LIST (BY CHAPTER)

Amount required is specified for each lab group.

Chapter	Item	Size	# Req.	Remarks
1	none			
2	beaker	300 mL	1	
	chromatography paper		1 pc.	
	marker, water-based		3	three different colors
	paper clip		1	
	watch glass		1	
3	paper ruler		3	
4	observation boxes		1 set	can be purchased under the name Ob-Scertainer from science suppliers such as Flinn Scientific
5	different light sources			
	diffraction grating		1	
	index card		1	
	rubber band		1	
	shoebox with lid		1	
	tape, clear			
	utility knife or scissors		1	
7	hot plate		1	
	marker, permanent		1	
	paraffin wax		1	
	pie pan, aluminum	9 in.	1	
	sugar		1 tsp	
	table salt		1 tsp	
8	beaker	50 mL	2	
	dime		1	
	disposable pipette		2	
	isopropyl alcohol		25 mL	
	water	25 mL		
9	molecular modeling set		1	
10	molecular modeling set		1	
11	baking soda		15 g	
	balance, laboratory		1	
	balloon		5	
	Erlenmeyer flask	500 mL	5	
	goggles		1 pair	
	weighing paper		1 pc.	
	white vinegar		1000 mL	
12	balloon		1	
	bucket		1	
	ice			enough to fill bucket
	marker, permanent		1	
	spoon		1	
	string	25 cm	1	

Chapter	Item	Size	# Req.	Remarks
13	bromothymol blue (BTB)		1 drop	
	petri dish with cover		1	
	vinegar		1 drop	
14	balance, laboratory		1	
	beaker	250 mL	4	
	granulated sugar		11 g	
	marker		1	
	stirring rod		1	
	stopwatch		1	
	sugar cube		1	
	water, hot		100 mL	
	water, room temperature		300 mL	
	weighing dish		4	
15	beaker	400 mL	1	
	density cube, aluminum		1	
	density cube, nickel		1	
	goggles		1 pair	
	hot plate		1	
	thermometer		2	
	tongs		1	
16	copper strip	2 cm	1	
	graduated cylinder	25 mL	1	
	magnesium strips	2 cm	3	
	marker		1	
	test tube		4	
	test tube rack		1	
	vinegar		55 mL	
	water		25 mL	
18	acids and bases	10 mL	6	six different acids and/or bases, each 10 mL; suitable acids and bases are lemon juice, orange juice, coffee, milk, salt water, soapy water
	beaker	50 mL	6	
	universal pH indicator paper		6 pcs.	
19	beaker	100 mL	2	
	connecting wires		2	
	copper strip	6 cm	1	
	copper(II) sulfate solution, 1 M		75 mL	
	salt bridge strip		1	
	voltmeter		1	
	zinc strip	6 cm	1	
	zinc sulfate solution, 1 M		75 mL	
20	molecular modeling set		1	
21	molecular modeling set		1	
22	dominoes		30	
	stopwatch		1	

Appendix O

EXPLAINING THE GOSPEL

One of the greatest desires of Christian teachers is to see their students repent and believe in Christ. Relying on the Holy Spirit, you should take advantage of the opportunities that arise for presenting the gospel. You may find the following outline helpful, especially when dealing individually with a young person.

1. The Lord God is King over all His creation (Rev. 4:11).

God created everything that is (Gen. 1–2).

God created the world with laws about how His world is to work and the way that people are to live.

2. All have sinned—including me (Rom. 3:23).

Since Adam first sinned, all people are born rebels against the rule of God (Rom. 5:12).

God has made me in His own image so that I might declare His glory by being like Him (Gen. 1:26–27).

But I am a sinner. I disobey God's Word. The Bible teaches that I am to love God more than anything or anyone (Mark 12:30). It also teaches that I should love other people at all times (Mark 12:31). But sometimes I don't enjoy doing what God wants me to do, I don't always delight in obeying my parents, and I don't always like being kind to other people.

God will punish me for my rebellion and sin (Rom. 6:23). God hates sin, and there is nothing I can do to get rid of my sin. I can try to change my behavior, but I can never change my heart.

3. Jesus died and rose again for me (Rom. 5:8).

God loves me even though I am a sinner.

He sent His Son, Jesus Christ, to live a perfect life and to die on the cross, suffering the punishment for my sin.

Three days later God raised Jesus from the dead and made Him the ruler of His eternal kingdom. Jesus is alive today. This is the gospel of Jesus Christ: He died on the cross and was raised up to be God's appointed King (1 Cor. 15:1–4).

God desires to restore me to bear His image fully by making me like His Son, the perfect image-bearer of God (Rom. 8:29).

God gives a new heart—new loves and desires—to every one of His children (Ezek. 36:26–27).

4. I need to put my trust in Jesus (Rom. 10:9–10).

I must repent of, or turn away from, my sin and let Jesus control my life. I must also believe what God has done through Jesus (Mark 1:15).

If I repent and believe in what Jesus has done, I am putting my trust in Jesus.

Everyone who has trusted in Jesus is forgiven of sin.

Everyone who has trusted in Jesus submits to having Him as his King.

Everyone who has been saved by God will continue to trust and obey Jesus for the rest of his life (Heb. 3:14).

When talking individually with a young person, ask questions to discern sincerity or any misunderstanding. What is sin? Are you a sinner? What is the gospel? What does it mean to repent? Read the verses from your Bible. If a student shows genuine sorrow for sin and a sufficiently accurate understanding of the basics of the gospel, encourage him to call on the Lord as you listen. Perhaps he will pray something like the following:

"God, I know that You hate sin. But I also know that You love me. I believe that Jesus died for me and rose from the dead for me. I now turn away from my sin, and I am trusting in Jesus to forgive me and to be my King forever. I want to follow Him wherever He leads me."

Show the student the Bible's command that believers unite together in regular fellowship (Heb. 10:24–25) and encourage him to get involved right away in a gospel-preaching church. Tell him that whenever he sins, he will be forgiven as he confesses his sins to God (1 John 1:9).

Glossary

A

absorption. The ability of a fluid substance to seep into the pores or interstitial spaces between the molecules of a solid.

accuracy. An evaluation of how close a measured value is to the expected or accepted value of a dimension being measured.

acid-base indicator. A substance that will change colors when it reacts with an acid or base, making it helpful in identifying acidic or basic solutions.

acid-base titration. A controlled neutralization reaction that scientists use to determine the unknown concentration of a solution.

acidic solution. A solution with a pH less than 7 and a pOH greater than 7.

acid-ionization constant (K_a)**.** The equilibrium constant for the dissociation of an acid. Higher values indicate stronger acids.

acoustic energy. The energy carried in a sound wave.

actinoid series. A set of elements typically placed at the bottom of the periodic table that consists of the *f*-block elements from Period 7.

activated complex. An intermediate substance that forms during a chemical reaction as reactants transition into products.

activation energy (E_a)**.** The minimum energy necessary for a chemical reaction to occur when reactants collide in the proper orientation.

actual yield. The amount of product produced when a chemical reaction is done in a laboratory.

addition reaction. A reaction in organic chemistry in which a multiple bond of a molecule is broken and two atoms or groups of atoms are added.

adhesion. The attraction between the particles of a liquid and the particles of other materials.

adsorption. A process similar to absorption but in which one substance collects on the surface of another and does not enter into the pores or interstitial space of the other substance.

alchemy. An ancient philosophy that blended astrology and mysticism with observation and experimentation and was the precursor of chemistry.

alcohol. A substituted hydrocarbon in which a hydroxyl group has replaced at least one of the hydrogen atoms.

aldehyde. A substituted hydrocarbon that contains a carbonyl group at one or both ends of a carbon chain.

aliphatic compound. An organic compound, either branched, unbranched, or a ring that does not contain delocalized electrons.

alkali metal. An element of Group 1 on the periodic table. It is a soft, highly reactive metal that has one valence electron that it easily loses to form a 1+ cation.

alkaline battery. A type of primary battery that contains a hydroxide electrolyte.

alkaline-earth metal. An element of Group 2 on the periodic table. It is a reactive metal, having two valence electrons that it easily loses to form a 2+ cation.

alkaline solution. See *basic solution.*

alkane. The simplest class of hydrocarbons consisting of substances that contain only single bonds.

alkene. A hydrocarbon that contains at least one double bond between two of its carbon atoms.

alkyl group. A hydrocarbon branch connected to another hydrocarbon.

alkyne. A hydrocarbon that contains at least one triple bond between two of its carbon atoms.

allotrope. One of the different forms that an element can have.

allotropic element. An element that can be found in different forms.

alloy. A homogenous mixture of a metal with another element, often a second metal.

alpha decay. Radioactivity that emits an alpha particle and energy, causing a decrease to both the mass number and the atomic number of the parent nuclide.

alpha helix. A secondary structure of polypeptides consisting of a tight spiral of amino acids held in place by hydrogen bonds.

alpha particle (α or ${}^{4}_{2}He$)**.** A particle consisting of two protons and two neutrons and having a 2+ charge.

amide. A substituted hydrocarbon in which an ammonia molecule replaces the hydroxyl group in a carboxylic acid.

amine. A substituted hydrocarbon in which an ammonia molecule combines with a hydrocarbon.

amino acid. A biochemical molecule made up of a carbon atom with an amine group, a carboxyl group, a hydrogen atom, and a side chain; a monomer of a protein.

amorphous solid. A solid that has no distinct shape or underlying pattern.

amount concentration (c_{solute})**.** A measure of concentration that compares the moles of a solute with the volume of an entire solution in liters; also known as *molar concentration* or *molarity.*

amphiphilic. A term used to describe a molecule that has both a polar end and a nonpolar end. The polar end of the molecule is water soluble, while the nonpolar end is not water soluble.

amphoteric substance. A substance that can act as both a Brønsted-Lowry acid and a Brønsted-Lowry base.

anabolism. Any biochemical process that combines small molecules or particles into larger molecules.

anhydrous compound. A compound without water in its crystalline structure; used to describe a hydrate with its water removed.

anion. A charged atom or group of atoms with a net negative charge due to the gain of electrons.

anode. The electrode at which oxidation occurs in an electrochemical cell. It is positively charged in an electrolytic cell and negatively charged in a voltaic cell.

applied science. The use of science to solve real-world problems.

aromatic compound. An organic compound that contains highly stable ring structures consisting in part of delocalized electrons.

Arrhenius acid. A chemical substance that when dissolved in water will ionize to form hydrogen ions (H^+) or hydronium (H_3O^+) ions; the earliest and most restrictive definition of acids.

Arrhenius base. A chemical substance that when dissolved in water will dissociate to form hydroxide ions (OH^-); the earliest and most restrictive definition of bases.

atom. The smallest particle that makes up an element and is capable of chemical interactions.

atomic crystal. A crystalline solid that forms from atoms of noble gases when they freeze.

atomic mass. The weighted average of the masses of all the naturally occurring isotopes of an element.

atomic number (Z)**.** The unique number that identifies a specific element. It is equal to the number of protons in an atom of that element.

atomic radius. The distance from the center of an atom's nucleus to its outermost electron.

atomism. An ancient Greek model of matter that stated that matter consisted of discrete particles, called *atoms*, which established a limit on how far matter could be divided.

aufbau principle. A principle that states that electrons will fill the lowest available energy sublevels before any can occupy higher-energy sublevels.

Avogadro's law. The law that states that the volume of a gas at a constant temperature and pressure is directly proportional to the number of moles of the gas.

Avogadro's number (N)**.** The number of particles in one mole: $6.022\ 140\ 76 \times 10^{23}$ particles.

B

band of stability. The group of stable nuclides plotted on a graph of the number of neutrons versus the number of protons.

base-ionization constant (K_b)**.** The equilibrium constant for the dissociation of a base. Higher values indicate stronger bases.

basic solution. A solution with a pH greater than 7 and a pOH less than 7; also known as an *alkaline solution*.

battery. A device that contains one or more voltaic cells, storing chemical energy to provide an on-demand electrical energy supply.

becquerel (Bq)**.** The SI unit for measuring the radioactivity emitted by a source.

bent molecule. A molecule shape characterized by three or four regions of electrons and two outer atoms surrounding a central atom.

benzene. A six-carbon, ring-structured hydrocarbon with delocalized electrons forming its carbon-carbon bonds; a common component of many aromatic hydrocarbons.

beta decay. Radioactivity that emits a beta particle (electron) and energy. The electron forms as a neutron changes to a proton, increasing the parent nuclide's atomic number but not its mass number.

beta particle (β or ${}^{0}_{-1}e$)**.** An electron emitted from a nucleus during beta decay.

beta plus decay. See *positron emission*.

beta sheet. A secondary structure of polypeptides consisting of strands of amino acids held in place by hydrogen bonds.

Big Bang model. The most popular evolutionary theory for the origin of the universe. It suggests that all matter in the universe began in a highly dense, high-energy state and expanded rapidly to form the universe over the past 13.8 billion years.

binary acid. An acid containing hydrogen and a nonmetal.

binary compound. A compound made of only two elements.

biochemistry. The field of chemistry that focuses on the chemistry of living things: genetics, cellular respiration, and other cellular functions.

Glossary

Bohr model. A model of atoms proposed by Niels Bohr in which electrons move around the nucleus in well-defined orbits. Each orbit represents a specific energy level for electrons. Also known as the *planetary model*.

boiling. The process of vaporization caused by the vapor pressure in regions of a liquid exceeding the atmospheric pressure, allowing liquid particles to transition to the gaseous phase.

boiling point. The temperature at which the vapor pressure of a liquid is equal to the current atmospheric pressure.

boiling point elevation (ΔT_b)**.** The increase of the boiling point of a solvent due to the presence of dissolved solute particles.

bond axis. The line formed between two atoms involved in bonding.

bonding pair. The two shared valence electrons participating in a covalent bond.

Boyle's law. The law that states that the pressure and volume of a sample of gas at a constant temperature are inversely related; $PV = k$.

branched hydrocarbon. A hydrocarbon that has alkyl groups attached such that no single chain of carbon atoms can be traced.

brine. A concentrated sodium chloride solution.

Brønsted-Lowry acid. A chemical substance that donates a proton.

Brønsted-Lowry base. A chemical substance that accepts a proton.

Brownian motion. The constant motion of fluid particles in random directions due to their kinetic energy.

buffer. A solution that resists pH changes when acids or bases are added; usually consists of a weak acid and its conjugate base or a weak base and its conjugate acid.

C

calorimeter. An insulated container, similar to a thermos, in which a thermometer detects the temperature change that occurs during a chemical reaction.

capillary action. The process of a liquid in a container moving upward against gravity due to the adhesive force between the liquid and container molecules.

capillary tube. A narrow glass tube that will draw liquids through the action of adhesion between the glass and liquid molecules.

carbohydrate. An organic compound that consists of carbon, hydrogen, and oxygen; collectively used to refer to sugars, starches, and cellulose.

carbonyl group. A functional group consisting of a carbon atom double bonded to an oxygen atom (C = O); a key feature of aldehydes and ketones.

carboxyl group. A functional group consisting of a carbon atom double bonded to an oxygen atom and to a hydroxyl group (C = OOH).

carboxylic acid. A substituted hydrocarbon containing a carboxyl group at one end.

catabolism. Any biochemical process that breaks large molecules down into smaller particles, providing building materials and energy for other processes.

catalyst. A substance that changes a reaction rate without being consumed in the chemical reaction.

catalyzed reaction. A reaction that occurs in the presence of a catalyst. The reaction rate of a catalyzed reaction is faster than the rate of the uncatalyzed reaction.

cathode. The electrode at which reduction occurs in an electrochemical cell. It is negatively charged in an electrolytic cell and positively charged in a voltaic cell.

cathode ray. The stream of electrons emitted from the cathode in a cathode-ray tube.

cation. A charged atom or group of atoms with a net positive charge due to the loss of electrons.

cellulose. A polysaccharide that forms the basis for structural components in plants.

Celsius scale. A temperature scale with one hundred degrees between the normal boiling point (100 °C) and freezing point (0 °C) of water.

chain reaction. An ongoing fission process in which the neutrons released by one reaction trigger additional reactions.

Charles's law. The law that states that the Kelvin temperature and volume of a sample of gas at a constant pressure are directly related; $\frac{V}{T} = k$.

chemical bond. A durable electrostatic attraction that forms between atoms.

chemical change. Any change that causes a substance to change its chemical identity; also known as a *chemical reaction*.

chemical energy. The potential energy stored in chemical substances.

chemical equation. A model of a chemical reaction that shows the chemicals used (reactants) and the chemicals produced (products).

chemical equilibrium. The state in a reversible chemical reaction in which the forward and reverse reaction rates are equal and the concentration of each substance is stable.

chemical formula. A combination of chemical symbols, coefficients, and subscripts that identifies the elements and number of atoms of each element in a compound.

chemical property. Any property that describes the way that matter acts in the presence of other materials or the way that it changes composition under certain conditions.

chemical reaction. Any change that causes a substance to change its chemical identity; also known as a *chemical change*.

chemical symbol. A one- or two-letter symbol that identifies an element.

chemistry. The study of matter and the changes that it undergoes.

chirality. The characteristic of a molecule that indicates that it can have either a left- or right-handed arrangement.

chromosome. A strand of DNA containing some or all of the genetic code of a cell.

coagulation. The clumping together of particles. In solutions, this refers to the clumping together of impurities in the solution that are to be removed.

coefficient. A number placed before a chemical substance in a chemical equation that indicates the number of particles of that substance in the reaction.

cohesion. The attraction between the particles of a liquid.

colligative property. A property of a solvent that changes as the number of solute particles in a solution changes.

collision theory. A theory explaining how chemical reactions occur that states that for a reaction to occur the substances (1) must collide (2) in the proper orientation and (3) with sufficient energy, called the *activation energy*.

colloid. A heterogeneous mixture formed when medium-sized particles (> 1 nm and < 1 μm) are dispersed in a dispersing medium.

combination reaction. See *synthesis reaction*.

combined gas law. The law that states that the pressure, volume, and Kelvin temperature of a sample of a gas vary jointly; $\frac{PV}{T} = k$.

combustion reaction. A chemical reaction that combines a reactant with oxygen and releases energy in various forms.

common ion. The ion that exists in two different solutes when mixed together. The concentration of both solutes must be considered when dealing with a common ion.

common-ion effect. The effect when there is a common ion in a mixture of solutions that causes the ion concentration product to exceed the K_{sp} of the less soluble salt, which will then precipitate out.

complete iconic equation. An expanded form of the chemical equation for a double-replacement reaction showing all the dissociated ions.

complex reaction. A chemical reaction that occurs in two or more elementary steps.

compound. A pure substance that consists of two or more elements chemically combined in a fixed ratio.

compressibility. The ability of a substance to be squeezed into a smaller volume by applying pressure.

concentration. A measure of the amount of a solute in a certain volume or mass of either a solvent alone or of an entire solution.

condensation. The phase change from a vapor to a liquid due to a loss of thermal energy.

condensation reaction. A reaction in organic chemistry in which molecules combine to form a larger molecule.

condensed structure formula. An abbreviated form of a structural formula that omits some components of a molecule and their bonds.

conductivity. The property of a material that enables it to transfer thermal energy or electricity.

conjugate acid. A Brønsted-Lowry base that has gained a proton.

conjugate acid-base pair. A Brønsted-Lowry acid and base that have exchanged a proton.

conjugate base. A Brønsted-Lowry acid that has given up a proton.

continuous spectrum. A complete set of all the items along a continuum.

continuous theory of matter. An ancient Greek model of matter that stated that matter could be divided infinitely into smaller portions.

conversion factor. The ratio of two equivalent measures, used to perform unit conversions.

covalent bond. A chemical bond characterized by the sharing of valence electrons between two atoms.

covalent molecular crystal. A molecular solid that is made of covalently bonded atoms held in a crystal lattice by its intermolecular forces.

covalent network solid. A nonmetallic element that is able to bond covalently to form a large network of atoms, as in diamond.

Creation Mandate. God's commandment to mankind to have dominion over the world that He created.

Glossary

critical mass. The minimum mass required to maintain a chain reaction.

critical pressure. The pressure that is needed to liquefy a gas at just below its critical temperature.

critical temperature. The temperature at which a gas can not be liquefied regardless of pressure.

crystal lattice. The orderly repeated arrangement of cations and anions in an ionic compound.

crystalline solid. A solid that has a naturally orderly shape, forming a regular three-dimensional pattern with distinct edges and sharp angles.

cyclic aliphatic compound. Any aliphatic organic compound that exists in a ring form rather than in an open chain.

D

Dalton's law of partial pressures. The law that states that the total pressure of a mixture of gases equals the sum of the pressures of each individual gas, called the *partial pressures*; $P_{total} = \Sigma P_i$.

daughter nuclide. The nuclide that is produced by any nuclear transmutation.

de Broglie hypothesis. The idea that if waves can behave like particles, then particles can behave like waves.

decanting. A process for separating mixtures in which a less dense medium is poured off the top of a more dense medium.

decomposition reaction. A chemical reaction that splits a single reactant into two or more products, having the general form $AB \longrightarrow A + B$.

deductive reasoning. The process of logically proceeding from general statements to a specific conclusion.

dehydration reaction. An elimination reaction in which water is removed from a molecule.

dehydrogenation reaction. An elimination reaction in which hydrogen atoms are removed from a molecule.

delocalized electron. A bonding electron that is associated with a group of atoms rather than forming part of a particular bond.

denaturing. The loss of protein structure caused by high heat, radiation, or toxins; results in a loss of a protein's function.

density (ρ)**.** The amount of matter in a unit of volume.

deoxyribonucleic acid. See *DNA*.

dependent variable. The variable in a controlled experiment that changes in response to variations in the independent variable.

deposition. The change of state directly from vapor to solid without transitioning through liquid due to a loss of thermal energy.

derived unit. Units in the SI that are mathematical combinations of fundamental units.

descriptive chemistry. The study of elements and the compounds they form.

diagonal rule. A visual aid to help remember the order of energy sublevels in the quantum-mechanical model of an atom.

diatomic element. An element that naturally occurs as molecules of two atoms.

diffusibility. The ability of a fluid substance to spread throughout and mix with another fluid.

diffusion. The process by which fluid matter and energy spread from a region of higher concentration to a region of lower concentration.

dilution. The process of making a solution less concentrated.

dimension. A measurable property of a phenomenon.

dipeptide. A molecule formed by the bonding of two amino acids.

dipole-dipole force. An intermolecular force between the positive end of one polar molecule and the negative end of another.

diprotic acid. An acid that can donate two protons.

disaccharide. A complex carbohydrate that is comprised of two sugar units.

dispersed phase. The medium-sized particles (> 1 nm and < 1 μm) that are spread through the dispersing medium of a colloid.

dispersing medium. The medium in which the medium-sized particles (> 1 nm and < 1 μm) of a colloid are spread.

dispersion force. See *London dispersion force.*

dissociation. The process by which ionic solutes dissolve when their ions are physically separated from each other by a solvent.

distillation. A process for separating a mixture on the basis of the different boiling points of its components.

DNA. A nucleic acid that contains deoxyribose as the sugar in its nucleotides and which encodes genetic information; the abbreviation for *deoxyribonucleic acid*.

dosimeter. A wearable device that collects data about the amount of radiation that a wearer has been exposed to.

double bond. A covalent bond that forms when two pairs of valence electrons are shared between atoms.

double-displacement reaction. See *double-replacement reaction.*

double-replacement reaction. A chemical reaction between two compounds in which the cations or the anions switch places. It has the general form $AX + BY \longrightarrow BX + AY$ (cation switching) or $AX + BY \longrightarrow AY + BX$ (anion switching). Also known as a *double-displacement reaction.*

ductility. The property of a material that enables it to be drawn into wire.

E

effusion. The process by which particles pass through a tiny opening into an evacuated chamber.

electrical energy. The potential energy of a charged particle due to its position in an electric field.

electrochemical cell. A device that uses either a spontaneous chemical reaction to produce electricity or electricity to drive a nonspontaneous chemical reaction.

electrochemistry. The field of chemistry that studies how electricity and redox reactions are related.

electrodepositing. The general term for processes that apply layers of material on an electrode through electrochemistry.

electrolysis. The process of forcing an otherwise nonspontaneous redox reaction to occur with the aid of an electrical current in an electrochemical cell.

electrolyte. Any substance that produces ions, which conduct electricity in a solution.

electrolytic cell. An electrochemical cell that use electrical energy to force a nonspontaneous chemical reaction to occur.

electromagnetic energy. The energy carried in electromagnetic waves that is produced by the vibration of charged particles and that disrupts the electromagnetic field.

electron (e^-). A subatomic particle located in the electron cloud around the nucleus of an atom. It has a negative charge and very little mass—less than 1/1800 the mass of a proton or neutron.

electron affinity. The change in energy when an electron is added to a neutral atom to form an anion.

electron capture. A nuclear transformation caused when a low-energy-level electron is absorbed by a nucleus. The transformation changes a proton to a neutron, causing a decrease in the parent nuclide's atomic number but not to its mass number.

electron cloud. The combination of all the orbitals of an atom that forms a roughly spherical region containing all the electrons of an atom.

electron configuration. In general, the arrangement of electrons in an atom of an element in its ground state. Specifically, the notation of an atom's electron configuration, consisting of its energy sublevels and superscripts that indicate the number of electrons in each.

electron deficiency. The state of a molecule that forms with one or more of the atoms having less than eight valence electrons.

electron dot notation. A shorthand method of representing atoms and their valence electrons, consisting of the atom's chemical symbol with surrounding dots representing its valence electrons.

electron sea model. A model for explaining bonding in metals and the properties of metals that states that metals consist of an extensive crystal lattice of metal cations surrounded by and submerged in a "sea" of mobile electrons; also known as the *free-electron model.*

electronegativity. The measure of the attraction between the nucleus of an atom and shared electrons in chemical bonds.

electroplating. A type of electrolysis in which the cathode is a metal object to be plated and the anode is the metal that is to cover the object.

electrostatic force. The force between electric charges. Opposite charges attract and like charges repel.

element. A pure substance that consists of only one kind of atom.

elementary step. An individual step in a reaction mechanism.

elimination reaction. A reaction in organic chemistry in which two atoms or groups of atoms are removed and a multiple bond fulfills the octet rule for the remaining atoms.

emission spectrum. An incomplete spectrum, in the form of a series of colored lines, that is unique for each element.

empirical formula. A formula that indicates the smallest whole-number ratio of atoms in a compound.

empirical science. Science that is based on data gathered from observations or an experiment.

enantiomer. An isomer based on chirality, being either right- or left-handed.

endothermic process. A process that absorbs more energy than it releases.

end point. The point in a titration at which some change in a property of the solution is detected. Typically the end point is when an indicator changes color.

energy. The ability to do work.

Glossary

energy diagram. A graph of the energy in reactants and products during a chemical reaction.

energy shell. See *principal energy level.*

energy sublevel. Divisions of principal energy levels within an atom that are further divided into orbitals.

enthalpy (ΔH)**.** The thermal energy content of a system at a constant pressure.

enthalpy of reaction (ΔH_r)**.** The change in enthalpy that occurs during a reaction. Positive values indicate an endothermic reaction and negative values indicate an exothermic reaction. Also known as the *heat of reaction*.

enthalpy of solution. The net energy change during the dissolving process; the energy required to form a solution; also known as the *heat of solution*.

entropy (S)**.** A mathematical measure of the dispersal of energy in a system.

enzyme. A naturally occurring biochemical catalyst.

equilibrium. In general, any condition in which competing influences are balanced. In chemistry, any condition in which reactions or processes are in balance.

equilibrium constant (K_{eq})**.** A mathematical representation of the equilibrium position for a chemical reaction at a particular temperature.

equilibrium position. The concentrations of reactants and products at equilibrium in a reversible chemical reaction.

equivalence point. The point in a titration at which an equivalent of titrant is added; that is, the point at which the number of H_3O^+ ions equals the number of OH^- ions.

essential amino acid. One of the eight amino acids that are necessary for human health but which cannot be produced by the body and must be obtained from diet.

essential oil. A mixture of volatile organic compounds, that is, carbon-based molecules that vaporize easily.

ester. A substituted hydrocarbon in which a carboxyl group connects two hydrocarbon chains; usually formed by the reaction of a carboxylic acid with an alcohol.

ether. A substituted hydrocarbon in which two hydrocarbon chains are connected by an oxygen atom.

ethics. The application of moral principles to how a person lives, including the use of chemistry.

evaporation. The process of vaporization caused by random liquid particles close to the surface of a liquid obtaining sufficient kinetic energy to leave the liquid phase.

excess reactant. A reactant that remains after a limiting reactant is consumed.

excited state. Any energy state, other than the ground state, resulting from an electron absorbing energy.

exothermic process. A process that releases more energy than it absorbs.

expansibility. The ability of a substance to spontaneously fill its available space.

experiment. An orderly process to observe a phenomenon, ideally under controlled conditions.

F

family. See *group.*

fat. A saturated ester of fatty acids and glycerol having relatively high intermolecular forces and which is typically solid at room temperature.

fatty acid. A carboxylic acid found in plant and animal fats with an even number of carbon atoms (normally twelve to eighteen).

filtration. A process for separating mixtures on the basis of particle size.

first law of thermodynamics. See *law of conservation of mass-energy.*

flammability. The property of a substance that enables it to burn in the presence of oxygen.

flocculation. The process by which coagulated material precipitates out of a solution as part of a water purification system.

fluid. Any substance that can flow.

formula unit. The chemical formula that represents the smallest whole number ratio of the elements in an ionic compound.

forward reaction. The chemical reaction depicted in an equation for a reversible reaction with the reactants on the left forming the products on the right.

fractional distillation. A process for separating mixtures in which the components have significantly different boiling points.

free-electron model. See *electron sea model.*

freezing. The phase change from a liquid to a solid due to a loss of thermal energy.

freezing point depression (ΔT_f)**.** The decrease in the freezing point of a solvent due to the presence of dissolved solute particles.

fuel cell. A highly efficient voltaic cell in which a fuel is provided to drive a chemical reaction that produces electrical energy.

functional group. An atom or group of atoms that replaces one or more hydrogen atoms in a hydrocarbon. Also called a *substituent.*

fundamental unit. One of seven units in the SI that is based on a physical constant. The seven fundamental units are the basis for almost all the derived units in the SI.

G

gamma decay. Radioactivity that emits energy, producing an isotope that differs only in having a lower energy state.

gamma ray. The high-energy electromagnetic radiation emitted during gamma decay.

gas. A fluid state of matter characterized by widely spaced particles that interact only in momentary collisions, resulting in a changeable shape and volume; also known as *vapor*.

Gay-Lussac's law. The law that states that the Kelvin temperature and pressure of a sample of gas at a constant volume are directly related; $\frac{P}{T} = k$.

Geiger counter. A device used to measure ionizing radiation by measuring the current produced by ionized gases in the counter.

gene. A subunit on a chromosome that contains information for the sequencing of amino acids in a protein.

Gibbs free energy (ΔG)**.** A mathematical measure of a chemical system that incorporates changes in enthalpy and entropy. A negative value for Gibbs free energy indicates a spontaneous reaction; a positive value indicates a reaction that is nonspontaneous.

glass. See *supercooled liquid.*

glycerol. A three-carbon alcohol with a hydroxyl group on each carbon; forms the backbone of triglycerides.

glycogen. A polysaccharide that stores energy in humans and animals.

Graham's law of diffusion. See *Graham's law of effusion.*

Graham's law of effusion. The law that states that the rate of effusion for a gas is inversely proportional to the square root of its molar mass; also known as *Graham's law of diffusion.*

gray (Gy)**.** The SI unit for measuring the radioactivity absorbed by an object.

Greek prefix system. A system used to name covalently bonded compounds that includes prefixes to indicate the number of atoms of each element in the compound.

greenhouse gas. Any atmospheric gas that transmits incident radiant energy but absorbs reflected energy, retaining the energy as thermal energy in the atmosphere.

ground state. The lowest energy level of an electron in the Bohr model.

group. A column of the periodic table that includes elements that have similar properties because they have similar electron configurations. Sometimes called a *family.*

H

Haber process. A chemical process that converts nitrogen gas into ammonia, which is vital to producing artificial fertilizers. Also known as the *Haber-Bosch process.*

half-cell. One of the two halves of a voltaic cell in which either the oxidation or the reduction occurs.

half-life. The amount of time required for half of a radioactive sample to decay.

half-reaction. Either of the separate oxidation and reduction reactions that occurs in a half-cell of a voltaic cell.

halide. Compounds that contain a halogen, often a halogen combined with one other element.

Hall-Héroult process. An electrolysis process used to produce aluminum.

haloaromatic. A substituted aromatic hydrocarbon in which a halogen has replaced at least one of the hydrogen atoms.

halocarbon. A substituted hydrocarbon in which a halogen has replaced at least one of the hydrogen atoms.

halogen. An element of Group 17 on the periodic table. It is a highly reactive nonmetal with seven valence electrons. It easily gains an additional electron to make a 1− anion.

heat. The movement of thermal energy due to a temperature difference.

heat of reaction. See *enthalpy of reaction.*

heat of solution. See *enthalpy of solution.*

Heisenberg uncertainty principle. A fundamental property of all submicroscopic systems described as the impossibility of simultaneously knowing both the energy, or momentum, and the exact position of a particle.

Henry's law. The law that states that the solubility of a gas is directly proportional to the partial pressure of that gas above the solution.

Hess's law. The law that states that the enthalpy change of a reaction equals the sum of the enthalpy changes for each step of the process.

heterogeneous catalyst. A catalyst that is in a different phase, or state of matter, as the substances in a chemical reaction.

heterogeneous equilibrium. The state of equilibrium between substances that are in different states of matter.

Glossary

heterogeneous mixture. A mixture that has two or more distinct regions, which give it a nonuniform appearance.

historical science. The body of scientific knowledge acquired by making inferences about events and processes in the past on the basis of observations of evidence in the present.

HIV. Two species of retrovirus that cause AIDS. Acronym for *human immunodeficiency virus*.

homogeneous catalyst. A catalyst that is in the same phase, or state of matter, as the substances in a chemical reaction.

homogeneous equilibrium. The state of equilibrium between substances that are all in the same state of matter.

homogeneous mixture. A mixture that has only one phase, which gives it a uniform appearance.

human immunodeficiency virus. See *HIV*.

Hund's rule. The rule stating that electrons fill a sublevel by a single electron occupying each orbital before a second electron can occupy any orbital.

hydrate. Compounds that hold a certain amount of water within their crystalline structures.

hydride. Compounds that contain hydrogen acting as an anion, often hydrogen combined with one metallic element.

hydrocarbon. An organic compound that contains only carbon and hydrogen.

hydrogen bond. An especially strong type of dipole-dipole force that forms between hydrogen in one molecule and nitrogen, oxygen, or fluorine in another molecule.

hydroxide. Compounds, often ionic, that contain a hydroxide ion (OH^-).

hydroxyl group. A functional group having the formula OH; a key feature of alcohols.

hypervalent molecule. A molecule that forms with one or more of the atoms having more than eight valence electrons.

hypothesis. A testable explanation for a phenomenon that forms the basis for scientific inquiry.

I

ideal gas. A gas whose behavior is perfectly predicted by the kinetic-molecular theory.

ideal gas law. The law that relates the pressure, temperature, volume, and the number of moles in any sample of a gas; $PV = nRT$.

immiscibility. The tendency of two liquids to not mutually dissolve. They remain in distinct layers.

independent variable. The variable in a controlled experiment that is manipulated by a scientist.

inductive reasoning. The process of logically proceeding from specific statements to a general conclusion.

inhibitor. A substance that reduces the effectiveness of a catalyst, slowing its action.

inner transition metal. An element from the *f* block of the periodic table (lanthanoid and actinoid series).

intermediate. A chemical substance that is formed during one elementary step of a reaction mechanism and is consumed in a later elementary step.

intermolecular force. A type of electrostatic attraction that forms between molecules and explains many bulk properties of matter. Also known as a *van der Waals force*.

International Union of Pure and Applied Chemistry (IUPAC). An international organization responsible for standardization in chemistry.

ion. A charged atom or group of atoms due to the gain or loss of electrons.

ionic bond. A chemical bond due to the attraction between ions formed by the transfer of valence electrons.

ionic crystal. An ionic solid made of a repeating network of ions defined by a unit cell.

ionization. The process by which covalent solutes dissolve as a solvent separates out ions from a solute.

ionization constant of water (K_w). The equilibrium constant for the self-ionization of water. The value at 25 °C is 1.0×10^{-14}.

ionization energy. The amount of energy required to remove an electron from an atom.

ionizing radiation. Any radioactivity of sufficient energy to ionize atoms with which it collides.

irreversible reaction. A reaction that can occur only in the forward direction.

island of stability. A theoretical group of stable nuclides with atomic numbers higher than those for presently known stable nuclides.

isomer. A substance whose molecular formula is identical to that of another substance but which has a different structural formula.

isotope. One of two or more variants of atoms of the same element, having the same number of protons but different numbers of neutrons, resulting in them having different mass numbers.

isotope notation. A special notation, used to identify important information about an isotope, consisting of a chemical symbol, atomic number, and mass number.

J

joule (J). The SI derived unit for work, energy, and heat; $1\ J = 1 N \cdot m = 1 \frac{kg \cdot m^2}{s^2}$.

K

Kelvin scale. An absolute temperature scale with 100 kelvins between the normal boiling point (373.15 K) and freezing point (273.15 K) of water.

ketone. A substituted hydrocarbon in which a carbonyl group exists anywhere between the end carbons of a carbon chain.

kinetic energy. The energy that an object has due to its motion.

kinetic-molecular theory. The model of matter that states that properties of matter can be explained by the interrelationships between the forces between particles and the particles' kinetic energy.

kinetics. The study of the rates of chemical reactions and the steps by which they occur.

L

lanthanoid series. A set of elements typically placed at the bottom of the periodic table that consists of the *f*-block elements from Period 6.

latent heat. The thermal energy that produces a phase change when transferred to or from a substance.

lattice energy. The energy released when gaseous particles form crystals.

law. A scientific model that describe a phenomenon, often in mathematical terms.

law of charges. The law that states that opposite charges attract and like charges repel.

law of chemical equilibrium. The law that states that at a specific temperature a chemical system may reach a point at which the ratio of the concentration of the products to the reactants is constant.

law of combining volumes. The law that states that under equivalent conditions, the volumes of reacting gases and their gaseous products can be expressed in ratios of small whole numbers.

law of conservation of mass-energy. The law that states that matter and energy cannot be created or destroyed but can change from one form to another, including changes between the two; also known as the *first law of thermodynamics*.

law of definite proportion. The law that states that every compound is formed of elements combined in specific ratios by mass that are unique for that compound.

law of energy conservation. The law that states that energy cannot be created or destroyed but can change from one form to another.

law of entropy. The law that states that the entropy of an isolated system will always increase; that is, its energy will become more spread out; also known as the *second law of thermodynamics*.

law of multiple proportions. The law that states that whenever a fixed amount of one element can combine with different masses of a second element, the ratio of masses can be reduced to small, whole numbers.

law of octaves. An early form of the periodic law devised by John Newlands as he noticed that every eighth known element had similar properties when ordered by increasing atomic mass.

Le Châtelier's principle. The principle that states that when a stress is put on a system in chemical equilibrium, the system will adjust in order to reduce the effect of the stress.

Lewis acid. Any substance that can accept a pair of electrons; the broadest definition of an acid.

Lewis base. A substance that can donate a pair of electrons; the broadest definition of a base.

Lewis structure. A visual, two-dimensional representation of a molecule that shows its atoms, bonds, and unbonded electron pairs.

limiting reactant. The reactant that is completely consumed in a chemical reaction.

linear hydrocarbon. A hydrocarbon without any alkyl groups attached; a hydrocarbon with only a single chain of carbon atoms.

linear molecule. A molecule shape characterized by two regions of electrons and two outer atoms on either side of a central atom.

lipid. A nonpolar biochemical molecule that is insoluble in water and is vital for energy storage; includes fats, oils, waxes, and steroids.

liquid. A fluid state of matter characterized by closely spaced particles that can slide past each other, resulting in a fixed volume but changeable shape.

litmus paper. Paper that has been treated with an acid-base indicator that changes color in the presence of an acid or a base. Blue litmus paper turns red in the presence of an acid, and red litmus paper turns blue in the presence of a base.

localized electron theory. See *valence bond theory*.

London dispersion force. An intermolecular force that forms between both polar and nonpolar molecules due to temporary dipoles formed from the random motion of the valence electrons in the participating molecules; also known as a *dispersion force* or *London force*.

Glossary

London force. See *London dispersion force.*

lone pair. A pair of electrons in a bonded atom that are not involved in bonding; also known as a *nonbonding pair.*

M

magic number. The number of protons or neutrons associated with a full nuclear shell. Nuclides with a magic number of protons or neutrons tend to be stable.

malleability. The property of a material that enables it to be hammered or pressed into a sheet.

mass defect. The mass difference between a nucleus and the sum of the masses of the components that make up that nucleus.

mass fraction (w_{solute})**.** A measure of concentration that compares the mass of a solute with the mass of an entire solution and is reported as a decimal or percent; also known as *percent by mass.*

mass number (A)**.** The sum of the protons and neutrons in an atom that is used to identify specific isotopes of an element.

matter. Anything that takes up space and has mass.

measurement. A comparison of an unknown quantity to a known standard unit.

melting. The phase change from a solid to a liquid due to a gain of thermal energy.

melting point. The temperature at which a solid changes to a liquid.

meniscus. The curved surface of a liquid caused by the interplay between cohesion and adhesion.

messenger RNA. RNA that carries protein synthesis instructions from the nucleus to the ribosomes; also known as *mRNA.*

metabolism. A collective term for all the chemical reactions that take place within cells.

metabolite. An intermediate in a chemical reaction that carries out metabolism.

metal. One of a general group of elements with similar characteristics, such as being solid at room temperature, lustrous, malleable, ductile, and a good conductor of heat and electricity.

metallic bond. A chemical bond characterized by the attraction between all the metal ions in a sample and their shared valence electrons.

metallic crystal. A network of positive metal ions surrounded by a sea of valence electrons.

metalloid. One of a general group of elements with characteristics that are between those of metals and nonmetals; also known as a *semiconductor*.

miscibility. A measure of the tendency of two liquids to mutually dissolve and mix in a solution.

mixture. The combination of two or more substances that are physically combined in a changeable ratio.

model. A workable explanation, description, or representation of a phenomenon.

molal. A term used to indicate the molality of a solution.

molal boiling point constant (K_b)**.** A constant for a solvent that indicates the change to the boiling point of a solution effected by the presence of solute particles.

molal freezing point constant (K_f)**.** A constant for a solvent that indicates the change to the freezing point of a solution affected by the presence of solute particles.

molality (b_{solute})**.** A measure of concentration that compares the moles of a solute with the mass of a solvent in kilograms.

molar. A term used to indicate the amount concentration of a solution.

molar concentration. See *amount concentration.*

molar enthalpy of fusion (ΔH_{fus})**.** The quantity of energy required to melt one mole of a solid to a liquid with no temperature change; also known as the *molar heat of fusion.*

molar enthalpy of vaporization (ΔH_{vap})**.** The quantity of energy required to vaporize one mole of a liquid to a gas with no temperature change; also known as the *molar heat of vaporization.*

molar heat of fusion. See *molar enthalpy of fusion.*

molar heat of vaporization. See *molar enthalpy of vaporization.*

molar mass. The mass of one mole of any pure substance.

molarity. See *amount concentration.*

mole. The amount of any substance that contains exactly $6.022\,140\,76 \times 10^{23}$ particles.

mole ratio. The ratio of coefficients in a balanced chemical equation that is used in stoichiometric calculations.

molecular dipole moment. The measure of the polar nature of a molecule.

molecular formula. The formula that indicates the types and numbers of atoms found in a molecule, ion, or formula unit.

molecular orbital theory. A model of chemical bonding that states that atoms obtain full valence shells by the formation of new molecular orbitals.

molecule. A distinct group of atoms that are covalently bonded together.

monatomic element. An element that can naturally occur as an individual atom.

monomer. A small molecule-like structure that forms the basis for creating a polymer.

monoprotic acid. An acid that can donate only one proton.

monosaccharide. A simple carbohydrate consisting of a single sugar unit.

monounsaturated fat. A lipid that contains one carbon-carbon double bond.

mRNA. See *messenger RNA*.

N

naturalism. A worldview that is based on a belief that matter is all that exists and that human reasoning informed by science is the only reliable path to truth.

net ionic equation. An abbreviated form of the chemical equation for a double-replacement reaction showing only the ions involved in the chemical change. Spectator ions are removed.

network covalent substance. A covalent substance that forms into a crystalline structure instead of forming distinct molecules (e.g., diamond).

neutralization reaction. A chemical reaction in which an acid and a base react to form water and a salt.

neutral solution. A solution with a pH and pOH both equal to 7.

neutron (n^0 or n)**.** A subatomic particle located in the nucleus of most atoms. It has no charge and a mass of approximately 1 u.

noble gas. An element of Group 18 on the periodic table. It is a nonreactive (inert) nonmetallic gas with a full valence shell.

noble gas notation. An abbreviated form of electron configuration consisting of the last noble gas in the configuration in brackets followed by any additional electron configuration for that element.

nomenclature. A system of naming that follows a standardized set of rules. The International Union of Pure and Applied Chemistry (IUPAC) has developed and oversees a nomenclature for compounds.

nonbonding pair. A pair of electrons in a bonded atom that are not involved in bonding; also known as a *lone pair*.

nonelectrolyte. Any substance that will not conduct electricity when dissolved.

nonmetal. One of a general group of elements with similar characteristics, such as generally being a gas or a soft, crumbly solid at room temperature, and being a poor conductor of heat and electricity.

nonrechargeable battery. A single-use battery that is not designed to be rechargeable. Its electrochemical process cannot be safely reversed. Also known as a *primary battery*.

normal boiling point. The temperature at which the vapor pressure of a liquid is equal to the standard atmospheric pressure of 101.325 kPa.

nuclear binding energy. The energy that holds a nucleus together. It is equivalent to the energy released as the nucleus is formed and is related to the mass defect of the nucleus.

nuclear bombardment reaction. Any type of nuclear transformation that is triggered by striking a nucleus with another particle.

nuclear chemistry. The study of the nuclei of elements, particularly their composition as they undergo nuclear changes.

nuclear energy. The potential energy in the nucleus of an atom due to the interaction of the subatomic particles and the electromagnetic, weak nuclear, and strong nuclear forces.

nuclear equation. An equation used to model nuclear reactions. Nuclear equations are balanced by balancing both the mass numbers and the atomic numbers across the equation.

nuclear fission. The nuclear process in which a heavy nucleus is split apart into smaller, more stable nuclei.

nuclear fusion. The transmutation process of combining light nuclei to form a more massive nucleus.

nuclear radiation. The energy and particles emitted from unstable nuclei as they move toward stability.

nucleic acid. A chain of nucleotides that encodes the information needed for the production of proteins.

nucleon. Any particle found in a nucleus, whether proton or neutron.

nucleotide. A monomer of a nucleic acid that consists of a five-carbon sugar, a phosphate group, and a nitrogenous base.

nucleus. The extremely small and dense center of an atom that contains the protons and neutrons and is surrounded by an electron cloud.

nuclide. A unique atom of an element with a specific set of protons and neutrons and a specific energy state.

O

octet rule. A rule that states that elements are most chemically stable when they have a full valence electron shell, typically with eight valence electrons.

oil. An unsaturated ester of a fatty acid and glycerol having relatively low intermolecular forces and which is typically liquid at room temperature.

Glossary

operational science. The body of scientific knowledge acquired by methods of investigation that involve real-time observations of present-day phenomena or first-person observations of events in the past.

orbital. A three-dimensional region representing the most probable position for an electron according to the quantum-mechanical model.

orbital hybridization. The formation of a new orbital due to the overlapping of atomic orbitals.

orbital notation. A notation or diagram used to illustrate the electron configuration of an atom, consisting of horizontal lines, representing the orbitals and labeled by sublevel, and arrows, representing the electrons in that orbital.

organic chemistry. The study of covalently bonded carbon compounds, with the exception of carbonates, carbon oxides, and carbides.

organic compound. Any covalently bonded carbon compound, with the exception of carbonates, carbon oxides, and carbides.

osmosis. The movement of a solvent across a semipermeable membrane due to differences in the solution concentration on each side of the membrane.

osmotic pressure. The amount of pressure required to prevent osmosis from occurring.

oxidation. A chemical process in which an element loses electrons, increasing the oxidation number of the element.

oxidation number. The number of electrons that an atom loses or gains when it bonds; also known as *oxidation state*.

oxidation-reduction reaction. A class of chemical reactions that involves the transfer of electrons; also known as a *redox reaction*.

oxidation state. See *oxidation number*.

oxide. A compound that contains oxygen, often oxygen combined with one other element.

oxidizing agent. A chemical substance that causes the oxidation of another substance in a redox reaction. The oxidizing agent is reduced in a redox reaction.

oxyanion. An anion that contains oxygen and one other element.

P

paramagnetism. The attraction of a molecule to a magnetic field.

parent nuclide. The starting nuclide in any nuclear transmutation.

partial pressure. The pressure contributed by an individual gas to the total pressure of a mixture of gases.

pascal (Pa). The SI unit of pressure; $1\ Pa = 1\ N/m^2$.

Pauli exclusion principle. A principle that states that the two electrons in an orbital must have opposite spins.

peer review. The process of having other scientists review scientific work by which the research is evaluated.

peptide bond. The bond formed between the carboxyl group of one amino acid and the amine group of another amino acid.

percent by mass. See *mass fraction*.

percent by volume. See *volume fraction*.

percent composition. The percent ratio of the mass of a component of a compound to the total mass of the compound.

percent yield. The percent ratio of an actual yield to its corresponding theoretical yield.

period. A row in the periodic table that includes elements that have their valence electrons in the same energy level. The period number represents the valence shell. Also known as a *series*.

periodic law. The law that states that the properties of elements vary periodically with their atomic numbers.

periodic table. A table of all the known elements ordered by increasing atomic number and arranged in a manner that models the atomic structure of the elements.

periodic trend. The pattern of change in particular properties as one moves along periods and groups in the periodic table.

periodicity. A repeating pattern in a characteristic; demonstrated in the periodic table as elements in the same family having similar properties.

pH. The potential of hydrogen ions is a simple indication of the acidity of a solution ($pH = -\log[H_3O^+]$); related to pOH by the equation $pH + pOH = 14$.

pH meter. An electronic device that reports a numerical value of the pH of a solution.

pharmacokinetics. The study of how the human body processes medications.

phase change. The transition between different states, or phases, of matter due to the transfer of thermal energy.

phase diagram. A graph of temperature and pressure that shows the states of matter and phase changes for a particular substance.

phospholipid. A lipid consisting of two fatty acid chains bonded to a phosphate group instead of to glycerol.

photon. A massless particle of light consisting of a bundle of wave energy.

physical change. Any change in the appearance, shape, or state of matter of a material that does not cause a change in its chemical composition.

physical property. Any property of matter that can be observed or measured without altering a substance's chemical composition.

pi (π) bond. A bond that forms when side by side orbitals overlap, forming two separate regions of the same bond.

planetary model. See *Bohr model.*

plum pudding model. The atomic model suggested by J. J. Thomson that viewed an atom as a sphere of positive charge in which numerous negative electrons are embedded.

pOH. A simple indication of the alkalinity of a solution ($pOH = -\log[OH^-]$).

polar covalent bond. A covalent bond with positive and negative ends caused by the unequal sharing of valence electrons.

polar molecule. A molecule with both a positive end and a negative end due to the polar nature of its bonds and the shape of the molecule.

polarity. The tendency of an object to form two localized regions of opposite character or charge.

polyatomic element. An element that naturally occurs as molecules of two or more atoms.

polyatomic ion. A charged group of covalently bonded atoms that act as a single ion.

polymer. A large molecule made of regularly repeated smaller subunits called *monomers.*

polymerization. Any process that combines monomers into polymers.

polymorph. A crystalline solid that can form different crystal lattices.

polypeptide. A molecule formed by the bonding of three or more amino acids.

polyprotic acid. An acid that can donate more than one proton.

polysaccharide. A complex carbohydrate that is composed of many sugar units.

polyunsaturated fat. A lipid, typically an oil, that contains two or more carbon-carbon double bonds.

positron ($^{0}_{+1}e$)**.** A subatomic particle identical to an electron, but having a positive charge. It is emitted from a nucleus during positron emission.

positron emission. Radioactivity that emits a positron (positive electron, 1+ charge) and energy. The positron forms as a proton changes to a neutron, causing a decrease in the parent nuclide's atomic number but not its mass number. Also known as *beta plus decay.*

post-transition metal. A metallic element in Groups 13–16. It easily loses electrons to form a 2+ cation.

potential energy. The energy that an object has due to its position or condition.

precipitate. A solid that settles out of a solution as the result of physical or chemical changes.

precision. An evaluation of the exactness of a measurement or a measuring instrument. It indicates how repeatable a measurement is or how exactly one can make a measurement.

premise. A statement that forms the basis of a logical argument.

pressure (*P*)**.** The force per unit area caused by the collisions of fluid particles with their container.

presupposition. An assumption about the world. The sum total of a person's presuppositions forms the basis of his worldview.

primary battery. A single-use battery that is not designed to be rechargeable. Its electrochemical process cannot be safely reversed. Also known as a *nonrechargeable battery.*

primary structure. The basic order of amino acids in polypeptide chains.

principal energy level (*n*)**.** The orbits or energy levels in atomic models; also known as *energy shells.*

principal quantum number. The quantum number that identifies the principal or main energy level of an electron.

product. A chemical substance that is formed in a chemical reaction. It is found on the right side of a chemical equation.

protein. An organic polymer comprised of amino acids.

protein complex. A large biomolecule formed by the combination of two or more protein subunits.

protein subunit. A finished polypeptide that combines with other protein subunits to form a protein complex.

protein turnover. The process in living things of breaking down and replacing worn-out proteins.

proton (p^+ or p)**.** A subatomic particle located in the nucleus of every atom. It has a positive charge and a mass of approximately 1 u. The number of protons in an atom is equal to the atomic number of that element.

pure science. The effort to understand how and why things work the way that they do.

pure substance. Any material that consists of only one type of matter (an element or a compound).

Glossary

Q

qualitative data. Data in the form of words that is used to describe something.

quantitative data. Data in the form of numbers that is determined through measuring.

quantized. The condition of a phenomenon having only discrete values for a particular dimension.

quantum-mechanical model. The current model of the atom in which protons and neutrons are located in the nucleus with electrons in orbitals around the nucleus. Orbitals represent the regions of highest probability for the locations of electrons.

quantum mechanics. The study of the mechanics of matter at the atomic and subatomic levels, with an emphasis on the quantized nature of their energies and momentums.

quantum numbers. A series of four numbers that uniquely identifies the placement of an electron in an atom according to the quantum-mechanical model.

R

radioactive decay. See *radioactivity*.

radioactive decay series. A sequence of radioactive decays through which an isotope proceeds in order to become a stable nuclide.

radioactivity. The spontaneous emission of nuclear radiation from the nuclei of unstable atoms as they endeavor to become more stable; also known as *radioactive decay*.

radioisotope. Any isotope that emits nuclear radiation.

rate-determining step. The elementary step in a reaction mechanism that determines how fast the overall reaction can occur. The reaction can go no faster than the slowest elementary step.

rate law. A mathematical law relating the concentration of reactants to the rate of a reaction. Rate laws can be determined only empirically.

reactant. A chemical substance that is consumed in a chemical reaction. It is found on the left side of a chemical equation.

reaction mechanism. The series of steps that make up a chemical reaction.

reaction order. An indication of the effect that the concentration of a particular reactant has on a reaction rate.

reaction rate. A measure of how quickly reactants change into products.

reactivity. The property of a substance that enables it to interact with another specific chemical.

rechargeable battery. A battery that is designed so that its electrochemical process can be reversed, allowing the battery to be recharged; also known as a *secondary battery*.

redox reaction. A class of chemical reactions that involves the transfer of electrons; also known as an *oxidation-reduction reaction*.

reducing agent. A chemical substance that causes the reduction of another substance in a redox reaction. The reducing agent is oxidized in a redox reaction.

reduction. A chemical process in which an element gains electrons, decreasing the oxidation number of the element.

resonance. The state of molecules that can have two or more possible Lewis structures. The observed state of the molecule is intermediate to the possible structures.

reverse osmosis. The process by which a solvent is forced to move "backward" across a semipermeable membrane by applying a force to the system.

reverse reaction. A chemical reaction that occurs when the concentration of products increases and the products react to form the original reactants. A reverse reaction is the opposite of the corresponding forward reaction.

reversible reaction. A reaction that can occur in both the forward and the reverse directions.

ribonucleic acid. See *RNA*.

ribosomal RNA. RNA of which the ribosomes in a cell are made; also known as *rRNA*.

RNA. A nucleic acid that contains ribose as the sugar in its nucleotides and which encodes the instructions needed for protein synthesis in cells; the abbreviation for *ribonucleic acid*.

roman numeral system. See *Stock system*.

rRNA. See *ribosomal RNA*.

S

salt. A substance formed when the anion of an acid and the cation of a base combine.

salt bridge. A tube of electrolytic gel that connects the two half-cells of a voltaic cell in order to permit the movement of ions to complete a circuit.

saturated hydrocarbon. A hydrocarbon in which all the carbons are surrounded by four other atoms, the maximum number possible. Saturated hydrocarbons have only single bonds between their carbon atoms.

saturated solution. A solution that contains the maximum amount of solute that it can hold at current conditions.

scientific inquiry. The process by which scientists answer scientific questions; also known as the *scientific method.*

scientific survey. A process that involves randomly selected representative samples from a larger population.

scintillation counter. A device used to measure ionizing radiation by measuring the light produced by ionized gases in the counter.

secondary battery. A battery that is designed so that its electrochemical process can be reversed, allowing the battery to be recharged; also known as a *rechargeable battery.*

secondary structure. A more complex structure of polypeptides in which the amino acids in one part of a chain bond with amino acids in other parts of the chain. Alpha helixes and beta sheets are the most common secondary structures.

second law of thermodynamics. See *law of entropy.*

self-ionization of water. A reaction that occurs in water in which two water molecules react to form a hydronium ion and a hydroxide ion.

semiconductor. See *metalloid.*

sensible heat. The transfer of thermal energy that produces a temperature change in a substance.

series. See *period.*

SI. The modern metric system used for science and adopted almost worldwide for daily usage. An abbreviation for the French *système international d'unités* for "international system of units."

sievert (Sv)**.** The SI unit for measuring the biological effect of radioactivity on an organism.

sigma (σ) bond. A bond that forms when orbitals overlap along the bond axis.

significant figure. The digits in a measurement that include those that are known with certainty plus one estimated digit. An indication of the precision of a measurement.

single-displacement reaction. See *single-replacement reaction.*

single-replacement reaction. A chemical reaction in which a more reactive element replaces a less reactive element in a compound. It has the general form $A + BX \longrightarrow AX + B$ (cation being replaced) or $X + AY \longrightarrow AX + Y$ (anion being replaced). Also known as a *single-displacement reaction.*

smelting. The process of melting an ore in order to separate a metal from its ore.

solid. A state of matter characterized by closely spaced particles vibrating in fixed positions, which give a material a fixed shape and volume.

solubility. The maximum amount of a solute that can dissolve in a specific solvent under specific conditions, such as temperature and pressure.

solubility product constant (K_{sp})**.** The equilibrium constant for the process of dissolving a solute.

solute. The substance that is dissolved by a solvent; the substance(s) in lower abundance in a solution.

solution. A homogeneous mixture of variable composition in a single phase.

solvation. The dissolving process in solid-in-liquid solutions in which the solvent particles separate the solute particles and then surround them.

solvent. The most abundant substance in a solution; the substance that dissolves the solute.

specific heat (c_{sp})**.** The amount of thermal energy required to raise the temperature of 1 g of a substance by 1 °C.

specific rate constant. The empirically determined value for the rate law for a particular chemical reaction.

spectator ion. An ion in a double-replacement reaction that is not involved in the chemical reaction.

spectroscopy. The analysis of light emitted or absorbed by matter.

spin. A measure of the angular moment of an electron in an orbital. Each of the two electrons in an orbital must have opposite spins.

spontaneous combustion. A combustion reaction that starts without an ignition source due to existing conditions, typically high temperatures.

standard molar enthalpy of combustion ($\Delta H°_c$)**.** The thermal energy released by the complete burning of 1 mol of a substance at standard conditions; also known as the *standard molar heat of combustion.*

standard molar enthalpy of formation ($\Delta H°_f$)**.** The enthalpy change to produce 1 mol of a compound in its standard state from its elements in their standard states; also known as the *standard molar heat of formation.*

standard molar heat of combustion. See *standard molar enthalpy of combustion.*

standard molar heat of formation. See *standard molar enthalpy of formation.*

standard molar volume. The property of gases that states that a mole of a gas at standard temperature and pressure occupies a volume of 22.4 L.

standard temperature and pressure (STP). A temperature and pressure agreed upon by chemists for comparison of research. STP is 0 °C (273.15 K) and 101.325 kPa.

starch. A complex carbohydrate that contains multiple glucose molecules.

Glossary

steroid. A lipid comprised of three six-carbon rings and a five-carbon ring.

Stock system. A system for naming ionic compounds with cations that can have more than one oxidation number; also known as the *roman numeral system*.

stoichiometry. The mathematical relationship between the quantities of substances involved in a chemical reaction.

strong acid. A substance that ionizes easily, freely giving up at least one proton.

strong base. A substance that easily accepts protons.

strong nuclear force. The short-range force that holds protons and neutrons together in a nucleus.

subcritical mass. A mass less than the minimum mass required to maintain a chain reaction.

sublimation. The change of state directly from solid to vapor without transitioning through liquid due to a gain of thermal energy.

substituent. See *functional group*.

substituted hydrocarbon. Any hydrocarbon in which a hydrogen has been removed and replaced by a functional group.

substitution reaction. A reaction in organic chemistry in which one part of a molecule is replaced with a new element or functional group.

sugar. A generic term for sweet-tasting saccharides.

sulfide. A compound that contains sulfur, often sulfur combined with one other element.

supercooled liquid. A term used for some amorphous solids that are cooled so fast that they cannot form a crystalline structure; also known as *glass*.

supersaturated solution. A solution that contains more than the maximum amount of solute that it can normally hold at current conditions.

surface tension. The elastic "skin" that forms on the surface of liquids, caused by the imbalance of intermolecular forces at the liquid's surface.

surfactant. Any substance that breaks down normal surface tension by interfering with hydrogen bonds.

suspension. A heterogeneous mixture formed when large particles (> 1 µm) are suspended in another substance. The suspended particles are so large that they will eventually settle out.

synthesis reaction. A chemical reaction that combines two or more reactants into a single product, having the general form $A + B \longrightarrow AB$; also known as a *combination reaction*.

system. Everything within a set of boundaries, defined by a scientist, that is being studied.

T

temperature. A measure of the average kinetic energy of all the particles within a substance.

ternary acid. An acid containing more than two elements, namely hydrogen, oxygen, and at least one other nonmetal.

tertiary structure. The three-dimensional shape of polypeptides resulting from combinations of turns, helixes, sheets, and random coils.

tetrahedral molecule. A molecule shape characterized by four regions of electrons and four outer atoms surrounding a central atom. An outer atom is at each vertex of a tetrahedron.

theoretical yield. The predicted amount of product produced by a chemical reaction as determined by a stoichiometric calculation.

theory. A scientific model that explains a phenomenon.

thermal energy. The sum of the kinetic energy of all the particles within a substance.

thermochemical equation. A chemical equation that shows the reactants, products, and amount of energy that is released or absorbed as heat.

thermochemistry. The branch of science that studies the transfer of energy during phase or chemical changes.

thermodynamics. The study of the movement and conversion of energy, especially thermal energy.

thermometric property. A physical property that changes in a predictable way with changes in temperature.

third law of thermodynamics. The law that states that we can never decrease a system's entropy to an absolute minimum.

titrant. The solution of known concentration used in a titration.

titration curve. A graph showing the pH of a system during titration as an acid and base are combined.

toxicity. The property of a substance that makes it harmful to living organisms.

transfer RNA. RNA that transports appropriate amino acids to ribosomes for protein synthesis; also known as *tRNA*.

transition interval. The range of pH values over which an indicator transitions from one color to another.

transition metal. An element from the *d* block of the periodic table (Groups 3–12). It is a metal that typically has one or two valence electrons that it easily loses to form a 1+ or 2+ cation.

translation. The process of building a polypeptide on the basis of information encoded in mRNA.

transmutation. Any process by which an atom of one kind of element changes into another kind of element as a result of a change in the number of protons in the atom's nucleus.

transuranium element. An element with an atomic number greater than 92, the atomic number of uranium.

triad. A group of three elements with similar characteristics that demonstrates periodicity.

triglyceride. A biochemical molecule formed by three fatty acids bonded to a glycerol molecule.

trigonal planar molecule. A molecule shape characterized by three regions of electrons and three outer atoms surrounding a central atom.

trigonal pyramidal molecule. A molecule shape characterized by four regions of electrons and three outer atoms surrounding a central atom. Three outer atoms and one unbonded pair of electrons are at the four vertices of a tetrahedron.

triple bond. A covalent bond that forms when three pairs of valence electrons are shared between atoms.

triple point. The specific pressure and temperature at which a substance will be in the solid, liquid, and vapor forms in equilibrium.

triprotic acid. An acid that can donate three protons.

tRNA. See *transfer RNA.*

Tyndall effect. An effect demonstrated by colloids in which a beam of light is visible due to the scattering of light by the dispersed phase.

U

uncatalyzed reaction. A reaction that occurs without a catalyst.

unified atomic mass unit (u)**.** The unit used to measure the mass of an atom; also known as a *dalton* (Da).

unit cell. The smaller structure within a crystalline solid identified by scientists as that which is repeated to form a crystal lattice.

unit conversion. The mathematical process used to change a measurement in one unit into an equivalent measurement using a different unit.

universal indicator. A substance that will change colors when it reacts with an acid or base and works throughout the entire range of pH values.

unsaturated hydrocarbon. A hydrocarbon that has fewer than four atoms surrounding at least some of its carbon atoms. These hydrocarbons contain at least one double or triple bond.

unsaturated solution. A solution that contains less than the maximum amount of solute that it could hold at current conditions.

V

valence bond theory. A model of chemical bonding that states that atoms fill their valence shells by filling vacancies in particular orbitals; also known as the *localized electron theory.*

valence electron. The electrons in the outermost energy level of an atom that are the ones most likely to be involved in chemical bonding.

valence shell electron pair repulsion (VSEPR) theory. A model for explaining the shapes of molecules that states that the atoms in a molecule will be arranged in such a way as to minimize the repulsive force between bonded and unbonded electrons.

van der Waals force. A collective term for the various intermolecular forces. See *intermolecular force.*

vapor. See *gas.*

vapor pressure depression. The lowering of the vapor pressure of a solvent due to the presence of dissolved solute particles.

vaporization. The phase change from liquid to vapor due to a gain of thermal energy that can occur by evaporation or boiling.

viscosity. A liquid's ability to resist flowing.

voltaic cell. An electrochemical cell that uses a spontaneous chemical reaction to produce electrical energy.

volume fraction (φ_{solute})**.** A measure of concentration that compares the volume of a solute with the volume of an entire solution and is reported as a decimal or percent; also known as *percent by volume.*

W

wave-particle duality. The current description of both light and matter as having characteristics of waves and particles simultaneously.

weak acid. A substance that doesn't ionize easily, releasing relatively few protons.

weak base. A substance that doesn't easily accept protons.

worldview. The perspective from which a person sees and interprets all of life. It is made up of what one believes about the most important things in life.

Index

A **boldface** page number denotes the page on which the vocabulary term is defined.

C

Index

F

G

Index

M

N

Index

Q

R

S

Index

T

Photo Credits

Key: (t) top; (c) center; (b) bottom; (l) left; (r) right; (bg) background

COVER

Nick Poon/Moment/Getty Images

FRONT MATTER

i real444/iStock/Getty Images Plus/Getty Images; **vii**tl dotted zebra/Alamy Stock Photo; **vii**tr UPI/Alamy Stock Photo; **vii**trc LWM/NASA/LANDSAT/Alamy Stock Photo; **vii**b LightField Studios Inc./Alamy Stock Photo; **viii**l © DETLEV VAN RAVENSWAAY/SCIENCE SOURCE; **viii**r ivan-96 /Digital Vision Vectors/Getty Images; **ix**t NASA/Handout /Getty Images; **ix**c © USTC Institute of Advanced Technology & Tsinghua University Press/SCIENCE SOURCE; **ix**bl Roongrote Amnuaysook/EyeEm/Getty Images; **ix**br Michael Marfell/Moment/Getty Images; **x**tl Aerogel hand by Courtesy NASA/JPL-Caltech/Wikimedia Commons /Public Domain/Cropped; **x**tr ranasu/iStock/Getty Images; **x**b Ashley Cooper/Alamy Stock Photo; **xi**t Jose A. Bernat Bacete/Moment/Getty Images; **xi**c Floortje/iStock/Getty Images; **xi**b MARTIN BERNETTI/AFP/Getty Images

CHAPTER 1

xiv Paul Starosta/Stone/Getty Images; **2** (philosophers) "Sanzio 01 Plato Aristotle" by Raphael/Wikimedia Commons/Public Domain/cropped; **2–3** (gutter) ilbusca /DigitalVision Vectors/Getty Images; **3**t benoitb/Digital Vision Vectors/Getty Images; **3**b anyaivanova/iStock/Getty Images Plus/Getty Images; **4–5**bg TommoT/Shutterstock .com; **5**l Public Domain; **6–7** georgeclerk/E+/Getty Images; **8**r Klaus Vedfelt/DigitalVision/Getty Images; **8–9** (gutter), **17**l Neil Thomas/Corbis News/Getty Images; **10–11** dra_ schwartz/E+/Getty Images; **12**bg Tommy Trenchard/Alamy Stock Photo; **12**r Edwin Remsberg/Alamy Stock Photo; **13** AFP/Getty Images; **14** Worldwide Picture Library /Alamy Stock Photo; **15, 17**r Hailshadow/iStock/Getty Images Plus/Getty Images; **16** Florilegius/Alamy Stock Photo; **19** Everett Collection Inc/Alamy Stock Photo

CHAPTER 2

20–21, 34l blackphobos/iStock/Getty Images; **21** studio casper/iStock/Getty Images; **22**l PHOTO RESEARCHERS, INC./Science Source/Getty Images; **22**tr Jennifer A Smith /Moment/Getty Images; **22**br, **45**t FactoryTh/iStock /Getty Images; **23**tr Fuse/Corbis/Getty Images; **23**l Jose A. Bernat Bacete/Moment/Getty Images; **23**br jarun011 /iStock/Getty Images; **24**t Sebastian Janicki/Shutterstock .com; **24**c Mandy Disher Photography/Moment/Getty Images; **24**b pederk/iStock Unreleased/Getty images; **25**t Spiderstock/iStock/Getty Images; **25**b gameover2012 /iStock/Getty Images; **27** © Vincent Boisvert, all right reserved/Moment/Getty Images; **28** Andrew Brookes /Cultura/Getty Images; **29** NASA/Handout/Getty Images; **31** Mimadeo/iStock/Getty Images; **32–33**t Jose A. Bernat Bacete/Moment/Getty Images; **32**b Floortje/iStock/Getty Images; **33**b, **45**b duncan1890/Digital Vision Vectors /Getty Images; **34**r emilyhayward/iStock/Getty Images; **35** © Richard J. Green/SCIENCE SOURCE; **36–37** JTSorrell /E+/Getty Images; **39** UniversalImagesGroup/Getty Images; **40, 46** jonnysek/iStock/Getty Images; **41**t videophoto /E+/Getty Images; **41**b E.R. Degginger/Alamy Stock Photo; **42** Allan Wallberg/EyeEm/Getty Images; **43** Instants/E+ /Getty Images; **44** MARIIA VASILEVA/iStock/Getty Images

CHAPTER 3

48 © DETLEV VAN RAVENSWAAY/SCIENCE SOURCE; **49** ivan-96/Digital Vision Vectors/Getty Images; **50**t, **71**tr studiocasper/iStock/Getty Images; **50**b INTERFOTO/Alamy Stock Photo; **51** (Ampere's Stand) World History Archive /Alamy Stock Photo; **51** (Candle) ilbusca/Digital Vision Vectors/Getty Images; **51** (thermometer) benoitb/Digital Vision Vectors/Getty Images; **51** (weights) ivan-96/Digital Vision Vectors/Getty Images; **51** (measuring tape) ivan-96 /Digital Vision Vectors/Getty Images; **51** (molecule) Book end/Alamy Stock Photo; **51** (watch) pictore/Digital Vision Vectors/Getty Images; **51** (scale) Mark Weiss/Photodisc /Getty Images; **51** (gauge) ChuckSchugPhotography /iStock/Getty images; **52** Bryan Mullennix/Getty Images; **53** HHakim/E+/Getty Images; **54**tl macroworld/E+/Getty Images; **54**tr Universal History Archive/Universal Images Group/Getty Images; **54**b lucato/iStock/Getty Images; **55** malerapaso/iStock/Getty Images; **56** picture alliance /Getty Images; **57** agafapaperiapunta/iStock/Getty Images; **58**t tdub303/E+/Getty Images; **58**b, **60**c, **71**cl Rawpixel /iStock/Getty Images; **59** Jenny E. Ross/Corbis Documentary/Getty Images; **60**t TEK IMAGE/SCIENCE PHOTO LIBRARY/Getty Images; **61** ilbusca/Digital Vision Vectors /Getty Images; **62** Tomas Ragina/iStock/Getty images; **63** Mailson Pignata/EyeEm/Getty Images; **64** AlexLMX /iStock/Getty Images; **65**t, **71**br shotsstudio/iStock/Getty Images; **65**b channarongsds/iStock/Getty Images; **66–67** Virojt Changyencham/Moment/Getty Images; **68** Casarsa Guru/E+/Getty Images; **69** EmirMemedovski/E+/Getty Images; **70** Kativ/E+/Getty Images; **72** tdub303/E+/Getty Images; **74** Plan Shoot/Multi-bits/Taxi/Getty Images

CHAPTER 4

76 Prof. Erwin Mueller/Science Source; **79**bg MARK GARLICK/Science Photo Library/Getty Images Plus/Getty Images; **79**c Dalton's Element List by John Dalton/Wikimedia Commons/Public Domain/Edited; **80**bl ZU_09/Getty Images/DigitalVision Vectors/Getty Images; **80**br, **90**c Artwork by Ina Stanimirova Chronicle/Alamy Stock Photo Archive / Alamy Stock Photo; **82** Artwork by Frank Ramspott Universal Images Group North America LLC/Alamy Stock Photo; **83**t Artwork by Ina Stanimirova Universal Images Group North America LLC/Alamy Stock Photo; **83**br Artwork by Ina Stanimirova derivative of "James Chadwick"/Los Alamos National Laboratory. Unless otherwise indicated, this information has been authored by an employee or employees of the Los Alamos National Security, LLC (LANS, operator of the Los Alamos National Laboratory under Contract No. DE-AC52-06NA25396 with the US Department of Energy.) /Wikimedia Commons; **85** Patrice Loiez, CERN/Science

Source; **87** BJU Photo Services; **89** SPL/Science Source; **93**t "Radium Dial"/Arma95/Wikimedia Commons/CC BY-SA 3 /cropped; **93**b Daily Herald Archive/SSPL/Getty Images

CHAPTER 5

94 ATLAS Collaboration/CERN/Science Source; **95**, **113** Adobe Stock/Morphart; **100** standing wave electron cloud /CK-12 Foundation/Wikimedia Commons/CC BY SA 3.0 /modified; **101**cl Artwork by Ina Stanimirova derivative of "Werner Heisenberg"/Bundesarchiv, Bild 183-R57262 /Wikimedia Commons/CC-BY-SA 3.0; **109** Artwork by Leib Chigrin derivative of Hund, Friedrich 1920er Göttingen by GFHund/Wikimdia Commons/CC BY 3.0

CHAPTER 6

116 Science History Images/Alamy Stock Photo; **117**cl Artwork by Ina Stanimirova derivative of "Lavoisier explaining to his wife the result of his experiment" by Ernest Board/WelcomeImages/Wikimedia Commons/CC By-SA 4.0; **117**t © SPL/SCIENCE SOURCE; **117**b Photos .com/Getty Images; **118**tl © Turtle Rock Scientific/SCIENCE SOURCE; **118**tr Artwork by Ina Stanimirova INTERFOTO /Alamy Stock Photo; **118**cl © Charles D. Winters/SCIENCE SOURCE; **118**c Newlands periodiska system 1866/John Alexander Reina Newlands/Wikimedia Commons/Public Domain/modified; **118**bl Editorial Image, LLC/Alamy Stock Photo; **119**t Science History Images/Alamy Stock Photo; **119**b Phil Degginger/Alamy Stock Photo; **124** (hydrogen), **134**t © SPL/SCIENCE SOURCE; **124**, **136** (lithium) Bjoern Wylezich/Shutterstock.com; **124**, **136** (sodium) Andraž Cerar/Shutterstock.com; **124**, **136** (potassium) © Turtle Rock Scientific/SCIENCE SOURCE; **124**, **136** (rubidium) © SPL/SCIENCE SOURCE; **124**, **136** (cesium) © SPL/SCIENCE SOURCE; **124**, **137** (beryllium) Bjoern Wylezich/Shutter stock.com; **124**, **137** (magnesium) Bjoern Wylezich/Shut terstock.com; **124**, **137** (calcium) Bjoern Wylezich/Shutter stock.com; **124**, **137** (strontium) © SPL/SCIENCE SOURCE; **124**, **137** (barium) © Turtle Rock Scientific/SCIENCE SOURCE; **124**, **138** (scandium) © SPL/SCIENCE SOURCE; **124**, **138** (titanium) Bjoern Wylezich/Shutterstock.com; **124**, **138** (vanadium) Bjoern Wylezich/Shutterstock.com; **124**, **138** (chromium) Bjoern Wylezich/Shutterstock.com; **124**, **138** (manganese) Bjoern Wylezich/Shutterstock.com; **124**, **138** (iron) Iron electrolytic and 1cm3 cube/Alchemist -hp/Wikimedia Commons/CC By-Sa 3.0/modified; **124**, **138** (cobalt) ALFRED PASIEKA/SCIENCE PHOTO LIBRARY/Getty Images; **124**, **138** (yttrium) Yttrium sublimed dendritic and 1cm3 cube/Alchemist-hp/Wikimedia Commons/CC By SA 3.0/modified; **124**, **138** (zirconium) Bjoern Wylezich/Shut terstock.com; **124**, **138**, **149** (niobium) Bjoern Wylezich /Shutterstock.com; **124**, **138** (molybdenum) © Science Stock Photography/SCIENCE SOURCE; **124**, **138** (ruthenium) © SPL/SCIENCE SOURCE; **124**, **138** (rhodium) © SPL/SCIENCE SOURCE; **124**, **138** (lanthanum) Bjoern Wylezich/Shutterstock.com; **124**, **138** (hafnium) Bjoern Wylezich/Shutterstock.com; **124**, **138** (tantalum) Bjoern Wylezich/Shutterstock.com; **124**, **138** (tungsten) Wolfram evaporated crystals and 1cm3 cube/Alchemist-hp /Wikimedia Commons/CC By-SA 1.2/modified; **124**, **138** (rhenium) Rhenium single crystal bar and 1cm3 cube /Alchemist-hp/Wikimedia Commons/CC By-SA 3.0/modified; **124**, **138** (osmium) LuYago/Shutterstock.com; **124**, **138** (iridium) © SPL/SCIENCE SOURCE; **124**, **139** (cerium) Bjoern Wylezich/Shutterstock.com; **124**, **139** (praseodymium) Bjoern Wylezich/Shutterstock.com; **124**, **139** (neodymium) Kim Christensen/Shutterstock.com; **124**, **139** (samarium) Bjoern Wylezich/Shutterstock.com; **124**, **139** (thorium) Thorium sample 0.1g/Alchemist-hp/Wikimedia Commons/CC By-SA 3.0/modified; **124**, **139** (uranium) abadonian/iStock/Getty Images; **125**, **138** (nickel) Bjoern Wylezich/Shutterstock.com; **125**, **138** (copper) Bjoern Wylezich/Shutterstock.com; **125**, **138** (zinc) © Turtle Rock Scientific/SCIENCE SOURCE; **125**, **138** (palladium) RHJ-Phtotoandilustration/Shutterstock.com; **125**, **138** (silver) Bjoern Wylezich/Shutterstock.com; **125**, **138** (cadmium) Bjoern Wylezich/Shutterstock.com; **125**, **138** (platinum) Bjoern Wylezich/Shutterstock.com; **125**, **138** (gold) studiocasper/iStock/Getty Images; **125**, **138** (mercury) MarcelC/iStock/Getty Images; **125**, **139** (europium) © SPL /SCIENCE SOURCE; **125**, **139** (gadolinium) Bjoern Wylezich /Shutterstock.com; **125**, **139** (terbium) Bjoern Wylezich /Shutterstock.com; **125**, **139** (dysprosium) Bjoern Wylezich /Shutterstock.com; **125**, **139** (holmium) Bjoern Wylezich /Shutterstock.com; **125**, **139** (erbium) © SPL/SCIENCE SOURCE; **125**, **139** (thulium) © SPL/SCIENCE SOURCE; **125**, **139** (ytterbium) Bjoern Wylezich/Shutterstock.com; **125**, **139** (lutetium) © SPL/SCIENCE SOURCE; **125**, **139** (americium) Americium microscope/Bionerd/Wikimedia Commons/CC By-SA 3.0/cropped; **125**, **141** (boron) Kim Christensen/Shutterstock.com; **125**, **140**b, **141** (aluminum) Bjoern Wylezich/Shutterstock.com; **125**, **141** (gallium) © Turtle Rock Scientific/SCIENCE SOURCE; **125**, **141** (indium) Bjoern Wylezich/Shutterstock.com; **125**, **141** (thallium) © SPL/SCIENCE SOURCE; **125**, **142** (carbon) PjrStudio/Alamy Stock Photo; **125**, **142** (silicon) Bjoern Wylezich/Shutter stock.com; **125**, **142** (geranium) ALFRED PASIEKA/SCIENCE PHOTO LIBRARY/Getty images; **125**, **142** (tin) Bjoern Wylezich/Shutterstock.com; **125**, **142** (lead) Lead electrolytic and 1cm3 cube/Alchemist-hp/Wikimedia Commons /CC By-SA 3.0/cropped; **125**, **143** (phosphorus) © SPL /SCIENCE SOURCE; **125**, **143** (arsenic) Harry Taylor/Dorling Kindersley/Getty Images; **125**, **143** (antimony) Bjoern Wylezich/Shutterstock.com; **125**, **143** (bismuth) MarcelC /iStock/Getty Images; **125**, **144** (sulfur) Bjoern Wylezich /Shutterstock.com; **125**, **144** (selenium) Bjoern Wylezich /Shutterstock.com; **125**, **144** (tellurium) Bjoern Wylezich /Shutterstock.com; **125**, **145** (fluorine) Dorling Kindersley /Getty Images; **125**, **145** (chlorine) Unusual Films; **125**, **145** (bromine) © Martyn F. Chillmaid/SCIENCE SOURCE; **125**, **145** (iodine) Bjoern Wylezich/Shutterstock.com; **125**, **146** (helium) Helium discharge tube/Alchemist-hp/Wikimedia Commons/CC By-SA 3.0/modified; **125**, **146** (neon) Neon discharge tube/Alchemist-hp/Wikimedia Commons/CC By-SA 3.0/modified; **125**, **146** (argon) Argon discharge tube/Alchemist-hp/Wikimedia Commons/CC By-SA 3.0

Photo Credits

/modified; **125**, **146** (Krypton) Krypton discharge tube /Alchemist-hp/Wikimedia Commons/CC By-SA 3.0/modified; **125**, **146** (xenon) Xenon discharge tube by Alchemist-hp/Wikimedia Commons/CC By-SA 3.0/modified; **126** Steve Allen/DigitalVision/Getty Images; **129** BJU Press artwork derivative of First Ionization Energy/Sponk/Wikimedia Commons/CC By-SA 3.0; **132** Atlantide Phototravel /Corbis Documentary/Getty Images; **133** Bjoern Wylezich /Shutterstock.com; **134** © Martyn F. Chillmaid/SCIENCE SOURCE; **135** GIPhotoStock X/Alamy Stock Photo; **136**t sciencephotos/Alamy Stock Photo; **136**b © Charles D. Winters/SCIENCE SOURCE; **137**b E.R. Degginger/Alamy Stock Photo; **138**l MarcelClemens/Shutterstock.com; **138**r Eddie Jordan Photos/Shutterstock.com; **140**t © Turtle Rock Scientific/SCIENCE SOURCE; **141**t Sean Gallup/Getty Images; **141**b KrimKate/iStock/Getty Images; **142**r sankai/iStock /Getty Images; **143**t jz86/iStock/Getty Images; **143**b © Charles D. Winters/SCIENCE SOURCE; **144**t R.M. Nunes /iStock/Getty Images; **144**b © Charles D. Winters/SCIENCE SOURCE; **145**l © Turtle Rock Scientific/SCIENCE SOURCE; **145**r © Charles D. Winters/SCIENCE SOURCE; **146**r hudiemm/iStock/Getty Images; **147**l dpa picture alliance archive/Alamy Stock Photo; **147**r Dr. Yuki Abe; **151** HAYKIRDI/E+/Getty images

CHAPTER 7

152 FotografiaBasica/E+/Getty Images; **153** DOE Photo /Alamy Stock Photo; **156**b Artwork by Ina Stanimirova World History Archive/Alamy Stock Photo; **157** Deepak Aggarwal/Dorling Kindersley/Getty Images; **159**t Artwork by Ina Stanimirova Science History Images/Alamy Stock Photo; **159–61**bg Photo by Alex Tihonov/Moment/Getty images; **162–63** © Turtle Rock Scientific/SCIENCE SOURCE; **164**t, **171** Artwork by David Lompe derivative of Xtals combined 2 300ppi/Paburr/Wikimedia Commons/CC By-SA 4.0; **164**l Edwin Remsberg/Photolibrary/Getty Images; **165–66**l Gregory_DUBUS/iStock/Getty images; **166–67**r Science Photo Library/Getty Images; **168**t Bjoern Wylezich/ Shutter
stock.com; **168**l © Turtle Rock Scientific/SCIENCE SOURCE; **168**b mizikm/iStock/Getty Images; **169** Aryfahmed/iStock /Getty Images; **173** MARTIN BERNETTI/AFP/Getty Images

CHAPTER 8

174 Paul Taylor/Stone/Getty Images; **177** Vadim Petrakov /Shutterstock.com; **178–79**bg Christian Schulze/EyeEm /Getty Images; **179**tc stocknshares/iStock/Getty Images; **180** © Charles D. Winters/SCIENCE SOURCE; **184** Zagursky /iStock/Getty Images; **186** BNBB Studio/Moment/Getty Images; **188**l JanMiko/iStock/Getty Images; **188**r Gregory S. Paulson/Cultura/Getty Images; **191** Xuanyu Han /Moment/Getty Images; **192** Simon Annable/Shutter stock.com; **195** Jason Doiy/iStock/Getty images

CHAPTER 9

196 wektorygrafika/iStock/Getty Images; **197** Alpha Stock /Alamy Stock Photo; **198–99**, **215**tl © CMEABG-UCBL /SCIENCE SOURCE; **200–201** hekakoskinen/iStock/Getty images; **202** David Wall Photo/Lonely Planet Images/Getty Images; **203**cl © Turtle Rock Scientific/SCIENCE SOURCE; **203**cc Phil Degginger/Alamy Stock Photo; **203**cr Andy Crawford & Tim Ridley/Dorling Kindersley/Getty Images; **203**bl © Turtle Rock Scientific/SCIENCE SOURCE; **203**bc © Turtle Rock Scientific/SCIENCE SOURCE; **204** (aluminum oxide) © Turtle Rock Scientific/SCIENCE SOURCE; **204** (magnesium oxide) © Turtle Rock Scientific/SCIENCE SOURCE; **204** (potassium sulfide) Potassium sulfide /Leiem/Wikimedia Commons/CC By-SA 4.0/modified; **204** (sodium chloride) mariusFM77/E+/Getty Images; **205** © Turtle Rock Scientific/SCIENCE SOURCE; **206–7** MICHAEL W DAVIDSON/Science Source/Getty Images; **208** BraunS/E+/Getty Images; **210–11**, **215**cl THOMAS DEERINCK, NCMIR/Science Photo Library/Getty Images; **213–14**, **215**bl © Vincent Boisvert, all right reserved /Moment/Getty Images; **217** RapidEye/E+/Getty Images

CHAPTER 10

218 Juergen Ritterbach/The Image Bank/Getty Images; **219**tl filipfoto/iStock/Getty Images; **219**tr Dorling Kindersley ltd/Alamy Stock Photo; **219**bl © MARTYN F. CHILLMAID /SCIENCE SOURCE; **219**br Scott O'Neill/iStock/Getty Images / babyblueut/iStock/Getty Images; **221** © Turtle Rock Scientific/SCIENCE SOURCE; **222** Bigyy/iStock/Getty Images; **223** Dennis Macdonald/Photolibrary/Getty Images; **224**, **237**tl © USTC Institute of Advanced Technology & Tsinghua University Press/SCIENCE SOURCE; **227** © USTC Institute of Advanced Technology & Tsinghua University Press/SCIENCE SOURCE; **228–29**tl unkas_photo/iStock/Getty Images; **228**b, **237**br Michael Marfell/Moment/Getty Images; **229**r © Turtle Rock Scientific/SCIENCE SOURCE; **230** Cavan Images/Cavan/Getty Images; **231** © Alexandre Dotta /SCIENCE SOURCE; **233**t © GIPhotoStock/Cultura/Getty Images; **233**b Stocktrek Images, Inc./Alamy Stock Photo; **234** © Turtle Rock Scientific/SCIENCE SOURCE; **235** Xvision /Moment/Getty Images; **236–37**l Roongrote Amnuaysook /EyeEm/Getty Images; **239**t World History Archive/Alamy Stock Photo; **239**b Bob_Eastman/iStock/Getty Images

CHAPTER 11

240 Дерябин Андрей Николаевич/iStock/Getty Images; **242** dehooks/iStock/Getty Images; **243** - - /123RF; **244** TibiP03/iStock/Getty Images; **245** Yon Marsh/Alamy Stock Photo; **246** Robert Daly/Stone/Getty Images; **248** nicolas_ /E+/Getty Images; **250–51** © Jonathan Knowles 2015 /Stone/Getty Images; **252–53**tl, **263**cr Sarah Marchant /Shutterstock.com; **252**bl Prostock-Studio/iStock/Getty Images; **253**tr AnthonyRosenberg/E+/Getty Images; **254** membio/iStock/Getty Images; **255** Ashley Cooper /Alamy Stock Photo; **257** gaffera/E+/Getty Images; **259**, **263**b grandriver/E+/Getty Images; **260–61** georgeclerk

/E+/Getty Images; **262** Muslianshah Masrie/Alamy Stock Photo; **267** AndreyPopov/iStock/Getty Images

CHAPTER 12

268 fStop Images - Caspar Benson/Brand X Pictures /Getty Images; **271** dml5050/iStock/Getty; **272**t Artwork by David Lompe Universal Images Group North America LLC/Alamy Stock Photo; **272**cl Alter_photo/iStock/Getty Images; **272**cr ilbusca/Digital Vision Vectors/Getty Images; **272**bl Alter_photo/iStock/Getty Images; **272**br nicoolay /iStock/Getty Images; **273** Zero Creatives/Image Source /Getty Images; **274–75**t Mr.Nino/Shutterstock.com; **274**b Science History Images/Alamy Stock Photo; **276** Nastasic /Digital Vision Vectors/Getty Images; **278–79**, **294**c Le-Manna/iStock/Getty Images; **280** Luis Javier Sandoval /Stockbyte/Getty Images; **282–83** Kalistratova/iStock /Getty Images; **285** fmajor/E+/Getty Images; **286** sarote pruksachat/Moment/Getty Images; **287** jacquesdurocher /iStock/Getty Images; **290**t B toy Anucha/Shutterstock .com; **290**b Maurice Savage/Alamy Stock Photo; **291** Leon Neal/Getty Images; **292** Westend61/Getty Images; **293**l Eric BOUVET/Gamma-Rapho/Getty Images; **293**r Fabian Plock /iStock/Getty Images; **297** Kohei Hara/Stone/Getty Images

CHAPTER 13

298 Ben Edwards/The Image Bank/Getty Images; **299** ZU_09/Digital Vision Vectors/Getty Images; **301** Maxi-photo/E+/Getty Images; **302–3** Rudi Sebastian/The Image Bank/Getty Images; **304**tl rep0rter/iStock/Getty Images; **304–5**tr, **322** Danita Delimont/Gallo Images/Getty Images; **304**b © Charles D. Winters/SCIENCE SOURCE; **305**bl Dafinchi/iStock/Getty Images; **305**br MahirAtes/iStock /Getty Images; **306**l HadelProductions/E+/Getty Images; **306**r Matt Meadows/Photolibrary/Getty Images; **307**t Jay Freis/Stone/Getty Images; **307**b Kubra Cavus/E+/Getty Images; **308** (Fluorite) Epitavi/iStock/Getty Images; **308** (Wulfenite) Coldmoon_photo/iStock/Getty Images; **308** (Tanzanite) Albert Russ/Shutterstock.com; **308** (Azurite) Kerrick/iStock/Getty Images; **308** (Amazonite) MarcelC /iStock/Getty Images; **308** (Emerald) photo-world/Shutter stock.com; **308** (Rhodochrosite) WILDLIFE GmbH/Alamy Stock Photo; **308–9**bg Bkamprath/iStock/Getty Images; **309**t Nikolai Gavriliukov/Shutterstock.com; **309**b Reload_ Studio/iStock/Getty Images; **310**l Argon ice 1/Deglr6328 ~commonswiki/Wikimedia Commons/CC By-SA 30 /modified; **310**r AlasdairJames/iStock/Getty Images; **311**t J-Palys/iStock/Getty Images; **311**cr Dafinchi/Shutterstock .com; **311**cl ROBERT BROOK/SCIENCE PHOTO LIBRARY /Getty Images; **312–13** Nick Poon/Moment/Getty Images; **314–15**bg Patrick Boelens/iStock/Getty Images; **314**b MarcelC/iStock/Getty Images; **315**b © Sinclair Stammers /SCIENCE SOURCE; **316** Kis Arpad/EyeEm/Getty Images; **317** ssuaphoto/iStock/Getty Images; **318**, **323** game-over2012/iStock/Getty Images; **320** imageBROKER/Alamy Stock Photo; **321** uchar/E+/Getty Images; **325**l 1939 Ted Williams/Apex Photo Company/Wikimedia Commons /Public Domain; **325**r Alcor-Dewar2/Alcor Life Extension Foundation/Wikimedia Commons/Public Domain

CHAPTER 14

326 hadynyah/E+/Getty Images; **327**l Shawshots/Alamy Stock Photo; **327**r pederk/iStock Unreleased/Getty images; **328–29**tl Jeff Rotman/The Image Bank/Getty Images; **328**c Cobalt88/iStock/Getty images; **328**bl ChrisEllis85 /iStock/Getty Images; **328**br Epitavi/iStock/Getty Images; **329**tr Creative Frame Studio/Moment/Getty Images; **329**b abadonian/iStock/Getty Images; **332–33**tbg rudchenko /iStock/Getty Images; **332**cl © Martyn F. Chillmaid/SCIENCE SOURCE; **333**tc © Turtle Rock Scientific/SCIENCE SOURCE; **334**t © Turtle Rock Scientific/SCIENCE SOURCE; **334**c © Turtle Rock Scientific/SCIENCE SOURCE; **334**b © Turtle Rock Scientific/SCIENCE SOURCE; **335**t VICTOR DE SCHWANBERG/Science Photo Library/Getty Images; **335**b Man_Half-tube/DigitalVision Vectors/Getty Images; **337** © Turtle Rock Scientific/SCIENCE SOURCE; **338**tl, **341**bl, **352** © Turtle Rock Scientific/SCIENCE SOURCE; **338–39**tr cookelma/iStock/Getty Images; **341**tr rrocio/iStock/Getty Images; **342** © Eye of Science/SCIENCE SOURCE; **343** robcocquyt/iStock/Getty Images; **344** RyersonClark/iStock /Getty Images; **346**t Helen King/The Image Bank/Getty Images; **346**b Steven White/iStock/Getty Images; **347** Pongsak Tawansaeng/EyeEm/Getty Images; **348** Tetiana Garkusha/iStock/Getty Images; **349**cl antonioiacobelli /RooM/Getty Images; **349**cr Ashva/iStock/Getty Images; **349**b, **353** Anton Petrus/Moment/Getty Images; **350**l Art-work by Leib Chigrin INTERFOTO/Alamy Stock Photo; **350**cr © Charles D. Winters/SCIENCE SOURCE; **350**bl De Agostini /P. Castano/De Agostini Picture Library/Getty Images; **351** dszc/E+/Getty Images; **355** robas/iStock/Getty Images

CHAPTER 15

356 Dimitri Otis/Stone/Getty Images; **357** benoitb/Digital Vision Vectors/Getty Images; **358–59**bg, **382**t Martin Puddy/Stone/Getty Images; **359**l © ADAM HART-DAVIS /SCIENCE SOURCE; **359**r © Turtle Rock Scientific/SCIENCE SOURCE; **360–61**l Jasmin Merdan/Moment/Getty Images; **361**r Lena_Zajchikova/iStock/Getty Images; **362** © Turtle Rock Scientific/SCIENCE SOURCE; **365**t Xvision/Moment /Getty Images; **365**b © SPL/SCIENCE SOURCE; **366**tl Daniel Grill/Getty Images; **366**tr NaturaLight/Alamy Stock Photo; **366**b, **382**b © TREVOR CLIFFORD PHOTOGRAPHY/SCIENCE SOURCE; **367** TANGOART/iStock/Getty Images; **368**, **368–69** (border) azerberber/iStock/Getty Images; **370** Leonid Ikan/iStock/Getty images; **371**bg Ivan/Moment/Getty Images; **371**, **383** duncan1890/Digital Vision Vectors/Getty Images; **372** Bruno Gori/Cultura/Getty Images; **373** Alatom /E+/Getty Images; **374** Trevor Williams/DigitalVision/Getty Images; **375** Artwork by Leib Chigrin derivative of Josiah Willard Gibbs -from MMS-/Wikimedia Commons/Public Domain; **375** ss404045/Alamy Stock Photo; **376**, **378** Sunny/Stone/Getty Images; **380** Alina Rosanova/iStock /Getty Images; **381** Melinda Podor/Moment/Getty Images

Photo Credits

CHAPTER 16

386 ljubaphoto/iStock/Getty Images; **387**l Koichi Yajima /EyeEm/Getty Images; **387**c Leonid Ikan/iStock/Getty Images; **387**r © Turtle Rock Scientific/SCIENCE SOURCE; **390–91** changyu lu/Moment/Getty Images; **392**cl © Charles D. Winters/SCIENCE SOURCE; **392**cc © Charles D. Winters/SCIENCE SOURCE; **392**b © Turtle Rock Scientific /SCIENCE SOURCE; **392**r © Turtle Rock Scientific/SCIENCE SOURCE; **393**tl © Turtle Rock Scientific/SCIENCE SOURCE; **393**tr CTK/Alamy Stock Photo; **393**bl © Turtle Rock Scientific/SCIENCE SOURCE; **393**br Xvision/Moment/Getty Images; **394**tr Aleksandr Zubkov/Moment/Getty Images; **394**bl © SPL/SCIENCE SOURCE; **395** SilvanBachmann /Shutterstock.com; **396**bl © Charles D. Winters/SCIENCE SOURCE; **396–97**bg Kitsana1980/Shutterstock.com; **397**tr Editorial Image, LLC/Alamy Stock Photo; **398–99**bg, **404–5**bg rudchenko/iStock/Getty Images; **399**br Dorling Kindersley ltd/Alamy Stock Photo; **400** E.R. Degginger /Alamy Stock Photo; **401**t Motortion Films/Shutterstock .com; **401**b Michael Moloney/Shutterstock.com; **402** Yulia Reznikov/Moment/Getty Images; **403**t ilbusca/Digital Vision Vectors/Getty Images; **403**b KatarzynaZakowska /Shutterstock.com; **407** Sara Stathas/Alamy Stock Photo

CHAPTER 17

408 Jevtic/iStock/Getty Images; **409** Sueddeutsche Zeitung Photo/Alamy Stock Photo; **410**tl, **430**r © Charles D. Winters/SCIENCE SOURCE; **410**tr © ANDREW LAMBERT PHOTOGRAPHY/SCIENCE SOURCE; **410**b Westend61/Getty Images; **411** © Editorial Image/SCIENCE SOURCE; **412** © Turtle Rock Scientific/SCIENCE SOURCE; **413**t © Charles D. Winters/SCIENCE SOURCE; **413**c © Charles D. Winters /SCIENCE SOURCE; **413**b © Charles D. Winters/SCIENCE SOURCE; **416–17** Nik Merkulov/Shutterstock.com; **419** Cultura RF/Joseph Giacomin/Cultura/Getty Images; **420** Nivellen77/iStock/Getty Images; **421**b Artwork by David Lompe derivative of Haber-Bosch-En/by Francis E Williams /Wikimedia Commons CC By-SA 2.5; **422**t Chuanthit Kunlayanamitre/Shutterstock.com; **422**b istetiana/Moment /Getty Images; **423** Science History Images/Alamy Stock Photo; **424–25**t Savany/iStock/Getty Images; **424**b © Turtle Rock Scientific/SCIENCE SOURCE; **425**br durk gardenier /Alamy Stock Photo; **426** Anna Usova/iStock/Getty images; **427**, **428**cl, **431** © Turtle Rock Scientific/SCIENCE SOURCE; **428–29**t NagyDodo/iStock/Getty Images; **432–33** Sergio Ballivian/500px Prime/Getty Images

CHAPTER 18

434 RossHelen/Shutterstock.com; **435**tr channarongsds /iStock/Getty Images; **435**bl © Turtle Rock Scientific /SCIENCE SOURCE; **436–38**bg Savushkin/iStock/Getty Images; **438** Artwork by Leib Chigrin GL Archive/Alamy Stock Photo; **439** KrivoTIFF/iStock/Getty Images; **440**tl Vesna Jovanovic/EyeEm/Getty Images; **440–41**tr borchee /iStock/Getty Images; **442–43** Artwork by Ina Stanimirova © Turtle Rock Scientific/SCIENCE SOURCE; **442** New Africa /Shutterstock.com; **444** fcafotodigital/E+/Getty Images; **445**, **459** © SCIENCE PHOTO LIBRARY/SCIENCE SOURCE; **446** © Turtle Rock Scientific/SCIENCE SOURCE; **447** © Turtle Rock Scientific/SCIENCE SOURCE; **448** kosmos111 /iStock/Getty Images; **449** Abstract Aerial Art/Digital Vision /Getty Images; **450** © Andrew Lambert Photography /SCIENCE SOURCE; **451**tr © Turtle Rock Scientific/SCIENCE SOURCE; **451**bl © Turtle Rock Scientific/SCIENCE SOURCE; **453**t © Turtle Rock Scientific/SCIENCE SOURCE; **453**b © GIPhotoStock/SCIENCE SOURCE; **454**, **460** © GIPhotoStock Images/SCIENCE SOURCE; **455** simonkr/E+/Getty Images; **456** © Turtle Rock Scientific/SCIENCE SOURCE; **457** Nazar Abbas Photography/Moment/Getty Images; **458** undefined /iStock/Getty Images

CHAPTER 19

462 Westend61/Getty Images; **463** © Charles D. Winters /SCIENCE SOURCE; **464** JGI/Jamie Grill/Getty Images; **465** ra2studio/iStock/Getty Images; **467**tr benoitb/Digital VisionVectors/Getty Images; **467**br Tsuji/E+/Getty Images; **467**bg, **481**t Xuanyu Han/Moment/Getty Images; **468** onlyyouqj/iStock/Getty Images; **471**t Chesky_W/iStock /Getty Images; **471**br © Turtle Rock Scientific/SCIENCE SOURCE © Turtle Rock Scientific/SCIENCE SOURCE; **474**tl benoitb/DigitalVisionVectors/Getty Images; **474**tr ilbusca /DigitalVision Vectors/Getty Images; **474**bl DAMRONG RATTANAPONG/Shutterstock.com; **476** MileA/iStock /Getty Images; **476**t Artwork by David Lompe derivative of Secondary Cell Diagram by Barrie Lawson/Wikimedia Commons/CC By-SA 3.0; **476**b Artwork by David Lompe © Argonne National Laboratory/SCIENCE SOURCE; **477**t, **481**b Matveev Aleksandr/Shutterstock.com; **477**b Artwork by David Lompe derivative of Zincbattery (1)/by Mcy jerry /Wikimedia Commons/CC By-SA 2.5; **478** Tribune Content Agency LLC/Alamy Stock Photo; **483** Sven Loeffler/iStock /Getty Images

CHAPTER 20

484 Anna Ok/Shutterstock.com; **487** SeanShot/E+/Getty Images; **488–89**t freemixer/E+/Getty Images; **490** wolv/E+ /Getty Images; **492** Shelly Still/iStock/Getty Images; **493** Picture Store/Shutterstock.com; **494** Syda Productions /Shutterstock.com; **495** Charles Gatewood/iStock/Getty Images; **497** FactoryTh/iStock/Getty Images; **499** sirawit 99/iStock/Getty Images; **500** Studio Doros/iStock/Getty Images; **501** Alina Yudina/Shutterstock.com; **502**t Isabel Pavia/Moment/Getty Images; **502**b Westend61/Getty Images; **503** Michal Kin/EyeEm/Getty Images; **504–5**bg Tunatura/iStock/Getty Images; **505**t Elizaveta Galitckaia /Shutterstock.com; **506–7**l, **511** Lorna Roberts/Shutter stock.com; **507**r photograph by dorisj/Moment/Getty Images; **508** AmyLv/Shutterstock.com; **509** © Turtle Rock Scientific/SCIENCE SOURCE

CHAPTER 21

514 RGB Ventures/SuperStock/Alamy Stock Photo; **516**, **533**t Paul Souders/Stone/Getty Images; **517**t didecs /iStock/Getty Images; **517**b MediaProduction/E+/Getty Images; **518** fcafotodigital/E+/Getty Images; **519**t Vesna Jovanovic/EyeEm/Getty Images; **519**b benoitb/E+/Getty Images; **520**t Aerogel hand by Courtesy NASA/JPL-Caltech /Wikimedia Commons/Public Domain/cropped; **520**r–**21** ranasu/iStock/Getty Images; **522**l Fattyplace/iStock/Getty Images; **522**r–**23**t, **533**b apomares/E+/Getty Images; **524**t Artwork by Ina Stanimirova Science History Images/Alamy Stock Photo; **525** virtustudio/iStock/Getty Images; **526**t Yulia Furman/Shutterstock.com; **526**b Artwork by Frank Ramspott derivative of Oxy-Hemoglobin by Belle2018 /Wikimedia Commons/CC By-SA 4.0; **527** robynmac /iStock/Getty Images; **528**tl, **534** Steven Puetzer/Photographer's Choice RF/Getty Images; **528**tr–**29**t Varavin88 /Shutterstock.com; **530** Science Picture Co/Alamy Stock Photo; **531** Science Photo Library - NASA/ESA/STSCI/M. ROBBERTO,HST ORION TREASURY TEAM/Brand X Pictures /Getty Images; **532** AvigatorPhotographer/iStock/Getty Images; **535** Fascinadora/Shutterstock.com

CHAPTER 22

536 guowei ying/Moment/Getty Images; **537**tr Artwork by Ina Stanimirova derivative of Würzburg, Germany - DSC04289/by Daderot/Wikimedia Commons/CC By-SA 1.0; **537** UniversalImagesGroup/Getty Images; **537**b Artwork by Ina Stanimirova Sueddeutsche Zeitung Photo /Alamy Stock Photo; **538** abadonian/iStock/Getty Images; **538**b, **546** Artwork by Ina Stanimirova derivative of Ernest Rutherford 1905/Wikimedia Commons/CC By-SA 4.0; **539** Rost9/Shutterstock.com; **540** Table isotopes ru by Sjlegg /Wikimedia Commons/CC By-SA 3.0/modified; **541** H. Mark Weidman Photography/Alamy Stock Photo; **543** well-photo/iStock/Getty Images; **544–45**t cigdem/Shutterstock.com; **544**b alexkuehni/iStock/Getty Images; **548–49** cokada/iStock/Getty Images; **552** Massimo Dallaglio/Alamy Stock Photo; **555**t Ian Dagnall/Alamy Stock Photo; **555**b Collection Christophel/Alamy Stock Photo; **556** JESPER KLAUSEN/SCIENCE PHOTO LIBRARY /Getty Images; **558** Evdoha_spb/Shutterstock.com; **559** AFP/Getty Images; **560** zhongguo/E+/Getty Images; **562–63** IngaNielsen/iStock/Getty Images; **562** Artwork by Frank Ramspott derivative of FusionintheSun by Borb /Wikimedia Commons/CC By-SA 2.0; **564**t mmac72/E+ /Getty Images; **564**b Mark Kostich/E+/Getty Images; **565**t Jupiter radio by NASA Jet Propulsion Laboratory/Wikimedia Commons/Public Domain/Cropped; **565**b Lisa Schaetzle /Moment/Getty Images; **569** DKosig/E+/Getty Images

BACK MATTER

571 ilbusca/DigitalVision Vectors/Getty Images; **572** SolStock/E+/Getty Images; **573** Morphart Creation /Shutterstock.com; **577** Look Studio/Shutterstock.com

Periodic Table

OF THE ELEMENTS

Key (example: Radon)

atomic number	86
radioactive	☢
name	Radon
symbol	**Rn**
atomic mass	(222)
electron structure by energy level	2, 8, 18, 32, 18, 8

atomic mass
- rounded to hundredths place
- mass number of isotope with longest known half-life indicated by ( )

Period	1	2	3	4	5	6	7	8	9
1	1 Hydrogen **H** 1.01 *1*								
2	3 Lithium **Li** 6.94 *2, 1*	4 Beryllium **Be** 9.01 *2, 2*							
3	11 Sodium **Na** 22.99 *2, 8, 1*	12 Magnesium **Mg** 24.31 *2, 8, 2*							
4	19 Potassium **K** 39.10 *2, 8, 8, 1*	20 Calcium **Ca** 40.08 *2, 8, 8, 2*	21 Scandium **Sc** 44.96 *2, 8, 9, 2*	22 Titanium **Ti** 47.87 *2, 8, 10, 2*	23 Vanadium **V** 50.94 *2, 8, 11, 2*	24 Chromium **Cr** 52.00 *2, 8, 13, 1*	25 Manganese **Mn** 54.94 *2, 8, 13, 2*	26 Iron **Fe** 55.85 *2, 8, 14, 2*	27 Cobalt **Co** 58.93 *2, 8, 15, 2*
5	37 Rubidium **Rb** 85.47 *2, 8, 18, 8, 1*	38 Strontium **Sr** 87.62 *2, 8, 18, 8, 2*	39 Yttrium **Y** 88.91 *2, 8, 18, 9, 2*	40 Zirconium **Zr** 91.22 *2, 8, 18, 10, 2*	41 Niobium **Nb** 92.91 *2, 8, 18, 12, 1*	42 Molybdenum **Mo** 95.95 *2, 8, 18, 13, 1*	43 ☢ Technetium **Tc** (98) *2, 8, 18, 13, 2*	44 Ruthenium **Ru** 101.07 *2, 8, 18, 15, 1*	45 Rhodium **Rh** 102.91 *2, 8, 18, 16, 1*
6	55 Cesium **Cs** 132.91 *2, 8, 18, 18, 8, 1*	56 Barium **Ba** 137.33 *2, 8, 18, 18, 8, 2*	57 Lanthanum **La** 138.91 *2, 8, 18, 18, 9, 2*	72 Hafnium **Hf** 178.49 *2, 8, 18, 32, 10, 2*	73 Tantalum **Ta** 180.95 *2, 8, 18, 32, 11, 2*	74 Tungsten **W** 183.84 *2, 8, 18, 32, 12, 2*	75 Rhenium **Re** 186.21 *2, 8, 18, 32, 13, 2*	76 Osmium **Os** 190.23 *2, 8, 18, 32, 14, 2*	77 Iridium **Ir** 192.22 *2, 8, 18, 32, 15, 2*
7	87 ☢ Francium **Fr** (223) *2, 8, 18, 32, 18, 8, 1*	88 ☢ Radium **Ra** (226) *2, 8, 18, 32, 18, 8, 2*	89 ☢ Actinium **Ac** (227) *2, 8, 18, 32, 18, 9, 2*	104 ☢ Rutherfordium **Rf** (267) *2, 8, 18, 32, 32, 10, 2*	105 ☢ Dubnium **Db** (268) *2, 8, 18, 32, 32, 11, 2*	106 ☢ Seaborgium **Sg** (269) *2, 8, 18, 32, 32, 12, 2*	107 ☢ Bohrium **Bh** (270) *2, 8, 18, 32, 32, 13, 2*	108 ☢ Hassium **Hs** (277) *2, 8, 18, 32, 32, 14, 2*	109 ☢ Meitnerium **Mt** (278) *2, 8, 18, 32, 32, 15, 2*

(after La)	58 Cerium **Ce** 140.12 *2, 8, 18, 19, 9, 2*	59 Praseodymium **Pr** 140.91 *2, 8, 18, 21, 8, 2*	60 Neodymium **Nd** 144.24 *2, 8, 18, 22, 8, 2*	61 ☢ Promethium **Pm** (145) *2, 8, 18, 23, 8, 2*	62 Samarium **Sm** 150.36 *2, 8, 18, 24, 8, 2*
(after Ac)	90 ☢ Thorium **Th** 232.04 *2, 8, 18, 32, 18, 10, 2*	91 ☢ Protactinium **Pa** 231.04 *2, 8, 18, 32, 20, 9, 2*	92 ☢ Uranium **U** 238.03 *2, 8, 18, 32, 21, 9, 2*	93 ☢ Neptunium **Np** (237) *2, 8, 18, 32, 22, 9, 2*	94 ☢ Plutonium **Pu** (244) *2, 8, 18, 32, 24, 8, 2*

- Alkali metals
- Alkaline-earth metals
- Transition metals
- Inner transition metals
- Post-transition metals
- Metalloids
- Nonmetals
- Halogens (also nonmetals)
- Noble gases
- ☢ Radioactive isotopes

10	11	12	13	14	15	16	17	18
								2 Helium **He** 4.00 2
			5 Boron **B** 10.81 2, 3	6 Carbon **C** 12.01 2, 4	7 Nitrogen **N** 14.01 2, 5	8 Oxygen **O** 16.00 2, 6	9 Fluorine **F** 19.00 2, 7	10 Neon **Ne** 20.18 2, 8
			13 Aluminum **Al** 26.98 2, 8, 3	14 Silicon **Si** 28.09 2, 8, 4	15 Phosphorus **P** 30.97 2, 8, 5	16 Sulfur **S** 32.06 2, 8, 6	17 Chlorine **Cl** 35.45 2, 8, 7	18 Argon **Ar** 39.95 2, 8, 8
28 Nickel **Ni** 58.69 2, 8, 17, 1	29 Copper **Cu** 63.55 2, 8, 18, 1	30 Zinc **Zn** 65.38 2, 8, 18, 2	31 Gallium **Ga** 69.72 2, 8, 18, 3	32 Germanium **Ge** 72.63 2, 8, 18, 4	33 Arsenic **As** 74.92 2, 8, 18, 5	34 Selenium **Se** 78.97 2, 8, 18, 6	35 Bromine **Br** 79.90 2, 8, 18, 7	36 Krypton **Kr** 83.80 2, 8, 18, 8
46 Palladium **Pd** 106.42 2, 8, 18, 18	47 Silver **Ag** 107.87 2, 8, 18, 18, 1	48 Cadmium **Cd** 112.41 2, 8, 18, 18, 2	49 Indium **In** 114.82 2, 8, 18, 18, 3	50 Tin **Sn** 118.71 2, 8, 18, 18, 4	51 Antimony **Sb** 121.76 2, 8, 18, 18, 5	52 Tellurium **Te** 127.60 2, 8, 18, 18, 6	53 Iodine **I** 126.90 2, 8, 18, 18, 7	54 Xenon **Xe** 131.29 2, 8, 18, 18, 8
78 Platinum **Pt** 195.08 2, 8, 18, 32, 17, 1	79 Gold **Au** 196.97 2, 8, 18, 32, 18, 1	80 Mercury **Hg** 200.59 2, 8, 18, 32, 18, 2	81 Thallium **Tl** 204.38 2, 8, 18, 32, 18, 3	82 Lead **Pb** 207.2 2, 8, 18, 32, 18, 4	83 Bismuth **Bi** 208.98 2, 8, 18, 32, 18, 5	84 ☢ Polonium **Po** (209) 2, 8, 18, 32, 18, 6	85 ☢ Astatine **At** (210) 2, 8, 18, 32, 18, 7	86 ☢ Radon **Rn** (222) 2, 8, 18, 32, 18, 8
110 ☢ Darmstadtium **Ds** (281) 2, 8, 18, 32, 32, 17, 1	111 ☢ Roentgenium **Rg** (282) 2, 8, 18, 32, 32, 17, 2	112 ☢ Copernicium **Cn** (285) 2, 8, 18, 32, 32, 18, 2	113 ☢ Nihonium **Nh** (286) 2, 8, 18, 32, 32, 18, 3	114 ☢ Flerovium **Fl** (289) 2, 8, 18, 32, 32, 18, 4	115 ☢ Moscovium **Mc** (290) 2, 8, 18, 32, 32, 18, 5	116 ☢ Livermorium **Lv** (293) 2, 8, 18, 32, 32, 18, 6	117 ☢ Tennessine **Ts** (294) 2, 8, 18, 32, 32, 18, 7	118 ☢ Oganesson **Og** (294) 2, 8, 18, 32, 32, 18, 8

63 Europium **Eu** 151.96 2, 8, 18, 25, 8, 2	64 Gadolinium **Gd** 157.25 2, 8, 18, 25, 9, 2	65 Terbium **Tb** 158.93 2, 8, 18, 27, 8, 2	66 Dysprosium **Dy** 162.50 2, 8, 18, 28, 8, 2	67 Holmium **Ho** 164.93 2, 8, 18, 29, 8, 2	68 Erbium **Er** 167.26 2, 8, 18, 30, 8, 2	69 Thulium **Tm** 168.93 2, 8, 18, 31, 8, 2	70 Ytterbium **Yb** 173.05 2, 8, 18, 32, 8, 2	71 Lutetium **Lu** 174.97 2, 8, 18, 32, 9, 2
95 ☢ Americium **Am** (243) 2, 8, 18, 32, 25, 8, 2	96 ☢ Curium **Cm** (247) 2, 8, 18, 32, 25, 9, 2	97 ☢ Berkelium **Bk** (247) 2, 8, 18, 32, 27, 8, 2	98 ☢ Californium **Cf** (251) 2, 8, 18, 32, 28, 8, 2	99 ☢ Einsteinium **Es** (252) 2, 8, 18, 32, 29, 8, 2	100 ☢ Fermium **Fm** (257) 2, 8, 18, 32, 30, 8, 2	101 ☢ Mendelevium **Md** (258) 2, 8, 18, 32, 31, 8, 2	102 ☢ Nobelium **No** (259) 2, 8, 18, 32, 32, 8, 2	103 ☢ Lawrencium **Lr** (266) 2, 8, 18, 32, 32, 8, 3